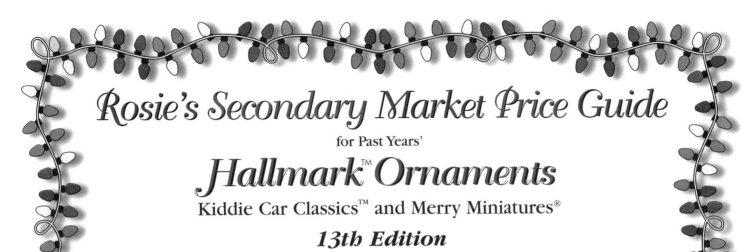

Rosie's Secondary Market Price Guide

for Past Years'

Hallmark™ Ornaments

Kiddie Car Classics™ and Merry Miniatures®

13th Edition

Rosie Wells
Editor & Collector

If you're looking for an older ornament...
Look to
The Ornament Collector™
magazine's classified ads
found within
The Collectors' Bulletin™
1-800-445-8745

Published by
Rosie Wells Enterprises, Inc.
22341 E. Wells Rd.
Canton, IL 61520

Check us out on the World Wide Web! – http:/www.RosieWells.com
Order line: **1-800-445-8745 or 1-800-Hi Rosie**
Question line: 309-668-2211

Buy and sell Hallmark Ornaments in the comfort of your own home through
www.ClAuction.com!

Rosalie "Rosie" Wells
Getting to know her

Author, Editor, Collector,
Wife, Mother, Grandma
Bringing Collectors Together Since 1983

Even as a child growing up in central Illinois, Rosie was a collector. She cherished her comic books, pins, little steel cars (instead of dolls) and WWII bubble gum. She ordered by radio all the *Straight Arrow* drums she could get with Shredded Wheat box tops and collected Cracker Jack toys!

Rosie and her husband, Dave, live "down on the farm," and have two grown children, Tim and Beth. They have also been blessed with two precious, outstanding, super-smart and cute little grandchildren, Hunter and Sydnie. They regularly visit the farm, and Grandma Rosie and Grandpa Dave feel very fortunate that they get to share their farm heritage with them.

Rosie's career in publishing began at her kitchen table. Seventeen years later, with her dedicated staff of over 50 employees, she works in a separate office building just across the road from her farm home. Rosie's love for animals is apparent, as she enjoys her chickens, peacocks, swans, turkeys, rheas and ostriches, as well as Dave's White Park cattle. Three loyal dogs also make their home with Rosie and Dave. Many species of woodland animals are seen on the farm, and part of the fields are planted to provide winter food for wildlife. Canadian geese inhabit the land year 'round; whitetail deer are frequently spotted from the view at the office. A log cabin was built in the woods to give a hide-away to do some writing in a quiet, calm atmosphere!

Rosie's Secondary Market Price Guides for Hallmark™ Ornaments, Precious Moments® Collectibles, *Charming Tails*™, Enesco's *Cherished Teddies*®, *The Boyds Collection, Ltd*®, *Rosie's Price Guide For Ty's Beanie Babies*®, as well as the *Collectors' Bulletin*™, are enjoyed by many all around the world. The *Collectors' Bulletin,*™ which is four magazines in one, is published six times throughout the year to inform collectors of what is happening in the world of collecting. Each *Collectors' Bulletin*™ now includes sections on Precious Moments® Collectibles, Hallmark™ Ornaments, Bean Bag Collectibles and many, many other collectibles. Rosie also publishes a *Weekly Collectors' Gazette*™, filled with news on Hallmark™

collectibles and other limited edition collectibles. Rosie and Dave host the Midwest Collectibles Fest in Westmont, Illinois, twice a year. (The largest in the nation with over 250 dealer tables each time!)

Rosie is a noted authority on collectibles and can spot a "hot"collectible in the making almost from day one! She has helped many collectibles gain recognition through her international collectors' magazine and through shows and seminars throughout the United States. Having a sensational collectible knowledge, a sense of humor and a loving heart, which collectors can relate to through the many articles she has written, draws collectors to Rosie. Hallmark™ Ornaments have always fascinated Rosie; she has a collection of several hundred ornaments. Rosie has also collected Hallmark Merry Miniatures® which are now included in this guide. Rosie says, "If I have only one life to live, then I hope to collect as much as my basement, shelves, drawers and walls can hold. Then everyone will know I was a fun lovin', crazy collector! Collectors are fun folks, you know!"

Visit Rosie's award winning Web site at http://www.RosieWells.com, or write to our e-mail address Rosie@RosieWells.com. Our web site was honored with the Gold Service Award by The Public Eye, an internet watchdog group that gives this award out only to "Internet companies who demonstrate the highest and most extraordinary level of customer service excellence." This award is the ultimate symbol of distinction for any company doing business on the Internet, as it is only given to businesses that pass rigorous standards in the areas of "service, accessibility, warranties, references and stability." We received this award after one of their people went "undercover" to purchase one of our products. They found our services to be exceptional and that made us happy, too! I hope this guide adds to your joy of collecting!

As mentioned above, I invite you to attend the largest of all Collectible shows which I have hosted along with my husband, Dave, and my staff. At the Midwest Collectibles Fest, you will find "older" Hallmark ornaments to purchase for your collection. The show is held every March and October in the Chicago area. I also meet with collectors every spring at my booth during the Collectibles Exposition Show in Long Beach, California, Rosemont, Illinois and New Jersey. For more information, contact Rosie Wells Enterprises.

Rosie

Table of Contents

Secondary Market Prices of Hallmark Keepsake Ornaments

Secondary Market Prices of Hallmark Mini Ornaments

Secondary Market Prices of Hallmark Easter Ornaments

(In 1997, Hallmark changed the "Hallmark Easter Ornaments" name to "Hallmark Spring Ornaments.")

Secondary Market Prices of Hallmark Spring Ornaments

New to Collecting? Read This!

Did you know that buying "just one more" Hallmark Ornament is what thousands do to ease their Hallmark fever? There are many reasons to purchase Hallmark Ornaments! People purchase their favorites! They purchase Hallmark Ornaments for gifts! They purchase them for sentimental reasons and they purchase the ones which remind them of a special person, special event or "just because." Boy, do I purchase for "just because!"

Yes, some people even purchase Hallmark Ornaments as an investment in hopes of making a little extra cash later on. There's a good chance, if you're involved in the buyers' circle, you may double your money, or more maybe, on the scarce ornaments and the "popular" first in series ornaments. For example, the 1993 *Holiday Barbie*, with a retail price of $14.75, went to $50 within two months on the secondary market; it has now risen to $170. (Not all first in series ornaments are a sure thing; in comparison, *Winter Surprise* did not see such an increase on the secondary market as quickly though, as others. So study the market. Use the prices within this guide as that, a guide!)

Of course, collectors and dealers were caught unaware of how popular the 1991 *Starship Enterprise* would become. The scarcity of this ornament caused the price to climb to the $400 mark, with seekers still out there looking. After a "hot" ornament is produced, don't get overly excited thinking that the second edition will be as scarce. Retailers remember the response to the "firsts" and usually order extra of "number two." Study the market carefully.

Fads come and go and "pop culture" ornaments are good sellers, such as the 1994 *Beatles* set. Retailers may not have ordered many of these because of the $48 retail price, but one must study the market! Someone, somewhere had over 1,000 of these to release on the secondary market and the 1994 *Beatles* secondary market was affected for a long period of time!

In my opinion, the only way the personalized ornaments will rise in value on the secondary market will be if you have a clever saying placed on it, maybe a famous name. For example, on the 1995 *Reindeer Rooters* (QP 605-6) I would put, "Hey Santa, may we ride too?" on the sign to be displayed with the 1993 *Cheery Cyclists* (QX 578-6) or "Vote for Clinton" - or "Vote for Dole" - or "Vote for Rosie!" Ha! That would be a real doozie!

Most light, motion and talking ornaments have not been favorites for secondary market folks to invest in. Many collectors are cautious about the life expectancy of the motors. Of course, if one holds the ornaments a year or two, one could easily make a few folks happy. I feel the 1996 *Chicken Coop Chorus* and the *Wizard of Oz* light and motion will be *Hot* soon!

If you're lucky to find ornaments from the '70s and early '80s at a bargain price, these would be great to resell on the secondary market. (Only a few of the ball ornaments are money makers. They're priced high, but few buy!)

Before you decide to invest in ornaments, my advice is to attend several swap meets and watch what sells. *Although 99% of the listed ornaments in this guide have a higher value than their original retail, it's still not a guarantee they will all "sell" immediately at these prices.* THESE PRICES ARE AVERAGED FROM SALE PRICES ACROSS THE COUNTRY AND SHOULD BE USED ONLY AS A GUIDE TO INSURE YOUR COLLECTION. WE MAKE NO WARRANTY ON THE PRICES CONTAINED IN THIS GUIDE.

Write to me if you have any questions. I also may be able to help you locate a much sought after ornament. Thank you for purchasing our guide; we hope you enjoy reading and learning the values for your ornaments. Our goal is to "Bring Collectors Together." I know the family who prays together stays together and I've also found that when families collect together they enjoy being together. I hope to see you sometime at a Collectibles Show! (Ask about our two Collectibles Shows, in Illinois, for March and October, 1999.)

Boxes, Boxes

This guide is the first to research "no box" (NB) prices on the majority of the ornaments. NB prices are not given for ornaments produced in '96-'98 because it is very unlikely that these ornaments would be found without a box. When insuring '96 through '98 ornaments that do not have a box, deduct up to 15% of the secondary market value. When insuring NB prices for Merry Miniatures, deduct up to 25% on those which originally came in boxes.

We have found that the older the ornament is, the harder it becomes to find anywhere... so a collector wanting it badly will be happy to own it even without a box. Collectors will buy what they want with or without the box. Collectors do pay more for an older ornament with a box. Why? Because 20 years ago, many of those who bought Hallmark ornaments didn't keep the boxes and didn't know what boxes would mean to collectors in the future. It wasn't even in the minds of many that in 15 to 20 years a Hallmark ornament might be looked upon as a collectible valued at many times its original retail price! So having an older ornament, mint in box, can be reason enough to ask a higher price.

When you have an original box with a popular ornament, such as the first in series *Here Comes Santa*, you will be able to sell it for more than the same ornament without a box. Boxes are a plus with older ornaments, but we've found that, with or without the box, sought-after ornaments will still bring a good price and should be insured accordingly.

Most recent ornaments are easily found at shows and from secondary market dealers, so it's felt that collectors should be aware of keeping the boxes should there be a decision to sell in the future. These ornaments will be offered to a new generation of well-informed collectors who may want the boxes. This guide reflects selling prices of "no box" ornaments. Once an ornament becomes older, then you may find the "no box" price will escalate. There are differences of opinion on this subject, each with valid points to be made.

To locate an ornament/collectibles show in your area, search the ads in the *Collectors' Bulletin*™ magazine! Shows are a lot of fun and you can find some of your favorite ornaments, since secondary market dealers offer hundreds of ornaments for sale. In *Collectors' Bulletin*™ magazine, *"We Bring Ornament Collectors Together"* to enjoy their collections. Ask about our shows.

Ball Ornaments

Generally speaking, ball ornaments have not proven to be as collectible as the other Hallmark ornaments, although some are very difficult to locate, especially "mint in box" condition. Many older ball ornaments are found with discoloration, spotting and with no boxes.

According to an article written by Shirley Trexler, which appeared in the June 1994 issue of *The Ornament Collector*™ magazine: *"Difficulty faces ball ornament collectors who try, in vain, to find ball ornaments that had low production and a high breakage and spotting potential. Few secondary market dealers have any ball or yarn ornaments listed on price lists or show tables. Many times collectors are unable to replace a broken, cherished ball ornament because these ornaments are so few in number anymore. A few examples of such rare older ball ornaments include: 1973 Manger Scene and Christmas Is Love; 1974 Angel ball and Snow Goose ball; 1975 Buttons and Bo collection and Little Miracles group of balls; 1976 Rudolph and Santa; and the Baby's First Christmas and Drummer Boy ball ornaments; 1979 Light of Christmas ball; 1980 Christmas Choir ball and the 1983 Christmas Wonderland ball. These are just a few of many which are fading from existence."*

Some ball ornaments are scarce, not because of tremendous popularity but because of the reasons listed above; low production, breakage and spotting. Some of the older ball ornaments are sought after, but not many. If you're thinking of the future secondary market for ball ornaments, don't go "overboard." Three or four of each of the new ones per secondary market dealer would overload the supply, in my opinion. Ball ornaments are lovely and enjoyable, but not easy to hold for investment, in my opinion, unless they are extra rare or unusual.

Collections Should be Insured

You can be sure this guide will be especially helpful when insuring your collection; many insurance companies use it as proof of value in settling claims. Collectibles usually are not covered with a general homeowner's insurance policy, but require a "rider" policy. Your agent may need additional documentation, such as photos of your collection and inventory records. Before appraising your collection for insuring, you may wish to contact your insurance agent and ask about the actual details which he/she requires. Be sure your agent insures your collection at today's replacement prices, not the original retail price.

In this guide, you will find space to record your ornament purchases as well as the condition of each ornament (mint in box, damaged box, etc.). It is very important to have a current inventory of your collection in the event you need to file a claim.

One should also be aware of the value of these ornaments in "estate planning." Sadly, many valuable Hallmark ornaments have been sold in a group for a very few dollars because of a lack of knowledge. Although you might never sell your collection, it's always best to keep a record of its monetary value.

Also...

☆ Usually attractive first editions increase in value immediately after Christmas. Always buy the first editions of the ornaments that you like as soon as they debut, or the next year you'll pay more!

☆ The 1998 African-American Holiday Barbie™ is the first in a new series.

☆ *Nolan Ryan* ornament was first release with a copyright reading "NLB 1996" on his back. It was corrected to "MLB 1996" which stands for Major League Baseball.

☆ Collectors should be cautious when using the Light and Motion ornaments with their Christmas light strings. Not all light strings carry the same current. Some of the ultra brites and super brites may have too strong a current! Be sure to read the instructions included with the light strings and Light and Motion ornaments.

☆ Duane Unruh designed Hallmark's 1996 NFL figural ornaments. However, the box the ornaments are packaged in say they were designed by Bob Seidler.

☆ In 1996, Hallmark launched a new program to benefit retailers and collectors alike. Retailers who carry an over abundance of a particular item may call Hallmark and request an item they need. Hallmark keeps track of what retailers have and what they are looking for and match up the retailers for a trade. For example, one retailer may have an overabundance of Barbie ornaments, but not many Larry Bird ornaments. With this new program, Hallmark matches the retailer with another and a trade is made. This could eliminate future half-off sales.

☆ The 1998 introduction, *Angelic Flight*, limited to 25,000, was not a dated ornament.

☆ The Kiddie Car Classics *1935 Steelcraft* car by Murray® limited edition sold out at Hallmark in less than three months!

☆ Although the ball ornaments are not in demand, they are becoming harder to locate. Watch for age marks on ball ornaments.

☆ A 1998 miniature ornament introduced in the Hallmark *Dream Book* as *Fishing Surprise* was actually named *Tasty Surprise*.

☆ The 1996 *Pansy*, first in the *Language of Flowers* series, and the *Nolan Ryan* ornament quickly sold out after their debut.

☆ *Freedom 7* features the voice of John Glenn. He says, "Roger, Zero G and I feel fine… Capsule is turning around. Oh, that view is tremendous."

☆ The 1980 *Cool Yule* is a very coveted ornament in the Hallmark line. *Here Comes Santa, Rocking Horse, Tin Locomotive, Classic American Cars* and *Barbie* are also very popular Hallmark series.

☆ Errors, such as missing decals, upside down sleeves on ball ornaments and missing painted parts, are sometimes found on ornaments. Errors are few; secondary market prices rise on these pieces, but there are few buyers for these errored pieces. An error found on an ornament is not highly sought after unless the error is corrected and the ornament re-released.

☆ A few ornaments through the years debuted in the *Dream Book* but were recalled due to production problems. Other ornaments were produced for retailers' displays and then pulled from production, such as the 1990 *Country Angel* and the changed 1994 *Lion King*, with light and music.

☆ There are local collector clubs in many states. Ask your favorite dealer, or call the Hallmark Keepsake Ornament Club in Kansas City at 1-800-523-5839.

☆ Many children, when they marry and leave home, leave the family dog and take their ornaments with them.

☆ *Merry Miniatures®* are boxed to protect them and make them more valuable to collectors. Large boxed sets have been eliminated and future pieces will be in two-piece sets or individually packaged.

☆ Remember, not all ornaments produced by Hallmark are "Keepsake Ornaments." Some are "Tree Trimmers." They are not in this guide and are not as sought after as the Keepsake Collection.

☆ It's best to put your favorite ornaments on layaway when they debut in July and August. Many people were accustomed to waiting for after Christmas sales to purchase their Hallmark ornaments, but in years past some collectors have been very disappointed, finding that many ornaments were gone from the shelves forever.

☆ This guide is available on CD-Rom. See inside front cover.

☆ Many collectors display their ornaments all year 'round. *Many,* I say *many,* collectors put up three, four, five or even more trees at Christmas time! Each year we give a Tree of the Year award! You'd be amazed at the photo entries we receive. Be sure to send in your photos!

☆ A collector found her 1995 *Holiday Barbie* ornament had two different earrings. One earring was red with silver on it and the other earring was silver with red on it. Fun!

☆ Back yard sales and auctions bring great finds to collectors. Advertise in your local paper for these collectibles!

☆ The *Rocking Horse* series ended with the 16th Edition, dated 1996. This has been a very popular series sculpted by Linda Sickman. Also, the 1997 *Springtime Barbie* was the last in the *Springtime Barbie™* series.

☆ "Personalized" ornaments, on which you have your own name or message placed, usually do not escalate in value; they have only heirloom value.

☆ The 1987 Hallmark Crayola® ornament, *Bright Christmas Dreams,* was not actually a part of the Hallmark *Crayola® Crayon* series, which officially started in 1989 with *Bright Journey,* although many collectors consider it a "must have" to accompany this series.

☆ Be careful when packing and unpacking ornaments. The 1994 *Beatles* have been found with Ringo having broken drum sticks. Ornaments which become unglued can usually be repaired without loss in value. Those ornaments which actually become broken or which have loose parts suffer the most loss in value.

☆ Starting with the 1996 ornaments, Hallmark included imprints of artists' signatures on many ornaments. There were some exceptions, of course. No signatures are found on miniature ornaments, on ornaments where there was no appropriate place that would not detract from the design of the ornament, and no signatures were found on ornaments where the licensees did not give permission.

☆ In lieu of one large convention, as in 1991 and 1993, Hallmark hosted one-day Ornament Expos across the country in 1994 and 1995, and Artist Signings in 1996. A special piece, *Mrs. Claus' Cupboard,* was available for purchase at the 1994 Expo, *Christmas Eve Bake-Off* was available at the 1995 Expo and *Santa's Toy Shop* was available at the 1996 Artist Signing. Hallmark also produced variations of popular ornaments which were given away at the Expos as door prizes and other special Expo offerings which collectors could purchase. (The 1995 miniature Pewter *Rocking Horse* is Hot!) Also, Artist Signing Events are held throughout the country each year, giving collectors a chance to meet Hallmark artists and have their favorite ornaments signed.

☆ In 1995 there were three souvenir ornaments available only at Hallmark Expo. These included a Hallmark Artists' Caricature ball ornament, a miniature pewter *Rocking Horse* and a Cookie tree ornament. The three ornaments were limited to one each per registered membership. The pewter *Rocking Horse* was the most popular!

☆ There was no Expo in 1996; instead there were several scheduled artist signings at special locations. Available at the 1996 Artists Signings were *Toy Shop Santa* and a Gold Miniature *Rocking Horse.* The *Rocking Horse* commemorated the retirement of the *Rocking Horse* series.

☆ Did you know that Hallmark Keepsake Ornaments are sold at 15,000 retailers, including nearly 5,000 Hallmark Gold Crown stores nationwide?

☆ The 1997 *Lone Ranger™* lunch box ornament has "Hi Yo" instead of "Hi Ho" imprinted on it. This is correct… as kids we said, "Hi Ho" didn't we? Ha!

☆ The full size Kiddie Car Classic '56 Golden Eagle convertible, introduced in May, 1997, quickly retired in August of 1997.

☆ Sleepers are ornaments which sell out at dealers more quickly than originally predicted. This is because there are usually fewer available.

☆ Generally, any train or Classic Car ornament is good for secondary market holdings. Just watch the market for the 700E Hudson Steam Locomotive, the first in the LIONEL® Train series.

☆ Did you know there are many channels through which you may find the older ornaments? These include ornament swap meets, secondary market dealers' ads; and some Hallmark stores have added rooms for older ornaments. Advertise, you'll probably find what you want! Check out our Web site at http://www.RosieWells.com! Call us – we'll try to help you!

☆ Know who you are dealing with when buying, selling and trading through the mail. Generally, most collectors are trustworthy folks, but there's always that one bad onion! There's a very good method to use to mark your ornaments when selling. Use a blacklight marking pen to put a dot or two on each ornament, in case a broken or scratched ornament is returned that is not yours. These marks will show up under a blacklight, proving whether or not the ornament that's returned is the one you sent. When shipping UPS, we advise shipping with the label AOD (Acknowledgment of Delivery). The recipient must "sign" for the package delivered by UPS, or insure it through U.S. mail.

☆ In the future we may see new series of different dog breeds, cat breeds, actual nursery rhyme characters, more licensed product ornaments, bicycles, football stars, mermaids and computers, plus Victorian dolls, Nativity pieces, a special line of Santas, trains and definitely a new series of angels. The farmers have hoped for antique tractors; replicas of old toys and mechanical banks have been thought about, as well as whimsical little vegetables! Mice will be around for years to come and surely, before the fad is over, a few black and white cows will debut. Hallmark artists plan designs several years ahead; as you read this next year's Christmas ornaments are well ahead on the production line in the Far East.

☆ The Classic American Cars series is very popular, as many men receive them as gifts. In the future we may see a similar line of foreign cars. Car enthusiasts are offering these at their Swap 'n Sells also. Who knows? We may see lighthouses debut as ornaments. What about Harley Davidson motorcycles? A great suggestion, eh?!

☆ For Hallmark Artist interviews, read Collectors' Bulletin™ magazine. Subscribe NOW! Call 1-800-445-8745.

☆ Sometimes the value of an ornament may fall after a peak, later to rise or level off. It pays to study the market.

☆ Many collectors feel that ornaments shouldn't be stored in the original bubble wrap packing, as this bubble wrap may emit a gas which discolors the ornament. As of 1994, Hallmark replaced bubble wrap with tissue paper as packing material. One reason for this change is that tissue paper is more environmentally friendly. However, we saw bubble wrap used as packing again in 1995. Many collectors also store their ornaments in sectioned storage boxes, thus eliminating the wear and tear on individual ornament boxes, if they decide to keep them. This also makes it simpler when decorating or putting away ornaments for the year. Ornament boxes may then be carefully flattened and stored.

☆ Many collectors want to know the relationship between Ambassador and Hallmark. Ambassador was a subsidiary of Hallmark and produced ornaments in the early '80s. Packaging for the Ambassador line consisted of white boxes with green inner boxes and a clear, see-through front. Printed on the outside of each box is The Holiday House Collection. It is difficult to find Ambassador ornaments in their original boxes.

☆ You have joined the National Hallmark Keepsake Collector's Club, haven't you? Pick up the forms from your Hallmark dealer.

☆ The 1986 Cinnamon Teddy has two different stock numbers. Hallmark was obtaining the ornament from more than one manufacturer, and they identified them with different numerals to regulate inventory.

☆ Upside down decals are sometimes found on ornaments. Such was the case on the '94 third in series, Betsey's Country Christmas; also, recently found on a 1997 Lone Ranger lunch box ornament.

☆ The 1995 Tobin Fraley Holiday Carrousel had a manufacturing defect. The designed side of the horse is on the inside and the plain side of the horse is facing outside.

☆ Six Keepsake Ornaments were issued in the 1996 Olympic Spirit Collection. They were: Invitation to the Games, two dated, trading-card size ceramic plaque ornaments; Lighting the Flame, a Magic Ornament which features flickering light and plays Bugler's Dream; Olympic Triumph; Cloisonné Medallion; Parade of Nations plate; and Izzy, the 1996 Olympic mascot. The medallion and plate sold best.

☆ The 1996 Mary Had a Little Lamb does not have an error. According to Hallmark, this ornament is a figural book. When opened, there is a 3-D figure of Mary and her little lamb. Mary's face was left unpainted on all the ornaments. That's what I call a blank expression!

We have conducted extensive research in recording values for ornaments found in this guide. Use these values as a "guide" in insuring, as well as buying and selling. We make no warranty on the prices contained in this guide. Expect prices on recent years' ornaments to increase proportionally more in the next few years than ornaments from early years.

MIB Sec. Mkt. prices quoted are for ornaments which are in mint condition and in their original boxes with price tab still attached to the box. The price tab is the removable perforated price tag found on each Hallmark ornament box. There were also "strips" running across the box or "gift tags" on some earlier boxes (i.e. 1977-1978 Trimmer Collection). When purchasing new ornaments, be sure the perforated price tab remains on the box if you plan to resell later. If you give Hallmark ornaments as gifts to friends or loved ones who are collectors, they may want you to leave the tabs on. (Normally, this would be considered a breach in good manners, but collectors are a rare breed!)

Photos of each ornament have been included next to each listing in this guide. Unfortunately, where a good clear color photo is unavailable a black and white photo is used. Collectors who would like to contribute to our search for replacement photos may contact the Guide Dept., Rosie Wells Enterprises, Inc. This guide includes all ornaments up through 1999 Spring. A secondary market price has been given for each ornament through 1996. Only a projected value has been given for 1998 ornaments through 1999 Spring ornaments. Looking at last year's guide, we were proven to be 99% correct on our projected values!

Read the *Collectors' Bulletin*™ *(actually four magazines in one)* for price updates and current news on Hallmark™ ornaments! Each issue is packed with hot news on Hallmark ornaments and other fabulous collectibles, Collectors' Comments, classified ads, show listings, club information and much more! $23.95 Yr./6 issues.
Rosie Wells Enterprises, Inc.
22341 E. Wells Rd., Dept. G, Canton, IL 61520
Phone: 1-800-445-8745; Fax: 309/668-2795

May be found on most newsstands!

Check us out on the Internet! http://www.RosieWells.com

E-Mail address: Rosie@RosieWells.com

This guide is arranged first by year of production, then each ornament is listed in alphabetical order by name. Ornaments in a series or collection are listed by the name of the series or collection.

① ② QX 478-4   POLAR BOWLER ③   ⑨ ☐
Comments: Handcrafted, 2-1/4" tall.
④ Santa shows great form with his polished green bowling ball at the "North Pole Bowl." **Artist:** Bob Siedler
☐ Purchased 19___ Pd $___   MIB   NB   DB   BNT
⑤ ☐ Want ⑥ Orig. Ret. $5.00 ⑦ **NB** $16 ⑧ **MIB** Sec. Mkt. **$20**

1 **PHOTOGRAPH** of the Ornament. If "Not Shown," then no photo of the piece was available. Photos welcomed!

2 **NUMBER:** Ornament's style number.

3 **NAME** of the Ornament. If the ornament is part of a series, the name of the series will appear first.

4 **COMMENTS:** Descriptions of each ornament include: Whether or not the ornament is part of a series and its standing in that series; if it is a ball ornament, acrylic, hand crafted, etc.; the size of the ornament (if available); whether or not it is dated; a short descriptive phrase; anything unusual or out of the ordinary.

This guide can also be used as a personal inventory book, keeping a record of ornaments you want or already own and the condition of your ornaments. MIB = mint in box, NB = no box, DB = damaged box and BNT = box with original price tab removed, NE = not established.

6 **ORIG. RET.:** Retail price of the ornament when it debuted.

7 **NB:** The value of the ornament without its original box. (NB-P signifies the fact that there is a plentiful supply of the ornament with No Box.)

8 **MIB** Sec. Mkt.: Today's secondary market price (collectors' and dealers' selling/buying prices). In most cases only one secondary market price was given, but there were cases where there was such a range in very high and very low selling prices for the ornament that only a range would do. Ninety-nine percent of the time you'll be able to find that special ornament at these prices. To sell a large collection quickly, expect to reduce your prices by 20%-30%. When selling to dealers, it may be necessary to deduct 50%-60%, as they buy to resell. REMEMBER, USE THESE PRICES ONLY AS A GUIDE TO HELP YOU EVALUATE THE REPLACEMENT VALUE FOR INSURANCE PURPOSES, ETC... YOU CAN ALSO RESEARCH PRICES BY STUDYING ADS BY COLLECTORS, ETC...

9 This box is for your convenience. You may mark the box so that you are able to tell immediately which ornaments you have and those which you do not have. Place a check in the box if it's in your collection.

Merry Miniatures

Today, Merry Miniatures collectors have become more selective than in the past. This, I feel, is mainly due to the change in the art-plas look, price difference and size, since the popular '70's Merry Miniatures were introduced.

The first pieces, through about 1986-1988, still had the "old look," size and familiar low prices. In 1989, a new look created a stir in the collectors' desire to add these Merry Miniatures with the now $3.50 and up prices.

Recently, coming boxed and in sets has been the policy. These have been, no doubt, marketed to sell more and to help prevent easy shoplifting. Yet, it was easier in the past to purchase one from the display, and even go back several times to purchase more later because they seemed less expensive. Collectors are saying that buying a Merry Miniatures boxed set as a quick, last minute purchase has not been that easily done. Buying the sets has meant spending more money. It had to be a planned purchase. This may have contributed to the slower interest of Merry Miniatures. Rumor now has it that Hallmark may be going back to individual plastic Merry Miniatures. If this is true, watch for the 1999 Ornament Premiere to debut the first ones. I predict that this will encourage Merry Miniatures collectors, perhaps even interest new collectors to the line. Remember, this is only a rumor and at present, Hallmark has announced a resin boxed set for Spring 1999.

My early collection is still being displayed at home and at the office. My li'l grandson likes the Santas. I find them hiding everywhere after he goes home. It won't be long until my li'l granddaughter will enjoy them. I imagine she'll like kitties and the li'l mice. This spring of 1999 be sure to purchase Bashful Boy and Girl at Garden Gate. This two-piece set may be scarce and will be limited, as it is a Preview Exclusive.

Happy Collecting!

Rosie

This portion of the guide is arranged first by year of production, then each Merry Miniatures is listed in a seasonal category, then by the Merry Miniatures' name.

① ② EPF1433   ③ RAGGEDY ANDY   □ ⑧
④ Issued 1974
□ Purch 19__ Pd $____ Orig. Ret. $1.25 ⑥
⑤ □ Want   Sec. Mkt. **$120** ⑦

1 **PHOTOGRAPH** of the Figurine. If "Not Shown," then no photo of the piece was available. Photos welcomed!

2 **NUMBER:** Figurine's style number.

3 **NAME** of the Figurine.

4 **COMMENTS:** In this area you will find when the piece was issued, series information and any other pertinent information on the piece.

5 This guide can also be used as a personal inventory book, keeping a record of Merry Miniatures you want or already own.

6 **ORIG. RET.:** Retail price of the figurine when it debuted.

7 **Sec. Mkt.:** Today's secondary market price (collectors' and dealers' selling/buying prices) for Merry Miniatures available from 1974-1995. Ninety-nine percent of the time you'll be able to find those special Merry Miniatures at these prices. To sell a large collection quickly, expect to reduce your prices by 20%-30%. When selling to secondary market dealers, it may be necessary to deduct 50%-60%, as they buy to resell. Starting in 1996, Merry Miniatures were available only in boxes, thus **MIB** values will be used when secondary market values are established.

REMEMBER, USE THESE PRICES ONLY AS A GUIDE TO HELP YOU EVALUATE THE REPLACEMENT VALUE FOR INSURANCE PURPOSES, ETC... YOU CAN ALSO RESEARCH PRICES BY STUDYING ADS BY COLLECTORS, ETC...

8 This box is for your convenience. You may mark the box so that you are able to tell immediately which Merry Miniatures you have and which you do not have. Place a check in the box if it's in your collection.

Collectible Ornament Series

African-American Holiday Barbie™   Complete series $20-25 Proj.

Series #	Year	Price	Item #	Description
1	1998	$20-25	QX 693-6	Black and silver dress

A Pony for Christmas   Complete series $15-20 Proj.

1	1998		QX 631-6	Toy bear riding toy pony

All American Trucks, Dated   Complete series $95-100 MIB

1	1995	$32	QX 552-7	1956 Ford Truck
2	1996	$25	QX 524-1	1955 Chevrolet Camaro
3	1997	$18	QX 610-5	1953 GMC
4	1998	$20-25	QX 626-3	1937 Ford V-8

All God's Children, Dated   Complete series $50-55 MIB

1	1996	$23	QX 556-4	Christy
2	1997	$12	QX 614-2	Nikki
3	1998	$15-20	QX 636-3	Ricky

Art Masterpiece, Padded Satin   Complete series $68 MIB

1	1984	$20	QX 349-4	Madonna and Child and St. John
2	1985	$18	QX 377-2	Madonna of the Pomegranate
3/Final	1986	$30	QX 350-6	Madonna and Child w/Infant and St. John

At the Ball Park, Dated   Complete series $72-77 MIB

1	1996	$30	QXI 571-1	Nolan Ryan
2	1997	$22	QXI 615-2	Hank Aaron
3	1998	$20-25	QXI 403-3	Cal Ripken Jr.

Barbie™, Dated   Complete series $131-136 MIB

1	1994	$40	QX 500-6	Black and White Swimsuit
2	1995	$30	QXI 504-9	Solo in the Spotlight
3	1996	$25	QXI 654-1	Enchanted Evening
4	1997	$16	QXI 681-2	Wedding Day 1959-1962
5	1998	$20-25	QXI 404-3	Silken Flame™

Baseball Heroes, Dated   Complete series $119 MIB

Series #	Year	Price	Item #	Description
1	1994	$55	QX 532-3	Babe Ruth
2	1995	$24	QX 502-9	Lou Gehrig
3	1996	$24	QX 530-4	Satchel Paige
4/Final	1997	$16	QX 620-2	Jackie Robinson

Bellringers, The, Dated   Complete series $872 MIB

1	1979	$400	QX 147-9	The Bellsringer (Elf on Bell Clapper)
2	1980	$85	QX 157-4	The Bellringers (Angels w/ Stars)
3	1981	$100	QX 441-5	Swingin' Bellringer (Mouse/Candycane)
4	1982	$100	QX 455-6	Angel Bellringer
5	1983	$137	QX 403-9	Teddy Bellringer
6/Final	1984	$50	QX 438-4	Elfin Artist

Betsey Clark, Dated Balls   Complete series $1,135 MIB

1	1973	$132	XHD 110-2	Christmas 1973
2	1974	$85	QX 108-1	Musicians
3	1975	$80	QX 133-1	Caroling Trio
4	1976	$115	QX 195-1	Christmas 1976
5	1977	$425	QX 264-2	Truest Joys of Christmas
6	1978	$60	QX 201-6	Christmas Spirit
7	1979	$32	QX 201-9	Holiday Fun
8	1980	$31	QX 215-4	Joy-in-the-Air
9	1981	$40	QX 802-2	Christmas 1982
10	1982	$35	QX 215-6	Joys of Christmas
11	1983	$30	QX 211-9	Christmas Happiness
12	1984	$35	QX 249-4	Days are Merry
13/Final	1985	$35	QX 263-2	Special Kind of Feeling

Betsey Clark: Home for Christmas, Dated   Complete series $177 MIB

1	1986	$35	QX 277-6	Decorating the Christmas Tree
2	1987	$25	QX 272-7	There's No Place Like Christmas
3	1988	$25	QX 271-4	A Homemade Touch...
4	1989	$37	QX 230-2	Filling Birdbath w/Water
5	1990	$25	QX 203-3	Christmas Duet
6/Final	1991	$30	QX 210-9	Getting Favorite Friends Together...

Betsey's Country Christmas, Dated   Complete series $68 MIB

1	1992	$30	QX 210-4	Christmas Sets Our Hearts A Dancing!
2	1993	$20	QX 206-2	Happy Is The Memory Of Bringing Home The Christmas Tree!
3/Final	1994	$18	QX 240-3	It's the simple joys, the simple pleasures, the heart remembers and dearly treasures.

Candlelight Services, Dated — Complete series $21-26 Proj.

Series #	Year	Price	Item #	Description
1	1998	$21-26	QLX 763-6	The Stone Church

Carrousel, Dated — Complete series $1,000 MIB

Series #	Year	Price	Item #	Description
1	1978	$410	QX 146-3	Antique Toys
2	1979	$185	QX 146-7	Christmas Carrousel
3	1980	$165	QX 141-4	Merry Carrousel
4	1981	$90	QX 427-5	Skaters' Carrousel
5	1982	$100	QX 478-3	Snowman Carrousel
6/Final	1983	$50	QX 401-9	Santa and Friends

Cat Naps, The, Dated — Complete series $126-131 MIB

Series #	Year	Price	Item #	Description
1	1994	$50	QX 531-3	Kitten Sleeping in Cookie Jar
2	1995	$30	QX 509-7	Kitten Sleeping on Mitten
3	1996	$20	QX 564-1	Kitten Sleeping in a Wicker Basket
4	1997	$11	QX 620-5	Kitten Sleeping in Suitcase
5/Final	1998	$15-20	QX 638-3	Kitten in Laundry Basket

Celebration of Angels — Complete series $87-92 MIB

Series #	Year	Price	Item #	Description
1	1995	$25	QX 507-7	Celebrates African-American Holiday
2	1996	$26	QX 563-4	Celebrates African-American Holiday
3	1997	$16	QX 617-5	Celebrates African-American Holiday
4/Final	1998	$20-25	QX 636-6	Celebrates African-American Holiday

Christmas Kitty, Porcelain — Complete series $84 MIB

Series #	Year	Price	Item #	Description
1	1989	$33	QX 544-5	White/Yellow Kitten in White Dress
2	1990	$31	QX 450-6	Grey Kitten in Blue/White Coat & Hat
3/Final	1991	$20	QX 437-7	Yellow Kitten in Pink Nightgown

Christmas Visitors, Dated — Complete series $73 MIB

Series #	Year	Price	Item #	Description
1	1995	$30	QX 508-7	St. Nicholas
2	1996	$25	QX 563-1	Christkindl
3/Final	1997	$18	QX 617-2	Kolyada

Classic American Cars, The, Dated — Complete series $381.50-406.50MIB

Series #	Year	Price	Item #	Description
1	1991	$175-195	QX 431-9	1957 Corvette
2	1992	$50	QX 428-4	1966 Mustang
3	1993	$40	QX 527-5	1956 Thunderbird
4	1994	$30	QX 542-2	1957 Chevrolet Bel Air
5	1995	$24	QX 523-9	1969 Camaro
6	1996	$25	QX 538-4	1959 Cadillac De Ville

Series #	Year	Price	Item #	Description
7	1997	$17.50	QX 610-2	1969 Hurst Oldsmobile 442
8	1998	$20-25	QX 625-6	1970 Plymouth®

Clauses on Vacation, Dated — Complete series $36-39 MIB

Series #	Year	Price	Item #	Description
1	1997	$18	QX 611-2	The Clauses Carrying Fishing Gear
2	1998	$18-21	QX 627-6	The Clauses in a Reindeer Float Tube

Clothespin Soldier — Complete series $292 MIB

Series #	Year	Price	Item #	Description
1	1982	$130	QX 458-3	British
2	1983	$42	QX 402-9	Early American
3	1984	$30	QX 447-1	Canadian Mountie
4	1985	$30	QX 471-5	Scottish Highlander
5	1986	$30	QX 406-3	French Officer
6/Final	1987	$30	QX 480-7	Sailor

Collector's Plate, Dated on Back — Complete series $246 MIB

Series #	Year	Price	Item #	Description
1	1987	$75	QX 481-7	Light Shines at Christmas
2	1988	$50	QX 406-1	Waiting for Santa
3	1989	$31	QX 461-2	Morning of Wonder
4	1990	$35	QX 443-6	Cookies for Santa
5	1991	$30	QX 436-9	Let It Snow!
6/Final	1992	$25	QX 446-1	Sweet Holiday Harmony

Club-exclusive: Barbie™ — Complete series $111 MIB

Series #	Year	Price	Item #	Description
1	1996	$33		Club-exclusive: Holiday BARBIE™
2	1997	$38		Club-exclusive: Holiday BARBIE™
3	1998	$40		Club-exclusive: Holiday BARBIE™

CRAYOLA® Crayon — Complete series $305.50-310.50 MIB

Series #	Year	Price	Item #	Description
1	1989	$50	QX 435-2	Bright Journey
2	1990	$45	QX 458-6	Bright Moving Colors
3	1991	$40	QX 421-9	Bright Vibrant Carols
4	1992	$33	QX 426-4	Bright Blazing Colors
5	1993	$30	QX 442-2	Bright Shining Castle
6	1994	$30	QX 527-3	Bright Playful Colors
7	1995	$19	QX 524-7	Bright 'n Sunny Tepee
8	1996	$25	QX 539-1	Bright Flying Colors
9	1997	$18.50	QX 623-5	Bright Rocking Colors
10/Final	1998	$15-20	QX 616-6	Bright Sledding Colors

Dickens' Caroler Bell Special Ed. — Complete series $165 MIB

Series #	Year	Price	Item #	Description
1	1990	$55	QX 505-6	Mr. Ashbourne
2	1991	$40	QX 503-9	Mrs. Beaumont
3	1992	$40	QX 455-4	Lord Chadwick
4/Final	1993	$30	QX 550-5	Lady Daphne

Dolls of the World, Dated — Complete series $66-76 MIB

Series #	Year	Price	Item #	Description
1	1996	$30-35	QX 556-1	Native American Barbie™
2	1997	$16	QX 616-2	Chinese Barbie™
3	1998	$20-25	QX 635-6	Mexican Barbie™

Fabulous Decade, Dated — Complete series $216-218 MIB

Series #	Year	Price	Item #	Description
1	1990	$30	QX 446-6	Squirrel w/Brass 1990
2	1991	$40	QX 411-9	Raccoon w/Brass 1991
3	1992	$40	QX 424-4	Bear w/Brass 1992
4	1993	$20	QX 447-5	Skunk w/Brass 1993
5	1994	$20	QX 526-3	Rabbit w/Brass 1994
6	1995	$22	QX 514-7	Otter w/Brass 1995
7	1996	$20	QX 566-1	Fox w/Brass 1996
8	1997	$14	QX 623-2	Porcupine w/Brass 1997
9	1998	$10-12	QX 639-3	Bear w/Brass 1998

Football Legends, Dated — Complete series $113-118 MIB

Series #	Year	Price	Item #	Description
1	1995	$50	QXI 575-9	Joe Montana
2	1996	$25	QXI 502-1	Troy Aikman
3	1997	$18	QXI 618-2	Joe Namath
4	1998	$20-25	QXI 403-6	Emmitt Smith

Frosty Friends, Dated Eskimo — Complete series $2,489-2,569 MIB

Series #	Year	Price	Item #	Description
1	1980	$675	QX 137-4	A Cool Yule
2	1981	$480	QX 433-5	Igloo
3	1982	$295	QX 452-3	Icicle
4	1983	$328	QX 400-7	Rubbing Noses w/White Seal
5	1984	$90	QX 437-1	Ice Fishing/Gift
6	1985	$75	QX 482-2	Kayak
7	1986	$75	QX 405-3	Wreath Around Baby Reindeer's Neck
8	1987	$60	QX 440-9	Seal w/Gift on Nose
9	1988	$65	QX 403-1	Wrapping Red Ribbon Around N. Pole
10	1989	$70	QX 457-2	Sled
11	1990	$40	QX 439-6	Sliding Down Iceberg
12	1991	$40	QX 432-7	Ice Hockey
13	1992	$35	QX 429-1	Whale
14	1993	$40	QX 414-2	Dog/Doghouse
15	1994	$37	QX 529-3	Polar Bear Jumping Through Wreath
16	1995	$32	QX 516-9	Eskimo on Snow Mobile
17	1996	$19	QX 568-1	Playing Pool
18	1997	$18	QX 625-5	Eskimo on Parasail
19	1998	$15-20	QX 622-6	Conducting a Chorus of Penguins

Gift Bringers, The, Dated Balls — Complete series $115 MIB

Series #	Year	Price	Item #	Description
1	1989	$25	QX 279-5	St. Nicholas
2	1990	$25	QX 280-3	St. Lucia
3	1991	$25	QX 211-7	Christkindl
4	1992	$20	QX 212-4	Kolyada
5/Final	1993	$20	QX 206-5	The Magi

Greatest Story, Dated — Complete series $77 MIB

Series #	Year	Price	Item #	Description
1	1990	$25	QX 465-6	Brass Snowflake w/White Porcelain Nativity
2	1991	$27	QX 412-9	Shepherds Gaze At the Star
3/Final	1992	$25	QX 425-1	Wise Men Offer Their Gifts

Hark! It's Herald, Dated — Complete series $85 MIB

Series #	Year	Price	Item #	Description
1	1989	$20	QX 455-5	Elf w/Xylophone
2	1990	$25	QX 446-3	Elf w/Drum
3	1991	$20	QX 437-9	Elf w/Golden Fife
4/Final	1992	$20	QX 446-4	Elf w/Baritone

Heart of Christmas, Dated — Complete series $196 MIB

Series #	Year	Price	Item #	Description
1	1990	$80	QX 472-6	Santa Filling the Stockings
2	1991	$27	QX 435-7	Bringing Home the Tree
3	1992	$29	QX 441-1	Decorating the Tree
4	1993	$30	QX 448-2	Sleigh Ride
5/Final	1994	$30	QX 526-6	Family/Christmas Dinner

Heavenly Angels, Dated — Complete series $58 MIB

Series #	Year	Price	Item #	Description
1	1991	$18	QX 436-7	Baroque Angels, ivory antique
2	1992	$20	QX 445-4	Angel w/Trumpet
3/Final	1993	$20	QX 494-5	Angel w/Dove

Here Comes Santa, Dated — Complete series $2,447-2,450 MIB

Series #	Year	Price	Item #	Description
1	1979	$650	QX 155-9	Santa's Motorcar
2	1980	$195	QX 143-4	Santa's Express
3	1981	$400	QX 438-2	Rooftop Deliveries
4	1982	$140	QX 464-3	Jolly Trolley
5	1983	$280	QX 403-7	Santa Express
6	1984	$90	QX 432-4	Santa's Deliveries
7	1985	$65	QX 496-5	Santa's Fire Engines
8	1986	$80	QX 404-3	Kringle's Kool Treats
9	1987	$95	QX 484-7	Santa's Woody
10	1988	$50	QX 400-1	Kringle Koach
11	1989	$50	QX 458-5	Christmas Caboose
12	1990	$45	QX 492-3	Festive Surrey

Seasons Greetings!

Series #	Year	Price	Item #	Description
13	1991	$60	QX 434-9	Antique Car
14	1992	$45	QX 434-1	Kringle Tours
15	1993	$40	QX 410-2	Happy Haul-idays
16	1994	$60	QX 529-6	Makin' Tractor Tracks
17	1995	$30	QX 517-9	Santa's Roadster
18	1996	$32	QX 568-4	Santa's 4x4
19	1997	$22	QX 626-2	The Claus-Mobile
20	1998	$18-21	QX 628-3	Santa's Bumper Car

Hockey Greats, Dated — Complete series $39-44 MIB

1	1997	$19	QXI 627-5	Wayne Gretzky
2	1998	$20-25	QXI 647-6	Mario Lemieux

Holiday Barbie™, Dated — Complete series $340-345 MIB

1	1993	$170	QX 572-5	Red Gown
2	1994	$60	QX 521-6	Gold/Ivory Gown
3	1995	$40	QXI 505-7	Green/White
4	1996	$30	QXI 537-1	Gold Gown w/Red Overcoat
5	1997	$20	QXI 621-2	Red/White
6	1998	$20-25	QXI 402-3	Black/Silver

Holiday Heirloom — Complete series $99 MIB

1	1987	$25	QX 485-7	Glass Bell in Wreath
2	1988	$35	QX 406-4	Silver Angels Above Glass Bell
3/Final	1989	$39	QXC 460-5	Toys Above Glass Bell

Holiday Homecoming — Complete series $35-40 MIB

1	1997	$15	Holiday Traditions™ Barbie®
2	1998	$20-25	Holiday Voyage™ Barbie®

Holiday Wildlife — Complete series $580 MIB

1	1982	$375	QX 313-3	Cardinalis Cardinalis
2	1983	$60	QX 309-9	Black-Capped Chickadees
3	1984	$30	QX 347-4	Ring-Necked Pheasant
4	1985	$30	QX 376-5	California Partridge
5	1986	$30	QX 321-6	Cedar Waxwing
6	1987	$27	QX 371-7	Snow Goose
7/Final	1988	$28	QX 371-1	Purple Finch

Hoop Stars, Dated — Complete series $118-123 MIB

1	1995	$55	QXI 551-7	Shaquille O'Neal
2	1996	$25	QXI 501-4	Larry Bird

Series #	Year	Price	Item #	Description
3	1997	$18	QXI 683-2	Magic Johnson
4	1998	$20-25	QXI 684-6	Grant Hill

Kiddie Car Classics, Dated — Complete series $164.50-169.50 MIB

1	1994	$65	QX 542-6	Murray® Champion
2	1995	$35	QX 502-7	Murray® Fire Truck
3	1996	$26	QX 536-4	Murray® Airplane
4	1997	$18.50	QX 619-5	Murray® Dump Truck
5	1998	$20-25	QX 637-6	Murray® Tractor and Trailer

Lionel®, Dated — Complete series $100-104 MIB

1	1996	$45	QX 553-1	700E Hudson Steam Locomotive
2	1997	$32	QX 614-5	1950 Santa Fe F3 Diesel Locomotive
3	1998	$23-27	QX 634-6	Pennsylvania GG - 1

Madame Alexander, Dated — Complete series $79-82 MIB

1	1996	$35	QX 631-1	Cinderella
2	1997	$26	QX 615-5	Little Red Riding Hood – 1991
3	1998	$18-21	QX 635-3	Mop Top Wendy

Madame Alexander Holiday Angels — Complete series $17-19 Proj.

1	1998	$17-19	QX 649-3	Glorious Angel

Majestic Wilderness, Dated — Complete series $37-40 MIB

1	1997	$22	QX 569-4	Snowshoe Rabbits in Winter
2	1998	$15-18	QX 627-3	Timber Wolves at Play

Marilyn Monroe, Dated — Complete series $38-43 MIB

1	1997	$18	QX 570-4	Marilyn Monroe: Marilyn Monroe
2	1998	$20-25	QX 633-3	Marilyn Monroe: Seven Year Itch

Mary's Angels — Complete series $382-384 MIB

1	1988	$45	QX 407-4	Buttercup
2	1989	$95	QX 454-5	Bluebell
3	1990	$40	QX 442-3	Rosebud
4	1991	$40	QX 427-9	Iris
5	1992	$50	QX 427-4	Lily
6	1993	$28	QX 428-2	Ivy
7	1994	$22	QX 527-6	Jasmine
8	1995	$22	QX 514-9	Camellia
9	1996	$16	QX 566-4	Violet
10	1997	$14	QX 624-2	Daisy
11	1998	$10-12	QX 615-3	Daphne

Merry Olde Santa, Dated — Complete series $377-379 MIB

Series #	Year	Price	Item #	Description
1	1990	$78	QX 473-6	Santa Holding Mini – Christmas Tree
2	1991	$83	QX 435-9	Santa w/ Bag of Toys, Cane w/Bell
3	1992	$40	QX 441-4	Santa Filling a Stocking
4	1993	$40	QX 484-2	Santa w/Bell and Ice Skates
5	1994	$33	QX 525-6	Santa w/Wreath and Lantern
6	1995	$29	QX 513-9	Santa w/Bag of Goodies
7	1996	$32	QX 565-4	Fourth of July Santa
8	1997	$24	QX 622-5	Santa w/Cardinals on Hands
9	1998	$18-21	QX 638-6	Santa Raising Arms Above Head

Miniature Creche — Complete series $182 MIB

Series #	Year	Price	Item #	Description
1	1985	$25	QX 482-5	Wood and Woven Straw
2	1986	$62	QX 407-6	Fine Porcelain
3	1987	$40	QX 481-9	Multi-Plated Brass
4	1988	$35	QX 403-4	Acrylic
5/Final	1989	$20	QX 459-2	Handcrafted

Mother Goose — Complete series $148 MIB

Series #	Year	Price	Item #	Description
1	1993	$45	QX 528-2	Humpty-Dumpty
2	1994	$40	QX 521-3	Hey Diddle, Diddle
3	1995	$25	QX 509-9	Jack and Jill
4	1996	$20	QX 564-4	Mary Had a Little Lamb
5/Final	1997	$18	QX 621-5	Little Boy Blue

Mr. and Mrs. Claus — Complete series $576 MIB

Series #	Year	Price	Item #	Description
1	1986	$105	QX 402-6	Merry Mistletoe Time
2	1987	$69	QX 483-7	Home Cooking
3	1988	$60	QX 401-1	Shall We Dance
4	1989	$50	QX 457-5	Holiday Duet
5	1990	$80	QX 439-3	Popcorn Party
6	1991	$50	QX 433-9	Checking His List
7	1992	$45	QX 429-4	Gift Exchange
8	1993	$45	QX 420-2	A Fitting Moment
9	1994	$40	QX 528-3	A Handwarming Present
10/Final	1995	$32	QX 515-7	Christmas Eve Kiss

Norman Rockwell — Complete series $514 MIB

Series #	Year	Price	Item #	Description
1	1980	$250	QX 306-1	Santa's Visitors
2	1981	$50	QX 511-5	The Carolers
3	1982	$32	QX 305-3	Filling the Stockings
4	1983	$35	QX 300-7	Dress Rehearsal
5	1984	$35	QX 341-1	Caught Napping
6	1985	$35	QX 374-5	Jolly Postman
7	1986	$30	QX 321-3	Checking Up

Series #	Year	Price	Item #	Description
8	1987	$25	QX 370-7	The Christmas Dance
9/Final	1988	$22	QX 370-4	And To All a Good Night

Nostalgic Houses and Shops — Complete series $1,276-1,281 MIB

Series #	Year	Price	Item #	Description
1	1984	$215	QX 448-1	Victorian Doll house
2	1985	$155	QX 497-5	Old-Fashioned Toy Shop
3	1986	$300	QX 403-3	Christmas Candy Shoppe
4	1987	$80	QX 483-9	House on Main Street
5	1988	$70	QX 401-4	Hall Bro's. Card Shop
6	1989	$70	QX 458-2	U.S. Post Office
7	1990	$80	QX 469-6	Holiday Home
8	1991	$70	QX 413-9	Fire Station
9	1992	$45	QX 425-4	Five-and-Ten-Cent Store
10	1993	$53	QX 417-5	Cozy Home
11	1994	$40	QX 528-6	Neighborhood Drugstore
12	1995	$32	QX 515-9	Town Church
13	1996	$26	QX 567-1	Victorian Painted Lady
14	1997	$20	QX 624-5	Cafe
15	1998	$20-25	QX 626-6	Grocery Store

Owliver — Complete series $56 MIB

Series #	Year	Price	Item #	Description
1	1992	$18	QX 454-4	Owliday Tales
2	1993	$18	QX 542-5	Owliver Sleeping by Squirrel
3/Final	1994	$20	QX 522-6	Owliver/Woodpeckers Trimming Tree Stump

Old West, The, Dated — Complete series $16-19 Proj.

Series #	Year	Price	Item #	Description
1	1998	$16-19	QX6323	Pony Express Rider

Peace On Earth, Dated — Complete series $73 MIB

Series #	Year	Price	Item #	Description
1	1991	$25	QX 512-9	Italy
2	1992	$23	QX 517-4	Spain
3/Final	1993	$25	QX 524-2	Poland

Peanuts® Gang — Complete series $129 MIB

Series #	Year	Price	Item #	Description
1	1993	$65	QX 531-5	Charlie Brown and Snow Man
2	1994	$25	QX 520-3	Lucy/Football w/Red Ribbon
3	1995	$24	QX 505-9	Linus on Sled
4/Final	1996	$15	QX 538-1	Sally Making Her List

Porcelain Bear — Complete series $374 MIB

Series #	Year	Price	Item #	Description
1	1983	$90	QX 428-9	Cinnamon Bear w/Top
2	1984	$50	QX 454-1	Cinnamon Bear w/Jingle Bell
3	1985	$60	QX 479-2	Cinnamon Bear w/Candy Cane
4	1986	$40	QX 405-6	Cinnamon Bear w/Gift Behind Back
5	1987	$40	QX 442-7	Cinnamon Bear Digging in Sock

Series #	Year	Price	Item #	Description
6	1988	$39	QX 404-4	Cinnamon Bear w/Heart
7	1989	$35	QX 461-5	Cinnamon Bear Eating Candy
8/Final	1990	$20	QX 442-6	Cinnamon Bear w/Christmas Tree

Puppy Love   Complete series $217-219 MIB

Series #	Year	Price	Item #	Description
1	1991	$60	QX 537-9	Cocker Spaniel on Candy Cane
2	1992	$40	QX 448-4	Grey/White Terrier in Basket
3	1993	$30	QX 504-5	Golden Retriever on Sled
4	1994	$25	QX 525-3	White Poodle Tangled Green Garland
5	1995	$22	QX 513-7	Puppy Helping Wrap Presents
6	1996	$18	QX 565-1	Brown Puppy Begging for Bone
7	1997	$12	QX 622-2	Beagle Puppy Holding Stocking
8	1998	$10-12	QX 616-3	Gray Puppy Tangled in Christmas Lights

Reindeer Champs   Complete series $395 MIB

Series #	Year	Price	Item #	Description
1	1986	$155	QX 422-3	Dasher
2	1987	$55	QX 480-9	Dancer
3	1988	$35	QX 405-1	Prancer
4	1989	$25	QX 456-2	Vixen
5	1990	$30	QX 443-3	Comet
6	1991	$30	QX 434-7	Cupid
7	1992	$35	QX 528-4	Donder
8/Final	1993	$30	QX 433-1	Blitzen

Rocking Horse, Dated   Complete series $2,032 MIB

Series #	Year	Price	Item #	Description
1	1981	$495	QX 422-2	Dappled
2	1982	$420	QX 502-3	Black
3	1983	$300	QX 417-7	Russet
4	1984	$100	QX 435-4	Appaloosa
5	1985	$95	QX 493-2	Pinto
6	1986	$65	QX 401-6	Palomino
7	1987	$80	QX 482-9	White
8	1988	$70	QX 402-4	Dappled Gray
9	1989	$70	QX 462-2	Bay
10	1990	$100	QX 464-6	Brown/White Dappled
11	1991	$60	QX 414-7	Buckskin
12	1992	$45	QX 426-1	Brown w/White Feet
13	1993	$50	QX 416-2	Gray w/White Feet
14	1994	$30	QX 501-6	Dark Brown w/White Stockings
15	1995	$30	QX 516-7	Painted pony w/Red Saddle
16/Final	1996	$22	QX 567-4	Black w/White Mane and Tail

Scarlett O'Hara, Dated   Complete series $38.50-43.50 MIB

Series #	Year	Price	Item #	Description
1	1997	$18.50	QX 612-5	Scarlett in Red Dress
2	1998	$20-25	QX 633-6	Scarlett as Debutante

Sky's the Limit, Dated   Complete series $40-43 MIB

Series #	Year	Price	Item #	Description
1	1997	$22	QX 557-4	Flight at Kitty Hawk, The
2	1998	$20-25	QX 628-6	1917 Curtiss JN- 4D "Jenny"

SNOOPY® and Friends, Dated   Complete series $545 MIB

Series #	Year	Price	Item #	Description
1	1979	$100	QX 141-9	Ice-Hockey Holiday
2	1980	$115	QX 154-1	Ski Holiday
3	1981	$130	QX 436-2	SNOOPY® and Friends (Sledding)
4	1982	$100	QX 480-3	SNOOPY® and Friends (Sleigh on Chimney)
5/Final	1983	$100	QX 416-9	Santa SNOOPY®

Snow Buddies   Complete series $10-12 Proj.

Series #	Year	Price	Item #	Description
1	1998	$10-12	QX 685-3	Snowman w/Bunny

Spotlight on Snoopy   Complete series $15-20 Proj.

Series #	Year	Price	Item #	Description
1	1998	$15-20	QX 645-3	Joe Cool

Star Wars, Dated   Complete series $44-49 MIB

Series #	Year	Price	Item #	Description
1	1997	$25	QXI 548-4	Luke Skywalker™
2	1998	$19-24	QXI 402-6	Princess Leia ™

Stock Car Champions   Complete series $38-49 MIB

Series #	Year	Price	Item #	Description
1	1997	$18-24	QXI 616-5	Jeff Gordon®
2	1998	$20-25	QXI 414-3	Richard Petty

Thimble   Complete series $1,102 MIB

Series #	Year	Price	Item #	Description
1	1978	$295	QX 133-6	Mouse in a Thimble
2	1979	$175	QX 131-9	A Christmas Salute
3	1980	$150	QX 132-1	Thimble Elf
4	1981	$160	QX 413-5	Thimble Angel
5	1982	$75	QX 451-3	Thimble Mouse
6	1983	$40	QX 401-7	Thimble Elf
7	1984	$60	QX 430-4	Thimble Angel
8	1985	$35	QX 472-5	Thimble Santa
9	1986	$30	QX 406-6	Thimble Partridge
10	1987	$30	QX 441-9	Thimble Drummer
11	1988	$25	QX 405-4	Thimble Snowman
12/Final	1989	$27	QX 455-2	Thimble Puppy

Thomas Kinkade, Dated   Complete series $32-36 MIB

Series #	Year	Price	Item #	Description
1	1997	$18	QXI 613-5	Victorian Christmas
2	1998	$14-18	QX 634-3	Victorian Christmas II

Tin Locomotive   Complete series $1,465 MIB

Series #	Year	Price	Item #	Description
1	1982	$750	QX 460-3	Blue
2	1983	$300	QX 404-9	Green and Red
3	1984	$70	QX 440-4	Red w/Blue and Gray
4	1985	$80	QX 497-2	Black
5	1986	$80	QX 403-6	Red and Yellow
6	1987	$65	QX 484-9	Green and Blue
7	1988	$60	QX 400-4	Brown and Blue
8/Final	1989	$60	QX 460-2	Gray and Green

Tobin Fraley Carrousel   Complete series $245 MIB

1	1992	$75	QX 489-1	White
2	1993	$60	QX 550-2	White
3	1994	$60	QX 522-3	White
4/Final	1995	$50	QX 506-9	White

Twelve Days of Christmas, Dated   Complete series $657 MIB

1	1984	$300	QX 348-4	Partridge in a Pear Tree
2	1985	$70	QX 371-2	Two Turtle Doves
3	1986	$45	QX 378-6	Three French Hens
4	1987	$40	QX 370-9	Four Colly Birds
5	1988	$30	QX 371-4	Five Golden Rings
6	1989	$20	QX 381-2	Six Geese A-Laying
7	1990	$32	QX 303-3	Seven Swans A Swimming
8	1991	$30	QX 308-9	Eight Maids A Milking
9	1992	$25	QX 303-1	Nine Ladies Dancing
10	1993	$25	QX 301-2	Ten Lords a Leaping
11	1994	$20	QX 318-3	Eleven Pipers Piping
12/Final	1995	$20	QX 300-9	Twelve Drummers Drumming

U.S. Christmas Stamps   Complete series $65 MIB

1	1993	$20	QX 529-2	1983 Santa Stamp
2	1994	$20	QX 520-6	1982 Snow Scene from Snow, OK
3/Final	1995	$25	QX 506-7	.25 Greeting w/Christmas tree

Windows of the World, Dated   Complete series $285 MIB

1	1985	$75	QX 490-2	Feliz Navidad
2	1986	$65	QX 408-3	Vrolyk Kerstfeest
3	1987	$40	QX 482-7	Mele Kalikimaka
4	1988	$35	QX 402-1	Joyeaux Noel
5	1989	$30	QX 462-5	Frohliche Weihnachten
6/Final	1990	$40	QX 463-6	Nollaig Shona

Winter Surprise   Complete series $86 MIB

1	1989	$20	QX 427-2	Decorating a Christmas Tree

Series #	Year	Price	Item #	Description
2	1990	$20	QX 444-3	Ice Skating
3	1991	$23	QX 427-7	Polar Carols
4/Final	1992	$23	QX 427-1	Building a Snowman

Winnie the Pooh, Dated   Complete series $20-25 Proj.

1	1998	$20-25	QXD 408-6	A Visit From Piglet

Wood Childhood Ornaments   Complete series $162 MIB

1	1984	$30	QX 439-4	Wood Lamb
2	1985	$30	QX 472-2	Wood Train
3	1986	$30	QX 407-3	Wood Reindeer
4	1987	$27	QX 441-7	Wood Horse
5	1988	$20	QX 404-1	Wood Airplane
6/Final	1989	$25	QX 459-5	Wood Truck

Yuletide Central, Dated   Complete series $168-173 MIB

1	1994	$50	QX 531-6	Locomotive
2	1995	$30	QX 507-9	Coal Car
3	1996	$38	QX 501-1	Mail Car
4	1997	$28-30	QX 581-2	Cargo Car
5/Final	1998	$22-25	QX 637-3	Caboose

Disney Collection Series

Enchanted Memories Collection, Dated   Complete series $42-47 MIB

1	1997	$22	QXD 404-5	Disney: Cinderella
2	1998	$20-25	QXD 405-6	Disney: Snow White

Hallmark Archives, Dated   Complete series $37-42 MIB

1	1997	$22	QXD 402-5	Donald's Surprising Gift
2	1998	$15-20	QXD 400-6	Ready for Christmas

Mickey's Holiday Parade, Dated   Complete series $45-50 MIB

1	1997	$26	QXD 402-2	Bandleader Mickey
2	1998	$19-24	QXD 410-6	Minnie Plays the Flute

Romantic Vacations, Dated   Complete series $20-25 Proj.

1	1998	$20-25	QXD 410-3	Donald and Daisy in Venice

Unforgettable Villains				Complete series $20-25 Proj.
Series #	Year	Price	Item #	Description
1	1998	$20-25	QXD 406-3	Cruella de Vil

Lighted Ornament Series

Chris Mouse, Dated, Lighted				Complete series $603 MIB
1	1985	$90	QLX 703-2	Chris Mouse
2	1986	$75	QLX 705-6	Chris Mouse Dreams
3	1987	$60	QLX 705-7	Chris Mouse Glow
4	1988	$60	QLX 715-4	Chris Mouse Star
5	1989	$45	QLX 722-5	Chris Mouse Cookout
6	1990	$50	QLX 729-6	Chris Mouse Wreath
7	1991	$40	QLX 720-7	Chris Mouse Mail
8	1992	$30	QLX 707-4	Chris Mouse Tales
9	1993	$35	QLX 715-2	Chris Mouse Flight
10	1994	$30	QLX 739-3	Chris Mouse Jelly
11	1995	$30	QLX 730-7	Chris Mouse Tree
12	1996	$30	QLX 737-1	Chris Mouse Inn
13/Final	1997	$28	QLX 752-5	Chris Mouse Luminaria

Christmas Classics, Dated, Lighted				Complete series $283 MIB
1	1986	$85	QLX 704-3	The Nutcracker Ballet - Sugarplum Fairy
2	1987	$75	QLX 702-9	A Christmas Carol
3	1988	$30	QLX 716-1	Night Before Christmas
4	1989	$43	QLX 724-2	Little Drummer Boy
5/Final	1990	$50	QLX 730-3	The Littlest Angel

Forest Frolics, Dated, Lighted				Complete series $449 MIB
1	1989	$95	QLX 728-2	Animals Skiing around Candy Cane
2	1990	$60	QLX 723-6	Animals in Tree House
3	1991	$70	QLX 721-9	Ice Show
4	1992	$65	QLX 725-4	Animals on Seesaw
5	1993	$53	QLX 716-5	Animals Decorating Christmas Tree
6	1994	$60	QLX 743-6	Animals Circle a Lighted Tree
7/Final	1995	$46	QLX 729-9	Forest Animals Swinging

Journeys into Space, Dated				Complete series $110-114 MIB
1	1996	$50	QLX 752-4	Freedom 7
2	1997	$32	QLX 753-2	Journeys Into Space: Friendship 7
3	1998	$28-32	QLX 754-3	Apollo Lunar Module

Lighthouse Greeting, Dated				Complete series $56-58 MIB
Series #	Year	Price	Item #	Description
1	1997	$30	QLX 744-2	Light House With Flashig Lights
2	1998	$26-28	QLX 753-6	Light House With Flashig Lights

Peanuts®, Dated, Lighted				Complete series $280 MIB
1	1991	$75	QLX 722-9	The Stockings Were Hung ...
2	1992	$50	QLX 721-4	Snoopy and Woodstock on Doghouse
3	1993	$50	QLX 715-5	Snoopy and Woodstock w/Tree
4	1994	$50	QLX 740-6	Snoopy and Woodstock Ringing Bells
5/Final	1995	$55	QLX 727-7	Snoopy Ice Skating

Santa and Sparky, Dated, Lighted				Complete series $215 MIB
1	1986	$95	QLX 703-3	Lighting the Tree
2	1987	$75	QLX 701-9	Perfect Portrait
3/Final	1988	$45	QLX 719-1	On W/the Show

Tobin Fraley, Dated, Lighted & Music				Complete series $180 MIB
1	1994	$75	QLX 749-6	Skater's Waltz
2	1995	$55	QLX 726-9	Over the Waves
3/Final	1996	$50	QLX 746-1	On the Beautiful blue Danube

Show Case Ornaments

Language of Flowers, Dated				Complete series $84-86 MIB
1	1996	$45	QK 117-1	Pansy
2	1997	$21	QX 109-5	Snowdrop Angel
3	1998	$18-20	QX 615-6	Iris Angel

Turn of the Century Parade, Dated				Complete series $89 MIB
1	1995	$39	QK 102-7	The Fireman
2	1996	$30	QK 108-4	Uncle Sam
3/Final	1997	$20	QX 121-5	Santa Claus

Collectible Mini Ornament Series

Alice in Wonderland, Dated				Complete series $51 MIB
1	1995	$15	QXM 477-7	Alice Sitting on a Thimble
2	1996	$15	QXM 407-4	Mad Hatter
3	1997	$12	QXM 414-2	White Rabbit
4/Final	1998	$9	QXM 418-6	Cheshire Cat

Antique Tractor, Dated   Complete series   **$25 MIB**

Series #	Year	Price	Item #	Description
1	1997	$16	QXM 418-5	Antique Tractor
2	1998	$9	QXM 416-6	Antique Tractor

Bearymores, The, Dated   Complete series   **$54 MIB**

1	1992	$18	QXM 554-4	Decorating the Tree
2	1993	$19	QXM 512-5	Caroling
3/Final	1994	$17	QXM 513-3	Building a Snowman

Centuries of Santa, Dated   Complete series   **$83 MIB**

1	1994	$25	QXM 515-3	Santa w/Tree
2	1995	$22	QXM 478-9	Santa w/Bunch of Goodies
3	1996	$16	QXM 409-1	Santa w/Walking Stick and Lantern
4	1997	$12	QXM 429-5	Santa in Kings Suit
5	1998	$8	QXM 420-6	Santa w/Toy Polar Bear

Christmas Bells, Dated   Complete series   **$50-52 MIB**

1	1995	$20	QXM 400-7	Angel on Top of Bell
2	1996	$15	QXM 407-1	Santa on Top of Bell
3	1997	$8-10	QXM 416-2	Snowman on Top of Bell
4	1998	$7	QXM 419-6	Bear on Top of Bell

Kittens in Toyland   Complete series   **$104 MIB**

1	1988	$25	QXM 562-1	Kitten w/Locomotive
2	1989	$21	QXM 561-2	Kitten on Scooter
3	1990	$20	QXM 573-6	Kitten in Sailboat
4	1991	$20	QXM 563-9	Kitten in Airplane
5/Final	1992	$18	QXM 539-1	Kitten on Pogo Stick

Kringles, The, Dated   Complete series   **$127 MIB**

1	1989	$33	QXM 562-5	Santa w/Package Behind Back
2	1990	$30	QXM 575-3	Santa Getting Ready to Leave
3	1991	$25	QXM 564-7	Mr. and Mrs. Kringle w/Plate of Cookies
4	1992	$23	QXM 538-1	Mr. and Mrs. Kringle Caroling
5/Final	1993	$16	QXM 513-5	Mr. and Mrs. Kringle Holding Wreath

March of the Teddy Bears, Dated   Complete series   **$64 MIB**

1	1993	$17	QXM 400-5	Teddy Holding Baton
2	1994	$20	QXM 510-6	Teddy w/Drum
3	1995	$14	QXM 479-9	Teddy Bear w/Trumpet
4/Final	1996	$13	QXM 409-4	Teddy Bear w/Trombone

Miniature Clothespin Soldier   Complete series   **$45 MIB**

Series #	Year	Price	Item #	Description
1	1995	$17	QXM 409-7	Miniature Clothespin Soldier
2	1996	$13	QXM 414-4	Miniature Clothespin Soldier
3	1997	$8	QXM 415-5	Miniature Clothespin Soldier
4	1998	$7	QXM 419-3	Miniature Clothespin Soldier

Miniature Kiddie Car Classics, Dated   Complete series   **$62 MIB**

1	1995	$20	QXM 407-9	Murray® Blue "Champion"
2	1996	$18	QXM 403-1	Murray® "Fire Truck"
3	1997	$14	QXM 413-2	Murray Inc.® "Pursuit" Airplane
4	1998	$10	QXM 418-3	Murray Inc.® "Dump Truck"

Miniature Kiddie Car Luxury Edition   Complete series   **$10 Proj.**

| 1 | 1998 | $10 | QXM 414-3 | 1937 Steelcraft Auburn |

Nativity, The   Complete series   **$9 Proj.**

| 1 | 1998 | $9 | QXM 415-6 | Joseph, Mary and Baby Jesus |

Nature's Angels   Complete series   **$134 MIB**

1	1990	$26	QXM 573-3	Rabbit Angel in White
2	1991	$23	QXM 565-7	Puppy Angel in Blue
3	1992	$20	QXM 545-1	Bear Angel w/Wreath
4	1993	$20	QXM 512-2	Kitty Angel
5	1994	$12	QXM 512-6	Skunk Angel
6	1995	$20	QXM 480-9	Bear Angel
7/Final	1996	$13	QXM 411-1	Squirrel Angel w/Nut

Night Before Christmas, The, Dated   Complete series   **$102 MIB**

1	1992	$30	QXM 554-1	Tin House/Mouse in Rocking Chair
2	1993	$23	QXM 511-5	Children Sleeping in Bed
3	1994	$15	QXM 512-3	Pa in His Kerchief
4	1995	$20	QXM 480-7	Santa w/Bag of Gifts
5/Final	1996	$14	QXM 410-4	Santa in Sleigh

Noel R.R., Dated   Complete series   **$247 MIB**

1	1989	$43	QXM 576-2	Blue Locomotive
2	1990	$34	QXM 575-6	Red Coal Car w/Toys
3	1991	$50	QXM 564-9	Passenger Car
4	1992	$15	QXM 544-1	Box Car
5	1993	$25	QXM 510-5	Flatbed Car
6	1994	$22	QXM 511-3	Stock Car
7	1995	$18	QXM 481-7	Tank Car
8	1996	$20	QXM 411-4	Cookie Car
9	1997	$10	QXM 417-5	Candy Car
10/Final	1998	$10	QXM 421-6	Caboose

Nutcracker Ballet, Dated — Complete series $47 MIB

Series #	Year	Price	Item #	Description
1	1996	$30	QXM 406-4	Girl in Pink Dress
2	1997	$9	QXM 413-5	Herr Drosselmeyer
3	1998	$8	QXM 414-6	Nutcracker

Nutcracker Guild, Dated — Complete series $78 MIB

Series #	Year	Price	Item #	Description
1	1994	$23	QXM 514-6	Nutcracker w/Rolling Pin
2	1995	$20	QXM 478-7	Nutcracker w/Gifts
3	1996	$16	QXM 404-4	Nutcracker w/Fishing Supplies
4	1997	$10	QXM 416-5	Nutcracker w/Flower Pot
5	1998	$9	QXM 420-3	Nutcracker w/Skis

Old English Village Series, Dated — Complete series $237 MIB

Series #	Year	Price	Item #	Description
1	1988	$45	QXM 563-4	Family Home
2	1989	$20	QXM 561-5	Sweet Shop
3	1990	$25	QXM 576-3	School
4	1991	$30	QXM 562-7	Inn
5	1992	$35	QXM 538-4	Church
6	1993	$22	QXM 513-2	Toy Shop
7	1994	$17	QXM 514-3	Hat Shop
8	1995	$19	QXM 481-9	Tudor House
9	1996	$16	QXM 412-4	Village Mill
10/Final	1997	$8	QXM 418-2	Village Depot

On the Road, Dated — Complete series $88 MIB

Series #	Year	Price	Item #	Description
1	1993	$22	QXM 400-2	Pressed Tin Station Wagon
2	1994	$17	QXM 510-3	Pressed Tin Van
3	1995	$16	QXM 479-7`	Pressed Tin Fire Engine
4	1996	$13	QXM 410-1	Pressed Tin Truck
5	1997	$12	QXM 417-2	Pressed Tin Police Car
6/Final	1998	$8	QXM 421-3	Pressed Tin Mail Car

Penguin Pal — Complete series $80 MIB

Series #	Year	Price	Item #	Description
1	1988	$25	QXM 563-1	Penguin w/Gift
2	1989	$20	QXM 560-2	Penguin w/Candy Cane
3	1990	$20	QXM 574-6	Penguin on Green Skis
4/Final	1991	$15	QXM 562-9	Penguin on Ice Skates

Rocking Horse, Dated — Complete series $225 MIB

Series #	Year	Price	Item #	Description
1	1988	$45	QXM 562-4	Dappled horse w/Red Rockers
2	1989	$30	QXM 560-5	Palomino w/Blue Rockers
3	1990	$25	QXM 574-3	Pinto w/Turquoise Rockers
4	1991	$30	QXM 563-7	Grey Arabian w/Red Rockers
5	1992	$23	QXM 545-4	Brown w/Green Rockers
6	1993	$15	QXM 511-2	Appalosa Black w/Red Rockers
7	1994	$18	QXM 511-6	White w/Tan Rockers
8	1995	$15	QXM 482-7	Brown Spotted Horse w/Blue & Green Rocker
9	1996	$16	QXM 412-1	Spotted Horse w/Red Rockers
10/Final	1997	$8	QXM 430-2	Gray Horse w/Brown and Black Rockers

Santa's Little Big Top, Dated — Complete series $42 MIB

Series #	Year	Price	Item #	Description
1	1995	$19	QXM 477-9	Santa is Putting on his Circus Show
2	1996	$15	QXM 408-1	Clowns on Balls
3/Final	1997	$8	QXM 415-2	Santa Putting on an Elephant Show

Snowflake Ballet, Dated — Complete series $23 MIB

Series #	Year	Price	Item #	Description
1	1997	$15	QXM 419-2	Snowflake Ballet
2	1998	$8	QXM 417-3	Snowflake Ballet

Teddy-Bear Style, Dated — Complete series $18 MIB

Series #	Year	Price	Item #	Description
1	1997	$10	QXM 421-5	Teddy Dressed in Hat and Vest
2	1998	$8	QXM 417-6	Teddy Dressed in Party Hat and Collar

Thimble Bells, Dated Porcelain — Complete series $83 MIB

Series #	Year	Price	Item #	Description
1	1990	$18	QXM 554-3	Rabbits
2	1991	$27	QXM 565-9	Year w/Holly Enclosure
3	1992	$23	QXM 546-1	Teddy Bear and Holly
4/Final	1993	$15	QXM 514-2	Poinsettia

Welcome Friends, Dated — Complete series $19 MIB

Series #	Year	Price	Item #	Description
1	1997	$10	QXM 420-5	Birds and Squirrel at Feeder
2	1998	$9	QXM 415-3	Birds at Bird House

Winter Fun With SNOOPY®, Dated — Complete series $10 Proj.

Series #	Year	Price	Item #	Description
1	1998	$10	QXM 424-3	Snoop in Dog Bowl

Woodland Babies — Complete series $49 MIB

Series #	Year	Price	Item #	Description
1	1991	$18	QXM 566-7	Baby Squirrel in Nutshell Cradle
2	1992	$15	QXM 544-4	Baby Raccoon Sleeping in a Leaf
3/Final	1993	$16	QXM 510-2	Baby Beaver on Tree Branch

Easter & Spring Ornament Series

Apple Blossom Lane, Dated — Complete series $56 MIB

Series #	Year	Price	Item #	Description
1	1995	$20	QEO 820-7	Apple Blossom Lane
2	1996	$18	QEO 808-4	Rabbit's house
3/Final	1997	$18	QEO 866-2	Apple Blossom Lane

Beatrix Potter — Complete series $109 MIB

1	1996	$75	QEO 807-1	Peter Rabbit™
2	1997	$20	QEO 864-5	Jemima Puddle-duck™
3	1998	$14	QEO 838-3	Benjamin Bunny™

Children's Collector Barbie™ — Complete series $43 MIB

1	1997	$25	QEO 863-5	Barbie™ as Rapunzel
2	1998	$18	QEO 837-3	Barbie as Little Bo Peep

Collector's Plate, Dated, Porcelain — Complete series $84 MIB

1	1994	$32	QEO 823-3	"Gathering Sunny Memories 1994"
2	1995	$19	QEO 821-9	"Catching the Breeze"
3	1996	$16	QEO 822-1	"Keeping a Secret"
4/Final	1997	$17	QEO 867-5	"Sunny Sunday Best"

Cotton Tail Express, Dated — Complete series $68 MIB

1	1996	$40	QEO 807-4	Locomotive
2	1997	$16	QEO 865-2	Coal Car
3	1998	$12	QEO 837-6	Passenger Car

Easter Parade, Dated — Complete series $70 MIB

1	1992	$30	QEO 930-1	Rabbit Conductor
2	1993	$20	QEO 832-5	Rabbit Playing Xylophone
3/Final	1994	$20	QEO 813-6	Rabbit Trumpeter

Eggs in Sports — Complete series $75 MIB

1	1992	$35	QEO 934-1	Baseball
2	1993	$20	QEO 833-2	Tennis
3/Final	1994	$20	QEO 813-3	Golf

Garden Club, Dated — Complete series $60 MIB

1	1995	$21	QEO 820-9	Chipmunk w/Flowers
2	1996	$15	QEO 809-1	Skunk SmellingFlowers
3	1997	$14	QEO 866-5	Garden Club
4/Final	1998	$10	QEO 842-6	Garden Club

Here Comes Easter, Dated — Complete series $81 MIB

Series #	Year	Price	Item #	Description
1	1994	$30	QEO 809-3	Rabbit in Car
2	1995	$19	QEO 821-7	Helicopter
3	1996	$17	QEO 809-4	Rabbit w/Chick in Bed of Truck
4/Final	1997	$15	QEO 868-2	Duck in Boat

Joyful Angels — Complete series $63 MIB

1	1996	$30	QEO 818-4	Joyful Ange in Pink
2	1997	$18	QEO 865-5	Joyful Angel in Yellow
3/Final	1998	$15	QEO 838-6	Joyful Angel in Blue

Sidewalk Cruisers — Complete series $36 MIB

1	1997	$19	QEO 863-2	1935 Velocipede by Murray®
2	1998	$17	QEO 839-3	1939 Mobo Horse

Springtime Barbie, Dated — Complete series $80 MIB

1	1995	$35	QEO 806-9	Floral Lavender Dress
2	1996	$28	QEO 808-1	Pink Dress
3/Final	1997	$17	QEO 864-2	Pink and White Dress

Springtime Bonnets, Dated — Complete series $112 MIB

1	1993	$30	QEO 832-2	Rabbit in Purple and White Dress
2	1994	$25	QEO 809-6	Rabbit in Pink Dress
3	1995	$18	QEO 822-7	Rabbit in Light Blue Dress
4	1996	$25	QEO 813-4	Rabbit in Green Dress/Umbrella
5/Final	1997	$14	QEO 867-2	Rabbit in Pink and Lavender Dress

Vintage Roadsters, Dated — Complete series $20 MIB

1	1998	$20	QEO 841-6	1931 Ford Model A Roadster

Hallmark Keepsake Ornament Collector's Club Ornaments

Year	Item #	Description	Comments	Price
1987	QXC 580-9	Wreath of Memories, Dated	Membership	$65
1987	QXC 581-7	Carrousel Reindeer	Members Only	$65
1988	QXC 580-4	Our Clubhouse, Dated	Membership	$45
1988	QXC 570-4	Hold On Tight, Mini	Early Renewal Gift	$75
1988	QXC 580-1	Sleighful of Dreams	Members Only	$75
1988	QX 406-4	Holiday Heirloom, II	Club - LE 34,600	$35

Year	Item #	Description	Comments	Price
1988	QX 408-4	Angelic Minstrel	Club - LE 49,900	$60
1988	QX 407-1	Christmas Is Sharing	Club - LE 49,900	$50
1989	QXC 580-2	Visit From Santa, Dated	Membership	$60
1989	QXC 428-5	Collect A Dream	Members Only	$65
1989	QXC 581-2	Sitting Purty, Mini	Special Gift	$45
1989	QXC 451-2	Christmas Is Peaceful	Club - LE 49,900	$45
1989	QXC 448-3	Noelle	Club - LE 49,900	$60
1989	QXC 460-5	Holiday Heirloom, III	Club- LE 34,600	$39
1990	QXC 445-6	Club Hollow, Dated	Membership	$35
1990	QXC 445-3	Armful of Joy	Members Only	$45
1990	QXC 560-3	Crown Prince, Mini	Special Gift	$35
1990	QXC 447-6	Dove of Peace	Club - LE 25,400	$75
1990	QXC 476-6	Christmas Limited	Club - LE 38,700	$125
1990	QXC 447-3	Sugar Plum Fairy	Club - LE 25,400	$60
1991	QXC 476-9	Hidden Treasure/Li'l Keeper	Membership	$38
1991	QXC 315-9	Five Years Together	Charter Mbr. Gift	$45
1991	QXC 725-9	Beary Artistic (Lighted)	Members Only	$40
1991	QXC 479-7	Secrets for Santa	Club - LE 28,700	$50
1991	QXC 477-9	Galloping Into Christmas	Club - LE 28,400	$125
1992	QXC 508-1	Rodney Takes Flight	Membership	$23
1992	QXC 729-1	Santa's Club List	Members Only	$40
1992	QXC 519-4	Chipmunk Parcel Service, Mini	Special Gift	$10
1992	QXC 546-4	Christmas Treasures	Club - LE 15,500	$125-$150
1992	QXC 406-7	Victorian Skater	Club - LE 14,700	$75
1993	QXC 527-2	It's in the Mail	Membership	$23
1993	QXC 543-2	Trimmed W/Memories	Members Only	$40
1993	QXC 543-5	Sharing Christmas	Club - LE 16,500	$45
1993	QXC 544-2	Gentle Tidings	Club - LE 17,500	$48
1993	QXC 529-4	Forty Winks, Mini	Membership	$20
1994	QXC 825-6	Tilling Time	Membership	$60
1994	QXC 484-6	First Hello	Membership	N.E.
1994	QXC 480-3	Happy Collecting MM Dog in Bag	Renewal Bonus	$30
1994	QXC 482-3	Holiday Pursuit	Membership	$24
1994	QXC 483-3	Jolly Holly Santa	Club - LE	$50
1994	QXC 483-6	Majestic Deer	Club - LE	$50
1994	QXC 485-3	On Cloud Nine	Members Only	$30
1994	QXC 480-6	Sweet Bouquet - Mini	Membership	$25
1995	QXC 416-7	1958 Ford Edsel Citation Conv.	Members Only	$75
1995	QXC 539-7	Barbie™: Brunette Debut - 1959	Members Only	$75
1995	QXC 105-9	Home From The Woods	Members Only	$59
1995	QXC 412-9	A Gift From Rodney - Mini	Membership	$17
1995	QXC 411-7	Collecting Memories	Membership	$15

Year	Item #	Description	Comments	Price
1995	QXC 445-7	Cool Santa - Mini	Membership	$12
1995	QXC 520-7	Fishing for Fun	Membership	$20
1995	QXC 411-9	Cozy Christmas	Early Renewal	$15
1996	QXC 419-1	Holiday Bunny	Membership	$13
1996	QXC 416-4	Santa, Dated	Membership	$18
1996	QXC 734-1	Rudolph the Red-Nosed Reindeer®, Dated	Membership	$25
1996	QXC 417-1	Rudolph®'s Helper, Dated	Membership	$10
1996	QXC 418-1	Happy Holidays® Barbie®, Dated	Members Only	$33
1996	QXC 417-4	Steelcraft Auburn by Murray®, Dated	Members Only	$50
1996	QXC 416-1	The Wizard of OZ™	Members Only	$50
1996	QXC 419-1	Airmail for Santa, Dated	Special Gift	$20
1997	QXC 514-2	Ready for Santa - Mini	Membership	$9
1997	QXC 513-5	Away to the Window, Dated	Membership	$20
1997	QXC 514-5	Jolly Old Santa	Membership	$12
1997	QXC 513-2	Happy Christmas to All	Membership	$18
1997	QXC 516-2	Happy Holidays® Barbie® Doll–1989, Dated	Members Only	$38
1997	QXC 518-5	1937 Steelcraft Airflow by Murray®, Dated	Members Only	$55
1997	QXC 518-2	Tender Touches: Farmer's Market, Dated	Members Only	$24
1998	QXC 4486-A	Kringle Bells	Members Only	$15
1998	QXC 4516-A	New Christmas Friend	Members Only	$22-25
1998	QXC 4523-A	Making His Way	Members Only	$15-17
1998	QXC 449-3	Based on the 1990 Happy Holidays BARBIE ®	Members Only	$40
1998	QXC 449-6	1935 Steelcraft by Murray®	Members Only	$20-25
1998	QXC 4503	Follow the Leader	Members Only	$20-23

Special Edition Mini – Ornaments

Year	Item #	Description	Price
1989	QXM 563-2	Santa's Magic Ride	$20
1990	QXM 553-3	Cloisonné Poinsettia	$13
1994	QXM 410-6	Noah's Ark	$60
1995	QXM 483-9	A Moustershire Christmas	$45
1996	QXM 420-4	O Holy Night	$40

Precious Edition Mini – Ornaments

Year	Item #	Description	Price
1991	QXM 567-9	Silvery Santa	$24
1992	QXM 536-4	Holiday Holly, gold plated	$20
1993	QXM 401-2	Cloisonné Snowflake	$20
1994	QXM 402-6	Dazzling Reindeer	$20
1995	QXM 401-7	Cloisonné Partridge	$20
1996	QXM 426-4	Sparkling Crystal Angel	$15

Series #	Year	Price	Item #	Description	
1997	QXM 427-5			Our Lady of Guadalupe	$10
1998	QXM 4283			Angel Chime	$11

Star Trek Ornaments

Series #	Year	Price	Item #	Description	
1991	QLX 719-9			Starship Enterprise	$400
1992	QLX 733-1			Shuttlecraft Galileo	$50
1993	QLX 741-2			U.S.S. Enterprise™	$50
1994	QLX 738-6			Klingon Bird of Prey™	$40
1995	QXI 553-9			Captain James T. Kirk	$22
1995	QXI 573-7			Captain Jean-Luc Picard	$22
1995	QXI 726-7			Romulan Warbird™	$35
1995	QXI 410-9			Ships of Star Trek	$22
1996	QXI 554-4			Mr. Spock	$31
1996	QXI 753-4			U.S.S. Enterprise™ and Galileo Shuttlecraft™	$75
1996	QLX 555-1			Commander Will Riker™	$20
1996	QXI 754-4			U.S.S Voyager™	$45
1997	QXI 635-2			Dr. Leonard H. McCoy™	$20
1997	QXI 634-5			Commander Data™	$20
1997	QXI 748-1			U.S.S. Defiant™	$30
1998	QXI 763-3			U.S.S. Enterprise™ NCC-1701-E	$30-35
1998	QXI 404-6			Captain Kathryn Janeway™	$20-25

Star Wars Ornaments

Series #	Year	Price	Item #	Description	
1996	QLX 747-4			Millennium Falcon	$47
1996	QXM 402-4			The Vehicles of Star Wars™	$35
1997	QXI 753-1			Darth Vader™	$25
1997	QXI 548-4			Luke Skywalker™	$25
1997	QXI 635-5			Yoda™	$32
1997	QXI 426-5			C-3PO™ and R2-D2™	$18
1998	QXI 759-6			X-wing Starfighter™	$30-35
1998	QXI 405-3			Boba Fett™	$20-25
1998	QXI 402-6			Princess Leia™	$19-24
1998	QXI 422-3			Ewoks™	$20

Special Edition Ornaments

Series #	Year	Price	Item #	Description	
1986	QX 429-6			Jolly St. Nick	$75
1987	QX 445-7			Favorite Santa	$45
1988	QX 411-4			The Wonderful Santacycle	$45
1989	QX 580-5			The Ornament Express	$30
1994	QX 481-3			Lucinda and Teddy	$33
1995	QX 525-9			Beverly and Teddy	$30
1996	QX 571-4			Evergreen Santa	$38

The Wizard of Oz Ornaments

Series#	Year	Price	Item#	Description	
1994	QX 544-6			Cowardly Lion	$40
1994	QX 543-3			Dorothy and Toto	$70
1994	QX 543-6			Scarecrow	$40
1994	QX 544-3			Tin Man	$40
1995	QX 574-9			Glinda, Witch of the North	$30
1996	QX 555-4			Witch of the West	$25
1996	QXC 416-1			Wizard	$50
1997	QX 637-2			Miss Gulch	$20
1997	QXM 426-2			King of the Forest	$30
1998	QX 643-3			Munchkinland™	$25-30
1998	QXM 423-3			Glinda, The Good Witch	$20

Limited Edition Ornaments

Year	Item#	Description			
1984	QX 459-1	Classical Angel, Dated	24,700	$50
1985	QX 405-2	Heavenly Trumpeter	24,700	$80
1986	QX 429-3	Magical Unicorn	24,700	$80
1987	QX 444-9	Christmas Is Gentle	24,700	$65
1987	QX 442-9	Christmas Time Mime	24,700	$55

Kiddie Car Classics

Bill's Boards — Complete series N.E.

	Year	Price	Item#	Description
1	1997	$35	QHG 360-6	Welcome Sign
2	1998	N.E.	QHG 361-4	Famous Food Sign

Luxury Edition — Complete series $675-825 MIB

	Year	Price	Item#	Description
1	1995	$150-200	QHG 902-1	1937 Steelcraft Auburn
2	1995	$125-150	QHG 902-4	1937 Steelcraft Airflow by Murray®
3	1996	$150-175	QHG 902-9	1935 Steelcraft by Murray®
4	1997	$125-150	QHG 903-5	1937 Garton® Ford
5	1997	$125-150	QHG 903-8	1938 Garton® Lincoln Zephyr

Vintage Speedster Collection, Luxury Edition — Complete series N.E.

	Year	Price	Description
1	1998	N.E.	1926 Steelcraft Speedster by Murray®

Winner's Circle Series — Complete series N.E.

	Year	Price	Item#	Description
1	1996	$60-85	QHG 902-8	1956 Garton® Hot Rod Racer
2	1997	$55-65	QHG 903-7	1940 Gendron "Red Hot Roadster"
3	1998	N.E.	QHG 903-9	1960 Eight Ball Racer

1973 Collection

(Deduct $15-$20 if there are "age spots.")
Ball ornaments are not in demand but would be hard to find if looking for one.

XHD 100-2   BETSEY CLARK   ☐
Comments: White Glass Ball, 3-1/4" dia.
Five girls sing joyful carols as they gather around their
Christmas tree.
☐ Purchased 19_____   Pd $_____   MIB   NB   DB   BNT
☐ Want   Orig. Ret. $2.50   **NB** $75   **MIB** Sec. Mkt. **$95**

XHD 110-2   BETSEY CLARK SERIES   ☐
Comments: **FIRST IN SERIES,** Dated 1973, White Glass
Ball, 3-1/4" dia. One little girl is feeding a deer; the other is cud-
dling a lamb.
☐ Purchased 19_____   Pd $_____   MIB   NB   DB   BNT
☐ Want   Orig. Ret. $2.50   **NB** $100   **MIB** Sec. Mkt. **$132**

XHD 106-2   CHRISTMAS IS LOVE   ☐
Comments: White Glass Ball, 3-1/4" dia.
Two angels play mandolins; in shades of green and lavender.
Caption: "Christmas Is Love - Christmas Is You."
☐ Purchased 19_____   Pd $_____   MIB   NB   DB   BNT
☐ Want   Orig. Ret. $2.50   **NB** $65   **MIB** Sec. Mkt. **$75**

XHD 103-5   ELVES   ☐
Comments: White Glass Ball, 3-1/4" dia. Ice skating elves.
☐ Purchased 19_____   Pd $_____   MIB   NB   DB   BNT
☐ Want   Orig. Ret. $2.50   **NB** $75   **MIB** Sec. Mkt. **$85**

XHD 102-2   MANGER SCENE   ☐
Comments: White Glass Ball, 3-1/4" dia.
Designed scene on dark red background.
☐ Purchased 19_____   Pd $_____MIB   NB   DB   BNT
☐ Want   Orig. Ret. $2.50   **NB** $85   **MIB** Sec. Mkt. **$95**

XHD 101-5   SANTA WITH ELVES   ☐
Comments: White Glass Ball, 3-1/4" dia.
☐ Purchased 19_____   Pd $_____   MIB   NB   DB   BNT
☐ Want   Orig. Ret. $2.50   **NB** $70   **MIB** Sec. Mkt. **$88**

No secondary market value has been established for yarn and fabric
ornaments found in original cellophane package.

XHD 78-5   YARN ORNAMENT - ANGEL   ☐
Comments: 4-1/2" tall.
☐ Purchased 19_____   Pd $_____   MIB   NB   DB   BNT
☐ Want   Orig. Ret. $1.25   White Wings: **$32**
                                          Gold Wings: **$32**

XHD 85-2   YARN ORNAMENT - BLUE GIRL   ☐
Comments: 4-1/2" tall.
☐ Purchased 19_____   Pd $_____   MIB   NB   DB   BNT
☐ Want   Orig. Ret. $1.25   Sec. Mkt. **$27**

XHD 83-2   YARN ORNAMENT - BOY CAROLER   ☐
Comments: 4-1/2" tall.
☐ Purchased 19_____   Pd $_____   MIB   NB   DB   BNT
☐ Want   Orig. Ret. $1.25   Sec. Mkt. **$25**

XHD 80-5   YARN ORNAMENT - CHOIR BOY   ☐
Comments: 4-1/2" tall.
☐ Purchased 19_____   Pd $_____   MIB   NB   DB   BNT
☐ Want   Orig. Ret. $1.25   Sec. Mkt. **$26**

XHD 79-2   YARN ORNAMENT - ELF   ☐
Comments: 4-1/2" tall.
☐ Purchased 19_____   Pd $_____   MIB   NB   DB   BNT
☐ Want   Orig. Ret. $1.25   Sec. Mkt. **$28**

XHD 84-5   YARN ORNAMENT - GREEN GIRL   ☐
Comments: 4-1/2" tall.
☐ Purchased 19_____   Pd $_____   MIB   NB   DB   BNT
☐ Want   Orig. Ret. $1.25   Sec. Mkt. **$28**

XHD 82-5   YARN ORNAMENT - LITTLE GIRL   ☐
Comments: 4-1/2" tall.
☐ Purchased 19____   Pd $_____   MIB   NB   DB   BNT
☐ Want   Orig. Ret. $1.25   Sec. Mkt. **$27**

XHD 74-5   YARN ORNAMENT - MR. SANTA   ☐
Comments: 4-1/2" tall.
☐ Purchased 19____   Pd $_____   MIB   NB   DB   BNT
☐ Want   Orig. Ret. $1.25   Sec. Mkt. **$25**

XHD 75-2   YARN ORNAMENT - MRS. SANTA   ☐
Comments: 4-1/2" tall.
☐ Purchased 19____   Pd $_____   MIB   NB   DB   BNT
☐ Want   Orig. Ret. $1.25   Sec. Mkt. **$25**

XHD 76-5   YARN ORNAMENT - MR. SNOWMAN   ☐
Comments: 4-1/2" tall.
☐ Purchased 19____   Pd $_____   MIB   NB   DB   BNT
☐ Want   Orig. Ret. $1.25   Sec. Mkt. **$25**

XHD 77-2   YARN ORNAMENT - MRS. SNOWMAN   ☐
Comments: 4-1/2" tall.
☐ Purchased 19____   Pd $_____   MIB   NB   DB   BNT
☐ Want   Orig. Ret. $1.25   Sec. Mkt. **$25**

XHD 81-2   YARN ORNAMENT - SOLDIER   ☐
Comments: 4-1/2" tall.
☐ Purchased 19____   Pd $_____   MIB   NB   DB   BNT
☐ Want   Orig. Ret. $1.00   Sec. Mkt. **$24**

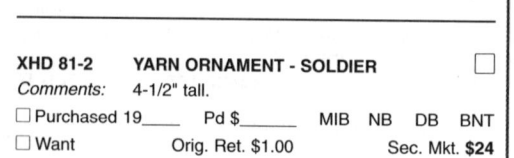

1974 Collection

QX 110-1   ANGEL   ☐
Comments: White Glass Ball, 3-1/4" dia.
☐ Purchased 19____   Pd $_____   MIB   NB   DB   BNT
☐ Want   Orig. Ret. $2.50   **NB** $67   **MIB** Sec. Mkt. **$80**

QX 108-1   BETSEY CLARK SERIES   ☐
Comments: **Second in Series,** Dated 1974.
White Glass Ball, 3-1/4" dia. An orchestra and choir of
youngsters prepare for a Christmas celebration.
☐ Purchased 19____   Pd $_____   MIB   NB   DB   BNT
☐ Want   Orig. Ret. $2.50   **NB** $70   **MIB** Sec. Mkt. **$85**
ERROR - Sleeve Upside Down . Other ornaments have also
been reported with the sleeves upside down. Add $25-$30
over the secondary market to these.

QX 113-1   BUTTONS & BO   ☐
Comments: White Glass Ball, 2-1/4" dia., Set of 2.
☐ Purchased 19____   Pd $_____   MIB   NB   DB   BNT
☐ Want   Orig. Ret. $3.50   **NB** $45   **MIB** Sec. Mkt. **$65**

QX 109-1   CHARMERS   ☐
Comments: White Glass Ball, 3-1/4" dia., Dated 1974.
☐ Purchased 19____   Pd $_____   MIB   NB   DB   BNT
☐ Want   Orig. Ret. $2.50   **NB** $35   **MIB** Sec. Mkt. **$55**

QX 112-1   CURRIER & IVES   ☐
Comments: White Glass Ball, 2-1/4" dia., Set of 2.
Country scenes of a winter farmstead and horse-drawn
sleigh are captured on two ornaments.
☐ Purchased 19____   Pd $_____   MIB   NB   DB   BNT
☐ Want   Orig. Ret. $3.50   **NB** $45   **MIB** Sec. Mkt. **$57.50**

QX 115-1   LITTLE MIRACLES   ☐
Comments: White Glass Ball, 1-3/4" dia., Set of 4.
A little boy and his rabbit companion play together.
☐ Purchased 19____   Pd $_____   MIB   NB   DB   BNT
☐ Want   Orig. Ret. $4.50   **NB** $55   **MIB** Sec. Mkt. **$65**

QX 111-1　NORMAN ROCKWELL ☐
Comments:　White Glass Ball, 3-1/4" dia.
Santa wears an apron with tools in his pockets. He naps in a chair while the elves work. The opposite side shows Santa with two boys.
☐ Purchased 19____　Pd $_____　MIB　NB　DB　BNT
☐ Want　Orig. Ret. $2.50　**NB** $70　**MIB** Sec. Mkt. **$88**

QX 106-1　NORMAN ROCKWELL SERIES ☐
Comments:　White Glass Ball, 3-1/4" dia., Dated 1974.
Two of Rockwell's famous illustrations on this ball include the "Jolly Postman" and, on the back, a father and son bringing home the perfect Christmas tree.
☐ Purchased 19____　Pd $_____　MIB　NB　DB　BNT
☐ Want　Orig. Ret. $2.50　**NB** $70　**MIB** Sec. Mkt. **$95**

QX 114-1　RAGGEDY ANN™ AND RAGGEDY ANDY™ ☐
Comments:　White Glass Ball, 1-3/4" dia.
A pretty set of 4.
☐ Purchased 19____　Pd $_____　MIB　NB　DB　BNT
☐ Want　Orig. Ret. $4.50　**NB** $70　**MIB** Sec. Mkt. **$75**

QX 107-1　SNOWGOOSE ☐
Comments:　White Glass Ball, 3-1/4" dia.
☐ Purchased 19____　Pd $_____　MIB　NB　DB　BNT
☐ Want　Orig. Ret. $2.50　**NB** $70　**MIB** Sec. Mkt. **$75**

No secondary market value has been established for yarn and fabric ornaments found in original cellophane package.
Seldom found in original packaging.

QX 103-1　YARN ORNAMENT - ANGEL ☐
Comments:　4-3/4" tall.
☐ Purchased 19____　Pd $_____　MIB　NB　DB　BNT
☐ Want　Orig. Ret. $1.50　Sec. Mkt. **$32**

QX 101-1　YARN ORNAMENT - ELF ☐
Comments:　4-3/4" tall.
☐ Purchased 19____　Pd $_____　MIB　NB　DB　BNT
☐ Want　Orig. Ret. $1.50　Sec. Mkt. **$28**

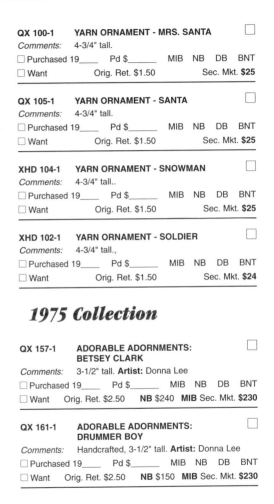

QX 100-1　YARN ORNAMENT - MRS. SANTA ☐
Comments:　4-3/4" tall.
☐ Purchased 19____　Pd $_____　MIB　NB　DB　BNT
☐ Want　Orig. Ret. $1.50　Sec. Mkt. **$25**

QX 105-1　YARN ORNAMENT - SANTA ☐
Comments:　4-3/4" tall.
☐ Purchased 19____　Pd $_____　MIB　NB　DB　BNT
☐ Want　Orig. Ret. $1.50　Sec. Mkt. **$25**

XHD 104-1　YARN ORNAMENT - SNOWMAN ☐
Comments:　4-3/4" tall..
☐ Purchased 19____　Pd $_____　MIB　NB　DB　BNT
☐ Want　Orig. Ret. $1.50　Sec. Mkt. **$25**

XHD 102-1　YARN ORNAMENT - SOLDIER ☐
Comments:　4-3/4" tall.,
☐ Purchased 19____　Pd $_____　MIB　NB　DB　BNT
☐ Want　Orig. Ret. $1.50　Sec. Mkt. **$24**

1975 Collection

**QX 157-1　ADORABLE ADORNMENTS:
　　　　　　BETSEY CLARK** ☐
Comments:　3-1/2" tall. **Artist:** Donna Lee
☐ Purchased 19____　Pd $_____　MIB　NB　DB　BNT
☐ Want　Orig. Ret. $2.50　**NB** $240　**MIB** Sec. Mkt. **$230**

**QX 161-1　ADORABLE ADORNMENTS:
　　　　　　DRUMMER BOY** ☐
Comments:　Handcrafted, 3-1/2" tall. **Artist:** Donna Lee
☐ Purchased 19____　Pd $_____　MIB　NB　DB　BNT
☐ Want　Orig. Ret. $2.50　**NB** $150　**MIB** Sec. Mkt. **$230**

QX 156-1   ADORABLE ADORNMENTS: ☐
                    MRS. SANTA
Comments: Handcrafted, 3-1/2" tall.
This ornament came in an individual package. Reissued with Mr.
Santa in 1981 in a box as "Mr. and Mrs. Claus." Only the original
packaging proves whether or not this ornament is the 1975 version
or the reissued 1981 ornament. This is why the no box price is
considerably lower than MIB price. **Artist:** Donna Lee

☐ Purchased 19_____   Pd $_____   MIB NB DB BNT
☐ Want   Orig. Ret. $2.50   **NB $55**   **MIB** Sec. Mkt. **$220**

QX 159-1   ADORABLE ADORNMENTS: ☐
                    RAGGEDY ANN™
Comments: Handcrafted, 3-1/2" tall.
RARE! Collectors are willing to pay nearly the same with or
without the box. **Artist:** Donna Lee

☐ Purchased 19_____   Pd $_____   MIB NB DB BNT
☐ Want   Orig. Ret. $2.50   **NB $300**   **MIB** Sec. Mkt. **$330**

QX 160-1   ADORABLE ADORNMENTS: ☐
                    RAGGEDY ANDY™
Comments: Handcrafted, 3-1/2" tall.
RARE! **Artist:** Donna Lee

☐ Purchased 19_____   Pd $_____   MIB NB DB BNT
☐ Want   Orig. Ret. $2.50   **NB $300**   **MIB** Sec. Mkt. **$375**

QX 155-1   ADORABLE ADORNMENTS: SANTA ☐
Comments: Handcrafted, 3-1/2" tall.
This ornament came in an individual package. Reissued with
Mrs. Santa in 1981 in box as "Mr. and Mrs. Claus." No real differ-
ence between these two years' ornaments. **Artist:** Donna Lee

☐ Purchased 19_____   Pd $_____   MIB NB DB BNT
☐ Want   Orig. Ret. $2.50   **NB $65**   **MIB** Sec. Mkt. **$220**

QX 168-1   BETSEY CLARK ☐
Comments: White Satin Ball, Dated 1975, 2" dia., Set of 4.
Caption: "Christmas 1975." Four different scenes of children
with animals and birds.

☐ Purchased 19_____   Pd $_____   MIB NB DB BNT
☐ Want   Orig. Ret. $4.50   **NB $45**   **MIB** Sec. Mkt. **$55**

QX 167-1   BETSEY CLARK ☐
Comments: White Satin Ball, 2-1/2" dia., Set of 2.
Caption: "Christmas 1975." Two skaters on one ornament and
a girl wearing a stocking cap on the other ornament.

☐ Purchased 19_____   Pd $_____   MIB NB DB BNT
☐ Want   Orig. Ret. $3.50   **NB $40**   **MIB** Sec. Mkt. **$48**

QX 163-1   BETSEY CLARK ☐
Comments: White Satin Ball, Dated 1975, 3" dia.
A youngster in pajamas says her bedtime prayers.
Artist: Linda Sickman

☐ Purchased 19_____   Pd $_____   MIB NB DB BNT
☐ Want   Orig. Ret. $2.50   **NB $29**   **MIB** Sec. Mkt. **$45**

QX 133-1   BETSEY CLARK SERIES ☐
Comments: **Third in Series,** White Glass Ball, 3-1/4" dia.
Caption: "Christmas 1975." Three girls dressed in pink,
blue and yellow calico sing carols.

☐ Purchased 19_____   Pd $_____   MIB NB DB BNT
☐ Want   Orig. Ret. $3.00   **NB $50**   **MIB** Sec. Mkt. **$80**

QX 139-1   BUTTONS & BO ☐
Comments: White Glass Ball, 1-3/4" dia., Set of 4.
Dated 1975 on back.

☐ Purchased 19_____   Pd $_____   MIB NB DB BNT
☐ Want   Orig. Ret. $5.00   **NB $37**   **MIB** Sec. Mkt. **$50**

QX 135-1   CHARMERS ☐
Comments: White Glass Ball, 3-1/2" dia., Dated 1975 on
back.

☐ Purchased 19_____   Pd $_____   MIB NB DB BNT
☐ Want   Orig. Ret. $3.00   **NB $32**   **MIB** Sec. Mkt. **$45**

QX 137-1   CURRIER & IVES ☐
Comments: White Glass Ball, 2-1/4" dia., Set of 2.
Snow scenes of Victorian ice skaters and old mill.
Artist: Linda Sickman

☐ Purchased 19_____   Pd $_____   MIB NB DB BNT
☐ Want   Orig. Ret. $4.00   **NB $25**   **MIB** Sec. Mkt. **$40**

QX 164-1   CURRIER & IVES ☐
Comments: White Satin Ball, 3" dia.
Winter scene of farm house and farm buildings.
Artist: Linda Sickman

☐ Purchased 19_____   Pd $_____   MIB NB DB BNT
☐ Want   Orig. Ret. $2.50   **NB $35**   **MIB** Sec. Mkt. **$40**

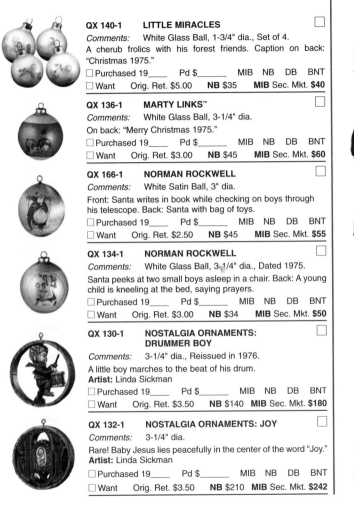

QX 140-1   LITTLE MIRACLES ☐
Comments: White Glass Ball, 1-3/4" dia., Set of 4.
A cherub frolics with his forest friends. Caption on back:
"Christmas 1975."
☐ Purchased 19____   Pd $_____   MIB NB DB BNT
☐ Want   Orig. Ret. $5.00   **NB** $35   **MIB** Sec. Mkt. **$40**

QX 136-1   MARTY LINKS™ ☐
Comments: White Glass Ball, 3-1/4" dia.
On back: "Merry Christmas 1975."
☐ Purchased 19____   Pd $_____   MIB NB DB BNT
☐ Want   Orig. Ret. $3.00   **NB** $45   **MIB** Sec. Mkt. **$60**

QX 166-1   NORMAN ROCKWELL ☐
Comments: White Satin Ball, 3" dia.
Front: Santa writes in book while checking on boys through
his telescope. Back: Santa with bag of toys.
☐ Purchased 19____   Pd $_____   MIB NB DB BNT
☐ Want   Orig. Ret. $2.50   **NB** $45   **MIB** Sec. Mkt. **$55**

QX 134-1   NORMAN ROCKWELL ☐
Comments: White Glass Ball, 3-1/4" dia., Dated 1975.
Santa peeks at two small boys asleep in a chair. Back: A young
child is kneeling at the bed, saying prayers.
☐ Purchased 19____   Pd $_____   MIB NB DB BNT
☐ Want   Orig. Ret. $3.00   **NB** $34   **MIB** Sec. Mkt. **$50**

**QX 130-1   NOSTALGIA ORNAMENTS:
DRUMMER BOY** ☐
Comments: 3-1/4" dia., Reissued in 1976.
A little boy marches to the beat of his drum.
Artist: Linda Sickman
☐ Purchased 19____   Pd $_____   MIB NB DB BNT
☐ Want   Orig. Ret. $3.50   **NB** $140   **MIB** Sec. Mkt. **$180**

QX 132-1   NOSTALGIA ORNAMENTS: JOY ☐
Comments: 3-1/4" dia.
Rare! Baby Jesus lies peacefully in the center of the word "Joy."
Artist: Linda Sickman
☐ Purchased 19____   Pd $_____   MIB NB DB BNT
☐ Want   Orig. Ret. $3.50   **NB** $210   **MIB** Sec. Mkt. **$242**

**QX 127-1   NOSTALGIA ORNAMENTS:
LOCOMOTIVE** ☐
Comments: 3-1/4" dia., Dated 1975.
Artist: Linda Sickman
☐ Purchased 19____   Pd $_____   MIB NB DB BNT
☐ Want   Orig. Ret. $3.50   **NB** $135   **MIB** Sec. Mkt. **$180**

**QX 131-1   NOSTALGIA ORNAMENTS:
PEACE ON EARTH** ☐
Comments: 3-1/4" dia., Dated 1975.
"Peace On Earth" is the perfect caption for this
snowy village scene. **Artist:** Linda Sickman
☐ Purchased 19____   Pd $_____   MIB NB DB BNT
☐ Want   Orig. Ret. $3.50   **NB** $110   **MIB** Sec. Mkt. **$165**

**QX 128-1   NOSTALGIA ORNAMENTS:
ROCKING HORSE** ☐
Comments: 3-1/4" dia., Reissued in 1976.
Artist: Linda Sickman
☐ Purchased 19____   Pd $_____   MIB NB DB BNT
☐ Want   Orig. Ret. $3.50   **NB** $140   **MIB** Sec. Mkt. **$175**

**QX 129-1   NOSTALGIA ORNAMENTS:
SANTA AND SLEIGH** ☐
Comments: 3-1/4" dia., RARE!
Artist: Linda Sickman
☐ Purchased 19____   Pd $_____   MIB NB DB BNT
☐ Want   Orig. Ret. $3.50   **NB** $230   **MIB** Sec. Mkt. **$260**

QX 165-1   RAGGEDY ANN™ ☐
Comments: White Satin Ball, 3" dia., Dated 1975.
A cute one! **Artist:** Linda Sickman
☐ Purchased 19____   Pd $_____   MIB NB DB BNT
☐ Want   Orig. Ret. $2.50   **NB** $45   **MIB** Sec. Mkt. **$55**

QX 138-1   RAGGEDY ANN™ AND RAGGEDY ANDY™ ☐
Comments: White Glass Ball, 2-1/4" dia., Set of 2.
Front: Ann and Andy are seated beside each other; a green
wreath encircles them. Back: They hold a "Merry Christmas"
banner. Front of second ornament: "Decorating the tree" Back:
"Christmas 1975." **Artist:** Linda Sickman
☐ Purchased 19____   Pd $_____   MIB NB DB BNT
☐ Want   Orig. Ret. $4.00   **NB** $55   **MIB** Sec. Mkt. **$70**

No secondary market value has been established for yarn and fabric ornaments found in original cellophane package.

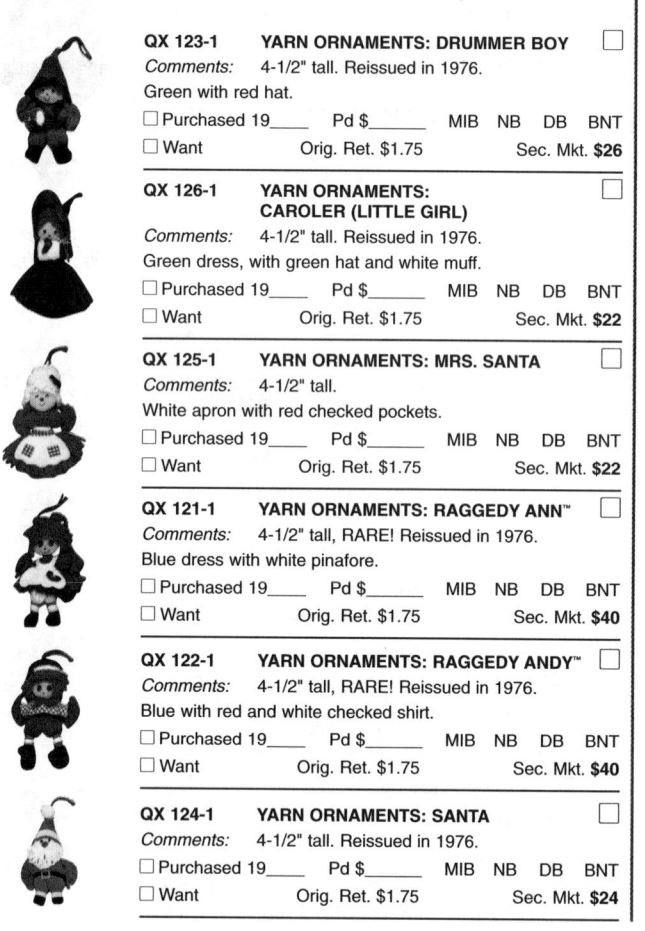

QX 123-1   YARN ORNAMENTS: DRUMMER BOY   ☐
Comments: 4-1/2" tall. Reissued in 1976.
Green with red hat.
☐ Purchased 19___   Pd $_____   MIB   NB   DB   BNT
☐ Want   Orig. Ret. $1.75   Sec. Mkt. **$26**

**QX 126-1   YARN ORNAMENTS:
CAROLER (LITTLE GIRL)**   ☐
Comments: 4-1/2" tall. Reissued in 1976.
Green dress, with green hat and white muff.
☐ Purchased 19___   Pd $_____   MIB   NB   DB   BNT
☐ Want   Orig. Ret. $1.75   Sec. Mkt. **$22**

QX 125-1   YARN ORNAMENTS: MRS. SANTA   ☐
Comments: 4-1/2" tall.
White apron with red checked pockets.
☐ Purchased 19___   Pd $_____   MIB   NB   DB   BNT
☐ Want   Orig. Ret. $1.75   Sec. Mkt. **$22**

QX 121-1   YARN ORNAMENTS: RAGGEDY ANN™   ☐
Comments: 4-1/2" tall, RARE! Reissued in 1976.
Blue dress with white pinafore.
☐ Purchased 19___   Pd $_____   MIB   NB   DB   BNT
☐ Want   Orig. Ret. $1.75   Sec. Mkt. **$40**

QX 122-1   YARN ORNAMENTS: RAGGEDY ANDY™   ☐
Comments: 4-1/2" tall, RARE! Reissued in 1976.
Blue with red and white checked shirt.
☐ Purchased 19___   Pd $_____   MIB   NB   DB   BNT
☐ Want   Orig. Ret. $1.75   Sec. Mkt. **$40**

QX 124-1   YARN ORNAMENTS: SANTA   ☐
Comments: 4-1/2" tall. Reissued in 1976.
☐ Purchased 19___   Pd $_____   MIB   NB   DB   BNT
☐ Want   Orig. Ret. $1.75   Sec. Mkt. **$24**

1976 Collection

QX 211-1   BABY'S FIRST CHRISTMAS   ☐
Comments: White Satin Ball, 3" dia., Dated 1976.
Caption: "Baby's First Christmas."
☐ Purchased 19___   Pd $_____   MIB   NB   DB   BNT
☐ Want   Orig. Ret. $2.50   **NB** $100   **MIB** Sec. Mkt. **$150**

QX 210-1   BETSEY CLARK   ☐
Comments: White Satin Ball, 3" dia.
Caption: "Christmas 1976."
☐ Purchased 19___   Pd $_____   MIB   NB   DB   BNT
☐ Want   Orig. Ret. $2.50   **NB** $45   **MIB** Sec. Mkt. **$60**

QX 218-1   BETSEY CLARK   ☐
Comments: White Satin Ball, 2" dia., Set of 3.
All dated 1976 on back.
☐ Purchased 19___   Pd $_____   MIB   NB   DB   BNT
☐ Want   Orig. Ret. $4.50   **NB** $30   **MIB** Sec. Mkt. **$60**

QX 195-1   BETSEY CLARK SERIES   ☐
Comments: **Fourth in Series**
White Glass Ball, 3-1/4" dia. Caption: "Christmas 1976."
Reports of several selling with "spots" at $45-$50.
☐ Purchased 19___   Pd $_____   MIB   NB   DB   BNT
☐ Want   Orig. Ret. $3.00   **NB** $75   **MIB** Sec. Mkt. **$115**

QX 203-1   BICENTENNIAL '76 COMMEMORATIVE   ☐
Comments: White Satin Ball, 3" dia.
Charmers dressed in 1776 fashions. Caption: "1976 Commemorative."
☐ Purchased 19___   Pd $_____   MIB   NB   DB   BNT
☐ Want   Orig. Ret. $2.50   **NB** $45   **MIB** Sec. Mkt. **$65**

QX 198-1   BICENTENNIAL CHARMERS   ☐
Comments: White Glass Ball, 3-1/4" dia.
Caption: "Merry Christmas 1976."
Very little trading found since 1992.
☐ Purchased 19___   Pd $_____   MIB   NB   DB   BNT
☐ Want   Orig. Ret. $3.00   **NB** $55   **MIB** Sec. Mkt. **$95**

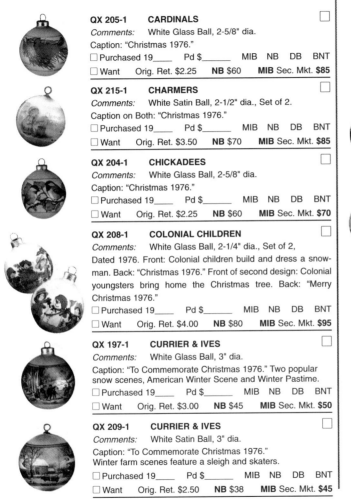

QX 205-1　CARDINALS ☐
Comments:　White Glass Ball, 2-5/8" dia.
Caption: "Christmas 1976."
☐ Purchased 19＿＿　Pd $＿＿＿　MIB　NB　DB　BNT
☐ Want　Orig. Ret. $2.25　**NB** $60　**MIB** Sec. Mkt. **$85**

QX 215-1　CHARMERS ☐
Comments:　White Satin Ball, 2-1/2" dia., Set of 2.
Caption on Both: "Christmas 1976."
☐ Purchased 19＿＿　Pd $＿＿＿　MIB　NB　DB　BNT
☐ Want　Orig. Ret. $3.50　**NB** $70　**MIB** Sec. Mkt. **$85**

QX 204-1　CHICKADEES ☐
Comments:　White Glass Ball, 2-5/8" dia.
Caption: "Christmas 1976."
☐ Purchased 19＿＿　Pd $＿＿＿　MIB　NB　DB　BNT
☐ Want　Orig. Ret. $2.25　**NB** $60　**MIB** Sec. Mkt. **$70**

QX 208-1　COLONIAL CHILDREN ☐
Comments:　White Glass Ball, 2-1/4" dia., Set of 2,
Dated 1976. Front: Colonial children build and dress a snow-
man. Back: "Christmas 1976." Front of second design: Colonial
youngsters bring home the Christmas tree. Back: "Merry
Christmas 1976."
☐ Purchased 19＿＿　Pd $＿＿＿　MIB　NB　DB　BNT
☐ Want　Orig. Ret. $4.00　**NB** $80　**MIB** Sec. Mkt. **$95**

QX 197-1　CURRIER & IVES ☐
Comments:　White Glass Ball, 3" dia.
Caption: "To Commemorate Christmas 1976." Two popular
snow scenes, American Winter Scene and Winter Pastime.
☐ Purchased 19＿＿　Pd $＿＿＿　MIB　NB　DB　BNT
☐ Want　Orig. Ret. $3.00　**NB** $45　**MIB** Sec. Mkt. **$50**

QX 209-1　CURRIER & IVES ☐
Comments:　White Satin Ball, 3" dia.
Caption: "To Commemorate Christmas 1976."
Winter farm scenes feature a sleigh and skaters.
☐ Purchased 19＿＿　Pd $＿＿＿　MIB　NB　DB　BNT
☐ Want　Orig. Ret. $2.50　**NB** $38　**MIB** Sec. Mkt. **$45**

QX 225-1　HAPPY HOLIDAYS KISSING BALL ☐
Comments:　White Satin Ball, 5-6" dia.
Caption: "Happy Holidays." Decorated with red ribbon and
green holly, this ball comes complete with mistletoe to hang in
a doorway.
☐ Purchased 19＿＿　Pd $＿＿＿　MIB　NB　DB　BNT
☐ Want　Orig. Ret. $5.00　**NB** $220　**MIB** Sec. Mkt. **$225**

QX 216-1　HAPPY THE SNOWMAN ☐
Comments:　White Satin Ball, 2-1/2" dia., Set of 2.
Captions: "Merry Christmas" on one side; "Happy Holidays" on
the other. **Artist:** Linda Sickman
☐ Purchased 19＿＿　Pd $＿＿＿　MIB　NB　DB　BNT
☐ Want　Orig. Ret. $3.50　**NB** $45　**MIB** Sec. Mkt. **$50**

QX 207-1　MARTY LINKS™ ☐
Comments:　White Glass Ball, 2-1/2" dia., Set of 2.
Captions: "Noel 1976" and "Merry Christmas 1976."
☐ Purchased 19＿＿　Pd $＿＿＿　MIB　NB　DB　BNT
☐ Want　Orig. Ret. $4.00　**NB** $55　**MIB** Sec. Mkt. **$65**

QX 196-1　NORMAN ROCKWELL ☐
Comments:　White Glass Ball, 3-1/4" dia.
Front: Santa convalesces from his travels.
Back: Santa feeds his reindeer. Caption: "Christmas 1976."
☐ Purchased 19＿＿　Pd $＿＿＿　MIB　NB　DB　BNT
☐ Want　Orig. Ret. $3.00　**NB** $60　**MIB** Sec. Mkt. **$65**

**QX 130-1　NOSTALGIA ORNAMENTS:
DRUMMER BOY** ☐
Comments:　3-1/4" dia. Reissued from 1975.
Artist: Linda Sickman
☐ Purchased 19＿＿　Pd $＿＿＿　MIB　NB　DB　BNT
☐ Want　Orig. Ret. $4.00　**NB** $160　**MIB** Sec. Mkt. **$175**

**QX 222-1　NOSTALGIA ORNAMENTS:
LOCOMOTIVE** ☐
Comments:　3-1/4" dia., Dated 1976. Same design as 1975,
but fewer available. **Artist:** Linda Sickman
☐ Purchased 19＿＿　Pd $＿＿＿　MIB　NB　DB　BNT
☐ Want　Orig. Ret. $4.00　**NB** $155　**MIB** Sec. Mkt. **$160**

QX 223-1   **NOSTALGIA ORNAMENTS: PEACE ON EARTH** ☐

Comments: 3-1/4" dia., Dated 1976. Same design as 1975.
Artist: Linda Sickman

☐ Purchased 19____   Pd $_____   MIB   NB   DB   BNT
☐ Want   Orig. Ret. $4.00   **NB** $130   **MIB** Sec. Mkt. **$135**

QX 128-1   **NOSTALGIA ORNAMENTS: ROCKING HORSE** ☐

Comments: 3-1/4" dia. Reissued from 1975.
Artist: Linda Sickman

☐ Purchased 19____   Pd $_____   MIB   NB   DB   BNT
☐ Want   1976 Retail $4.00   **NB** $140   **MIB** Sec. Mkt. **$150**

QX 212-1   **RAGGEDY ANN™** ☐

Comments: White Satin Ball, 2-1/2" dia., Dated 1976.
Ann is hanging stockings at fireplace. Caption on back: "Merry Christmas 1976." Very cute!

☐ Purchased 19____   Pd $_____   MIB   NB   DB   BNT
☐ Want   Orig. Ret. $2.50   **NB** $50   **MIB** Sec. Mkt. **$65**

QX 213-1   **RUDOLPH AND SANTA** ☐

Comments: White Satin Ball, 2-1/2" dia., Dated 1976.
Front: "Rudolph the Red-Nosed Reindeer."
Back: "Merry Christmas 1976."

☐ Purchased 19____   Pd $_____   MIB   NB   DB   BNT
☐ Want   Orig. Ret. $2.50   **NB** $75   **MIB** Sec. Mkt. **$85**

QX 176-1   **TREE TREATS: ANGEL** ☐

Comments: Vary in size from 2-3/4" to 3-5/8" tall.
Resembles baker's dough. Caption: "Merry Christmas 1976."

☐ Purchased 19____   Pd $_____   MIB   NB   DB   BNT
☐ Want   Orig. Ret. $3.0   **NB** $175   **MIB** Sec. Mkt. **$195**

QX 178-1   **TREE TREATS: REINDEER** ☐

Comments: Vary in size from 2-3/4" to 3-5/8" tall, Dated 1976. Made from material resembling baker's dough.
Caption: "Merry Christmas 1976."

☐ Purchased 19____   Pd $_____   MIB   NB   DB   BNT
☐ Want   Orig. Ret. $3.00   **NB** $100   **MIB** Sec. Mkt. **$115**

QX 177-1   **TREE TREATS: SANTA** ☐

Comments: Vary in size from 2-3/4" to 3-5/8" tall, Dated 1976. Made from material resembling baker's dough.
Caption: "Season's Greetings 1976."

☐ Purchased 19____   Pd $_____   MIB   NB   DB   BNT
☐ Want   Orig. Ret. $3.00   **NB** $180   **MIB** Sec. Mkt. **$200**

QX 175-1   **TREE TREATS: SHEPHERD** ☐

Comments: Vary in size from 2-3/4" to 3-5/8" tall. Made from material resembling baker's dough.
Caption: "Season's Greetings 1976."

☐ Purchased 19____   Pd $_____   MIB   NB   DB   BNT
☐ Want   Orig. Ret. $3.00   **NB** $100   **MIB** Sec. Mkt. **$100**

QX 171-1   **TWIRL-ABOUTS: ANGEL** ☐

Comments: Vary in size from 3-1/2" to 4" tall, Dated 1976. Center figure rotates on a brass pin. Angel in Christmas Tree.
Caption: "Merry Christmas 1976." **Artist:** Linda Sickman

☐ Purchased 19____   Pd $_____   MIB   NB   DB   BNT
☐ Want   Orig. Ret. $4.50   **NB** $149   **MIB** Sec. Mkt. **$165**

QX 174-1   **TWIRL-ABOUTS: PARTRIDGE** ☐

Comments: Vary in size from 3-1/2" to 4" tall, Dated 1976. Partridge rotates on a brass pin in the center of a pear wreath.
Artist: Linda Sickman

☐ Purchased 19____   Pd $_____   MIB   NB   DB   BNT
☐ Want   Orig. Ret. $4.50   **NB** $165   **MIB** Sec. Mkt. **$185**

QX 172-1   **TWIRL-ABOUTS: SANTA** ☐

Comments: Vary in size from 3-1/2" to 4" tall.
Santa rotates on a brass pin in the center of a wreath.
Artist: Linda Sickman

☐ Purchased 19____   Pd $_____   MIB   NB   DB   BNT
☐ Want   Orig. Ret. $4.50   **NB** $100   **MIB** Sec. Mkt. **$125**

QX 173-1   **TWIRL-ABOUTS: SOLDIER** ☐

Comments: Vary in size from 3-1/2" to 4" tall, Dated 1976. Soldier rotates on a brass pin in the center of Guard House.
Artist: Linda Sickman

☐ Purchased 19____   Pd $_____   MIB   NB   DB   BNT
☐ Want   Orig. Ret. $4.50   **NB** $84   **MIB** Sec. Mkt. **$95**

No secondary market value has been established for yarn and fabric ornaments found in original cellophane package.

QX 126-1   YARN ORNAMENTS: CAROLER (LITTLE GIRL)

Comments: 4-1/2" tall. Reissued from 1975.
Green, with white muff and green hat.

☐ Purchased 19____   Pd $_____   MIB   NB   DB   BNT
☐ Want   Orig. Ret. $1.75   Sec. Mkt. **$22**

QX 123-1   YARN ORNAMENTS: DRUMMER BOY

Comments: 4-1/2" tall. Reissued from 1975.
Green with red hat.

☐ Purchased 19____   Pd $_____   MIB   NB   DB   BNT
☐ Want   Orig. Ret. $1.75   Sec. Mkt. **$26**

QX 125-1   YARN ORNAMENTS: MRS. SANTA

Comments: 4-1/2" tall. Reissued from 1975.
White apron with red checked pockets.

☐ Purchased 19____   Pd $_____   MIB   NB   DB   BNT
☐ Want   Orig. Ret. $1.75   Sec. Mkt. **$22**

QX 121-1   YARN ORNAMENTS: RAGGEDY ANN™

Comments: 4-1/2" tall, RARE!
Reissued from 1975. Blue dress with white pinafore.

☐ Purchased 19____   Pd $_____   MIB   NB   DB   BNT
☐ Want   Orig. Ret. $1.75   Sec. Mkt. **$40**

QX 122-1   YARN ORNAMENTS: RAGGEDY ANDY™

Comments: 4-1/2" tall, RARE!
Reissued from 1975. Blue with red and white checked shirt.

☐ Purchased 19____   Pd $_____   MIB   NB   DB   BNT
☐ Want   Orig. Ret. $1.75   Sec. Mkt. **$40**

QX 124-1   YARN ORNAMENTS: SANTA

Comments: 4-1/2" tall. Reissued from 1975.

☐ Purchased 19____   Pd $_____   MIB   NB   DB   BNT
☐ Want   Orig. Ret. $1.75   Sec. Mkt. **$23**

QX 184-1   YESTERYEARS: DRUMMER BOY

Comments: Vary in size from 2-3/4" to 4" tall. Dated 1976.
This "wooden" soldier has been designed in "old world" tradition.

☐ Purchased 19____   Pd $_____   MIB   NB   DB   BNT
☐ Want   Orig. Ret. $5.00   **NB** $140   **MIB** Sec. Mkt. **$150**

QX 183-1   YESTERYEARS: PARTRIDGE

Comments: Vary in size from 2-3/4" to 4" tall. Dated 1976.
"Wood look" design in "old world" character.

☐ Purchased 19____   Pd $_____   MIB   NB   DB   BNT
☐ Want   Orig. Ret. $5.00   **NB** $100   **MIB** Sec. Mkt. **$118**

QX 182-1   YESTERYEARS: SANTA

Comments: Vary in size from 2-3/4" to 4" tall. Dated 1976.
Simulated wood design in "old world" character. Price up in '97.

☐ Purchased 19____   Pd $_____   MIB   NB   DB   BNT
☐ Want   Orig. Ret. $5.00   **NB** $150   **MIB** Sec. Mkt. **$165**

QX 181-1   YESTERYEARS: TRAIN

Comments: Vary in size from 2-3/4" to 4" tall. Dated 1976.
"Wood look" designs in "old world" character.

☐ Purchased 19____   Pd $_____   MIB   NB   DB   BNT
☐ Want   Orig. Ret. $5.00   **NB** $155   **MIB** Sec. Mkt. **$155**

1977 Collection

QX 220-2   ANGEL

Comments: 4" tall.
Quilted and stuffed doll made from silk-screened fabric.

☐ Purchased 19____   Pd $_____   MIB   NB   DB   BNT
☐ Want   Orig. Ret. $1.75   Sec. Mkt. **$50**

QSD 230-2   ANGEL TREE TOPPER

Comments: 6-1/2" tall. Country style simulated wood angel.
Dress is in cream, pink, turquoise and gold.

☐ Purchased 19____   Pd $_____   MIB   NB   DB   BNT
☐ Want   Orig. Ret. $9.00   **NB** $255   **MIB** Sec. Mkt. **$375**

QX 131-5   BABY'S FIRST CHRISTMAS

Comments: White Satin Ball, 3-1/4" dia., Dated 1977.
Caption: "Baby's First Christmas."

☐ Purchased 19____   Pd $_____   MIB   NB   DB   BNT
☐ Want   Orig. Ret. $3.50   **NB** $45   **MIB** Sec. Mkt. **$70**

QX 159-5   BEAUTY OF AMERICA COLLECTION: ☐
            DESERT

Comments: White Glass Ball, 2-5/8" dia.
A desert mission at sunset. Caption: "Ring Out Christmas Bells And Let All The World Hear Your Joyful Song."

☐ Purchased 19____   Pd $_____   MIB NB DB BNT
☐ Want   Orig. Ret. $2.25   **NB** $30   **MIB** Sec. Mkt. **$45**

QX 158-2   BEAUTY OF AMERICA COLLECTION: ☐
            MOUNTAINS

Comments: White Glass Ball, 2-5/8" dia.
Caption: "The Spirit Of Christmas Is Peace... The Message Of Christmas Is Love." The beauty of the mountains is captured on this ornament.

☐ Purchased 19____   Pd $_____   MIB NB DB BNT
☐ Want   Orig. Ret. $2.50   **NB** $30   **MIB** Sec. Mkt. **$45**

QX 160-2   BEAUTY OF AMERICA COLLECTION: ☐
            SEASHORE

Comments: White Glass Ball, 2-5/8" dia.
Caption: "Christmas Is - The Company Of Good Friends, The Warmth Of Goodwill And The Memory Of Good Times."

☐ Purchased 19____   Pd $_____   MIB NB DB BNT
☐ Want   Orig. Ret. $2.50   **NB** $45   **MIB** Sec. Mkt. **$58**

QX 161-5   BEAUTY OF AMERICA COLLECTION: ☐
            WHARF

Comments: White Glass Ball, 2-5/8" dia.
Caption: "Christmas... When The World Stands Silent And The Spirit Of Hope Touches Every Heart."

☐ Purchased 19____   Pd $_____   MIB NB DB BNT
☐ Want   Orig. Ret. $2.50   **NB** $25   **MIB** Sec. Mkt. **$40**

QX 264-2   BETSEY CLARK SERIES ☐

Comments: **Fifth in Series,** White Glass Ball, 3-1/4" dia.
Captions: "Christmas 1977" and "The Truest Joys Of Christmas Come From Deep Inside." Most scarce of Betsey Clark Series.

☐ Purchased 19____   Pd $_____   MIB NB DB BNT
☐ Want   Orig. Ret. $3.50   **NB** $400   **MIB** Sec. Mkt. **$425**

QX 153-5   CHARMERS ☐

Comments: Gold Glass Ball, 3-1/4" dia. Dated 1977.
Caption: "We Wish You A Merry Christmas."

☐ Purchased 19____   Pd $_____   MIB NB DB BNT
☐ Want   Orig. Ret. $3.50   **NB** $52   **MIB** Sec. Mkt. **$65**

QX 154-2   CHRISTMAS EXPRESSIONS: BELL ☐

Comments: White Glass Ball, 3-1/4" dia.
Caption: "I heard the bells on Christmas Day, Their old familiar carols play, And wild and sweet, the words repeat, Of peace on earth, good will to men." Henry Wadsworth Longfellow.

☐ Purchased 19____   Pd $_____   MIB NB DB BNT
☐ Want   Orig. Ret. $3.50   **NB** $28   **MIB** Sec. Mkt. **$40**

QX 157-5   CHRISTMAS EXPRESSIONS: ☐
            MANDOLIN

Comments: White Glass Ball, 3-1/4" dia.
Caption: "Sing a song of seasons; Something bright in all..." Robert Louis Stevenson.

☐ Purchased 19____   Pd $_____   MIB NB DB BNT
☐ Want   Orig. Ret. $3.50   **NB** $28   **MIB** Sec. Mkt. **$40**

QX 155-5   CHRISTMAS EXPRESSIONS: ☐
            ORNAMENTS

Comments: White Glass Ball, 3-1/4" dia.
Caption: "The Spirit of Christmas is Peace... The Message of Christmas is love." Marjorie Frances Ames.

☐ Purchased 19____   Pd $_____   MIB NB DB BNT
☐ Want   Orig. Ret. $3.50   **NB** $22   **MIB** Sec. Mkt. **$40**

QX 156-2   CHRISTMAS EXPRESSIONS: WREATH ☐

Comments: White Glass Ball, 3-1/4" dia.
Caption: "Christmas Is A Special Time. A Season Set Apart - A Warm And Glad Remembering Time. A Season Of The Heart." Thomas Malloy.

☐ Purchased 19____   Pd $_____   MIB NB DB BNT
☐ Want   Orig. Ret. $3.50   **NB** $22   **MIB** Sec. Mkt. **$35**

QX 134-2   CHRISTMAS MOUSE ☐

Comments: White Satin Ball, 3-1/4" dia.
Mice decorate their tree. Caption: "Tinsel And Lights Make The Season So Bright."

☐ Purchased 19____   Pd $_____   MIB NB DB BNT
☐ Want   Orig. Ret. $3.50   **NB** $45   **MIB** Sec. Mkt. **$65**

QX 200-2   COLORS OF CHRISTMAS: BELL ☐

Comments: Acrylic, 3-1/4" dia.
Stained glass look. Bell with green ribbon.
Artist: Linda Sickman

☐ Purchased 19____   Pd $_____   MIB NB DB BNT
☐ Want   Orig. Ret. $3.50   **NB** $42   **MIB** Sec. Mkt. **$50**

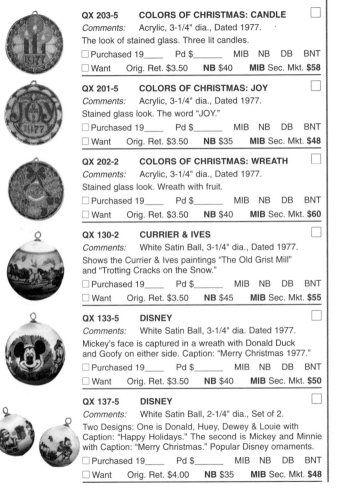

QX 203-5   COLORS OF CHRISTMAS: CANDLE ☐
Comments: Acrylic, 3-1/4" dia., Dated 1977.
The look of stained glass. Three lit candles.
☐ Purchased 19_____   Pd $_____   MIB NB DB BNT
☐ Want   Orig. Ret. $3.50   **NB** $40   **MIB** Sec. Mkt. **$58**

QX 201-5   COLORS OF CHRISTMAS: JOY ☐
Comments: Acrylic, 3-1/4" dia., Dated 1977.
Stained glass look. The word "JOY."
☐ Purchased 19_____   Pd $_____   MIB NB DB BNT
☐ Want   Orig. Ret. $3.50   **NB** $35   **MIB** Sec. Mkt. **$48**

QX 202-2   COLORS OF CHRISTMAS: WREATH ☐
Comments: Acrylic, 3-1/4" dia., Dated 1977.
Stained glass look. Wreath with fruit.
☐ Purchased 19_____   Pd $_____   MIB NB DB BNT
☐ Want   Orig. Ret. $3.50   **NB** $40   **MIB** Sec. Mkt. **$60**

QX 130-2   CURRIER & IVES ☐
Comments: White Satin Ball, 3-1/4" dia., Dated 1977.
Shows the Currier & Ives paintings "The Old Grist Mill"
and "Trotting Cracks on the Snow."
☐ Purchased 19_____   Pd $_____   MIB NB DB BNT
☐ Want   Orig. Ret. $3.50   **NB** $45   **MIB** Sec. Mkt. **$55**

QX 133-5   DISNEY ☐
Comments: White Satin Ball, 3-1/4" dia. Dated 1977.
Mickey's face is captured in a wreath with Donald Duck
and Goofy on either side. Caption: "Merry Christmas 1977."
☐ Purchased 19_____   Pd $_____   MIB NB DB BNT
☐ Want   Orig. Ret. $3.50   **NB** $40   **MIB** Sec. Mkt. **$50**

QX 137-5   DISNEY ☐
Comments: White Satin Ball, 2-1/4" dia., Set of 2.
Two Designs: One is Donald, Huey, Dewey & Louie with
Caption: "Happy Holidays." The second is Mickey and Minnie
with Caption: "Merry Christmas." Popular Disney ornaments.
☐ Purchased 19_____   Pd $_____   MIB NB DB BNT
☐ Want   Orig. Ret. $4.00   **NB** $35   **MIB** Sec. Mkt. **$48**

QX 132-2   FIRST CHRISTMAS TOGETHER ☐
Comments: White Satin Ball, 3-1/4" dia., Dated 1977.
Caption: "Our First Christmas Together." Date and
caption printed in gold.
☐ Purchased 19_____   Pd $_____   MIB NB DB BNT
☐ Want   Orig. Ret. $3.50   **NB** $35   **MIB** Sec. Mkt. **$55**

QX 263-5   FOR YOUR NEW HOME ☐
Comments: Gold Glass Ball, 3-1/4" dia.
Dated 1977 on doormat.
☐ Purchased 19_____   Pd $_____   MIB NB DB BNT
☐ Want   Orig. Ret. $3.50   **NB** $18   **MIB** Sec. Mkt. **$35**

QX 208-2   GRANDDAUGHTER ☐
Comments: White Satin Ball, 3-1/4" dia.
Caption: "A Granddaughter Is A Gift Whose Worth Cannot
Be Measured Except By The Heart." Very little trading
in past few years.
☐ Purchased 19_____   Pd $_____   MIB NB DB BNT
☐ Want   Orig. Ret. $3.50   **NB** $18   **MIB** Sec. Mkt. **$25**

QX 150-2   GRANDMA MOSES ☐
Comments: White Glass Ball, 3-1/4" dia.
RARE! Two snow scenes from the paintings "Green Sleigh"
and "Sugartime." A pamphlet giving the history of Grandma
Moses and her paintings was included with each ornament.
☐ Purchased 19_____   Pd $_____   MIB NB DB BNT
☐ Want   Orig. Ret. $3.50   **NB** $45 (without pamphlet)
                                    MIB Sec. Mkt. **$55**

QX 260-2   GRANDMOTHER ☐
Comments: Gold Glass Ball, 3-1/4" dia.
Caption: "Grandmother Is Another Word For Love."
☐ Purchased 19_____   Pd $_____   MIB NB DB BNT
☐ Want   Orig. Ret. $3.50   **NB** $25   **MIB** Sec. Mkt. **$40**

QX 209-5   GRANDSON ☐
Comments: White Satin Ball, 3-1/2" dia.
Caption: "A Grandson Is... A Joy Bringer... A Memory Maker...
A Grandson Is Love."
☐ Purchased 19_____   Pd $_____   MIB NB DB BNT
☐ Want   Orig. Ret. $3.50   **NB** $15   **MIB** Sec. Mkt. **$25**

QX 312-2   HOLIDAY HIGHLIGHTS: DRUMMER BOY ☐

Comments: Acrylic, 3-1/4" dia.

A drummer boy keeps the beat as he marches with his drum. Caption repeated around border: "Rum-Pa-Pum-Pum."

☐ Purchased 19____   Pd $_____   MIB NB DB BNT
☐ Want   Orig. Ret. $3.50   **NB** $40   **MIB** Sec. Mkt. **$60**

QX 310-2   HOLIDAY HIGHLIGHTS: JOY ☐

Comments: Acrylic, 3-1/4" dia. Caption: "JOY 1977."

☐ Purchased 19____   Pd $_____   MIB NB DB BNT
☐ Want   Orig. Ret. $3.50   **NB** $20   **MIB** Sec. Mkt. **$45**

QX 311-5   HOLIDAY HIGHLIGHTS: PEACE ON EARTH ☐

Comments: Acrylic, 3-1/4" dia.

A picturesque village scene with snow-covered houses, pine trees and a church in the center. Caption: "Peace On Earth, Good Will Toward Men. 1977"

☐ Purchased 19____   Pd $_____   MIB NB DB BNT
☐ Want   Orig. Ret. $3.50   **NB** $40   **MIB** Sec. Mkt. **$55**

QX 313-5   HOLIDAY HIGHLIGHTS: STAR ☐

Comments: Acrylic, 3-1/4" dia.

A bright shining star radiates beams over the ornament's surface. Caption: "Once For A Shining Hour Heaven Touched Earth."

☐ Purchased 19____   Pd $_____   MIB NB DB BNT
☐ Want   Orig. Ret. $3.50   **NB** $50   **MIB** Sec. Mkt. **$55**

OHD 320-2   HOLLY & POINSETTIA TABLE DECORATION ☐

Comments: With special base. Wood look.

☐ Purchased 19____   Pd $_____   MIB NB DB BNT
☐ Want   Orig. Ret. $8.00   **NB** $125   **MIB** Sec. Mkt. **$135**

QX 262-2   LOVE ☐

Comments: Gold Glass Ball, 3-1/4" dia. Caption: "Christmas 1977."

☐ Purchased 19____   Pd $_____   MIB NB DB BNT
☐ Want   Orig. Ret. $3.50   **NB** $10   **MIB** Sec. Mkt. **$25**

QX 210-2   METAL ORNAMENTS: SNOWFLAKES ☐

Comments: Chrome Plated Zinc, 2-1/8" dia.

Set of 4 die-cast in lightweight, chrome plated zinc. Packaged in peek-through gift box. This is the only year the snowflake set was offered. This set is hard to find. **Artist:** Linda Sickman

☐ Purchased 19____   Pd $_____   MIB NB DB BNT
☐ Want   Orig. Ret. $5.00   **NB** $70   **MIB** Sec. Mkt. **$95**

QX 261-5   MOTHER ☐

Comments: White Glass Ball, 3-1/4" dia.

Pink roses and green holly. Caption: "In a Mother's heart, there is love... the very heart of Christmas."

☐ Purchased 19____   Pd $_____   MIB NB DB BNT
☐ Want   Orig. Ret. $3.50   **NB** $12   **MIB** Sec. Mkt. **$20**

QX 225-2   MR. AND MRS. SNOWMAN KISSING BALL ☐

Comments: Says "Happy Holidays."

☐ Purchased 19____   Pd $_____   MIB NB DB BNT
☐ Want   Orig. Ret. $5.00   **NB** $85   **MIB** Sec. Mkt. **$100**

QX 151-5   NORMAN ROCKWELL ☐

Comments: White Glass Ball, 3-1/4" dia., Dated 1977.

Four favorite Rockwell designs are reproduced in separate panels. Caption: "Christmas 1977."

☐ Purchased 19____   Pd $_____   MIB NB DB BNT
☐ Want   Orig. Ret. $3.50   **NB** $50   **MIB** Sec. Mkt. **$65**

QX 182-2   NOSTALGIA COLLECTION: ANGEL ☐

Comments: Handcrafted, 3-1/4" dia.

An angel flies in the center of a wide outer ring which features the caption: "Peace on earth" and "Good will toward men." Gift tag was included. **Artist:** Donna Lee

☐ Purchased 19____   Pd $_____   MIB NB DB BNT
☐ Want   Orig. Ret. $5.00   **NB** $75   **MIB** Sec. Mkt. **$125**

QX 180-2   NOSTALGIA COLLECTION: ANTIQUE CAR ☐

Comments: Handcrafted, 3-1/4" dia.

Green car trimmed in red. Caption: "Season's Greetings 1977." Gift tag was included. **Artist:** Linda Sickman

☐ Purchased 19____   Pd $_____   MIB NB DB BNT
☐ Want   Orig. Ret. $5.00   **NB** $35   **MIB** Sec. Mkt. **$50**

QX 181-5   NOSTALGIA COLLECTION: NATIVITY ☐
Comments: Handcrafted, 3-1/4" dia.
The Holy Family and animals in a stable with pine trees on either side. Caption: "O Come, Let Us Adore Him." Gift tag was included.
☐ Purchased 19____   Pd $_____   MIB NB DB BNT
☐ Want   Orig. Ret. $5.00   **NB** $120   **MIB** Sec. Mkt. **$145**

QX 183-5   NOSTALGIA COLLECTION: TOYS ☐
Comments: Handcrafted, 3-1/4" dia., Dated 1977.
Toys in the center of a red and yellow ring. Gift tag was included. **Artist:** Linda Sickman
☐ Purchased 19____   Pd $_____   MIB NB DB BNT
☐ Want   Orig. Ret. $5.00   **NB** $85   **MIB** Sec. Mkt. **$155**

QX 225-5   OLD FASHIONED CUSTOMS ☐
**   KISSING BALL**
Comments: White Satin Ball.
☐ Purchased 19____   Pd $_____   MIB NB DB BNT
☐ Want   Orig. Ret. $5.00   **NB** $125   **MIB** Sec. Mkt. **$150**

QX 135-5   PEANUTS® ☐
Comments: White Satin Ball, 3-1/4" dia., Dated 1977.
Front: Snoopy is tangled in Christmas tree lights.
Back: Charlie Brown and Lucy.
☐ Purchased 19____   Pd $_____   MIB NB DB BNT
☐ Want   Orig. Ret. $3.50   **NB** $53   **MIB** Sec. Mkt. **$75**

QX 162-2   PEANUTS® ☐
Comments: White Glass Ball, 2-5/8" dia.
Front: Charlie Brown and his sister, Sally, watch the stockings on the fireplace. Caption: "A Watched Stocking Never Fills." Back: Schroeder plays the piano as Lucy gives him a gift. Caption: "Merry Christmas." Packaged in Snoopy's Christmas-decorated doghouse.
☐ Purchased 19____   Pd $_____   MIB NB DB BNT
☐ Want   Orig. Ret. $2.50   **NB** $40   **MIB** Sec. Mkt. **$50**

QX 163-5   PEANUTS® ☐
Comments: White Glass Ball, 2-1/4" dia., Set of 2, Dated 1977. Two Designs: Santa Snoopy is pulled in a sleigh. Charlie Brown, Linus, Woodstock, Snoopy and Peppermint Patty play in the snow.
☐ Purchased 19____   Pd $_____   MIB NB DB BNT
☐ Want   Orig. Ret. $4.00   **NB** $65   **MIB** Sec. Mkt. **$85**

QX 139-5   RABBIT ☐
Comments: White Satin Ball, 2-5/8" dia. A rabbit looks at a little bird on a broken tree limb. Caption: "Nature's ever-changing beauty brings never-ending joy." Karl Lawrence.
☐ Purchased 19____   Pd $_____   MIB NB DB BNT
☐ Want   Orig. Ret. $2.50   **NB** $95   **MIB** Sec. Mkt. **$105**

QX 221-5   SANTA ☐
Comments: 4" tall. RARE!
Stuffed and quilted doll made from silk-screened fabric. A jingle bell is attached to his hat. Hard to find!
☐ Purchased 19____   Pd $_____   MIB NB DB BNT
☐ Want   Orig. Ret. $1.75   **NB** $60   **MIB** Sec. Mkt. **$75**

QX 138-2   SQUIRREL ☐
Comments: White Satin Ball, 2-5/8" dia. Caption: "Each Moment Of The Year Has Its Own Beauty..." Emerson.
☐ Purchased 19____   Pd $_____   MIB NB DB BNT
☐ Want   Orig. Ret. $2.50   **NB** $95   **MIB** Sec. Mkt. **$100**

QX 152-2   STAINED GLASS ☐
Comments: Chrome Glass Ball, 3-1/4" dia. A look of art deco stained glass. Caption: "Merry Christmas 1977."
☐ Purchased 19____   Pd $_____   MIB NB DB BNT
☐ Want   Orig. Ret. $3.50   **NB** $35   **MIB** Sec. Mkt. **$45**

QX 192-2   TWIRL-ABOUT COLLECTION: ☐
**   BELLRINGER**
Comments: Handcrafted, 3-11/16" tall, Dated 1977.
A little boy strikes a bell as he rotates inside an arched gate decorated with red bows.
☐ Purchased 19____   Pd $_____   MIB NB DB BNT
☐ Want   Orig. Ret. $6.00   **NB** $30   **MIB** Sec. Mkt. **$55**

QX 193-5   TWIRL-ABOUT COLLECTION: ☐
**   DELLA ROBIA WREATH**
Comments: Handcrafted, 3-9/16" tall, Dated 1977.
A little girl, kneeling in prayer, twirls in the center of the traditional Della Robia wreath. **Artist:** Donna Lee
☐ Purchased 19____   Pd $_____   MIB NB DB BNT
☐ Want   Orig. Ret. $4.50   **NB** $60   **MIB** Sec. Mkt. **$120**

QX 190-2   TWIRL-ABOUT COLLECTION: ☐
SNOWMAN
Comments: Handcrafted, 3-3/4" tall, Dated 1977.
A snowman rotates in the center of a three-dimensional snowflake. **Artist:** Linda Sickman
☐ Purchased 19____   Pd $_____   MIB NB DB BNT
☐ Want   Orig. Ret. $4.50   **NB** $30   **MIB** Sec. Mkt. **$70**

QX 191-5   TWIRL-ABOUT COLLECTION: ☐
WEATHER HOUSE
Comments: Handcrafted, 3-15/16" tall, Dated 1977. Swiss dressed boy and girl rotate through the doors of a country chalet.
☐ Purchased 19____   Pd $_____   MIB NB DB BNT
☐ Want   Orig. Ret. $6.00   **NB** $65   **MIB** Sec. Mkt. **$95**

QX 172-2   YESTERYEARS COLLECTION: ANGEL ☐
Comments: Handcrafted, 3-1/2" tall. This lovely folk-art angel is similar to the Angel Tree Topper, except for the color in the dress is light blue. Caption: "Joy to the world 1977."
☐ Purchased 19____   Pd $_____   MIB NB DB BNT
☐ Want   Orig. Ret. $6.00   **NB** $65   **MIB** Sec. Mkt. **$120**

QX 170-2   YESTERYEARS COLLECTION: HOUSE ☐
Comments: Handcrafted, 3-11/16" tall.
This quaint cottage has a red roof and red shutters with painted designs. Caption: "Happy Holidays 1977."
☐ Purchased 19____   Pd $_____   MIB NB DB BNT
☐ Want   Orig. Ret. $6.00   **NB** $80 **MIB** Sec. Mkt. **$100**

QX 171-5   YESTERYEARS COLLECTION: ☐
JACK-IN-THE-BOX
Comments: Handcrafted, 3-13/16" tall.
Green, blue and red Jack in a red and pink box. Caption: "Merry Christmas 1977." More readily available than most of 1970's ornaments.
☐ Purchased 19____   Pd $_____   MIB NB DB BNT
☐ Want   Orig. Ret. $6.00   **NB-P** $75   **MIB** Sec. Mkt. **$125**

QX 173-5   YESTERYEARS COLLECTION: ☐
REINDEER
Comments: Handcrafted, 4-1/4" tall, Dated 1977.
Ivory painted reindeer on wheels has the look of a nostalgic child's toy.
☐ Purchased 19____   Pd $_____   MIB NB DB BNT
☐ Want   Orig. Ret. $6.00   **NB** $85   **MIB** Sec. Mkt. **$135**

1978 Collection

QX 139-6   ANGEL ☐
Comments: Handcrafted, 2-15/16" tall, Reissued in 1981.
Made with the bread-dough look, a barefoot angel dressed in blue and white holds a star. **Artist:** Donna Lee
☐ Purchased 19____   Pd $_____   MIB NB DB BNT
☐ Want   Orig. Ret. $4.50   **NB** $80   **MIB** Sec. Mkt. **$95**

QX 150-3   ANGELS ☐
Comments: Handcrafted, 3-7/8" tall, Dated 1978.
Angels fly around decorating a Christmas tree.
☐ Purchased 19____   Pd $_____   MIB NB DB BNT
☐ Want   Orig. Ret. $8.00   **NB** $200 **MIB** Sec. Mkt. **$345**

QX 149-6   ANIMAL HOME ☐
Comments: Handcrafted, 2-9/16" tall.
A darling little mushroom has become "home sweet home" to a family of mice. **Artist:** Donna Lee
☐ Purchased 19____   Pd $_____   MIB NB DB BNT
☐ Want   Orig. Ret. $6.00   **NB** $125 **MIB** Sec. Mkt. **$150**

QX 200-3   BABY'S FIRST CHRISTMAS ☐
Comments: White Satin Ball, 3-1/4" dia.
A baby dressed in yellow plays with a stuffed teddy bear and a kitten. Caption: "Baby's First Christmas 1978."
☐ Purchased 19____   Pd $_____   MIB NB DB BNT
☐ Want   Orig. Ret. $3.50   **NB** $47   **MIB** Sec. Mkt. **$85**

QX 201-6   BETSEY CLARK SERIES ☐
Comments: **Sixth in series,** Ecru Soft-Sheen Satin Ball, 3-1/4" dia. Dated 1978. A little girl wraps a gift and delivers it to a friend. Caption: "The Christmas Spirit Seems To Bring A Cheerful Glow To Everything."
☐ Purchased 19____   Pd $_____   MIB NB DB BNT
☐ Want   Orig. Ret. $3.50   **NB** $30   **MIB** Sec. Mkt. **$60**

QX 137-6   CALICO MOUSE ☐
Comments: Handcrafted, 3-7/16" tall.
Smiling red calico mouse, with green ears and nose, holds a sprig of holly. Similar to the Merry Miniature.
☐ Purchased 19____   Pd $_____   MIB NB DB BNT
☐ Want   Orig. Ret. $4.50   **NB** $95   **MIB** Sec. Mkt. **$175**

QX 146-3   CARROUSEL SERIES ☐

*Comments: **FIRST IN SERIES,** Handcrafted, 3" tall.*
Caption: "Christmas 1978." This carrousel has toys that spin around, hand painted.
☐ Purchased 19____   Pd $_____   MIB NB DB BNT
☐ Want   Orig. Ret. $6.00   **NB** $250 **MIB** Sec. Mkt. **$410**

QX 702-3   CHRISTMAS STAR TREE TOPPER ☐

Comments: Acrylic, 9-3/4" tall.
A nine-point acrylic star with an etched snowflake in the center makes a lovely addition to any Christmas tree.
☐ Purchased 19____   Pd $_____   MIB NB DB BNT
☐ Want   Orig. Ret. $7.50   **NB** $31   **MIB** Sec. Mkt. **$42**

QX 354-3   COLORS OF CHRISTMAS: ANGEL ☐

Comments: Acrylic, stained glass look, 3-5/8" tall.
This golden haired angel wears a red dress and halo.
☐ Purchased 19____   Pd $_____   MIB NB DB BNT
☐ Want   Orig. Ret. $3.50   **NB** $32   **MIB** Sec. Mkt. **$50**

QX 357-6   COLORS OF CHRISTMAS: CANDLE ☐

Comments: Acrylic, stained glass look, 3-5/8" tall.
Classic Christmas candle, with holly and berries at the base.
☐ Purchased 19____   Pd $_____   MIB NB DB BNT
☐ Want   Orig. Ret. $3.50   **NB** $65   **MIB** Sec. Mkt. **$78**

**QX 356-3   COLORS OF CHRISTMAS:
              LOCOMOTIVE** ☐

Comments: Acrylic, stained glass look, 3-1/4" tall.
Dated 1978.
☐ Purchased 19____   Pd $_____   MIB NB DB BNT
☐ Want   Orig. Ret. $3.50   **NB** $45   **MIB** Sec. Mkt. **$60**

**QX 355-6   COLORS OF CHRISTMAS:
              MERRY CHRISTMAS** ☐

Comments: Acrylic, stained glass look, 4-1/8" tall.
"Merry Christmas" in gold on a red and green oval ornament.
Artist: Don Palmiter
☐ Purchased 19____   Pd $_____   MIB NB DB BNT
☐ Want   Orig. Ret. $3.50   **NB** $37   **MIB** Sec. Mkt. **$50**

QX 207-6   DISNEY ☐

Comments: White Satin Ball, 3-1/4" dia., Dated 1978.
Disney characters ride a wooden train. Mickey, as Santa, rings a bell.
☐ Purchased 19____   Pd $_____   MIB NB DB BNT
☐ Want   Orig. Ret. $3.50   **NB** $70   **MIB** Sec. Mkt. **$95**

QX 190-3   DOVE ☐

Comments: Handcrafted, 3-9/16" tall, Dated 1978.
A white dove twirls in the center of a white lacy snowflake.
Artist: Linda Sickman
☐ Purchased 19____   Pd $_____   MIB NB DB BNT
☐ Want   Orig. Ret. $4.50   **NB** $75   **MIB** Sec. Mkt. **$85**

QX 252-3   DRUMMER BOY ☐

Comments: Gold Glass Ball, 3-1/4" dia., Dated 1978.
Followed by sheep and geese, a little drummer boy leads the parade to the Christ Child in the manger.
☐ Purchased 19____   Pd $_____   MIB NB DB BNT
☐ Want   Orig. Ret. $3.50   **NB** $35   **MIB** Sec. Mkt. **$50**

QX 218-3   FIRST CHRISTMAS TOGETHER ☐

Comments: White Satin Ball, 3-1/4" dia. Red hearts, fruits,
flowers, greenery and pair of red birds. Caption: "Sharing Is The Heart Of Loving" and "First Christmas Together 1978."
☐ Purchased 19____   Pd $_____   MIB NB DB BNT
☐ Want   Orig. Ret. $3.50   **NB** $45   **MIB** Sec. Mkt. **$55**

QX 217-6   FOR YOUR NEW HOME ☐

Comments: White Satin Ball, 3-1/4" dia.; Christmas 1978.
A wreath with a glowing candle hangs from a brightly lighted window. Caption: "Home... Where The Light Of Love Shines Brightest."
☐ Purchased 19____   Pd $_____   MIB NB DB BNT
☐ Want   Orig. Ret. $3.50   **NB** $20   **MIB** Sec. Mkt. **$22**

QX 216-3   GRANDDAUGHTER ☐

Comments: White Satin Ball, 3-1/4" dia.
A little girl decorates her Christmas tree. Caption: "A Grand-daughter... Never Far From Thought, Ever Near In Love."
☐ Purchased 19____   Pd $_____   MIB NB DB BNT
☐ Want   Orig. Ret. $3.50   **NB** $30   **MIB** Sec. Mkt. **$55**

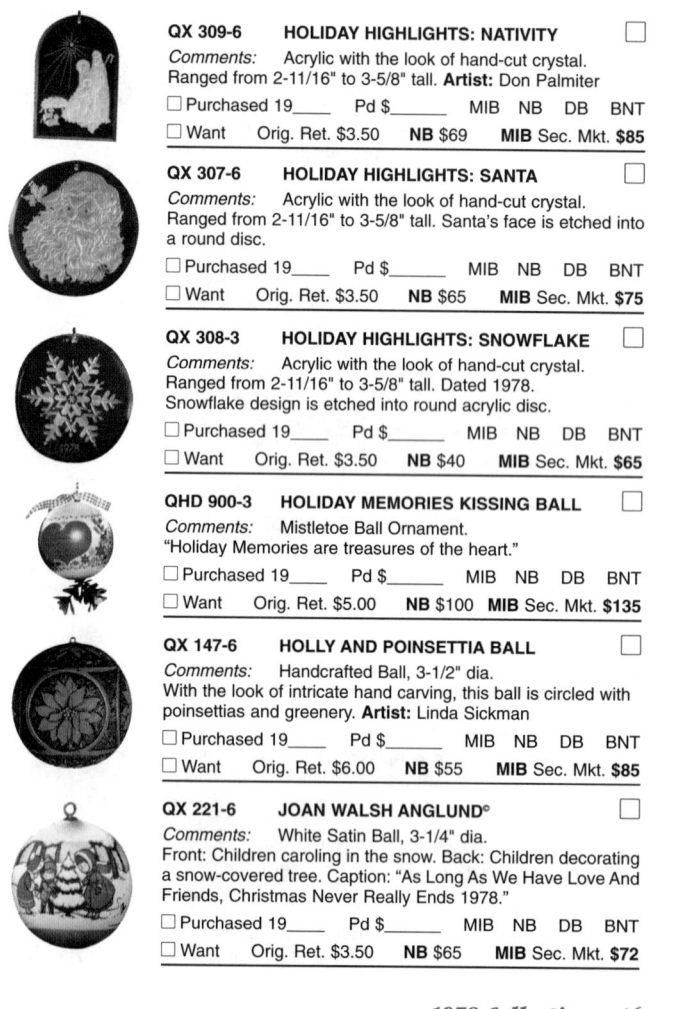

QX 267-6   GRANDMOTHER ☐
Comments: White Satin Ball, 3-1/4" dia.
Red American Beauty roses and holly. Caption: "A Grand-mother Has A Special Way Of Bringing Joy To Every Day."
☐ Purchased 19____   Pd $_____   MIB NB DB BNT
☐ Want   Orig. Ret. $3.50   **NB** $40   **MIB** Sec. Mkt. **$50**

QX 215-6   GRANDSON ☐
Comments: White Satin Ball, 3-1/4" dia.
Raccoons have fun ice skating, building a snowman and sled-ding. Caption: "A Grandson Is Loved In A Special Way For The Special Joy He Brings."
☐ Purchased 19____   Pd $_____   MIB NB DB BNT
☐ Want   Orig. Ret. $3.50   **NB** $35   **MIB** Sec. Mkt. **$45**

QX 220-3   HALLMARK'S ANTIQUE ☐
　　　　　　　CARD COLLECTION DESIGN
Comments: Ecru Soft-Sheen Satin Ball, 3-1/4" dia.
Reproduced from an antique Hallmark card. Caption: "Christmas Is A Special Time, A Season Set Apart – A Warm And Glad Remembering Time, A Season Of The Heart."
☐ Purchased 19____   Pd $_____   MIB NB DB BNT
☐ Want   Orig. Ret. $3.50   **NB** $40   **MIB** Sec. Mkt. **$47**

QHD 921-9   HEAVENLY MINSTREL TABLETOP ☐
Comments: Very similar to the Heavenly Minstrel ornament. Comes with walnut base with stained-glass look and brass background.
☐ Purchased 19____   Pd $_____   MIB NB DB BNT
☐ Want   Orig. Ret. $35.00   **NB** $350   **MIB** Sec. Mkt. **$425**

QX 320-3   HOLIDAY CHIMES: REINDEER CHIMES ☐
Comments: Reissued in 1979, Chrome plated brass, 5-1/2" tall. Three prancing reindeer are suspended from a large snowflake. **Artist:** Linda Sickman
☐ Purchased 19____   Pd $_____   MIB NB DB BNT
☐ Want   Orig. Ret. $4.50   **NB** $45   **MIB** Sec. Mkt. **$60**

QX 310-3   HOLIDAY HIGHLIGHTS: DOVE ☐
Comments: Acrylic with the look of hand-cut crystal. Ranged from 2-11/16" to 3-5/8" tall. RARE! This dove in flight is produced in frosted acrylic with clear acrylic wing tips.
☐ Purchased 19____   Pd $_____   MIB NB DB BNT
☐ Want   Orig. Ret. $3.50   **NB** $125   **MIB** Sec. Mkt. **$120**

QX 309-6   HOLIDAY HIGHLIGHTS: NATIVITY ☐
Comments: Acrylic with the look of hand-cut crystal. Ranged from 2-11/16" to 3-5/8" tall. **Artist:** Don Palmiter
☐ Purchased 19____   Pd $_____   MIB NB DB BNT
☐ Want   Orig. Ret. $3.50   **NB** $69   **MIB** Sec. Mkt. **$85**

QX 307-6   HOLIDAY HIGHLIGHTS: SANTA ☐
Comments: Acrylic with the look of hand-cut crystal. Ranged from 2-11/16" to 3-5/8" tall. Santa's face is etched into a round disc.
☐ Purchased 19____   Pd $_____   MIB NB DB BNT
☐ Want   Orig. Ret. $3.50   **NB** $65   **MIB** Sec. Mkt. **$75**

QX 308-3   HOLIDAY HIGHLIGHTS: SNOWFLAKE ☐
Comments: Acrylic with the look of hand-cut crystal. Ranged from 2-11/16" to 3-5/8" tall. Dated 1978. Snowflake design is etched into round acrylic disc.
☐ Purchased 19____   Pd $_____   MIB NB DB BNT
☐ Want   Orig. Ret. $3.50   **NB** $40   **MIB** Sec. Mkt. **$65**

QHD 900-3   HOLIDAY MEMORIES KISSING BALL ☐
Comments: Mistletoe Ball Ornament.
"Holiday Memories are treasures of the heart."
☐ Purchased 19____   Pd $_____   MIB NB DB BNT
☐ Want   Orig. Ret. $5.00   **NB** $100 **MIB** Sec. Mkt. **$135**

QX 147-6   HOLLY AND POINSETTIA BALL ☐
Comments: Handcrafted Ball, 3-1/2" dia.
With the look of intricate hand carving, this ball is circled with poinsettias and greenery. **Artist:** Linda Sickman
☐ Purchased 19____   Pd $_____   MIB NB DB BNT
☐ Want   Orig. Ret. $6.00   **NB** $55   **MIB** Sec. Mkt. **$85**

QX 221-6   JOAN WALSH ANGLUND© ☐
Comments: White Satin Ball, 3-1/4" dia.
Front: Children caroling in the snow. Back: Children decorating a snow-covered tree. Caption: "As Long As We Have Love And Friends, Christmas Never Really Ends 1978."
☐ Purchased 19____   Pd $_____   MIB NB DB BNT
☐ Want   Orig. Ret. $3.50   **NB** $65   **MIB** Sec. Mkt. **$72**

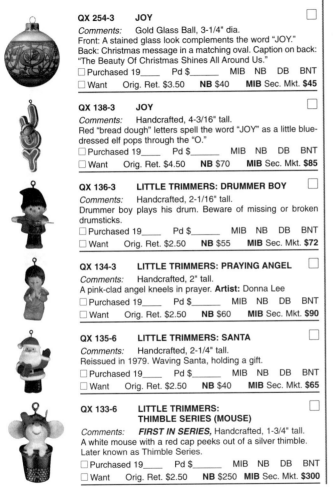

QX 254-3   JOY
Comments: Gold Glass Ball, 3-1/4" dia.
Front: A stained glass look complements the word "JOY."
Back: Christmas message in a matching oval. Caption on back: "The Beauty Of Christmas Shines All Around Us."
☐ Purchased 19____   Pd $_____   MIB   NB   DB   BNT
☐ Want   Orig. Ret. $3.50   **NB** $40   **MIB** Sec. Mkt. **$45**

QX 138-3   JOY
Comments: Handcrafted, 4-3/16" tall.
Red "bread dough" letters spell the word "JOY" as a little blue-dressed elf pops through the "O."
☐ Purchased 19____   Pd $_____   MIB   NB   DB   BNT
☐ Want   Orig. Ret. $4.50   **NB** $70   **MIB** Sec. Mkt. **$85**

QX 136-3   LITTLE TRIMMERS: DRUMMER BOY
Comments: Handcrafted, 2-1/16" tall.
Drummer boy plays his drum. Beware of missing or broken drumsticks.
☐ Purchased 19____   Pd $_____   MIB   NB   DB   BNT
☐ Want   Orig. Ret. $2.50   **NB** $55   **MIB** Sec. Mkt. **$72**

QX 134-3   LITTLE TRIMMERS: PRAYING ANGEL
Comments: Handcrafted, 2" tall.
A pink-clad angel kneels in prayer. **Artist:** Donna Lee
☐ Purchased 19____   Pd $_____   MIB   NB   DB   BNT
☐ Want   Orig. Ret. $2.50   **NB** $60   **MIB** Sec. Mkt. **$90**

QX 135-6   LITTLE TRIMMERS: SANTA
Comments: Handcrafted, 2-1/4" tall.
Reissued in 1979. Waving Santa, holding a gift.
☐ Purchased 19____   Pd $_____   MIB   NB   DB   BNT
☐ Want   Orig. Ret. $2.50   **NB** $40   **MIB** Sec. Mkt. **$65**

QX 133-6   LITTLE TRIMMERS: THIMBLE SERIES (MOUSE)
Comments: **FIRST IN SERIES,** Handcrafted, 1-3/4" tall.
A white mouse with a red cap peeks out of a silver thimble. Later known as Thimble Series.
☐ Purchased 19____   Pd $_____   MIB   NB   DB   BNT
☐ Want   Orig. Ret. $2.50   **NB** $250   **MIB** Sec. Mkt. **$300**

QX 132-3   LITTLE TRIMMER COLLECTION
Comments: Handcrafted, Set of 4.
Miniature versions of Thimble Mouse, Praying Angel, Drummer Boy and Santa. RARE!
☐ Purchased 19____   Pd $_____   MIB   NB   DB   BNT
☐ Want   Orig. Ret. $9.00   **NB** $300   **MIB** Sec. Mkt. **$340**

QX 268-3   LOVE
Comments: Gold Glass Ball, 3-1/4" dia., Dated 1978.
A heart which contains "1978" is surrounded by poinsettias and birds. Caption: "Of Life's Many Treasures, The Most Beautiful Is Love."
☐ Purchased 19____   Pd $_____   MIB   NB   DB   BNT
☐ Want   Orig. Ret. $3.50   **NB** $40   **MIB** Sec. Mkt. **$55**

QX 202-3   MERRY CHRISTMAS (SANTA)
Comments: White Satin Ball, 3-1/4" dia., Dated 1978.
Santa with his pack of gifts is later seen flying over rooftops on Christmas Eve. Caption: "Merry Christmas."
☐ Purchased 19____   Pd $_____   MIB   NB   DB   BNT
☐ Want   Orig. Ret. $3.50   **NB** $44   **MIB** Sec. Mkt. **$55**

QX 266-3   MOTHER
Comments: White Glass Ball, 3-1/4" dia.
Caption: "The Wonderful Meaning Of Christmas Is Found In A Mother's Love" and "Christmas 1978."
☐ Purchased 19____   Pd $_____   MIB   NB   DB   BNT
☐ Want   Orig. Ret. $3.50   **NB** $42   **MIB** Sec. Mkt. **$45**

QX 253-6   NATIVITY
Comments: White Glass Ball, 3-1/4" dia.
An "old world" Nativity scene. Caption: "The Joy Of Heaven Is Come To Earth."
☐ Purchased 19____   Pd $_____   MIB   NB   DB   BNT
☐ Want   Orig. Ret. $3.50   **NB** $90   **MIB** Sec. Mkt. **$150**

QX 145-6   PANORAMA BALL
Comments: Handcrafted Panorama Ball, 3-5/8" dia.
A little boy has fallen on the ice, viewed through a peek-through window in the ornament. Caption: "Merry Christmas 1978."
☐ Purchased 19____   Pd $_____   MIB   NB   DB   BNT
☐ Want   Orig. Ret. $6.00   **NB** $115   **MIB** Sec. Mkt. **$135**

QX 203-6   PEANUTS®

Comments: White Satin Ball, 2-5/8" dia. Charlie Brown is wrapped up in the Christmas tree lights. Snoopy decorates his doghouse. Caption: "Have A Delightful Christmas."

☐ Purchased 19_____   Pd $_____   MIB   NB   DB   BNT
☐ Want   Orig. Ret. $2.50   **NB** $50   **MIB** Sec. Mkt. **$65**

QX 204-3   PEANUTS®

Comments: White Satin Ball, 2-5/8" dia., Dated 1978. Snoopy and Woodstock decorate their freshly cut Christmas tree.

☐ Purchased 19_____   Pd $_____   MIB   NB   DB   BNT
☐ Want   Orig. Ret. $2.50   **NB** $60   **MIB** Sec. Mkt. **$68**

QX 205-6   PEANUTS®

Comments: White Satin Ball, 3-1/4" dia. The gang sings while Linus holds a dated wreath. Caption: "Joy to the World 1978."

☐ Purchased 19_____   Pd $_____   MIB   NB   DB   BNT
☐ Want   Orig. Ret. $3.50   **NB** $55   **MIB** Sec. Mkt. **$62**

QX 206-3   PEANUTS®

Comments: White Satin Ball, 3-1/4" dia., Dated 1978. Front: Snoopy, Woodstock and his flock are playing in a toy store. Back: Snoopy plays Santa.

☐ Purchased 19_____   Pd $_____   MIB   NB   DB   BNT
☐ Want   Orig. Ret. $3.50   **NB** $45   **MIB** Sec. Mkt. **$55**

QX 251-6   QUAIL, THE

Comments: Gold Glass Ball, 3-1/4" dia., Dated 1978. Caption: "Nature Has A Wonderful Way Of Making A Wonder-filled World."

☐ Purchased 19_____   Pd $_____   MIB   NB   DB   BNT
☐ Want   Orig. Ret. $3.50   **NB** $38   **MIB** Sec. Mkt. **$45**

QX 144-3   RED CARDINAL

Comments: Handcrafted, 4" tall. This cardinal clips on the branch of the tree.

☐ Purchased 19_____   Pd $_____   MIB   NB   DB   BNT
☐ Want   Orig. Ret. $4.50   **NB** $100   **MIB** Sec. Mkt. **$175**

QX 148-3   ROCKING HORSE

Comments: Handcrafted, 3-9/16" tall, Dated 1978. Hand-painted, polka-dot horse with white yarn mane and red rockers.

☐ Purchased 19_____   Pd $_____   MIB   NB   DB   BNT
☐ Want   Orig. Ret. $6.00   **NB** $75   **MIB** Sec. Mkt. **$85**

QX 152-3   SCHNEEBERG BELL

Comments: Handcrafted, 4" tall. Reproduction of an intricate Schneeberg wood carving collage (82 decorating steps were required to achieve the natural wood look). Caption: "Christmas 1978."

☐ Purchased 19_____   Pd $_____   MIB   NB   DB   BNT
☐ Want   Orig. Ret. $8.00   **NB** $140   **MIB** Sec. Mkt. **$190**

QX 142-3   SKATING RACCOON

Comments: Handcrafted, 2-3/4" tall. Reissued in 1979. Raccoon with red mittens and scarf wears real metal skates. **Artist:** Donna Lee

☐ Purchased 19_____   Pd $_____   MIB   NB   DB   BNT
☐ Want   Orig. Ret. $6.00   **NB** $70   **MIB** Sec. Mkt. **$95**

QX 219-6   SPENCER™ SPARROW, ESQ.

Comments: Ecru Soft-Sheen Satin Ball, 3-1/4" dia. A little sparrow named Spencer sits in a wreath and on the reverse, pulls a sled loaded with gifts. Caption: "Holly Days Are Jolly Days" and "Christmas 1978."

☐ Purchased 19_____   Pd $_____   MIB   NB   DB   BNT
☐ Want   Orig. Ret. $3.50   **NB** $45   **MIB** Sec. Mkt. **$50**

QX 133-6   THIMBLE SERIES: MOUSE

Comments: **FIRST IN SERIES**, Handcrafted, 1-3/4" tall. Reissued from Little Trimmers Series - Thimble Mouse.

☐ Purchased 19_____   Pd $_____   MIB   NB   DB   BNT
☐ Want   Orig. Ret. $2.50   **NB** $200   **MIB** Sec. Mkt. **$295**

QX 269-6   TWENTY-FIFTH CHRISTMAS TOGETHER

Comments: White Glass Ball, 3-1/4" dia., Dated 1978. Front: Caption "25th Christmas Together." Back: Caption "Time Endears But Cannot Fade The Memories That Love Has Made."

☐ Purchased 19_____   Pd $_____   MIB   NB   DB   BNT
☐ Want   Orig. Ret. $3.50   **NB** $20   **MIB** Sec. Mkt. **$35**

No secondary market value has been established for yarn and fabric ornaments found in original cellophane package.

QX 123-1   YARN ORNAMENTS – GREEN BOY ☐
Comments: 4-1/2" tall.
Slight changes from 1975. Reissued in 1979.
☐ Purchased 19____   Pd $_____   MIB   NB   DB   BNT
☐ Want   Orig. Ret. $2.00   Sec. Mkt. **$30**

QX 126-1   YARN ORNAMENTS – GREEN GIRL ☐
Comments: 4-1/2" tall.
Slight changes from 1975. Reissued in 1979.
☐ Purchased 19____   Pd $_____   MIB   NB   DB   BNT
☐ Want   Orig. Ret. $2.00   Sec. Mkt. **$25**

QX 340-3   YARN ORNAMENTS – MR. CLAUS ☐
Comments: 4-1/2" tall. Identical to 1975. Reissued in 1979.
☐ Purchased 19____   Pd $_____   MIB   NB   DB   BNT
☐ Want   Orig. Ret. $2.00   Sec. Mkt. **$22**

QX 125-1   YARN ORNAMENTS: – MRS. CLAUS ☐
Comments: 4-1/2" tall. Identical to 1975. Reissued in 1979.
White apron with red checked pockets.
☐ Purchased 19____   Pd $_____   MIB   NB   DB   BNT
☐ Want   Orig. Ret. $2.00   Sec. Mkt. **$22**

QX 250-3   YESTERDAY'S TOYS ☐
Comments: Gold Glass Ball, 3-1/4" dia., Dated 1978.
Caption: "Every Joy Of Yesterday Is A Memory For Tomorrow,. 1978."
☐ Purchased 19____   Pd $_____   MIB   NB   DB   BNT
☐ Want   Orig. Ret. $3.50   **NB** $15   **MIB** Sec. Mkt. **$25**

1979 Collection

QX 134-7   A CHRISTMAS TREAT ☐
Comments: Handcrafted, 4-3/4" tall. Reissued in 1980.
A teddy bear holds a giant candy cane. The 1979 ornament has "grooves" around the candy cane; the 1980 ornament does not.
☐ Purchased 19____   Pd $_____   MIB   NB   DB   BNT
☐ Want   Orig. Ret. $5.00   **NB** $45   **MIB** Sec. Mkt. **$85**

QX 343-9   ANGEL MUSIC ☐
Comments: Sewn Fabric. Vary in size from 4" to 5" tall.
Reissued in 1980.
Flying angel in blue flowered gown with pink and white wings, carries a harp.
☐ Purchased 19____   Pd $_____   MIB   NB   DB   BNT
☐ Want   Orig. Ret. $2.00   **NB** $12   **MIB** Sec. Mkt. **$22**

QX 154-7   BABY'S FIRST CHRISTMAS ☐
Comments: Handcrafted, 4" tall, Dated 1979.
RARE!! Knitted stocking filled with toys. The first handcrafted ornament for Baby's First Christmas. Caption: "Baby's First Christmas 1979."
☐ Purchased 19____   Pd $_____   MIB   NB   DB   BNT
☐ Want   Orig. Ret. $8.00   **NB** $75   **MIB** Sec. Mkt. **$115**

QX 208-7   BABY'S FIRST CHRISTMAS ☐
Comments: White Satin Ball, 3-1/4" dia., Dated 1979.
Toys and gifts are pulled on a sleigh. Back: A Christmas tree is decorated by birds. Caption: "Baby's First Christmas 1979."
☐ Purchased 19____   Pd $_____   MIB   NB   DB   BNT
☐ Want   Orig. Ret. $3.50   **NB** $11   **MIB** Sec. Mkt. **$32**

QX 255-9   BEHOLD THE STAR ☐
Comments: White Satin Ball, 3-1/4" dia.
Caption: "And the light was for all time; And the love was for all men."
☐ Purchased 19____   Pd $_____   MIB   NB   DB   BNT
☐ Want   Orig. Ret. $3.50   **NB** $21   **MIB** Sec. Mkt. **$40**

QX 147-9   BELLRINGER - "BELLSWINGER" ☐
Comments: **FIRST IN SERIES,** Dated 1979.
Porcelain and Handcrafted, 4" tall. A happy elf swings on the clapper of a white porcelain bell decorated with a wreath.
☐ Purchased 19____   Pd $_____   MIB   NB   DB   BNT
☐ Want   Orig. Ret. $10.00   **NB** $225   **MIB** Sec. Mkt. **$400**

QX 201-9   BETSEY CLARK SERIES ☐
Comments: **Seventh in Series,** White Satin Ball, 3-1/4" dia.
Children sit at home reading and then they pull a sled with a tree and gifts. Caption: "Holiday Fun Times Make Memories To Treasure, 1979."
☐ Purchased 19____   Pd $_____   MIB   NB   DB   BNT
☐ Want   Orig. Ret. $3.50   **NB** $25   **MIB** Sec. Mkt. **$32**

QX 207-9   BLACK ANGEL   ☐
Comments: Gold Glass Ball, 3-1/4" dia., Dated 1979.
Young adult angel dressed in a red and white robe.
Caption: "Merry Christmas 1979." **Artist:** Thomas Blackshear

☐ Purchased 19____   Pd $_____   MIB   NB   DB   BNT

☐ Want   Orig. Ret. $3.50   **NB** $20   **MIB** Sec. Mkt. **$25**

QX 146-7   CARROUSEL SERIES: ☐
CHRISTMAS CARROUSEL
Comments: **Second in Series,** Handcrafted, 3-1/2" tall.
Four angel musicians revolve on a carrousel.
Caption: "Christmas 1979."

☐ Purchased 19____   Pd $_____   MIB   NB   DB   BNT

☐ Want   Orig. Ret. $6.50   **NB** $150   **MIB** Sec. Mkt. **$185**

QX 204-7   CHRISTMAS CHICKADEES   ☐
Comments: Gold Glass Ball, 3-1/4" dia.
A pair of chickadees enjoy holly berries. Caption: "Beauty Is A
Gift Nature Gives Every Day" and "Christmas 1979."

☐ Purchased 19____   Pd $_____   MIB   NB   DB   BNT

☐ Want   Orig. Ret. $3.50   **NB** $18   **MIB** Sec. Mkt. **$35**

QX 257-9   CHRISTMAS COLLAGE   ☐
Comments: Gold Glass Ball, 3-1/4" dia., Dated 1979.
Old fashioned toys reproduced from a photograph of a
Schneeberg collage. Caption: "Season's Greetings."

☐ Purchased 19____   Pd $_____   MIB   NB   DB   BNT

☐ Want   Orig. Ret. $3.50   **NB** $25   **MIB** Sec. Mkt. **$40**

QX 157-9   CHRISTMAS EVE SURPRISE   ☐
Comments: Handcrafted, 4-1/4" tall, Dated 1979. A wood-
look shadow box shows Santa going down the chimney.

☐ Purchased 19____   Pd $_____   MIB   NB   DB   BNT

☐ Want   Orig. Ret. $6.50   **NB** $50   **MIB** Sec. Mkt. **$65**

QX 140-7   CHRISTMAS HEART   ☐
Comments: Handcrafted, 3-1/2" tall, Dated 1979.
Two doves rotate through the center of this heart-shaped orna-
ment. **Artist:** Linda Sickman

☐ Purchased 19____   Pd $_____   MIB   NB   DB   BNT

☐ Want   Orig. Ret. $6.50   **NB** $75   **MIB** Sec. Mkt. **$120**

QX 135-9   CHRISTMAS IS FOR CHILDREN   ☐
Comments: Handcrafted, 4-1/4" tall. Reissued in 1980.
A young girl dressed in a green bonnet and red dress holds a
white kitten as she swings.

☐ Purchased 19____   Pd $_____   MIB   NB   DB   BNT

☐ Want   Orig. Ret. $5.00   **NB** $65   **MIB** Sec. Mkt. **$95**

QX 253-9   CHRISTMAS TRADITIONS   ☐
Comments: Gold Glass Ball, 3-1/4" dia., Dated 1979.
Homey Christmas traditions are portrayed. Caption: "The old
may be replaced with new, traditions rearranged, but the won-
der that is Christmas will never ever change."
Artist: Linda Sickman

☐ Purchased 19____   Pd $_____   MIB   NB   DB   BNT

☐ Want   Orig. Ret. $3.50   **NB** $25   **MIB** Sec. Mkt. **$35**

QX 353-9   COLORS OF CHRISTMAS: ☐
HOLIDAY WREATH
Comments: Acrylic, 3-1/2" tall, Dated 1979.
Stained-Glass Look. Wreath decorated with colorful ornaments
and a red bow.

☐ Purchased 19____   Pd $_____   MIB   NB   DB   BNT

☐ Want   Orig. Ret. $3.50   **NB** $35   **MIB** Sec. Mkt. **$45**

QX 351-9   COLORS OF CHRISTMAS: ☐
PARTRIDGE IN A PEAR TREE
Comments: Acrylic, 3-1/4" dia., Dated 1979.
Stained-Glass Look. A richly colored partridge surrounded by
golden pears and green leaves.

☐ Purchased 19____   Pd $_____   MIB   NB   DB   BNT

☐ Want   Orig. Ret. $3.50   **NB** $35   **MIB** Sec. Mkt. **$45**

QX 352-7   COLORS OF CHRISTMAS: ☐
STAR OVER BETHLEHEM
Comments: Acrylic, 3-1/2" dia. Stained-Glass Look.
The shepherds gaze in wonder at the star which shines bright-
ly over Bethlehem. **Artist:** Linda Sickman

☐ Purchased 19____   Pd $_____   MIB   NB   DB   BNT

☐ Want   Orig. Ret. $3.50   **NB** $60   **MIB** Sec. Mkt. **$75**

QX 350-7   COLORS OF CHRISTMAS: ☐
WORDS OF CHRISTMAS
Comments: Acrylic, 3-3/4" tall, Stained-Glass Look.
Caption: "The Message Of Christmas Is Love."

☐ Purchased 19____   Pd $_____   MIB   NB   DB   BNT

☐ Want   Orig. Ret. $3.50   **NB** $67   **MIB** Sec. Mkt. **$85**

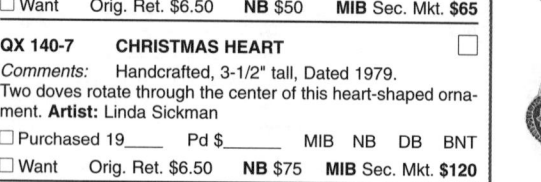

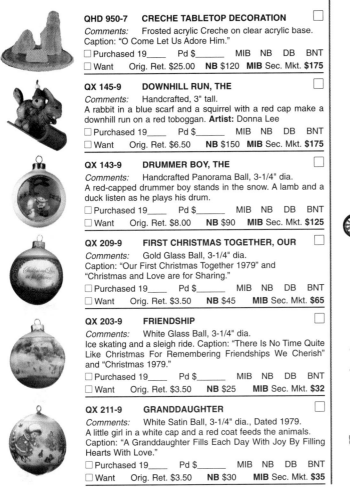

QHD 950-7   CRECHE TABLETOP DECORATION ☐

Comments: Frosted acrylic Creche on clear acrylic base.
Caption: "O Come Let Us Adore Him."

☐ Purchased 19____   Pd $_____   MIB   NB   DB   BNT
☐ Want   Orig. Ret. $25.00   **NB** $120   **MIB** Sec. Mkt. **$175**

QX 145-9   DOWNHILL RUN, THE ☐

Comments: Handcrafted, 3" tall.
A rabbit in a blue scarf and a squirrel with a red cap make a downhill run on a red toboggan. **Artist:** Donna Lee

☐ Purchased 19____   Pd $_____   MIB   NB   DB   BNT
☐ Want   Orig. Ret. $6.50   **NB** $150   **MIB** Sec. Mkt. **$175**

QX 143-9   DRUMMER BOY, THE ☐

Comments: Handcrafted Panorama Ball, 3-1/4" dia.
A red-capped drummer boy stands in the snow. A lamb and a duck listen as he plays his drum.

☐ Purchased 19____   Pd $_____   MIB   NB   DB   BNT
☐ Want   Orig. Ret. $8.00   **NB** $90   **MIB** Sec. Mkt. **$125**

QX 209-9   FIRST CHRISTMAS TOGETHER, OUR ☐

Comments: Gold Glass Ball, 3-1/4" dia.
Caption: "Our First Christmas Together 1979" and "Christmas and Love are for Sharing."

☐ Purchased 19____   Pd $_____   MIB   NB   DB   BNT
☐ Want   Orig. Ret. $3.50   **NB** $45   **MIB** Sec. Mkt. **$65**

QX 203-9   FRIENDSHIP ☐

Comments: White Glass Ball, 3-1/4" dia.
Ice skating and a sleigh ride. Caption: "There Is No Time Quite Like Christmas For Remembering Friendships We Cherish" and "Christmas 1979."

☐ Purchased 19____   Pd $_____   MIB   NB   DB   BNT
☐ Want   Orig. Ret. $3.50   **NB** $25   **MIB** Sec. Mkt. **$32**

QX 211-9   GRANDDAUGHTER ☐

Comments: White Satin Ball, 3-1/4" dia., Dated 1979.
A little girl in a white cap and a red coat feeds the animals. Caption: "A Granddaughter Fills Each Day With Joy By Filling Hearts With Love."

☐ Purchased 19____   Pd $_____   MIB   NB   DB   BNT
☐ Want   Orig. Ret. $3.50   **NB** $30   **MIB** Sec. Mkt. **$35**

QX 252-7   GRANDMOTHER ☐

Comments: White Glass Ball, 3-1/4" dia., Dated 1979.
Birds fly about a basket of Christmas flowers. Caption: "Grandmothers Bring Happy Times — Time And Time Again."

☐ Purchased 19____   Pd $_____   MIB   NB   DB   BNT
☐ Want   Orig. Ret. $3.50   **NB** $14   **MIB** Sec. Mkt. **$22**

QX 210-7   GRANDSON ☐

Comments: White Satin Ball, 3-1/4" dia.
Snoopy and Woodstock sledding in the snow. Caption: "A Grandson... A Special Someone Whose Merry Ways Bring Extra Joy To The Holidays. Christmas 1979."

☐ Purchased 19____   Pd $_____   MIB   NB   DB   BNT
☐ Want   Orig. Ret. $3.50   **NB** $24   **MIB** Sec. Mkt. **$30**

QX 155-9   HERE COMES SANTA SERIES:
SANTA'S MOTORCAR ☐

Comments: **FIRST IN SERIES,** Handcrafted, 3-1/2" tall, Dated 1979. Turning wheels on the antique car that Santa drives makes this a special ornament.

☐ Purchased 19____   Pd $_____   MIB   NB   DB   BNT
☐ Want   Orig. Ret. $9.00   **NB** $475   **MIB** Sec. Mkt. **$650**

QX 320-3   HOLIDAY CHIMES: REINDEER CHIMES ☐

Comments: Chrome plated brass, 5-1/2" tall.
Issued in 1978, 1979 and 1980. **Artist:** Linda Sickman

☐ Purchased 19____   Pd $_____   MIB   NB   DB   BNT
☐ Want   Orig. Ret. $4.50   **NB** $45   **MIB** Sec. Mkt. **$60**

QX 137-9   HOLIDAY CHIMES: STAR CHIMES ☐

Comments: Chrome Plate, 4" tall, Dated 1979.
Stars circle within stars. Year date is in the center star.
Artist: Linda Sickman

☐ Purchased 19____   Pd $_____   MIB   NB   DB   BNT
☐ Want   Orig. Ret. $4.50   **NB** $60   **MIB** Sec. Mkt. **$75**

QX 300-7   HOLIDAY HIGHLIGHTS:
CHRISTMAS ANGEL ☐

Comments: Acrylic, 4-1/4" wide, Hard to Find.
Flying angel with long floral dress, feathery wings and halo, holding a nosegay of flowers. Caption: "Christmas 1979."

☐ Purchased 19____   Pd $_____   MIB   NB   DB   BNT
☐ Want   Orig. Ret. $3.50   **NB** $75   **MIB** Sec. Mkt. **$110**

QX 303-9   HOLIDAY HIGHLIGHTS: CHRISTMAS CHEER ☐

Comments: Acrylic, 3-1/2" dia., Dated 1979.
A little bird with berries in its beak is perched on a holly bough.

☐ Purchased 19____   Pd $_____   MIB   NB   DB   BNT
☐ Want   Orig. Ret. $3.50   **NB** $50   **MIB** Sec. Mkt. **$80**

QX 302-7   HOLIDAY HIGHLIGHTS: CHRISTMAS TREE ☐

Comments: Acrylic, 4-1/2" tall, Dated 1979.
A tree of leaves and flowers with a dove near the top. The date is stamped in silver foil.

☐ Purchased 19____   Pd $_____   MIB   NB   DB   BNT
☐ Want   Orig. Ret. $3.50   **NB** $60   **MIB** Sec. Mkt. **$75**

QX 304-7   HOLIDAY HIGHLIGHTS: LOVE ☐

Comments: Acrylic, 3-1/2" tall.
The caption is stamped in silver foil on this heart: "Time Of Memories And Dreams… Time Of Love. Christmas 1979."

☐ Purchased 19____   Pd $_____   MIB   NB   DB   BNT
☐ Want   Orig. Ret. $3.50   **NB** $88   **MIB** Sec. Mkt. **$90**

QX 301-9   HOLIDAY HIGHLIGHTS SNOWFLAKE ☐

Comments: Acrylic, 3-1/2" dia., Dated 1979. This lovely snowflake has the date "etched" in the center hexagon.

☐ Purchased 19____   Pd $_____   MIB   NB   DB   BNT
☐ Want   Orig. Ret. $3.50   **NB** $30   **MIB** Sec. Mkt. **$45**

QX 152-7   HOLIDAY SCRIMSHAW ☐

Comments: Handcrafted, 3-1/2" tall.
Ivory angel with widespread wings resembles scrimshaw carving. Caption: "Peace - Love - Joy 1979."

☐ Purchased 19____   Pd $_____   MIB   NB   DB   BNT
☐ Want   Orig. Ret. $4.00   **NB** $165   **MIB** Sec. Mkt. **$225**

QX 205-9   JOAN WALSH ANGLUND© ☐

Comments: White Satin Ball, 3-1/4" dia., Dated 1979.
Children hang their stockings by the fireplace. Back: Children with their gifts. Caption: "The Smallest Pleasure Is Big Enough To Share."

☐ Purchased 19____   Pd $_____   MIB   NB   DB   BNT
☐ Want   Orig. Ret. $3.50   **NB** $30   **MIB** Sec. Mkt. **$35**

QX 256-7   LIGHT OF CHRISTMAS, THE ☐

Comments: Chrome Glass Ball, 3-1/4" dia., Dated 1979.
Stained Glass Art Deco design. Caption: "There's No Light As Bright As Christmas To Adorn And Warm The Night."

☐ Purchased 19____   Pd $_____   MIB   NB   DB   BNT
☐ Want   Orig. Ret. $3.50   **NB** $20   **MIB** Sec. Mkt. **$30**

QX 132-7   LITTLE TRIMMER COLLECTION: A MATCHLESS CHRISTMAS ☐

Comments: Handcrafted, 2-1/2" long.
A little white mouse wearing a red nightcap makes a cozy bed from a red match box.

☐ Purchased 19____   Pd $_____   MIB   NB   DB   BNT
☐ Want   Orig. Ret. $4.00   **NB** $60   **MIB** Sec. Mkt. **$85**

QX 130-7   LITTLE TRIMMER COLLECTION: ANGEL DELIGHT ☐

Comments: Handcrafted, 1-3/4" tall.
A little angel rides in her walnut shell.

☐ Purchased 19____   Pd $_____   MIB   NB   DB   BNT
☐ Want   Orig. Ret. $3.00   **NB** $70   **MIB** Sec. Mkt. **$95**

QX 135-6   LITTLE TRIMMERS: SANTA ☐

Comments: Handcrafted, 2-1/4" tall. Reissued from 1978.

☐ Purchased 19____   Pd $_____   MIB   NB   DB   BNT
☐ Want   Orig. Ret. $3.00   **NB** $40   **MIB** Sec. Mkt. **$65**

QX 133-6   LITTLE TRIMMERS: THIMBLE SERIES ☐

Comments: **FIRST IN SERIES,** Handcrafted, 1-3/4" tall. Reissued from 1978.

☐ Purchased 19____   Pd $_____   MIB   NB   DB   BNT
☐ Want   Orig. Ret. $3.00   **NB** $250   **MIB** Sec. Mkt. **$300**

QX 159-9   LITTLE TRIMMER SET ☐

Comments: Handcrafted.
The Angel, Matchless Christmas and Soldier were packaged together as a trio of Trimmers.

☐ Purchased 19____   Pd $_____   MIB   NB   DB   BNT
☐ Want   Orig. Ret. $9.00   **NB** $180   **MIB** Sec. Mkt. **$300**

QX 258-7   LOVE ☐

Comments: White Glass Ball, 3-1/4" dia.
Caption: "Love... Warm As Candle Glow, Wondrous As
Snowfall, Welcome As Christmas" and "Christmas 1979."

☐ Purchased 19____   Pd $_____   MIB   NB   DB   BNT
☐ Want   Orig. Ret. $3.50   **NB** $24   **MIB** Sec. Mkt. **$44**

QX 254-7   MARY HAMILTON ☐

Comments: Ecru Soft-Sheen Satin Ball, 3-1/4" dia.
Dated 1979. A choir of angels sing to forest creatures.
Caption: "... And Heaven And Nature Sing."

☐ Purchased 19____   Pd $_____   MIB   NB   DB   BNT
☐ Want   Orig. Ret. $3.50   **NB** $20   **MIB** Sec. Mkt. **$30**

QX 342-7   MERRY SANTA ☐

Comments: Fabric, 4"-5" tall. Reissued in 1980.
Whimsical Santa with a pack of toys on his back.

☐ Purchased 19____   Pd $_____   MIB   NB   DB   BNT
☐ Want   Orig. Ret. $2.00   Sec. Mkt. **$20**

QX 251-9   MOTHER ☐

Comments: White Glass Ball, 3-1/4" dia.
Caption: "It's Love That Makes Christmas So Special - And
Mother Who Makes Us Feel Loved."

☐ Purchased 19____   Pd $_____   MIB   NB   DB   BNT
☐ Want   Orig. Ret. $3.50   **NB** $18   **MIB** Sec. Mkt. **$23**

QX 212-7   NEW HOME ☐

Comments: Ecru Soft-Sheen Satin Ball, 3-1/4" dia.
Dated 1979. A colorful snow-covered village and pond.
Caption: "Christmas... When Love Fills The Heart, When
Hearts Look To Home."

☐ Purchased 19____   Pd $_____   MIB   NB   DB   BNT
☐ Want   Orig. Ret. $3.50   **NB** $25   **MIB** Sec. Mkt. **$45**

QX 214-7   NIGHT BEFORE CHRISTMAS ☐

Comments: White Satin Ball, 3-1/4" dia., Dated 1979.
Santa fills the stockings and continues on his journey.
Caption: "... I Heard Him Exclaim, Ere He Drove Out Of Sight,
Happy Christmas To All, And To All A Good Night." C. C. Moore

☐ Purchased 19____   Pd $_____   MIB   NB   DB   BNT
☐ Want   Orig. Ret. $3.50   **NB** $32   **MIB** Sec. Mkt. **$40**

QX 150-7   OUTDOOR FUN ☐

Comments: Handcrafted, 3" tall.
A little girl swings between two fir trees. **Artist:** Linda Sickman

☐ Purchased 19____   Pd $_____   MIB   NB   DB   BNT
☐ Want   Orig. Ret. $8.00   **NB** $80   **MIB** Sec. Mkt. **$110**

QX 202-7   PEANUTS® (TIME TO TRIM) ☐

Comments: White Satin Ball, 3-1/4" dia., Dated 1979.
Woodstock and his green-capped flock decorate their
Christmas tree with candy canes Snoopy is giving them.
Caption: "Merry Christmas 1979."

☐ Purchased 19____   Pd $_____   MIB   NB   DB   BNT
☐ Want   Orig. Ret. $3.50   **NB** $28   **MIB** Sec. Mkt. **$40**

QX 133-9   READY FOR CHRISTMAS ☐

Comments: Handcrafted, 3" tall, Dated 1979.
White birdhouse with snow-capped roof and green garland over
the door. **Artist:** Donna Lee

☐ Purchased 19____   Pd $_____   MIB   NB   DB   BNT
☐ Want   Orig. Ret. $6.50   **NB** $100   **MIB** Sec. Mkt. **$150**

QX 340-7   ROCKING HORSE, THE ☐

Comments: Quilted Fabric, 4" - 5" tall. Reissued in 1980.
A brown spotted rocking horse rides into Christmas on blue
rockers. The ornament is trimmed in red.

☐ Purchased 19____   Pd $_____   MIB   NB   DB   BNT
☐ Want   Orig. Ret. $2.00   Sec. Mkt. **$23**

QX 138-7   SANTA'S HERE ☐

Comments: Handcrafted, 4" dia., Dated 1979.
Santa, with his pack, waves as he rotates inside a white
snowflake. **Artist:** Linda Sickman

☐ Purchased 19____   Pd $_____   MIB   NB   DB   BNT
☐ Want   Orig. Ret. $5.00   **NB** $65   **MIB** Sec. Mkt. **$80**

QX 142-3   SKATING RACCOON ☐

Comments: Handcrafted, 2" tall. Reissued from 1978.
Artist: Donna Lee

☐ Purchased 19____   Pd $_____   MIB   NB   DB   BNT
☐ Want   Orig. Ret. $6.50   **NB** $60   **MIB** Sec. Mkt. **$95**

QX 139-9 SKATING SNOWMAN, THE ☐

Comments: Handcrafted, 4-1/4" tall, Reissued in 1980.
This happy snowman wears metal ice skates, a black top hat and a green and white scarf.

☐ Purchased 19____   Pd $_____   MIB NB DB BNT
☐ Want   Orig. Ret. $5.00   **NB** $70   **MIB** Sec. Mkt. **$82**

QX 141-9 SNOOPY & FRIENDS SERIES: ☐
ICE HOCKEY HOLIDAY

Comments: **FIRST IN SERIES,** 3-1/4" dia., Dated 1979.
Handcrafted Panorama Ball. Snoopy and Woodstock play ice hockey on a frozen pond.

☐ Purchased 19____   Pd $_____   MIB NB DB BNT
☐ Want   Orig. Ret. $8.00   **NB** $80   **MIB** Sec. Mkt. **$100**

QX 200-7 SPENCER™ SPARROW, ESQ. ☐

Comments: Ecru Soft-Sheen Satin Ball, 3-1/4" dia.
Dated 1979. Spencer swings on a garland of popcorn and cranberries. Caption: "Christmas Time Means Decorating, Spreading Cheer And Celebrating."

☐ Purchased 19____   Pd $_____   MIB NB DB BNT
☐ Want   Orig. Ret. $3.50   **NB** $25   **MIB** Sec. Mkt. **$41**

QX 341-9 STUFFED FULL STOCKING ☐

Comments: Quilted Fabric, 4" - 5" tall, Reissued in 1980.
Blue patchwork stocking holds a doll and other gifts to delight a child.

☐ Purchased 19____   Pd $_____   MIB NB DB BNT
☐ Want   Orig. Ret. $2.00   Sec. Mkt. **$26**

QX 213-9 TEACHER ☐

Comments: White Satin Ball, 3-1/4" dia., Dated 1979.
Front: A raccoon writes a message to the teacher. Back: A sleigh with a gift. Caption: "To a Special Teacher" and "Merry Christmas 1979."

☐ Purchased 19____   Pd $_____   MIB NB DB BNT
☐ Want   Orig. Ret. $3.50   **NB** $5   **MIB** Sec. Mkt. **$15**

QX 131-9 THIMBLE SERIES: ☐
A CHRISTMAS SALUTE

Comments: **Second in Series,** Handcrafted, 2-1/4" tall.
Reissued in 1980. A cute soldier dressed in red and blue wears a thimble hat.

☐ Purchased 19____   Pd $_____   MIB NB DB BNT
☐ Want   Orig. Ret. $3.00   **NB** $95   **MIB** Sec. Mkt. **$175**

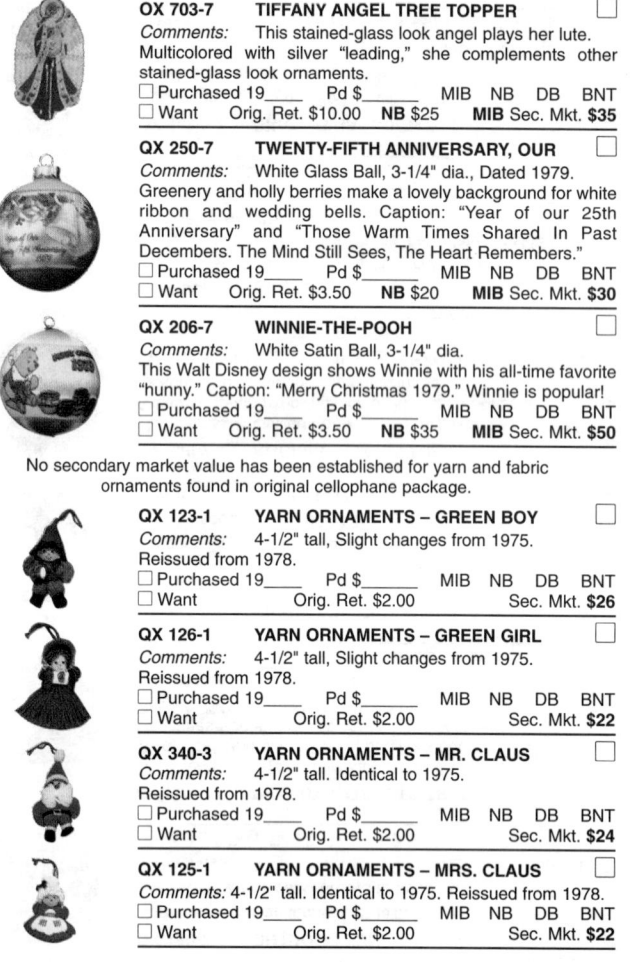

OX 703-7 TIFFANY ANGEL TREE TOPPER ☐

Comments: This stained-glass look angel plays her lute.
Multicolored with silver "leading," she complements other stained-glass look ornaments.

☐ Purchased 19____   Pd $_____   MIB NB DB BNT
☐ Want   Orig. Ret. $10.00   **NB** $25   **MIB** Sec. Mkt. **$35**

QX 250-7 TWENTY-FIFTH ANNIVERSARY, OUR ☐

Comments: White Glass Ball, 3-1/4" dia., Dated 1979.
Greenery and holly berries make a lovely background for white ribbon and wedding bells. Caption: "Year of our 25th Anniversary" and "Those Warm Times Shared In Past Decembers. The Mind Still Sees, The Heart Remembers."

☐ Purchased 19____   Pd $_____   MIB NB DB BNT
☐ Want   Orig. Ret. $3.50   **NB** $20   **MIB** Sec. Mkt. **$30**

QX 206-7 WINNIE-THE-POOH ☐

Comments: White Satin Ball, 3-1/4" dia.
This Walt Disney design shows Winnie with his all-time favorite "hunny." Caption: "Merry Christmas 1979." Winnie is popular!

☐ Purchased 19____   Pd $_____   MIB NB DB BNT
☐ Want   Orig. Ret. $3.50   **NB** $35   **MIB** Sec. Mkt. **$50**

No secondary market value has been established for yarn and fabric ornaments found in original cellophane package.

QX 123-1 YARN ORNAMENTS – GREEN BOY ☐

Comments: 4-1/2" tall, Slight changes from 1975.
Reissued from 1978.

☐ Purchased 19____   Pd $_____   MIB NB DB BNT
☐ Want   Orig. Ret. $2.00   Sec. Mkt. **$26**

QX 126-1 YARN ORNAMENTS – GREEN GIRL ☐

Comments: 4-1/2" tall, Slight changes from 1975.
Reissued from 1978.

☐ Purchased 19____   Pd $_____   MIB NB DB BNT
☐ Want   Orig. Ret. $2.00   Sec. Mkt. **$22**

QX 340-3 YARN ORNAMENTS – MR. CLAUS ☐

Comments: 4-1/2" tall. Identical to 1975.
Reissued from 1978.

☐ Purchased 19____   Pd $_____   MIB NB DB BNT
☐ Want   Orig. Ret. $2.00   Sec. Mkt. **$24**

QX 125-1 YARN ORNAMENTS – MRS. CLAUS ☐

Comments: 4-1/2" tall. Identical to 1975. Reissued from 1978.

☐ Purchased 19____   Pd $_____   MIB NB DB BNT
☐ Want   Orig. Ret. $2.00   Sec. Mkt. **$22**

1980 Collection

QX 134-7   A CHRISTMAS TREAT ☐
Comments: Handcrafted, 4-3/4" tall.
Reissued from 1979. The 1979 ornament has "grooves" around the candy cane; the 1980 ornament does not.
☐ Purchased 19_____   Pd $_____   MIB   NB   DB   BNT
☐ Want   Orig. Ret. $5.50   **NB** $65   **MIB** Sec. Mkt. **$85**

QX 144-1   A CHRISTMAS VIGIL ☐
Comments: Handcrafted Panorama Ball, 3-13/16" tall.
A little boy and his dog look through a window in time to see Santa and his reindeer. Panorama Balls are usually not MIB.
Artist: Donna Lee
☐ Purchased 19_____   Pd $_____   MIB   NB   DB   BNT
☐ Want   Orig. Ret. $9.00   **NB** $95   **MIB** Sec. Mkt. **$105**

QX 139-4   A HEAVENLY NAP ☐
Comments: Handcrafted, 3-1/2" tall. Reissued in 1981.
A frosted acrylic moon, sound asleep, holds a sleeping angel.
Artist: Donna Lee
☐ Purchased 19_____   Pd $_____   MIB   NB   DB   BNT
☐ Want   Orig. Ret. $6.50   **NB** $35   **MIB** Sec. Mkt. **$55**

QX 153-4   A SPOT OF CHRISTMAS CHEER ☐
Comments: Handcrafted, 2-47/64" tall, Dated 1980.
A chipmunk trims a Christmas tree inside a teapot decorated with green garland. **Artist:** Donna Lee
☐ Purchased 19_____   Pd $_____   MIB   NB   DB   BNT
☐ Want   Orig. Ret. $8.00   **NB** $100   **MIB** Sec. Mkt. **$150**

QX 343-9   ANGEL MUSIC ☐
Comments: Quilted Fabric. Reissued from 1979.
☐ Purchased 19_____   Pd $_____   MIB   NB   DB   BNT
☐ Want   Orig. Ret. $2.00   Sec. Mkt. **$20**

Subscribe to the
***Weekly Collectors' Gazette*™**
to keep yourself posted on the latest Hot Tips!
Call Today! 1-800-445-8745

QX 150-1   ANIMALS' CHRISTMAS, THE ☐
Comments: Handcrafted, 2-37/64" tall.
A brown rabbit and a brown bird decorate a tree with red ribbon and a gold star. **Artist:** Donna Lee
☐ Purchased 19_____   Pd $_____   MIB   NB   DB   BNT
☐ Want   Orig. Ret. $8.00   **NB** $47   **MIB** Sec. Mkt. **$57**

QX 200-1   BABY'S FIRST CHRISTMAS ☐
Comments: White Satin Ball, 3-1/4" dia.
Santa stops to wish a Merry Christmas to baby.
Caption: "Baby's First Christmas, 1980."
☐ Purchased 19_____   Pd $_____   MIB   NB   DB   BNT
☐ Want   Orig. Ret. $4.00   **NB** $20   **MIB** Sec. Mkt. **$30**

QX 156-1   BABY'S FIRST CHRISTMAS ☐
Comments: Handcrafted, 3-57/64" tall, Dated 1980.
A shadow box in the shape of a Christmas tree is filled with baby's toys. Caption: "Baby's First Christmas."
Artist: Linda Sickman
☐ Purchased 19_____   Pd $_____   MIB   NB   DB   BNT
☐ Want   Orig. Ret. $12.00   **NB** $40   **MIB** Sec. Mkt. **$50**

QX 303-4   BEAUTY OF FRIENDSHIP ☐
Comments: Acrylic, 3-1/4" dia., Dated 1980.
Caption: "Friendship Brings Beauty To Our Days, Joy To Our World. Christmas 1980."
☐ Purchased 19_____   Pd $_____   MIB   NB   DB   BNT
☐ Want   Orig. Ret. $4.00   **NB** $50   **MIB** Sec. Mkt. **$65**

QX 157-4   BELLRINGERS SERIES ☐
Comments: **Second in Series,** Handcrafted, 2-7/64" tall.
Dated 1980. Two angels in blue gowns circle and ring a white porcelain bell with the star "clappers" they are holding.
☐ Purchased 19_____   Pd $_____   MIB   NB   DB   BNT
☐ Want   Orig. Ret. $15.00   **NB** $70   **MIB** Sec. Mkt. **$85**

QX 215-4   BETSEY CLARK SERIES ☐
Comments: **Eighth in Series,** White Glass Ball, 3-1/4" dia.
Two children sled past a sign that says "Christmas 1980."
Caption: "It's Joy-In-The-Air Time, Love Everywhere Time, Good-Fun-To-Share Time, It's Christmas."
☐ Purchased 19_____   Pd $_____   MIB   NB   DB   BNT
☐ Want   Orig. Ret. $4.00   **NB** $25   **MIB** Sec. Mkt. **$31**

QX 307-4   BETSEY CLARK

Comments: Cameo, 3-3/8" dia., Dated 1980.

Angel is kneeling in prayer. Caption: "Love Came Down At Christmas, Love All Lovely, Love Divine: Love Was Born At Christmas, Star And Angels Gave The Sign" and "Christmas 1980."

☐ Purchased 19____   Pd $_____   MIB   NB   DB   BNT
☐ Want   Orig. Ret. $6.50   **NB** $44   **MIB** Sec. Mkt. **$60**

QX 149-4   BETSEY CLARK'S CHRISTMAS

Comments: Handcrafted, 4" tall, Dated 1980. A shadow box trimmed in white and red shows a girl in a three-dimensional snow scene.

☐ Purchased 19____   Pd $_____   MIB   NB   DB   BNT
☐ Want   Orig. Ret. $7.50   **NB** $24   **MIB** Sec. Mkt. **$40**

QX 229-4   AN AFRICAN-AMERICAN BABY'S FIRST CHRISTMAS

Comments: White Satin Ball, 3-1/4" dia., Dated 1980.

An African-American baby sits by a decorated tree that holds nested birds. Toys surround the tree. Caption: "Baby's First Christmas, 1980."

☐ Purchased 19____   Pd $_____   MIB   NB   DB   BNT
☐ Want   Orig. Ret. $4.00   **NB** $25   **MIB** Sec. Mkt. **$30**

OX 705-4   BRASS STAR TREE TOPPER

Comments: A lacy design was used for this interlocking brass star.

☐ Purchased 19____   Pd $_____   MIB   NB   DB   BNT
☐ Want   Orig. Ret. $25.00   **NB** $50   **MIB** Sec. Mkt. **$65**

QX 140-1   CAROLING BEAR

Comments: Handcrafted, 3-7/33" tall, Dated 1980. A brown bear sings a duet with a red bird on his arm. Caption: "Carols 1980." **Artist:** Donna Lee

☐ Purchased 19____   Pd $_____   MIB   NB   DB   BNT
☐ Want   Orig. Ret. $7.50   **NB** $120   **MIB** Sec. Mkt. **$150**

QX 141-4   CARROUSEL SERIES: MERRY CARROUSEL

Comments: **Third in Series.** Handcrafted, 3-1/8" tall, Dated 1980. Santa and his reindeer make their "rounds." Caption on top: "Christmas 1980."

☐ Purchased 19____   Pd $_____   MIB   NB   DB   BNT
☐ Want   Orig. Ret. $7.50   **NB** $150   **MIB** Sec. Mkt. **$165**

QX 158-4   CHECKING IT TWICE

Comments: Handcrafted, 5-15/16" tall, Special Edition. Reissued in 1981. Santa checks his list. He wears spectacles of real metal. **Artist:** Thomas Blackshear

☐ Purchased 19____   Pd $_____   MIB   NB   DB   BNT
☐ Want   Orig. Ret. $20.00   **NB** $175   **MIB** Sec. Mkt. **$200**

QX 210-1   CHRISTMAS AT HOME

Comments: Gold Glass Ball, 3-1/4" dia., Dated 1980. Caption: "A Home That's Filled With Christmas Glows With The Joyful Light Of the special warmth and happiness that makes the season bright. Christmas 1980."

☐ Purchased 19____   Pd $_____   MIB   NB   DB   BNT
☐ Want   Orig. Ret. $4.00   **NB** $20   **MIB** Sec. Mkt. **$38**

QX 224-1   CHRISTMAS CARDINALS

Comments: White Glass Ball, 3-1/4" dia., Dated 1980. Two cardinals sit on berry-laden branches of holly. Caption: "Nature at Christmas... a wonderland of wintry art. Christmas 1980."

☐ Purchased 19____   Pd $_____   MIB   NB   DB   BNT
☐ Want   Orig. Ret. $4.00   **NB** $17   **MIB** Sec. Mkt. **$30**

QX 228-1   CHRISTMAS CHOIR

Comments: Gold Glass Ball, 3-1/4" dia., Dated 1980. Three children dressed in choir robes sing the message of Christmas. Caption: "Go Tell It On The Mountain... Jesus Christ Is Born!" and "Christmas 1980."

☐ Purchased 19____   Pd $_____   MIB   NB   DB   BNT
☐ Want   Orig. Ret. $4.00   **NB** $60   **MIB** Sec. Mkt. **$85**

QX 135-9   CHRISTMAS IS FOR CHILDREN

Comments: Handcrafted, 4-1/4" tall.

Reissued from 1979.

☐ Purchased 19____   Pd $_____   MIB   NB   DB   BNT
☐ Want   1980 Retail. $5.00   **NB** $65   **MIB** Sec. Mkt. **$95**

QX 353-4   CHRISTMAS KITTEN TEST ORNAMENT

Comments: *VERY RARE! ONLY 200 MADE.* Very limited "known" sold prices in past years. Until recently we had not seen this ornament in a box. No sales found for two years.

☐ Purchased 19____   Pd $_____   MIB   NB   DB   BNT
☐ Want   Orig. Ret. $4.00   **NB** $200   **MIB** Sec. Mkt. **$300**

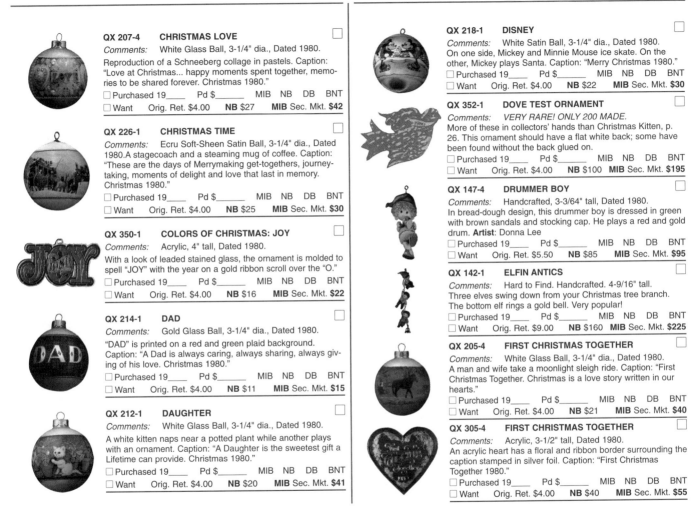

QX 207-4　CHRISTMAS LOVE　☐
Comments:　White Glass Ball, 3-1/4" dia., Dated 1980.
Reproduction of a Schneeberg collage in pastels. Caption:
"Love at Christmas... happy moments spent together, memo-
ries to be shared forever. Christmas 1980."
☐ Purchased 19＿＿＿　Pd $＿＿＿＿　MIB　NB　DB　BNT
☐ Want　Orig. Ret. $4.00　**NB** $27　**MIB** Sec. Mkt. **$42**

QX 226-1　CHRISTMAS TIME　☐
Comments:　Ecru Soft-Sheen Satin Ball, 3-1/4" dia., Dated
1980.A stagecoach and a steaming mug of coffee. Caption:
"These are the days of Merrymaking get-togethers, journey-
taking, moments of delight and love that last in memory.
Christmas 1980."
☐ Purchased 19＿＿＿　Pd $＿＿＿＿　MIB　NB　DB　BNT
☐ Want　Orig. Ret. $4.00　**NB** $25　**MIB** Sec. Mkt. **$30**

QX 350-1　COLORS OF CHRISTMAS: JOY　☐
Comments:　Acrylic, 4" tall, Dated 1980.
With a look of leaded stained glass, the ornament is molded to
spell "JOY" with the year on a gold ribbon scroll over the "O."
☐ Purchased 19＿＿＿　Pd $＿＿＿＿　MIB　NB　DB　BNT
☐ Want　Orig. Ret. $4.00　**NB** $16　**MIB** Sec. Mkt. **$22**

QX 214-1　DAD　☐
Comments:　Gold Glass Ball, 3-1/4" dia., Dated 1980.
"DAD" is printed on a red and green plaid background.
Caption: "A Dad is always caring, always sharing, always giv-
ing of his love. Christmas 1980."
☐ Purchased 19＿＿＿　Pd $＿＿＿＿　MIB　NB　DB　BNT
☐ Want　Orig. Ret. $4.00　**NB** $11　**MIB** Sec. Mkt. **$15**

QX 212-1　DAUGHTER　☐
Comments:　White Glass Ball, 3-1/4" dia., Dated 1980.
A white kitten naps near a potted plant while another plays
with an ornament. Caption: "A Daughter is the sweetest gift a
Lifetime can provide. Christmas 1980."
☐ Purchased 19＿＿＿　Pd $＿＿＿＿　MIB　NB　DB　BNT
☐ Want　Orig. Ret. $4.00　**NB** $20　**MIB** Sec. Mkt. **$41**

QX 218-1　DISNEY　☐
Comments:　White Satin Ball, 3-1/4" dia., Dated 1980.
On one side, Mickey and Minnie Mouse ice skate. On the
other, Mickey plays Santa. Caption: "Merry Christmas 1980."
☐ Purchased 19＿＿＿　Pd $＿＿＿＿　MIB　NB　DB　BNT
☐ Want　Orig. Ret. $4.00　**NB** $22　**MIB** Sec. Mkt. **$30**

QX 352-1　DOVE TEST ORNAMENT　☐
Comments:　*VERY RARE! ONLY 200 MADE.*
More of these in collectors' hands than Christmas Kitten, p.
26. This ornament should have a flat white back; some have
been found without the back glued on.
☐ Purchased 19＿＿＿　Pd $＿＿＿＿　MIB　NB　DB　BNT
☐ Want　Orig. Ret. $4.00　**NB** $100　**MIB** Sec. Mkt. **$195**

QX 147-4　DRUMMER BOY　☐
Comments:　Handcrafted, 3-3/64" tall, Dated 1980.
In bread-dough design, this drummer boy is dressed in green
with brown sandals and stocking cap. He plays a red and gold
drum. **Artist:** Donna Lee
☐ Purchased 19＿＿＿　Pd $＿＿＿＿　MIB　NB　DB　BNT
☐ Want　Orig. Ret. $5.50　**NB** $85　**MIB** Sec. Mkt. **$95**

QX 142-1　ELFIN ANTICS　☐
Comments:　Hard to Find. Handcrafted. 4-9/16" tall.
Three elves swing down from your Christmas tree branch.
The bottom elf rings a gold bell. Very popular!
☐ Purchased 19＿＿＿　Pd $＿＿＿＿　MIB　NB　DB　BNT
☐ Want　Orig. Ret. $9.00　**NB** $160　**MIB** Sec. Mkt. **$225**

QX 205-4　FIRST CHRISTMAS TOGETHER　☐
Comments:　White Glass Ball, 3-1/4" dia., Dated 1980.
A man and wife take a moonlight sleigh ride. Caption: "First
Christmas Together. Christmas is a love story written in our
hearts."
☐ Purchased 19＿＿＿　Pd $＿＿＿＿　MIB　NB　DB　BNT
☐ Want　Orig. Ret. $4.00　**NB** $21　**MIB** Sec. Mkt. **$40**

QX 305-4　FIRST CHRISTMAS TOGETHER　☐
Comments:　Acrylic, 3-1/2" tall, Dated 1980.
An acrylic heart has a floral and ribbon border surrounding the
caption stamped in silver foil. Caption: "First Christmas
Together 1980."
☐ Purchased 19＿＿＿　Pd $＿＿＿＿　MIB　NB　DB　BNT
☐ Want　Orig. Ret. $4.00　**NB** $40　**MIB** Sec. Mkt. **$55**

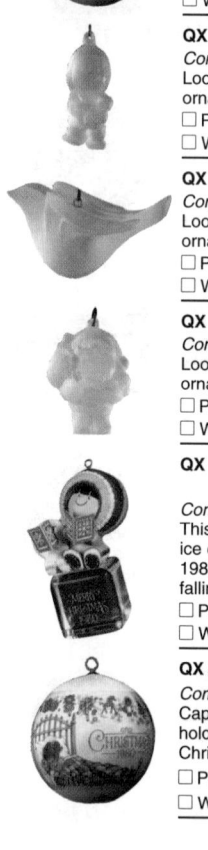

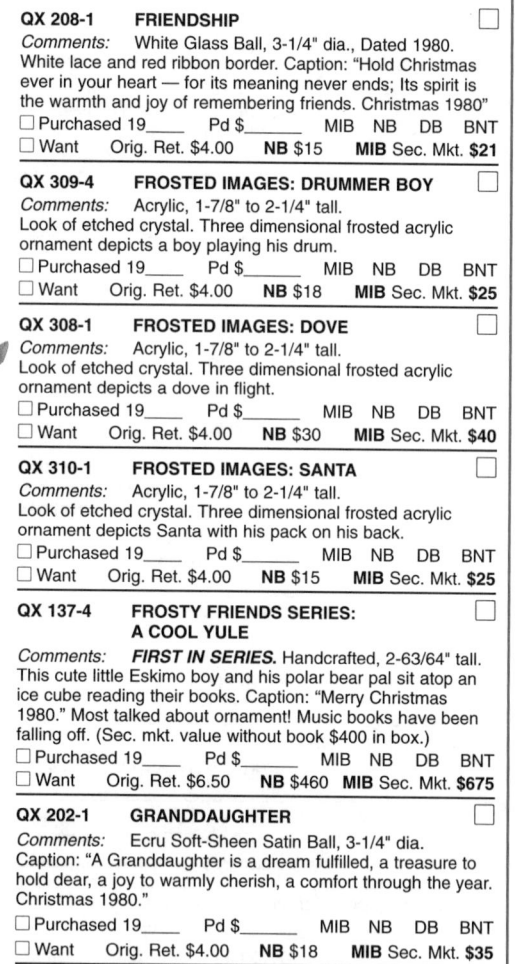

QX 208-1 FRIENDSHIP ☐

Comments: White Glass Ball, 3-1/4" dia., Dated 1980.
White lace and red ribbon border. Caption: "Hold Christmas
ever in your heart — for its meaning never ends; Its spirit is
the warmth and joy of remembering friends. Christmas 1980"
☐ Purchased 19____ Pd $_____ MIB NB DB BNT
☐ Want Orig. Ret. $4.00 **NB** $15 **MIB** Sec. Mkt. **$21**

QX 309-4 FROSTED IMAGES: DRUMMER BOY ☐

Comments: Acrylic, 1-7/8" to 2-1/4" tall.
Look of etched crystal. Three dimensional frosted acrylic
ornament depicts a boy playing his drum.
☐ Purchased 19____ Pd $_____ MIB NB DB BNT
☐ Want Orig. Ret. $4.00 **NB** $18 **MIB** Sec. Mkt. **$25**

QX 308-1 FROSTED IMAGES: DOVE ☐

Comments: Acrylic, 1-7/8" to 2-1/4" tall.
Look of etched crystal. Three dimensional frosted acrylic
ornament depicts a dove in flight.
☐ Purchased 19____ Pd $_____ MIB NB DB BNT
☐ Want Orig. Ret. $4.00 **NB** $30 **MIB** Sec. Mkt. **$40**

QX 310-1 FROSTED IMAGES: SANTA ☐

Comments: Acrylic, 1-7/8" to 2-1/4" tall.
Look of etched crystal. Three dimensional frosted acrylic
ornament depicts Santa with his pack on his back.
☐ Purchased 19____ Pd $_____ MIB NB DB BNT
☐ Want Orig. Ret. $4.00 **NB** $15 **MIB** Sec. Mkt. **$25**

**QX 137-4 FROSTY FRIENDS SERIES:
A COOL YULE** ☐

Comments: **FIRST IN SERIES.** Handcrafted, 2-63/64" tall.
This cute little Eskimo boy and his polar bear pal sit atop an
ice cube reading their books. Caption: "Merry Christmas
1980." Most talked about ornament! Music books have been
falling off. (Sec. mkt. value without book $400 in box.)
☐ Purchased 19____ Pd $_____ MIB NB DB BNT
☐ Want Orig. Ret. $6.50 **NB** $460 **MIB** Sec. Mkt. **$675**

QX 202-1 GRANDDAUGHTER ☐

Comments: Ecru Soft-Sheen Satin Ball, 3-1/4" dia.
Caption: "A Granddaughter is a dream fulfilled, a treasure to
hold dear, a joy to warmly cherish, a comfort through the year.
Christmas 1980."
☐ Purchased 19____ Pd $_____ MIB NB DB BNT
☐ Want Orig. Ret. $4.00 **NB** $18 **MIB** Sec. Mkt. **$35**

QX 231-4 GRANDFATHER ☐

Comments: White Glass Ball, 3-1/4" dia., Dated 1980.
Two snow scenes, one of a covered bridge and the other of
an old wagon in a barn yard. Caption: "A Grandfather is...
strong in his wisdom, gentle in his love. Christmas 1980."
☐ Purchased 19____ Pd $_____ MIB NB DB BNT
☐ Want Orig. Ret. $4.00 **NB** $12 **MIB** Sec. Mkt. **$20**

QX 204-1 GRANDMOTHER ☐

Comments: White Glass Ball, 3-1/4" dia., Dated 1980.
The caption and date are framed by flowers, birds and ani-
mals. Caption: "Love and joy And Comfort And Cheer Are
Gifts A Grandmother Gives All Year. Christmas 1980."
☐ Purchased 19____ Pd $_____ MIB NB DB BNT
☐ Want Orig. Ret. $4.00 **NB** $12 **MIB** Sec. Mkt. **$19**

QX 213-4 GRANDPARENTS ☐

Comments: Gold Glass Ball, 3-1/4" dia., Dated 1980.
Reproduced from the Currier & Ives print, "Early Winter," the
design is a large home by a pond. Caption: "Grandparents
have beautiful ways of giving, of helping, of teaching...
especially of loving."
☐ Purchased 19____ Pd $_____ MIB NB DB BNT
☐ Want Orig. Ret. $4.00 **NB** $30 **MIB** Sec. Mkt. **$40**

QX 201-4 GRANDSON ☐

Comments: White Satin Ball, 3-1/4" dia.
Front: Raccoons pull a snowman on a sled. Back: A Snow-
man Adds A Candy Cane To A Tree. Caption: "Grandsons And
Christmas Are Joys That Go Together. Christmas 1980."
☐ Purchased 19____ Pd $_____ MIB NB DB BNT
☐ Want Orig. Ret. $4.00 **NB** $30 **MIB** Sec. Mkt. **$35**

QX 222-1 HAPPY CHRISTMAS ☐

Comments: Ecru Soft-Sheen Satin Ball, 3-1/4" dia.
A Koala bear waters a potted tree which grows into a "pear
tree" with a small bird at the top. Caption: "Tis The Season
When Hearts Are Glowing, Love Is Growing, And Happiness
Rounds Out The Year!" and "Christmas 1980."
☐ Purchased 19____ Pd $_____ MIB NB DB BNT
☐ Want Orig. Ret. $4.00 **NB** $30 **MIB** Sec. Mkt. **$30**

QX 156-7   HEAVENLY MINSTREL ☐
Comments: S**pecial Edition,** Handcrafted, 6-1/4" tall.
A beautiful old world angel with widespread wings plays a
lute. **Artist:** Donna Lee
☐ Purchased 19____   Pd $_____   MIB   NB   DB   BNT
☐ Want   Orig. Ret. $15.00   **NB** $300   **MIB** Sec. Mkt. **$345**

QX 152-1   HEAVENLY SOUNDS ☐
Comments: Handcrafted, 3-30/64" tall, Dated 1980.
Angels dressed in pink and blue ring a gold metal bell as they
twirl around in the center of a wood-look pink ring.
☐ Purchased 19____   Pd $_____   MIB   NB   DB   BNT
☐ Want   Orig. Ret. $7.50   **NB** $64   **MIB** Sec. Mkt. **$95**

QX 143-4   HERE COMES SANTA SERIES: ☐
SANTA'S EXPRESS
Comments: **Second in Series,** Handcrafted, 3" tall.
Dated 1980. Santa waves from an old-fashioned locomotive in
red and green; the wheels turn. Tends to be more NB sales
than MIB.
☐ Purchased 19____   Pd $_____   MIB   NB   DB   BNT
☐ Want   Orig. Ret. $12.00   **NB** $150   **MIB** Sec. Mkt. **$195**

QX 320-3   HOLIDAY CHIMES: REINDEER CHIMES ☐
Comments: Chrome plated brass, 5-1/2" tall.
Issued in 1978, 1979 and 1980. **Artist:** Linda Sickman
☐ Purchased 19____   Pd $_____   MIB   NB   DB   BNT
☐ Want   Orig. Ret. $5.50   **NB** $45   **MIB** Sec. Mkt. **$60**

QX 136-1   HOLIDAY CHIMES: SANTA MOBILE ☐
Comments: Chrome Plate, 3-57/64" tall. Reissued in 1981.
His sleigh pulled by three reindeer, Santa flies over three
homes with smoking chimneys.
☐ Purchased 19____   Pd $_____   MIB   NB   DB   BNT
☐ Want   Orig. Ret. $5.50   **NB** $45   **MIB** Sec. Mkt. **$50**

QX 165-4   HOLIDAY CHIMES: SNOWFLAKE CHIMES ☐
Comments: Chrome Plate, 1-59/64" dia., Reissued in 1981.
Three lacy snowflakes are suspended from a fourth
snowflake. **Artist:** Linda Sickman
☐ Purchased 19____   Pd $_____   MIB   NB   DB   BNT
☐ Want   Orig. Ret. $5.50   **NB** $30   **MIB** Sec. Mkt. **$35**

QX 300-1   HOLIDAY HIGHLIGHTS: ☐
THREE WISE MEN
Comments: Acrylic, 4" tall, Dated 1980.
Three wise men follow the star to Bethlehem.
Caption: "Christmas 1980."
☐ Purchased 19____   Pd $_____   MIB   NB   DB   BNT
☐ Want   Orig. Ret. $4.00   **NB** $25   **MIB** Sec. Mkt. **$31**

QX 301-4   HOLIDAY HIGHLIGHTS: WREATH ☐
Comments: Acrylic, 3-1/4" dia., Dated 1980.
Leaves and holly in frosted acrylic are set off by clear fruit and
berries. Date is stamped in silver foil on a clear center.
☐ Purchased 19____   Pd $_____   MIB   NB   DB   BNT
☐ Want   Orig. Ret. $4.00   **NB** $56   **MIB** Sec. Mkt. **$85**

QX 217-4   JOAN WALSH ANGLUND® ☐
Comments: White Satin Ball, 3-1/4" dia., Dated 1980.
Three children ice skate on a frozen lake. Caption: "Each and
every bright December brings the best times to remember.
Christmas 1980."
☐ Purchased 19____   Pd $_____   MIB   NB   DB   BNT
☐ Want   Orig. Ret. $4.00   **NB** $20   **MIB** Sec. Mkt. **$30**

QX 227-4   JOLLY SANTA ☐
Comments: White Glass Ball, 3-1/4" dia., Dated 1980.
Santa and his reindeer spell out Christmas messages with ice
skates. Caption: "Merry Christmas" and "Christmas 1980."
☐ Purchased 19____   Pd $_____   MIB   NB   DB   BNT
☐ Want   Orig. Ret. $4.00   **NB** $20   **MIB** Sec. Mkt. **$31**

QX 131-4   LITTLE TRIMMERS: CHRISTMAS OWL ☐
Comments: Handcrafted, 1-27/32" tall. Reissued in 1982.
This cute little owl wearing a Santa cap holds a sprig of holly
in its beak.
☐ Purchased 19____   Pd $_____   MIB   NB   DB   BNT
☐ Want   Orig. Ret. $4.00   **NB** $20   **MIB** Sec. Mkt. **$40**

QX 135-4   LITTLE TRIMMERS: CHRISTMAS TEDDY ☐
Comments: Handcrafted, 1-1/4".
A small brown teddy bear with a big smile painted on his face
has a bread dough look.
☐ Purchased 19____   Pd $_____   MIB   NB   DB   BNT
☐ Want   Orig. Ret. $2.50   **NB** $89   **MIB** Sec. Mkt. **$90**

QX 134-1   LITTLE TRIMMERS:
CLOTHESPIN SOLDIER

Comments: Handcrafted, 2-15/16" tall.

Clothespin style soldier stands at attention.

☐ Purchased 19____   Pd $_____   MIB NB DB BNT
☐ Want   Orig. Ret. $3.50   **NB** $25   **MIB** Sec. Mkt. **$40**

QX 160-1   LITTLE TRIMMERS: MERRY REDBIRD ☐

Comments: Handcrafted-Flocked, 1-27/32" long.

This little redbird wears flocked "feathers" and holds a sprig of holly in his bill.

☐ Purchased 19____   Pd $_____   MIB NB DB BNT
☐ Want   Orig. Ret. $3.50   **NB** $47   **MIB** Sec. Mkt. **$65**

QX 130-1   LITTLE TRIMMERS:
SWINGIN' ON A STAR

Comments: Handcrafted, 2-5/32" tall.

A tiny white mouse with a red and green striped cap swings on a brass star.

☐ Purchased 19____   Pd $_____   MIB NB DB BNT
☐ Want   Orig. Ret. $4.90   **NB** $65   **MIB** Sec. Mkt. **$85**

QX 302-1   LOVE ☐

Comments: Acrylic, 4" tall, Dated 1980.

The word LOVE is enhanced by silver foil stamping. Caption: "Where There Is Love, There Is The Spirit Of Christmas."

☐ Purchased 19____   Pd $_____   MIB NB DB BNT
☐ Want   Orig. Ret. $4.00   **NB** $50   **MIB** Sec. Mkt. **$65**

QX 221-4   MARTY LINKS™ ☐

Comments: White Satin Ball, 3-1/4" dia.

A little boy and animals carol in the snow under the direction of a little girl. Caption: "We Wish You A Merry Christmas And A Happy New Year" and "Christmas 1980."

☐ Purchased 19____   Pd $_____   MIB NB DB BNT
☐ Want   Orig. Ret. $4.00   **NB** $10   **MIB** Sec. Mkt. **$824**

QX 219-4   MARY HAMILTON ☐

Comments: Gold Glass Ball, 3-1/4" dia.

Caption: "Christmas – The Warmest, Brightest Season Of All" and "Christmas 1980."

☐ Purchased 19____   Pd $_____   MIB NB DB BNT
☐ Want   Orig. Ret. $4.00   **NB** $14   **MIB** Sec. Mkt. **$24**

QX 342-7   MERRY SANTA ☐

Comments: Quilted Fabric.

Reissued from 1979.

☐ Purchased 19____   Pd $_____   MIB NB DB BNT
☐ Want   Orig. Ret. $2.00   Sec. Mkt. **$20**

QX 203-4   MOTHER ☐

Comments: White Satin Ball, 3-1/4" dia., Dated 1980.

Large poinsettias and other Christmas flowers. Caption: "A Mother Has The Special Gift Of Giving Of Herself. Christmas 1980."

☐ Purchased 19____   Pd $_____   MIB NB DB BNT
☐ Want   Orig. Ret. $4.00   **NB** $15   **MIB** Sec. Mkt. **$23**

QX 304-1   MOTHER ☐

Comments: Acrylic, 3-1/2" tall, Dated 1980.

Heart-shaped with a ribbon tied floral border. Caption and date are stamped in silver foil: "Mother Is Another Word For Love. Christmas 1980."

☐ Purchased 19____   Pd $_____   MIB NB DB BNT
☐ Want   Orig. Ret. $4.00   **NB** $27   **MIB** Sec. Mkt. **$35**

QX 230-1   MOTHER & DAD ☐

Comments: White Glass Ball, 3-1/4" dia.

Sprigs of holly and berries. Caption: "When Homes Are Decked With Holly And Hearts Are Feeling Glad, It's A Wonderful Time To Remember A Wonderful Mother And Dad. Christmas 1980."

☐ Purchased 19____   Pd $_____   MIB NB DB BNT
☐ Want   Orig. Ret. $4.00   **NB** $15   **MIB** Sec. Mkt. **$23**

QX 220-1   MUPPETS™ ☐

Comments: White Satin Ball, 3-1/4" dia.

Kermit waves a greeting on the front. The Muppets sing carols. Caption: "Merry Christmas 1980."

☐ Purchased 19____   Pd $_____   MIB NB DB BNT
☐ Want   Orig. Ret. $4.00   **NB** $26   **MIB** Sec. Mkt. **$40**

QX 225-4   NATIVITY ☐

Comments: Gold Glass Ball, 3-1/4" dia.

Animals and birds draw near children in prayer at the manger. Caption: "Silent Night…Holy Night…" and "Christmas 1980."

☐ Purchased 19____   Pd $_____   MIB NB DB BNT
☐ Want   Orig. Ret. $4.00   **NB** $24   **MIB** Sec. Mkt. **$34**

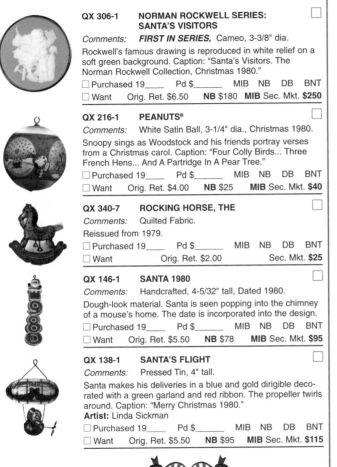

QX 306-1   NORMAN ROCKWELL SERIES: SANTA'S VISITORS

Comments: ***FIRST IN SERIES***, Cameo, 3-3/8" dia.
Rockwell's famous drawing is reproduced in white relief on a soft green background. Caption: "Santa's Visitors. The Norman Rockwell Collection, Christmas 1980."
☐ Purchased 19____   Pd $_____   MIB NB DB BNT
☐ Want   Orig. Ret. $6.50   **NB** $180   **MIB** Sec. Mkt. **$250**

QX 216-1   PEANUTS®

Comments: White Satin Ball, 3-1/4" dia., Christmas 1980.
Snoopy sings as Woodstock and his friends portray verses from a Christmas carol. Caption: "Four Colly Birds... Three French Hens... And A Partridge In A Pear Tree."
☐ Purchased 19____   Pd $_____   MIB NB DB BNT
☐ Want   Orig. Ret. $4.00   **NB** $25   **MIB** Sec. Mkt. **$40**

QX 340-7   ROCKING HORSE, THE

Comments: Quilted Fabric.
Reissued from 1979.
☐ Purchased 19____   Pd $_____   MIB NB DB BNT
☐ Want   Orig. Ret. $2.00   Sec. Mkt. **$25**

QX 146-1   SANTA 1980

Comments: Handcrafted, 4-5/32" tall, Dated 1980.
Dough-look material. Santa is seen popping into the chimney of a mouse's home. The date is incorporated into the design.
☐ Purchased 19____   Pd $_____   MIB NB DB BNT
☐ Want   Orig. Ret. $5.50   **NB** $78   **MIB** Sec. Mkt. **$95**

QX 138-1   SANTA'S FLIGHT

Comments: Pressed Tin, 4" tall.
Santa makes his deliveries in a blue and gold dirigible decorated with a green garland and red ribbon. The propeller twirls around. Caption: "Merry Christmas 1980."
Artist: Linda Sickman
☐ Purchased 19____   Pd $_____   MIB NB DB BNT
☐ Want   Orig. Ret. $5.50   **NB** $95   **MIB** Sec. Mkt. **$115**

QX 223-4   SANTA'S WORKSHOP

Comments: White Satin Ball, 3-1/4" dia.
Santa adds a scarf to his usual costume and checks his list. Caption: "What Merriment Is All Around When Dear Old Santa Comes To Town" and "Christmas 1980."
☐ Purchased 19____   Pd $_____   MIB NB DB BNT
☐ Want   Orig. Ret. $4.00   **NB** $24   **MIB** Sec. Mkt. **$30**

QHD 925-4   SANTA'S WORKSHOP TABLETOP DECORATIONS

Comments: Handcrafted, 8" tall.
☐ Purchased 19____   Pd $_____   MIB NB DB BNT
☐ Want   Orig. Ret. $40.00   **NB** $130   **MIB** Sec. Mkt. **$185**

QX 139-9   SKATING SNOWMAN, THE

Comments: Handcrafted, 4-1/4" tall.
Reissued from 1979. **Artist:** Donna Lee
☐ Purchased 19____   Pd $_____   MIB NB DB BNT
☐ Want   Orig. Ret. $40.00   **NB** $130   **MIB** Sec. Mkt. **$185**

QX 154-1   SNOOPY AND FRIENDS SERIES: SNOOPY SKI HOLIDAY

Comments: **Second in Series,** Dated 1980.
Handcrafted Panorama Ball, 3-1/4" dia. Snoopy, on skis, wears a red and green stocking cap and Woodstock rides in Snoopy's personalized feeding bowl. Several of this style ornament have been found with scratched surfaces.
Artist: John Francis (Collin)
☐ Purchased 19____   Pd $_____   MIB NB DB BNT
☐ Want   Orig. Ret. $9.00   **NB** $100   **MIB** Sec. Mkt. **$115**

QX 133-4   SNOWFLAKE SWING, THE

Comments: Handcrafted, 3" tall.
An angel swings from an acrylic snowflake.
☐ Purchased 19____   Pd $_____   MIB NB DB BNT
☐ Want   Orig. Ret. $4.00   **NB** $32   **MIB** Sec. Mkt. **$45**

QX 211-4   SON

Comments: Gold Glass Ball, 3-1/4" dia.
A scene of a boy's favorite toys. Caption: "A Son Is... A Maker Of Memories, A Source Of Pride... A Son Is Love" and "Christmas 1980."
☐ Purchased 19____   Pd $_____   MIB NB DB BNT
☐ Want   Orig. Ret. $4.00   **NB** $21   **MIB** Sec. Mkt. **$35**

QX 341-9   STUFFED FULL STOCKING ☐

Comments: Quilted Fabric.

Reissued from 1979.

☐ Purchased 19____   Pd $_____   MIB   NB   DB   BNT
☐ Want   Orig. Ret. $2.00   Sec. Mkt. **$26**

QX 209-4   TEACHER ☐

Comments: White Satin Ball, 3-1/4" dia.

Kitten dressed in warm clothing is walking to school with a gift. Back: He's placing the gift on the teacher's desk. Caption: "Merry Christmas, Teacher" and "Christmas 1980."

☐ Purchased 19____   Pd $_____   MIB   NB   DB   BNT
☐ Want   Orig. Ret. $4.00   **NB $14**   **MIB** Sec. Mkt. **$21**

QX 131-9   THIMBLE SERIES:
A CHRISTMAS SALUTE ☐

Comments: **Second in Series,** Handcrafted, 2-1/4" tall.

Reissued from 1979.

☐ Purchased 19____   Pd $_____   MIB   NB   DB   BNT
☐ Want   Orig. Ret. $4.00   **NB $95**   **MIB** Sec. Mkt. **$175**

QX 132-1   THIMBLE SERIES: THIMBLE ELF ☐

Comments: **Third in Series,** Handcrafted, 2-31/32" tall.

Cute little elf dressed in red and green is swinging on a thimble "bell" which hangs from a golden rope.

☐ Purchased 19____   Pd $_____   MIB   NB   DB   BNT
☐ Want   Orig. Ret. $4.00   **NB $95**   **MIB** Sec. Mkt. **$150**

QX 206-1   TWENTY-FIFTH CHRISTMAS TOGETHER ☐

Comments: White Glass Ball, 3-1/4" dia., Dated 1980.

Garlands, bells and ribbons frame the captions. "The good times of the present blend with memories of the past to make each Christmas season even dearer than the last" and "25th Christmas Together 1980." A collector has reported this ball ornament being found without the date.

☐ Purchased 19____   Pd $_____   MIB   NB   DB   BNT
☐ Want   Orig. Ret. $4.00   **NB $13**   **MIB** Sec. Mkt. **$23**

QX 162-1   YARN & FABRIC – ANGEL ☐

Comments: Yarn with lace and felt accents, 5" tall.

Reissued in 1981. This lovely blue angel with white wings, white pinafore and golden hair holds a green wreath.

☐ Purchased 19____   Pd $_____   MIB   NB   DB   BNT
☐ Want   Orig. Ret. $3.00   Sec. Mkt. **$5**

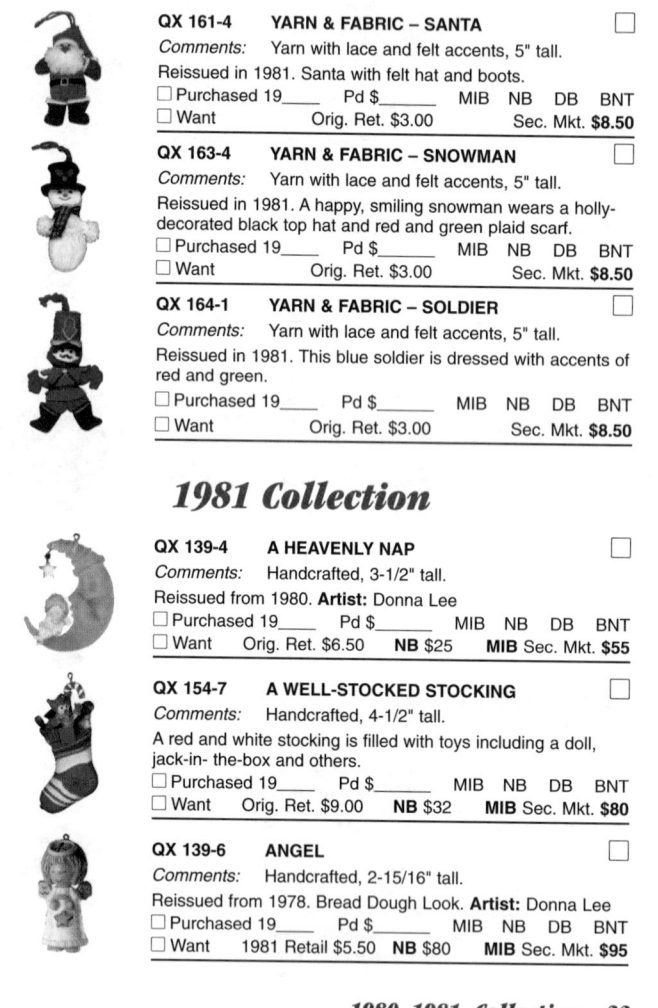

QX 161-4   YARN & FABRIC – SANTA ☐

Comments: Yarn with lace and felt accents, 5" tall.

Reissued in 1981. Santa with felt hat and boots.

☐ Purchased 19____   Pd $_____   MIB   NB   DB   BNT
☐ Want   Orig. Ret. $3.00   Sec. Mkt. **$8.50**

QX 163-4   YARN & FABRIC – SNOWMAN ☐

Comments: Yarn with lace and felt accents, 5" tall.

Reissued in 1981. A happy, smiling snowman wears a holly-decorated black top hat and red and green plaid scarf.

☐ Purchased 19____   Pd $_____   MIB   NB   DB   BNT
☐ Want   Orig. Ret. $3.00   Sec. Mkt. **$8.50**

QX 164-1   YARN & FABRIC – SOLDIER ☐

Comments: Yarn with lace and felt accents, 5" tall.

Reissued in 1981. This blue soldier is dressed with accents of red and green.

☐ Purchased 19____   Pd $_____   MIB   NB   DB   BNT
☐ Want   Orig. Ret. $3.00   Sec. Mkt. **$8.50**

1981 Collection

QX 139-4   A HEAVENLY NAP ☐

Comments: Handcrafted, 3-1/2" tall.

Reissued from 1980. **Artist:** Donna Lee

☐ Purchased 19____   Pd $_____   MIB   NB   DB   BNT
☐ Want   Orig. Ret. $6.50   **NB $25**   **MIB** Sec. Mkt. **$55**

QX 154-7   A WELL-STOCKED STOCKING ☐

Comments: Handcrafted, 4-1/2" tall.

A red and white stocking is filled with toys including a doll, jack-in- the-box and others.

☐ Purchased 19____   Pd $_____   MIB   NB   DB   BNT
☐ Want   Orig. Ret. $9.00   **NB $32**   **MIB** Sec. Mkt. **$80**

QX 139-6   ANGEL ☐

Comments: Handcrafted, 2-15/16" tall.

Reissued from 1978. Bread Dough Look. **Artist:** Donna Lee

☐ Purchased 19____   Pd $_____   MIB   NB   DB   BNT
☐ Want   1981 Retail $5.50   **NB $80**   **MIB** Sec. Mkt. **$95**

QX 440-2   BABY'S FIRST CHRISTMAS

Comments: Handcrafted, 3-3/4" long.
Baby is in a "wicker" carriage. The wheels roll and the caption is on the fabric blanket: "Baby's First Christmas, 1981."
☐ Purchased 19_____   Pd $_____   MIB   NB   DB   BNT
☐ Want   Orig. Ret. $13.00   **NB** $45   **MIB** Sec. Mkt. **$50**

QX 513-5   BABY'S FIRST CHRISTMAS

Comments: Lt. Green Cameo, 3-3/8" dia.
A large, gift-wrapped box, rocking horse on wheels and toys. Caption: "Baby's First Christmas 1981" and "A Baby Adds A Special Joy To All The Joys Of Christmas."
☐ Purchased 19_____   Pd $_____   MIB   NB   DB   BNT
☐ Want   Orig. Ret. $8.50   **NB** $12   **MIB** Sec. Mkt. **$20**

QX 516-2   BABY'S FIRST CHRISTMAS

Comments: Acrylic, 4" dia., Dated 1981.
The wreath frames a photograph opening.
Caption: "Baby's First Christmas."
☐ Purchased 19_____   Pd $_____   MIB   NB   DB   BNT
☐ Want   Orig. Ret. $5.50   **NB** $27   **MIB** Sec. Mkt. **$30**

QX 602-2   BABY'S FIRST CHRISTMAS

Comments: Ecru Soft-Sheen Satin Ball, 3-1/4" dia.
A baby with his toys is playing peekaboo. Caption: "Baby's First Christmas 1981" and "A Baby Is A Gift Of Joy, A Gift Of Love At Christmas".
☐ Purchased 19_____   Pd $_____   MIB   NB   DB   BNT
☐ Want   Orig. Ret. $4.50   **NB** $15   **MIB** Sec. Mkt. **$25**

QX 601-5   BABY'S FIRST CHRISTMAS – BOY

Comments: White Satin Ball, 3-1/4" dia.
Caption: "Baby's First Christmas 1981" and "There's nothing like a baby boy to bring a world of special joy at Christmas."
☐ Purchased 19_____   Pd $_____   MIB   NB   DB   BNT
☐ Want   Orig. Ret. $4.50   **NB** $18   **MIB** Sec. Mkt. **$25**

QX 600-2   BABY'S FIRST CHRISTMAS – GIRL

Comments: White Satin Ball, 3-1/4" dia.
Caption: "Baby's First Christmas 1981" and "There's Nothing Like A Baby Girl To Cheer And Brighten All The World At Christmas."
☐ Purchased 19_____   Pd $_____   MIB   NB   DB   BNT
☐ Want   Orig. Ret. $4.50   **NB** $18   **MIB** Sec. Mkt. **$25**

QX 441-5   BELLRINGER SERIES: SWINGIN' BELLRINGER

Comments: **Third in Series,** Handcrafted, 4" tall.
Dated 1981. A mouse swings on the candy cane clapper of this gold-rimmed bell.
☐ Purchased 19_____   Pd $_____   MIB   NB   DB   BNT
☐ Want   Orig. Ret. $15.00   **NB** $85   **MIB** Sec. Mkt. **$100**

QX 802-2   BETSEY CLARK SERIES

Comments: **Ninth in Series,** White Glass Ball, 3-1/4" dia.
A little girl leaves a gift for her friend. Back: She pulls a gift-filled sleigh. Caption: "Christmas 1981" and "The Greatest Joy Of Christmas Day Comes From The Joy We Give Away."
☐ Purchased 19_____   Pd $_____   MIB   NB   DB   BNT
☐ Want   Orig. Ret. $4.50   **NB** $30   **MIB** Sec. Mkt. **$40**

QX 423-5   BETSEY CLARK

Comments: Handcrafted, 3-9/32" tall.
Betsey and a fawn look at a tree topped with a brilliant star.
Artist: John Francis (Collin)
☐ Purchased 19_____   Pd $_____   MIB   NB   DB   BNT
☐ Want   Orig. Ret. $9.00   **NB** $60   **MIB** Sec. Mkt. **$75**

QX 512-2   BETSEY CLARK BLUE CAMEO

Comments: Cameo, 3-3/8" dia.
A little girl pets a fawn. Caption: "Christmas, When Hearts Reach Out To Give And Receive The Gentle Gifts Of Love" and "Christmas 1981."
☐ Purchased 19_____   Pd $_____   MIB   NB   DB   BNT
☐ Want   Orig. Ret. $8.50   **NB** $25   **MIB** Sec. Mkt. **$30**

QX 403-5   CALICO KITTY

Comments: Sewn Fabric, 3" tall.
Yellow Christmas fabric kitty has red bow.
☐ Purchased 19_____   Pd $_____   MIB   NB   DB   BNT
☐ Want   Orig. Ret. $3.00   **NB** $15   **MIB** Sec. Mkt. **$20**

QX 418-2   CANDYVILLE EXPRESS

Comments: Handcrafted, 3" long.
Locomotive appears as if it has been crafted from gumdrops, cookies and licorice. Easily found Mint in Box.
☐ Purchased 19_____   Pd $_____   MIB   NB   DB   BNT
☐ Want   Orig. Ret. $7.50   **NB** $70   **MIB** Sec. Mkt. **$100**

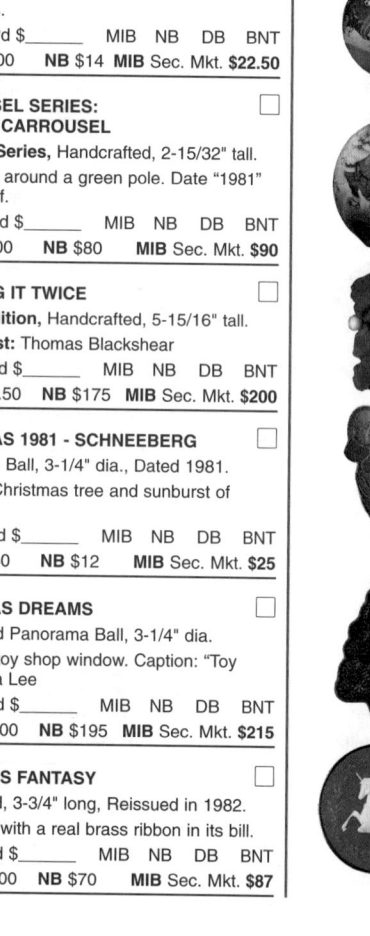

QX 400-2　CARDINAL CUTIE ☐
Comments:　Sewn Fabric, 3" tall.
Red fabric with white dots.
☐ Purchased 19____　Pd $_____　MIB　NB　DB　BNT
☐ Want　Orig. Ret. $3.00　**NB** $14　**MIB** Sec. Mkt. **$22.50**

QX 427-5　CARROUSEL SERIES: ☐
　　　　　SKATERS CARROUSEL
Comments:　**Fourth in Series,** Handcrafted, 2-15/32" tall.
A family of four ice skates around a green pole. Date "1981"
stamped on the top of roof.
☐ Purchased 19____　Pd $_____　MIB　NB　DB　BNT
☐ Want　Orig. Ret. $9.00　**NB** $80　**MIB** Sec. Mkt. **$90**

QX 158-4　CHECKING IT TWICE ☐
Comments:　**Special Edition,** Handcrafted, 5-15/16" tall.
Reissued from 1980. **Artist:** Thomas Blackshear
☐ Purchased 19____　Pd $_____　MIB　NB　DB　BNT
☐ Want　Orig. Ret. $22.50　**NB** $175　**MIB** Sec. Mkt. **$200**

QX 809-5　CHRISTMAS 1981 - SCHNEEBERG ☐
Comments:　White Satin Ball, 3-1/4" dia., Dated 1981.
Schneeberg collage of a Christmas tree and sunburst of
beads and colored glass.
☐ Purchased 19____　Pd $_____　MIB　NB　DB　BNT
☐ Want　Orig. Ret. $4.50　**NB** $12　**MIB** Sec. Mkt. **$25**

QX 437-5　CHRISTMAS DREAMS ☐
Comments:　Handcrafted Panorama Ball, 3-1/4" dia.
Little boy looks through a toy shop window. Caption: "Toy
Shop 1981." **Artist:** Donna Lee
☐ Purchased 19____　Pd $_____　MIB　NB　DB　BNT
☐ Want　Orig. Ret. $12.00　**NB** $195　**MIB** Sec. Mkt. **$215**

QX 155-4　CHRISTMAS FANTASY ☐
Comments:　Handcrafted, 3-3/4" long, Reissued in 1982.
An elf rides a white goose with a real brass ribbon in its bill.
☐ Purchased 19____　Pd $_____　MIB　NB　DB　BNT
☐ Want　Orig. Ret. $13.00　**NB** $70　**MIB** Sec. Mkt. **$87**

QX 813-5　CHRISTMAS IN THE FOREST ☐
Comments:　White Glass Ball, 3-1/4" dia., Dated 1981. RARE!
Caption: "Softly… Gently… Joyfully… Christmas Arrives In
The Heart" and "Christmas 1981."
☐ Purchased 19____　Pd $_____　MIB　NB　DB　BNT
☐ Want　Orig. Ret. $4.50　**NB** $110　**MIB** Sec. Mkt. **$145**

QX 810-2　CHRISTMAS MAGIC ☐
Comments:　White Satin Ball, 3-1/4" dia., Dated 1981.
A gnome-like Santa ice skates with the animals. Caption:
"Christmas 1981" and "It's here, there, everywhere…
Christmas magic's in the air."
☐ Purchased 19____　Pd $_____　MIB　NB　DB　BNT
☐ Want　Orig. Ret. $4.50　**NB** $18　**MIB** Sec. Mkt. **$27**

QX 404-2　CHRISTMAS TEDDY ☐
Comments:　Plush, 4" tall, packed in gift box.
Cute little teddy with a green/red plaid bow and red stocking cap.
☐ Purchased 19____　Pd $_____　MIB　NB　DB　BNT
☐ Want　Orig. Ret. $5.50　**NB** $20　**MIB** Sec. Mkt. **$25**

QX 507-5　CROWN CLASSICS COLLECTION: ☐
　　　　　ANGEL
Comments:　Acrylic, 3-3/4" tall, stained glass look.
Golden-haired angel with white wings.
☐ Purchased 19____　Pd $_____　MIB　NB　DB　BNT
☐ Want　Orig. Ret. $4.50　**NB** $21　**MIB** Sec. Mkt. **$26**

QX 515-5　CROWN CLASSICS COLLECTION: ☐
　　　　　TREE PHOTOHOLDER
Comments:　Acrylic, 3-27/32" tall, Dated 1981.
Decorated tree has opening for photo. Caption: "Christmas
1981."
☐ Purchased 19____　Pd $_____　MIB　NB　DB　BNT
☐ Want　Orig. Ret. $5.50　**NB** $19　**MIB** Sec. Mkt. **$30**

QX 516-5　CROWN CLASSICS COLLECTION: ☐
　　　　　UNICORN
Comments:　Cameo, 3-3/8" dia., Dated 1981.
White unicorn on light green background. Caption: "A Time Of
Magical Moments, Dreams Come True… Christmas 1981."
☐ Purchased 19____　Pd $_____　MIB　NB　DB　BNT
☐ Want　Orig. Ret. $8.50　**NB** $19　**MIB** Sec. Mkt. **$28**

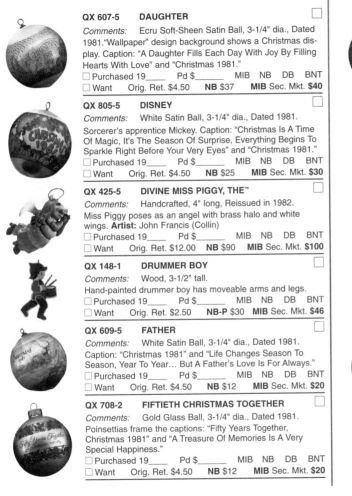

QX 607-5   DAUGHTER

Comments: Ecru Soft-Sheen Satin Ball, 3-1/4" dia., Dated 1981. "Wallpaper" design background shows a Christmas display. Caption: "A Daughter Fills Each Day With Joy By Filling Hearts With Love" and "Christmas 1981."

☐ Purchased 19____   Pd $_____   MIB   NB   DB   BNT
☐ Want   Orig. Ret. $4.50   **NB** $37   **MIB** Sec. Mkt. **$40**

QX 805-5   DISNEY

Comments: White Satin Ball, 3-1/4" dia., Dated 1981. Sorcerer's apprentice Mickey. Caption: "Christmas Is A Time Of Magic, It's The Season Of Surprise, Everything Begins To Sparkle Right Before Your Very Eyes" and "Christmas 1981."

☐ Purchased 19____   Pd $_____   MIB   NB   DB   BNT
☐ Want   Orig. Ret. $4.50   **NB** $25   **MIB** Sec. Mkt. **$30**

QX 425-5   DIVINE MISS PIGGY, THE™

Comments: Handcrafted, 4" long, Reissued in 1982. Miss Piggy poses as an angel with brass halo and white wings. **Artist:** John Francis (Collin)

☐ Purchased 19____   Pd $_____   MIB   NB   DB   BNT
☐ Want   Orig. Ret. $12.00   **NB** $90   **MIB** Sec. Mkt. **$100**

QX 148-1   DRUMMER BOY

Comments: Wood, 3-1/2" tall. Hand-painted drummer boy has moveable arms and legs.

☐ Purchased 19____   Pd $_____   MIB   NB   DB   BNT
☐ Want   Orig. Ret. $2.50   **NB-P** $30   **MIB** Sec. Mkt. **$46**

QX 609-5   FATHER

Comments: White Satin Ball, 3-1/4" dia., Dated 1981. Caption: "Christmas 1981" and "Life Changes Season To Season, Year To Year… But A Father's Love Is For Always."

☐ Purchased 19____   Pd $_____   MIB   NB   DB   BNT
☐ Want   Orig. Ret. $4.50   **NB** $12   **MIB** Sec. Mkt. **$20**

QX 708-2   FIFTIETH CHRISTMAS TOGETHER

Comments: Gold Glass Ball, 3-1/4" dia., Dated 1981. Poinsettias frame the captions: "Fifty Years Together, Christmas 1981" and "A Treasure Of Memories Is A Very Special Happiness."

☐ Purchased 19____   Pd $_____   MIB   NB   DB   BNT
☐ Want   Orig. Ret. $4.50   **NB** $12   **MIB** Sec. Mkt. **$20**

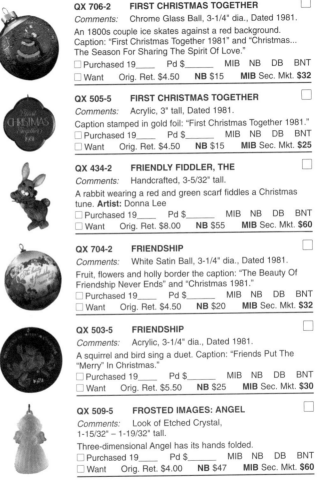

QX 706-2   FIRST CHRISTMAS TOGETHER

Comments: Chrome Glass Ball, 3-1/4" dia., Dated 1981. An 1800s couple ice skates against a red background. Caption: "First Christmas Together 1981" and "Christmas... The Season For Sharing The Spirit Of Love."

☐ Purchased 19____   Pd $_____   MIB   NB   DB   BNT
☐ Want   Orig. Ret. $4.50   **NB** $15   **MIB** Sec. Mkt. **$32**

QX 505-5   FIRST CHRISTMAS TOGETHER

Comments: Acrylic, 3" tall, Dated 1981. Caption stamped in gold foil: "First Christmas Together 1981."

☐ Purchased 19____   Pd $_____   MIB   NB   DB   BNT
☐ Want   Orig. Ret. $4.50   **NB** $15   **MIB** Sec. Mkt. **$25**

QX 434-2   FRIENDLY FIDDLER, THE

Comments: Handcrafted, 3-5/32" tall. A rabbit wearing a red and green scarf fiddles a Christmas tune. **Artist:** Donna Lee

☐ Purchased 19____   Pd $_____   MIB   NB   DB   BNT
☐ Want   Orig. Ret. $8.00   **NB** $55   **MIB** Sec. Mkt. **$60**

QX 704-2   FRIENDSHIP

Comments: White Satin Ball, 3-1/4" dia., Dated 1981. Fruit, flowers and holly border the caption: "The Beauty Of Friendship Never Ends" and "Christmas 1981."

☐ Purchased 19____   Pd $_____   MIB   NB   DB   BNT
☐ Want   Orig. Ret. $4.50   **NB** $20   **MIB** Sec. Mkt. **$32**

QX 503-5   FRIENDSHIP

Comments: Acrylic, 3-1/4" dia., Dated 1981. A squirrel and bird sing a duet. Caption: "Friends Put The 'Merry' In Christmas."

☐ Purchased 19____   Pd $_____   MIB   NB   DB   BNT
☐ Want   Orig. Ret. $5.50   **NB** $25   **MIB** Sec. Mkt. **$30**

QX 509-5   FROSTED IMAGES: ANGEL

Comments: Look of Etched Crystal, 1-15/32" – 1-19/32" tall. Three-dimensional Angel has its hands folded.

☐ Purchased 19____   Pd $_____   MIB   NB   DB   BNT
☐ Want   Orig. Ret. $4.00   **NB** $47   **MIB** Sec. Mkt. **$60**

QX 508-2   FROSTED IMAGES: MOUSE

Comments: Look of Etched Crystal,
1-15/32" – 1-19/32" tall.

Three-dimensional Mouse holds a stocking.

☐ Purchased 19____   Pd $_____   MIB   NB   DB   BNT
☐ Want   Orig. Ret. $4.00   **NB** $24   **MIB** Sec. Mkt. **$28**

QX 510-2   FROSTED IMAGES: SNOWMAN

Comments: Look of Etched Crystal,
1-15/32" – 1-19/32" tall.

Three-dimensional Snowman is waving.

☐ Purchased 19____   Pd $_____   MIB   NB   DB   BNT
☐ Want   Orig. Ret. $4.00   **NB** $19   **MIB** Sec. Mkt. **$26**

QX 433-5   FROSTY FRIENDS

Comments: **Second in Series,** Handcrafted, 2" tall.

Dated 1981. An Eskimo and Husky puppy keep cozy in their igloo.

☐ Purchased 19____   Pd $_____   MIB   NB   DB   BNT
☐ Want   Orig. Ret. $8.00   **NB** $350   **MIB** Sec. Mkt. **$480**

QX 705-5   GIFT OF LOVE, THE

Comments: Gold Glass Ball, 3-1/4" dia., Dated 1981.

Red roses and holly frame the date and caption: "Christmas 1981" and "Love Is A Precious Gift, Priceless And Perfect, Cherished Above All Life's Treasures."

☐ Purchased 19____   Pd $_____   MIB   NB   DB   BNT
☐ Want   Orig. Ret. $4.50   **NB** $18   **MIB** Sec. Mkt. **$25**

QX 402-2   GINGHAM DOG

Comments: Sewn Fabric, 3" tall.

Cute blue/white gingham dog has a red bow.

☐ Purchased 19____   Pd $_____   MIB   NB   DB   BNT
☐ Want   Orig. Ret. $3.00   Sec. Mkt. **$20**

QX 603-5   GODCHILD

Comments: White Satin Ball, 3-1/4" dia.

An angel and puppy on a cloud are placing stars in a bag. Caption: "Christmas 1981" and "For A Special Godchild."

☐ Purchased 19____   Pd $_____   MIB   NB   DB   BNT
☐ Want   Orig. Ret. $4.50   **NB** $19   **MIB** Sec. Mkt. **$23**

QX 605-5   GRANDDAUGHTER

Comments: White Satin Ball, 3-1/4" dia., Dated 1981.

A white rocking horse and toys are featured. Caption: "A Granddaughter Adds A Magical Touch To The Beauty And Joy Of Christmas."

☐ Purchased 19____   Pd $_____   MIB   NB   DB   BNT
☐ Want   Orig. Ret. $4.50   **NB** $21   **MIB** Sec. Mkt. **$30**

QX 701-5   GRANDFATHER

Comments: Gold Glass Ball, 3-1/4" dia. The caption in red and gold is bordered by sprigs of holly: Grandfather Holds A Special Place In The Heart" and "Christmas 1981."

☐ Purchased 19____   Pd $_____   MIB   NB   DB   BNT
☐ Want   Orig. Ret. $4.50   **NB** $17   **MIB** Sec. Mkt. **$20**

QX 702-2   GRANDMOTHER

Comments: Ecru Soft-Sheen Satin Ball, 3-1/4" dia. Caption: "Christmas 1981" and "A Grandmother Is So Loving And Dear At Christmas And Throughout The Year."

☐ Purchased 19____   Pd $_____   MIB   NB   DB   BNT
☐ Want   Orig. Ret. $4.50   **NB** $19   **MIB** Sec. Mkt. **$25**

QX 703-5   GRANDPARENTS

Comments: White Glass Ball, 3-1/4" dia., Dated 1981. Caption: "Grandparents Give The Gift Of Love At Christmas And All Year 'Round."

☐ Purchased 19____   Pd $_____   MIB   NB   DB   BNT
☐ Want   Orig. Ret. $4.50   **NB** $16   **MIB** Sec. Mkt. **$21**

QX 604-2   GRANDSON

Comments: White Satin Ball, 3-1/4" dia. Santa and reindeer are making toys. Caption: "A Grandson Makes The 'Holly Days' Extra Bright And Jolly Days" and "Christmas 1981."

☐ Purchased 19____   Pd $_____   MIB   NB   DB   BNT
☐ Want   Orig. Ret. $4.50   **NB** $18   **MIB** Sec. Mkt. **$30**

**QX 438-2   HERE COMES SANTA SERIES:
                 ROOFTOP DELIVERIES**

Comments: **Third in Series,** Handcrafted, 4-1/16" tall. Santa's making deliveries in a vehicle which resembles an old milk truck. Caption: "1981 S. Claus & Co. Rooftop Deliveries."

☐ Purchased 19____   Pd $_____   MIB   NB   DB   BNT
☐ Want   Orig. Ret. $13.00   **NB** $250   **MIB** Sec. Mkt. **$400**

QX 136-1   HOLIDAY CHIMES: SANTA MOBILE ☐
Comments: Chrome Plated.
Reissued from 1980.
☐ Purchased 19____   Pd $_____   MIB   NB   DB   BNT
☐ Want   Orig. Ret. $5.50   **NB** $45   **MIB** Sec. Mkt. **$50**

QX 445-5   HOLIDAY CHIMES: SNOWMAN CHIMES ☐
Comments: Chrome Plate, 4" tall.
Mr. and Mrs. Snowman and Snowchild are suspended from a large snowflake.
☐ Purchased 19____   Pd $_____   MIB   NB   DB   BNT
☐ Want   Orig. Ret. $5.50   Sec. Mkt. **$30**

QX 165-4   HOLIDAY CHIMES: ☐
SNOWFLAKE CHIMES
Comments: Chrome Plated.
Reissued from 1980. **Artist:** Linda Sickman
☐ Purchased 19____   Pd $_____   MIB   NB   DB   BNT
☐ Want   Orig. Ret. $5.50   **NB** $30   **MIB** Sec. Mkt. **$35**

QX 501-5   HOLIDAY HIGHLIGHTS: ☐
CHRISTMAS STAR
Comments: Clear Acrylic, 3-1/2" tall, Dated 1981.
Star with raised, faceted border has emerald shapes between the points. Caption stamped in silver foil: "Christmas 1981."
☐ Purchased 19____   Pd $_____   MIB   NB   DB   BNT
☐ Want   Orig. Ret. $5.50   **NB** $15   **MIB** Sec. Mkt. **$30**

QX 500-2   HOLIDAY HIGHLIGHTS: ☐
SHEPHERD SCENE
Comments: Clear Acrylic, 4" tall.
A shepherd and his sheep watch the star over Bethlehem.
☐ Purchased 19____   Pd $_____   MIB   NB   DB   BNT
☐ Want   Orig. Ret. $5.50   **NB** $19   **MIB** Sec. Mkt. **$28**

QX 709-5   HOME ☐
Comments: White Satin Ball, 3-1/4" dia., Dated 1981.
Victorian winter village scene. Caption: "Christmas 1981" and "Love In The Home Puts Joy In The Heart."
☐ Purchased 19____   Pd $_____   MIB   NB   DB   BNT
☐ Want   Orig. Ret. $4.50   **NB** $17   **MIB** Sec. Mkt. **$20**

QX 431-5   ICE FAIRY ☐
Comments: Acrylic & Handcrafted, 4-1/8" tall.
A white frosted ice fairy with acrylic wings holds a clear acrylic snowflake. **Artist:** Donna Lee
☐ Purchased 19____   Pd $_____   MIB   NB   DB   BNT
☐ Want   Orig. Ret. $6.50   **NB** $75   **MIB** Sec. Mkt. **$100**

QX 432-2   ICE SCULPTOR, THE ☐
Comments: Handcrafted, 3-1/32" tall.
A bear artist sculpts his self portrait in ice (clear acrylic).
Artist: Donna Lee
☐ Purchased 19____   Pd $_____   MIB   NB   DB   BNT
☐ Want   Orig. Ret. $8.00   **NB** $75   **MIB** Sec. Mkt. **$100**

QX 804-2   JOAN WALSH ANGLUND© ☐
Comments: White Satin Ball, 3-1/4" dia.
Three children read a book together, then decorate the stair rail. Caption: " 'Tis The Time Of Dreams Come True. 'Tis The Time For Merrymaking" and "Christmas 1981."
☐ Purchased 19____   Pd $_____   MIB   NB   DB   BNT
☐ Want   Orig. Ret. $4.50   **NB** $18   **MIB** Sec. Mkt. **$30**

QX 424-2   KERMIT THE FROG™ ☐
Comments: Handcrafted, 3-11/32" long.
Kermit, in a red stocking cap, races downhill on his sled.
Artist: John Francis (Collin)
☐ Purchased 19____   Pd $_____   MIB   NB   DB   BNT
☐ Want   Orig. Ret. $9.00   **NB** $85   **MIB** Sec. Mkt. **$95**

QX 811-5   LET US ADORE HIM ☐
Comments: Gold Glass Ball, 3-1/4" dia.
Cherubs adore the Christ child on this lovely ball.
Caption: "Christmas 1981" and "O Come Let Us Adore Him."
☐ Purchased 19____   Pd $_____   MIB   NB   DB   BNT
☐ Want   Orig. Ret. $4.50   **NB** $60   **MIB** Sec. Mkt. **$67**

QX 408-2   LITTLE TRIMMERS: ☐
CLOTHESPIN DRUMMER BOY
Comments: Handcrafted, 2-13/16" tall.
Drummer boy in black and brown beats a red drum.
☐ Purchased 19____   Pd $_____   MIB   NB   DB   BNT
☐ Want   Orig. Ret. $4.50   **NB** $37   **MIB** Sec. Mkt. **$44**

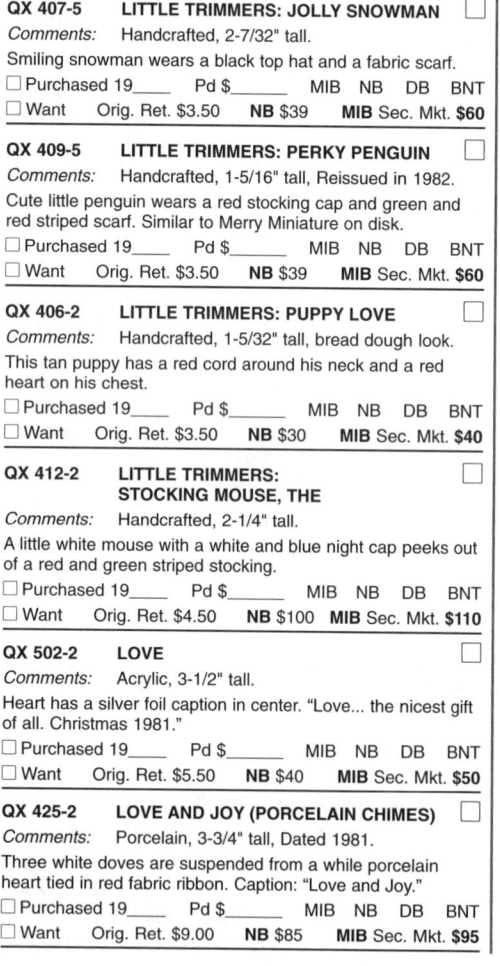

QX 407-5   LITTLE TRIMMERS: JOLLY SNOWMAN ☐
Comments: Handcrafted, 2-7/32" tall.
Smiling snowman wears a black top hat and a fabric scarf.
☐ Purchased 19____   Pd $_____   MIB NB DB BNT
☐ Want   Orig. Ret. $3.50   **NB** $39   **MIB** Sec. Mkt. **$60**

QX 409-5   LITTLE TRIMMERS: PERKY PENGUIN ☐
Comments: Handcrafted, 1-5/16" tall, Reissued in 1982.
Cute little penguin wears a red stocking cap and green and
red striped scarf. Similar to Merry Miniature on disk.
☐ Purchased 19____   Pd $_____   MIB NB DB BNT
☐ Want   Orig. Ret. $3.50   **NB** $39   **MIB** Sec. Mkt. **$60**

QX 406-2   LITTLE TRIMMERS: PUPPY LOVE ☐
Comments: Handcrafted, 1-5/32" tall, bread dough look.
This tan puppy has a red cord around his neck and a red
heart on his chest.
☐ Purchased 19____   Pd $_____   MIB NB DB BNT
☐ Want   Orig. Ret. $3.50   **NB** $30   **MIB** Sec. Mkt. **$40**

QX 412-2   LITTLE TRIMMERS:
STOCKING MOUSE, THE ☐
Comments: Handcrafted, 2-1/4" tall.
A little white mouse with a white and blue night cap peeks out
of a red and green striped stocking.
☐ Purchased 19____   Pd $_____   MIB NB DB BNT
☐ Want   Orig. Ret. $4.50   **NB** $100   **MIB** Sec. Mkt. **$110**

QX 502-2   LOVE ☐
Comments: Acrylic, 3-1/2" tall.
Heart has a silver foil caption in center. "Love... the nicest gift
of all. Christmas 1981."
☐ Purchased 19____   Pd $_____   MIB NB DB BNT
☐ Want   Orig. Ret. $5.50   **NB** $40   **MIB** Sec. Mkt. **$50**

QX 425-2   LOVE AND JOY (PORCELAIN CHIMES) ☐
Comments: Porcelain, 3-3/4" tall, Dated 1981.
Three white doves are suspended from a while porcelain
heart tied in red fabric ribbon. Caption: "Love and Joy."
☐ Purchased 19____   Pd $_____   MIB NB DB BNT
☐ Want   Orig. Ret. $9.00   **NB** $85   **MIB** Sec. Mkt. **$95**

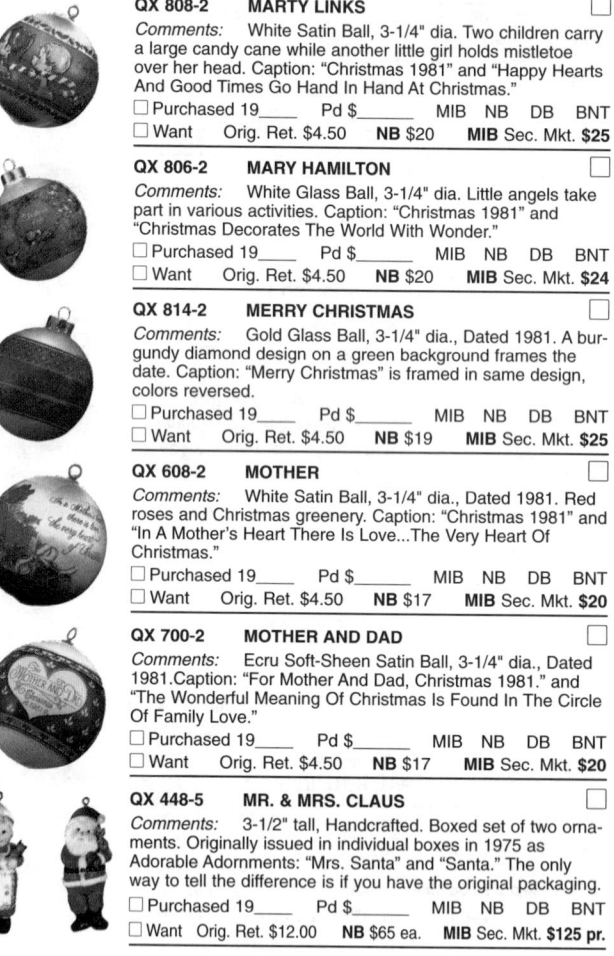

QX 808-2   MARTY LINKS ☐
Comments: White Satin Ball, 3-1/4" dia. Two children carry
a large candy cane while another little girl holds mistletoe
over her head. Caption: "Christmas 1981" and "Happy Hearts
And Good Times Go Hand In Hand At Christmas."
☐ Purchased 19____   Pd $_____   MIB NB DB BNT
☐ Want   Orig. Ret. $4.50   **NB** $20   **MIB** Sec. Mkt. **$25**

QX 806-2   MARY HAMILTON ☐
Comments: White Glass Ball, 3-1/4" dia. Little angels take
part in various activities. Caption: "Christmas 1981" and
"Christmas Decorates The World With Wonder."
☐ Purchased 19____   Pd $_____   MIB NB DB BNT
☐ Want   Orig. Ret. $4.50   **NB** $20   **MIB** Sec. Mkt. **$24**

QX 814-2   MERRY CHRISTMAS ☐
Comments: Gold Glass Ball, 3-1/4" dia., Dated 1981. A burgundy diamond design on a green background frames the
date. Caption: "Merry Christmas" is framed in same design,
colors reversed.
☐ Purchased 19____   Pd $_____   MIB NB DB BNT
☐ Want   Orig. Ret. $4.50   **NB** $19   **MIB** Sec. Mkt. **$25**

QX 608-2   MOTHER ☐
Comments: White Satin Ball, 3-1/4" dia., Dated 1981. Red
roses and Christmas greenery. Caption: "Christmas 1981" and
"In A Mother's Heart There Is Love...The Very Heart Of
Christmas."
☐ Purchased 19____   Pd $_____   MIB NB DB BNT
☐ Want   Orig. Ret. $4.50   **NB** $17   **MIB** Sec. Mkt. **$20**

QX 700-2   MOTHER AND DAD ☐
Comments: Ecru Soft-Sheen Satin Ball, 3-1/4" dia., Dated
1981.Caption: "For Mother And Dad, Christmas 1981." and
"The Wonderful Meaning Of Christmas Is Found In The Circle
Of Family Love."
☐ Purchased 19____   Pd $_____   MIB NB DB BNT
☐ Want   Orig. Ret. $4.50   **NB** $17   **MIB** Sec. Mkt. **$20**

QX 448-5   MR. & MRS. CLAUS ☐
Comments: 3-1/2" tall, Handcrafted. Boxed set of two orna-
ments. Originally issued in individual boxes in 1975 as
Adorable Adornments: "Mrs. Santa" and "Santa." The only
way to tell the difference is if you have the original packaging.
☐ Purchased 19____   Pd $_____   MIB NB DB BNT
☐ Want Orig. Ret. $12.00   **NB** $65 ea.   **MIB** Sec. Mkt. **$125 pr.**

QX 807-5　MUPPETS™

Comments:　White Satin Ball, 3-1/4" dia., Dated 1981.
Kermit "Santa" starts down the chimney; Miss Piggy awaits
his visit. Caption: "Let's Hear It For Christmas" and "Let's
Hear It For Santa."

☐ Purchased 19____　Pd $_____　MIB　NB　DB　BNT
☐ Want　Orig. Ret. $4.50　**NB** $19　**MIB** Sec. Mkt. **$30**

**QX 511-5　NORMAN ROCKWELL SERIES:
　　　　　　 CAROLERS**

Comments:　**Second in Series,** Cameo, 3-3/8" dia.
Rockwell's "Carolers" are depicted on dark blue background.
Caption: "Carolers, Second In A Series, The Norman Rockwell
Collection Christmas 1981."

☐ Purchased 19____　Pd $_____　MIB　NB　DB　BNT
☐ Want　Orig. Ret. $8.50　**NB** $38　**MIB** Sec. Mkt. **$50**

QX 803-5　PEANUTS™

Comments:　White Satin Ball, 3-1/4" dia.
Snoopy, Woodstock and friends sing. Caption: "Deck the halls
with boughs of holly... Christmas 1981."

☐ Purchased 19____　Pd $_____　MIB　NB　DB　BNT
☐ Want　Orig. Ret. $4.50　**NB** $28　**MIB** Sec. Mkt. **$40**

QX 401-5　PEPPERMINT MOUSE

Comments:　Sewn Fabric, 3" tall.
White mouse with red/white striped clothes.

☐ Purchased 19____　Pd $_____　MIB　NB　DB　BNT
☐ Want　Orig. Ret. $3.00　**NB** $24　**MIB** Sec. Mkt. **$37**

QX 405-5　RACCOON TUNES

Comments:　Plush, 4" tall.
Raccoon caroler wears a felt vest and holds a felt song book.

☐ Purchased 19____　Pd $_____　MIB　NB　DB　BNT
☐ Want　Orig. Ret. $5.50　**NB** $15　**MIB** Sec. Mkt. **$22**

QX 422-2　ROCKING HORSE

Comments:　***FIRST IN SERIES,*** Handcrafted 2" tall, Dated
1981.Brown/white Palomino horse on red rockers. Very much
sought after. **Artist:** Linda Sickman

☐ Purchased 19____　Pd $_____　MIB　NB　DB　BNT
☐ Want　Orig. Ret. $9.00　**NB** $425　**MIB** Sec. Mkt. **$495**

QX 439-5　SAILING SANTA

Comments:　Handcrafted, 5" tall, Dated 1981. Santa sails
away in a red hot air balloon. Caption: "Merry Christmas
1981."

☐ Purchased 19____　Pd $_____　MIB　NB　DB　BNT
☐ Want　Orig. Ret. $13.00　**NB** $200　**MIB** Sec. Mkt. **$300**

QX 812-2　SANTA'S COMING

Comments:　White Satin Ball, 3-1/4" dia., Dated 1981. Mrs.
Santa makes sure Santa is ready for his trip while reindeer fly
through a moonlit night. Caption: "Christmas 1981" and
"Hustle, Bustle, Hurry, Scurry, Santa's Coming... Never Worry."

☐ Purchased 19____　Pd $_____　MIB　NB　DB　BNT
☐ Want　Orig. Ret. $4.50　**NB** $17　**MIB** Sec. Mkt. **$28**

QX 815-5　SANTA'S SURPRISE

Comments:　White Satin Ball, 3-1/4" dia., Dated 1981.
Santa uses the stars from the sky to decorate a small ever-
green. Caption: "Twinkle, Glimmer, Sparkle, Shimmer... Let
The Christmas Season Shine" and "Christmas 1981."

☐ Purchased 19____　Pd $_____　MIB　NB　DB　BNT
☐ Want　Orig. Ret. $4.50　**NB** $16　**MIB** Sec. Mkt. **$25**

QX 436-2　SNOOPY AND FRIENDS

Comments:　**Third in Series,** Handcrafted Panorama Ball.
3-1/4" dia. Dated 1981. A "birdsled" pulls Snoopy past a snow
Snoopy. **Artist:** John Francis (Collin)

☐ Purchased 19____　Pd $_____　MIB　NB　DB　BNT
☐ Want　Orig. Ret. $12.00　**NB** $80　**MIB** Sec. Mkt. **$130**

QX 606-2　SON

Comments:　White Satin Ball, 3-1/4" dia., Dated 1981.
A variety of Christmas scenes are shown in various colored
squares. Caption: "Christmas 1981" and "A Son Puts The
Merry In Christmas."

☐ Purchased 19____　Pd $_____　MIB　NB　DB　BNT
☐ Want　Orig. Ret. $4.50　**NB** $21　**MIB** Sec. Mkt. **$30**

QX 430-2　SPACE SANTA

Comments:　Handcrafted, 3" tall, Dated 1981. Santa flies in
for a Christmas hello, wearing a silver space suit.

☐ Purchased 19____　Pd $_____　MIB　NB　DB　BNT
☐ Want　Orig. Ret. $6.50　**NB** $95　**MIB** Sec. Mkt. **$125**

QX 446-2   ST. NICHOLAS

Comments: Pressed Tin, 4-3/8" tall.

Traditional European St. Nicholas carries a lantern to light his way. **Artist:** Linda Sickman

☐ Purchased 19____   Pd $_____   MIB NB DB BNT
☐ Want   Orig. Ret. $5.50   **NB $44**   **MIB** Sec. Mkt. **$50**

QX 421-5   STAR SWING

Comments: Brass & Handcrafted, 3-5/8" tall, Dated 1981.

A little girl swings from a chrome-plated brass star.
Artist: Linda Sickman

☐ Purchased 19____   Pd $_____   MIB NB DB BNT
☐ Want   Orig. Ret. $5.50   **NB $25**   **MIB** Sec. Mkt. **$30**

QX 800-2   TEACHER

Comments: White Satin Ball, 3-1/4" dia., Dated 1981.

Multi-colored stocking in white oval, red background. Caption: "For a special teacher 1981."

☐ Purchased 19____   Pd $_____   MIB NB DB BNT
☐ Want   Orig. Ret. $4.50   **NB $10**   **MIB** Sec. Mkt. **$14**

QX 413-5   THIMBLE SERIES: ANGEL

Comments: **Fourth in Series,** Handcrafted, 1-1/2" dia.

Flying angel with white wings carries a tree that is potted in a thimble. HARD TO FIND!

☐ Purchased 19____   Pd $_____   MIB NB DB BNT
☐ Want   Orig. Ret. $4.50   **NB $110**   **MIB** Sec. Mkt. **$160**

QX 429-5   TOPSY-TURVY TUNES

Comments: Handcrafted, 3" tall.

An opossum hangs by his tail while a redbird sits on his book of Carols. **Artist:** Donna Lee

☐ Purchased 19____   Pd $_____   MIB NB DB BNT
☐ Want   Orig. Ret. $7.50   **NB $70**   **MIB** Sec. Mkt. **$80**

QX 801-5   TRADITIONAL (BLACK SANTA)

Comments: RARE! White Satin Ball, 3-1/4" dia., Dated 1981. A black Santa feeds the animals in the forest. Caption: "It's Christmas. It's time for Sharing... And dreaming, and caring and merry gift bearing..."

☐ Purchased 19____   Pd $_____   MIB NB DB BNT
☐ Want   Orig. Ret. $4.50   **NB $80**   **MIB** Sec. Mkt. **$98**

QX 504-2   TWENTY-FIFTH CHRISTMAS TOGETHER

Comments: Clear Acrylic, 4-1/2" tall.

Two wedding bells with frosted border designs have caption in silver foil. "25 Years Together, Christmas 1981."

☐ Purchased 19____   Pd $_____   MIB NB DB BNT
☐ Want   Orig. Ret. $5.50   **NB $20**   **MIB** Sec. Mkt. **$23**

QX 707-5   TWENTY-FIFTH CHRISTMAS TOGETHER

Comments: White Glass Ball, 3-1/4" dia.

White bells on a background of red ribbon and Christmas greenery. Caption: "25 Years Together, Christmas 1981" and "Christmas season of the heart, time of sweet remembrance."

☐ Purchased 19____   Pd $_____   MIB NB DB BNT
☐ Want   Orig. Ret. $4.50   **NB $15**   **MIB** Sec. Mkt. **$23**

QX 162-1   YARN & FABRIC ORNAMENT ANGEL

Comments: Yarn with lace and felt accents, 5" tall.
Reissued from 1980.

☐ Purchased 19____   Pd $_____   MIB NB DB BNT
☐ Want   Orig. Ret. $3.00   Sec. Mkt. **$5**

QX 161-4   YARN & FABRIC ORNAMENT SANTA

Comments: Yarn with lace and felt accents, 5" tall.
Reissued from 1980.

☐ Purchased 19____   Pd $_____   MIB NB DB BNT
☐ Want   Orig. Ret. $3.00   Sec. Mkt. **$8.50**

QX 163-4   YARN & FABRIC ORNAMENT SNOWMAN

Comments: Yarn with lace and felt accents, 5" tall.
Reissued from 1980.

☐ Purchased 19____   Pd $_____   MIB NB DB BNT
☐ Want   Orig. Ret. $3.00   Sec. Mkt. **$8.50**

QX 164-1   YARN & FABRIC ORNAMENT SOLDIER

Comments: Yarn with lace and felt accents, 5" tall.
Reissued from 1980.

☐ Purchased 19____   Pd $_____   MIB NB DB BNT
☐ Want   Orig. Ret. $3.00   Sec. Mkt. **$8.50**

1982 Collection

QX 300-3 ARCTIC PENGUIN
Comments: Clear Acrylic, 1-1/2" tall.
Penguin molded to resemble an ice sculpture.
☐ Purchased 19____ Pd $_____ MIB NB DB BNT
☐ Want Orig. Ret. $4.00 **NB** $15 **MIB** Sec. Mkt. **$20**

QX 455-3 BABY'S FIRST CHRISTMAS
Comments: Handcrafted, 3" tall, Dated 1982. Baby's rattle with panorama window. Caption: "Baby's First Christmas."
Artist: Ed Seale
☐ Purchased 19____ Pd $_____ MIB NB DB BNT
☐ Want Orig. Ret. $13.00 **NB** $35 **MIB** Sec. Mkt. **$50**

QMB 900-7 BABY'S FIRST CHRISTMAS
Comments: Musical, Classic Shape, 4-1/2" tall, Dated 1982. Caption: "First Christmas 1982." Plays Brahms' Lullaby.
☐ Purchased 19____ Pd $_____ MIB NB DB BNT
☐ Want Orig. Ret. $16.00 **NB** $50 **MIB** Sec. Mkt. **$65**

QX 216-3 BABY'S FIRST CHRISTMAS (BOY)
Comments: Light Blue Satin Ball, 3-1/4" dia., Dated 1982. Design was hand-embroidered, then photographed. Caption: "Baby's First Christmas 1982" and "A baby boy is a precious gift – a blessing from above."
☐ Purchased 19____ Pd $_____ MIB NB DB BNT
☐ Want Orig. Ret. $4.50 **NB** $22 **MIB** Sec. Mkt. **$27**

QX 207-3 BABY'S FIRST CHRISTMAS (GIRL)
Comments: Light Pink Satin Ball, 3-1/4" dia., Dated 1982. Embroidered toys form a quilt. Caption: "Baby's First Christmas 1982" and "A baby girl is the sweetest gift a lifetime can provide."
☐ Purchased 19____ Pd $_____ MIB NB DB BNT
☐ Want Orig. Ret. $4.50 **NB** $20 **MIB** Sec. Mkt. **$28**

QX 312-6 BABY'S FIRST CHRISTMAS: PHOTOHOLDER
Comments: Acrylic, 4-1/4" tall, Dated 1982. A stocking filled with toys. Caption: "Baby's First Christmas 1982" and "Oh what joy and sweet surprise Christmas brings to little eyes."
☐ Purchased 19____ Pd $_____ MIB NB DB BNT
☐ Want Orig. Ret. $6.50 **NB** $18 **MIB** Sec. Mkt. **$25**

QX 302-3 BABY'S FIRST CHRISTMAS
Comments: Acrylic, 3-17/32" tall.
Teddy Bear in frosted acrylic with block. Caption: "Baby's First Christmas 1982." **Artist:** Ed Seale
☐ Purchased 19____ Pd $_____ MIB NB DB BNT
☐ Want Orig. Ret. $5.50 **NB** $25 **MIB** Sec. Mkt. **$40**

QX 456-6 BAROQUE ANGEL
Comments: Brass & Handcrafted, 4-7/16" tall.
A cherub flies with a brass banner. Caption: "Joyeux Noel."
Artist: Donna Lee
☐ Purchased 19____ Pd $_____ MIB NB DB BNT
☐ Want Orig. Ret. $15.00 **NB** $120 **MIB** Sec. Mkt. **$175**

QX 455-6 BELLRINGER, THE: ANGEL
Comments: **Fourth in Series,** Handcrafted, 2-27/32" tall.
Dated 1982. The clapper is a red and green wreath with an angel in its center. **Artist:** Donna Lee
☐ Purchased 19____ Pd $_____ MIB NB DB BNT
☐ Want Orig. Ret. $15.00 **NB** $80 **MIB** Sec. Mkt. **$100**

QX 305-6 BETSEY CLARK
Comments: Blue Cameo, 3-3/8" dia.
Angel decorates a tree on a cloud. Caption: "Christmas 1982" and "'Tis The Season For Trimming Trees And Making Merry Memories."
☐ Purchased 19____ Pd $_____ MIB NB DB BNT
☐ Want Orig. Ret. $8.50 **NB** $15 **MIB** Sec. Mkt. **$25**

QX 215-6 BETSEY CLARK SERIES
Comments: **Tenth in Series,** White Satin Ball, 3-1/4" dia.
Three children share a bedtime story. Caption: "Christmas 1982" and "The joys of Christmas are multiplied when shared with those we love."
☐ Purchased 19____ Pd $_____ MIB NB DB BNT
☐ Want Orig. Ret. $4.50 **NB** $25 **MIB** Sec. Mkt. **$35**

QX 460-6 BRASS BELL
Comments: Polished Brass, 2-11/32" tall.
Design of holly leaves and berries are stamped into the bell. Red ribbon and bow for hanging. **Artist:** Donna Lee
☐ Purchased 19____ Pd $_____ MIB NB DB BNT
☐ Want Orig. Ret. $12.00 **NB** $20 **MIB** Sec. Mkt. **$35**

No Number **BRASS PROMOTIONAL ORNAMENT** ☐
Comments: Dimensional Brass, 2-3/8" tall.
24 k. gold tone coating. Victorian couple in sleigh are shown in front of a sleeping village.
☐ Purchased 19_____ Pd $_____ MIB NB DB BNT
☐ Want Orig. Ret. $3.50 **NB** $35 **MIB** Sec. Mkt. **$45**

QX 478-3 CARROUSEL ☐
Comments: **Fifth in Series,** Handcrafted, 3" tall, Dated 1982. Snowmen ice skate around a pole. Caption: "Merry Christmas 1982" on snow-covered top. **Artist:** Ed Seale
☐ Purchased 19_____ Pd $_____ MIB NB DB BNT
☐ Want Orig. Ret. $10.00 **NB** $90 **MIB** Sec. Mkt. **$100**

QX 220-6 CHRISTMAS ANGEL ☐
Comments: Gold Glass Ball, 3-1/4" dia., Dated 1982.
Angel shelters the flame of a glowing candle. Caption: "From Heaven above the light of love shines into our hearts at Christmas."
☐ Purchased 19_____ Pd $_____ MIB NB DB BNT
☐ Want Orig. Ret. $4.50 **NB** $15 **MIB** Sec. Mkt. **$25**

QX 155-4 CHRISTMAS FANTASY ☐
Comments: Brass and Handcrafted, 3-3/4" long.
Reissued from 1981.
☐ Purchased 19_____ Pd $_____ MIB NB DB BNT
☐ Want Orig. Ret. $13.00 **NB** $70 **MIB** Sec. Mkt. **$87**

QX 311-6 CHRISTMAS MEMORIES ☐
Comments: Acrylic, 4-1/8" tall, Dated 1982.
Square white photoholder with green holly leaves and red bow. Caption: "How bright the joys of Christmas, how warm the memories." **Artist:** Linda Sickman
☐ Purchased 19_____ Pd $_____ MIB NB DB BNT
☐ Want Orig. Ret. $6.50 **NB** $8 **MIB** Sec. Mkt. **$15**

QX 145-4 CLOISONNÉ ANGEL ☐
Comments: Cloisonné, 2-21/32" tall.
An angel flies in the center of an open heart.
Caption: "Peace, Love, Joy."
☐ Purchased 19_____ Pd $_____ MIB NB DB BNT
☐ Want Orig. Ret. $12.00 **NB** $80 **MIB** Sec. Mkt. **$100**

QX 458-3 CLOTHESPIN SOLDIER: BRITISH ☐
Comments: **FIRST IN SERIES,** Handcrafted, 3-5/32" tall.
This soldier has a black mustache, tall black hat, red/white/blue uniform and carries a black baton. **Artist:** Linda Sickman
☐ Purchased 19_____ Pd $_____ MIB NB DB BNT
☐ Want Orig. Ret. $5.00 **NB** $100 **MIB** Sec. Mkt. **$130**

QX 308-6 COLORS OF CHRISTMAS: SANTA'S FLIGHT ☐
Comments: Acrylic, 4-1/4" tall, Dated Christmas 1982.
Stained glass look; Santa in a hot air balloon.
☐ Purchased 19_____ Pd $_____ MIB NB DB BNT
☐ Want Orig. Ret. $4.50 **NB** $37 **MIB** Sec. Mkt. **$50**

QX 308-3 COLORS OF CHRISTMAS: NATIVITY ☐
Comments: Acrylic, 4" tall, Stained glass look.
Traditional view of the Holy Family.
☐ Purchased 19_____ Pd $_____ MIB NB DB BNT
☐ Want Orig. Ret. $4.50 **NB** $40 **MIB** Sec. Mkt. **$55**

QX 480-6 COWBOY SNOWMAN ☐
Comments: Handcrafted, 2-27/32" tall.
Snowman is dressed in red scarf, boots and hat with a candy cane "pistol."
☐ Purchased 19_____ Pd $_____ MIB NB DB BNT
☐ Want Orig. Ret. $8.00 **NB** $45 **MIB** Sec. Mkt. **$57**

QX 201-3 CURRIER & IVES ☐
Comments: White Porcelain Glass Ball, 3-1/4" dia.
Reproduction of "The Road – Winter." Caption: "Christmas 1982" and "The Road – Winter" and "Currier and Ives." This print was "registered according to an Act of Congress in 1853."
☐ Purchased 19_____ Pd $_____ MIB NB DB BNT
☐ Want Orig. Ret. $4.50 **NB** $19 **MIB** Sec. Mkt. **$25**

QX 435-5 CYCLING SANTA ☐
Comments: Handcrafted, 4-3/8" tall, Reissued in 1983.
Santa rides an old "velocipede" with his pack on the back. The wheels turn and three brass bells attached to his pack jingle.
☐ Purchased 19_____ Pd $_____ MIB NB DB BNT
☐ Want Orig. Ret. $20.00 **NB** $105 **MIB** Sec. Mkt. **$150**

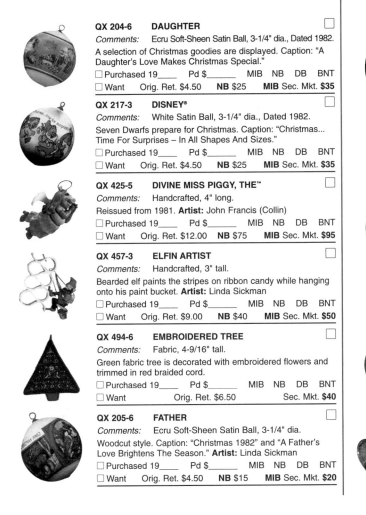

QX 204-6   DAUGHTER ☐

Comments: Ecru Soft-Sheen Satin Ball, 3-1/4" dia., Dated 1982.
A selection of Christmas goodies are displayed. Caption: "A Daughter's Love Makes Christmas Special."

☐ Purchased 19____   Pd $_____   MIB   NB   DB   BNT
☐ Want   Orig. Ret. $4.50   **NB** $25   **MIB** Sec. Mkt. **$35**

QX 217-3   DISNEY® ☐

Comments: White Satin Ball, 3-1/4" dia., Dated 1982.
Seven Dwarfs prepare for Christmas. Caption: "Christmas... Time For Surprises – In All Shapes And Sizes."

☐ Purchased 19____   Pd $_____   MIB   NB   DB   BNT
☐ Want   Orig. Ret. $4.50   **NB** $25   **MIB** Sec. Mkt. **$35**

QX 425-5   DIVINE MISS PIGGY, THE™ ☐

Comments: Handcrafted, 4" long.
Reissued from 1981. **Artist:** John Francis (Collin)

☐ Purchased 19____   Pd $_____   MIB   NB   DB   BNT
☐ Want   Orig. Ret. $12.00   **NB** $75   **MIB** Sec. Mkt. **$95**

QX 457-3   ELFIN ARTIST ☐

Comments: Handcrafted, 3" tall.
Bearded elf paints the stripes on ribbon candy while hanging onto his paint bucket. **Artist:** Linda Sickman

☐ Purchased 19____   Pd $_____   MIB   NB   DB   BNT
☐ Want   Orig. Ret. $9.00   **NB** $40   **MIB** Sec. Mkt. **$50**

QX 494-6   EMBROIDERED TREE ☐

Comments: Fabric, 4-9/16" tall.
Green fabric tree is decorated with embroidered flowers and trimmed in red braided cord.

☐ Purchased 19____   Pd $_____   MIB   NB   DB   BNT
☐ Want   Orig. Ret. $6.50   Sec. Mkt. **$40**

QX 205-6   FATHER ☐

Comments: Ecru Soft-Sheen Satin Ball, 3-1/4" dia.
Woodcut style. Caption: "Christmas 1982" and "A Father's Love Brightens The Season." **Artist:** Linda Sickman

☐ Purchased 19____   Pd $_____   MIB   NB   DB   BNT
☐ Want   Orig. Ret. $4.50   **NB** $15   **MIB** Sec. Mkt. **$20**

QX 212-3   FIFTIETH CHRISTMAS TOGETHER ☐

Comments: Gold Glass Ball, 3-1/4" dia., Dated 1982.
Burgundy lettering, highlighted with white. Caption: "50th Christmas Together 1982" and "We Measure Our Time, Not By Years Alone, But By The Love And Joy We've Known."

☐ Purchased 19____   Pd $_____   MIB   NB   DB   BNT
☐ Want   Orig. Ret. $4.50   **NB** $15   **MIB** Sec. Mkt. **$20**

QMB 901-9   FIRST CHRISTMAS TOGETHER ☐

Comments: Musical, Classic Shape, 4-1/2" tall, Dated 1982.
Plays "White Christmas." Caption: "First Christmas Together 1982."

☐ Purchased 19____   Pd $_____   MIB   NB   DB   BNT
☐ Want   Orig. Ret. $16.00   **NB** $60   **MIB** Sec. Mkt. **$75**

QX 211-3   FIRST CHRISTMAS TOGETHER ☐

Comments: Silver Chrome Glass Ball, 3-1/4" dia., Dated 1982. Two redbirds soar against a frosty background. Caption: "First Christmas Together 1982" and "Quiet Moments Together, Love That Lasts Forever."

☐ Purchased 19____   Pd $_____   MIB   NB   DB   BNT
☐ Want   Orig. Ret. $4.50   **NB** $28   **MIB** Sec. Mkt. **$40**

QX 302-6   FIRST CHRISTMAS TOGETHER ☐

Comments: Acrylic, 4-1/4" tall, Dated 1982.
Tree. Caption: "First Christmas Together."

☐ Purchased 19____   Pd $_____   MIB   NB   DB   BNT
☐ Want   Orig. Ret. $5.50   **NB** $13   **MIB** Sec. Mkt. **$23**

QX 306-6   FIRST CHRISTMAS TOGETHER ☐

Comments: Turquoise Cameo, 3-3/8" dia., Dated 1982.
A couple ice skates. Caption: "First Christmas Together" and "Christmas Is For Sharing With The Special One You Love."

☐ Purchased 19____   Pd $_____   MIB   NB   DB   BNT
☐ Want   Orig. Ret. $8.50   **NB** $26   **MIB** Sec. Mkt. **$44**

QX 456-3   FIRST CHRISTMAS TOGETHER – LOCKET ☐

Comments: Polished Brass, 2-5/8" tall, Dated 1982.
Hinged, heart-shaped locket opens with inserts for two photos. Includes brass hanger. Caption: "First Christmas Together 1982." **Artist:** Ed Seale

☐ Purchased 19____   Pd $_____   MIB   NB   DB   BNT
☐ Want   Orig. Ret. $15.00   **NB** $22   **MIB** Sec. Mkt. **$25**

QX 208-6   FRIENDSHIP

Comments: White Satin Ball, 3-1/4" dia.

Happy animals ice skate together. Caption: "Christmas 1982" and "Hearts Are Happy When Friends Are Together."

☐ Purchased 19____   Pd $_____   MIB NB DB BNT
☐ Want   Orig. Ret. $4.50   **NB** $15   **MIB** Sec. Mkt. **$20**

QX 304-6   FRIENDSHIP

Comments: Acrylic, 3-1/4" tall, Dated 1982.

Kitten/puppy together. Caption: "Christmas Is For Friends."

☐ Purchased 19____   Pd $_____   MIB NB DB BNT
☐ Want   Orig. Ret. $5.50   **NB** $18   **MIB** Sec. Mkt. **$25**

QX 452-3   FROSTY FRIENDS

Comments: **Third in Series,** Handcrafted, 4-1/8" tall.

Dated 1982. A little Eskimo Climbs An Icicle "Mountain." His Husky puppy waits at the top. Many no boxed ones out there. **Artist:** Ed Seale

☐ Purchased 19____   Pd $_____   MIB NB DB BNT
☐ Want   Orig. Ret. $8.00   **NB** $140   **MIB** Sec. Mkt. **$295**

QX 222-6   GODCHILD

Comments: White Glass Ball, 3-1/4" dia., Dated 1982.

A little angel reaches for a snowflake. Caption: "Merry Christmas To A Special Godchild."

☐ Purchased 19____   Pd $_____   MIB NB DB BNT
☐ Want   Orig. Ret. $4.50   **NB** $15   **MIB** Sec. Mkt. **$23**

QX 224-3   GRANDDAUGHTER

Comments: White Satin Ball, 3-1/4" dia.

Puppies, teddy bears and bunnies carry a rope of green garland. Caption: "Christmas 1982" and "A Granddaughter Has A Special Gift For Giving Special Joy."

☐ Purchased 19____   Pd $_____   MIB NB DB BNT
☐ Want   Orig. Ret. $4.50   **NB** $15   **MIB** Sec. Mkt. **$30**

QX 207-6   GRANDFATHER

Comments: Dark Blue Satin Ball, 3-1/4" dia.

Caption: "Grandfather... In His Strength He Teaches, In His Gentleness He Loves" and "Christmas 1982."

☐ Purchased 19____   Pd $_____   MIB NB DB BNT
☐ Want   Orig. Ret. $4.50   **NB** $15   **MIB** Sec. Mkt. **$21**

QX 200-3   GRANDMOTHER

Comments: Dark Pink Satin Ball, 3-1/4" dia., Dated 1982.

Caption: "Christmas 1982" and "A Grandmother Is Love."

☐ Purchased 19____   Pd $_____   MIB NB DB BNT
☐ Want   Orig. Ret. $4.50   **NB** $15   **MIB** Sec. Mkt. **$18**

QX 214-6   GRANDPARENTS

Comments: White Glass Ball, 3-1/4" dia., Dated 1982.

Covered bridge and winter scenes. Caption: "Christmas 1982" and "With Thoughts Of Grandparents Come Thoughts Of Days The Heart Will Always Treasure."

☐ Purchased 19____   Pd $_____   MIB NB DB BNT
☐ Want   Orig. Ret. $4.50   **NB** $10   **MIB** Sec. Mkt. **$18**

QX 224-6   GRANDSON

Comments: White Satin Ball, 3-1/4" dia., Dated 1982.

Bunnies sled in the snow. Caption: "Christmas 1982" and "A Grandson... Makes Days Bright, Hearts Light And Christmas Time A Real Delight."

☐ Purchased 19____   Pd $_____   MIB NB DB BNT
☐ Want   Orig. Ret. $4.50   **NB** $18   **MIB** Sec. Mkt. **$30**

QX 464-3   HERE COMES SANTA: JOLLY TROLLEY

Comments: **Fourth in Series,** Handcrafted, 3-3/8" tall.

Santa's in the driver's seat of an old trolley car. Caption: "1982 Jolly Trolley." **Artist:** Linda Sickman

☐ Purchased 19____   Pd $_____   MIB NB DB BNT
☐ Want   Orig. Ret. $15.00   **NB** $100   **MIB** Sec. Mkt. **$140**

QX 502-6   HOLIDAY CHIMES: ANGEL CHIMES

Comments: Chrome-Plated Brass, 4-1/2" tall.

Three angels, each holding a poinsettia, are suspended from a large snowflake. Collectors have not been aware of these being produced until recent years.

☐ Purchased 19____   Pd $_____   MIB NB DB BNT
☐ Want   Orig. Ret. $5.50   **NB** $20   **MIB** Sec. Mkt. **$25**

QX 494-3   HOLIDAY CHIMES: BELL CHIMES

Comments: Chrome-Plated Brass, 3" tall.

Three stamped bells, each with different snowflake cutouts, hang from a snowflake. **Artist:** Linda Sickman

☐ Purchased 19____   Pd $_____   MIB NB DB BNT
☐ Want   Orig. Ret. $5.50   **NB** $20   **MIB** Sec. Mkt. **$30**

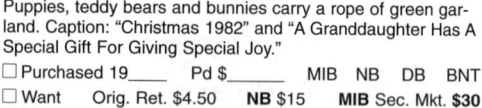
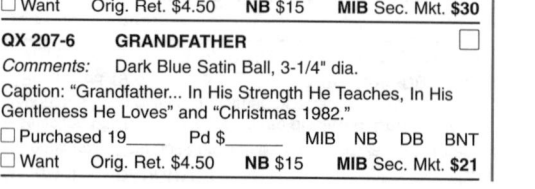
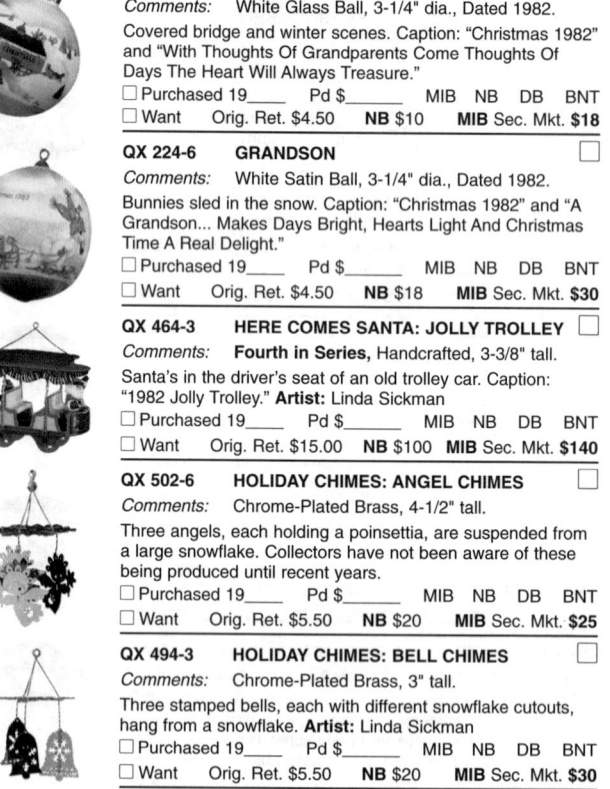

QX 484-6 HOLIDAY CHIMES: TREE CHIMES ☐
Comments: Stamped Brass, 4-7/16" tall.
Lacy, stamped brass tree has five bells and two doves incorporated into its leafy branches. **Artist:** Ed Seale
☐ Purchased 19____   Pd $_____   MIB NB DB BNT
☐ Want   Orig. Ret. $5.50   **MIB** Sec. Mkt. **$40**

QX 309-6 HOLIDAY HIGHLIGHTS: ANGEL ☐
Comments: Acrylic, 3-1/2" tall.
Angel plays harp. Gold Foil Caption: "Rejoice."
☐ Purchased 19____   Pd $_____   MIB NB DB BNT
☐ Want   Orig. Ret. $5.50   **NB** $25   **MIB** Sec. Mkt. **$35**

**QX 311-3 HOLIDAY HIGHLIGHTS:
CHRISTMAS MAGIC** ☐
Comments: Acrylic, 3-13/16" tall.
Rabbit looks at an ornament hanging from a tree branch.
Caption: "Christmas... season of magical moments."
☐ Purchased 19____   Pd $_____   MIB NB DB BNT
☐ Want   Orig. Ret. $5.50   **NB** $20   **MIB** Sec. Mkt. **$30**

**QX 309-3 HOLIDAY HIGHLIGHTS:
CHRISTMAS SLEIGH** ☐
Comments: Acrylic, 3-23/32" tall.
A sleigh filled with gifts and a Christmas tree.
Caption: "Christmas 1982."
☐ Purchased 19____   Pd $_____   MIB NB DB BNT
☐ Want   Orig. Ret. $5.50   **NB** $60   **MIB** Sec. Mkt. **$75**

QX 313-3 HOLIDAY WILDLIFE: CARDINALIS ☐
Comments: **FIRST IN SERIES,** Wood and Decoform, 4" dia.
Two cardinals are perched on a pine bough. Caption:
"Cardinalis, Cardinalis. First in a series, Wildlife Collection.
Christmas 1982." Scarce!
☐ Purchased 19____   Pd $_____   MIB NB DB BNT
☐ Want   Orig. Ret. $7.00   **NB** $320 **MIB** Sec. Mkt. **$375**

QX 432-2 ICE SCULPTOR, THE ☐
Comments: Handcrafted, 3-1/32" tall.
Reissued from 1981. **Artist:** Donna Lee
☐ Purchased 19____   Pd $_____   MIB NB DB BNT
☐ Want   Orig. Ret. $8.00   **NB** $75   **MIB** Sec. Mkt. **$100**

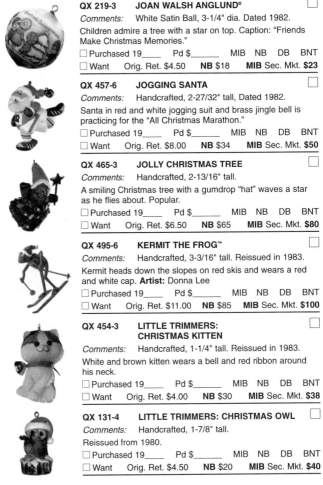

QX 219-3 JOAN WALSH ANGLUND© ☐
Comments: White Satin Ball, 3-1/4" dia. Dated 1982.
Children admire a tree with a star on top. Caption: "Friends
Make Christmas Memories."
☐ Purchased 19____   Pd $_____   MIB NB DB BNT
☐ Want   Orig. Ret. $4.50   **NB** $18   **MIB** Sec. Mkt. **$23**

QX 457-6 JOGGING SANTA ☐
Comments: Handcrafted, 2-27/32" tall, Dated 1982.
Santa in red and white jogging suit and brass jingle bell is
practicing for the "All Christmas Marathon."
☐ Purchased 19____   Pd $_____   MIB NB DB BNT
☐ Want   Orig. Ret. $8.00   **NB** $34   **MIB** Sec. Mkt. **$50**

QX 465-3 JOLLY CHRISTMAS TREE ☐
Comments: Handcrafted, 2-13/16" tall.
A smiling Christmas tree with a gumdrop "hat" waves a star
as he flies about. Popular.
☐ Purchased 19____   Pd $_____   MIB NB DB BNT
☐ Want   Orig. Ret. $6.50   **NB** $65   **MIB** Sec. Mkt. **$80**

QX 495-6 KERMIT THE FROG™ ☐
Comments: Handcrafted, 3-3/16" tall. Reissued in 1983.
Kermit heads down the slopes on red skis and wears a red
and white cap. **Artist:** Donna Lee
☐ Purchased 19____   Pd $_____   MIB NB DB BNT
☐ Want   Orig. Ret. $11.00   **NB** $85   **MIB** Sec. Mkt. **$100**

**QX 454-3 LITTLE TRIMMERS:
CHRISTMAS KITTEN** ☐
Comments: Handcrafted, 1-1/4" tall. Reissued in 1983.
White and brown kitten wears a bell and red ribbon around
his neck.
☐ Purchased 19____   Pd $_____   MIB NB DB BNT
☐ Want   Orig. Ret. $4.00   **NB** $30   **MIB** Sec. Mkt. **$38**

QX 131-4 LITTLE TRIMMERS: CHRISTMAS OWL ☐
Comments: Handcrafted, 1-7/8" tall.
Reissued from 1980.
☐ Purchased 19____   Pd $_____   MIB NB DB BNT
☐ Want   Orig. Ret. $4.50   **NB** $20   **MIB** Sec. Mkt. **$40**

QX 454-6 LITTLE TRIMMERS: COOKIE MOUSE ☐

Comments: Handcrafted, 2-1/16" tall, Dated 1982.
A cute white mouse sits on top of a star shaped cookie, eating one of its "points." **Artist:** Linda Sickman

☐ Purchased 19____ Pd $_____ MIB NB DB BNT
☐ Want Orig. Ret. $4.50 **NB** $44 **MIB** Sec. Mkt. **$60**

QX 462-3 LITTLE TRIMMERS: DOVE LOVE ☐

Comments: Acrylic, 2-1/16" tall.
A white dove swings in the center of an open red heart. **Artist:** Linda Sickman

☐ Purchased 19____ Pd $_____ MIB NB DB BNT
☐ Want Orig. Ret. $4.50 **NB** $44 **MIB** Sec. Mkt. **$50**

QX 477-6 LITTLE TRIMMERS: JINGLING TEDDY ☐

Comments: Flocked, Brass, 2-1/8" tall.
A brown flocked teddy bear holds a brass bell. **Artist:** Ed Seale

☐ Purchased 19____ Pd $_____ MIB NB DB BNT
☐ Want Orig. Ret. $4.00 **NB** $28 **MIB** Sec. Mkt. **$40**

QX 415-5 LITTLE TRIMMERS: MERRY MOOSE ☐

Comments: Handcrafted, 1-3/4" tall.
Young moose on ice skates.

☐ Purchased 19____ Pd $_____ MIB NB DB BNT
☐ Want Orig. Ret. $5.50 **NB** $40 **MIB** Sec. Mkt. **$55**

QX 459-6 LITTLE TRIMMERS: MUSICAL ANGEL ☐

Comments: Handcrafted, 1-15/16" tall.
A tiny angel wearing a brass halo, sits on a cloud playing his lyre. **Artist:** Donna Lee

☐ Purchased 19____ Pd $_____ MIB NB DB BNT
☐ Want Orig. Ret. $5.50 **NB** $90 **MIB** Sec. Mkt. **$130**

QX 409-5 LITTLE TRIMMERS: PERKY PENGUIN ☐

Comments: Handcrafted, 1-5/16" tall.
Reissued from 1981.

☐ Purchased 19____ Pd $_____ MIB NB DB BNT
☐ Want Orig. Ret. $4.00 **NB** $39 **MIB** Sec. Mkt. **$60**

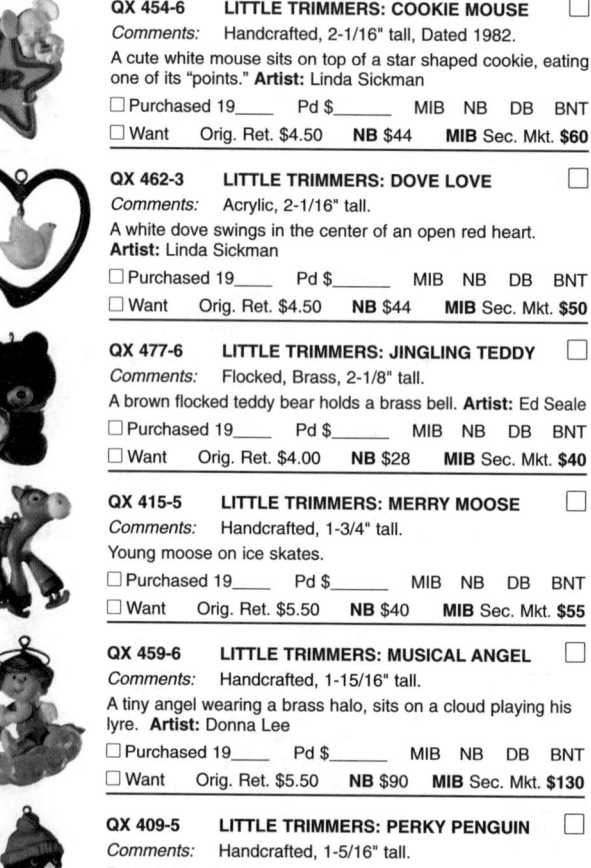

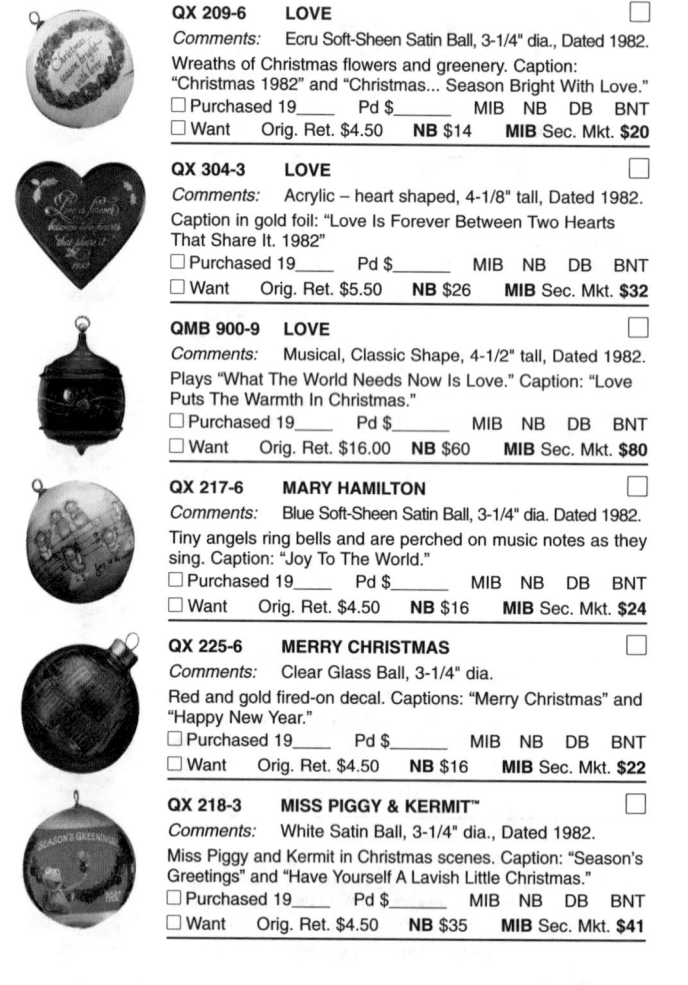

QX 209-6 LOVE ☐

Comments: Ecru Soft-Sheen Satin Ball, 3-1/4" dia., Dated 1982.
Wreaths of Christmas flowers and greenery. Caption: "Christmas 1982" and "Christmas... Season Bright With Love."

☐ Purchased 19____ Pd $_____ MIB NB DB BNT
☐ Want Orig. Ret. $4.50 **NB** $14 **MIB** Sec. Mkt. **$20**

QX 304-3 LOVE ☐

Comments: Acrylic – heart shaped, 4-1/8" tall, Dated 1982.
Caption in gold foil: "Love Is Forever Between Two Hearts That Share It. 1982"

☐ Purchased 19____ Pd $_____ MIB NB DB BNT
☐ Want Orig. Ret. $5.50 **NB** $26 **MIB** Sec. Mkt. **$32**

QMB 900-9 LOVE ☐

Comments: Musical, Classic Shape, 4-1/2" tall, Dated 1982.
Plays "What The World Needs Now Is Love." Caption: "Love Puts The Warmth In Christmas."

☐ Purchased 19____ Pd $_____ MIB NB DB BNT
☐ Want Orig. Ret. $16.00 **NB** $60 **MIB** Sec. Mkt. **$80**

QX 217-6 MARY HAMILTON ☐

Comments: Blue Soft-Sheen Satin Ball, 3-1/4" dia. Dated 1982.
Tiny angels ring bells and are perched on music notes as they sing. Caption: "Joy To The World."

☐ Purchased 19____ Pd $_____ MIB NB DB BNT
☐ Want Orig. Ret. $4.50 **NB** $16 **MIB** Sec. Mkt. **$24**

QX 225-6 MERRY CHRISTMAS ☐

Comments: Clear Glass Ball, 3-1/4" dia.
Red and gold fired-on decal. Captions: "Merry Christmas" and "Happy New Year."

☐ Purchased 19____ Pd $_____ MIB NB DB BNT
☐ Want Orig. Ret. $4.50 **NB** $16 **MIB** Sec. Mkt. **$22**

QX 218-3 MISS PIGGY & KERMIT™ ☐

Comments: White Satin Ball, 3-1/4" dia., Dated 1982.
Miss Piggy and Kermit in Christmas scenes. Caption: "Season's Greetings" and "Have Yourself A Lavish Little Christmas."

☐ Purchased 19____ Pd $_____ MIB NB DB BNT
☐ Want Orig. Ret. $4.50 **NB** $35 **MIB** Sec. Mkt. **$41**

QX 209-3   MOMENTS OF LOVE

Comments: Blue Soft-Sheen Satin Ball, 3-1/4" dia., Dated 1982. A horse-drawn stagecoach is silhouetted in white. Caption: "Christmas 1982" and "Each Moment Of Love Lives Forever In Memory."

☐ Purchased 19_____   Pd $_____   MIB   NB   DB   BNT
☐ Want   Orig. Ret. $4.50   **NB** $14   **MIB** Sec. Mkt. **$18**

QX 205-3   MOTHER

Comments: White Glass Ball, 3-1/4" dia., Dated 1982. Holly and pine garland and poinsettia bouquet. Caption: "Christmas 1982" and "The Spirit Of Christmas Lives In A Mother's Loving Heart."

☐ Purchased 19_____   Pd $_____   MIB   NB   DB   BNT
☐ Want   Orig. Ret. $4.50   **NB** $10   **MIB** Sec. Mkt. **$20**

QX 222-3   MOTHER AND DAD

Comments: White Porcelain Glass Ball, 3-1/4" dia., Dated 1982. Holly leaves, berries and evergreens. Caption: "Christmas 1982" and "A Mother And Dad Know So Many Ways To Warm A Heart With Love."

☐ Purchased 19_____   Pd $_____   MIB   NB   DB   BNT
☐ Want   Orig. Ret. $4.50   **NB** $10   **MIB** Sec. Mkt. **$18**

QX 218-6   MUPPETS™ PARTY

Comments: White Satin Ball, 3-1/4" dia., Dated 1982. The whole Muppets gang is gathered for a party. Caption: "Merry Christmas 1982."

☐ Purchased 19_____   Pd $_____   MIB   NB   DB   BNT
☐ Want   Orig. Ret. $4.50   **NB** $30   **MIB** Sec. Mkt. **$40**

QX 212-6   NEW HOME

Comments: Dk. Blue Satin Ball, 3-1/4" dia., Dated 1982. Snow covered village homes. Caption: "Christmas Time Fills Hearts With Love And Homes With Warmth And Joy."

☐ Purchased 19_____   Pd $_____   MIB   NB   DB   BNT
☐ Want   Orig. Ret. $4.50   **NB** $15   **MIB** Sec. Mkt. **$24**

QX 202-3   NORMAN ROCKWELL

Comments: Red Soft-Sheen Satin Ball, 3-1/4" dia., Dated 1982. Caption: "From The Norman Rockwell Collection 1982. Hearts Are Light, Smiles Are Bright, Child's Delight, It's Christmas."

☐ Purchased 19_____   Pd $_____   MIB   NB   DB   BNT
☐ Want   Orig. Ret. $4.50   **NB** $18   **MIB** Sec. Mkt. **$28**

QX 305-3   NORMAN ROCKWELL SERIES

Comments: **Third in Series,** Red Cameo, 3-3/8" dia. Dated 1982. Caption: "Filling The Stockings. Third In A Series. The Norman Rockwell Collection. Christmas 1982."

☐ Purchased 19_____   Pd $_____   MIB   NB   DB   BNT
☐ Want   Orig. Ret. $8.50   **NB** $25   **MIB** Sec. Mkt. **$32**

QX 227-6   OLD FASHIONED CHRISTMAS

Comments: White Porcelain Glass Ball, 3-1/4" dia. Reproduction of antique English greeting cards from late 1800s. Caption: "Merry Christmas" and "Happy New Year."

☐ Purchased 19_____   Pd $_____   MIB   NB   DB   BNT
☐ Want   Orig. Ret. $4.50   **NB** $34   **MIB** Sec. Mkt. **$48**

QX 226-3   OLD WORLD ANGELS

Comments: White Porcelain Glass Ball, 3-1/4" dia. Old-world angels hold lighted candles and float amid stars and streamers.

☐ Purchased 19_____   Pd $_____   MIB   NB   DB   BNT
☐ Want   Orig. Ret. $4.50   **NB** $18   **MIB** Sec. Mkt. **$25**

QX 226-6   PATTERNS OF CHRISTMAS

Comments: Gold Glass Ball, 3-1/4" dia. Oriental designs of poinsettias and holly are highlighted in gold.

☐ Purchased 19_____   Pd $_____   MIB   NB   DB   BNT
☐ Want   Orig. Ret. $4.50   **NB** $16   **MIB** Sec. Mkt. **$24**

QX 200-6   PEANUTS®

Comments: Light Blue Satin Ball, 3-1/4" dia., Dated 1982. Snoopy, Woodstock and friends ride a tandem bike. Caption: "Christmas 1982."

☐ Purchased 19_____   Pd $_____   MIB   NB   DB   BNT
☐ Want   Orig. Ret. $4.50   **NB** $29   **MIB** Sec. Mkt. **$42**

QX 419-5   PEEKING ELF

Comments: Handcrafted, 3-3/32" tall. An elf peeks over the top of a silver ball ornament tied with a red ribbon.

☐ Purchased 19_____   Pd $_____   MIB   NB   DB   BNT
☐ Want   Orig. Ret. $6.50   **NB** $28   **MIB** Sec. Mkt. **$40**

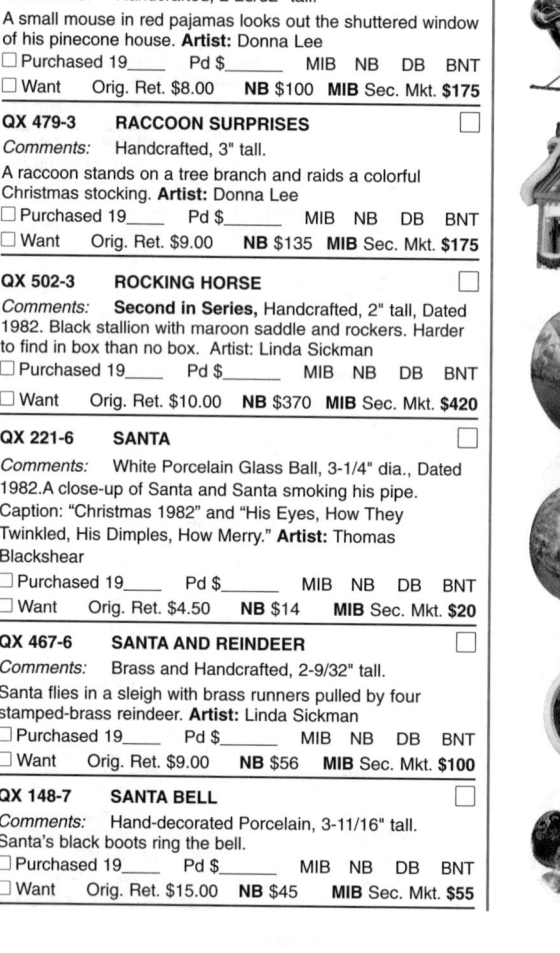

QX 461-3   PINECONE HOME ☐
Comments: Handcrafted, 2-23/32" tall.
A small mouse in red pajamas looks out the shuttered window of his pinecone house. **Artist:** Donna Lee
☐ Purchased 19_____   Pd $_____   MIB   NB   DB   BNT
☐ Want   Orig. Ret. $8.00   **NB** $100   **MIB** Sec. Mkt. **$175**

QX 479-3   RACCOON SURPRISES ☐
Comments: Handcrafted, 3" tall.
A raccoon stands on a tree branch and raids a colorful Christmas stocking. **Artist:** Donna Lee
☐ Purchased 19_____   Pd $_____   MIB   NB   DB   BNT
☐ Want   Orig. Ret. $9.00   **NB** $135   **MIB** Sec. Mkt. **$175**

QX 502-3   ROCKING HORSE ☐
Comments: **Second in Series,** Handcrafted, 2" tall, Dated 1982. Black stallion with maroon saddle and rockers. Harder to find in box than no box. Artist: Linda Sickman
☐ Purchased 19_____   Pd $_____   MIB   NB   DB   BNT
☐ Want   Orig. Ret. $10.00   **NB** $370   **MIB** Sec. Mkt. **$420**

QX 221-6   SANTA ☐
Comments: White Porcelain Glass Ball, 3-1/4" dia., Dated 1982. A close-up of Santa and Santa smoking his pipe. Caption: "Christmas 1982" and "His Eyes, How They Twinkled, His Dimples, How Merry." **Artist:** Thomas Blackshear
☐ Purchased 19_____   Pd $_____   MIB   NB   DB   BNT
☐ Want   Orig. Ret. $4.50   **NB** $14   **MIB** Sec. Mkt. **$20**

QX 467-6   SANTA AND REINDEER ☐
Comments: Brass and Handcrafted, 2-9/32" tall.
Santa flies in a sleigh with brass runners pulled by four stamped-brass reindeer. **Artist:** Linda Sickman
☐ Purchased 19_____   Pd $_____   MIB   NB   DB   BNT
☐ Want   Orig. Ret. $9.00   **NB** $56   **MIB** Sec. Mkt. **$100**

QX 148-7   SANTA BELL ☐
Comments: Hand-decorated Porcelain, 3-11/16" tall.
Santa's black boots ring the bell.
☐ Purchased 19_____   Pd $_____   MIB   NB   DB   BNT
☐ Want   Orig. Ret. $15.00   **NB** $45   **MIB** Sec. Mkt. **$55**

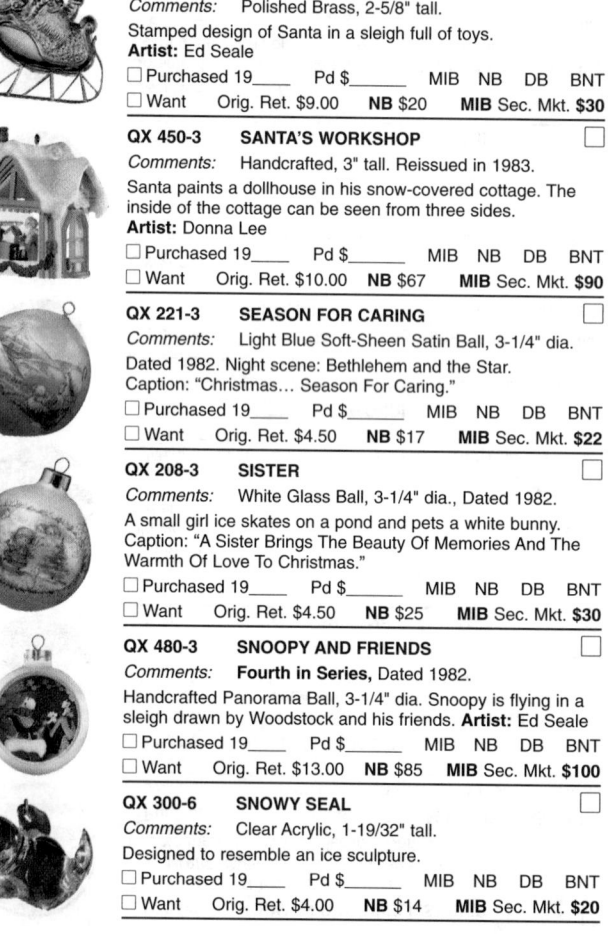

QX 478-6   SANTA'S SLEIGH ☐
Comments: Polished Brass, 2-5/8" tall.
Stamped design of Santa in a sleigh full of toys. **Artist:** Ed Seale
☐ Purchased 19_____   Pd $_____   MIB   NB   DB   BNT
☐ Want   Orig. Ret. $9.00   **NB** $20   **MIB** Sec. Mkt. **$30**

QX 450-3   SANTA'S WORKSHOP ☐
Comments: Handcrafted, 3" tall. Reissued in 1983.
Santa paints a dollhouse in his snow-covered cottage. The inside of the cottage can be seen from three sides. **Artist:** Donna Lee
☐ Purchased 19_____   Pd $_____   MIB   NB   DB   BNT
☐ Want   Orig. Ret. $10.00   **NB** $67   **MIB** Sec. Mkt. **$90**

QX 221-3   SEASON FOR CARING ☐
Comments: Light Blue Soft-Sheen Satin Ball, 3-1/4" dia.
Dated 1982. Night scene: Bethlehem and the Star. Caption: "Christmas… Season For Caring."
☐ Purchased 19_____   Pd $_____   MIB   NB   DB   BNT
☐ Want   Orig. Ret. $4.50   **NB** $17   **MIB** Sec. Mkt. **$22**

QX 208-3   SISTER ☐
Comments: White Glass Ball, 3-1/4" dia., Dated 1982.
A small girl ice skates on a pond and pets a white bunny. Caption: "A Sister Brings The Beauty Of Memories And The Warmth Of Love To Christmas."
☐ Purchased 19_____   Pd $_____   MIB   NB   DB   BNT
☐ Want   Orig. Ret. $4.50   **NB** $25   **MIB** Sec. Mkt. **$30**

QX 480-3   SNOOPY AND FRIENDS ☐
Comments: **Fourth in Series,** Dated 1982.
Handcrafted Panorama Ball, 3-1/4" dia. Snoopy is flying in a sleigh drawn by Woodstock and his friends. **Artist:** Ed Seale
☐ Purchased 19_____   Pd $_____   MIB   NB   DB   BNT
☐ Want   Orig. Ret. $13.00   **NB** $85   **MIB** Sec. Mkt. **$100**

QX 300-6   SNOWY SEAL ☐
Comments: Clear Acrylic, 1-19/32" tall.
Designed to resemble an ice sculpture.
☐ Purchased 19_____   Pd $_____   MIB   NB   DB   BNT
☐ Want   Orig. Ret. $4.00   **NB** $14   **MIB** Sec. Mkt. **$20**

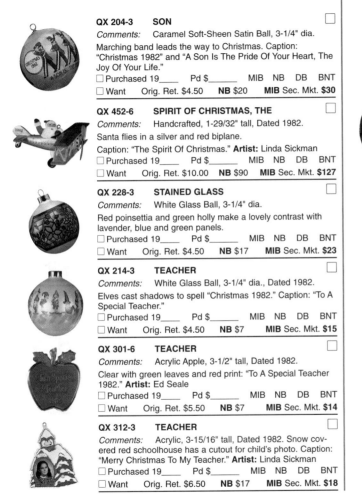

QX 204-3　SON ☐

Comments: Caramel Soft-Sheen Satin Ball, 3-1/4" dia.
Marching band leads the way to Christmas. Caption: "Christmas 1982" and "A Son Is The Pride Of Your Heart, The Joy Of Your Life."
☐ Purchased 19____ 　 Pd $_____ 　 MIB　NB　DB　BNT
☐ Want 　 Orig. Ret. $4.50 　 **NB** $20 　 **MIB** Sec. Mkt. **$30**

QX 452-6　SPIRIT OF CHRISTMAS, THE ☐

Comments: Handcrafted, 1-29/32" tall, Dated 1982.
Santa flies in a silver and red biplane.
Caption: "The Spirit Of Christmas." **Artist:** Linda Sickman
☐ Purchased 19____ 　 Pd $_____ 　 MIB　NB　DB　BNT
☐ Want 　 Orig. Ret. $10.00 　 **NB** $90 　 **MIB** Sec. Mkt. **$127**

QX 228-3　STAINED GLASS ☐

Comments: White Glass Ball, 3-1/4" dia.
Red poinsettia and green holly make a lovely contrast with lavender, blue and green panels.
☐ Purchased 19____ 　 Pd $_____ 　 MIB　NB　DB　BNT
☐ Want 　 Orig. Ret. $4.50 　 **NB** $17 　 **MIB** Sec. Mkt. **$23**

QX 214-3　TEACHER ☐

Comments: White Glass Ball, 3-1/4" dia., Dated 1982.
Elves cast shadows to spell "Christmas 1982." Caption: "To A Special Teacher."
☐ Purchased 19____ 　 Pd $_____ 　 MIB　NB　DB　BNT
☐ Want 　 Orig. Ret. $4.50 　 **NB** $7 　 **MIB** Sec. Mkt. **$15**

QX 301-6　TEACHER ☐

Comments: Acrylic Apple, 3-1/2" tall, Dated 1982.
Clear with green leaves and red print: "To A Special Teacher 1982." **Artist:** Ed Seale
☐ Purchased 19____ 　 Pd $_____ 　 MIB　NB　DB　BNT
☐ Want 　 Orig. Ret. $5.50 　 **NB** $7 　 **MIB** Sec. Mkt. **$14**

QX 312-3　TEACHER ☐

Comments: Acrylic, 3-15/16" tall, Dated 1982. Snow covered red schoolhouse has a cutout for child's photo. Caption: "Merry Christmas To My Teacher." **Artist:** Linda Sickman
☐ Purchased 19____ 　 Pd $_____ 　 MIB　NB　DB　BNT
☐ Want 　 Orig. Ret. $6.50 　 **NB** $17 　 **MIB** Sec. Mkt. **$18**

QX 451-3　THIMBLE – MOUSE ☐

Comments: **Fifth in Series,** Handcrafted, 2-11/32" tall.
Little mouse "soldier" with big ears and silver needle "baton" wears a thimble as a hat.
☐ Purchased 19____ 　 Pd $_____ 　 MIB　NB　DB　BNT
☐ Want 　 Orig. Ret. $5.00 　 **NB** $58 　 **MIB** Sec. Mkt. **$75**

QX 307-3　THREE KINGS ☐

Comments: Blue Cameo, 3-3/8" dia., Dated 1982.
Caption: "By A Star Shining Brightly, Three Kings Set Their Course And Followed The Heavenly Light To Its Source."
Artist: Thomas Blackshear
☐ Purchased 19____ 　 Pd $_____ 　 MIB　NB　DB　BNT
☐ Want 　 Orig. Ret. $8.50 　 **NB** $17 　 **MIB** Sec. Mkt. **$27**

QX 460-3　TIN LOCOMOTIVE ☐

Comments: **FIRST IN SERIES,** Pressed Tin, 3-5/8" tall.
Dated 1982. Decorated in red, blue and silver, with a brass bell that hangs in front of the cab.
Artist: Linda Sickman
☐ Purchased 19____ 　 Pd $_____ 　 MIB　NB　DB　BNT
☐ Want 　 Orig. Ret. $13.00 　 **NB** $525 　 **MIB** Sec. Mkt. **$750**

QX 483-6　TIN SOLDIER ☐

Comments: Pressed Tin, 4-7/8" tall.
A British soldier stands at stiff attention.
☐ Purchased 19____ 　 Pd $_____ 　 MIB　NB　DB　BNT
☐ Want 　 Orig. Ret. $6.50 　 **NB** $40 　 **MIB** Sec. Mkt. **$50**

QX 203-6　TWELVE DAYS OF CHRISTMAS ☐

Comments: White Pebbled Glass Ball, 3-1/4" dia., Dated 1982. Illustration of the verses of the Christmas carol. Caption: "The Twelve Days Of Christmas 1982."
☐ Purchased 19____ 　 Pd $_____ 　 MIB　NB　DB　BNT
☐ Want 　 Orig. Ret. $4.50 　 **NB** $20 　 **MIB** Sec. Mkt. **$25**

QX 211-6　TWENTY-FIFTH CHRISTMAS TOGETHER ☐

Comments: White Porcelain Glass Ball, 3-1/4" dia., Dated 1982. Caption: "Twenty-Fifth Christmas Together 1982" and "Christmas... As Timeless As Snow-Fall, As Forever As Candleglow, As Always As Love."
☐ Purchased 19____ 　 Pd $_____ 　 MIB　NB　DB　BNT
☐ Want 　 Orig. Ret. $4.50 　 **NB** $15 　 **MIB** Sec. Mkt. **$20**

1983 Collection

When purchasing ball ornaments, watch for "spots." Deduct from price.

QX 220-9   1983

Comments: Raspberry Glass Ball, 3-1/4" dia. Date is printed in gold on a narrow band. Trimmed in platinum colored stripes.

☐ Purchased 19____   Pd $_____   MIB   NB   DB   BNT
☐ Want   Orig. Ret. $4.50   **NB** $18   **MIB** Sec. Mkt. **$30**

QX 217-9   AN OLD FASHIONED CHRISTMAS

Comments: Green Porcelain Glass Ball, 3-1/4" dia. Christmas scenes reminiscent of old greeting cards.

☐ Purchased 19____   Pd $_____   MIB   NB   DB   BNT
☐ Want   Orig. Ret. $4.50   **NB** $19   **MIB** Sec. Mkt. **$35**

QX 408-7   ANGEL MESSENGER

Comments: Brass, Handcrafted, 2" tall, Dated 1983. The brass year date is carried by an angel dressed in a blue robe. **Artist:** Ed Seale

☐ Purchased 19____   Pd $_____   MIB   NB   DB   BNT
☐ Want   Orig. Ret. $6.50   **NB** $80   **MIB** Sec. Mkt. **$95**

QX 219-7   ANGELS

Comments: Clear Glass Ball, 3-1/4" dia. The inside of the ball has a gold tinsel starburst. Design is of old world angels in soft pastels.

☐ Purchased 19____   Pd $_____   MIB   NB   DB   BNT
☐ Want   Orig. Ret. $5.00   **NB** $15   **MIB** Sec. Mkt. **$25**

QX 216-7   ANNUNCIATION, THE

Comments: White Porcelain Glass Ball, 3-1/4" dia. Reproduction of Fra Filippo Filippi of "The Annunciation." Caption from Luke 1:35 (RSVB).

☐ Purchased 19____   Pd $_____   MIB   NB   DB   BNT
☐ Want   Orig. Ret. $4.50   **NB** $16   **MIB** Sec. Mkt. **$25**

QX 301-9   BABY'S FIRST CHRISTMAS

Comments: Red Cameo, 3-3/4" wide, Dated 1983. Old fashioned rocking horse. Caption: "Baby's First Christmas 1983" and "A Baby Fills Each Day With Joy By Filling Hearts With Love." **Artist:** Linda Sickman

☐ Purchased 19____   Pd $_____   MIB   NB   DB   BNT
☐ Want   Orig. Ret. $7.50   **NB** $9   **MIB** Sec. Mkt. **$18**

QX 402-7   BABY'S FIRST CHRISTMAS

Comments: Handcrafted, 3-5/32" tall, Dated 1983. Cradle painted in folk art motif. Caption: "Baby's First Christmas." **Artist:** Donna Lee

☐ Purchased 19____   Pd $_____   MIB   NB   DB   BNT
☐ Want   Orig. Ret. $14.00   **NB** $32   **MIB** Sec. Mkt. **$40**

QMB 903-9   BABY'S FIRST CHRISTMAS

Comments: Musical, Classic Shape, 4-1/2" tall, Dated 1983. Babies crawl up and down the candy cane letters that form the caption. Caption: "Baby's First Christmas." Plays "Schubert's Lullaby."

☐ Purchased 19____   Pd $_____   MIB   NB   DB   BNT
☐ Want   Orig. Ret. $16.00   **NB** $50   **MIB** Sec. Mkt. **$90**

QX 200-9   BABY'S FIRST CHRISTMAS – BOY

Comments: Light Blue Soft-Sheen Satin Ball, 3-1/4" dia. Dated 1983. Six teddies tumble around the ornament. Caption: "Baby's First Christmas 1983" and "A Baby Boy Is Love And Joy... And Pride That Lasts A Lifetime."

☐ Purchased 19____   Pd $_____   MIB   NB   DB   BNT
☐ Want   Orig. Ret. $4.50   **NB** $15   **MIB** Sec. Mkt. **$30**

QX 200-7   BABY'S FIRST CHRISTMAS – GIRL

Comments: White Soft-Sheen Satin Ball, 3-1/4" dia., Dated 1983. Baby's red dress with white polka dots and pinafore. Caption: "Baby's First Christmas 1983" and "A Baby Girl Is A Special Gift Of Love."

☐ Purchased 19____   Pd $_____   MIB   NB   DB   BNT
☐ Want   Orig. Ret. $4.50   **NB** $25   **MIB** Sec. Mkt. **$30**

QX 302-9   BABY'S FIRST CHRISTMAS – PHOTOHOLDER

Comments: Acrylic, 3-7/8" tall, Dated 1983. An open baby book holds baby's photo. Caption: "Baby's First Christmas 1983." and "A Baby Is A Dream Fulfilled, A Treasure To Hold Dear — A Baby Is A Love That Grows More Precious Every Year."

☐ Purchased 19____   Pd $_____   MIB   NB   DB   BNT
☐ Want   Orig. Ret. $7.00   **NB** $16   **MIB** Sec. Mkt. **$28**

QX 226-7   BABY'S SECOND CHRISTMAS

Comments: White Soft-Sheen Satin Ball, 3-1/4" dia. Dated 1983. Caption: "Baby's Second Christmas 1983" and "A child knows such special ways to jolly up the holidays!"

☐ Purchased 19____   Pd $_____   MIB   NB   DB   BNT
☐ Want   Orig. Ret. $4.50   **NB** $21   **MIB** Sec. Mkt. **$36**

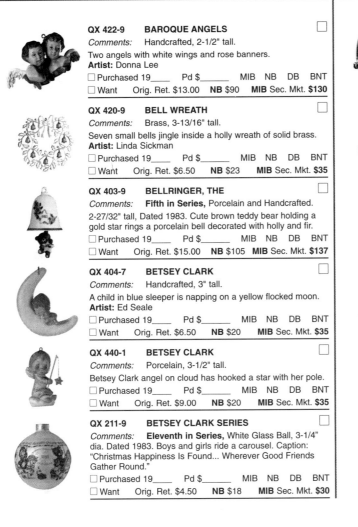

QX 422-9   BAROQUE ANGELS

Comments: Handcrafted, 2-1/2" tall.
Two angels with white wings and rose banners.
Artist: Donna Lee

☐ Purchased 19____   Pd $_____   MIB NB DB BNT
☐ Want   Orig. Ret. $13.00   **NB** $90   **MIB** Sec. Mkt. **$130**

QX 420-9   BELL WREATH

Comments: Brass, 3-13/16" tall.
Seven small bells jingle inside a holly wreath of solid brass.
Artist: Linda Sickman

☐ Purchased 19____   Pd $_____   MIB NB DB BNT
☐ Want   Orig. Ret. $6.50   **NB** $23   **MIB** Sec. Mkt. **$35**

QX 403-9   BELLRINGER, THE

Comments: **Fifth in Series,** Porcelain and Handcrafted.
2-27/32" tall, Dated 1983. Cute brown teddy bear holding a
gold star rings a porcelain bell decorated with holly and fir.

☐ Purchased 19____   Pd $_____   MIB NB DB BNT
☐ Want   Orig. Ret. $15.00   **NB** $105   **MIB** Sec. Mkt. **$137**

QX 404-7   BETSEY CLARK

Comments: Handcrafted, 3" tall.
A child in blue sleeper is napping on a yellow flocked moon.
Artist: Ed Seale

☐ Purchased 19____   Pd $_____   MIB NB DB BNT
☐ Want   Orig. Ret. $6.50   **NB** $20   **MIB** Sec. Mkt. **$35**

QX 440-1   BETSEY CLARK

Comments: Porcelain, 3-1/2" tall.
Betsey Clark angel on cloud has hooked a star with her pole.

☐ Purchased 19____   Pd $_____   MIB NB DB BNT
☐ Want   Orig. Ret. $9.00   **NB** $20   **MIB** Sec. Mkt. **$35**

QX 211-9   BETSEY CLARK SERIES

Comments: **Eleventh in Series,** White Glass Ball, 3-1/4"
dia. Dated 1983. Boys and girls ride a carousel. Caption:
"Christmas Happiness Is Found... Wherever Good Friends
Gather Round."

☐ Purchased 19____   Pd $_____   MIB NB DB BNT
☐ Want   Orig. Ret. $4.50   **NB** $18   **MIB** Sec. Mkt. **$30**

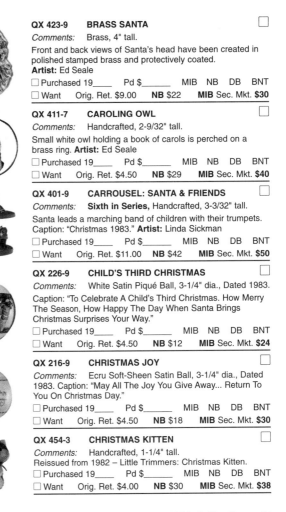

QX 423-9   BRASS SANTA

Comments: Brass, 4" tall.
Front and back views of Santa's head have been created in
polished stamped brass and protectively coated.
Artist: Ed Seale

☐ Purchased 19____   Pd $_____   MIB NB DB BNT
☐ Want   Orig. Ret. $9.00   **NB** $22   **MIB** Sec. Mkt. **$30**

QX 411-7   CAROLING OWL

Comments: Handcrafted, 2-9/32" tall.
Small white owl holding a book of carols is perched on a
brass ring. **Artist:** Ed Seale

☐ Purchased 19____   Pd $_____   MIB NB DB BNT
☐ Want   Orig. Ret. $4.50   **NB** $29   **MIB** Sec. Mkt. **$40**

QX 401-9   CARROUSEL: SANTA & FRIENDS

Comments: **Sixth in Series,** Handcrafted, 3-3/92" tall.
Santa leads a marching band of children with their trumpets.
Caption: "Christmas 1983." **Artist:** Linda Sickman

☐ Purchased 19____   Pd $_____   MIB NB DB BNT
☐ Want   Orig. Ret. $11.00   **NB** $42   **MIB** Sec. Mkt. **$50**

QX 226-9   CHILD'S THIRD CHRISTMAS

Comments: White Satin Piqué Ball, 3-1/4" dia., Dated 1983.
Caption: "To Celebrate A Child's Third Christmas. How Merry
The Season, How Happy The Day When Santa Brings
Christmas Surprises Your Way."

☐ Purchased 19____   Pd $_____   MIB NB DB BNT
☐ Want   Orig. Ret. $4.50   **NB** $12   **MIB** Sec. Mkt. **$24**

QX 216-9   CHRISTMAS JOY

Comments: Ecru Soft-Sheen Satin Ball, 3-1/4" dia., Dated
1983. Caption: "May All The Joy You Give Away... Return To
You On Christmas Day."

☐ Purchased 19____   Pd $_____   MIB NB DB BNT
☐ Want   Orig. Ret. $4.50   **NB** $18   **MIB** Sec. Mkt. **$30**

QX 454-3   CHRISTMAS KITTEN

Comments: Handcrafted, 1-1/4" tall.
Reissued from 1982 – Little Trimmers: Christmas Kitten.

☐ Purchased 19____   Pd $_____   MIB NB DB BNT
☐ Want   Orig. Ret. $4.00   **NB** $30   **MIB** Sec. Mkt. **$38**

QX 419-9 CHRISTMAS KOALA ☐

Comments: Handcrafted, 2-3/16" tall. A flocked koala bear holds a sprig of evergreen. **Artist:** Ed Seale

☐ Purchased 19____ Pd $_____ MIB NB DB BNT
☐ Want Orig. Ret. $4.00 **NB** $26 **MIB** Sec. Mkt. **$32**

QX 221-9 CHRISTMAS WONDERLAND ☐

Comments: Clear Glass Ball, 3-1/4" dia., Rare! The animals celebrate Christmas in the forest. Another scene inside the ball may be seen through a "peek through" area of the design.

☐ Purchased 19____ Pd $_____ MIB NB DB BNT
☐ Want Orig. Ret. $4.50 **NB** $110 **MIB** Sec. Mkt. **$125**

QX 402-9 CLOTHESPIN SOLDIER: ☐
EARLY AMERICAN

Comments: **Second in Series,** Handcrafted, 2-7/16" tall. American Revolutionary soldier beats his bass drum with arms that move. **Artist:** Linda Sickman

☐ Purchased 19____ Pd $_____ MIB NB DB BNT
☐ Want Orig. Ret. $5.00 **NB** $30 **MIB** Sec. Mkt. **$42**

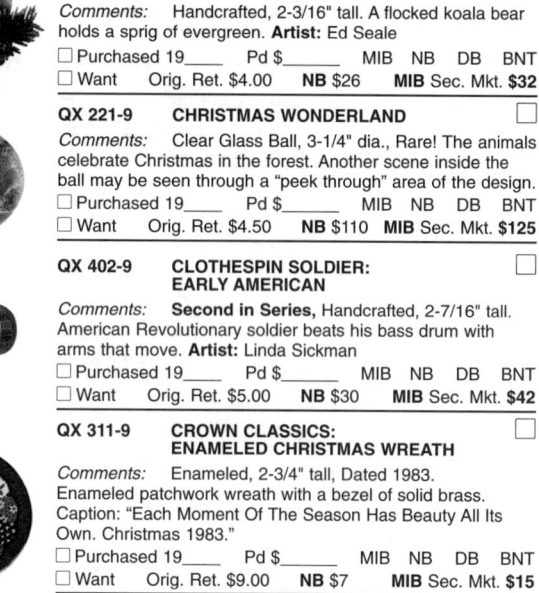

QX 311-9 CROWN CLASSICS: ☐
ENAMELED CHRISTMAS WREATH

Comments: Enameled, 2-3/4" tall, Dated 1983. Enameled patchwork wreath with a bezel of solid brass. Caption: "Each Moment Of The Season Has Beauty All Its Own. Christmas 1983."

☐ Purchased 19____ Pd $_____ MIB NB DB BNT
☐ Want Orig. Ret. $9.00 **NB** $7 **MIB** Sec. Mkt. **$15**

QX 303-7 CROWN CLASSICS: ☐
MEMORIES TO TREASURE

Comments: Acrylic, 4-1/4" tall, Dated 1983. Santa's beard holds your favorite photograph. Caption: "Holiday Fun Times Make Memories To Treasure."

☐ Purchased 19____ Pd $_____ MIB NB DB BNT
☐ Want Orig. Ret. $7.00 **NB** $23 **MIB** Sec. Mkt. **$30**

QX 302-7 CROWN CLASSICS: MOTHER & CHILD ☐

Comments: Blue Oval Cameo, 3-3/4" tall. Madonna and Child design with a translucent appearance. Caption: "Come Let Us Celebrate His Love For This Is The Season Of Rejoicing."

☐ Purchased 19____ Pd $_____ MIB NB DB BNT
☐ Want Orig. Ret. $7.50 **NB** $27 **MIB** Sec. Mkt. **$42**

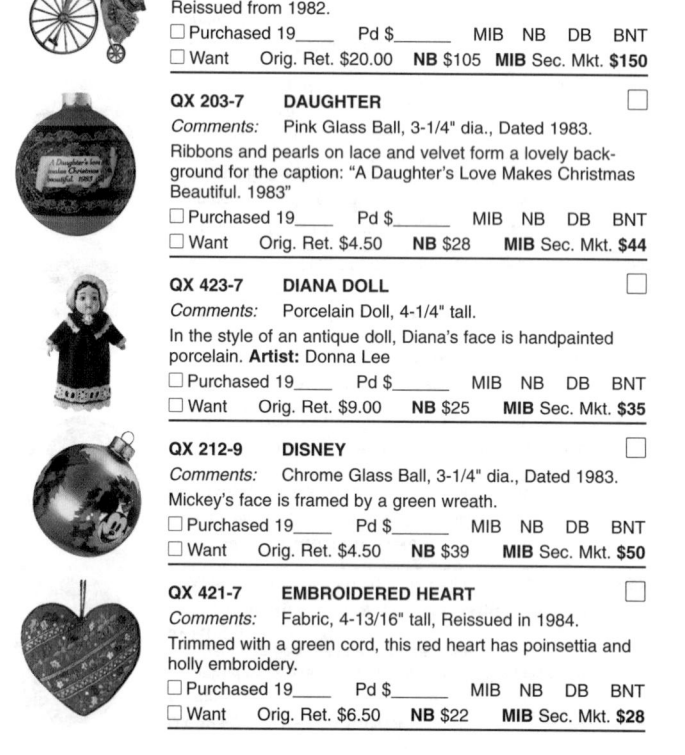

QX 215-9 CURRIER & IVES ☐

Comments: White Porcelain Glass Ball, 3-1/4" dia., Dated 1983. Caption: "Christmas 1983, Central Park Winter, The Skating Pond, Currier and Ives."

☐ Purchased 19____ Pd $_____ MIB NB DB BNT
☐ Want Orig. Ret. $4.50 **NB** $17 **MIB** Sec. Mkt. **$25**

QX 435-5 CYCLING SANTA ☐

Comments: Handcrafted, 4-3/8" tall. Reissued from 1982.

☐ Purchased 19____ Pd $_____ MIB NB DB BNT
☐ Want Orig. Ret. $20.00 **NB** $105 **MIB** Sec. Mkt. **$150**

QX 203-7 DAUGHTER ☐

Comments: Pink Glass Ball, 3-1/4" dia., Dated 1983. Ribbons and pearls on lace and velvet form a lovely background for the caption: "A Daughter's Love Makes Christmas Beautiful. 1983"

☐ Purchased 19____ Pd $_____ MIB NB DB BNT
☐ Want Orig. Ret. $4.50 **NB** $28 **MIB** Sec. Mkt. **$44**

QX 423-7 DIANA DOLL ☐

Comments: Porcelain Doll, 4-1/4" tall. In the style of an antique doll, Diana's face is handpainted porcelain. **Artist:** Donna Lee

☐ Purchased 19____ Pd $_____ MIB NB DB BNT
☐ Want Orig. Ret. $9.00 **NB** $25 **MIB** Sec. Mkt. **$35**

QX 212-9 DISNEY ☐

Comments: Chrome Glass Ball, 3-1/4" dia., Dated 1983. Mickey's face is framed by a green wreath.

☐ Purchased 19____ Pd $_____ MIB NB DB BNT
☐ Want Orig. Ret. $4.50 **NB** $39 **MIB** Sec. Mkt. **$50**

QX 421-7 EMBROIDERED HEART ☐

Comments: Fabric, 4-13/16" tall, Reissued in 1984. Trimmed with a green cord, this red heart has poinsettia and holly embroidery.

☐ Purchased 19____ Pd $_____ MIB NB DB BNT
☐ Want Orig. Ret. $6.50 **NB** $22 **MIB** Sec. Mkt. **$28**

QX 479-6 EMBROIDERED STOCKING ☐

Comments: Fabric, 3-1/4" tall, Reissued in 1984.
Quilted red stocking, accented with embroidery, is trimmed in lace and filled with toys. **Artist:** Linda Sickman

☐ Purchased 19___ Pd $_____ MIB NB DB BNT
☐ Want Orig. Ret. $6.50 **NB** $20 **MIB** Sec. Mkt. **$25**

QX 208-9 FIRST CHRISTMAS TOGETHER ☐

Comments: White Glass Ball, 3-1/4" dia., Dated 1983.
Candy canes form hearts which surround the caption and the date. The design is printed directly on the ball. Caption: "First Christmas Together." **Artist:** Linda Sickman

☐ Purchased 19___ Pd $_____ MIB NB DB BNT
☐ Want Orig. Ret. $4.50 **NB** $24 **MIB** Sec. Mkt. **$30**

QX 301-7 FIRST CHRISTMAS TOGETHER ☐

Comments: Dark Blue Cameo, 3-3/4" wide, Dated 1983.
Couple on sleigh ride. Caption: "First Christmas Together 1983."

☐ Purchased 19___ Pd $_____ MIB NB DB BNT
☐ Want Orig. Ret. $7.50 **NB** $17 **MIB** Sec. Mkt. **$25**

QX 306-9 FIRST CHRISTMAS TOGETHER ☐

Comments: Acrylic, 4-1/4" tall, Dated 1983.
Bell shape design with caption: "First Christmas Together 1983."

☐ Purchased 19___ Pd $_____ MIB NB DB BNT
☐ Want Orig. Ret. $6.00 **NB** $15 **MIB** Sec. Mkt. **$22**

QX 310-7 FIRST CHRISTMAS TOGETHER ☐

Comments: Classic Shape, 3-1/4" dia., Dated 1983.
Winter forest scene. Caption: "First Christmas Together 1983" and "All The World Is Beautiful When Seen Through Eyes Of Love."

☐ Purchased 19___ Pd $_____ MIB NB DB BNT
☐ Want Orig. Ret. $6.00 **NB** $24 **MIB** Sec. Mkt. **$40**

QX 432-9 FIRST CHRISTMAS TOGETHER ☐

Comments: Polished Brass, 2-5/8" tall, Dated 1983.
Locket opens; space for two photos. Caption: "First Christmas Together 1983." **Artist:** Ed Seale

☐ Purchased 19___ Pd $_____ MIB NB DB BNT
☐ Want Orig. Ret. $15.00 **NB** $28 **MIB** Sec. Mkt. **$40**

QX 207-7 FRIENDSHIP ☐

Comments: White Classic Glass, 3-1/4" dia., Dated 1983.
Eskimo in Christmas scenes. Caption: "Christmas 1983" and "Friendship Is A Special Gift That Gives Your Heart A Happy Lift."

☐ Purchased 19___ Pd $_____ MIB NB DB BNT
☐ Want Orig. Ret. $4.50 **NB** $15 **MIB** Sec. Mkt. **$21**

QX 305-9 FRIENDSHIP ☐

Comments: Acrylic, Classic shape, 5" tall, Dated 1983.
Caption: "Christmas 1983" and "Friendship Grows More Beautiful With Each Passing Season."

☐ Purchased 19___ Pd $_____ MIB NB DB BNT
☐ Want Orig. Ret. $6.00 **NB** $10 **MIB** Sec. Mkt. **$20**

QMB 904-7 FRIENDSHIP ☐

Comments: Musical, Classic Shape, 4-1/2" tall.
Muffin celebrates Christmas. Caption: "It's Song-in-the-Air Time, Lights-Everywhere Time, Good Fun-to-Share Time, It's Christmas." Plays "We Wish You A Merry Christmas."

☐ Purchased 19___ Pd $_____ MIB NB DB BNT
☐ Want Orig. Ret. $16.00 **NB** $80 **MIB** Sec. Mkt. **$125**

QX 400-7 FROSTY FRIENDS ☐

Comments: **Fourth in Series,** Handcrafted, 1-59/64" tall.
Dated 1983. Frosty and his baby seal rub noses as they float on an iceberg. Caption: "Merry Christmas 1983." **Artist:** Ed Seale

☐ Purchased 19___ Pd $_____ MIB NB DB BNT
☐ Want Orig. Ret. $8.00 **NB** $290 **MIB** Sec. Mkt. **$328**

QX 201-7 GODCHILD ☐

Comments: White Classical Glass, 3-1/4" dia., Dated 1983.
Angel and red bird sing a duet. Caption: "To Wish A Special Godchild A Very Merry Christmas."

☐ Purchased 19___ Pd $_____ MIB NB DB BNT
☐ Want Orig. Ret. $4.50 **NB** $10 **MIB** Sec. Mkt. **$20**

QX 430-9 GRANDCHILD'S FIRST CHRISTMAS ☐

Comments: Handcrafted, 3-3/4" long, Dated 1983.
Baby rides in a white, wicker-look buggy. Caption: "Grandchild's First Christmas 1983."

☐ Purchased 19___ Pd $_____ MIB NB DB BNT
☐ Want Orig. Ret. $14.00 **NB** $20 **MIB** Sec. Mkt. **$30**

QX 312-9　　GRANDCHILD'S FIRST CHRISTMAS

Comments:　　White Classic Shape, 3-1/4" dia., Dated 1983.
A baby and its toys. Caption: "Grandchild's First Christmas
1983" and "A Grandchild Is A Special Reason Why Christmas
Is Such A Merry Season."

☐ Purchased 19____　　Pd $_____　　MIB　NB　DB　BNT
☐ Want　　Orig. Ret. $6.00　　**NB** $19　　**MIB** Sec. Mkt. **$25**

QX 202-7　　GRANDDAUGHTER

Comments:　　White Porcelain Glass Ball, 3-1/4" dia., Dated
1983. Artwork from the Hallmark Historical Collection.
Caption: "A Granddaughter Brings Beautiful Moments And
Memories To Treasure" and "Christmas 1983."

☐ Purchased 19____　　Pd $_____　　MIB　NB　DB　BNT
☐ Want　　Orig. Ret. $4.50　　**NB** $20　　**MIB** Sec. Mkt. **$30**

QX 205-7　　GRANDMOTHER

Comments:　　White Porcelain Glass Ball, 3-1/4" dia., Dated
1983. Family in a horse-drawn sleigh with fenced farm house
in the background. Caption: "Over The River And Through
The Woods To Grandmother's House We Go... Christmas
1983."

☐ Purchased 19____　　Pd $_____　　MIB　NB　DB　BNT
☐ Want　　Orig. Ret. $4.50　　**NB** $20　　**MIB** Sec. Mkt. **$29**

QX 429-9　　GRANDPARENTS

Comments:　　Ceramic, 3" tall, Dated 1983.
White Bell. Caption: "Grandparents Are Love."

☐ Purchased 19____　　Pd $_____　　MIB　NB　DB　BNT
☐ Want　　Orig. Ret. $6.50　　**NB** $15　　**MIB** Sec. Mkt. **$23**

QX 201-9　　GRANDSON

Comments:　　Ecru Soft-Sheen Satin Ball, 3-1/4" dia., Dated
1983. A kitten and puppy play with the tree ornaments.
Caption: "Christmas 1983" and "A Grandson, Like Christmas,
Brings Joy To The Heart."

☐ Purchased 19____　　Pd $_____　　MIB　NB　DB　BNT
☐ Want　　Orig. Ret. $4.50　　**NB** $20　　**MIB** Sec. Mkt. **$30**

QX 217-7　　HERE COMES SANTA

Comments:　　Red Glass Ball, 3-1/4" dia., Dated 1983.
Four views of Santa's face. Caption: "Merry Christmas 1983."

☐ Purchased 19____　　Pd $_____　　MIB　NB　DB　BNT
☐ Want　　Orig. Ret. $4.50　　**NB** $22　　**MIB** Sec. Mkt. **$45**

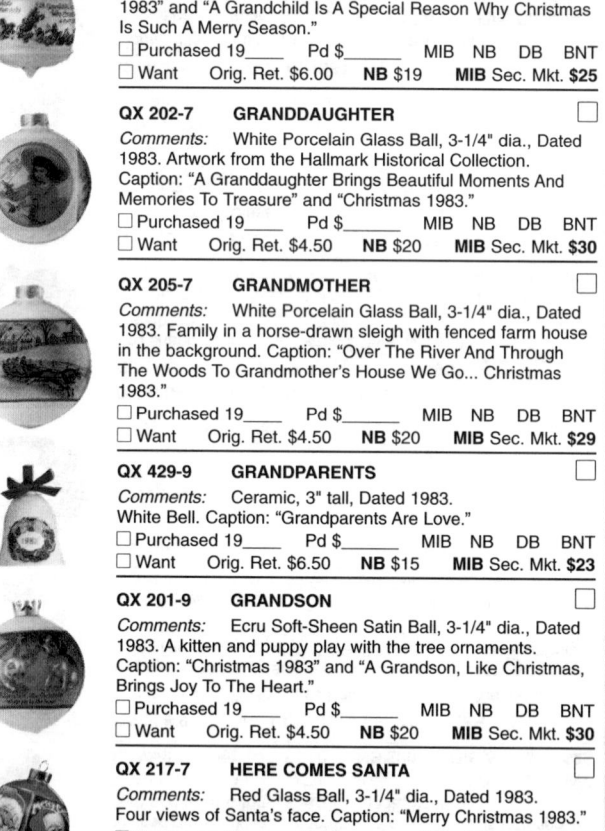

QX 403-7　　HERE COMES SANTA: SANTA EXPRESS

Comments:　　**Fifth in Series,** Handcrafted, 3-7/16" tall,
Dated 1983. Santa pumps a "wooden" railroad car with gifts.
The wheels turn. **Artist:** Donna Lee

☐ Purchased 19____　　Pd $_____　　MIB　NB　DB　BNT
☐ Want　　Orig. Ret. $13.00　　**NB** $200　　**MIB** Sec. Mkt. **$280**

QX 424-7　　HITCHHIKING SANTA

Comments:　　Handcrafted, 2-21/32" tall. Santa in sunglasses
and white shorts is holding a sign that reads "Goin' South" as
he "thumbs" a ride. **Artist:** Ed Seale

☐ Purchased 19____　　Pd $_____　　MIB　NB　DB　BNT
☐ Want　　Orig. Ret. $8.00　　**NB** $30　　**MIB** Sec. Mkt. **$40**

**QX 303-9　　HOLIDAY HIGHLIGHTS:
　　　　　　　　CHRISTMAS STOCKING**

Comments:　　Acrylic, 4" tall, Dated 1983. "Etched" argyle
Christmas stocking is filled with gifts and toys. Caption: "Merry
Christmas 1983."

☐ Purchased 19____　　Pd $_____　　MIB　NB　DB　BNT
☐ Want　　Orig. Ret. $6.00　　**NB** $30　　**MIB** Sec. Mkt. **$40**

QX 304-7　　HOLIDAY HIGHLIGHTS: STAR OF PEACE

Comments:　　Acrylic, 4" tall. A four-pointed star with "reflec-
tions" is centered in an oval shape. Caption: "Peace."
Artist: Ed Seale

☐ Purchased 19____　　Pd $_____　　MIB　NB　DB　BNT
☐ Want　　Orig. Ret. $6.00　　**NB** $12　　**MIB** Sec. Mkt. **$21**

**QX 307-7　　HOLIDAY HIGHLIGHTS:
　　　　　　　　TIME FOR SHARING**

Comments:　　Acrylic, 4" tall, Dated 1983. Mary Hamilton
scene of a little girl tying a scarf around a kitten's neck.
Caption: "Christmas Is A Time For Sharing, Smiling, Loving,
Giving, Caring."

☐ Purchased 19____　　Pd $_____　　MIB　NB　DB　BNT
☐ Want　　Orig. Ret. $6.00　　**NB** $27　　**MIB** Sec. Mkt. **$40**

QX 412-7　　HOLIDAY PUPPY

Comments:　　Handcrafted, 1-19/32" tall. Cute brown and
white puppy with black nose and ears has a red fabric bow
around its neck.

☐ Purchased 19____　　Pd $_____　　MIB　NB　DB　BNT
☐ Want　　Orig. Ret. $3.50　　**NB** $18　　**MIB** Sec. Mkt. **$30**

QX 307-9   HOLIDAY SCULPTURE: HEART ☐
Comments: Translucent Acrylic, 2" tall.
Red, three-dimensional heart. **Artist:** Linda Sickman
☐ Purchased 19___   Pd $_____   MIB NB DB BNT
☐ Want   Orig. Ret. $4.00   **NB** $39   **MIB** Sec. Mkt. **$50**

QX 308-7   HOLIDAY SCULPTURE: SANTA ☐
Comments: Translucent Red Acrylic.
Three-dimensional Santa.
☐ Purchased 19___   Pd $_____   MIB NB DB BNT
☐ Want   Orig. Ret. $4.00   **NB** $26   **MIB** Sec. Mkt. **$34**

QX 309-9   HOLIDAY WILDLIFE: CHICKADEE ☐
Comments: **Second in Series,** Decoform and Wood, 3" dia.
Dated 1983. Porcelain look insert of a chickadee on a branch.
Caption: "Black-Capped Chickadees, Parus Atricapillus" and
"Second In A Series, Wildlife Collection – Christmas 1983."
☐ Purchased 19___   Pd $_____   MIB NB DB BNT
☐ Want   Orig. Ret. $7.00   **NB** $50   **MIB** Sec. Mkt. **$60**

QX 407-9   JACK FROST ☐
Comments: Handcrafted, 3-3/4" tall.
Scrolls of frost on the window panes are evidence of Jack's
special artistry.
☐ Purchased 19___   Pd $_____   MIB NB DB BNT
☐ Want   Orig. Ret. $9.00   **NB** $50   **MIB** Sec. Mkt. **$60**

QX 425-9   JOLLY SANTA ☐
Comments: Handcrafted, 1-15/16" tall.
Merry Santa is posing with his pack of toys.
☐ Purchased 19___   Pd $_____   MIB NB DB BNT
☐ Want   Orig. Ret. $3.50   **NB** $27   **MIB** Sec. Mkt. **$35**

QX 495-6   KERMIT THE FROG™ ☐
Comments: Handcrafted, 3-9/16" tall.
Reissued from 1982. **Artist:** Donna Lee
☐ Purchased 19___   Pd $_____   MIB NB DB BNT
☐ Want   Orig. Ret. $11.00   **NB** $85   **MIB** Sec. Mkt. **$100**

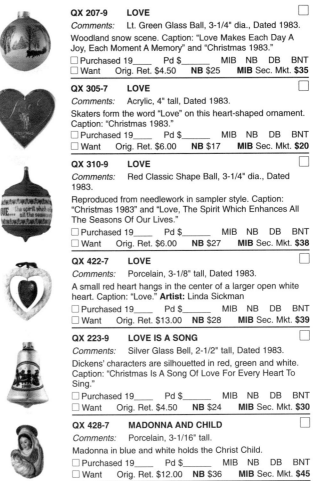

QX 207-9   LOVE ☐
Comments: Lt. Green Glass Ball, 3-1/4" dia., Dated 1983.
Woodland snow scene. Caption: "Love Makes Each Day A
Joy, Each Moment A Memory" and "Christmas 1983."
☐ Purchased 19___   Pd $_____   MIB NB DB BNT
☐ Want   Orig. Ret. $4.50   **NB** $25   **MIB** Sec. Mkt. **$35**

QX 305-7   LOVE ☐
Comments: Acrylic, 4" tall, Dated 1983.
Skaters form the word "Love" on this heart-shaped ornament.
Caption: "Christmas 1983."
☐ Purchased 19___   Pd $_____   MIB NB DB BNT
☐ Want   Orig. Ret. $6.00   **NB** $17   **MIB** Sec. Mkt. **$20**

QX 310-9   LOVE ☐
Comments: Red Classic Shape Ball, 3-1/4" dia., Dated
1983.
Reproduced from needlework in sampler style. Caption:
"Christmas 1983" and "Love, The Spirit Which Enhances All
The Seasons Of Our Lives."
☐ Purchased 19___   Pd $_____   MIB NB DB BNT
☐ Want   Orig. Ret. $6.00   **NB** $27   **MIB** Sec. Mkt. **$38**

QX 422-7   LOVE ☐
Comments: Porcelain, 3-1/8" tall, Dated 1983.
A small red heart hangs in the center of a larger open white
heart. Caption: "Love." **Artist:** Linda Sickman
☐ Purchased 19___   Pd $_____   MIB NB DB BNT
☐ Want   Orig. Ret. $13.00   **NB** $28   **MIB** Sec. Mkt. **$39**

QX 223-9   LOVE IS A SONG ☐
Comments: Silver Glass Bell, 2-1/2" tall, Dated 1983.
Dickens' characters are silhouetted in red, green and white.
Caption: "Christmas Is A Song Of Love For Every Heart To
Sing."
☐ Purchased 19___   Pd $_____   MIB NB DB BNT
☐ Want   Orig. Ret. $4.50   **NB** $24   **MIB** Sec. Mkt. **$30**

QX 428-7   MADONNA AND CHILD ☐
Comments: Porcelain, 3-1/16" tall.
Madonna in blue and white holds the Christ Child.
☐ Purchased 19___   Pd $_____   MIB NB DB BNT
☐ Want   Orig. Ret. $12.00   **NB** $36   **MIB** Sec. Mkt. **$45**

QX 415-7   MAILBOX KITTEN

Comments: Handcrafted, 1-9/16" tall, Dated 1983.
A kitten with letters in its paws peeks out of a red mailbox reading "1983 Peppermint Lane."

☐ Purchased 19____   Pd $_____   MIB   NB   DB   BNT
☐ Want   Orig. Ret. $6.50   **NB** $49   **MIB** Sec. Mkt. **$62**

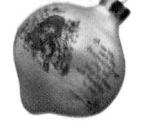

QX 213-7   MARY HAMILTON

Comments: White Classical Glass, 3-1/2" tall, Dated 1983.
A little girl prays with forest creatures. Caption: "A Wee Little, Warm Little Christmas Time Prayer – May God bless us always with friendships to share."

☐ Purchased 19____   Pd $_____   MIB   NB   DB   BNT
☐ Want   Orig. Ret. $4.50   **NB** $48   **MIB** Sec. Mkt. **$60**

QX 405-7   MISS PIGGY™

Comments: Handcrafted, 4-9/16" tall.
Dressed in a lavender skating costume, Miss Piggy leaps gracefully on her ice skates.

☐ Purchased 19____   Pd $_____   MIB   NB   DB   BNT
☐ Want   Orig. Ret. $13.00   **NB** $175   **MIB** Sec. Mkt. **$200**

QX 429-7   MOM & DAD

Comments: Ceramic Bell, 3" tall, Dated 1983.
Fired-on decals of poinsettias and holly frame the captions: "Mom and Dad" and "Christmas 1983." **Artist:** Sharon Pike

☐ Purchased 19____   Pd $_____   MIB   NB   DB   BNT
☐ Want   Orig. Ret. $6.50   **NB** $16   **MIB** Sec. Mkt. **$25**

QX 306-7   MOTHER

Comments: Acrylic, 4" tall, Dated 1983.
Heart-shaped design with white "etched" border carries the caption: "Mother... Always Caring, Always Sharing, Always There To Love."

☐ Purchased 19____   Pd $_____   MIB   NB   DB   BNT
☐ Want   Orig. Ret. $6.00   **NB** $14   **MIB** Sec. Mkt. **$20**

MDQ 340-7   MOTHER'S DAY – A MOTHER'S LOVE

Comments: Musical; White Glass Classical Ball.
Plays "Swan Lake."

☐ Purchased 19____   Pd $_____   MIB   NB   DB   BNT
☐ Want   Orig. Ret. $14.00   **NB** $25   **MIB** Sec. Mkt. **$40**

QX 407-7   MOUNTAIN CLIMBING SANTA

Comments: Handcrafted, 2-13/32" tall, Reissued in 1984.
Santa scales the cliffs using a real rope. **Artist:** Ed Seale

☐ Purchased 19____   Pd $_____   MIB   NB   DB   BNT
☐ Want   Orig. Ret. $6.50   **NB** $29   **MIB** Sec. Mkt. **$40**

QX 419-7   MOUSE IN BELL

Comments: Handcrafted-Glass, 4" tall.
A cute mouse with a leather tail and a brass ring in the top of his stocking cap is the "clapper" for this clear glass bell.

☐ Purchased 19____   Pd $_____   MIB   NB   DB   BNT
☐ Want   Orig. Ret. $10.00   **NB** $50   **MIB** Sec. Mkt. **$65**

QX 413-7   MOUSE ON CHEESE

Comments: Handcrafted, 2-37/64" tall.
An adorable gray mouse enjoys the gift-wrapped cheese on which he's sitting. **Artist:** Linda Sickman

☐ Purchased 19____   Pd $_____   MIB   NB   DB   BNT
☐ Want   Orig. Ret. $6.50   **NB** $40   **MIB** Sec. Mkt. **$50**

QX 214-7   MUPPETS™, THE

Comments: Lt. Blue Satin Ball, 3-1/4" dia., Dated 1983.
Kermit and Miss Piggy are in a biplane skywriting "Merry Christmas" while Fozzie floats in a hot air balloon.

☐ Purchased 19____   Pd $_____   MIB   NB   DB   BNT
☐ Want   Orig. Ret. $4.50   **NB** $40   **MIB** Sec. Mkt. **$50**

QMB 904-9   NATIVITY

Comments: Musical, Classic Shape, Dark Blue, 4-1/2" tall.
Three Kings bring gifts for the Holy Child. Caption: "The star shone bright with a holy light as heaven came to earth that night." Plays "Silent Night."

☐ Purchased 19____   Pd $_____   MIB   NB   DB   BNT
☐ Want   Orig. Ret. $16.00   **NB** $70   **MIB** Sec. Mkt. **$120**

QX 210-7   NEW HOME

Comments: White Soft-Sheen Satin Ball, 3-1/4" dia.
Dated 1983. Carolers spread Christmas cheer on a snowy night. Caption: "Christmas Is The Perfect Way Of Rounding Out Each Year, For Every Heart And Home's Aglow With Love And Warmth And Cheer."

☐ Purchased 19____   Pd $_____   MIB   NB   DB   BNT
☐ Want   Orig. Ret. $4.50   **NB** $29   **MIB** Sec. Mkt. **$33**

QX 215-7   NORMAN ROCKWELL   ☐
Comments: Light Green Glass Ball, 3-1/4" dia., Dated 1983.
Caption: "Things Are Humming, Santa's Coming, Hearts Are
Full Of Cheer. Lights Are Gleaming, Kids Are Dreaming...
Christmas Time Is Here." From the Norman Rockwell
Collection.

☐ Purchased 19____   Pd $_____   MIB NB DB BNT
☐ Want   Orig. Ret. $4.50   **NB** $40   **MIB** Sec. Mkt. **$50**

QX 300-7   NORMAN ROCKWELL SERIES   ☐
Comments: **Fourth in Series,** Dark Blue Cameo, 3" dia.
Dated 1983. Caption: "Dress Rehearsal. Fourth In A Series.
Christmas 1983." The Norman Rockwell Collection.

☐ Purchased 19____   Pd $_____   MIB NB DB BNT
☐ Want   Orig. Ret. $7.50   **NB** $29   **MIB** Sec. Mkt. **$35**

QX 409-9   OLD-FASHIONED SANTA   ☐
Comments: Handcrafted, 5-9/64" tall.
Jointed, realistic interpretation. Santa wears a knee-length red
suit with red and white striped hose. His arms and legs are
moveable. **Artist:** Linda Sickman

☐ Purchased 19____   Pd $_____   MIB NB DB BNT
☐ Want   Orig. Ret. $11.00   **NB** $50   **MIB** Sec. Mkt. **$65**

QX 218-7   ORIENTAL BUTTERFLIES   ☐
Comments: Turquoise Glass Ball, 3-1/4" dia.
Eight colorful butterflies; reproduced from original stitchery.

☐ Purchased 19____   Pd $_____   MIB NB DB BNT
☐ Want   Orig. Ret. $4.50   **NB** $25   **MIB** Sec. Mkt. **$30**

QX 212-7   PEANUTS®   ☐
Comments: White Soft-Sheen Satin Ball, 3-1/4" dia.
Dated 1983. Comic strip panels show Snoopy bringing
Woodstock and his friends out of the cold. Caption:
"Christmas 1983" and "May The Joy Of The Season Warm
Every Heart."

☐ Purchased 19____   Pd $_____   MIB NB DB BNT
☐ Want   Orig. Ret. $4.50   **NB** $27   **MIB** Sec. Mkt. **$38**

QX 408-9   PEPPERMINT PENGUIN   ☐
Comments: Handcrafted, 2-3/4" tall.
A red capped penguin pedals his "peppermint candy" unicycle.

☐ Purchased 19____   Pd $_____   MIB NB DB BNT
☐ Want   Orig. Ret. $6.50   **NB** $38   **MIB** Sec. Mkt. **$45**

QX 428-9   PORCELAIN BEAR: CINNAMON TEDDY   ☐
Comments: **FIRST IN SERIES,** Porcelain, 2-15/64" tall.
Made of fine porcelain and hand painted.
Artist: Peter Dutkin

☐ Purchased 19____   Pd $_____   MIB NB DB BNT
☐ Want   Orig. Ret. $7.00   **NB** $60   **MIB** Sec. Mkt. **$90**

QX 416-7   RAINBOW ANGEL   ☐
Comments: Handcrafted, 2-15/16" tall.
Angel with a brass halo slides down a rainbow. Trading
increase seen on this ornament. **Artist:** Donna Lee

☐ Purchased 19____   Pd $_____   MIB NB DB BNT
☐ Want   Orig. Ret. $5.50   **NB** $95   **MIB** Sec. Mkt. **$125**

QX 417-7   ROCKING HORSE   ☐
Comments: **Third in Series,** Handcrafted, 2-7/8" tall.
Dated 1983. Russet horse with green rockers. **Artist:** Linda
Sickman

☐ Purchased 19____   Pd $_____   MIB NB DB BNT
☐ Want   Orig. Ret. $10.00   **NB** $215   **MIB** Sec. Mkt. **$300**

QX 311-7   SANTA'S MANY FACES   ☐
Comments: Red Classic Shape Ball, 3-1/4" dia., Dated 1983.
Six Santa scenes circle the ornament. Caption: "Merry
Christmas."

☐ Purchased 19____   Pd $_____   MIB NB DB BNT
☐ Want   Orig. Ret. $6.00   **NB** $25   **MIB** Sec. Mkt. **$30**

QX 426-9   SANTA'S ON HIS WAY   ☐
Comments: Handcrafted, 3" tall.
Four handcrafted openings show Santa in three-dimensional,
handpainted scenes.

☐ Purchased 19____   Pd $_____   MIB NB DB BNT
☐ Want   Orig. Ret. $10.00   **NB** $20   **MIB** Sec. Mkt. **$35**

QX 450-3   SANTA'S WORKSHOP   ☐
Comments: Handcrafted, 3" tall. Reissued from 1982..
Artist: Donna Lee

☐ Purchased 19____   Pd $_____   MIB NB DB BNT
☐ Want   Orig. Ret. $10.00   **NB** $67   **MIB** Sec. Mkt. **$90**

QX 424-9   SCRIMSHAW REINDEER ☐

Comments: Handcrafted, 3-3/4" tall.
The leaping reindeer was created with the look of handcarved ivory scrimshaw accented in brown. **Artist:** Ed Seale
☐ Purchased 19___   Pd $_____   MIB   NB   DB   BNT
☐ Want   Orig. Ret. $8.00   **NB** $24   **MIB** Sec. Mkt. **$35**

QX 219-9   SEASON'S GREETINGS ☐

Comments: Chrome Glass Ball, 3-1/4" dia.
The caption, "Season's Greetings," is formed with neon lettering on a dark background.
☐ Purchased 19___   Pd $_____   MIB   NB   DB   BNT
☐ Want   Orig. Ret. $4.50   **NB** $17   **MIB** Sec. Mkt. **$24**

QX 214-9   SHIRT TALES™ ☐

Comments: White Classical Glass, 3-1/2" tall, Dated 1983.
A walrus, penguin and polar bear wear t-shirts that say, "Deck the Halls" and "Fa La-La-La-La." Caption: "Christmas 1983" and "Tis The Season To Be Jolly."
☐ Purchased 19___   Pd $_____   MIB   NB   DB   BNT
☐ Want   Orig. Ret. $4.50   **NB** $20   **MIB** Sec. Mkt. **$25**

OX 110-9   SILVER BELL ☐

Comments: Silverplated.
Came with red ribbon; made for J. C. Penney.
☐ Purchased 19___   Pd $_____   MIB   NB   DB   BNT
☐ Want   Orig. Ret. $12.00   **NB** $20   **MIB** Sec. Mkt. **$40**

QX 206-9   SISTER ☐

Comments: White Classical Glass, 3-1/4" dia., Dated 1983.
Wreath frames the caption: "A Sister Is A Forever Friend."
☐ Purchased 19___   Pd $_____   MIB   NB   DB   BNT
☐ Want   Orig. Ret. $4.50   **NB** $20   **MIB** Sec. Mkt. **$23**

QX 409-7   SKATING RABBIT ☐

Comments: Handcrafted, 3-1/4" tall.
This happy rabbit has a real cotton tail and a specially designed stocking cap which covers each ear separately.
☐ Purchased 19___   Pd $_____   MIB   NB   DB   BNT
☐ Want   Orig. Ret. $8.00   **NB** $42   **MIB** Sec. Mkt. **$56**

QX 418-7   SKI LIFT SANTA ☐

Comments: Handcrafted-Brass, 3-7/8" tall, Dated 1983.
Santa waves as he rides the ski lift. A brass bell is the pom-pon for his hat. Date is on his ski lift ticket. All boxes were printed Santa Ski Lift. No added value for this imprinting on the box.
☐ Purchased 19___   Pd $_____   MIB   NB   DB   BNT
☐ Want   Orig. Ret. $8.00   **NB** $57   **MIB** Sec. Mkt. **$72**

QX 420-7   SKIING FOX ☐

Comments: Handcrafted, 2-5/32" tall.
A fox with a green muffler is showing great form as he races downhill. **Artist:** Donna Lee
☐ Purchased 19___   Pd $_____   MIB   NB   DB   BNT
☐ Want   Orig. Ret. $8.00   **NB** $30   **MIB** Sec. Mkt. **$40**

QX 400-9   SNEAKER MOUSE ☐

Comments: Handcrafted, 1-11/16" tall.
A cute white mouse has made his bed in a red and white sneaker. **Artist:** Ed Seale
☐ Purchased 19___   Pd $_____   MIB   NB   DB   BNT
☐ Want   Orig. Ret. $4.50   **NB** $27   **MIB** Sec. Mkt. **$40**

QX 416-9   SNOOPY AND FRIENDS ☐

Comments: **Fifth in Series,** Handcrafted Panorama Ball. 3-1/4" dia., Dated 1983. Snoopy is dressed as Santa and delivers a bag of gifts to Woodstock. **Artist:** Linda Sickman
☐ Purchased 19___   Pd $_____   MIB   NB   DB   BNT
☐ Want   Orig. Ret. $13.00   **NB** $89   **MIB** Sec. Mkt. **$100**

QX 202-9   SON ☐

Comments: Deep Blue Satin Ball, 3-1/4" dia., Dated 1983.
A little boy, house, Christmas trees and a snowman riding a snowhorse are depicted. Caption: "A Son Brings A Bit Of Christmas Cheer To Every Day Throughout The Year."
☐ Purchased 19___   Pd $_____   MIB   NB   DB   BNT
☐ Want   Orig. Ret. $4.50   **NB** $30   **MIB** Sec. Mkt. **$40**

QHD 406-9   ST. NICHOLAS ☐

Comments: Porcelain Table Decoration.
An Old-World Santa makes his rounds on Christmas Eve with his pack of toys and a walking stick.
☐ Purchased 19___   Pd $_____   MIB   NB   DB   BNT
☐ Want   Orig. Ret. $27.50   **NB** $84   **MIB** Sec. Mkt. **$100**

QX 224-9   TEACHER ☐

Comments: Silver Glass Bell, 2-1/2" tall, Dated 1983.
Schoolhouse and red and green lettering are bordered with
green bands. Caption: "For a Special Teacher at Christmas."

☐ Purchased 19____   Pd $_____   MIB   NB   DB   BNT
☐ Want   Orig. Ret. $4.50   **NB** $10   **MIB** Sec. Mkt. **$15**

QX 304-9   TEACHER ☐

Comments: Acrylic, 3-3/4" tall, Dated 1983. A classic shape
design shows a raccoon writing the caption: "Merry
Christmas, Merry Christmas, Merry Christmas, Teacher!"

☐ Purchased 19____   Pd $_____   MIB   NB   DB   BNT
☐ Want   Orig. Ret. $6.00   **NB** $11   **MIB** Sec. Mkt. **$17**

QX 430-7   TENTH CHRISTMAS TOGETHER ☐

Comments: Ceramic Bell, 3" tall, Dated 1983. White ceramic bell is decorated with a golden French horn and hung with
red fabric ribbon. Caption: "Tenth Christmas Together 1983."

☐ Purchased 19____   Pd $_____   MIB   NB   DB   BNT
☐ Want   Orig. Ret. $6.50   **NB** $14   **MIB** Sec. Mkt. **$25**

QX 401-7   THIMBLE SERIES: THIMBLE ELF ☐

Comments: **Sixth in Series,** Handcrafted, 1-15/16" tall.
A little elf is licking his lips over a cherry-topped treat served
in a thimble.

☐ Purchased 19____   Pd $_____   MIB   NB   DB   BNT
☐ Want   Orig. Ret. $5.00   **NB-P** $29   **MIB** Sec. Mkt. **$40**

QX 404-9   TIN LOCOMOTIVE ☐

Comments: **Second in Series,** Pressed Tin, 3" tall, Dated
1983. This early locomotive is lithographed in red and green
and trimmed in gold. **Artist:** Linda Sickman

☐ Purchased 19____   Pd $_____   MIB   NB   DB   BNT
☐ Want   Orig. Ret. $13.00   **NB** $240   **MIB** Sec. Mkt. **$300**

QX 414-9   TIN ROCKING HORSE ☐

Comments: Pressed Tin, 3-11/64" tall. This three-dimensional lithographed tin rocking horse is a dappled gray and
resembles an Early American nursery toy. **Artist:** Linda
Sickman

☐ Purchased 19____   Pd $_____   MIB   NB   DB   BNT
☐ Want   Orig. Ret. $6.50   **NB** $44   **MIB** Sec. Mkt. **$50**

QMB 415-9   TWELVE DAYS OF CHRISTMAS MUSICAL ☐

Comments: Musical, Handcrafted, 3-3/4" tall. Reissued in
1984. Blue and white motifs of the song. Plays "Twelve Days
of Christmas." **Artist:** Ed Seale

☐ Purchased 19____   Pd $_____   MIB   NB   DB   BNT
☐ Want   Orig. Ret. $15.00   **NB** $95   **MIB** Sec. Mkt. **$130**

QX 224-7   TWENTY-FIFTH CHRISTMAS TOGETHER ☐

Comments: Silver Glass Bell, 2-1/2" tall, Dated 1983.
Bell with red print and white snowflakes.
Caption: "25th Christmas Together."

☐ Purchased 19____   Pd $_____   MIB   NB   DB   BNT
☐ Want   Orig. Ret. $4.50   **NB** $15   **MIB** Sec. Mkt. **$20**

QX 426-7   UNICORN ☐

Comments: Porcelain, 4" tall. Beautiful white porcelain
prancing unicorn has hand painted gold trim. Don't confuse
this with QX 429-3, 1986 Magical Unicorn.

☐ Purchased 19____   Pd $_____   MIB   NB   DB   BNT
☐ Want   Orig. Ret. $10.00   **NB** $50   **MIB** Sec. Mkt. **$65**

QX 220-7   WISE MEN, THE ☐

Comments: Gold Glass Ball, 3-1/4" dia.
Three kings raise their gifts to the star leading them.

☐ Purchased 19____   Pd $_____   MIB   NB   DB   BNT
☐ Want   Orig. Ret. $4.50   **NB** $46   **MIB** Sec. Mkt. **$60**

1984 Collection

QX 246-1   A CHRISTMAS PRAYER ☐

Comments: Blue Satin Ball, 2-7/8" dia. Mary Hamilton's
angels chase stars. Caption: "Little Prayer Be On Your Way...
Bless Our Friends On Christmas Day."

☐ Purchased 19____   Pd $_____   MIB   NB   DB   BNT
☐ Want   Orig. Ret. $4.50   **NB** $15   **MIB** Sec. Mkt. **$22**

QX 260-4   A GIFT OF FRIENDSHIP ☐

Comments: Peach Glass Ball, 3" dia. Scenes of Muffin and
her kitten. Caption: "Friendship Is The Happiest Gift Of All."

☐ Purchased 19____   Pd $_____   MIB   NB   DB   BNT
☐ Want   Orig. Ret. $4.50   **NB** $17   **MIB** Sec. Mkt. **$23**

QX 254-1   A SAVIOR IS BORN ☐

Comments: Purple Glass Ball, 2-7/8" dia. The Nativity flanks the caption which is printed in large gold lettering: "For Unto You Is Born This Day In The City Of David A Savior Which Is Christ The Lord. Luke 2:11."

☐ Purchased 19____   Pd $_____   MIB NB DB BNT
☐ Want   Orig. Ret. $4.50   **NB** $23   **MIB** Sec. Mkt. **$35**

QLX 704-4   ALL ARE PRECIOUS ☐

Comments: Lighted Acrylic, 4" tall, Reissued in 1985. A Shepherd, lamb and donkey watch the star. Caption in gold foil stamp: "All Are Precious In His Sight..."

☐ Purchased 19____   Pd $_____   MIB NB DB BNT
☐ Want   Orig. Ret. $8.00   **NB** $20   **MIB** Sec. Mkt. **$25**

QX 452-1   ALPINE ELF ☐

Comments: Handcrafted, 3-1/2" wide. A little elf, dressed in a red coat and hat, plays a long curved horn. **Artist:** Ed Seale

☐ Purchased 19____   Pd $_____   MIB NB DB BNT
☐ Want   Orig. Ret. $6.00   **NB** $33   **MIB** Sec. Mkt. **$40**

QX 432-1   AMANDA DOLL ☐

Comments: Fabric, Handpainted Porcelain, 4-3/4" tall. This doll is wearing a bright green ruffled dress and bonnet.

☐ Purchased 19____   Pd $_____   MIB NB DB BNT
☐ Want   Orig. Ret. $9.00   **NB** $25   **MIB** Sec. Mkt. **$30**

QTT 710-1   ANGEL TREE TOPPER ☐

Comments: Fabric and Porcelain. Golden accents on her wings and gown add to the charm of this lovely angel.

☐ Purchased 19____   Pd $_____   MIB NB DB BNT
☐ Want   Orig. Ret. $24.50   **NB** $30   **MIB** Sec. Mkt. **$40**

QX 349-4   ART MASTERPIECE ☐

Comments: **FIRST IN SERIES,** Bezeled Satin, 2-3/4" dia. Classic oil painting reproduced on padded satin. "Giuliano Bugiardini, Madonna And Child And St. John, (ca. 1505) The Nelson-Atkins Museum Of Art, Kansas City, Missouri (Nelson Fund)." **Artist:** Diana McGehee

☐ Purchased 19____   Pd $_____   MIB NB DB BNT
☐ Want   Orig. Ret. $6.50   **NB** $10   **MIB** Sec. Mkt. **$20**

QX 340-1   BABY'S FIRST CHRISTMAS ☐

Comments: Acrylic, 3-3/4" tall, Dated 1984. This etched teddy bear is holding a toy-filled stocking. Caption: "Baby's First Christmas."

☐ Purchased 19____   Pd $_____   MIB NB DB BNT
☐ Want   Orig. Ret. $6.00   **NB** $30   **MIB** Sec. Mkt. **$40**

QX 438-1   BABY'S FIRST CHRISTMAS ☐

Comments: Handcrafted, 3-1/2" wide, Dated 1984. A brown bear rides a sled full of toys. Caption: "Baby's First Christmas."

☐ Purchased 19____   Pd $_____   MIB NB DB BNT
☐ Want   Orig. Ret. $14.00   **NB** $35   **MIB** Sec. Mkt. **$50**

QX 240-4   BABY'S FIRST CHRISTMAS – BOY ☐

Comments: White Satin Ball, 2-7/8" dia., Dated 1984. A handcrafted mouse sits on top of the ornament. Caption: "Baby's First Christmas" and "A Baby Boy Is A Bundle Of Pleasure To Fill Every day With Love Beyond Measure."

☐ Purchased 19____   Pd $_____   MIB NB DB BNT
☐ Want   Orig. Ret. $4.50   **NB** $20   **MIB** Sec. Mkt. **$30**

QX 240-1   BABY'S FIRST CHRISTMAS – GIRL ☐

Comments: Cream Satin Ball, 2-7/8" dia., Dated 1984. A parade of little girls, animals and toys. Caption: "A Baby Girl Is Love That Grows In The Warmth Of Caring Hearts. Baby's First Christmas."

☐ Purchased 19____   Pd $_____   MIB NB DB BNT
☐ Want   Orig. Ret. $4.50   **NB** $20   **MIB** Sec. Mkt. **$28**

QX 904-1   BABY'S FIRST CHRISTMAS ☐

Comments: Musical, Classic Shape, 4-1/4" tall, Dated 1984. "A Baby Is... Happiness, Pleasure, A Gift From Above... A Wonderful, Magical Treasure Of Love. Baby's First Christmas." Plays "Babes In Toyland." **Artist:** Donna Lee

☐ Purchased 19____   Pd $_____   MIB NB DB BNT
☐ Want   Orig. Ret. $16.00   **NB** $35   **MIB** Sec. Mkt. **$50**

QX 300-1   BABY'S FIRST CHRISTMAS PHOTOHOLDER ☐

Comments: Fabric, 3-1/4" dia., Dated 1984. Embroidered holly sprigs with a white fabric photoholder. Caption: "Baby's First Christmas" and "A Baby Is A Special Dream Come True."

☐ Purchased 19____   Pd $_____   MIB NB DB BNT
☐ Want   Orig. Ret. $7.00   **NB** $17   **MIB** Sec. Mkt. **$20**

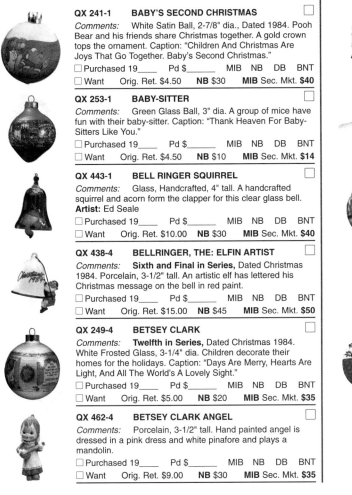

QX 241-1 BABY'S SECOND CHRISTMAS ☐
Comments: White Satin Ball, 2-7/8" dia., Dated 1984. Pooh Bear and his friends share Christmas together. A gold crown tops the ornament. Caption: "Children And Christmas Are Joys That Go Together. Baby's Second Christmas."

☐ Purchased 19____ Pd $_____ MIB NB DB BNT
☐ Want Orig. Ret. $4.50 **NB** $30 **MIB** Sec. Mkt. **$40**

QX 253-1 BABY-SITTER ☐
Comments: Green Glass Ball, 3" dia. A group of mice have fun with their baby-sitter. Caption: "Thank Heaven For Baby-Sitters Like You."

☐ Purchased 19____ Pd $_____ MIB NB DB BNT
☐ Want Orig. Ret. $4.50 **NB** $10 **MIB** Sec. Mkt. **$14**

QX 443-1 BELL RINGER SQUIRREL ☐
Comments: Glass, Handcrafted, 4" tall. A handcrafted squirrel and acorn form the clapper for this clear glass bell. **Artist:** Ed Seale

☐ Purchased 19____ Pd $_____ MIB NB DB BNT
☐ Want Orig. Ret. $10.00 **NB** $30 **MIB** Sec. Mkt. **$40**

QX 438-4 BELLRINGER, THE: ELFIN ARTIST ☐
Comments: **Sixth and Final in Series,** Dated Christmas 1984. Porcelain, 3-1/2" tall. An artistic elf has lettered his Christmas message on the bell in red paint.

☐ Purchased 19____ Pd $_____ MIB NB DB BNT
☐ Want Orig. Ret. $15.00 **NB** $45 **MIB** Sec. Mkt. **$50**

QX 249-4 BETSEY CLARK ☐
Comments: **Twelfth in Series,** Dated Christmas 1984. White Frosted Glass, 3-1/4" dia. Children decorate their homes for the holidays. Caption: "Days Are Merry, Hearts Are Light, And All The World's A Lovely Sight."

☐ Purchased 19____ Pd $_____ MIB NB DB BNT
☐ Want Orig. Ret. $5.00 **NB** $20 **MIB** Sec. Mkt. **$35**

QX 462-4 BETSEY CLARK ANGEL ☐
Comments: Porcelain, 3-1/2" tall. Hand painted angel is dressed in a pink dress and white pinafore and plays a mandolin.

☐ Purchased 19____ Pd $_____ MIB NB DB BNT
☐ Want Orig. Ret. $9.00 **NB** $30 **MIB** Sec. Mkt. **$35**

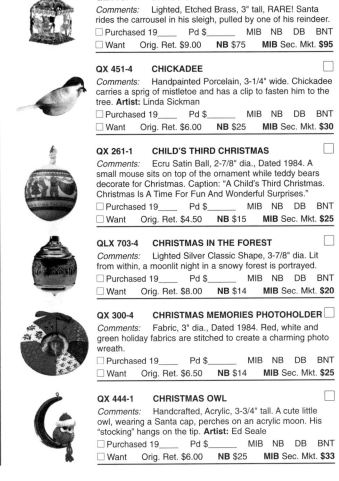

QLX 707-1 BRASS CARROUSEL ☐
Comments: Lighted, Etched Brass, 3" tall, RARE! Santa rides the carrousel in his sleigh, pulled by one of his reindeer.

☐ Purchased 19____ Pd $_____ MIB NB DB BNT
☐ Want Orig. Ret. $9.00 **NB** $75 **MIB** Sec. Mkt. **$95**

QX 451-4 CHICKADEE ☐
Comments: Handpainted Porcelain, 3-1/4" wide. Chickadee carries a sprig of mistletoe and has a clip to fasten him to the tree. **Artist:** Linda Sickman

☐ Purchased 19____ Pd $_____ MIB NB DB BNT
☐ Want Orig. Ret. $6.00 **NB** $25 **MIB** Sec. Mkt. **$30**

QX 261-1 CHILD'S THIRD CHRISTMAS ☐
Comments: Ecru Satin Ball, 2-7/8" dia., Dated 1984. A small mouse sits on top of the ornament while teddy bears decorate for Christmas. Caption: "A Child's Third Christmas. Christmas Is A Time For Fun And Wonderful Surprises."

☐ Purchased 19____ Pd $_____ MIB NB DB BNT
☐ Want Orig. Ret. $4.50 **NB** $15 **MIB** Sec. Mkt. **$25**

QLX 703-4 CHRISTMAS IN THE FOREST ☐
Comments: Lighted Silver Classic Shape, 3-7/8" dia. Lit from within, a moonlit night in a snowy forest is portrayed.

☐ Purchased 19____ Pd $_____ MIB NB DB BNT
☐ Want Orig. Ret. $8.00 **NB** $14 **MIB** Sec. Mkt. **$20**

QX 300-4 CHRISTMAS MEMORIES PHOTOHOLDER ☐
Comments: Fabric, 3" dia., Dated 1984. Red, white and green holiday fabrics are stitched to create a charming photo wreath.

☐ Purchased 19____ Pd $_____ MIB NB DB BNT
☐ Want Orig. Ret. $6.50 **NB** $14 **MIB** Sec. Mkt. **$25**

QX 444-1 CHRISTMAS OWL ☐
Comments: Handcrafted, Acrylic, 3-3/4" tall. A cute little owl, wearing a Santa cap, perches on an acrylic moon. His "stocking" hangs on the tip. **Artist:** Ed Seale

☐ Purchased 19____ Pd $_____ MIB NB DB BNT
☐ Want Orig. Ret. $6.00 **NB** $25 **MIB** Sec. Mkt. **$33**

QLX 701-4 CITY LIGHTS ☐

Comments: Lighted, Handcrafted, 3-1/2" tall. Santa and a squirrel are perched atop a four-way signal light which illuminates an animal. **Artist:** Bob Siedler

☐ Purchased 19____ Pd $_____ MIB NB DB BNT
☐ Want Orig. Ret. $10.00 **NB** $29 **MIB** Sec. Mkt. **$43**

QX 459-1 CLASSICAL ANGEL ☐

Comments: Limited Edition. 24,700, Handpainted Porcelain. 5" tall, Wood display stand, Dated 1984. In a gown of pink, yellow and white, this angel carries a chain of brass bells. **Artist:** Donna Lee

☐ Purchased 19____ Pd $_____ MIB NB DB BNT
☐ Want Orig. Ret. $27.50 **NB**/No Stand $30
MIB Sec. Mkt. **$50**

QX 447-1 CLOTHESPIN SOLDIER: CANADIAN MOUNTIE ☐

Comments: **Third in Series,** Handcrafted, 2-1/2" tall. Dressed in a red and black uniform, this little soldier carries a holiday flag. **Artist:** Linda Sickman

☐ Purchased 19____ Pd $_____ MIB NB DB BNT
☐ Want Orig. Ret. $5.00 **NB** $22 **MIB** Sec. Mkt. **$30**

QX 455-1 CUCKOO CLOCK ☐

Comments: Handcrafted, 3-1/4" tall. This intricately detailed clock, complete with pinecone pendulums, has a brass face with the time spelling out "Merry Christmas." The box for this ornament quotes the name as "Old-World Cuckoo clock". **Artist:** Donna Lee

☐ Purchased 19____ Pd $_____ MIB NB DB BNT
☐ Want Orig. Ret. $10.00 **NB** $40 **MIB** Sec. Mkt. **$50**

QX 250-1 CURRIER & IVES ☐

Comments: White Blown Glass Ball, 2-7/8" dia., Dated 1984. Caption: "American Winter Scenes, Evening, Christmas 1984."

☐ Purchased 19____ Pd $_____ MIB NB DB BNT
☐ Want Orig. Ret. $4.50 **NB** $15 **MIB** Sec. Mkt. **$23**

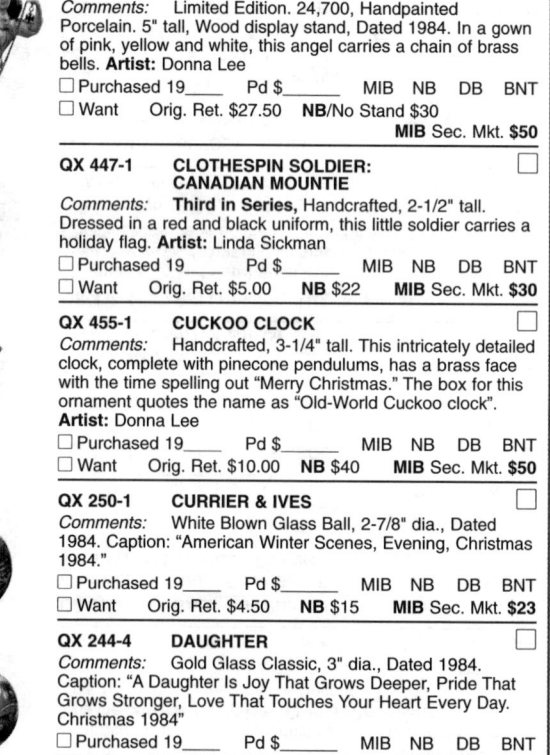

QX 244-4 DAUGHTER ☐

Comments: Gold Glass Classic, 3" dia., Dated 1984. Caption: "A Daughter Is Joy That Grows Deeper, Pride That Grows Stronger, Love That Touches Your Heart Every Day. Christmas 1984"

☐ Purchased 19____ Pd $_____ MIB NB DB BNT
☐ Want Orig. Ret. $4.50 **NB** $20 **MIB** Sec. Mkt. **$34**

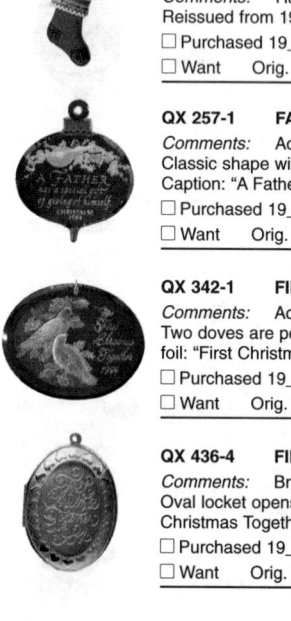

QX 250-4 DISNEY ☐

Comments: White Glass Ball, 2-7/8" dia., Dated 1984. The whole Disney gang sends Christmas greetings: "Friends Put The Merry In Christmas."

☐ Purchased 19____ Pd $_____ MIB NB DB BNT
☐ Want Orig. Ret. $4.50 **NB** $35 **MIB** Sec. Mkt. **$43**

QX 421-7 EMBROIDERED HEART ☐

Comments: Hand-Embroidered Fabric, 4-3/4" tall. Reissued from 1983.

☐ Purchased 19____ Pd $_____ MIB NB DB BNT
☐ Want Orig. Ret. $6.50 **NB** $22 **MIB** Sec. Mkt. **$28**

QX 479-6 EMBROIDERED STOCKING ☐

Comments: Hand-Embroidered Fabric, 3-1/4" tall. Reissued from 1983. **Artist:** Linda Sickman

☐ Purchased 19____ Pd $_____ MIB NB DB BNT
☐ Want Orig. Ret. $6.50 **NB** $20 **MIB** Sec. Mkt. **$25**

QX 257-1 FATHER ☐

Comments: Acrylic, 3-1/4" wide, Dated Christmas 1984. Classic shape with musical instruments and holly at the top. Caption: "A Father Has A Special Gift Of Giving Of Himself."

☐ Purchased 19____ Pd $_____ MIB NB DB BNT
☐ Want Orig. Ret. $6.00 **NB** $12 **MIB** Sec. Mkt. **$20**

QX 342-1 FIRST CHRISTMAS TOGETHER ☐

Comments: Acrylic, 3-5/8" dia., Dated 1984. Two doves are perched on a holly branch. Caption in silver foil: "First Christmas Together."

☐ Purchased 19____ Pd $_____ MIB NB DB BNT
☐ Want Orig. Ret. $6.00 **NB** $10 **MIB** Sec. Mkt. **$14**

QX 436-4 FIRST CHRISTMAS TOGETHER ☐

Comments: Brushed Brass, 2-1/2" tall, Dated 1984. Oval locket opens to hold two photos. Caption: "First Christmas Together" framed by hearts. **Artist:** Ed Seale

☐ Purchased 19____ Pd $_____ MIB NB DB BNT
☐ Want Orig. Ret. $15.00 **NB** $30 **MIB** Sec. Mkt. **$40**

QX 340-4   FIRST CHRISTMAS TOGETHER ☐

Comments: Cameo, 3-1/4" dia., Dated 1984. A couple waltz against a blue background. Caption: "Each Moment Spent Together Is A Special Celebration" and "First Christmas Together." **Artist:** Diana McGehee

☐ Purchased 19____   Pd $_____   MIB   NB   DB   BNT
☐ Want   Orig. Ret. $7.50   **NB** $20   **MIB** Sec. Mkt. **$30**

QX 904-4   FIRST CHRISTMAS TOGETHER ☐

Comments: Musical, Classic Shape, 4" tall, Dated 1984. Reindeer prance across a deep blue background to the tune of "Lara's Theme." Caption: "First Christmas Together." **Artist:** Diana McGehee

☐ Purchased 19____   Pd $_____   MIB   NB   DB   BNT
☐ Want   Orig. Ret. $16.00   **NB** $20   **MIB** Sec. Mkt. **$30**

QX 245-1   FIRST CHRISTMAS TOGETHER ☐

Comments: Silver Glass Ball, 3" dia., Dated 1984. Holiday birds, flowers and greenery create a contemporary pattern. Caption: "Love... A Joy For all Seasons. First Christmas Together."

☐ Purchased 19____   Pd $_____   MIB   NB   DB   BNT
☐ Want   Orig. Ret. $4.50   **NB** $20   **MIB** Sec. Mkt. **$30**

QX 256-4   FLIGHTS OF FANTASY ☐

Comments: Blue Glass Ball, 2-7/8" dia., Dated 1984. Beautiful birds are taking the elves on a flight. A ribbon banner is printed: "Christmas 1984."

☐ Purchased 19____   Pd $_____   MIB   NB   DB   BNT
☐ Want   Orig. Ret. $4.50   **NB** $15   **MIB** Sec. Mkt. **$20**

QX 452-4   FORTUNE COOKIE ELF ☐

Comments: Handcrafted, 2-1/2" tall. A little elf paints the fortune for the fortune cookie. Caption: "May Your Christmas Be Merry." **Artist:** Linda Sickman

☐ Purchased 19____   Pd $_____   MIB   NB   DB   BNT
☐ Want   Orig. Ret. $4.50   **NB** $30   **MIB** Sec. Mkt. **$40**

QX 248-1   FRIENDSHIP ☐

Comments: Blue-Green Glass Ball, 2-7/8" dia., Dated 1984. Silhouettes of carolers against the snow. Caption: "Let Us Sing A Christmas Song Of Friendship, Joy And Cheer."

☐ Purchased 19____   Pd $_____   MIB   NB   DB   BNT
☐ Want   Orig. Ret. $4.50   **NB** $10   **MIB** Sec. Mkt. **$23**

QX 444-4   FRISBEE® PUPPY ☐

Comments: Handcrafted, 2-3/4" tall. This energetic puppy has caught a holiday frisbee with a flying leap. "Merry Christmas" is written on the frisbee.

☐ Purchased 19____   Pd $_____   MIB   NB   DB   BNT
☐ Want   Orig. Ret. $5.00   **NB** $35   **MIB** Sec. Mkt. **$40**

QX 248-4   FROM OUR HOME TO YOURS ☐

Comments: Green Glass Ball, 2-7/8" dia., Dated 1984. Sampler design of a family and home in winter. Caption: "The Spirit Of Christmas Adorns A Home With Love. Christmas 1984."

☐ Purchased 19____   Pd $_____   MIB   NB   DB   BNT
☐ Want   Orig. Ret. $4.50   **NB** $30   **MIB** Sec. Mkt. **$50**

QX 437-1   FROSTY FRIENDS ☐

Comments: **Fifth in Series,** Handcrafted, 2-1/2" tall. Dated 1984. A little Eskimo and his penguin pal have gone ice fishing and have caught a gift. **Artist:** Ed Seale

☐ Purchased 19____   Pd $_____   MIB   NB   DB   BNT
☐ Want   Orig. Ret. $8.00   **NB** $70   **MIB** Sec. Mkt. **$90**

QX 343-1   FUN OF FRIENDSHIP, THE ☐

Comments: Acrylic, 3-3/4" tall, Dated 1984. Cute etched bell shows two arctic friends. Caption: "A Friend Is A Partner In Life's Merry Moments."

☐ Purchased 19____   Pd $_____   MIB   NB   DB   BNT
☐ Want   Orig. Ret. $6.00   **NB** $24   **MIB** Sec. Mkt. **$35**

QX 451-1   GIFT OF MUSIC ☐

Comments: Musical, Handcrafted, 3" tall. Tying his Christmas gift with red ribbon is a colorful, bearded elf. The tag reads "Jolly Holidays!" Plays "Jingle Bells." **Artist:** Ed Seale

☐ Purchased 19____   Pd $_____   MIB   NB   DB   BNT
☐ Want   Orig. Ret. $15.00   **NB** $85   **MIB** Sec. Mkt. **$100**

QX 242-1   GODCHILD ☐

Comments: Gold Glass Ball, 3" dia., Dated 1984. Elf children are painting the holly berries red.

☐ Purchased 19____   Pd $_____   MIB   NB   DB   BNT
☐ Want   Orig. Ret. $4.50   **NB** $16   **MIB** Sec. Mkt. **$20**

QX 257-4   GRANDCHILD'S FIRST CHRISTMAS ☐

Comments: Green Satin Ball, 2-7/8" dia., Dated 1984. A "torn paper" scene of Santa loading toys into his bag. Hand-crafted mouse sits atop the ornament. Caption: "A Baby Makes Christmas Delightfully Bright. Grandchild's First Christmas."

☐ Purchased 19____   Pd $_____   MIB NB DB BNT

☐ Want   Orig. Ret. $4.50   **NB** $10   **MIB** Sec. Mkt. **$18**

QX 460-1   GRANDCHILD'S FIRST CHRISTMAS ☐

Comments: Handcrafted, 3-3/8" tall, Dated 1984. A flocked white lamb stands on a colorful pull toy. Caption: "Grand-child's First Christmas."

☐ Purchased 19____   Pd $_____   MIB NB DB BNT

☐ Want   Orig. Ret. $11.00   **NB** $15   **MIB** Sec. Mkt. **$20**

QX 243-1   GRANDDAUGHTER ☐

Comments: Green Glass Ball, 2-7/8" dia., Dated 1984. Caption is written in a sampler design: "A Granddaughter Is Warmth, Hope And Promise. Christmas 1984."

☐ Purchased 19____   Pd $_____   MIB NB DB BNT

☐ Want   Orig. Ret. $4.50   **NB** $20   **MIB** Sec. Mkt. **$30**

QX 244-1   GRANDMOTHER ☐

Comments: Lt. Blue Glass Ball, 2-7/8" dia., Dated 1984. Pastel flowers frame the caption: "There's A Special Kind Of Beauty In A Grandmother's Special Love. Christmas 1984."

☐ Purchased 19____   Pd $_____   MIB NB DB BNT

☐ Want   Orig. Ret. $4.50   **NB** $17   **MIB** Sec. Mkt. **$23**

QX 256-1   GRANDPARENTS ☐

Comments: French Blue Glass Ball, 2-7/8" dia., Dated 1984. "Stitched" snow scene. Caption: "Grandparents... Wherever They Are, There Is Love. Christmas 1984."

☐ Purchased 19____   Pd $_____   MIB NB DB BNT

☐ Want   Orig. Ret. $4.50   **NB** $15   **MIB** Sec. Mkt. **$20**

QX 242-4   GRANDSON ☐

Comments: Blue Glass Ball, 3" dia., Dated Christmas 1984. A polar bear family enjoys Christmas together. Caption: "A Grandson Has A Wonderful Way Of Adding Love To Every Day."

☐ Purchased 19____   Pd $_____   MIB NB DB BNT

☐ Want   Orig. Ret. $4.50   **NB** $20   **MIB** Sec. Mkt. **$30**

QX 344-4   GRATITUDE ☐

Comments: Acrylic, Teardrop shape, 4-1/2" tall. Ribbon and sleigh bells. Caption: "The spirit of Christmas lives in every heart that gives."

☐ Purchased 19____   Pd $_____   MIB NB DB BNT

☐ Want   Orig. Ret. $6.00   **NB** $6   **MIB** Sec. Mkt. **$12**

QX 443-4   HEARTFUL OF LOVE ☐

Comments: Bone China, 3-3/4" wide, Dated 1984. White heart with pink roses. Caption: "Love... the most beautiful treasure of Christmas."

☐ Purchased 19____   Pd $_____   MIB NB DB BNT

☐ Want   Orig. Ret. $10.00   **NB** $25   **MIB** Sec. Mkt. **$45**

QX 432-4   HERE COMES SANTA - SANTA'S DELIVERIES ☐

Comments: **Sixth in Series,** Handcrafted, 3-1/4" tall, Dated 1984. "S. Claus Free Delivery" carries a load of Christmas trees. License plate: "1984." **Artist:** Linda Sickman

☐ Purchased 19____   Pd $_____   MIB NB DB BNT

☐ Want   Orig. Ret. $13.00   **NB** $80   **MIB** Sec. Mkt. **$90**

QX 445-1   HOLIDAY FRIENDSHIP ☐

Comments: Peek-Through Ball, 3-1/4" dia. A little girl and boy wave to each other through a frosty window as each hides gifts from the other.

☐ Purchased 19____   Pd $_____   MIB NB DB BNT

☐ Want   Orig. Ret. $13.00   **NB** $29   **MIB** Sec. Mkt. **$35**

QX 437-4   HOLIDAY JESTER ☐

Comments: Handcrafted, 5-1/4" tall. With movable arms and legs, this jester wears the traditional black and white cos-tume. **Artist:** Linda Sickman

☐ Purchased 19____   Pd $_____   MIB NB DB BNT

☐ Want   Orig. Ret. $11.00   **NB** $20   **MIB** Sec. Mkt. **$25**

QX 253-4   HOLIDAY STARBURST ☐

Comments: Clear Glass Ball, 2-7/8" dia., Dated 1984. Red, green and blue ribbons on the outside of this clear glass ball accent a silver starburst inside. Caption: "Christmas 1984."

☐ Purchased 19____   Pd $_____   MIB NB DB BNT

☐ Want   Orig. Ret. $5.00   **NB** $20   **MIB** Sec. Mkt. **$25**

QX 347-4   HOLIDAY WILDLIFE: PHEASANTS ☐

Comments: **Third in Series,** 3" dia., Dated 1984. Caption:
"Ring-Necked Pheasant, Phasianus Torquatus, Third In A
Series, Wildlife Collection, Christmas 1984."

☐ Purchased 19___   Pd $_____   MIB NB DB BNT
☐ Want   Orig. Ret. $7.25   **NB** $25   **MIB** Sec. Mkt. **$30**

QX 463-1   KATYBETH ☐

Comments: Handpainted Porcelain, 2-1/4" tall.
This freckle-faced angel holds a friendly, happy star.

☐ Purchased 19___   Pd $_____   MIB NB DB BNT
☐ Want   Orig. Ret. $9.00   **NB** $24   **MIB** Sec. Mkt. **$33**

QX 453-4   KIT ☐

Comments: Handcrafted, 2-3/4" tall. Wearing his classic
green cap, Muffin's friend Kit brings a candy cane to you.

☐ Purchased 19___   Pd $_____   MIB NB DB BNT
☐ Want   Orig. Ret. $5.50   **NB** $20   **MIB** Sec. Mkt. **$28**

QX 255-4   LOVE ☐

Comments: Chrome Glass Ball, 2-7/8" dia., Dated 1984.
Classic mimes share thoughts of love. Caption: "Love Can
Say The Special Things That Words Alone Cannot. Christmas
1984."

☐ Purchased 19___   Pd $_____   MIB NB DB BNT
☐ Want   Orig. Ret. $4.50   **NB** $15   **MIB** Sec. Mkt. **$25**

QX 247-4   LOVE... THE SPIRIT OF CHRISTMAS ☐

Comments: Chrome Glass Ball, 2-7/8" dia., Dated 1984. A
bright fruit and flower design on a black band resembles a
lacquer appearance. Caption: "Love, Which Is The Spirit And
The Heart Of Christmas, Blossoms All Year Through."

☐ Purchased 19___   Pd $_____   MIB NB DB BNT
☐ Want   Orig. Ret. $4.50   **NB** $35   **MIB** Sec. Mkt. **$43**

QX 344-1   MADONNA & CHILD ☐

Comments: Acrylic, 4" tall. This acrylic ornament features a
beautifully etched design of the Holy Child cradled in the arms
of the Madonna. Gold foil stamped caption: "All Is Calm, All Is
Bright..." **Artist:** Don Palmiter

☐ Purchased 19___   Pd $_____   MIB NB DB BNT
☐ Want   Orig. Ret. $6.00   **NB** $30   **MIB** Sec. Mkt. **$50**

QX 456-4   MARATHON SANTA ☐

Comments: Handcrafted, 2-1/4" tall, Dated 1984. Santa
runs with the Olympic flame; let the games begin!
Artist: Ed Seale

☐ Purchased 19___   Pd $_____   MIB NB DB BNT
☐ Want   Orig. Ret. $8.00   **NB** $30   **MIB** Sec. Mkt. **$43**

QX 342-4   MIRACLE OF LOVE, THE ☐

Comments: Acrylic, 4" tall, Dated Christmas 1984. Heart
etched with festive ribbon and holly design. Gold foil Caption:
"Love... A Miracle Of The Heart."

☐ Purchased 19___   Pd $_____   MIB NB DB BNT
☐ Want   Orig. Ret. $6.00   **NB** $25   **MIB** Sec. Mkt. **$34**

QX 343-4   MOTHER ☐

Comments: Acrylic, 3-1/4" wide, Dated 1984. Etched fir
branches help to highlight the caption: "A Mother Has A
Beautiful Way Of Adding Love To Every Day."

☐ Purchased 19___   Pd $_____   MIB NB DB BNT
☐ Want   Orig. Ret. $6.00   **NB** $12   **MIB** Sec. Mkt. **$18**

QX 258-1   MOTHER & DAD ☐

Comments: Bone China Bell, 3" tall, Dated Christmas 1984.
White bell has decal of Christmas design motifs.

☐ Purchased 19___   Pd $_____   MIB NB DB BNT
☐ Want   Orig. Ret. $6.50   **NB** $17   **MIB** Sec. Mkt. **$25**

QX 407-7   MOUNTAIN CLIMBING SANTA ☐

Comments: Handcrafted, 2-1/2" tall. Reissued from 1983.
Artist: Ed Seale

☐ Purchased 19___   Pd $_____   MIB NB DB BNT
☐ Want   Orig. Ret. $6.50   **NB** $29   **MIB** Sec. Mkt. **$40**

QX 442-1   MUFFIN ☐

Comments: Handcrafted, 2-3/4" tall. Muffin, wearing her
trademark red, knitted cap, holds a gift behind her back.
Artist: Donna Lee

☐ Purchased 19___   Pd $_____   MIB NB DB BNT
☐ Want   Orig. Ret. $5.50   **NB** $27   **MIB** Sec. Mkt. **$33**

QX 251-4   MUPPETS™, THE ☐

Comments: Chrome Glass Ball, 2-7/8" dia. Kermit dons a Santa cap to wish us "Hoppy, Hoppy Holidays!" as Miss Piggy says, "Merry Kissmas!" Both are framed in wreaths.

☐ Purchased 19____   Pd $_____   MIB NB DB BNT
☐ Want   Orig. Ret. $4.50   **NB** $20   **MIB** Sec. Mkt. **$35**

QX 434-4   MUSICAL ANGEL ☐

Comments: Handcrafted, 1-1/4" tall. This cute little angel, caught up by the hem of her dress, is playing a tune on her brass horn. The banner hanging from her horn says "Noel." **Artist:** Donna Lee

☐ Purchased 19____   Pd $_____   MIB NB DB BNT
☐ Want   Orig. Ret. $5.50   **NB** $60   **MIB** Sec. Mkt. **$70**

QX 435-1   NAPPING MOUSE ☐

Comments: Handcrafted, 1-3/4" tall. Sleeping soundly in a walnut shell, a little white mouse holds tightly onto his "teddy mouse."

☐ Purchased 19____   Pd $_____   MIB NB DB BNT
☐ Want   Orig. Ret. $5.50   **NB** $40   **MIB** Sec. Mkt. **$50**

QLX 700-1   NATIVITY ☐

Comments: Lighted Panorama Ball, 3-1/2" dia. A beautiful vision of Bethlehem at night as seen by the three wise men. Caption: "Christmas... Light Through The Darkness... Love Through The Ages." **Artist:** Ed Seale

☐ Purchased 19____   Pd $_____   MIB NB DB BNT
☐ Want   Orig. Ret. $12.00   **NB** $20   **MIB** Sec. Mkt. **$30**

QX 459-4   NEEDLEPOINT WREATH ☐

Comments: Needlepoint-Fabric, 3-1/2" dia. Bright holiday poinsettias have been stitched into a lovely wreath. **Artist:** Sharon Pike

☐ Purchased 19____   Pd $_____   MIB NB DB BNT
☐ Want   Orig. Ret. $6.50   **NB** $10   **MIB** Sec. Mkt. **$15**

QX 245-4   NEW HOME ☐

Comments: Pearl Blue Glass Ball, 2-7/8" dia., Dated 1984. Village holiday snow scene. Caption: "Home Is Where The Heart Is And A New Home Always Seems The Happiest Of Places, For It Is Filled With All Your Dreams. Christmas 1984."

☐ Purchased 19____   Pd $_____   MIB NB DB BNT
☐ Want   Orig. Ret. $4.50   **NB** $75   **MIB** Sec. Mkt. **$80**

QX 251-1   NORMAN ROCKWELL ☐

Comments: Gold Glass Ball, 2-7/8" dia., Dated 1984. Dickens' Christmas characters. "Good Friends, Good Times, Good Health, Good Cheer And Happy Holidays Throughout The Year." From the Norman Rockwell Collection, 1984. **Artist:** Diana McGehee

☐ Purchased 19____   Pd $_____   MIB NB DB BNT
☐ Want   Orig. Ret. $4.50   **NB** $20   **MIB** Sec. Mkt. **$30**

**QX 341-1   NORMAN ROCKWELL:
CAUGHT NAPPING** ☐

Comments: **Fifth in Series,** Cameo, 3" dia., Dated 1984. "Caught Napping, Fifth In A Series, The Norman Rockwell Collection, Christmas 1984." **Artist:** Diana McGehee

☐ Purchased 19____   Pd $_____   MIB NB DB BNT
☐ Want   Orig. Ret. $7.50   **NB** $22   **MIB** Sec. Mkt. **$35**

**QX 448-1   NOSTALGIC HOUSES AND SHOPS:
VICTORIAN DOLLHOUSE** ☐

Comments: **FIRST IN SERIES,** Handcrafted, 3-1/4" tall. Fully decorated interior is complete with wallpaper, furniture, Christmas tree and a miniature dollhouse. **Artist:** Donna Lee

☐ Purchased 19____   Pd $_____   MIB NB DB BNT
☐ Want   Orig. Ret. $13.00   **NB** $200   **MIB** Sec. Mkt. **$215**

QX 442-4   NOSTALGIC SLED ☐

Comments: Handcrafted, 3-1/2" wide, Reissued in 1985. Classic-style sled with real string rope and metal runners. Caption: "Season's Greetings." **Artist:** Linda Sickman

☐ Purchased 19____   Pd $_____   MIB NB DB BNT
☐ Want   Orig. Ret. $6.00   **NB** $20   **MIB** Sec. Mkt. **$30**

QX 346-4   OLD FASHIONED ROCKING HORSE ☐

Comments: Brass, Acrylic, 3-1/4" dia. A finely-etched brass rocking horse is embedded in acrylic.

☐ Purchased 19____   Pd $_____   MIB NB DB BNT
☐ Want   Orig. Ret. $7.50   **NB** $15   **MIB** Sec. Mkt. **$20**

QX 341-4   PEACE ON EARTH ☐

Comments: Red Oval Cameo, 3" tall. A beautiful old-world ivory angel plays a harp. Caption: "Peace On Earth."

☐ Purchased 19____   Pd $_____   MIB NB DB BNT
☐ Want   Orig. Ret. $7.50   **NB** $25   **MIB** Sec. Mkt. **$30**

QX 252-1   PEANUTS®

Comments: Light Blue Soft-Sheen Satin Ball, 2-7/8" dia. Dated 1984. Woodstock and his friends build a gallery of snowmen as Snoopy watches. His red banner says, "Merry Christmas."

☐ Purchased 19____   Pd $_____   MIB   NB   DB   BNT
☐ Want   Orig. Ret. $4.50   **NB** $28   **MIB** Sec. Mkt. **$35**

QX 456-1   PEPPERMINT 1984

Comments: Handcrafted, 2-3/4" wide, Dated 1984. The year 1984 is designed from peppermint candy. Two birds sit atop the "9." **Artist:** Donna Lee

☐ Purchased 19____   Pd $_____   MIB   NB   DB   BNT
☐ Want   Orig. Ret. $4.50   **NB** $42   **MIB** Sec. Mkt. **$50**

QX 430-1   POLAR BEAR DRUMMER

Comments: Handcrafted, 2-1/4" tall. A white polar bear plays his red drum. **Artist:** Ed Seale

☐ Purchased 19____   Pd $_____   MIB   NB   DB   BNT
☐ Want   Orig. Ret. $4.50   **NB** $20   **MIB** Sec. Mkt. **$30**

QX 454-1   PORCELAIN BEAR

Comments: **Second in Series,** Porcelain, 2-1/2" tall. Handpainted Cinnamon Bear holds a gold jingle bell with a red bow. Price up in '97.

☐ Purchased 19____   Pd $_____   MIB   NB   DB   BNT
☐ Want   Orig. Ret. $7.00   **NB** $30   **MIB** Sec. Mkt. **$50**

QX 447-4   RACCOON'S CHRISTMAS

Comments: Handcrafted, 2-3/4" tall. A raccoon and his neighbor have hung their Christmas stockings outside their "homes." **Artist:** Ed Seale

☐ Purchased 19____   Pd $_____   MIB   NB   DB   BNT
☐ Want   Orig. Ret. $9.00   **NB** $45   **MIB** Sec. Mkt. **$56**

QX 254-4   REINDEER RACETRACK

Comments: Red Glass Ball, 3" dia. The race has started and they're off! Santa shouts his encouragement from the stands: "On Comet! On Cupid! On Donder! On Blitzen!"

☐ Purchased 19____   Pd $_____   MIB   NB   DB   BNT
☐ Want   Orig. Ret. $4.50   **NB** $20   **MIB** Sec. Mkt. **$25**

QX 435-4   ROCKING HORSE

Comments: **Fourth in Series,** Handcrafted, 4" wide. Dated 1984. Blue and red saddle and rockers are a striking contrast to this black and white Appaloosa with gray mane and tail.

☐ Purchased 19____   Pd $_____   MIB   NB   DB   BNT
☐ Want   Orig. Ret. $10.00   **NB** $80   **MIB** Sec. Mkt. **$100**

QX 457-1   ROLLER SKATING RABBIT

Comments: Handcrafted, 2-1/2" wide, Reissued in 1985. A white bunny has snuggled down into a green and white roller skate boot for a fun ride. The red wheels really turn! **Artist:** Ed Seale

☐ Purchased 19____   Pd $_____   MIB   NB   DB   BNT
☐ Want   Orig. Ret. $5.00   **NB** $15   **MIB** Sec. Mkt. **$25**

QX 458-4   SANTA

Comments: Hand-embroidered Fabric, 4" tall. Santa rides a reindeer over lush green hillsides filled with blooming flowers.

☐ Purchased 19____   Pd $_____   MIB   NB   DB   BNT
☐ Want   Orig. Ret. $7.50   **NB** $15   **MIB** Sec. Mkt. **$20**

QX 433-4   SANTA MOUSE

Comments: Handcrafted, 2" tall. A cute little mouse has dressed up as Santa, complete with a furry "beard." **Artist:** Bob Siedler

☐ Purchased 19____   Pd $_____   MIB   NB   DB   BNT
☐ Want   Orig. Ret. $4.50   **NB** $30   **MIB** Sec. Mkt. **$40**

QX 450-4   SANTA STAR

Comments: Handcrafted, 3-1/2" tall. Santa is designed in the shape of a five-pointed star!

☐ Purchased 19____   Pd $_____   MIB   NB   DB   BNT
☐ Want   Orig. Ret. $5.50   **NB** $30   **MIB** Sec. Mkt. **$40**

QX 436-1   SANTA SULKY DRIVER

Comments: Etched Brass, 1-3/4" tall. Santa races along in his brass sulky rig. A banner reads "Season's Greetings."

☐ Purchased 19____   Pd $_____   MIB   NB   DB   BNT
☐ Want   Orig. Ret. $9.00   **NB** $25   **MIB** Sec. Mkt. **$35**

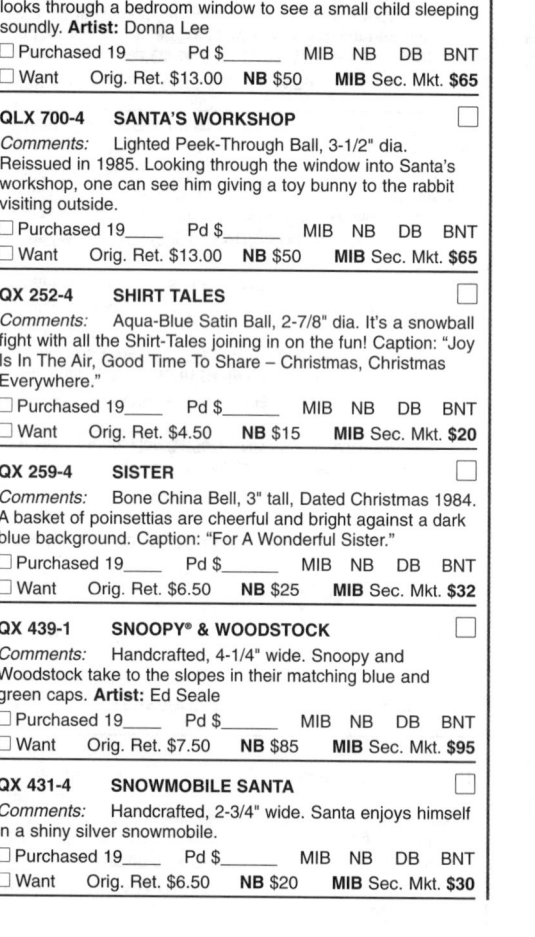

QLX 702-4   SANTA'S ARRIVAL

Comments: Lighted Peek-Through Ball, 3-1/2" dia. Santa looks through a bedroom window to see a small child sleeping soundly. **Artist:** Donna Lee

☐ Purchased 19___   Pd $_____   MIB   NB   DB   BNT
☐ Want   Orig. Ret. $13.00   **NB** $50   **MIB** Sec. Mkt. **$65**

QLX 700-4   SANTA'S WORKSHOP

Comments: Lighted Peek-Through Ball, 3-1/2" dia. Reissued in 1985. Looking through the window into Santa's workshop, one can see him giving a toy bunny to the rabbit visiting outside.

☐ Purchased 19___   Pd $_____   MIB   NB   DB   BNT
☐ Want   Orig. Ret. $13.00   **NB** $50   **MIB** Sec. Mkt. **$65**

QX 252-4   SHIRT TALES

Comments: Aqua-Blue Satin Ball, 2-7/8" dia. It's a snowball fight with all the Shirt-Tales joining in on the fun! Caption: "Joy Is In The Air, Good Time To Share – Christmas, Christmas Everywhere."

☐ Purchased 19___   Pd $_____   MIB   NB   DB   BNT
☐ Want   Orig. Ret. $4.50   **NB** $15   **MIB** Sec. Mkt. **$20**

QX 259-4   SISTER

Comments: Bone China Bell, 3" tall, Dated Christmas 1984. A basket of poinsettias are cheerful and bright against a dark blue background. Caption: "For A Wonderful Sister."

☐ Purchased 19___   Pd $_____   MIB   NB   DB   BNT
☐ Want   Orig. Ret. $6.50   **NB** $25   **MIB** Sec. Mkt. **$32**

QX 439-1   SNOOPY® & WOODSTOCK

Comments: Handcrafted, 4-1/4" wide. Snoopy and Woodstock take to the slopes in their matching blue and green caps. **Artist:** Ed Seale

☐ Purchased 19___   Pd $_____   MIB   NB   DB   BNT
☐ Want   Orig. Ret. $7.50   **NB** $85   **MIB** Sec. Mkt. **$95**

QX 431-4   SNOWMOBILE SANTA

Comments: Handcrafted, 2-3/4" wide. Santa enjoys himself in a shiny silver snowmobile.

☐ Purchased 19___   Pd $_____   MIB   NB   DB   BNT
☐ Want   Orig. Ret. $6.50   **NB** $20   **MIB** Sec. Mkt. **$30**

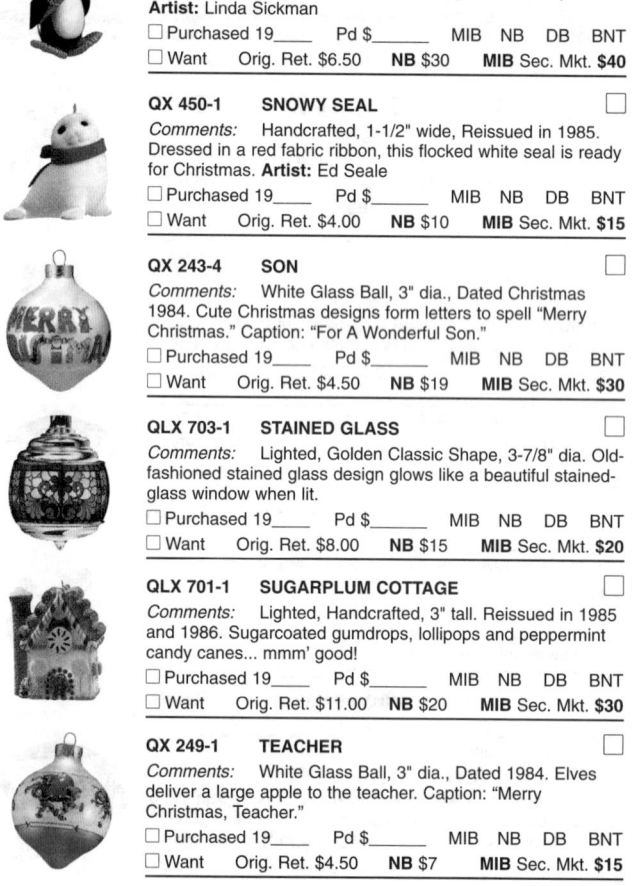

QX 453-1   SNOWSHOE PENGUIN

Comments: Handcrafted, 3" tall. Santa's neighbor has donned his snowshoes and is on his way to deliver a present. **Artist:** Linda Sickman

☐ Purchased 19___   Pd $_____   MIB   NB   DB   BNT
☐ Want   Orig. Ret. $6.50   **NB** $30   **MIB** Sec. Mkt. **$40**

QX 450-1   SNOWY SEAL

Comments: Handcrafted, 1-1/2" wide, Reissued in 1985. Dressed in a red fabric ribbon, this flocked white seal is ready for Christmas. **Artist:** Ed Seale

☐ Purchased 19___   Pd $_____   MIB   NB   DB   BNT
☐ Want   Orig. Ret. $4.00   **NB** $10   **MIB** Sec. Mkt. **$15**

QX 243-4   SON

Comments: White Glass Ball, 3" dia., Dated Christmas 1984. Cute Christmas designs form letters to spell "Merry Christmas." Caption: "For A Wonderful Son."

☐ Purchased 19___   Pd $_____   MIB   NB   DB   BNT
☐ Want   Orig. Ret. $4.50   **NB** $19   **MIB** Sec. Mkt. **$30**

QLX 703-1   STAINED GLASS

Comments: Lighted, Golden Classic Shape, 3-7/8" dia. Old-fashioned stained glass design glows like a beautiful stained-glass window when lit.

☐ Purchased 19___   Pd $_____   MIB   NB   DB   BNT
☐ Want   Orig. Ret. $8.00   **NB** $15   **MIB** Sec. Mkt. **$20**

QLX 701-1   SUGARPLUM COTTAGE

Comments: Lighted, Handcrafted, 3" tall. Reissued in 1985 and 1986. Sugarcoated gumdrops, lollipops and peppermint candy canes... mmm' good!

☐ Purchased 19___   Pd $_____   MIB   NB   DB   BNT
☐ Want   Orig. Ret. $11.00   **NB** $20   **MIB** Sec. Mkt. **$30**

QX 249-1   TEACHER

Comments: White Glass Ball, 3" dia., Dated 1984. Elves deliver a large apple to the teacher. Caption: "Merry Christmas, Teacher."

☐ Purchased 19___   Pd $_____   MIB   NB   DB   BNT
☐ Want   Orig. Ret. $4.50   **NB** $7   **MIB** Sec. Mkt. **$15**

QX 258-4   TEN YEARS TOGETHER ☐

Comments: Bone China Bell, 3" tall, Dated Christmas 1984. A frosty blue winter scene inside an oval is featured on this lovely bell. Caption: "Ten Years Together."

☐ Purchased 19____ Pd $_____ MIB NB DB BNT
☐ Want   Orig. Ret. $6.50 **NB** $20 **MIB** Sec. Mkt. **$25**

QX 430-4   THIMBLE: ANGEL ☐

Comments: **Seventh in Series,** Handcrafted, 1-3/4" tall. A cute little angel has caught a thimbleful of stars. **Artist:** Bob Siedler

☐ Purchased 19____ Pd $_____ MIB NB DB BNT
☐ Want   Orig. Ret. $5.00 **NB** $45 **MIB** Sec. Mkt. **$60**

QX 431-1   THREE KITTENS IN A MITTEN ☐

Comments: Handcrafted, 3-1/2" tall, Reissued in 1985. Three little kittens are hanging out of a knitted red and green mitten. **Artist:** Donna Lee

☐ Purchased 19____ Pd $_____ MIB NB DB BNT
☐ Want   Orig. Ret. $8.00 **NB** $22 **MIB** Sec. Mkt. **$40**

QX 440-4   TIN LOCOMOTIVE ☐

Comments: **Third in Series,** Pressed Tin, 2-1/2" tall. Dated 1984. Antique design locomotive has movable wheels in red, blue, and steel. **Artist:** Linda Sickman

☐ Purchased 19____ Pd $_____ MIB NB DB BNT
☐ Want   Orig. Ret. $14.00 **NB** $60 **MIB** Sec. Mkt. **$70**

QX 415-9   TWELVE DAYS OF CHRISTMAS ☐

Comments: Musical, Handcrafted, 3-3/4" tall. Issued in 1983 as part of the Musical Decoration line, it was reintroduced in 1984 as part of the Keepsake line. **Artist:** Ed Seale

☐ Purchased 19____ Pd $_____ MIB NB DB BNT
☐ Want   Orig. Ret. $15.00 **NB** $95 **MIB** Sec. Mkt. **$130**

QX 348-4   TWELVE DAYS OF CHRISTMAS ☐

Comments: **FIRST IN SERIES,** Acrylic, 3" tall, Dated 1984. Etched partridge in a pear tree. Gold foil lettering: "The Twelve Days Of Christmas" and "... And A Partridge In A Pear Tree.

☐ Purchased 19____ Pd $_____ MIB NB DB BNT
☐ Want   Orig. Ret. $6.00 **NB** $275 **MIB** Sec. Mkt. **$300**

QX 259-1   TWENTY-FIVE YEARS TOGETHER ☐

Comments: Bone China Bell, 3" tall, Dated Christmas 1984. A gold and silver sleigh filled with gifts graces this bone china bell. Caption: "Twenty-Five Years Together."

☐ Purchased 19____ Pd $_____ MIB NB DB BNT
☐ Want   Orig. Ret. $6.50 **NB** $25 **MIB** Sec. Mkt. **$30**

QX 449-1   UNCLE SAM ☐

Comments: Pressed Tin, 5" tall, Dated 1984. Uncle Sam is decked out in red, white, and blue holding a teddy bear. **Artist:** Linda Sickman

☐ Purchased 19____ Pd $_____ MIB NB DB BNT
☐ Want   Orig. Ret. $6.00 **NB** $40 **MIB** Sec. Mkt. **$40**

QLX 702-1   VILLAGE CHURCH ☐

Comments: Lighted, Handcrafted, 4-5/8" tall. Reissued in 1985. The tall steeple of this clapboard village church is topped with a gold cross. Holiday carolers may be seen through the open door. **Artist:** Donna Lee

☐ Purchased 19____ Pd $_____ MIB NB DB BNT
☐ Want   Orig. Ret. $15.00 **NB** $35 **MIB** Sec. Mkt. **$40**

QX 905-1   WHITE CHRISTMAS ☐

Comments: Musical, Classic Shape, 4-1/2" tall. A busy city at Christmas time. Plays White Christmas. Caption: "At Christmas Time, Love Shines In Every Smile, glows in Every Heart."

☐ Purchased 19____ Pd $_____ MIB NB DB BNT
☐ Want   Orig. Ret. $16.00 **NB** $80 **MIB** Sec. Mkt. **$95**

QX 439-4   WOOD CHILDHOOD ORNAMENTS: LAMB ☐

Comments: **FIRST IN SERIES,** Wood, Handcrafted, 2-1/4" tall. A little wooden lamb has red wheels and a fabric bow around its neck.

☐ Purchased 19____ Pd $_____ MIB NB DB BNT
☐ Want   Orig. Ret. $6.50 **NB** $25 **MIB** Sec. Mkt. **$30**

1985 Collection

QLX 704-4   ALL ARE PRECIOUS ☐
Comments: Lighted Acrylic, 4" tall. Reissued from 1984.
☐ Purchased 19____   Pd $_____   MIB NB DB BNT
☐ Want   Orig. Ret. $8.00   **NB** $20   **MIB** Sec. Mkt. **$25**

QX 377-2   ART MASTERPIECE ☐
Comments: **Second in Series,** Bezeled Satin, 2-3/4" dia.
Caption: "Madonna of the Pomegranate (ca. 1487), The Uffizi
Gallery, Florence, Italy." **Artist:** Diana McGehee
☐ Purchased 19____   Pd $_____   MIB NB DB BNT
☐ Want   Orig. Ret. $6.75   **NB** $10   **MIB** Sec. Mkt. **$18**

QX 401-2   BABY LOCKET ☐
Comments: Textured Brass, 2-1/4" dia. Embossed toys and
the word "Baby" decorate the locket. There is space for per-
sonalizing, as well as baby's photo. **Artist:** Diana McGehee
☐ Purchased 19____   Pd $_____   MIB NB DB BNT
☐ Want   Orig. Ret. $16.00   **NB** $15   **MIB** Sec. Mkt. **$22**

QX 260-2   BABY'S FIRST CHRISTMAS ☐
Comments: Green Soft-Sheen Satin Ball, 2-7/8" dia. Dated
1985. Topped with a handcrafted mouse. Caption: "A Baby
Keeps The Season Bright And Warms The Heart With Sweet
Delight. Baby's First Christmas."
☐ Purchased 19____   Pd $_____   MIB NB DB BNT
☐ Want   Orig. Ret. $5.00   **NB** $20   **MIB** Sec. Mkt. **$25**

QX 370-2   BABY'S FIRST CHRISTMAS ☐
Comments: Acrylic, 3-3/4" tall, Dated 1985. Baby cup, filled
with toys, carries the caption: "Baby's First Christmas."
Artist: Donna Lee
☐ Purchased 19____   Pd $_____   MIB NB DB BNT
☐ Want   Orig. Ret. $5.75   **NB** $18   **MIB** Sec. Mkt. **$22**

QX 478-2   BABY'S FIRST CHRISTMAS ☐
Comments: Embroidered Fabric, 4-1/2" tall, Dated 1985.
Decorated with ribbon and lace, this hand embroidered tree
says "Baby's First Christmas." **Artist:** LaDene Votruba
☐ Purchased 19____   Pd $_____   MIB NB DB BNT
☐ Want   Orig. Ret. $7.00   **NB** $10   **MIB** Sec. Mkt. **$18**

QX 499-2   BABY'S FIRST CHRISTMAS ☐
Comments: Handcrafted, 3-3/4" tall, Dated 1985. "Baby's
First Christmas" is delightful in a rattan look stroller with lace
trim and a red bow.
☐ Purchased 19____   Pd $_____   MIB NB DB BNT
☐ Want   Orig. Ret. $15.00   **NB** $45   **MIB** Sec. Mkt. **$55**

QX 499-5   BABY'S FIRST CHRISTMAS ☐
Comments: Musical, Fabric, 3-1/4" tall, Dated 1985.
Embroidered satin baby block. Plays "Schubert's Lullaby."
Caption: "Baby's First Christmas."
☐ Purchased 19____   Pd $_____   MIB NB DB BNT
☐ Want   Orig. Ret. $16.00   **NB** $38   **MIB** Sec. Mkt. **$45**

QLX 700-5   BABY'S FIRST CHRISTMAS ☐
Comments: Lighted, Handcrafted-Acrylic, 4" tall. This cute
carousel features teddy bears riding their frosted acrylic
ponies. **Artist:** Ed Seale
☐ Purchased 19____   Pd $_____   MIB NB DB BNT
☐ Want   Orig. Ret. $16.50   **NB** $28   **MIB** Sec. Mkt. **$40**

QX 478-5   BABY'S SECOND CHRISTMAS ☐
Comments: Handcrafted, 3-1/2" tall, Dated 1985. Brown
teddy in yellow t-shirt is riding his stick horse. Caption:
"Baby's Second Christmas."
☐ Purchased 19____   Pd $_____   MIB NB DB BNT
☐ Want   Orig. Ret. $6.00   **NB** $25   **MIB** Sec. Mkt. **$37**

QX 264-2   BABY-SITTER ☐
Comments: Green Glass Ball, 3" dia., Dated 1985. Panda
bears are preparing for Christmas. Caption: "A Baby-Sitter Is
A Special Kind Of Friend. Christmas 1985." **Artist:** Michele
Pyda-Sevcik
☐ Purchased 19____   Pd $_____   MIB NB DB BNT
☐ Want   Orig. Ret. $4.75   **NB** $8   **MIB** Sec. Mkt. **$13**

QX 491-2   BAKER ELF ☐
Comments: Handcrafted, 3" tall, Dated 1985. A cute elf
uses red and green "icing" to decorate the bell-shaped cookie
he has baked. **Artist:** Ed Seale
☐ Purchased 19____   Pd $_____   MIB NB DB BNT
☐ Want   Orig. Ret. $5.75   **NB** $20   **MIB** Sec. Mkt. **$30**

QX 480-5　BEARY SMOOTH RIDE ☐
Comments:　Handcrafted, 1-3/4" tall, Reissued in 1986. Teddy rides around on a colorful tricycle. **Artist:** Linda Sickman

☐ Purchased 19____　Pd $_____　MIB　NB　DB　BNT
☐ Want　Orig. Ret. $6.50　**NB** $15　**MIB** Sec. Mkt. **$20**

QX 263-2　BETSEY CLARK ☐
Comments:　**Thirteenth and Final in Series,** White Glass Ball. 3-1/4" dia., Dated 1985. Angelic children dust the stars and play on the clouds. Caption: "Christmas Brings A Special Kind Of Feeling." **Artist:** Sharon Pike

☐ Purchased 19____　Pd $_____　MIB　NB　DB　BNT
☐ Want　Orig. Ret. $5.00　**NB** $20　**MIB** Sec. Mkt. **$35**

QX 508-5　BETSEY CLARK ☐
Comments:　Handpainted Porcelain, 2-1/2" tall. A wee angle holds a little lamb.

☐ Purchased 19____　Pd $_____　MIB　NB　DB　BNT
☐ Want　Orig. Ret. $8.50　**NB** $18　**MIB** Sec. Mkt. **$30**

QX 481-5　BOTTLECAP FUN BUNNIES ☐
Comments:　Handcrafted, 2-1/4" tall. Mama and baby bunny go riding in a metal bottle cap from the "Santa Soda, North Pole Bottling Co." **Artist:** Bob Siedler

☐ Purchased 19____　Pd $_____　MIB　NB　DB　BNT
☐ Want　Orig. Ret. $7.75　**NB** $24　**MIB** Sec. Mkt. **$35**

QX 374-2　CANDLE CAMEO ☐
Comments:　Bezeled Cameo, 3" tall, Dated 1985. Traditional ivory Christmas symbols against a red cameo. Caption: "Christmas... The Season That Brightens The World." **Artist:** Sharon Pike

☐ Purchased 19____　Pd $_____　MIB　NB　DB　BNT
☐ Want　Orig. Ret. $6.75　**NB** $10　**MIB** Sec. Mkt. **$15**

QX 470-5　CANDY APPLE MOUSE ☐
Comments:　Handcrafted, 3-3/4" tall, Dated 1985. A white mouse is sleeping on a red candy apple. **Artist:** Linda Sickman

☐ Purchased 19____　Pd $_____　MIB　NB　DB　BNT
☐ Want　Orig. Ret. $6.50　**NB** $55　**MIB** Sec. Mkt. **$65**

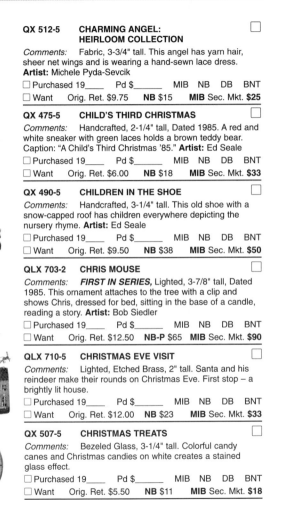

QX 512-5　CHARMING ANGEL: ☐
　　　　　　HEIRLOOM COLLECTION
Comments:　Fabric, 3-3/4" tall. This angel has yarn hair, sheer net wings and is wearing a hand-sewn lace dress. **Artist:** Michele Pyda-Sevcik

☐ Purchased 19____　Pd $_____　MIB　NB　DB　BNT
☐ Want　Orig. Ret. $9.75　**NB** $15　**MIB** Sec. Mkt. **$25**

QX 475-5　CHILD'S THIRD CHRISTMAS ☐
Comments:　Handcrafted, 2-1/4" tall, Dated 1985. A red and white sneaker with green laces holds a brown teddy bear. Caption: "A Child's Third Christmas '85." **Artist:** Ed Seale

☐ Purchased 19____　Pd $_____　MIB　NB　DB　BNT
☐ Want　Orig. Ret. $6.00　**NB** $18　**MIB** Sec. Mkt. **$33**

QX 490-5　CHILDREN IN THE SHOE ☐
Comments:　Handcrafted, 3-1/4" tall. This old shoe with a snow-capped roof has children everywhere depicting the nursery rhyme. **Artist:** Ed Seale

☐ Purchased 19____　Pd $_____　MIB　NB　DB　BNT
☐ Want　Orig. Ret. $9.50　**NB** $38　**MIB** Sec. Mkt. **$50**

QLX 703-2　CHRIS MOUSE ☐
Comments:　**FIRST IN SERIES,** Lighted, 3-7/8" tall, Dated 1985. This ornament attaches to the tree with a clip and shows Chris, dressed for bed, sitting in the base of a candle, reading a story. **Artist:** Bob Siedler

☐ Purchased 19____　Pd $_____　MIB　NB　DB　BNT
☐ Want　Orig. Ret. $12.50　**NB-P** $65　**MIB** Sec. Mkt. **$90**

QLX 710-5　CHRISTMAS EVE VISIT ☐
Comments:　Lighted, Etched Brass, 2" tall. Santa and his reindeer make their rounds on Christmas Eve. First stop – a brightly lit house.

☐ Purchased 19____　Pd $_____　MIB　NB　DB　BNT
☐ Want　Orig. Ret. $12.00　**NB** $23　**MIB** Sec. Mkt. **$33**

QX 507-5　CHRISTMAS TREATS ☐
Comments:　Bezeled Glass, 3-1/4" tall. Colorful candy canes and Christmas candies on white creates a stained glass effect.

☐ Purchased 19____　Pd $_____　MIB　NB　DB　BNT
☐ Want　Orig. Ret. $5.50　**NB** $11　**MIB** Sec. Mkt. **$18**

QX 471-5   CLOTHESPIN SOLDIER: SCOTTISH ☐

Comments: **Fourth in Series,** Handcrafted, 2-1/2" tall. The Scottish Highlander is dressed in a colorful fabric kilt with a blue pom-pom on his red tam. **Artist:** Linda Sickman

☐ Purchased 19____   Pd $_____   MIB   NB   DB   BNT
☐ Want   Orig. Ret. $5.50   **NB** $23   **MIB** Sec. Mkt. **$30**

QX 518-5   COUNTRY GOOSE ☐

Comments: Wood, 3" dia. A goose with a Christmas wreath around its neck graces this wood ornament. Caption: "This Original Design, Styled In The American Country Tradition, Has Been Printed On Hardwood." **Artist:** Michele Pyda-Sevcik

☐ Purchased 19____   Pd $_____   MIB   NB   DB   BNT
☐ Want   Orig. Ret. $7.75   **NB** $11   **MIB** Sec. Mkt. **$15**

QX 477-2   DAPPER PENGUIN ☐

Comments: Handcrafted, 2-1/4" tall. This cute little fellow is all decked out with a red top hat, green bow tie and gold cane. **Artist:** Ed Seale

☐ Purchased 19____   Pd $_____   MIB   NB   DB   BNT
☐ Want   Orig. Ret. $5.00   **NB** $22   **MIB** Sec. Mkt. **$30**

QX 503-2   DAUGHTER ☐

Comments: Wood, 3-1/4" dia., Dated Christmas 1985. "Silk-screened" design in an embroidery hoop. Caption: "A Daughter Decorates The Holidays With Love."

☐ Purchased 19____   Pd $_____   MIB   NB   DB   BNT
☐ Want   Orig. Ret. $5.50   **NB** $14   **MIB** Sec. Mkt. **$20**

QX 271-2   DISNEY® CHRISTMAS ☐

Comments: Pearl Blue Glass, 3" dia., Dated 1985. Mice hang their stockings for Christmas as Mickey dons a Santa suit.

☐ Purchased 19____   Pd $_____   MIB   NB   DB   BNT
☐ Want   Orig. Ret. $4.75   **NB** $23   **MIB** Sec. Mkt. **$30**

QX 481-2   DO NOT DISTURB BEAR ☐

Comments: Handcrafted, 3" wide, Reissued in 1986. A flocked bear snoozes comfortably in his hollow log with his "Do Not Disturb 'Til Christmas" sign. **Artist:** Ed Seale

☐ Purchased 19____   Pd $_____   MIB   NB   DB   BNT
☐ Want   Orig. Ret. $7.75   **NB** $16   **MIB** Sec. Mkt. **$23**

QX 474-2   DOGGY IN A STOCKING ☐

Comments: Handcrafted, 3" tall. A cute tan terrier is poking his head out of the red and green striped stocking.

☐ Purchased 19____   Pd $_____   MIB   NB   DB   BNT
☐ Want   Orig. Ret. $5.50   **NB** $25   **MIB** Sec. Mkt. **$40**

QX 473-5   ENGINEERING MOUSE ☐

Comments: Handcrafted, 2" tall. Designed to look like a windup toy, a little white mouse engineers a red and green locomotive. **Artist:** Bob Siedler

☐ Purchased 19____   Pd $_____   MIB   NB   DB   BNT
☐ Want   Orig. Ret. $5.50   **NB** $16   **MIB** Sec. Mkt. **$25**

QX 376-2   FATHER ☐

Comments: Wood, 3" dia., Dated Christmas 1985. Printed on wood to resemble hand painting is an old-fashioned sleigh filled with gifts and a Christmas tree. Caption: "A Father Sees Through The Eyes Of Love And Listens With His Heart." **Artist:** LaDene Votruba

☐ Purchased 19____   Pd $_____   MIB   NB   DB   BNT
☐ Want   Orig. Ret. $6.50   **NB** $9   **MIB** Sec. Mkt. **$13**

QX 370-5   FIRST CHRISTMAS TOGETHER ☐

Comments: Acrylic, 3-1/2" wide, Dated 1985. Doves carry a banner with the caption: "First Christmas Together." Framed in brass.

☐ Purchased 19____   Pd $_____   MIB   NB   DB   BNT
☐ Want   Orig. Ret. $6.75   **NB** $20   **MIB** Sec. Mkt. **$26**

QX 261-2   FIRST CHRISTMAS TOGETHER ☐

Comments: Lt. Blue Glass Ball, 2-7/8" dia., Dated 1985. Silhouettes of a couple at Christmas are shown in heart frames tied with red ribbons. Caption: "Love Is A Gift From Heart To Heart. First Christmas Together."

☐ Purchased 19____   Pd $_____   MIB   NB   DB   BNT
☐ Want   Orig. Ret. $4.75   **NB** $20   **MIB** Sec. Mkt. **$25**

QX 507-2   FIRST CHRISTMAS TOGETHER ☐

Comments: Fabric and Wood, 2-1/2" tall, Dated 1985. Red and white hearts are woven in a wooden frame. Caption: "First Christmas Together."

☐ Purchased 19____   Pd $_____   MIB   NB   DB   BNT
☐ Want   Orig. Ret. $8.00   **NB** $14   **MIB** Sec. Mkt. **$18**

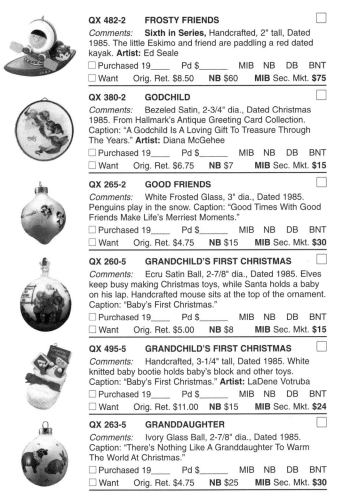

QX 400-5　FIRST CHRISTMAS TOGETHER ☐
Comments:　Polished Brass, 2-1/2" tall, Dated 1985.
Embossed hearts surround the caption: "First Christmas
Together." Locket holds two photos. **Artist:** Ed Seale
☐ Purchased 19____　Pd $_____　MIB　NB　DB　BNT
☐ Want　Orig. Ret. $16.75　**NB** $18　**MIB** Sec. Mkt. **$30**

QX 493-5　FIRST CHRISTMAS TOGETHER ☐
Comments:　Porcelain, 2" tall, Dated 1985.
Red porcelain hearts are the clappers of this pale green
porcelain bisque bell. Caption: "First Christmas Together."
Artist: Linda Sickman
☐ Purchased 19____　Pd $_____　MIB　NB　DB　BNT
☐ Want　Orig. Ret. $13.00　**NB** $20　**MIB** Sec. Mkt. **$25**

QX 265-5　FRAGGLE ROCK™ HOLIDAY ☐
Comments:　Lt. Blue Glass Ball, 3" dia., Dated 1985.
Sprocket, the dog, looks on at the Christmas activities of the
Fraggle Rock gang. Caption: "Happy Holidays 1985."
☐ Purchased 19____　Pd $_____　MIB　NB　DB　BNT
☐ Want　Orig. Ret. $4.75　**NB** $21　**MIB** Sec. Mkt. **$30**

QX 378-5　FRIENDSHIP ☐
Comments:　Bezeled Satin, 3" tall, Dated 1985. Christmas
time in an early American village. Printed on padded satin and
framed with a chrome bezel. Caption: "Christmas... Season
Bright With Friendship." **Artist:** Michele Pyda-Sevcik
☐ Purchased 19____　Pd $_____　MIB　NB　DB　BNT
☐ Want　Orig. Ret. $6.75　**NB** $12　**MIB** Sec. Mkt. **$20**

QX 506-2　FRIENDSHIP ☐
Comments:　Embroidered Satin, 2" tall, Dated 1985. A pine
branch and snowflakes are embroidered on Oriental red satin.
Includes gift card. Caption: "Christmas... A Special Time For
Friendship." **Artist:** Joyce Pattee
☐ Purchased 19____　Pd $_____　MIB　NB　DB　BNT
☐ Want　Orig. Ret. $7.75　**NB** $10　**MIB** Sec. Mkt. **$15**

QX 520-2　FROM OUR HOUSE TO YOURS ☐
Comments:　Needlepoint-Fabric, 4" tall, Dated 1985.
Caption: "A Happy Home Reflects The Joy Of Christmas All
Year Round." **Artist:** Joyce Pattee
☐ Purchased 19____　Pd $_____　MIB　NB　DB　BNT
☐ Want　Orig. Ret. $7.75　**NB** $10　**MIB** Sec. Mkt. **$12**

QX 482-2　FROSTY FRIENDS ☐
Comments:　**Sixth in Series,** Handcrafted, 2" tall, Dated
1985. The little Eskimo and friend are paddling a red dated
kayak. **Artist:** Ed Seale
☐ Purchased 19____　Pd $_____　MIB　NB　DB　BNT
☐ Want　Orig. Ret. $8.50　**NB** $60　**MIB** Sec. Mkt. **$75**

QX 380-2　GODCHILD ☐
Comments:　Bezeled Satin, 2-3/4" dia., Dated Christmas
1985. From Hallmark's Antique Greeting Card Collection.
Caption: "A Godchild Is A Loving Gift To Treasure Through
The Years." **Artist:** Diana McGehee
☐ Purchased 19____　Pd $_____　MIB　NB　DB　BNT
☐ Want　Orig. Ret. $6.75　**NB** $7　**MIB** Sec. Mkt. **$15**

QX 265-2　GOOD FRIENDS ☐
Comments:　White Frosted Glass, 3" dia., Dated 1985.
Penguins play in the snow. Caption: "Good Times With Good
Friends Make Life's Merriest Moments."
☐ Purchased 19____　Pd $_____　MIB　NB　DB　BNT
☐ Want　Orig. Ret. $4.75　**NB** $15　**MIB** Sec. Mkt. **$30**

QX 260-5　GRANDCHILD'S FIRST CHRISTMAS ☐
Comments:　Ecru Satin Ball, 2-7/8" dia., Dated 1985. Elves
keep busy making Christmas toys, while Santa holds a baby
on his lap. Handcrafted mouse sits at the top of the ornament.
Caption: "Baby's First Christmas."
☐ Purchased 19____　Pd $_____　MIB　NB　DB　BNT
☐ Want　Orig. Ret. $5.00　**NB** $8　**MIB** Sec. Mkt. **$15**

QX 495-5　GRANDCHILD'S FIRST CHRISTMAS ☐
Comments:　Handcrafted, 3-1/4" tall, Dated 1985. White
knitted baby bootie holds baby's block and other toys.
Caption: "Baby's First Christmas." **Artist:** LaDene Votruba
☐ Purchased 19____　Pd $_____　MIB　NB　DB　BNT
☐ Want　Orig. Ret. $11.00　**NB** $15　**MIB** Sec. Mkt. **$24**

QX 263-5　GRANDDAUGHTER ☐
Comments:　Ivory Glass Ball, 2-7/8" dia., Dated 1985.
Caption: "There's Nothing Like A Granddaughter To Warm
The World At Christmas."
☐ Purchased 19____　Pd $_____　MIB　NB　DB　BNT
☐ Want　Orig. Ret. $4.75　**NB** $25　**MIB** Sec. Mkt. **$30**

QX 262-5   GRANDMOTHER

Comments: Red Glass Ball, 3" dia., Dated Christmas 1985. Floral design and scroll banner decorate this red transparent ball. Caption: "A Grandmother Gives The Gift Of Love."
Artist: Joyce Pattee

☐ Purchased 19____   Pd $_____   MIB   NB   DB   BNT
☐ Want   Orig. Ret. $4.75   **NB** $10   **MIB** Sec. Mkt. **$20**

QX 380-5   GRANDPARENTS

Comments: Bezeled Lacquer-Look, 2-3/4" wide, Dated 1985. A white poinsettia against a red background is framed in brass and accented with gold. Caption: "Grandparents Have Beautiful Ways Of Adding Love To The Holidays. Christmas 1985." **Artist:** Sharon Pike

☐ Purchased 19____   Pd $_____   MIB   NB   DB   BNT
☐ Want   Orig. Ret. $7.00   **NB** $10   **MIB** Sec. Mkt. **$15**

QX 262-2   GRANDSON

Comments: Green Glass Ball, 2-7/8" dia., Dated 1985. A bright red, green and yellow train circles the ball. Caption: "A Grandson Makes Holiday Joys Shine Even Brighter! Christmas 1985." **Artist:** LaDene Votruba

☐ Purchased 19____   Pd $_____   MIB   NB   DB   BNT
☐ Want   Orig. Ret. $4.75   **NB** $20   **MIB** Sec. Mkt. **$30**

QX 378-2   HEART FULL OF LOVE

Comments: Bezeled Satin, 3" tall, Dated Christmas 1985. Winter scene is framed with a chrome ring. Caption: "The World Is Full Of Beauty When Hearts Are Full Of Love."

☐ Purchased 19____   Pd $_____   MIB   NB   DB   BNT
☐ Want   Orig. Ret. $6.75   **NB** $13   **MIB** Sec. Mkt. **$20**

QX 405-2   HEAVENLY TRUMPETER

Comments: Porcelain, 5" tall, Limited Edition of 24,700. Comes with a wooden display stand. A handpainted porcelain angel plays her golden trumpet.

☐ Purchased 19____   Pd $_____   MIB   NB   DB   BNT
☐ Want   Orig. Ret. $27.50   **NB** $70   **MIB** Sec. Mkt. **$80**

QX 496-5   HERE COMES SANTA: SANTA'S FIRE ENGINE

Comments: **Seventh in Series,** Handcrafted, 3" tall. Dated 1985. Santa's Fire Engine from the "North Pole Fire Department" has Santa in the driver's seat once again. **Artist:** Linda Sickman

☐ Purchased 19____   Pd $_____   MIB   NB   DB   BNT
☐ Want   Orig. Ret. $14.00   **NB** $57   **MIB** Sec. Mkt. **$65**

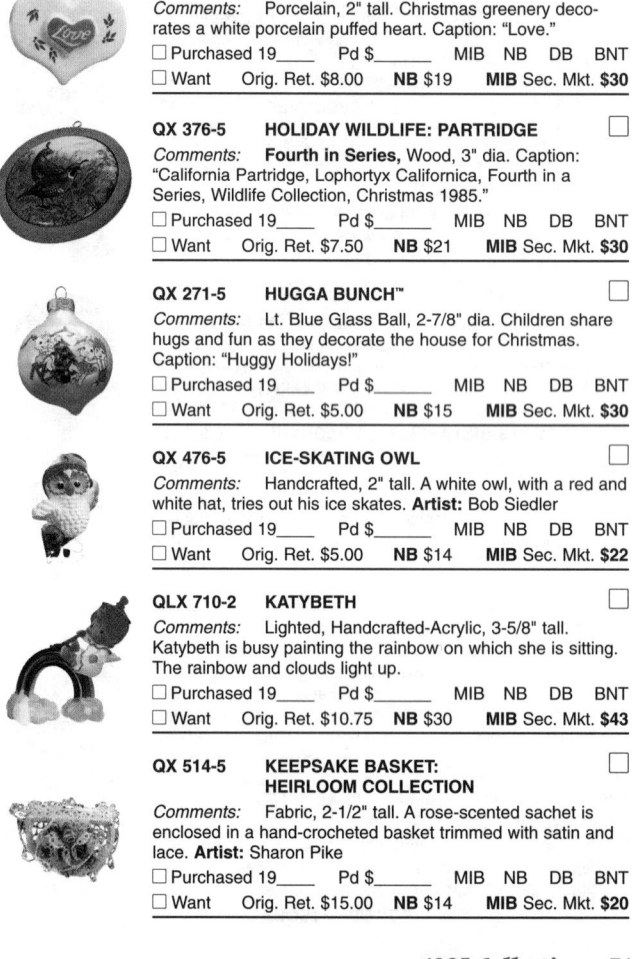

QX 498-2   HOLIDAY HEART

Comments: Porcelain, 2" tall. Christmas greenery decorates a white porcelain puffed heart. Caption: "Love."

☐ Purchased 19____   Pd $_____   MIB   NB   DB   BNT
☐ Want   Orig. Ret. $8.00   **NB** $19   **MIB** Sec. Mkt. **$30**

QX 376-5   HOLIDAY WILDLIFE: PARTRIDGE

Comments: **Fourth in Series,** Wood, 3" dia. Caption: "California Partridge, Lophortyx Californica, Fourth in a Series, Wildlife Collection, Christmas 1985."

☐ Purchased 19____   Pd $_____   MIB   NB   DB   BNT
☐ Want   Orig. Ret. $7.50   **NB** $21   **MIB** Sec. Mkt. **$30**

QX 271-5   HUGGA BUNCH™

Comments: Lt. Blue Glass Ball, 2-7/8" dia. Children share hugs and fun as they decorate the house for Christmas. Caption: "Huggy Holidays!"

☐ Purchased 19____   Pd $_____   MIB   NB   DB   BNT
☐ Want   Orig. Ret. $5.00   **NB** $15   **MIB** Sec. Mkt. **$30**

QX 476-5   ICE-SKATING OWL

Comments: Handcrafted, 2" tall. A white owl, with a red and white hat, tries out his ice skates. **Artist:** Bob Siedler

☐ Purchased 19____   Pd $_____   MIB   NB   DB   BNT
☐ Want   Orig. Ret. $5.00   **NB** $14   **MIB** Sec. Mkt. **$22**

QLX 710-2   KATYBETH

Comments: Lighted, Handcrafted-Acrylic, 3-5/8" tall. Katybeth is busy painting the rainbow on which she is sitting. The rainbow and clouds light up.

☐ Purchased 19____   Pd $_____   MIB   NB   DB   BNT
☐ Want   Orig. Ret. $10.75   **NB** $30   **MIB** Sec. Mkt. **$43**

QX 514-5   KEEPSAKE BASKET: HEIRLOOM COLLECTION

Comments: Fabric, 2-1/2" tall. A rose-scented sachet is enclosed in a hand-crocheted basket trimmed with satin and lace. **Artist:** Sharon Pike

☐ Purchased 19____   Pd $_____   MIB   NB   DB   BNT
☐ Want   Orig. Ret. $15.00   **NB** $14   **MIB** Sec. Mkt. **$20**

QX 484-5   KIT THE SHEPHERD ☐

Comments: Handcrafted, 2-1/2" tall. Kit has traded in his green cap for a shepherd's headdress for the Christmas play. **Artist:** Bob Siedler

☐ Purchased 19____   Pd $_____   MIB   NB   DB   BNT
☐ Want   Orig. Ret. $5.75   **NB** $20   **MIB** Sec. Mkt. **$25**

QX 474-5   KITTY MISCHIEF ☐

Comments: Handcrafted, 2" tall, Reissued in 1986. A ball of real yarn is used with this yellow and white kitten. **Artist:** Peter Dutkin

☐ Purchased 19____   Pd $_____   MIB   NB   DB   BNT
☐ Want   Orig. Ret. $5.00   **NB** $17   **MIB** Sec. Mkt. **$25**

QX 511-2   LACY HEART: HEIRLOOM COLLECTION ☐

Comments: Fabric, 3" tall. A padded white satin heart is trimmed with lace. Scented with a rose sachet.

☐ Purchased 19____   Pd $_____   MIB   NB   DB   BNT
☐ Want   Orig. Ret. $8.75   **NB** $14   **MIB** Sec. Mkt. **$20**

QX 480-2   LAMB IN LEGWARMERS ☐

Comments: Handcrafted, 3" tall. Green, red and white crocheted legwarmers keep this little flocked lamb warm and cozy.

☐ Purchased 19____   Pd $_____   MIB   NB   DB   BNT
☐ Want   Orig. Ret. $7.00   **NB** $14   **MIB** Sec. Mkt. **$20**

QLX 711-2   LITTLE RED SCHOOLHOUSE ☐

Comments: Lighted, Handcrafted 2-5/8" tall. Inside, three parents watch the children perform in a school Christmas pageant. There is a great amount of detail on this ornament. **Artist:** Donna Lee

☐ Purchased 19____   Pd $_____   MIB   NB   DB   BNT
☐ Want   Orig. Ret. $15.75   **NB** $70   **MIB** Sec. Mkt. **$75**

QX 371-5   LOVE AT CHRISTMAS ☐

Comments: Acrylic, 3-1/4" wide. This acrylic heart is raining red foil hearts. Caption: "The Spirit Of Christmas Is Love." **Artist:** Diana McGehee

☐ Purchased 19____   Pd $_____   MIB   NB   DB   BNT
☐ Want   Orig. Ret. $5.75   **NB** $30   **MIB** Sec. Mkt. **$40**

QLX 702-5   LOVE WREATH ☐

Comments: Lighted, Acrylic, 3-1/2" tall. A wreath, hearts and ribbon is etched in clear acrylic. Caption: "Christmas Happens In The Heart." **Artist:** LaDene Votruba

☐ Purchased 19____   Pd $_____   MIB   NB   DB   BNT
☐ Want   Orig. Ret. $8.50   **NB** $25   **MIB** Sec. Mkt. **$30**

QX 403-2   MERRY MOUSE ☐

Comments: Handcrafted, 2-1/2" tall, Reissued in 1986. This happy little fellow wears a Santa hat. His tail is made of leather. **Artist:** Peter Dutkin

☐ Purchased 19____   Pd $_____   MIB   NB   DB   BNT
☐ Want   Orig. Ret. $4.50   **NB** $20   **MIB** Sec. Mkt. **$30**

QX 267-2   MERRY SHIRT TALES™ ☐

Comments: Lt. Blue Glass, 3" dia., Dated Christmas 1985. The Shirt Tales gang is sledding, skating and skiing. Caption: "Every Day's A Holiday When Good Friends Get Together."

☐ Purchased 19____   Pd $_____   MIB   NB   DB   BNT
☐ Want   Orig. Ret. $4.75   **NB** $13   **MIB** Sec. Mkt. **$20**

QX 482-5   MINIATURE CRECHE ☐

Comments: **FIRST IN SERIES,** Wood and Straw, 3-1/2" tall. Wooden figures of the Holy Family grace the straw "stable." Price down from last guide. **Artist:** Ed Seale

☐ Purchased 19____   Pd $_____   MIB   NB   DB   BNT
☐ Want   Orig. Ret. $8.75   **NB** $10   **MIB** Sec. Mkt. **$25**

QX 372-2   MOTHER ☐

Comments: Acrylic, 3-3/8" tall, Dated Christmas 1985. Acrylic teardrop framed in gold, has a caption which reads: "Mother Is The Heart Of Our Happiest Holiday Memories." **Artist:** Sharon Pike

☐ Purchased 19____   Pd $_____   MIB   NB   DB   BNT
☐ Want   Orig. Ret. $6.75   **NB** $11   **MIB** Sec. Mkt. **$15**

QX 509-2   MOTHER & DAD ☐

Comments: Porcelain Bell, 3" tall, Dated Christmas 1985. White porcelain bell has a bas relief paisley design. Caption in soft blue: "Mother And Dad." **Artist:** LaDene Votruba

☐ Purchased 19____   Pd $_____   MIB   NB   DB   BNT
☐ Want   Orig. Ret. $7.75   **NB** $18   **MIB** Sec. Mkt. **$25**

QX 476-2   MOUSE WAGON ☐

Comments: Handcrafted, 2" tall, Dated 1985. Little white mouse rides his little red wagon bearing a gift of cheese.

☐ Purchased 19____   Pd $_____   MIB NB DB BNT
☐ Want   Orig. Ret. $5.75   **NB** $43   **MIB** Sec. Mkt. **$64**

QLX 705-2   MR. AND MRS. SANTA ☐

Comments: Lighted, Handcrafted, 3" tall, Reissued in 1986. Mrs. Santa decorates her Christmas tree while Santa waves to people passing by.

☐ Purchased 19____   Pd $_____   MIB NB DB BNT
☐ Want   Orig. Ret. $14.50   **NB** $50   **MIB** Sec. Mkt. **$70**

QX 483-5   MUFFIN THE ANGEL ☐

Comments: Handcrafted, 2-1/2" tall. Muffin is dressed as an angel and is ready for the Christmas play.
Artist: Bob Siedler

☐ Purchased 19____   Pd $_____   MIB NB DB BNT
☐ Want   Orig. Ret. $5.75   **NB** $19   **MIB** Sec. Mkt. **$25**

QLX 700-1   NATIVITY ☐

Comments: Lighted Panorama Ball, 3-1/2" dia. Reissued from 1984. **Artist:** Ed Seale

☐ Purchased 19____   Pd $_____   MIB NB DB BNT
☐ Want   Orig. Ret. $12.00   **NB** $25   **MIB** Sec. Mkt. **$32**

QX 264-5   NATIVITY SCENE ☐

Comments: Lt. Blue Glass Ball, 3" dia., Dated Christmas 1985. Hard to Find! Little angels welcome the Christ Child. Caption: "O Come, All Ye Faithful... Christmas 1985."

☐ Purchased 19____   Pd $_____   MIB NB DB BNT
☐ Want   Orig. Ret. $4.75   **NB** $15   **MIB** Sec. Mkt. **$30**

QX 269-5   NEW HOME ☐

Comments: Blue Glass Ball, 3" dia., Dated Christmas 1985. Victorian homes, decorated for Christmas, circle this blue tear-drop ball. Caption: "New Home, New Joys, New Memories To Cherish." **Artist:** Michele Pyda-Sevcik

☐ Purchased 19____   Pd $_____   MIB NB DB BNT
☐ Want   Orig. Ret. $4.75   **NB** $10   **MIB** Sec. Mkt. **$30**

QX 520-5   NIECE ☐

Comments: Acrylic, 3-3/4" tall, Dated Christmas 1985. Caption stamped in silver foil on teardrop shape: "A Niece Fills Hearts With A Special Kind Of Love."

☐ Purchased 19____   Pd $_____   MIB NB DB BNT
☐ Want   Orig. Ret. $5.75   **NB** $7   **MIB** Sec. Mkt. **$14**

QX 449-4   NIGHT BEFORE CHRISTMAS ☐

Comments: Panorama Ball, 3-1/4" dia. Push the button and the pages of this favorite Christmas story flip over (30 pages). Comes with special stand for off-tree display. **Artist:** Ed Seale

☐ Purchased 19____   Pd $_____   MIB NB DB BNT
☐ Want   Orig. Ret. $13.00   **NB** $20   **MIB** Sec. Mkt. **$30**

QX 266-2   NORMAN ROCKWELL ☐

Comments: White Glass Ball, 2-7/8" dia., Dated 1985. Caption: "... He Was Chubby And Plump, A Right Jolly Old Elf, And I Laughed When I Saw Him, In Spite Of Myself... C.C. Moore From the Norman Rockwell Collection 1985." **Artist:** Diana McGehee

☐ Purchased 19____   Pd $_____   MIB NB DB BNT
☐ Want   Orig. Ret. $4.75   **NB** $25   **MIB** Sec. Mkt. **$30**

QX 374-5   NORMAN ROCKWELL: JOLLY POSTMAN ☐

Comments: **Sixth in Series,** Light Green Cameo, 3" dia. Dated 1985. Caption: "Jolly Postman, Sixth In A Series, Christmas 1985, The Norman Rockwell Collection." **Artist:** Diana McGehee

☐ Purchased 19____   Pd $_____   MIB NB DB BNT
☐ Want   Orig. Ret. $7.50   **NB** $15   **MIB** Sec. Mkt. **$35**

QX 497-5   NOSTALGIC HOUSES AND SHOPS: TOY SHOP ☐

Comments: **Second in Series,** Handcrafted, 2-1/2" tall. Dated 1985. This Old-Fashioned Toy Shop boasts a counter, cash register, dollhouse and toy truck downstairs and the owner's furnished apartment upstairs
Artist: Donna Lee

☐ Purchased 19____   Pd $_____   MIB NB DB BNT
☐ Want   Orig. Ret. $13.75   **NB** $130   **MIB** Sec. Mkt. **$155**

QX 442-4   NOSTALGIC SLED ☐

Comments: Handcrafted, 3-1/2" wide. Reissued from 1984. **Artist:** Linda Sickman

☐ Purchased 19____   Pd $_____   MIB NB DB BNT
☐ Want   Orig. Ret. $6.00   **NB** $20   **MIB** Sec. Mkt. **$30**

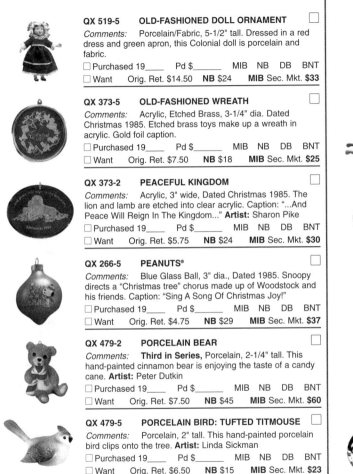

QX 519-5 OLD-FASHIONED DOLL ORNAMENT ☐

Comments: Porcelain/Fabric, 5-1/2" tall. Dressed in a red dress and green apron, this Colonial doll is porcelain and fabric.

☐ Purchased 19____ Pd $_____ MIB NB DB BNT
☐ Want Orig. Ret. $14.50 **NB** $24 **MIB** Sec. Mkt. **$33**

QX 373-5 OLD-FASHIONED WREATH ☐

Comments: Acrylic, Etched Brass, 3-1/4" dia. Dated Christmas 1985. Etched brass toys make up a wreath in acrylic. Gold foil caption.

☐ Purchased 19____ Pd $_____ MIB NB DB BNT
☐ Want Orig. Ret. $7.50 **NB** $18 **MIB** Sec. Mkt. **$25**

QX 373-2 PEACEFUL KINGDOM ☐

Comments: Acrylic, 3" wide, Dated Christmas 1985. The lion and lamb are etched into clear acrylic. Caption: "...And Peace Will Reign In The Kingdom..." **Artist:** Sharon Pike

☐ Purchased 19____ Pd $_____ MIB NB DB BNT
☐ Want Orig. Ret. $5.75 **NB** $24 **MIB** Sec. Mkt. **$30**

QX 266-5 PEANUTS® ☐

Comments: Blue Glass Ball, 3" dia., Dated 1985. Snoopy directs a "Christmas tree" chorus made up of Woodstock and his friends. Caption: "Sing A Song Of Christmas Joy!"

☐ Purchased 19____ Pd $_____ MIB NB DB BNT
☐ Want Orig. Ret. $4.75 **NB** $29 **MIB** Sec. Mkt. **$37**

QX 479-2 PORCELAIN BEAR ☐

Comments: **Third in Series,** Porcelain, 2-1/4" tall. This hand-painted cinnamon bear is enjoying the taste of a candy cane. **Artist:** Peter Dutkin

☐ Purchased 19____ Pd $_____ MIB NB DB BNT
☐ Want Orig. Ret. $7.50 **NB** $45 **MIB** Sec. Mkt. **$60**

QX 479-5 PORCELAIN BIRD: TUFTED TITMOUSE ☐

Comments: Porcelain, 2" tall. This hand-painted porcelain bird clips onto the tree. **Artist:** Linda Sickman

☐ Purchased 19____ Pd $_____ MIB NB DB BNT
☐ Want Orig. Ret. $6.50 **NB** $15 **MIB** Sec. Mkt. **$23**

QX 268-2 RAINBOW BRITE™ & FRIENDS ☐

Comments: Clear Glass Ball, 2-7/8" dia., Dated 1985. Rainbow Brite and the Sprites are shown against colorful stars and snowflakes. A gold starburst inside the clear glass ball shows through.

☐ Purchased 19____ Pd $_____ MIB NB DB BNT
☐ Want Orig. Ret. $4.75 **NB** $14 **MIB** Sec. Mkt. **$25**

QX 493-2 ROCKING HORSE ☐

Comments: **Fifth in Series,** Handcrafted, 4" wide, Dated 1985. A brown and white pinto with green saddle rides on blue rockers. Many NB prices averaged and large drop from last guide. **Artist:** Linda Sickman

☐ Purchased 19____ Pd $_____ MIB NB DB BNT
☐ Want Orig. Ret. $10.75 **NB** $65 **MIB** Sec. Mkt. **$95**

QX 518-2 ROCKING HORSE MEMORIES ☐

Comments: Wood/Fabric, 3-1/4" dia., Dated Christmas 1985. A silk-screen rocking horse is appliqued against a holly pattern and is framed in a wooden embroidery hoop. **Artist:** LaDene Votruba

☐ Purchased 19____ Pd $_____ MIB NB DB BNT
☐ Want Orig. Ret. $10.00 **NB** $11 **MIB** Sec. Mkt. **$15**

QX 457-1 ROLLER SKATING RABBIT ☐

Comments: Handcrafted, 2-1/2" wide. Reissued from 1984. **Artist:** Ed Seale

☐ Purchased 19____ Pd $_____ MIB NB DB BNT
☐ Want Orig. Ret. $5.00 **NB** $20 **MIB** Sec. Mkt. **$30**

QX 300-5 SANTA CLAUS – THE MOVIE™: SANTA CLAUS ☐

Comments: Lacquer-Look, 3-1/2" tall. Santa holds the reins of a sleigh overflowing with toys. "Elfmade" emblem foil stamped on back. No demand for the movie ornaments.

☐ Purchased 19____ Pd $_____ MIB NB DB BNT
☐ Want Orig. Ret. $6.75 **NB** $8 **MIB** Sec. Mkt. **$15**

QX 300-2 SANTA CLAUS – THE MOVIE™ SANTA'S VILLAGE ☐

Comments: Lacquer-Look, 2-1/4" tall. A portrait of Santa's magical village is set in a brass bezel. Caption: "Merry, Merry Christmas." "Elfmade" emblem foil stamped on the back.

☐ Purchased 19____ Pd $_____ MIB NB DB BNT
☐ Want Orig. Ret. $6.75 **NB** $8 **MIB** Sec. Mkt. **$14.50**

QX 494-2   SANTA PIPE ☐

Comments: Handcrafted, 4-1/2" tall. This pipe, with the look of carved antique meerschaum, depicts Santa and the reindeer on Christmas eve. **Artist:** Peter Dutkin

☐ Purchased 19____   Pd $_____   MIB NB DB BNT
☐ Want   Orig. Ret. $9.50   **NB** $15   **MIB** Sec. Mkt. **$20**

QX 496-2   SANTA'S SKI TRIP ☐

Comments: Handcrafted, 3-3/4" tall, Dated 1985. Santa rides a green cable car to the top of "Snowflake Mountain No. 1985." Don't drop your hat, Santa! **Artist:** Ed Seale

☐ Purchased 19____   Pd $_____   MIB NB DB BNT
☐ Want Orig. Ret. $12.00   **NB** $54   **MIB** Sec. Mkt. **$60**

QLX 700-4   SANTA'S WORKSHOP ☐

Comments: Lighted, Peek-Through Ball, 3-1/2" dia. Reissued from 1984.

☐ Purchased 19____   Pd $_____   MIB NB DB BNT
☐ Want   Orig. Ret. $13.00   **NB** $50   **MIB** Sec. Mkt. **$65**

QLX 712-2   SEASON OF BEAUTY ☐

Comments: Lighted, Red and Gold Classic Shape, 3-1/4" dia. A wintry scene reflects peace and beauty. Caption: "May Joy Come Into Your World As Christmas Comes Into Your Heart." **Artist:** Joyce A. Lyle

☐ Purchased 19____   Pd $_____   MIB NB DB BNT
☐ Want   Orig. Ret. $8.00   **NB** $17   **MIB** Sec. Mkt. **$30**

QX 379-5   SEWN PHOTOHOLDER ☐

Comments: Embroidered Fabric, 3-1/4" dia. Dated Christmas 1985. Red fabric photoholder is embroidered with holiday designs and hearts. Caption: "Cherished Times That Mean The Most Are Kept In Memory Ever Close." **Artist:** Sharon Pike

☐ Purchased 19____   Pd $_____   MIB NB DB BNT
☐ Want   Orig. Ret. $7.00   **NB** $20   **MIB** Sec. Mkt. **$35**

QX 517-5   SHEEP AT CHRISTMAS ☐

Comments: Handcrafted, 3-1/4" tall, Dated 1985. This wood-look sheep wears a bell. Caption: "Season's Greetings." **Artist:** Linda Sickman

☐ Purchased 19____   Pd $_____   MIB NB DB BNT
☐ Want   Orig. Ret. $8.25   **NB** $24   **MIB** Sec. Mkt. **$30**

QX 506-5   SISTER ☐

Comments: Porcelain, 2-3/4" tall, Dated Christmas 1985. White porcelain bell with red ribbon is designed with hearts and holly. Caption: "For Sister, With Love."
Artist: Joyce Pattee

☐ Purchased 19____   Pd $_____   MIB NB DB BNT
☐ Want   Orig. Ret. $7.25   **NB** $20   **MIB** Sec. Mkt. **$25**

QX 473-2   SKATEBOARD RACCOON ☐

Comments: Handcrafted, 2-1/2" tall, Reissued in 1986. A flocked raccoon is riding a red skateboard with green moveable wheels. **Artist:** Peter Dutkin

☐ Purchased 19____   Pd $_____   MIB NB DB BNT
☐ Want   Orig. Ret. $6.50   **NB** $33   **MIB** Sec. Mkt. **$43**

QX 491-5   SNOOPY® AND WOODSTOCK ☐

Comments: Handcrafted, 1-3/4" tall. Snoopy and Woodstock are practicing their hockey moves. **Artist:** Bob Siedler

☐ Purchased 19____   Pd $_____   MIB NB DB BNT
☐ Want   Orig. Ret. $7.50   **NB** $67   **MIB** Sec. Mkt. **$80**

QX 470-2   SNOW-PITCHING SNOWMAN ☐

Comments: Handcrafted, 2" tall, Reissued in 1986. A cute little snowman, dressed in a red and green baseball cap, is captured in the middle of pitching his snowball.
Artist: Donna Lee

☐ Purchased 19____   Pd $_____   MIB NB DB BNT
☐ Want   Orig. Ret. $4.50   **NB** $17   **MIB** Sec. Mkt. **$25**

It is better to light one candle than to curse the darkness.

QX 510-5 SNOWFLAKE: HEIRLOOM COLLECTION ☐

Comments: Fabric, 4-1/4" dia. Hand-crocheted snowflake covers padded burgundy satin. **Artist:** Joyce Pattee

☐ Purchased 19____ Pd $_____ MIB NB DB BNT
☐ Want Orig. Ret. $6.50 **NB** $9 **MIB** Sec. Mkt. **$23**

QX 450-1 SNOWY SEAL ☐

Comments: Handcrafted, 1-1/2" wide. Reissued from 1984. **Artist:** Ed Seale

☐ Purchased 19____ Pd $_____ MIB NB DB BNT
☐ Want Orig. Ret. $4.00 **NB** $10 **MIB** Sec. Mkt. **$15**

QX 477-5 SOCCER BEAVER ☐

Comments: Handcrafted, 2-1/2" tall, Reissued in 1986. This little fellow, dressed in a red shirt, is ready to play! **Artist:** Peter Dutkin

☐ Purchased 19____ Pd $_____ MIB NB DB BNT
☐ Want Orig. Ret. $6.50 **NB** $15 **MIB** Sec. Mkt. **$25**

QX 502-5 SON ☐

Comments: Handcrafted, 2" tall, Dated 1985. This charming little terrier with red bow, holds a message, "Merry Christmas Son." **Artist:** Bob Siedler

☐ Purchased 19____ Pd $_____ MIB NB DB BNT
☐ Want Orig. Ret. $5.50 **NB** $32 **MIB** Sec. Mkt. **$50**

QX 372-5 SPECIAL FRIENDS ☐

Comments: Acrylic, 3" wide, Dated 1985. A doll and a bear are etched with the message: "Special friends bring special joys to Christmas." **Artist:** Don Palmiter

☐ Purchased 19____ Pd $_____ MIB NB DB BNT
☐ Want Orig. Ret. $5.75 **NB** $5 **MIB** Sec. Mkt. **$10**

QX 498-5 SPIRIT OF SANTA CLAUS, THE ☐

Comments: Special Ed., Handcrafted, 4-3/4" tall. This elaborate reindeer and sleigh with Santa at the reins is beautiful! Came with a wishbone-shaped hanger. **Artist:** Donna Lee

☐ Purchased 19____ Pd $_____ MIB NB DB BNT
☐ Want Orig. Ret. $22.50 **NB** $55 **MIB** Sec. Mkt. **$75**

QX 475-2 STARDUST ANGEL ☐

Comments: Handcrafted, 2" tall. An adorable angel goes about her daily chores... cleaning stardust from the stars. **Artist:** Donna Lee

☐ Purchased 19____ Pd $_____ MIB NB DB BNT
☐ Want Orig. Ret. $5.75 **NB** $30 **MIB** Sec. Mkt. **$37**

QLX 701-1 SUGARPLUM COTTAGE ☐

Comments: Lighted, Handcrafted, 3" tall. Issued in 1984, 1985 and 1986.

☐ Purchased 19____ Pd $_____ MIB NB DB BNT
☐ Want Orig. Ret. $11.00 **NB** $20 **MIB** Sec. Mkt. **$30**

QX 492-2 SUN & FUN SANTA ☐

Comments: Handcrafted, 2-3/4" tall, Dated 1985. Santa's ready for the beach with his reindeer inner tube and bathing cap. **Artist:** Bob Siedler

☐ Purchased 19____ Pd $_____ MIB NB DB BNT
☐ Want Orig. Ret. $7.75 **NB** $30 **MIB** Sec. Mkt. **$40**

QX 492-5 SWINGING ANGEL BELL ☐

Comments: Handcrafted/Glass, 3-3/4" tall. An angel is the clapper of this clear glass bell. **Artist:** Bob Siedler

☐ Purchased 19____ Pd $_____ MIB NB DB BNT
☐ Want Orig. Ret. $11.00 **NB** $35 **MIB** Sec. Mkt. **$40**

QLX 706-5 SWISS CHEESE LANE ☐

Comments: Lighted, Handcrafted, 2-5/8" tall, Dated 1985. "Swiss Cheese Lane" turns a wedge of cheese into a comfortable home for a pair of mice. The brightly lit interior shows the details of the home.

☐ Purchased 19____ Pd $_____ MIB NB DB BNT
☐ Want Orig. Ret. $13.00 **NB** $30 **MIB** Sec. Mkt. **$40**

QX 505-2 TEACHER - OWL ☐

Comments: Handcrafted, 3" tall, "School Days 1985." An owl sits atop a slate reading a book. The slate reads "Merry Christmas to a Grade A Teacher." May be personalized on the back of the slate.

☐ Purchased 19____ Pd $_____ MIB NB DB BNT
☐ Want Orig. Ret. $6.00 **NB** $11 **MIB** Sec. Mkt. **$20**

QX 472-5   THIMBLE SERIES: SANTA ☐

Comments: **Eighth in Series,** Handcrafted, 2-3/8" tall. Santa carries a thimble "backpack" with a Christmas tree. **Artist:** Bob Siedler

☐ Purchased 19____   Pd $_____   MIB   NB   DB   BNT
☐ Want   Orig. Ret. $5.50   **NB** $20   **MIB** Sec. Mkt. **$35**

QX 431-1   THREE KITTENS IN A MITTEN ☐

Comments: Handcrafted, 3-1/2" tall. Reissued from 1984. **Artist:** Donna Lee

☐ Purchased 19____   Pd $_____   MIB   NB   DB   BNT
☐ Want   Orig. Ret. $8.00   **NB** $22   **MIB** Sec. Mkt. **$40**

QX 497-2   TIN LOCOMOTIVE ☐

Comments: **Fourth in Series,** 3-1/2" tall, Dated 1985. This black locomotive is embellished with colors and designs and a jingle bell. **Artist:** Linda Sickman

☐ Purchased 19____   Pd $_____   MIB   NB   DB   BNT
☐ Want   Orig. Ret. $14.75   **NB** $65   **MIB** Sec. Mkt. **$80**

QX 471-2   TRUMPET PANDA ☐

Comments: Handcrafted, 2" tall. A flocked panda plays a red trumpet. **Artist:** Ed Seale

☐ Purchased 19____   Pd $_____   MIB   NB   DB   BNT
☐ Want   Orig. Ret. $4.50   **NB** $17   **MIB** Sec. Mkt. **$25**

QX 371-2   TWELVE DAYS OF CHRISTMAS ☐

Comments: **Second in Series,** Acrylic, 3" tall, Dated 1985. Two turtle doves are represented for the Second Day of Christmas. Caption: "...two turtle doves." **Artist:** Sharon Pike

☐ Purchased 19____   Pd $_____   MIB   NB   DB   BNT
☐ Want   Orig. Ret. $6.50   **NB** $50   **MIB** Sec. Mkt. **$70**

QX 500-5   TWENTY-FIVE YEARS TOGETHER ☐

Comments: Porcelain, 3-1/4" dia., Dated 1985. A white porcelain plate is decorated with a blue, silver and gold wreath of holly and firs. Caption: "Twenty-Five Years Together."

☐ Purchased 19____   Pd $_____   MIB   NB   DB   BNT
☐ Want   Orig. Ret. $8.00   **NB** $11   **MIB** Sec. Mkt. **$20**

QX 513-2   VICTORIAN LADY ☐

Comments: Porcelain/Fabric, 3-3/4" tall. A hand-painted porcelain doll wears a dress of burgundy satin and lace trim.

☐ Purchased 19____   Pd $_____   MIB   NB   DB   BNT
☐ Want   Orig. Ret. $9.50   **NB** $15   **MIB** Sec. Mkt. **$25**

QLX 702-1   VILLAGE CHURCH ☐

Comments: Lighted, Handcrafted, 4-5/8" tall. Reissued from 1984. **Artist:** Donna Lee

☐ Purchased 19____   Pd $_____   MIB   NB   DB   BNT
☐ Want   Orig. Ret. $15.00   **NB** $35   **MIB** Sec. Mkt. **$40**

QX 519-2   WHIRLIGIG SANTA ☐

Comments: Wood, 4" tall. Modeled after a Colonial toy, this Santa has arms that move in a whirligig fashion.

☐ Purchased 19____   Pd $_____   MIB   NB   DB   BNT
☐ Want   Orig. Ret. $12.50   **NB** $20   **MIB** Sec. Mkt. **$30**

QX 490-2   WINDOWS OF THE WORLD: MEXICAN ☐

Comments: **FIRST IN SERIES,** Handcrafted, 3" tall, Dated 1985. A little Mexican boy sits in a brick and stucco window and plays. Caption: "Feliz Navidad." **Artist:** Donna Lee

☐ Purchased 19____   Pd $_____   MIB   NB   DB   BNT
☐ Want   Orig. Ret. $9.75   **NB** $60   **MIB** Sec. Mkt. **$75**

QX 375-2   WITH APPRECIATION ☐

Comments: Acrylic, 3-1/2" tall, Dated 1985. Silver foil snowflakes and gold caption: "Christmas... a time when we think of those who have given us so much." Framed in brass.

☐ Purchased 19____   Pd $_____   MIB   NB   DB   BNT
☐ Want   Orig. Ret. $6.75   **NB** $2   **MIB** Sec. Mkt. **$10**

QX 472-2   WOOD CHILDHOOD SERIES: TRAIN ☐

Comments: **Second in Series,** Wood, 3-1/2" wide. Handpainted locomotive carries a log car. Has a real pull string and wheels that turn. **Artist:** Peter Dutkin

☐ Purchased 19____   Pd $_____   MIB   NB   DB   BNT
☐ Want   Orig. Ret. $7.00   **NB** $20   **MIB** Sec. Mkt. **$30**

1986 Collection

QX 424-3 ACORN INN ☐

Comments: Handcrafted, 2" tall. Using a green wreath a squirrel decorates his snow-capped inn. **Artist:** Duane Unruh

☐ Purchased 19___ Pd $_____ MIB NB DB BNT
☐ Want Orig. Ret. $8.50 **NB** $17 **MIB** Sec. Mkt. $20

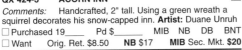

QX 350-6 ART MASTERPIECE: MADONNA & CHILD ☐

Comments: **Third and Final in Series,** Bezeled Satin, 3-1/4" tall. Caption: "Lorenzo Di Cridi, Madonna and Child with the Infant St. John, The Nelson-Atkins Museum Of Art, Kansas City, MO (Nelson Fund)." **Artist:** Diana McGehee

☐ Purchased 19___ Pd $_____ MIB NB DB BNT
☐ Want Orig. Ret. $6.75 **NB** $20 **MIB** Sec. Mkt. $30

QX 412-3 BABY LOCKET ☐

Comments: Textured Brass, 2-1/4" dia., Dated 1986. This brass locket includes embossed lettering and baby toy designs. Opens for Baby's photo and personalizing. Caption: "Baby." **Artist:** Diana McGehee

☐ Purchased 19___ Pd $_____ MIB NB DB BNT
☐ Want Orig. Ret. $16.00 **NB** $15 **MIB** Sec. Mkt. $27

QX 271-3 BABY'S FIRST CHRISTMAS ☐

Comments: Ecru Satin Ball 2-7/8" dia., Dated 1986. Caption: "A Baby's A Bundle Of Hope And Joy" and "Baby's First Christmas."

☐ Purchased 19___ Pd $_____ MIB NB DB BNT
☐ Want Orig. Ret. $5.50 **NB** $15 **MIB** Sec. Mkt. $25

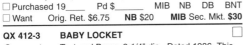

QLX 710-3 BABY'S FIRST CHRISTMAS ☐

Comments: Lighted Panorama Ball, 3-5/8" tall. Baby's First Christmas 1986. Caption: "There's Someone New On Santa's List, Someone Small And Dear, Someone Santa's Sure To Love And Visit Every Year!" **Artist:** Ken Crow

☐ Purchased 19___ Pd $_____ MIB NB DB BNT
☐ Want Orig. Ret. $19.50 **NB** $32 **MIB** Sec. Mkt. $45

QX 412-6 BABY'S FIRST CHRISTMAS ☐

Comments: Handcrafted, 3-1/2" tall, Dated 1986. Miniature mobile has a duck, Santa, teddy bear and stocking hanging from an acrylic cloud and star with the caption: "Baby's First Christmas." **Artist:** Linda Sickman

☐ Purchased 19___ Pd $_____ MIB NB DB BNT
☐ Want Orig. Ret. $9.00 **NB** $28 **MIB** Sec. Mkt. $40

QX 380-3 BABY'S FIRST CHRISTMAS ☐

Comments: Acrylic, 3-3/4" tall, Dated 1986. A lamb with curly etched "wool" carries a stocking for "Baby's First Christmas." **Artist:** Don Palmiter

☐ Purchased 19___ Pd $_____ MIB NB DB BNT
☐ Want Orig. Ret. $6.00 **NB** $10 **MIB** Sec. Mkt. $25

QX 379-2 BABY'S FIRST CHRISTMAS PHOTOHOLDER ☐

Comments: Fabric, 3-3/4" tall, Dated 1986. Green and white gingham photoholder. Caption: "Baby's First Christmas" and "A Baby Puts Special Magic In Holiday Moments." **Artist:** Joyce Pattee

☐ Purchased 19___ Pd $_____ MIB NB DB BNT
☐ Want Orig. Ret. $8.00 **NB** $10 **MIB** Sec. Mkt. $15

QX 413-3 BABY'S SECOND CHRISTMAS ☐

Comments: Handcrafted, 1-3/4" tall, Dated 1986. A little mouse with a diaper delivers a stocking that says "Baby's 2nd Christmas." **Artist:** Bob Siedler

☐ Purchased 19___ Pd $_____ MIB NB DB BNT
☐ Want Orig. Ret. $6.50 **NB** $15 **MIB** Sec. Mkt. $30

QX 275-6 BABY-SITTER ☐

Comments: Gold Glass Ball, 3" dia., Dated Christmas 1986. Antique toys circle the ball. Caption: "For Being The Best Friend A Child Could Ever Have." Baby sitter ornaments usually never go up on the Secondary Market.

☐ Purchased 19___ Pd $_____ MIB NB DB BNT
☐ Want Orig. Ret. $4.75 **NB** $5 **MIB** Sec. Mkt. $10

QX 480-5 BEARY SMOOTH RIDE ☐

Comments: Handcrafted, 1-3/4" tall. Reissued from 1985. **Artist:** Linda Sickman

☐ Purchased 19___ Pd $_____ MIB NB DB BNT
☐ Want Orig. Ret. $6.50 **NB** $15 **MIB** Sec. Mkt. $20

QX 277-6 BETSEY CLARK: HOME FOR CHRISTMAS ☐

Comments: **FIRST IN SERIES,** Pink Glass Ball, 2-7/8" dia. Dated 1986. Betsey and her friends are busy decorating. Caption: "May Christmas Love Fill Every Little Corner Of Your World." **Artist:** Sharon Pike

☐ Purchased 19___ Pd $_____ MIB NB DB BNT
☐ Want Orig. Ret. $5.00 **NB** $23 **MIB** Sec. Mkt. $35

QX 428-3   BLUEBIRD

Comments: Hand-Painted Fine Porcelain, 3-5/16" tall. Red-breasted bluebird, with wings spread wide, has just landed on a tree branch. Clip-on hanger. **Artist:** Linda Sickman

☐ Purchased 19____   Pd $_____   MIB NB DB BNT
☐ Want   Orig. Ret. $7.25   **NB** $43   **MIB** Sec. Mkt. **$60**

QX 417-6   CHATTY PENGUIN

Comments: Plush, 3-5/8" tall. Colorful penguin wearing a red Santa cap squeaks when you shake him. **Artist:** Ken Crow

☐ Purchased 19____   Pd $_____   MIB NB DB BNT
☐ Want   Orig. Ret. $5.75   **NB** $15   **MIB** Sec. Mkt. **$25**

QX 413-6   CHILD'S THIRD CHRISTMAS

Comments: Fabric, 2-11/32" tall, Dated 1986. This flocked panda is dressed in red cap and sleepers. Written on his green bib is "Child's Third Christmas." **Artist:** Joyce Pattee

☐ Purchased 19____   Pd $_____   MIB NB DB BNT
☐ Want   Orig. Ret. $6.50   **NB** $20   **MIB** Sec. Mkt. **$27**

QLX 705-6   CHRIS MOUSE: CHRIS MOUSE DREAMS

Comments: **Second in Series,** Lighted, Handcrafted, 3-3/4" tall. Dated 1986. Chris Mouse slumbers away. His "home" was molded from a real pinecone. **Artist:** Peter Dutkin

☐ Purchased 19____   Pd $_____   MIB NB DB BNT
☐ Want   Orig. Ret. $13.00   **NB** $55   **MIB** Sec. Mkt. **$75**

QX 322-3   CHRISTMAS BEAUTY

Comments: Lacquer-Look, 2-3/4" dia. The spirit of the season is depicted with Oriental flavor. Caption: "Christmas Comes Gently, Touching The World With Beauty, Filling It With Joy." **Artist:** Joyce Pattee

☐ Purchased 19____   Pd $_____   MIB NB DB BNT
☐ Want   Orig. Ret. $6.00   **NB** $5   **MIB** Sec. Mkt. **$10**

QLX 704-3   CHRISTMAS CLASSICS:
NUTCRACKER BALLET

Comments: **FIRST IN SERIES,** Lighted, Handcrafted, 4-1/2" tall. Dated 1986. Crafted in shimmering pastels, a ballerina strikes a classic pose, waiting for the ballet to begin. "Sugarplum Fairy."

☐ Purchased 19____   Pd $_____   MIB NB DB BNT
☐ Want   Orig. Ret. $17.50   **NB** $60   **MIB** Sec. Mkt. **$85**

QX 512-6   CHRISTMAS GUITAR

Comments: Handcrafted, 3" tall, Dated 1986. This miniature guitar is decorated with green and red holly. Hangs from fabric guitar strap. **Artist:** Duane Unruh

☐ Purchased 19____   Pd $_____   MIB NB DB BNT
☐ Want   Orig. Ret. $7.00   **NB** $15   **MIB** Sec. Mkt. **$25**

QLX 701-2   CHRISTMAS SLEIGH RIDE

Comments: Light and Motion, Handcrafted, 3-3/4" tall. A couple rides in a horse-drawn sleigh. The clear dome is sprinkled with "snow." Caption: "Love's Precious Moments Shine Forever In The Heart." **Artist:** Ed Seale

☐ Purchased 19____   Pd $_____   MIB NB DB BNT
☐ Want   Orig. Ret. $24.50   **NB** $125   **MIB** Sec. Mkt. **$150**

QX 406-3   CLOTHESPIN SOLDIERS:
FRENCH OFFICER

Comments: **Fifth in Series,** Handcrafted, 1-27/32" tall. Dressed in the style of Napoleon, this officer carries a telescope and is dressed in red and green. **Artist:** Linda Sickman

☐ Purchased 19____   Pd $_____   MIB NB DB BNT
☐ Want   Orig. Ret. $5.50   **NB** $23   **MIB** Sec. Mkt. **$30**

QXO279-6   COCA-COLA SANTA:
OPEN HOUSE ORNAMENT

Comments: Porcelain White Glass Ball, 2-7/8" dia. Three nostalgic paintings of Santa. Special offering for dealers' "Open House" events.

☐ Purchased 19____   Pd $_____   MIB NB DB BNT
☐ Want   Orig. Ret. $4.75   **NB** $12   **MIB** Sec. Mkt. **$22**

QX 414-6   COOKIES FOR SANTA

Comments: Handcrafted, 2-3/4" dia., Dated 1986. A plate carries a sign "For Santa" and holds a star shaped cookie and a gingerbread man. **Artist:** Diana McGehee

☐ Purchased 19____   Pd $_____   MIB NB DB BNT
☐ Want   Orig. Ret. $4.50   **NB** $18   **MIB** Sec. Mkt. **$30**

QX 511-3   COUNTRY SLEIGH

Comments: Handcrafted, 2" tall, Dated 1986. This red and gold sleigh was modeled after an antique sleigh and holds a plaid fabric blanket. **Artist:** Linda Sickman

☐ Purchased 19____   Pd $_____   MIB NB DB BNT
☐ Want   Orig. Ret. $10.00   **NB** $20   **MIB** Sec. Mkt. **$30**

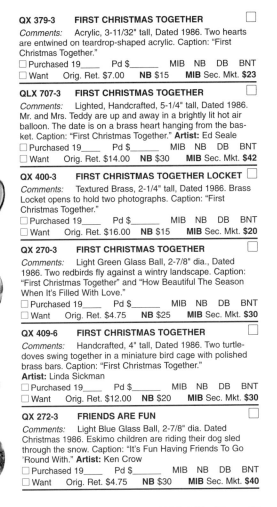

QX 430-6 DAUGHTER ☐

Comments: Handcrafted, 3-1/2" tall, Dated 1986.
A "wooden" doll, resembling an Old-World European toy, is in
a red and green knit stocking. Caption: "For Daughter."
Artist: Ed Seale

☐ Purchased 19____   Pd $_____   MIB NB DB BNT
☐ Want   Orig. Ret. $5.75   **NB** $39   **MIB** Sec. Mkt. **$50**

QX 481-2 DO NOT DISTURB BEAR ☐

Comments: Handcrafted, 3" wide.
Reissued from 1985. **Artist:** Ed Seale

☐ Purchased 19____   Pd $_____   MIB NB DB BNT
☐ Want   Orig. Ret. $7.75   **NB** $16   **MIB** Sec. Mkt. **$23**

QX 431-3 FATHER ☐

Comments: Wood, 3-1/4" dia., Dated Christmas 1986. A silver French horn, tied with a festive bow, decorates this wood-
en disc. Caption: "Nothing Can Ever Replace The Wisdom,
Guidance And Love Of A Father." **Artist:** LaDene Votruba

☐ Purchased 19____   Pd $_____   MIB NB DB BNT
☐ Want   Orig. Ret. $6.50   **NB** $10   **MIB** Sec. Mkt. **$15**

QX 514-3 FAVORITE TIN DRUM ☐

Comments: Tin, 2" dia., Dated 1986. The top and bottom of
this drum are decorated with holly and gold cord bindings.
Don't forget the drumsticks. **Artist:** Linda Sickman

☐ Purchased 19____   Pd $_____   MIB NB DB BNT
☐ Want   Orig. Ret. $8.50   **NB** $20   **MIB** Sec. Mkt. **$30**

QX 513-3 FESTIVE TREBLE CLEF ☐

Comments: Handcrafted, 3-7/8" tall. A golden treble clef is
accented with translucent red, a brass bell and a striped ribbon. **Artist:** Bob Siedler

☐ Purchased 19____   Pd $_____   MIB NB DB BNT
☐ Want   Orig. Ret. $8.75   **NB** $25   **MIB** Sec. Mkt. **$30**

QX 400-6 FIFTY YEARS TOGETHER ☐

Comments: Fine Porcelain, 3-13/32" tall. Dated Christmas
1986. White porcelain bell has a bas-relief holly design and a
sculpted "50" as the handle. Caption: "Fifty Years Together."

☐ Purchased 19____   Pd $_____   MIB NB DB BNT
☐ Want   Orig. Ret. $10.00   **NB** $12   **MIB** Sec. Mkt. **$20**

QX 379-3 FIRST CHRISTMAS TOGETHER ☐

Comments: Acrylic, 3-11/32" tall, Dated 1986. Two hearts
are entwined on teardrop-shaped acrylic. Caption: "First
Christmas Together."

☐ Purchased 19____   Pd $_____   MIB NB DB BNT
☐ Want   Orig. Ret. $7.00   **NB** $15   **MIB** Sec. Mkt. **$23**

QLX 707-3 FIRST CHRISTMAS TOGETHER ☐

Comments: Lighted, Handcrafted, 5-1/4" tall, Dated 1986.
Mr. and Mrs. Teddy are up and away in a brightly lit hot air
balloon. The date is on a brass heart hanging from the basket. Caption: "First Christmas Together." **Artist:** Ed Seale

☐ Purchased 19____   Pd $_____   MIB NB DB BNT
☐ Want   Orig. Ret. $14.00   **NB** $30   **MIB** Sec. Mkt. **$42**

QX 400-3 FIRST CHRISTMAS TOGETHER LOCKET ☐

Comments: Textured Brass, 2-1/4" tall, Dated 1986. Brass
Locket opens to hold two photographs. Caption: "First
Christmas Together."

☐ Purchased 19____   Pd $_____   MIB NB DB BNT
☐ Want   Orig. Ret. $16.00   **NB** $15   **MIB** Sec. Mkt. **$20**

QX 270-3 FIRST CHRISTMAS TOGETHER ☐

Comments: Light Green Glass Ball, 2-7/8" dia., Dated
1986. Two redbirds fly against a wintry landscape. Caption:
"First Christmas Together" and "How Beautiful The Season
When It's Filled With Love."

☐ Purchased 19____   Pd $_____   MIB NB DB BNT
☐ Want   Orig. Ret. $4.75   **NB** $25   **MIB** Sec. Mkt. **$30**

QX 409-6 FIRST CHRISTMAS TOGETHER ☐

Comments: Handcrafted, 4" tall, Dated 1986. Two turtle-
doves swing together in a miniature bird cage with polished
brass bars. Caption: "First Christmas Together."
Artist: Linda Sickman

☐ Purchased 19____   Pd $_____   MIB NB DB BNT
☐ Want   Orig. Ret. $12.00   **NB** $20   **MIB** Sec. Mkt. **$30**

QX 272-3 FRIENDS ARE FUN ☐

Comments: Light Blue Glass Ball, 2-7/8" dia. Dated
Christmas 1986. Eskimo children are riding their dog sled
through the snow. Caption: "It's Fun Having Friends To Go
'Round With." **Artist:** Ken Crow

☐ Purchased 19____   Pd $_____   MIB NB DB BNT
☐ Want   Orig. Ret. $4.75   **NB** $30   **MIB** Sec. Mkt. **$40**

QX 427-3 FRIENDSHIP GREETING ☐

Comments: Fabric, 2-3/4" tall, Dated 1986. Silk-screened fabric is stitched to create a colorful envelope ornament. Enclosed card reads: "Friends are forever." Back of envelope says "Merry Christmas."

☐ Purchased 19____ Pd $_____ MIB NB DB BNT
☐ Want Orig. Ret. $8.00 **NB** $5 **MIB** Sec. Mkt. **$15**

QX 381-6 FRIENDSHIP'S GIFT ☐

Comments: Acrylic, 3" tall, Dated Christmas 1986. A little mouse helps Santa deliver a gift. Caption: "Friendship Is A Gift."

☐ Purchased 19____ Pd $_____ MIB NB DB BNT
☐ Want Orig. Ret. $6.00 **NB** $10 **MIB** Sec. Mkt. **$15**

QX 383-3 FROM OUR HOME TO YOURS ☐

Comments: Acrylic, 3-1/4" tall, Dated Christmas 1986. A fruit-filled wicker basket graces this teardrop shaped ornament. Caption: "From Our Home To Yours."

☐ Purchased 19____ Pd $_____ MIB NB DB BNT
☐ Want Orig. Ret. $6.00 **NB** $8 **MIB** Sec. Mkt. **$15**

QX 405-3 FROSTY FRIENDS ☐

Comments: **Seventh in Series,** Handcrafted, 2-1/4" tall. Dated 1986. A flocked baby reindeer and the cute little Eskimo sit on an acrylic ice flow. **Artist:** Bob Siedler

☐ Purchased 19____ Pd $_____ MIB NB DB BNT
☐ Want Orig. Ret. $8.50 **NB** $60 **MIB** Sec. Mkt. **$75**

QLX 705-3 GENERAL STORE ☐

Comments: Lighted, Handcrafted, 2-11/16" tall. The store is bright with light and open for holiday business as it advertises "Christmas Trees 50¢." **Artist:** Donna Lee

☐ Purchased 19____ Pd $_____ MIB NB DB BNT
☐ Want Orig. Ret. $15.75 **NB** $55 **MIB** Sec. Mkt. **$60**

QLX 708-3 GENTLE BLESSINGS ☐

Comments: Lighted Panorama Ball, 3-5/8" tall. A glowing light shines on the Christ Child as the animals in the stable watch over Him. **Artist:** Linda Sickman

☐ Purchased 19____ Pd $_____ MIB NB DB BNT
☐ Want Orig. Ret. $15.00 **NB** $130 **MIB** Sec. Mkt. **$180**

QX 428-6 GLOWING CHRISTMAS TREE ☐

Comments: Embedded Acrylic, 3-1/4", Dated 1986. A brass Christmas tree, complete with colorful stars, is embedded in teardrop shaped acrylic. **Artist:** Joyce Pattee

☐ Purchased 19____ Pd $_____ MIB NB DB BNT
☐ Want Orig. Ret. $7.00 **NB** $11 **MIB** Sec. Mkt. **$15**

QX 271-6 GODCHILD ☐

Comments: White Satin Ball, 2-7/8" dia. Dated Christmas 1986. Colorful teddy bears circle the ornament capped with a gold crown. Caption: "A Godchild Is A Very Special Someone."

☐ Purchased 19____ Pd $_____ MIB NB DB BNT
☐ Want Orig. Ret. $4.75 **NB** $8 **MIB** Sec. Mkt. **$16**

QX 411-6 GRANDCHILD'S FIRST CHRISTMAS ☐

Comments: Handcrafted, 2-1/4" tall, Dated 1986. A flocked bear is sound asleep in a basket ready for "Baby's First Christmas."

☐ Purchased 19____ Pd $_____ MIB NB DB BNT
☐ Want Orig. Ret. $10.00 **NB** $10 **MIB** Sec. Mkt. **$16**

QX 273-6 GRANDDAUGHTER ☐

Comments: White Glass Ball, 2-7/8" dia. Dated Christmas 1986. Old-fashioned scenes of children and Christmas. Caption: "Season After Season, A Granddaughter Grows Dearer And Dearer." **Artist:** Joyce Lyle

☐ Purchased 19____ Pd $_____ MIB NB DB BNT
☐ Want Orig. Ret. $4.75 **NB** $21 **MIB** Sec. Mkt. **$33**

QX 274-3 GRANDMOTHER ☐

Comments: Ivory Satin Ball, 2-7/8" dia. Dated Christmas 1986. A country quilt design of Christmas trees carries the message: "A Grandmother's Love Is For Always." **Artist:** Joyce Pattee

☐ Purchased 19____ Pd $_____ MIB NB DB BNT
☐ Want Orig. Ret. $4.75 **NB** $8 **MIB** Sec. Mkt. **$16**

QX 432-3 GRANDPARENTS ☐

Comments: Porcelain, 5-1/2" tall, Dated Christmas 1986. Two doves in a Christmas stitch design decorate a white porcelain bell. Caption: "Grandparents Are Never Far From Thought... Ever Near In Love."

☐ Purchased 19____ Pd $_____ MIB NB DB BNT
☐ Want Orig. Ret. $7.50 **NB** $14 **MIB** Sec. Mkt. **$24**

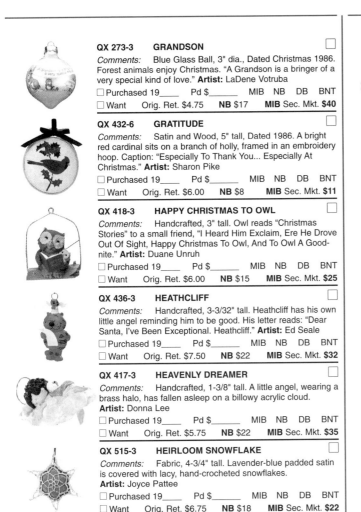

QX 273-3   GRANDSON

Comments: Blue Glass Ball, 3" dia., Dated Christmas 1986. Forest animals enjoy Christmas. "A Grandson is a bringer of a very special kind of love." **Artist:** LaDene Votruba

☐ Purchased 19____   Pd $_____   MIB NB DB BNT
☐ Want   Orig. Ret. $4.75   **NB** $17   **MIB** Sec. Mkt. **$40**

QX 432-6   GRATITUDE

Comments: Satin and Wood, 5" tall, Dated 1986. A bright red cardinal sits on a branch of holly, framed in an embroidery hoop. Caption: "Especially To Thank You... Especially At Christmas." **Artist:** Sharon Pike

☐ Purchased 19____   Pd $_____   MIB NB DB BNT
☐ Want   Orig. Ret. $6.00   **NB** $8   **MIB** Sec. Mkt. **$11**

QX 418-3   HAPPY CHRISTMAS TO OWL

Comments: Handcrafted, 3" tall. Owl reads "Christmas Stories" to a small friend, "I Heard Him Exclaim, Ere He Drove Out Of Sight, Happy Christmas To Owl, And To Owl A Goodnite." **Artist:** Duane Unruh

☐ Purchased 19____   Pd $_____   MIB NB DB BNT
☐ Want   Orig. Ret. $6.00   **NB** $15   **MIB** Sec. Mkt. **$25**

QX 436-3   HEATHCLIFF

Comments: Handcrafted, 3-3/32" tall. Heathcliff has his own little angel reminding him to be good. His letter reads: "Dear Santa, I've Been Exceptional. Heathcliff." **Artist:** Ed Seale

☐ Purchased 19____   Pd $_____   MIB NB DB BNT
☐ Want   Orig. Ret. $7.50   **NB** $22   **MIB** Sec. Mkt. **$32**

QX 417-3   HEAVENLY DREAMER

Comments: Handcrafted, 1-3/8" tall. A little angel, wearing a brass halo, has fallen asleep on a billowy acrylic cloud.
Artist: Donna Lee

☐ Purchased 19____   Pd $_____   MIB NB DB BNT
☐ Want   Orig. Ret. $5.75   **NB** $22   **MIB** Sec. Mkt. **$35**

QX 515-3   HEIRLOOM SNOWFLAKE

Comments: Fabric, 4-3/4" tall. Lavender-blue padded satin is covered with lacy, hand-crocheted snowflakes.
Artist: Joyce Pattee

☐ Purchased 19____   Pd $_____   MIB NB DB BNT
☐ Want   Orig. Ret. $6.75   **NB** $18   **MIB** Sec. Mkt. **$22**

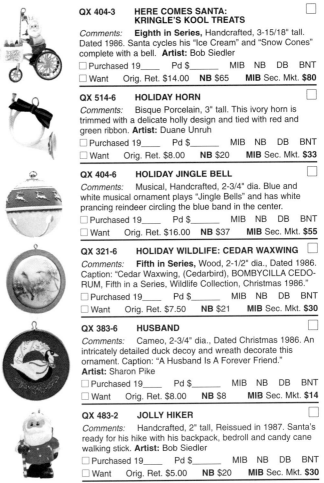

QX 404-3   HERE COMES SANTA: KRINGLE'S KOOL TREATS

Comments: **Eighth in Series,** Handcrafted, 3-15/18" tall. Dated 1986. Santa cycles his "Ice Cream" and "Snow Cones" complete with a bell. **Artist:** Bob Siedler

☐ Purchased 19____   Pd $_____   MIB NB DB BNT
☐ Want   Orig. Ret. $14.00   **NB** $65   **MIB** Sec. Mkt. **$80**

QX 514-6   HOLIDAY HORN

Comments: Bisque Porcelain, 3" tall. This ivory horn is trimmed with a delicate holly design and tied with red and green ribbon. **Artist:** Duane Unruh

☐ Purchased 19____   Pd $_____   MIB NB DB BNT
☐ Want   Orig. Ret. $8.00   **NB** $20   **MIB** Sec. Mkt. **$33**

QX 404-6   HOLIDAY JINGLE BELL

Comments: Musical, Handcrafted, 2-3/4" dia. Blue and white musical ornament plays "Jingle Bells" and has white prancing reindeer circling the blue band in the center.

☐ Purchased 19____   Pd $_____   MIB NB DB BNT
☐ Want   Orig. Ret. $16.00   **NB** $37   **MIB** Sec. Mkt. **$55**

QX 321-6   HOLIDAY WILDLIFE: CEDAR WAXWING

Comments: **Fifth in Series,** Wood, 2-1/2" dia., Dated 1986. Caption: "Cedar Waxwing, (Cedarbird), BOMBYCILLA CEDORUM, Fifth in a Series, Wildlife Collection, Christmas 1986."

☐ Purchased 19____   Pd $_____   MIB NB DB BNT
☐ Want   Orig. Ret. $7.50   **NB** $21   **MIB** Sec. Mkt. **$30**

QX 383-6   HUSBAND

Comments: Cameo, 2-3/4" dia., Dated Christmas 1986. An intricately detailed duck decoy and wreath decorate this ornament. Caption: "A Husband Is A Forever Friend."
Artist: Sharon Pike

☐ Purchased 19____   Pd $_____   MIB NB DB BNT
☐ Want   Orig. Ret. $8.00   **NB** $8   **MIB** Sec. Mkt. **$14**

QX 483-2   JOLLY HIKER

Comments: Handcrafted, 2" tall, Reissued in 1987. Santa's ready for his hike with his backpack, bedroll and candy cane walking stick. **Artist:** Bob Siedler

☐ Purchased 19____   Pd $_____   MIB NB DB BNT
☐ Want   Orig. Ret. $5.00   **NB** $20   **MIB** Sec. Mkt. **$30**

QX 429-6 JOLLY ST. NICK

Comments: Hand-Painted Fine Porcelain, 5-1/2" tall. Special Edition. Crafted from a Thomas Nast St. Nicholas introduced in the 1800s. **Artist:** Duane Unruh

☐ Purchased 19____ Pd $_____ MIB NB DB BNT
☐ Want   Orig. Ret. $22.50 **NB** $55   **MIB** Sec. Mkt. **$75**

QX 382-3 JOY OF FRIENDS

Comments: Bezeled Satin, 2-3/4" tall. Ice skaters, printed on padded satin, resemble American folk art. Framed in chrome. Caption: "Friends Make The Heart Warmer, The Day Merrier, The Season More Memorable." Artist: Joyce Pattee

☐ Purchased 19____ Pd $_____ MIB NB DB BNT
☐ Want   Orig. Ret. $6.75 **NB** $10   **MIB** Sec. Mkt. **$18**

QX 513-6 JOYFUL CAROLERS

Comments: Handcrafted, 3-1/4" dia., Dated 1986. Designed similar to the Nostalgia ornaments, carolers dressed in Dickens' style share their joy. Caption: "Joy To The World." **Artist:** Linda Sickman

☐ Purchased 19____ Pd $_____ MIB NB DB BNT
☐ Want   Orig. Ret. $9.75 **NB** $36   **MIB** Sec. Mkt. **$42**

QX 435-3 KATYBETH WITH STAR

Comments: Hand-Painted Fine Porcelain, 2-19/32" tall. Katybeth plays with a star that is passing by.

☐ Purchased 19____ Pd $_____ MIB NB DB BNT
☐ Want   Orig. Ret. $7.00 **NB** $15   **MIB** Sec. Mkt. **$25**

QLX 707-6 KEEP ON GLOWIN'!

Comments: Lighted, Handcrafted, 2-7/16" tall. Reissued in 1987. This bright icicle proves a source of fun for one of Santa's elves. **Artist:** Ken Crow

☐ Purchased 19____ Pd $_____ MIB NB DB BNT
☐ Want   Orig. Ret. $10.00 **NB** $40   **MIB** Sec. Mkt. **$52**

QX 474-5 KITTY MISCHIEF

Comments: Handcrafted, 2" tall. Reissued from 1985. **Artist:** Peter Dutkin

☐ Purchased 19____ Pd $_____ MIB NB DB BNT
☐ Want   Orig. Ret. $5.00 **NB** $19   **MIB** Sec. Mkt. **$28**

QX 419-3 LI'L JINGLER

Comments: Handcrafted, 2" tall, Reissued in 1987. A cute little raccoon in a red bow-tie hangs onto a stringer of brass jingle bells. Cute piece! **Artist:** Ed Seale

☐ Purchased 19____ Pd $_____ MIB NB DB BNT
☐ Want   Orig. Ret. $6.75 **NB** $28   **MIB** Sec. Mkt. **$42**

QX 511-6 LITTLE DRUMMERS

Comments: Handcrafted, 4" tall, Real Drumming Motion. Three little drummer boys play their drums when you tap or shake their platform. **Artist:** Ken Crow

☐ Purchased 19____ Pd $_____ MIB NB DB BNT
☐ Want   Orig. Ret. $12.50 **NB** $22   **MIB** Sec. Mkt. **$32**

QX 409-3 LOVING MEMORIES

Comments: Handcrafted, 5-1/4" tall, Dated 1986. A heart-shaped shadow box holds a brass bell, teddy bear and Christmas gift. **Artist:** Ed Seale

☐ Purchased 19____ Pd $_____ MIB NB DB BNT
☐ Want   Orig. Ret. $9.00 **NB** $20 **MIB** Sec. Mkt. **$37.50**

QX 272-6 MAGI, THE

Comments: Gold Glass Teardrop Ball, 3" dia. Dated Christmas 1986. The Magi bring their gifts to the Child. Caption: "O Come Let Us Adore Him." **Artist:** Sharon Pike

☐ Purchased 19____ Pd $_____ MIB NB DB BNT
☐ Want   Orig. Ret. $4.75 **NB** $10   **MIB** Sec. Mkt. **$24**

QX 429-3 MAGICAL UNICORN

Comments: Limited Edition 24,700, Wooden Display Stand. Hand-Painted Fine Porcelain, 4-1/2" tall. White porcelain unicorn has hand-painted pastel flowers and pastel ribbons. Beautiful! **Artist:** Duane Unruh

☐ Purchased 19____ Pd $_____ MIB NB DB BNT
☐ Want   Orig. Ret. $27.50 **NB** $65   **MIB** Sec. Mkt. **$80**

QX 402-3 MARIONETTE ANGEL

Comments: Handcrafted, 3-9/16" tall, Very rare! This whimsical little angel has authentic marionette features. Appeared in retailers' catalogs but was pulled from production.

☐ Purchased 19____ Pd $_____ MIB NB DB BNT
☐ Want   Orig. Ret. $8.50 **NB** $350 **MIB** Sec. Mkt. **$410**

QX 275-2   MARY EMMERLING: AMERICAN COUNTRY COLLECTION ☐

Comments: Glass Balls, 2-7/8" dia., Set of 4.
These four blue and white glass balls feature motifs from 19th Century American homes.

☐ Purchased 19_____   Pd $_____   MIB   NB   DB   BNT
☐ Want   Orig. Ret. $7.95   **NB** $10   **MIB** Sec. Mkt. **$22**

QX 427-6   MEMORIES TO CHERISH: PHOTOHOLDER ☐

Comments: Ceramic, 3-1/8" tall, Dated Christmas 1986. A white, braided wreath sports holly and a big red bow. Caption: "A Memory To Cherish."

☐ Purchased 19_____   Pd $_____   MIB   NB   DB   BNT
☐ Want   Orig. Ret. $7.50   **NB** $22   **MIB** Sec. Mkt. **$30**

QLX 709-3   MERRY CHRISTMAS BELL ☐

Comments: Lighted Acrylic, 5-9/16" tall. Bell-shaped acrylic has etched Christmas flowers. Caption: "Merry Christmas." **Artist:** LaDene Votruba

☐ Purchased 19_____   Pd $_____   MIB   NB   DB   BNT
☐ Want   Orig. Ret. $8.50   **NB** $15   **MIB** Sec. Mkt. **$25**

QX 415-3   MERRY KOALA ☐

Comments: Handcrafted, 2" tall, Reissued in 1987. Flocked koala is wearing an oversized Santa cap. **Artist:** Linda Sickman

☐ Purchased 19_____   Pd $_____   MIB   NB   DB   BNT
☐ Want   Orig. Ret. $5.00   **NB** $15   **MIB** Sec. Mkt. **$23**

QX 403-2   MERRY MOUSE ☐

Comments: Handcrafted, 2-1/2" tall. Reissued from 1985. **Artist:** Peter Dutkin

☐ Purchased 19_____   Pd $_____   MIB   NB   DB   BNT
☐ Want   Orig. Ret. $4.50   **NB** $20   **MIB** Sec. Mkt. **$30**

QX 407-6   MINIATURE CRECHE ☐

Comments: **Second in Series,** Fine Porcelain, 3-3/4" tall. Porcelain bisque figures of the Holy Family are set off beautifully with the graceful arch and brass star shining brightly above. **Artist:** Ed Seale

☐ Purchased 19_____   Pd $_____   MIB   NB   DB   BNT
☐ Want   Orig. Ret. $9.00   **NB** $45   **MIB** Sec. Mkt. **$62**

QX 382-6   MOTHER ☐

Comments: Acrylic, 2-3/4" dia., Dated 1986. A brass bezel frames this ornament with a heart etched in the center with the caption: "A Mother's Love Reflects The Warmth Of Christmas All Year Through."

☐ Purchased 19_____   Pd $_____   MIB   NB   DB   BNT
☐ Want   Orig. Ret. $7.00   **NB** $20   **MIB** Sec. Mkt. **$25**

QX 431-6   MOTHER AND DAD ☐

Comments: Fine Porcelain, 5-1/2" tall, Dated Christmas 1986. Brilliant, colorful candles make a striking contrast on this white bell tied up in red ribbon. Caption: "For A Mother And Dad Who Are Warmly Loved." **Artist:** Michele Pyda-Sevcik

☐ Purchased 19_____   Pd $_____   MIB   NB   DB   BNT
☐ Want   Orig. Ret. $7.50   **NB** $11   **MIB** Sec. Mkt. **$25**

QX 416-6   MOUSE IN THE MOON ☐

Comments: Handcrafted, 2-3/4" tall, Reissued in 1987. This cute little mouse, dressed in red sleepers, likes his reflection shown in the mirrored moon. **Artist:** Ed Seale

☐ Purchased 19_____   Pd $_____   MIB   NB   DB   BNT
☐ Want   Orig. Ret. $5.50   **NB** $16   **MIB** Sec. Mkt. **$22**

QX 402-6   MR. AND MRS. CLAUS: MERRY MISTLETOE TIME ☐

Comments: **FIRST IN SERIES,** Handcrafted, 3-7/16" tall. Dated 1986. Mrs. Claus gives Santa a big kiss as he stands under the mistletoe she's holding. **Artist:** Duane Unruh

☐ Purchased 19_____   Pd $_____   MIB   NB   DB   BNT
☐ Want   Orig. Ret. $13.00   **NB** $90   **MIB** Sec. Mkt. **$105**

QLX 705-2   MR. AND MRS. SANTA ☐

Comments: Lighted, Handcrafted, 3" tall. Reissued from 1985.

☐ Purchased 19_____   Pd $_____   MIB   NB   DB   BNT
☐ Want   Orig. Ret. $14.50   **NB** $50   **MIB** Sec. Mkt. **$70**

QX 381-3   NEPHEW ☐

Comments: Bezeled Lacquer-Look, 2-3/4" dia., Dated 1986. A white snowman, accented with a red scarf, contrasts vividly against the sky. Caption: "To Wish A Special Nephew A Happy Holiday Season!"

☐ Purchased 19_____   Pd $_____   MIB   NB   DB   BNT
☐ Want   Orig. Ret. $6.25   **NB** $10   **MIB** Sec. Mkt. **$15**

QX 274-6   NEW HOME

Comments: White Glass Ball, 3" dia., Dated 1986. Gingerbread people and animals run through a neighborhood of sweets. Caption: "Christmas Is So Special When It's Spent In A New Home." **Artist:** Ken Crow

☐ Purchased 19____   Pd $_____   MIB NB DB BNT
☐ Want   Orig. Ret. $4.75   **NB** $34   **MIB** Sec. Mkt. **$50**

QX 426-6   NIECE

Comments: Fabric and Wood, 4-1/2" tall. Dated Christmas 1986. A white cat with a big red bow around its neck sits on red and green cushions. Caption: "Nieces Give The Nicest Gifts... Beauty, Joy And Love."

☐ Purchased 19____   Pd $_____   MIB NB DB BNT
☐ Want   Orig. Ret. $6.00   **NB** $5   **MIB** Sec. Mkt. **$10**

QX 276-3   NORMAN ROCKWELL

Comments: Green Glass Ball, 2-7/8" dia. Christmas scenes reflect the excitement of Christmas. Caption: "Christmas Time Is Filled With Joy And Glad Anticipation, And All The Loving Reasons For A Happy Celebration."

☐ Purchased 19____   Pd $_____   MIB NB DB BNT
☐ Want   Orig. Ret. $4.75   **NB** $16   **MIB** Sec. Mkt. **$30**

QX 321-3   NORMAN ROCKWELL: CHECKING UP

Comments: **Seventh in Series,** Red Cameo, 3-1/4" dia. Caption: "Checking Up, Seventh In A Series, Christmas 1986, The Norman Rockwell Collection." **Artist:** Sharon Pike

☐ Purchased 19____   Pd $_____   MIB NB DB BNT
☐ Want   Orig. Ret. $7.75   **NB** $23   **MIB** Sec. Mkt. **$30**

QX 403-3   NOSTALGIC HOUSES AND SHOPS: CHRISTMAS CANDY SHOPPE

Comments: **Third in Series,** Handcrafted, 4-5/16" tall. Dated 1986. The baking is done upstairs and the candies are sold downstairs. Very popular ornament. Harder to find than the 1985 issue. **Artist:** Donna Lee

☐ Purchased 19____   Pd $_____   MIB NB DB BNT
☐ Want   Orig. Ret. $13.75   **NB** $250   **MIB** Sec. Mkt. **$300**

QX 512-3   NUTCRACKER SANTA

Comments: Handcrafted, 3-3/8" tall. Crafted to look like a nutcracker, Santa's mouth pops open when you lift the tassel on his cap. **Artist:** Duane Unruh

☐ Purchased 19____   Pd $_____   MIB NB DB BNT
☐ Want   Orig. Ret. $10.00   **NB** $35   **MIB** Sec. Mkt. **$50**

QXO440-3   OLD-FASHIONED SANTA: OPEN HOUSE ORN.

Comments: Handcrafted, 4-1/2" tall. Old World Santa, looking like hand-carved wood, carries a bag of toys. Special offering for dealers' "Open House" events. **Artist:** Linda Sickman

☐ Purchased 19____   Pd $_____   MIB NB DB BNT
☐ Want   Orig. Ret. $12.75   **NB** $37   **MIB** Sec. Mkt. **$50**

QSP 420-1   ON THE RIGHT TRACK: GOLD CROWN ORN.

Comments: Hand-Painted Fine Porcelain, 4-3/4" tall. The artist signed his name to this special promotional Santa. Santa, in his shirt sleeves, puts the finishing touches on a locomotive. **Artist:** Peter Dutkin

☐ Purchased 19____   Pd $_____   MIB NB DB BNT
☐ Want   Orig. Ret. $15.00   **NB** $37   **MIB** Sec. Mkt. **$50**

QX 422-6   OPEN ME FIRST

Comments: Handcrafted, 2-15/16" tall, Dated 1986. A child is delighted with the kitten inside a gift box titled "Open Me First."

☐ Purchased 19____   Pd $_____   MIB NB DB BNT
☐ Want   Orig. Ret. $7.25   **NB** $25   **MIB** Sec. Mkt. **$35**

QX 435-6   PADDINGTON™ BEAR

Comments: Handcrafted, 2-9/16" tall. This favorite bear is dressed in a bright blue coat and yellow hat, and carries a jar of honey. **Artist:** Bob Siedler

☐ Purchased 19____   Pd $_____   MIB NB DB BNT
☐ Want   Orig. Ret. $6.00   **NB** $28   **MIB** Sec. Mkt. **$40**

QX 276-6   PEANUTS®

Comments: Blue Glass Ball, 3" dia., Dated 1986. Snoopy, Woodstock and his feathered friends go ice skating. Caption: "Merry Christmas."

☐ Purchased 19____   Pd $_____   MIB NB DB BNT
☐ Want   Orig. Ret. $4.75   **NB** $25   **MIB** Sec. Mkt. **$30**

QX 425-3   PLAYFUL POSSUM

Comments: Handcrafted/Glass, 3-23/32" tall. An opossum is the clapper in a clear glass bell. **Artist:** Ken Crow

☐ Purchased 19____   Pd $_____   MIB NB DB BNT
☐ Want   Orig. Ret. $11.00   **NB** $25   **MIB** Sec. Mkt. **$35**

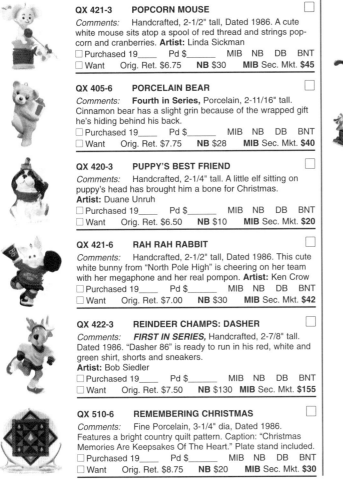

QX 421-3   POPCORN MOUSE ☐

Comments: Handcrafted, 2-1/2" tall, Dated 1986. A cute white mouse sits atop a spool of red thread and strings popcorn and cranberries. **Artist:** Linda Sickman
☐ Purchased 19____ Pd $_____ MIB NB DB BNT
☐ Want Orig. Ret. $6.75 **NB** $30 **MIB** Sec. Mkt. **$45**

QX 405-6   PORCELAIN BEAR ☐

Comments: **Fourth in Series,** Porcelain, 2-11/16" tall. Cinnamon bear has a slight grin because of the wrapped gift he's hiding behind his back.
☐ Purchased 19____ Pd $_____ MIB NB DB BNT
☐ Want Orig. Ret. $7.75 **NB** $28 **MIB** Sec. Mkt. **$40**

QX 420-3   PUPPY'S BEST FRIEND ☐

Comments: Handcrafted, 2-1/4" tall. A little elf sitting on puppy's head has brought him a bone for Christmas. **Artist:** Duane Unruh
☐ Purchased 19____ Pd $_____ MIB NB DB BNT
☐ Want Orig. Ret. $6.50 **NB** $10 **MIB** Sec. Mkt. **$20**

QX 421-6   RAH RAH RABBIT ☐

Comments: Handcrafted, 2-1/2" tall, Dated 1986. This cute white bunny from "North Pole High" is cheering on her team with her megaphone and her real pompon. **Artist:** Ken Crow
☐ Purchased 19____ Pd $_____ MIB NB DB BNT
☐ Want Orig. Ret. $7.00 **NB** $30 **MIB** Sec. Mkt. **$42**

QX 422-3   REINDEER CHAMPS: DASHER ☐

Comments: **FIRST IN SERIES,** Handcrafted, 2-7/8" tall. Dated 1986. "Dasher 86" is ready to run in his red, white and green shirt, shorts and sneakers. **Artist:** Bob Siedler
☐ Purchased 19____ Pd $_____ MIB NB DB BNT
☐ Want Orig. Ret. $7.50 **NB** $130 **MIB** Sec. Mkt. **$155**

QX 510-6   REMEMBERING CHRISTMAS ☐

Comments: Fine Porcelain, 3-1/4" dia, Dated 1986. Features a bright country quilt pattern. Caption: "Christmas Memories Are Keepsakes Of The Heart." Plate stand included.
☐ Purchased 19____ Pd $_____ MIB NB DB BNT
☐ Want Orig. Ret. $8.75 **NB** $20 **MIB** Sec. Mkt. **$30**

QX 401-6   ROCKING HORSE ☐

Comments: **Sixth in Series,** Handcrafted, 4" wide, Dated 1986. A golden palomino rides into the holidays on green rockers. Some collectors found this ornament with the number "QX 436-6." Others have found a gold sticker on the box stating "Made in Macau." **Artist:** Linda Sickman
☐ Purchased 19____ Pd $_____ MIB NB DB BNT
☐ Want Orig. Ret. $10.75 **NB** $40 **MIB** Sec. Mkt. **$65**

QXO440-6   SANTA & HIS REINDEER: OPEN HOUSE ORNAMENT ☐

Comments: Handcrafted, 2" tall and 14" wide. Two reindeer pull Santa in his sleigh full of toys. Special offering for "Open House" events. Very nice ornament!
☐ Purchased 19____ Pd $_____ MIB NB DB BNT
☐ Want Orig. Ret. $9.75 **NB** $15 **MIB** Sec. Mkt. **$25**

QLX 703-3   SANTA & SPARKY ☐

Comments: **FIRST IN SERIES,** Light and Motion, Handcrafted. 4-1/16" tall, Dated 1986. Santa lights the Christmas tree and moves backwards to admire this work, as Sparky penguin watches with excitement.
☐ Purchased 19____ Pd $_____ MIB NB DB BNT
☐ Want Orig. Ret. $22.00 **NB** $75 **MIB** Sec. Mkt. **$95**

QT 700-6   SANTA TREE TOPPER ☐

Comments: Open House, Fabric. This whimsical Santa is all set in his red and white suit with green mittens. He holds a gold wand.
☐ Purchased 19____ Pd $_____ MIB NB DB BNT
☐ Want Orig. Ret. $18.00 **NB** $28 **MIB** Sec. Mkt. **$38**

QX 426-3   SANTA'S HOT TUB ☐

Comments: Handcrafted, 3" tall. Santa and one of his reindeer are enjoying themselves in a hot tub from the "Polar Barrel Hot Tub Co." **Artist:** Ed Seale
☐ Purchased 19____ Pd $_____ MIB NB DB BNT
☐ Want Orig. Ret. $12.00 **NB** $35 **MIB** Sec. Mkt. **$60**

QLX 711-5   SANTA'S ON HIS WAY ☐

Comments: Light and Hologram Panorama Ball, 3-5/8" tall. Laser photography creates a three-dimensional effect of Santa and his reindeer flying above the city. **Artist:** Duane Unruh
☐ Purchased 19____ Pd $_____ MIB NB DB BNT
☐ Want Orig. Ret. $15.00 **NB** $60 **MIB** Sec. Mkt. **$75**

QXO 441-3   SANTA'S PANDA PAL: OPEN HOUSE ORN.

Comments: Handcrafted, 2-1/4" tall. Cute flocked panda wears a Santa hat. Special offering for dealers' "Open House" events.

☐ Purchased 19____   Pd $_____   MIB   NB   DB   BNT
☐ Want   Orig. Ret. $5.00   **NB** $18   **MIB** Sec. Mkt. **$30**

QLX 706-6   SANTA'S SNACK

Comments: Lighted, Handcrafted, 2-15/16" tall. Santa's midnight snack is a "mile-high" sandwich. Santa is dressed in reindeer slippers and a green striped nightshirt. **Artist:** Ken Crow

☐ Purchased 19____   Pd $_____   MIB   NB   DB   BNT
☐ Want   Orig. Ret. $10.00   **NB** $45   **MIB** Sec. Mkt. **$60**

QX 270-6   SEASON OF THE HEART

Comments: Red Glass Ball, 2-7/8" dia. A family enjoys a ride through the snow-covered countryside in a horse-drawn sleigh. Caption: "Christmas... Season Of The Heart, Time Of Fond Remembrance."

☐ Purchased 19____   Pd $_____   MIB   NB   DB   BNT
☐ Want   Orig. Ret. $4.75   **NB** $5   **MIB** Sec. Mkt. **$19**

QLX 706-3   SHARING FRIENDSHIP

Comments: Lighted Acrylic, 5-5/16" tall, Dated 1986. A poinsettia etched into clear acrylic accents the caption: "Friendship Is A Special Kind Of Sharing." **Artist:** LaDene Votruba

☐ Purchased 19____   Pd $_____   MIB   NB   DB   BNT
☐ Want   Orig. Ret. $8.50   **NB** $12   **MIB** Sec. Mkt. **$20**

QLT 709-6   SHINING STAR TREE TOPPER

Comments: Lighted, Acrylic. A partridge graces the center of this five-pointed star. Each of the five points include a design of a pear and leaf.

☐ Purchased 19____   Pd $_____   MIB   NB   DB   BNT
☐ Want   Orig. Ret. $17.50   **NB** $14   **MIB** Sec. Mkt. **$25**

QX 277-3   SHIRT TALES™ PARADE

Comments: Gold Glass Ball, 2-7/8" dia. The Shirt Tales Band parades around the ball. Caption: "Here Comes Christmas!" and "Merriment Is All Around Whenever Christmas Comes To Town!"

☐ Purchased 19____   Pd $_____   MIB   NB   DB   BNT
☐ Want   Orig. Ret. $4.75   **NB** $10   **MIB** Sec. Mkt. **$18**

QX 380-6   SISTER

Comments: Bezeled Satin, 2-3/4" dia., Dated 1986. Red padded satin carries a design of a grapevine wreath entwined with holly and ribbon, with a teddy bear for company. Caption: "With Every Christmas, Every Year, A Sister Grows More Loved... More Dear." **Artist:** LaDene Votruba

☐ Purchased 19____   Pd $_____   MIB   NB   DB   BNT
☐ Want   Orig. Ret. $6.75   **NB** $12   **MIB** Sec. Mkt. **$16**

QX 473-2   SKATEBOARD RACCOON

Comments: Handcrafted, 2-1/2" tall. Reissued from 1985. **Artist:** Peter Dutkin

☐ Purchased 19____   Pd $_____   MIB   NB   DB   BNT
☐ Want   Orig. Ret. $6.50   **NB** $33   **MIB** Sec. Mkt. **$43**

QX 420-6   SKI TRIPPER

Comments: Handcrafted, 2-1/8" tall. A young skier is ready for the slopes with her red jumpsuit and skis in hand. **Artist:** Bob Siedler

☐ Purchased 19____   Pd $_____   MIB   NB   DB   BNT
☐ Want   Orig. Ret. $6.75   **NB** $12   **MIB** Sec. Mkt. **$20**

QX 438-3   SNOOPY® AND WOODSTOCK

Comments: Handcrafted, 1-3/4" tall. These two friends enjoy their saucer ride down the hill on the "Beagle Express." **Artist:** Bob Siedler

☐ Purchased 19____   Pd $_____   MIB   NB   DB   BNT
☐ Want   Orig. Ret. $8.00   **NB** $32   **MIB** Sec. Mkt. **$45**

QX 423-6   SNOW BUDDIES

Comments: Handcrafted, 2-1/4" tall. A little mouse has created a "snowmouse" complete with a fabric muffler. His arms are molded from real sticks. **Artist:** Peter Dutkin

☐ Purchased 19____   Pd $_____   MIB   NB   DB   BNT
☐ Want   Orig. Ret. $8.00   **NB** $26   **MIB** Sec. Mkt. **$40**

QX 470-2   SNOW-PITCHING SNOWMAN

Comments: Handcrafted, 2" tall. Reissued from 1985. **Artist:** Donna Lee

☐ Purchased 19____   Pd $_____   MIB   NB   DB   BNT
☐ Want   Orig. Ret. $4.50   **NB** $17   **MIB** Sec. Mkt. **$25**

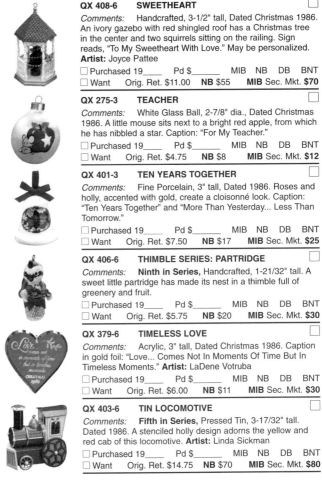

QX 477-5   SOCCER BEAVER

Comments: Handcrafted, 2-1/2" tall. Reissued from 1985.
Artist: Peter Dutkin

☐ Purchased 19＿＿＿   Pd $＿＿＿＿   MIB NB DB BNT
☐ Want   Orig. Ret. $6.50   **NB** $15   **MIB** Sec. Mkt. **$25**

QX 430-3   SON

Comments: Handcrafted, 4" tall, Dated 1986. A wooden boy toy is poking out of the top of a red and green striped knit stocking "For Son." **Artist:** Ed Seale

☐ Purchased 19＿＿＿   Pd $＿＿＿＿   MIB NB DB BNT
☐ Want   Orig. Ret. $5.75   **NB** $18   **MIB** Sec. Mkt. **$35**

QX 415-6   SPECIAL DELIVERY

Comments: Handcrafted, 2" tall. This little penguin is on his way to deliver a gift of sardines to one of his friends.
Artist: Bob Siedler

☐ Purchased 19＿＿＿   Pd $＿＿＿＿   MIB NB DB BNT
☐ Want   Orig. Ret. $5.00   **NB** $23   **MIB** Sec. Mkt. **$30**

QX 322-6   STAR BRIGHTENERS

Comments: Acrylic, 2-3/4" dia., Dated 1986. Two etched angels are polishing a star. Caption: "Joy At Christmas."
Artist: LaDene Votruba

☐ Purchased 19＿＿＿   Pd $＿＿＿＿   MIB NB DB BNT
☐ Want   Orig. Ret. $6.00   **NB** $15   **MIB** Sec. Mkt. **$20**

QX 384-3   STATUE OF LIBERTY, THE

Comments: Acrylic, 3-9/16" tall, Dated 1986. This special commemorative shows "The Lady" etched in clear acrylic and was created in honor of the statue's 100th birthday. Caption: "1886 Centennial 1986." **Artist:** Michele Pyda-Sevcik

☐ Purchased 19＿＿＿   Pd $＿＿＿＿   MIB NB DB BNT
☐ Want   Orig. Ret. $6.00   **NB** $12   **MIB** Sec. Mkt. **$25**

QLX 701-1   SUGARPLUM COTTAGE

Comments: Lighted, Handcrafted, 3" tall. Issued in 1984, 1985 and 1986.

☐ Purchased 19＿＿＿   Pd $＿＿＿＿   MIB NB DB BNT
☐ Want   Orig. Ret. $11.00   **NB** $20   **MIB** Sec. Mkt. **$30**

QX 408-6   SWEETHEART

Comments: Handcrafted, 3-1/2" tall, Dated Christmas 1986. An ivory gazebo with red shingled roof has a Christmas tree in the center and two squirrels sitting on the railing. Sign reads, "To My Sweetheart With Love." May be personalized.
Artist: Joyce Pattee

☐ Purchased 19＿＿＿   Pd $＿＿＿＿   MIB NB DB BNT
☐ Want   Orig. Ret. $11.00   **NB** $55   **MIB** Sec. Mkt. **$70**

QX 275-3   TEACHER

Comments: White Glass Ball, 2-7/8" dia., Dated Christmas 1986. A little mouse sits next to a bright red apple, from which he has nibbled a star. Caption: "For My Teacher."

☐ Purchased 19＿＿＿   Pd $＿＿＿＿   MIB NB DB BNT
☐ Want   Orig. Ret. $4.75   **NB** $8   **MIB** Sec. Mkt. **$12**

QX 401-3   TEN YEARS TOGETHER

Comments: Fine Porcelain, 3" tall, Dated 1986. Roses and holly, accented with gold, create a cloisonné look. Caption: "Ten Years Together" and "More Than Yesterday... Less Than Tomorrow."

☐ Purchased 19＿＿＿   Pd $＿＿＿＿   MIB NB DB BNT
☐ Want   Orig. Ret. $7.50   **NB** $17   **MIB** Sec. Mkt. **$25**

QX 406-6   THIMBLE SERIES: PARTRIDGE

Comments: **Ninth in Series,** Handcrafted, 1-21/32" tall. A sweet little partridge has made its nest in a thimble full of greenery and fruit.

☐ Purchased 19＿＿＿   Pd $＿＿＿＿   MIB NB DB BNT
☐ Want   Orig. Ret. $5.75   **NB** $20   **MIB** Sec. Mkt. **$30**

QX 379-6   TIMELESS LOVE

Comments: Acrylic, 3" tall, Dated Christmas 1986. Caption in gold foil: "Love... Comes Not In Moments Of Time But In Timeless Moments." **Artist:** LaDene Votruba

☐ Purchased 19＿＿＿   Pd $＿＿＿＿   MIB NB DB BNT
☐ Want   Orig. Ret. $6.00   **NB** $11   **MIB** Sec. Mkt. **$30**

QX 403-6   TIN LOCOMOTIVE

Comments: **Fifth in Series,** Pressed Tin, 3-17/32" tall. Dated 1986. A stenciled holly design adorns the yellow and red cab of this locomotive. **Artist:** Linda Sickman

☐ Purchased 19＿＿＿   Pd $＿＿＿＿   MIB NB DB BNT
☐ Want   Orig. Ret. $14.75   **NB** $70   **MIB** Sec. Mkt. **$80**

QX 418-6   TIPPING THE SCALES

Comments: Handcrafted, 2-11/16" tall, Dated 1986. Santa, in his red monogrammed robe, checks out his weight... "1986" while holding a cookie. **Artist:** Peter Dutkin

☐ Purchased 19_____   Pd $_____   MIB   NB   DB   BNT

☐ Want   Orig. Ret. $6.75   **NB** $23   **MIB** Sec. Mkt. **$30**

QX 423-3   TOUCHDOWN SANTA

Comments: Handcrafted, 2-15/16" tall, Dated 1986. Santa has the ball and he's headed for a touchdown! His red jersey is #86. **Artist:** Peter Dutkin

☐ Purchased 19_____   Pd $_____   MIB   NB   DB   BNT

☐ Want   Orig. Ret. $8.00   **NB** $33   **MIB** Sec. Mkt. **$43**

QX 425-6   TREETOP TRIO/BLUEBIRDS

Comments: Handcrafted, 2" tall, Reissued in 1987. The bluebird trio is chirping out a Christmas carol in a nest of real straw. **Artist:** Donna Lee

☐ Purchased 19_____   Pd $_____   MIB   NB   DB   BNT

☐ Want   Orig. Ret. $11.00   **NB** $25   **MIB** Sec. Mkt. **$33**

QX 378-6   TWELVE DAYS OF CHRISTMAS: THREE FRENCH HENS

Comments: **Third in Series,** Acrylic, 3-3/8" tall, Dated 1986. This acrylic teardrop has captions in gold and pictures three hens on holly leaves. **Artist:** LaDene Votruba

☐ Purchased 19_____   Pd $_____   MIB   NB   DB   BNT

☐ Want   Orig. Ret. $6.50   **NB** $30   **MIB** Sec. Mkt. **$45**

QX 410-3   TWENTY-FIVE YEARS TOGETHER

Comments: Fine Porcelain Plate, 3-1/4" tall. Dated Christmas 1986. Blue and silver bells tied up with ribbon and holly. Comes with acrylic stand. Caption: "Twenty-Five Years Together" and "Love Lights All The Seasons Of Our Years." **Artist:** LaDene Votruba

☐ Purchased 19_____   Pd $_____   MIB   NB   DB   BNT

☐ Want   Orig. Ret. $8.00   **NB** $13   **MIB** Sec. Mkt. **$25**

QLX 707-2   VILLAGE EXPRESS

Comments: Light/Motion, Handcrafted, 3-1/2" tall. Reissued in 1987. A train chugs through a peaceful mountain village and a tunnel. **Artist:** Linda Sickman

☐ Purchased 19_____   Pd $_____   MIB   NB   DB   BNT

☐ Want   Orig. Ret. $24.50   **NB** $100   **MIB** Sec. Mkt. **$125**

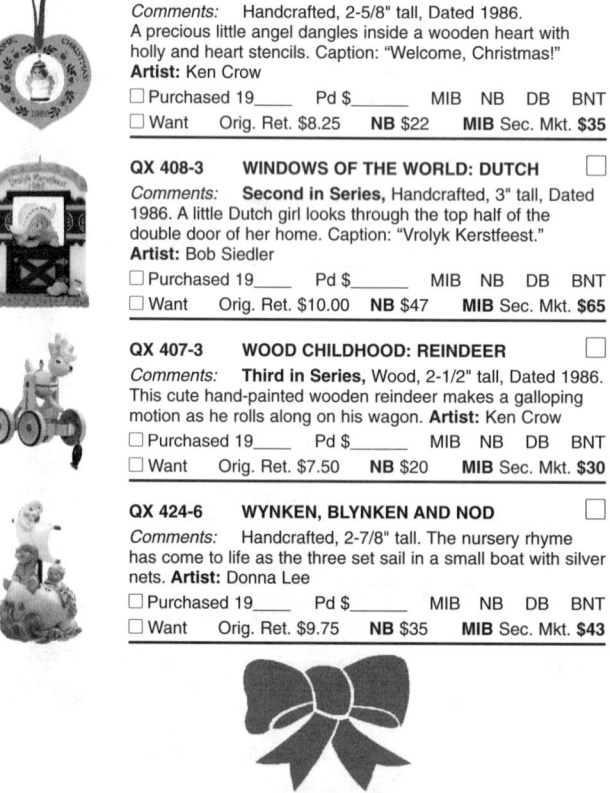

QX 419-6   WALNUT SHELL RIDER

Comments: Handcrafted, 1-3/4" tall, Reissued in 1987. An elf dressed in blue rides downhill in his walnut shell sled. **Artist:** Ed Seale

☐ Purchased 19_____   Pd $_____   MIB   NB   DB   BNT

☐ Want   Orig. Ret. $6.00   **NB** $19   **MIB** Sec. Mkt. **$23**

QX 510-3   WELCOME, CHRISTMAS

Comments: Handcrafted, 2-5/8" tall, Dated 1986. A precious little angel dangles inside a wooden heart with holly and heart stencils. Caption: "Welcome, Christmas!" **Artist:** Ken Crow

☐ Purchased 19_____   Pd $_____   MIB   NB   DB   BNT

☐ Want   Orig. Ret. $8.25   **NB** $22   **MIB** Sec. Mkt. **$35**

QX 408-3   WINDOWS OF THE WORLD: DUTCH

Comments: **Second in Series,** Handcrafted, 3" tall, Dated 1986. A little Dutch girl looks through the top half of the double door of her home. Caption: "Vrolyk Kerstfeest." **Artist:** Bob Siedler

☐ Purchased 19_____   Pd $_____   MIB   NB   DB   BNT

☐ Want   Orig. Ret. $10.00   **NB** $47   **MIB** Sec. Mkt. **$65**

QX 407-3   WOOD CHILDHOOD: REINDEER

Comments: **Third in Series,** Wood, 2-1/2" tall, Dated 1986. This cute hand-painted wooden reindeer makes a galloping motion as he rolls along on his wagon. **Artist:** Ken Crow

☐ Purchased 19_____   Pd $_____   MIB   NB   DB   BNT

☐ Want   Orig. Ret. $7.50   **NB** $20   **MIB** Sec. Mkt. **$30**

QX 424-6   WYNKEN, BLYNKEN AND NOD

Comments: Handcrafted, 2-7/8" tall. The nursery rhyme has come to life as the three set sail in a small boat with silver nets. **Artist:** Donna Lee

☐ Purchased 19_____   Pd $_____   MIB   NB   DB   BNT

☐ Want   Orig. Ret. $9.75   **NB** $35   **MIB** Sec. Mkt. **$43**

1987 Collection

QLX 711-3 ANGELIC MESSENGERS
Comments: Light and Changing Scene Panorama Ball, 3-5/8" dia. Angels suddenly appear before the shepherds. Caption: "Love Came Down At Christmas, Love All Lovely, Love Divine. Love Was Born At Christmas, Star And Angels Gave The Sign." **Artist:** Duane Unruh

☐ Purchased 19_____ Pd $_____ MIB NB DB BNT
☐ Want Orig. Ret. $18.75 **NB** $50 **MIB** Sec. Mkt. **$60**

QX 461-7 BABY LOCKET
Comments: Textured Metal, 2-1/4" dia., Dated 1987. This silvery locket has a space for baby's photo and for personalization. Has a wishbone hanger.

☐ Purchased 19_____ Pd $_____ MIB NB DB BNT
☐ Want Orig. Ret. $15.00 **NB** $25 **MIB** Sec. Mkt. **$30**

QLX 704-9 BABY'S FIRST CHRISTMAS
Comments: Lighted, Handcrafted, 3-3/4" tall, Dated 1987. Teddy paints "Baby's First Christmas" on the nursery window.

☐ Purchased 19_____ Pd $_____ MIB NB DB BNT
☐ Want Orig. Ret. $13.50 **NB** $30 **MIB** Sec. Mkt. **$38**

QX 461-9 BABY'S FIRST CHRISTMAS PHOTOHOLDER
Comments: Ecru Fabric, 3-1/4" dia., Dated 1987. Caption: "Baby's First Christmas" and "Welcome To Christmas, Baby Dear. Everyone Is Glad You're Here."

☐ Purchased 19_____ Pd $_____ MIB NB DB BNT
☐ Want Orig. Ret. $7.50 **NB** $25 **MIB** Sec. Mkt. **$30**

QX 372-9 BABY'S FIRST CHRISTMAS
Comments: Acrylic, 3-1/2" tall, Dated 1987. Hand-etched acrylic baby booties are decorated with jingle bells. Caption: "Baby's First Christmas."

☐ Purchased 19_____ Pd $_____ MIB NB DB BNT
☐ Want Orig. Ret. $6.00 **NB** $10 **MIB** Sec. Mkt. **$20**

QX 274-9 BABY'S FIRST CHRISTMAS: BABY BOY
Comments: White Satin Ball, 2-7/8" dia., Dated 1987. Baby's blocks spell "Baby Boy." Caption: "A Baby Boy, So Darling And Dear, Makes Christmas Extra Special This Year. Baby's First Christmas." **Artist:** Joyce Pattee

☐ Purchased 19_____ Pd $_____ MIB NB DB BNT
☐ Want Orig. Ret. $4.75 **NB** $15 **MIB** Sec. Mkt. **$30**

QX 274-7 BABY'S FIRST CHRISTMAS: BABY GIRL
Comments: White Satin Ball, 2-7/8" dia., Dated 1987. Caption: "A Baby Girl, So Dear And Sweet, Makes Your Christmas Joy Complete. Baby's First Christmas." More "girls" than "boys." **Artist:** Joyce Pattee

☐ Purchased 19_____ Pd $_____ MIB NB DB BNT
☐ Want Orig. Ret. $4.75 **NB** $17 **MIB** Sec. Mkt. **$28**

QX 411-3 BABY'S FIRST CHRISTMAS
Comments: Handcrafted, 4-1/4" tall, Dated 1987. Baby has lots of fun in this real spring seat. Caption: "Baby's First Christmas." **Artist:** Donna Lee

☐ Purchased 19_____ Pd $_____ MIB NB DB BNT
☐ Want Orig. Ret. $9.75 **NB** $28 **MIB** Sec. Mkt. **$30**

QX 460-7 BABY'S SECOND CHRISTMAS
Comments: Handcrafted, 2-3/4" tall, Dated 1987. A "Clown-in-the-Box" greets "Baby's 2nd Christmas." Attaches to the tree with a clip. **Artist:** Donna Lee

☐ Purchased 19_____ Pd $_____ MIB NB DB BNT
☐ Want Orig. Ret. $5.75 **NB** $19 **MIB** Sec. Mkt. **$33**

QX 279-7 BABYSITTER
Comments: Porcelain White Glass Ball, 3" dia., Dated 1987. Caption: "For Bringing Children Such Special Gifts... Gentleness, Caring, And Love. Merry Christmas." **Artist:** Sharon Pike

☐ Purchased 19_____ Pd $_____ MIB NB DB BNT
☐ Want Orig. Ret. $4.75 **NB** $15 **MIB** Sec. Mkt. **$20**

QX 455-7 BEARY SPECIAL
Comments: Handcrafted, 2-1/2" tall. A flocked brown bear reaches up to hang an ornament on the tree – it has his picture on it! **Artist:** Bob Siedler

☐ Purchased 19_____ Pd $_____ MIB NB DB BNT
☐ Want Orig. Ret. $4.75 **NB** $18 **MIB** Sec. Mkt. **$30**

QX 272-7 BETSEY CLARK: HOME FOR CHRISTMAS
Comments: **Second in Series,** Gold Glass Ball, 2-7/8" dia. Dated 1987. Betsey and her friends add final holiday decorating touches. Captions: "There's No Place Like Christmas" and "Noel." **Artist:** Sharon Pike

☐ Purchased 19_____ Pd $_____ MIB NB DB BNT
☐ Want Orig. Ret. $5.00 **NB** $15 **MIB** Sec. Mkt. **$25**

QX 473-7 BRIGHT CHRISTMAS DREAMS ☐

Comments: Handcrafted 4" tall, Dated Christmas 1987. Four white mice with brightly colored nightcaps have fallen asleep in a box of Crayola Crayons. The Crayola series began in '88. **Artist:** Bob Siedler

☐ Purchased 19___ Pd $_____ MIB NB DB BNT
☐ Want Orig. Ret. $7.25 **NB** $75 **MIB** Sec. Mkt. **$90**

QLX 705-9 BRIGHT NOEL ☐

Comments: Lighted Acrylic, 5-1/2" tall. An outline of an acrylic star is the framework for a bright red "Noel" in the center. **Artist:** LaDene Votruba

☐ Purchased 19___ Pd $_____ MIB NB DB BNT
☐ Want Orig. Ret. $7.00 **NB** $20 **MIB** Sec. Mkt. **$32**

QXC 581-7 CARROUSEL REINDEER: CHARTER CLUB MEMBERSHIP ORNAMENT ☐

Comments: Handcrafted, 3-3/4" tall, Dated 1987. A prancing reindeer rides a brass post inside a hoop. Caption: "1987 Charter Member." Club logo is printed in gold on bottom of hoop. **Artist:** Linda Sickman

☐ Purchased 19___ Pd $_____ MIB NB DB BNT
☐ Want Orig. Ret. $8.00 **NB** $45 **MIB** Sec. Mkt. **$65**

QX 459-9 CHILD'S THIRD CHRISTMAS ☐

Comments: Handcrafted, 3" tall, Dated 1987. A child dressed in red rides a reindeer, which makes a galloping motion when it is tapped. Caption: "My 3rd Christmas." **Artist:** Ken Crow

☐ Purchased 19___ Pd $_____ MIB NB DB BNT
☐ Want Orig. Ret. $5.75 **NB** $15 **MIB** Sec. Mkt. **$30**

QX 456-7 CHOCOLATE CHIPMUNK ☐

Comments: Handcrafted, 2" tall. This cute little fellow sits happily on a chocolate chip cookie and holds a chip in his paws. **Artist:** Ed Seale

☐ Purchased 19___ Pd $_____ MIB NB DB BNT
☐ Want Orig. Ret. $6.00 **NB** $40 **MIB** Sec. Mkt. **$55**

QLX 705-7 CHRIS MOUSE GLOW ☐

Comments: **Third in Series,** Lighted, Handcrafted, 4-1/8" tall. Dated 1987. In a blue nightshirt and red cap, Chris Mouse swings happily from his "stained glass" lamp. **Artist:** Bob Siedler

☐ Purchased 19___ Pd $_____ MIB NB DB BNT
☐ Want Orig. Ret. $11.00 **NB** $50 **MIB** Sec. Mkt. **$60**

QLX 702-9 CHRISTMAS CLASSICS: A CHRISTMAS CAROL ☐

Comments: **Second in Series,** Lighted, Handcrafted, 4-3/16" tall. Dated 1987. In this scene, Scrooge gives gifts to Tiny Tim while his parents look on. Setting is a stage draped in elegant curtains.

☐ Purchased 19___ Pd $_____ MIB NB DB BNT
☐ Want Orig. Ret. $16.00 **NB** $60 **MIB** Sec. Mkt. **$75**

QX 453-7 CHRISTMAS CUDDLE ☐

Comments: Handcrafted, 2-3/4" tall. A kitten and a white mouse, in matching Santa caps, snuggle together.

☐ Purchased 19___ Pd $_____ MIB NB DB BNT
☐ Want Orig. Ret. $5.75 **NB** $18 **MIB** Sec. Mkt. **$30**

QX 467-9 CHRISTMAS FUN PUZZLE ☐

Comments: Handcrafted, 2-1/2" dia. A Santa, mouse and reindeer take on new shapes and designs as this ornament is rotated to mix or match the characters. **Artist:** Donna Lee

☐ Purchased 19___ Pd $_____ MIB NB DB BNT
☐ Want Orig. Ret. $8.00 **NB** $14 **MIB** Sec. Mkt. **$30**

QX 444-9 CHRISTMAS IS GENTLE ☐

Comments: Limited Edition 24,700, Hand numbered. Handpainted Bone China, 3" tall. Two lambs sit peacefully in a basket edged with gold. **Artist:** Ed Seale

☐ Purchased 19___ Pd $_____ MIB NB DB BNT
☐ Want Orig. Ret. $17.50 **NB** $50 **MIB** Sec. Mkt. **$65**

QX 473-9 CHRISTMAS KEYS ☐

Comments: Handcrafted, 2" tall. An ivory upright piano is decorated with sprigs of bright green holly and red berries. **Artist:** Duane Unruh

☐ Purchased 19___ Pd $_____ MIB NB DB BNT
☐ Want Orig. Ret. $5.75 **NB** $25 **MIB** Sec. Mkt. **$30**

QLX 701-3 CHRISTMAS MORNING ☐

Comments: Light and Motion, Handcrafted, 4-5/16" tall. Reissued in 1988. Two children slide down the banister in anticipation of their Christmas gifts. **Artist:** Ken Crow

☐ Purchased 19___ Pd $_____ MIB NB DB BNT
☐ Want Orig. Ret. $24.50 **NB** $40 **MIB** Sec. Mkt. **$50**

QX 442-9   CHRISTMAS TIME MIME ☐

Comments: Limited Edition 24,700 w/stand. Hand-Painted Fine Porcelain, 2-1/2" tall. The mime shares Christmas with a teddy bear. He wears a Santa cap and beard; his bag is filled with stars. **Artist:** Duane Unruh

☐ Purchased 19____   Pd $_____   MIB   NB   DB   BNT
☐ Want   Orig. Ret. $27.50   **NB** $37   **MIB** Sec. Mkt. **$55**

QX 480-7   CLOTHESPIN SOLDIER: SAILOR ☐

Comments: **Sixth and Final in Series,** Handcrafted, 2-1/4" tall. "Christmas is here," this sailor seems to be saying as he waves his red flags with bright green trees. **Artist:** Linda Sickman

☐ Purchased 19____   Pd $_____   MIB   NB   DB   BNT
☐ Want   Orig. Ret. $5.50   **NB** $20   **MIB** Sec. Mkt. **$30**

QX 481-7   COLLECTOR'S PLATE: LIGHT SHINES AT CHRISTMAS ☐

Comments: **FIRST IN SERIES,** Fine Porcelain, 3-1/4" dia. Dated 1987. Three children happily decorate their Christmas tree in anticipation of Christmas. **Artist:** LaDene Votruba

☐ Purchased 19____   Pd $_____   MIB   NB   DB   BNT
☐ Want   Orig. Ret. $8.00   **NB** $50   **MIB** Sec. Mkt. **$75**

QX 377-7   CONSTITUTION, THE ☐

Comments: Acrylic, 2-1/2" tall, Dated 1987. Oval acrylic features gold foil lettering and a brass frame. Caption: "We the People, The Constitution of the United States, 200 Years, 1787-1987." A quill is etched in the acrylic. **Artist:** Joyce Pattee

☐ Purchased 19____   Pd $_____   MIB   NB   DB   BNT
☐ Want   Orig. Ret. $6.50   **NB** $10   **MIB** Sec. Mkt. **$20**

QX 470-9   COUNTRY WREATH ☐

Comments: Wood and Straw, 4-3/4" tall. This straw wreath is tied with red yarn and is decorated with wooden shapes. **Artist:** Michele Pyda-Sevcik

☐ Purchased 19____   Pd $_____   MIB   NB   DB   BNT
☐ Want   Orig. Ret. $5.75   **NB** $25   **MIB** Sec. Mkt. **$30**

QX 282-9   CURRIER & IVES: AMERICAN FARM SCENE ☐

Comments: Porcelain White Glass Ball, 2-7/8" dia., Dated 1987. The farm on a wintry morning is portrayed in this design. Caption: "Christmas 1987. American Farm Scene, Currier & Ives." **Artist:** Joyce Lyle

☐ Purchased 19____   Pd $_____   MIB   NB   DB   BNT
☐ Want   Orig. Ret. $4.75   **NB** $18   **MIB** Sec. Mkt. **$30**

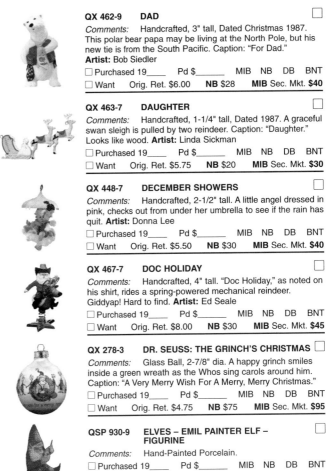

QX 462-9   DAD ☐

Comments: Handcrafted, 3" tall, Dated Christmas 1987. This polar bear papa may be living at the North Pole, but his new tie is from the South Pacific. Caption: "For Dad." **Artist:** Bob Siedler

☐ Purchased 19____   Pd $_____   MIB   NB   DB   BNT
☐ Want   Orig. Ret. $6.00   **NB** $28   **MIB** Sec. Mkt. **$40**

QX 463-7   DAUGHTER ☐

Comments: Handcrafted, 1-1/4" tall, Dated 1987. A graceful swan sleigh is pulled by two reindeer. Caption: "Daughter." Looks like wood. **Artist:** Linda Sickman

☐ Purchased 19____   Pd $_____   MIB   NB   DB   BNT
☐ Want   Orig. Ret. $5.75   **NB** $20   **MIB** Sec. Mkt. **$30**

QX 448-7   DECEMBER SHOWERS ☐

Comments: Handcrafted, 2-1/2" tall. A little angel dressed in pink, checks out from under her umbrella to see if the rain has quit. **Artist:** Donna Lee

☐ Purchased 19____   Pd $_____   MIB   NB   DB   BNT
☐ Want   Orig. Ret. $5.50   **NB** $30   **MIB** Sec. Mkt. **$40**

QX 467-7   DOC HOLIDAY ☐

Comments: Handcrafted, 4" tall. "Doc Holiday," as noted on his shirt, rides a spring-powered mechanical reindeer. Giddyap! Hard to find. **Artist:** Ed Seale

☐ Purchased 19____   Pd $_____   MIB   NB   DB   BNT
☐ Want   Orig. Ret. $8.00   **NB** $30   **MIB** Sec. Mkt. **$45**

QX 278-3   DR. SEUSS: THE GRINCH'S CHRISTMAS ☐

Comments: Glass Ball, 2-7/8" dia. A happy grinch smiles inside a green wreath as the Whos sing carols around him. Caption: "A Very Merry Wish For A Merry, Merry Christmas."

☐ Purchased 19____   Pd $_____   MIB   NB   DB   BNT
☐ Want   Orig. Ret. $4.75   **NB** $75   **MIB** Sec. Mkt. **$95**

QSP 930-9   ELVES – EMIL PAINTER ELF – FIGURINE ☐

Comments: Hand-Painted Porcelain.

☐ Purchased 19____   Pd $_____   MIB   NB   DB   BNT
☐ Want   Orig. Ret. $10.00   **NB** $25   **MIB** Sec. Mkt. **$38**

QSP 930-7　ELVES - HANS CARPENTER ELF - FIGURINE

Comments:　Hand-Painted Porcelain.

☐ Purchased 19____　　Pd $_____　　MIB　NB　DB　BNT

☐ Want　　Orig. Ret. $10.00　**NB** $25　**MIB** Sec. Mkt. **$38**

QSP 931-7　ELVES - KURT BLUE PRINT ELF - FIGURINE

Comments:　Hand-Painted Porcelain.

☐ Purchased 19____　　Pd $_____　　MIB　NB　DB　BNT

☐ Want　　Orig. Ret. $10.00　**NB** $25　**MIB** Sec. Mkt. **$35**

QX 445-7　FAVORITE SANTA

Comments:　Special Edition, Hand-Painted Fine Porcelain, 5-1/2" tall. A "Jolly Old Elf" indeed – Santa carries a long green, patched stocking full of gifts. **Artist:** Peter Dutkin

☐ Purchased 19____　　Pd $_____　　MIB　NB　DB　BNT

☐ Want　　Orig. Ret. $22.50　**NB** $28　**MIB** Sec. Mkt. **$45**

QX 443-7　FIFTY YEARS TOGETHER

Comments:　Fine Porcelain, 5" tall, Dated Christmas 1987. This lovely bell shows off a bas relief poinsettia and is rimmed in gold. Caption: "Fifty Years Together." Handle is a sculpted "50." **Artist:** Ed Seale

☐ Purchased 19____　　Pd $_____　　MIB　NB　DB　BNT

☐ Want　　Orig. Ret. $8.00　**NB** $10　**MIB** Sec. Mkt. **$25**

QX 272-9　FIRST CHRISTMAS TOGETHER

Comments:　White Glass Ball, 2-7/8" dia., Dated 1987.This ornament has a delicate design of lovebirds in a garden of pastel poinsettias. Caption: "First Christmas Together" and "To All Who Love, Love Is All The World." **Artist:** Joyce A. Lyle

☐ Purchased 19____　　Pd $_____　　MIB　NB　DB　BNT

☐ Want　　Orig. Ret. $4.75　**NB** $12　**MIB** Sec. Mkt. **$20**

QX 371-9　FIRST CHRISTMAS TOGETHER

Comments:　Acrylic, 2-1/2" tall, Dated 1987. Two etched swans glide gracefully among the tall grasses. Caption: "First Christmas Together."

☐ Purchased 19____　　Pd $_____　　MIB　NB　DB　BNT

☐ Want　　Orig. Ret. $6.50　**NB** $15　**MIB** Sec. Mkt. **$20**

QX 446-9　FIRST CHRISTMAS TOGETHER

Comments:　Textured Brass, 2-1/4" tall, Dated 1987. Heart-shaped brass locket is decorated with embossed lovebirds and caption.

☐ Purchased 19____　　Pd $_____　　MIB　NB　DB　BNT

☐ Want　　Orig. Ret. $15.00　**NB** $20　**MIB** Sec. Mkt. **$30**

QLX 708-7　FIRST CHRISTMAS TOGETHER

Comments:　Lighted, Handcrafted, 2-5/8" tall, Dated 1987. Two polar bears celebrate Christmas in their snow-capped igloo.

☐ Purchased 19____　　Pd $_____　　MIB　NB　DB　BNT

☐ Want　　Orig. Ret. $11.50　**NB** $37　**MIB** Sec. Mkt. **$50**

QX 445-9　FIRST CHRISTMAS TOGETHER

Comments:　Handcrafted, 2-1/2" tall, Dated 1987. Two raccoons "share" a red fabric sweatshirt. Caption: "First Christmas Together."

☐ Purchased 19____　　Pd $_____　　MIB　NB　DB　BNT

☐ Want　　Orig. Ret. $8.00　**NB** $29　**MIB** Sec. Mkt. **$39**

QX 446-7　FIRST CHRISTMAS TOGETHER

Comments:　Handcrafted, 3" tall, Dated 1987. Just add an attic and a roof to the heart and you have a cozy cottage for two! Sampler inside reads "Love, Sweet Love." **Artist:** Donna Lee

☐ Purchased 19____　　Pd $_____　　MIB　NB　DB　BNT

☐ Want　　Orig. Ret. $9.50　**NB** $20　**MIB** Sec. Mkt. **$30**

QX 474-9　FOLK ART SANTA

Comments:　Handcrafted, 4" tall. This Old-World Santa has been painted and antiqued to resemble folk art. His coat is accented with gold. **Artist:** Linda Sickman

☐ Purchased 19____　　Pd $_____　　MIB　NB　DB　BNT

☐ Want　　Orig. Ret. $5.25　**NB** $26　**MIB** Sec. Mkt. **$35**

QX 279-9　FROM OUR HOME TO YOURS

Comments:　White Glass Ball, 3" dia., Dated 1987. Holiday decorated doorways circle this frosted ball ornament. Caption: "From Our Home... To Yours... At Christmas." **Artist:** Michele Pyda-Sevcik

☐ Purchased 19____　　Pd $_____　　MIB　NB　DB　BNT

☐ Want　　Orig. Ret. $4.75　**NB** $40　**MIB** Sec. Mkt. **$50**

QX 440-9 FROSTY FRIENDS ☐

Comments: **Eighth in Series,** Handcrafted, 2" tall, Dated 1987. The little Eskimo is receiving a bright red gift from a flocked seal who has jumped up through a hole in the ice. **Artist:** Ed Seale

☐ Purchased 19____ Pd $_____ MIB NB DB BNT
☐ Want Orig. Ret. $8.50 **NB** $50 **MIB** Sec. Mkt. **$60**

QX 449-7 FUDGE FOREVER ☐

Comments: Handcrafted, 3" tall. A little white mouse has filled his tummy with the fudge in this blue spatterware ladle. **Artist:** Peter Dutkin

☐ Purchased 19____ Pd $_____ MIB NB DB BNT
☐ Want Orig. Ret. $5.00 **NB** $25 **MIB** Sec. Mkt. **$30**

QX 276-7 GODCHILD ☐

Comments: Blue Glass Ball, 2-7/8" dia., Dated 1987. A contemporary green tree with red balls and gold star are painted against a "snowy" blue ball. Caption: "A Godchild Makes Christmas Glow A Little Brighter." **Artist:** Michele Pyda-Sevcik

☐ Purchased 19____ Pd $_____ MIB NB DB BNT
☐ Want Orig. Ret. $4.75 **NB** $17 **MIB** Sec. Mkt. **$23**

QX 464-9 GOLDFINCH ☐

Comments: Hand-Painted Fine Porcelain, 2-1/2" tall. Poised in flight, this goldfinch is so realistically painted, you'd think it could fly away! **Artist:** Linda Sickman

☐ Purchased 19____ Pd $_____ MIB NB DB BNT
☐ Want Orig. Ret. $7.00 **NB** $55 **MIB** Sec. Mkt. **$90**

QLX 704-6 GOOD CHEER BLIMP ☐

Comments: Blinking Lights, Handcrafted, 3-1/16" tall. Santa leans over the side of his gondola to see where his next stop will be. **Artist:** Linda Sickman

☐ Purchased 19____ Pd $_____ MIB NB DB BNT
☐ Want Orig. Ret. $16.00 **NB** $30 **MIB** Sec. Mkt. **$50**

QX 460-9 GRANDCHILD'S FIRST CHRISTMAS ☐

Comments: Handcrafted, 1-3/4" tall, Dated 1987. A teddy bear sits on a red and green quilt inside a Jenny Lind style playpen. "Grandchild's First Christmas" is on the blanket over the side. **Artist:** Ed Seale

☐ Purchased 19____ Pd $_____ MIB NB DB BNT
☐ Want Orig. Ret. $9.00 **NB** $20 **MIB** Sec. Mkt. **$28**

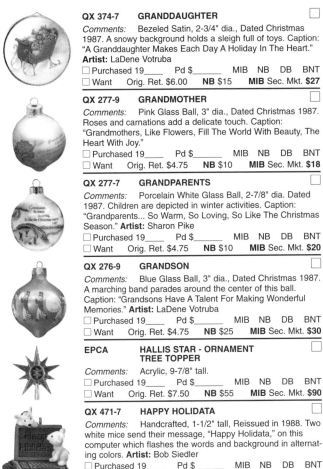

QX 374-7 GRANDDAUGHTER ☐

Comments: Bezeled Satin, 2-3/4" dia., Dated Christmas 1987. A snowy background holds a sleigh full of toys. Caption: "A Granddaughter Makes Each Day A Holiday In The Heart." **Artist:** LaDene Votruba

☐ Purchased 19____ Pd $_____ MIB NB DB BNT
☐ Want Orig. Ret. $6.00 **NB** $15 **MIB** Sec. Mkt. **$27**

QX 277-9 GRANDMOTHER ☐

Comments: Pink Glass Ball, 3" dia., Dated Christmas 1987. Roses and carnations add a delicate touch. Caption: "Grandmothers, Like Flowers, Fill The World With Beauty, The Heart With Joy."

☐ Purchased 19____ Pd $_____ MIB NB DB BNT
☐ Want Orig. Ret. $4.75 **NB** $10 **MIB** Sec. Mkt. **$18**

QX 277-7 GRANDPARENTS ☐

Comments: Porcelain White Glass Ball, 2-7/8" dia. Dated 1987. Children are depicted in winter activities. Caption: "Grandparents... So Warm, So Loving, So Like The Christmas Season." **Artist:** Sharon Pike

☐ Purchased 19____ Pd $_____ MIB NB DB BNT
☐ Want Orig. Ret. $4.75 **NB** $10 **MIB** Sec. Mkt. **$20**

QX 276-9 GRANDSON ☐

Comments: Blue Glass Ball, 3" dia., Dated Christmas 1987. A marching band parades around the center of this ball. Caption: "Grandsons Have A Talent For Making Wonderful Memories." **Artist:** LaDene Votruba

☐ Purchased 19____ Pd $_____ MIB NB DB BNT
☐ Want Orig. Ret. $4.75 **NB** $25 **MIB** Sec. Mkt. **$30**

EPCA HALLIS STAR - ORNAMENT TREE TOPPER ☐

Comments: Acrylic, 9-7/8" tall.

☐ Purchased 19____ Pd $_____ MIB NB DB BNT
☐ Want Orig. Ret. $7.50 **NB** $55 **MIB** Sec. Mkt. **$90**

QX 471-7 HAPPY HOLIDATA ☐

Comments: Handcrafted, 1-1/2" tall, Reissued in 1988. Two white mice send their message, "Happy Holidata," on this computer which flashes the words and background in alternating colors. **Artist:** Bob Siedler

☐ Purchased 19____ Pd $_____ MIB NB DB BNT
☐ Want Orig. Ret. $6.50 **NB** $25 **MIB** Sec. Mkt. **$30**

QX 456-9   HAPPY SANTA   ☐

Comments: Handcrafted, 2-1/2" tall. Santa hangs onto the tree branch with his candy cane. He also holds a gold jingle bell. **Artist:** Ken Crow

☐ Purchased 19____   Pd $_____   MIB NB DB BNT
☐ Want   Orig. Ret. $4.75   **NB $25**   **MIB** Sec. Mkt. **$30**

QX 372-7   HEART IN BLOSSOM   ☐

Comments: Acrylic, 2-3/4" tall, Dated Christmas 1987. An acrylic etched rose is growing around the edge of the heart shaped ornament and blooming into the center. "Love Is The Heart In Blossom." **Artist:** LaDene Votruba

☐ Purchased 19____   Pd $_____   MIB NB DB BNT
☐ Want   Orig. Ret. $6.00   **NB $15**   **MIB** Sec. Mkt. **$24**

QX 465-9   HEAVENLY HARMONY   ☐

Comments: Musical, Handcrafted, 4-1/4" tall. A little angel rings out "Joy To The World" as she pulls the rope to the bell tower. A key at the back activates the music. **Artist:** Ken Crow

☐ Purchased 19____   Pd $_____   MIB NB DB BNT
☐ Want   Orig. Ret. $15.00   **NB $28**   **MIB** Sec. Mkt. **$35**

QX 484-7   HERE COMES SANTA: SANTA'S WOODY   ☐

Comments: **Ninth in Series,** Handcrafted, 2" tall, Dated 1987. Santa's new car sports whitewall tires, custom paneling and a license plate that says "JOY-2-U." **Artist:** Ken Crow

☐ Purchased 19____   Pd $_____   MIB NB DB BNT
☐ Want   Orig. Ret. $14.00   **NB $75**   **MIB** Sec. Mkt. **$95**

QX 375-7   HOLIDAY GREETINGS   ☐

Comments: Bezeled Foil, 2-3/4" dia., Dated 1987. A silver tree and lettering against blue foil. Caption: "Season's Greetings" and "Wishing You Happiness At This Beautiful Time Of Year."

☐ Purchased 19____   Pd $_____   MIB NB DB BNT
☐ Want   Orig. Ret. $6.00   **NB $10**   **MIB** Sec. Mkt. **$15**

QX 485-7   HOLIDAY HEIRLOOM   ☐

Comments: Limited Edition 34,600, Dated 1987. Lead Crystal, Silver Plating, 3-1/4" tall. Hanging in the center of a silver-plated wreath is this clear crystal bell with bow and ribbon. Many were "bought up" in 1987 for the secondary market. **Artist:** Duane Unruh

☐ Purchased 19____   Pd $_____   MIB NB DB BNT
☐ Want   Orig. Ret. $25.00   **NB $10**   **MIB** Sec. Mkt. **$25**

QX 470-7   HOLIDAY HOURGLASS   ☐

Comments: Handcrafted, 3" tall. This snowman changes holidays as you turn him over - "Merry Christmas" and "Happy New Year." **Artist:** Duane Unruh

☐ Purchased 19____   Pd $_____   MIB NB DB BNT
☐ Want   Orig. Ret. $8.00   **NB $15**   **MIB** Sec. Mkt. **$25**

QX 371-7   HOLIDAY WILDLIFE: SNOW GOOSE   ☐

Comments: **Sixth in Series,** Wood, 2-1/2" dia. Caption: "Snow Goose, CHEN HYPERBOREA, Sixth In A Series, Wildlife Collection, Christmas 1987." **Artist:** LaDene Votruba

☐ Purchased 19____   Pd $_____   MIB NB DB BNT
☐ Want   Orig. Ret. $7.50   **NB $20**   **MIB** Sec. Mkt. **$27**

QX 471-9   HOT DOGGER   ☐

Comments: Handcrafted, 2-1/2" tall. Santa's a real "hot dogger" in his red ski suit, and has proven that he is a real champion. **Artist:** Duane Unruh

☐ Purchased 19____   Pd $_____   MIB NB DB BNT
☐ Want   Orig. Ret. $6.50   **NB $20**   **MIB** Sec. Mkt. **$30**

QX 373-9   HUSBAND   ☐

Comments: Blue Cameo, 3-1/4" dia., Dated 1987. A couple sit together in an ivory sleigh. Caption: "For My Husband" and "The Nicest Part Of Christmas Is Sharing It With You." **Artist:** LaDene Votruba

☐ Purchased 19____   Pd $_____   MIB NB DB BNT
☐ Want   Orig. Ret. $7.00   **NB $10**   **MIB** Sec. Mkt. **$12**

QX 278-9   I REMEMBER SANTA   ☐

Comments: Porcelain White Glass Ball, 2-7/8" dia. Dated 1987. Three antique postcard reproductions of Santa are captured on this porcelain ball. Caption: "At Christmastime, Especially, Those Magic Memories Start... Those Memories Of Yesterday That So Delight The Heart." **Artist:** Joyce A. Lyle

☐ Purchased 19____   Pd $_____   MIB NB DB BNT
☐ Want   Orig. Ret. $4.75   **NB $20**   **MIB** Sec. Mkt. **$33**

QX 450-9   ICY TREAT   ☐

Comments: Handcrafted, 2-1/4" tall. A penguin in a green stocking cap is enjoying his icy cherry treat. **Artist:** Bob Siedler

☐ Purchased 19____   Pd $_____   MIB NB DB BNT
☐ Want   Orig. Ret. $4.50   **NB $25**   **MIB** Sec. Mkt. **$30**

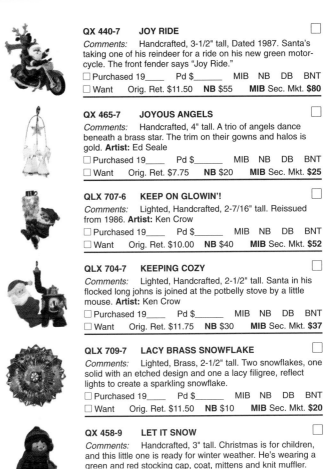

QX 469-7   IN A NUTSHELL

Comments: Handcrafted, 1-1/2" tall, Reissued in 1988. Open the walnut and inside are detailed Christmas scenes. **Artist:** Duane Unruh

☐ Purchased 19____   Pd $_____   MIB   NB   DB   BNT
☐ Want   Orig. Ret. $5.50   **NB** $25   **MIB** Sec. Mkt. **$35**

QX 449-9   JACK FROSTING

Comments: Handcrafted, 2-1/2" tall. Jack brushes a glittery frost onto each leaf to make the Christmas season sparkle. **Artist:** Ed Seale

☐ Purchased 19____   Pd $_____   MIB   NB   DB   BNT
☐ Want   Orig. Ret. $7.00   **NB** $40   **MIB** Sec. Mkt. **$50**

QX 283-9   JAMMIE PIES™

Comments: Porcelain White Glass Ball, 2-7/8" dia., Dated 1987. A child waits for the swan; it is bringing a visitor who knows many stories. Caption: "When Jammie Pies Are Close To You, All Your Christmas Dreams Come True."

☐ Purchased 19____   Pd $_____   MIB   NB   DB   BNT
☐ Want   Orig. Ret. $4.75   **NB** $8   **MIB** Sec. Mkt. **$18**

QX 457-7   JOGGING THROUGH THE SNOW

Comments: Handcrafted, 3" tall, Dated 1987. This perky rabbit is wearing his jogging shirt and shorts and has his radio and earphones on. **Artist:** Peter Dutkin

☐ Purchased 19____   Pd $_____   MIB   NB   DB   BNT
☐ Want   Orig. Ret. $7.25   **NB** $30   **MIB** Sec. Mkt. **$40**

QX 466-9   JOLLY FOLLIES

Comments: Handcrafted, 2" tall. When you pull the string three penguins in top hats, spats and red bow ties dance at the "Jolly Follies." **Artist:** Ken Crow

☐ Purchased 19____   Pd $_____   MIB   NB   DB   BNT
☐ Want   Orig. Ret. $8.50   **NB** $20   **MIB** Sec. Mkt. **$35**

QX 483-2   JOLLY HIKER

Comments: Handcrafted, 2" tall. Reissued from 1986. **Artist:** Bob Siedler

☐ Purchased 19____   Pd $_____   MIB   NB   DB   BNT
☐ Want   Orig. Ret. $5.00   **NB** $20   **MIB** Sec. Mkt. **$28**

QX 440-7   JOY RIDE

Comments: Handcrafted, 3-1/2" tall, Dated 1987. Santa's taking one of his reindeer for a ride on his new green motorcycle. The front fender says "Joy Ride."

☐ Purchased 19____   Pd $_____   MIB   NB   DB   BNT
☐ Want   Orig. Ret. $11.50   **NB** $55   **MIB** Sec. Mkt. **$80**

QX 465-7   JOYOUS ANGELS

Comments: Handcrafted, 4" tall. A trio of angels dance beneath a brass star. The trim on their gowns and halos is gold. **Artist:** Ed Seale

☐ Purchased 19____   Pd $_____   MIB   NB   DB   BNT
☐ Want   Orig. Ret. $7.75   **NB** $20   **MIB** Sec. Mkt. **$25**

QLX 707-6   KEEP ON GLOWIN'!

Comments: Lighted, Handcrafted, 2-7/16" tall. Reissued from 1986. **Artist:** Ken Crow

☐ Purchased 19____   Pd $_____   MIB   NB   DB   BNT
☐ Want   Orig. Ret. $10.00   **NB** $40   **MIB** Sec. Mkt. **$52**

QLX 704-7   KEEPING COZY

Comments: Lighted, Handcrafted, 2-1/2" tall. Santa in his flocked long johns is joined at the potbelly stove by a little mouse. **Artist:** Ken Crow

☐ Purchased 19____   Pd $_____   MIB   NB   DB   BNT
☐ Want   Orig. Ret. $11.75   **NB** $30   **MIB** Sec. Mkt. **$37**

QLX 709-7   LACY BRASS SNOWFLAKE

Comments: Lighted, Brass, 2-1/2" tall. Two snowflakes, one solid with an etched design and one a lacy filigree, reflect lights to create a sparkling snowflake.

☐ Purchased 19____   Pd $_____   MIB   NB   DB   BNT
☐ Want   Orig. Ret. $11.50   **NB** $10   **MIB** Sec. Mkt. **$20**

QX 458-9   LET IT SNOW

Comments: Handcrafted, 3" tall. Christmas is for children, and this little one is ready for winter weather. He's wearing a green and red stocking cap, coat, mittens and knit muffler.

☐ Purchased 19____   Pd $_____   MIB   NB   DB   BNT
☐ Want   Orig. Ret. $6.50   **NB** $15   **MIB** Sec. Mkt. **$20**

QX 419-3   LI'L JINGLER

Comments: Handcrafted, 2" tall. Reissued from 1986.
Artist: Ed Seale

☐ Purchased 19_____   Pd $_____   MIB   NB   DB   BNT
☐ Want   Orig. Ret. $6.75   **NB** $28   **MIB** Sec. Mkt. **$42**

QX 469-9   LITTLE WHITTLER

Comments: Handcrafted, 3" tall. With the look of hand-carved wood, this Santa is happy with the reindeer toy he is carving. **Artist:** Peter Dutkin

☐ Purchased 19_____   Pd $_____   MIB   NB   DB   BNT
☐ Want   Orig. Ret. $6.00   **NB** $27   **MIB** Sec. Mkt. **$33**

QX 278-7   LOVE IS EVERYWHERE

Comments: Chrome and Frosted Blue Glass Ball, 2-7/8" dia. Dated 1987. Two redbirds fly against a wintry landscape. Caption: "Beautifully, Peacefully, Christmas Touches Our Lives...Love Is Everywhere." **Artist:** Joyce A. Lyle

☐ Purchased 19_____   Pd $_____   MIB   NB   DB   BNT
☐ Want   Orig. Ret. $4.75   **NB** $15   **MIB** Sec. Mkt. **$25**

QLX 701-6   LOVING HOLIDAY

Comments: Light and Motion, Handcrafted, 3-5/8" tall. A couple move out of the house and meet under the clock in this reproduction of an old-fashioned glockenspiel. Caption: "Precious Times Are Spent With Those We Love." **Artist:** Ed Seale

☐ Purchased 19_____   Pd $_____   MIB   NB   DB   BNT
☐ Want   Orig. Ret. $22.00   **NB** $45   **MIB** Sec. Mkt. **$60**

QLX 706-7   MEMORIES ARE FOREVER PHOTOHOLDER

Comments: Lighted, Handcrafted, 3-7/8" tall. The design of this ornament illuminates your favorite photo. Caption: "Memory Keeps Each Christmas Forever Warm And Bright." **Artist:** Ed Seale

☐ Purchased 19_____   Pd $_____   MIB   NB   DB   BNT
☐ Want   Orig. Ret. $8.50   **NB** $20   **MIB** Sec. Mkt. **$33**

QLX 708-9   MEOWY CHRISTMAS

Comments: Lighted, Handcrafted, 2-1/2" tall. Two kittens play with the white fabric bow on a glowing red heart. **Artist:** Sharon Pike

☐ Purchased 19_____   Pd $_____   MIB   NB   DB   BNT
☐ Want   Orig. Ret. $10.00   **NB** $40   **MIB** Sec. Mkt. **$63**

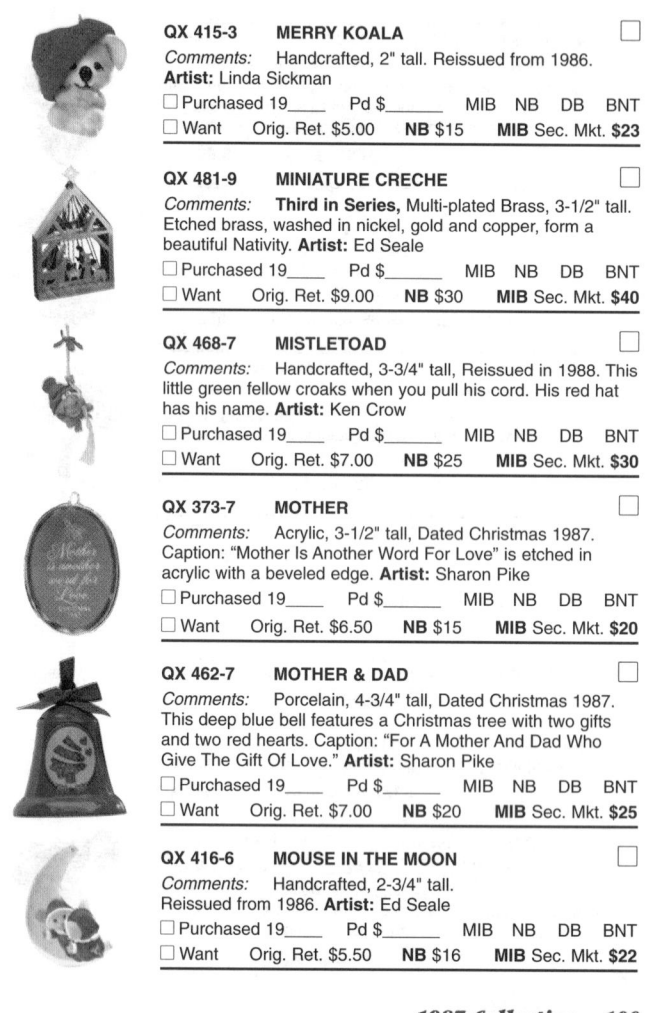

QX 415-3   MERRY KOALA

Comments: Handcrafted, 2" tall. Reissued from 1986.
Artist: Linda Sickman

☐ Purchased 19_____   Pd $_____   MIB   NB   DB   BNT
☐ Want   Orig. Ret. $5.00   **NB** $15   **MIB** Sec. Mkt. **$23**

QX 481-9   MINIATURE CRECHE

Comments: **Third in Series,** Multi-plated Brass, 3-1/2" tall. Etched brass, washed in nickel, gold and copper, form a beautiful Nativity. **Artist:** Ed Seale

☐ Purchased 19_____   Pd $_____   MIB   NB   DB   BNT
☐ Want   Orig. Ret. $9.00   **NB** $30   **MIB** Sec. Mkt. **$40**

QX 468-7   MISTLETOAD

Comments: Handcrafted, 3-3/4" tall, Reissued in 1988. This little green fellow croaks when you pull his cord. His red hat has his name. **Artist:** Ken Crow

☐ Purchased 19_____   Pd $_____   MIB   NB   DB   BNT
☐ Want   Orig. Ret. $7.00   **NB** $25   **MIB** Sec. Mkt. **$30**

QX 373-7   MOTHER

Comments: Acrylic, 3-1/2" tall, Dated Christmas 1987. Caption: "Mother Is Another Word For Love" is etched in acrylic with a beveled edge. **Artist:** Sharon Pike

☐ Purchased 19_____   Pd $_____   MIB   NB   DB   BNT
☐ Want   Orig. Ret. $6.50   **NB** $15   **MIB** Sec. Mkt. **$20**

QX 462-7   MOTHER & DAD

Comments: Porcelain, 4-3/4" tall, Dated Christmas 1987. This deep blue bell features a Christmas tree with two gifts and two red hearts. Caption: "For A Mother And Dad Who Give The Gift Of Love." **Artist:** Sharon Pike

☐ Purchased 19_____   Pd $_____   MIB   NB   DB   BNT
☐ Want   Orig. Ret. $7.00   **NB** $20   **MIB** Sec. Mkt. **$25**

QX 416-6   MOUSE IN THE MOON

Comments: Handcrafted, 2-3/4" tall. Reissued from 1986. **Artist:** Ed Seale

☐ Purchased 19_____   Pd $_____   MIB   NB   DB   BNT
☐ Want   Orig. Ret. $5.50   **NB** $16   **MIB** Sec. Mkt. **$22**

QX 483-7   MR. AND MRS. CLAUS: HOME COOKING ☐

Comments: **Second in Series,** Handcrafted, 3" tall. Dated 1987. Dec. 24. Mrs. Claus won't let Santa leave on his journey without a plate of cookies (chocolate chip, probably). **Artist:** Duane Unruh

☐ Purchased 19____   Pd $_____   MIB NB DB BNT
☐ Want   Orig. Ret. $13.25   **NB** $60   **MIB** Sec. Mkt. **$69**

QX 273-9   NATURE'S DECORATIONS ☐

Comments: Blue Glass Ball, 2-7/8" dia., Dated 1987. Forest animals enjoy the winter season. Caption: "The Nicest Christmas Decorations Start With Nature's Own Creations." **Artist:** LaDene Votruba

☐ Purchased 19____   Pd $_____   MIB NB DB BNT
☐ Want   Orig. Ret. $4.75   **NB** $17   **MIB** Sec. Mkt. **$35**

QX 376-7   NEW HOME ☐

Comments: Mirrored Acrylic, 2-3/4" dia., Dated Christmas 1987. Caption: "A New Home Is A Wonderful Beginning To Wonderful Memories." **Artist:** Joyce Pattee

☐ Purchased 19____   Pd $_____   MIB NB DB BNT
☐ Want   Orig. Ret. $6.00   **NB** $21   **MIB** Sec. Mkt. **$30**

QX 275-9   NIECE ☐

Comments: Turquoise Blue Glass Ball, 3" dia., Dated 1987. White fluffy sheep, accented in red, frolic around the ball. Caption: "Christmas Is Happier... Merrier... Cheerier... Because Of A Niece's Love."

☐ Purchased 19____   Pd $_____   MIB NB DB BNT
☐ Want   Orig. Ret. $4.75   **NB** $6   **MIB** Sec. Mkt. **$12**

QX 451-7   NIGHT BEFORE CHRISTMAS ☐

Comments: Handcrafted, 2-3/4" tall, Reissued in 1988. 'Twas the night before Christmas... not a creature was stirring, especially not this little mouse! He's got his teddy and some cheese and is all tucked away in Santa's flocked hat. **Artist:** Ken Crow

☐ Purchased 19____   Pd $_____   MIB NB DB BNT
☐ Want   Orig. Ret. $6.50   **NB** $21   **MIB** Sec. Mkt. **$33**

QX 282-7   NORMAN ROCKWELL: CHRISTMAS SCENES ☐

Comments: Gold Glass Ball, 2-7/8" dia., Dated 1987. Caption: "O Gather Friends, At Christmastime, To Sing A Song Of Cheer, To Reminisce The Days Gone By, To Toast The Bright New Year. From The Norman Rockwell Collection." **Artist:** Joyce A. Lyle

☐ Purchased 19____   Pd $_____   MIB NB DB BNT
☐ Want   Orig. Ret. $4.75   **NB** $20   **MIB** Sec. Mkt. **$30**

QX 370-7   NORMAN ROCKWELL: CHRISTMAS DANCE ☐

Comments: **Eighth in Series,** Light Blue Cameo, 3-1/4" dia. Caption: "The Christmas Dance, Eighth In A Series, Christmas 1987, The Norman Rockwell Collection." **Artist:** Don Palmiter

☐ Purchased 19____   Pd $_____   MIB NB DB BNT
☐ Want   Orig. Ret. $7.75   **NB** $15   **MIB** Sec. Mkt. **$25**

XPR 933-3   NORTH POLE POWER & LIGHT: OPEN HOUSE ☐

Comments: Handcrafted, 3" tall. A colorful elf is on 24-hour call to keep the lights on your Christmas tree in good order. He carries three replacement bulbs in his backpack. **Artist:** Ken Crow

☐ Purchased 19____   Pd $_____   MIB NB DB BNT
☐ Want   Orig. Ret. $2.95   **NB** $15   **MIB** Sec. Mkt. **$28**

QX 483-9   NOSTALGIC HOUSES AND SHOPS: HOUSE ON MAIN ST. ☐

Comments: **Fourth in Series,** Handcrafted, 4-1/4" tall. Dated 1987. This lovely Victorian home includes a lavender and mauve bedroom upstairs and a parlor decorated for Christmas. **Artist:** Donna Lee

☐ Purchased 19____   Pd $_____   MIB NB DB BNT
☐ Want   Orig. Ret. $14.00   **NB** $65   **MIB** Sec. Mkt. **$80**

QX 468-9   NOSTALGIC ROCKER ☐

Comments: Wood, 2-1/2" tall. Rocking horse is handcrafted in wood with fabric ears. **Artist:** Linda Sickman

☐ Purchased 19____   Pd $_____   MIB NB DB BNT
☐ Want   Orig. Ret. $6.50   **NB** $25   **MIB** Sec. Mkt. **$33**

QX 455-9   "OWLIDAY" WISH ☐

Comments: Handcrafted, 2" tall Reissued in 1988. This cute white owl in spectacles is pointing to the holiday message written on the eye chart: "Seasons Greetings To You." **Artist:** Sharon Pike

☐ Purchased 19____   Pd $_____   MIB NB DB BNT
☐ Want   Orig. Ret. $6.50   **NB** $20   **MIB** Sec. Mkt. **$25**

QX 472-7   PADDINGTON™ BEAR ☐

Comments: Handcrafted, 3" tall. Paddington wears a red apron and white chef's cap. On his hat is a tag that says, "Please Look After This Bear. Thank You." **Artist:** Sharon Pike

☐ Purchased 19____   Pd $_____   MIB NB DB BNT
☐ Want   Orig. Ret. $5.50   **NB** $25   **MIB** Sec. Mkt. **$35**

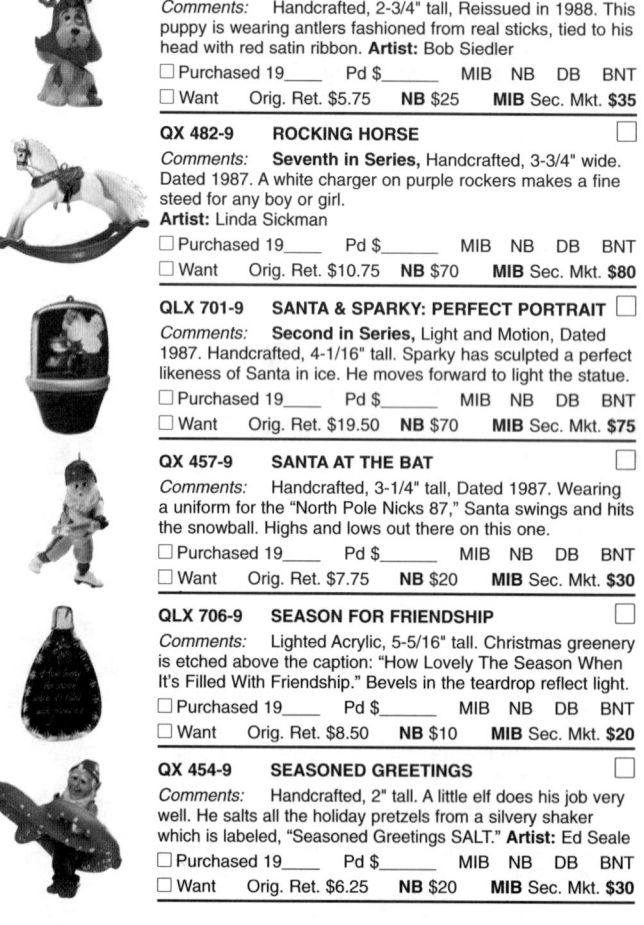

QX 281-9   PEANUTS®

Comments: Chrome Glass Ball, 3" dia., Dated 1987. "Everyone's Cool At Christmastime!" is depicted by Snoopy, Woodstock and his friends, as well as a snowman, all wearing their "shades."

☐ Purchased 19____   Pd $_____   MIB   NB   DB   BNT
☐ Want   Orig. Ret. $4.75   **NB** $30   **MIB** Sec. Mkt. **$40**

QX 442-7   PORCELAIN BEAR

Comments: **Fifth in Series,** Fine Porcelain, 2-1/8" tall. This hand-painted Cinnamon Bear is searching for something in the toe of his red stocking.

☐ Purchased 19____   Pd $_____   MIB   NB   DB   BNT
☐ Want   Orig. Ret. $7.75   **NB** $35   **MIB** Sec. Mkt. **$40**

QX 448-9   PRETTY KITTY

Comments: Handcrafted/Glass, 3-1/2" tall. A clear glass bell is a perfect display for a little kitten tangled in a red bead garland. **Artist:** Ken Crow

☐ Purchased 19____   Pd $_____   MIB   NB   DB   BNT
☐ Want   Orig. Ret. $11.00   **NB** $19   **MIB** Sec. Mkt. **$30**

QX 374-9   PROMISE OF PEACE

Comments: Acrylic, 2-3/4" dia., Framed in brass. A dove with a gold foil olive branch. The caption, "A Season Of Hope, A Reminder Of Miracles, A Promise Of Peace," is etched in the bevel in the front. **Artist:** Ken Crow

☐ Purchased 19____   Pd $_____   MIB   NB   DB   BNT
☐ Want   Orig. Ret. $11.00   **NB** $20   **MIB** Sec. Mkt. **$25**

QX 458-7   RACCOON BIKER

Comments: Handcrafted, 3" tall, Dated 1987. This little raccoon is pedaling his bicycle to deliver his special Christmas present. **Artist:** Bob Siedler

☐ Purchased 19____   Pd $_____   MIB   NB   DB   BNT
☐ Want   Orig. Ret. $7.00   **NB** $25   **MIB** Sec. Mkt. **$30**

QX 480-9   REINDEER CHAMPS: DANCER

Comments: **Second in Series,** Handcrafted, 3-1/2" tall. Dated 1987. Dancer is a vision of loveliness as she ice skates her way into the hearts and homes of collectors. **Artist:** Bob Siedler

☐ Purchased 19____   Pd $_____   MIB   NB   DB   BNT
☐ Want   Orig. Ret. $7.50   **NB** $40   **MIB** Sec. Mkt. **$55**

QX 452-7   REINDOGGY

Comments: Handcrafted, 2-3/4" tall, Reissued in 1988. This puppy is wearing antlers fashioned from real sticks, tied to his head with red satin ribbon. **Artist:** Bob Siedler

☐ Purchased 19____   Pd $_____   MIB   NB   DB   BNT
☐ Want   Orig. Ret. $5.75   **NB** $25   **MIB** Sec. Mkt. **$35**

QX 482-9   ROCKING HORSE

Comments: **Seventh in Series,** Handcrafted, 3-3/4" wide. Dated 1987. A white charger on purple rockers makes a fine steed for any boy or girl. **Artist:** Linda Sickman

☐ Purchased 19____   Pd $_____   MIB   NB   DB   BNT
☐ Want   Orig. Ret. $10.75   **NB** $70   **MIB** Sec. Mkt. **$80**

QLX 701-9   SANTA & SPARKY: PERFECT PORTRAIT

Comments: **Second in Series,** Light and Motion, Dated 1987. Handcrafted, 4-1/16" tall. Sparky has sculpted a perfect likeness of Santa in ice. He moves forward to light the statue.

☐ Purchased 19____   Pd $_____   MIB   NB   DB   BNT
☐ Want   Orig. Ret. $19.50   **NB** $70   **MIB** Sec. Mkt. **$75**

QX 457-9   SANTA AT THE BAT

Comments: Handcrafted, 3-1/4" tall, Dated 1987. Wearing a uniform for the "North Pole Nicks 87," Santa swings and hits the snowball. Highs and lows out there on this one.

☐ Purchased 19____   Pd $_____   MIB   NB   DB   BNT
☐ Want   Orig. Ret. $7.75   **NB** $20   **MIB** Sec. Mkt. **$30**

QLX 706-9   SEASON FOR FRIENDSHIP

Comments: Lighted Acrylic, 5-5/16" tall. Christmas greenery is etched above the caption: "How Lovely The Season When It's Filled With Friendship." Bevels in the teardrop reflect light.

☐ Purchased 19____   Pd $_____   MIB   NB   DB   BNT
☐ Want   Orig. Ret. $8.50   **NB** $10   **MIB** Sec. Mkt. **$20**

QX 454-9   SEASONED GREETINGS

Comments: Handcrafted, 2" tall. A little elf does his job very well. He salts all the holiday pretzels from a silvery shaker which is labeled, "Seasoned Greetings SALT." **Artist:** Ed Seale

☐ Purchased 19____   Pd $_____   MIB   NB   DB   BNT
☐ Want   Orig. Ret. $6.25   **NB** $20   **MIB** Sec. Mkt. **$30**

QX 474-7　SISTER

Comments:　Wood, 2-3/4" tall, Dated Christmas 1987. This wooden heart has a basket of brightly stenciled poinsettias on the front. Caption: "A Sister Brings Happiness Wrapped In Love." **Artist:** Linda Sickman

☐ Purchased 19＿＿＿　Pd $＿＿＿＿　MIB　NB　DB　BNT
☐ Want　Orig. Ret. $6.00　**NB** $10　**MIB** Sec. Mkt. **$15**

QX 450-7　SLEEPY SANTA

Comments:　Handcrafted, 2-3/4" tall. Santa relaxes in his favorite chair and soaks his feet — it's Dec. 26 and he deserves his rest! **Artist:** Ken Crow

☐ Purchased 19＿＿＿　Pd $＿＿＿＿　MIB　NB　DB　BNT
☐ Want　Orig. Ret. $6.25　**NB** $22　**MIB** Sec. Mkt. **$32**

QX 472-9　SNOOPY & WOODSTOCK

Comments:　Handcrafted, 2-1/2" tall. Woodstock plays "Angel" and perches on the top of Snoopy's bottle-brush tree. **Artist:** Bob Siedler

☐ Purchased 19＿＿＿　Pd $＿＿＿＿　MIB　NB　DB　BNT
☐ Want　Orig. Ret. $7.25　**NB** $35　**MIB** Sec. Mkt. **$50**

QX 463-9　SON

Comments:　Handcrafted, 1" tall, Dated Christmas 1987. Hanging from a red cord is an old-fashioned toy train with the words "For Son" painted in bright colors. **Artist:** Linda Sickman

☐ Purchased 19＿＿＿　Pd $＿＿＿＿　MIB　NB　DB　BNT
☐ Want　Orig. Ret. $5.75　**NB** $40　**MIB** Sec. Mkt. **$50**

QX 464-7　SPECIAL MEMORIES PHOTOHOLDER

Comments:　Fabric, 3-1/4" dia., Dated 1987. This fabric wreath with red satin rosette and green satin ribbon features embroidery and needlepoint. Caption: "Every Christmas Brings Special Moments To Remember."

☐ Purchased 19＿＿＿　Pd $＿＿＿＿　MIB　NB　DB　BNT
☐ Want　Orig. Ret. $6.75　**NB** $16　**MIB** Sec. Mkt. **$27**

QX 452-9　SPOTS 'N STRIPES

Comments:　Handcrafted, 2-1/4" tall. This little Dalmatian pup has received a red and white striped candy cane in the shape of a bone.

☐ Purchased 19＿＿＿　Pd $＿＿＿＿　MIB　NB　DB　BNT
☐ Want　Orig. Ret. $5.50　**NB** $18　**MIB** Sec. Mkt. **$25**

QX 453-9　ST. LOUIE NICK

Comments:　Handcrafted, 3-1/2" tall, Reissued in 1988. Santa plays the blues with his jazzy sax— he's also a cool cat in his spats, beret and dark glasses. **Artist:** Peter Dutkin

☐ Purchased 19＿＿＿　Pd $＿＿＿＿　MIB　NB　DB　BNT
☐ Want　Orig. Ret. $7.75　**NB** $17　**MIB** Sec. Mkt. **$30**

QX 447-9　SWEETHEART

Comments:　Handcrafted, 3-1/8" tall, Dated Christmas 1987. This lovely surrey with red fabric fringe contains a present "For My Sweetheart." On the back, "Sweet" is printed above two entwined hearts. **Artist:** Linda Sickman

☐ Purchased 19＿＿＿　Pd $＿＿＿＿　MIB　NB　DB　BNT
☐ Want　Orig. Ret. $11.00　**NB** $17　**MIB** Sec. Mkt. **$30**

QX 466-7　TEACHER

Comments:　Handcrafted, 2" tall, Dated 1987. Teddy has taken time to write a Christmas greeting: "Merry Christmas Teacher From (name)." **Artist:** Bob Siedler

☐ Purchased 19＿＿＿　Pd $＿＿＿＿　MIB　NB　DB　BNT
☐ Want　Orig. Ret. $5.75　**NB** $12　**MIB** Sec. Mkt. **$20**

QX 444-7　TEN YEARS TOGETHER

Comments:　Porcelain/Bell, 4-3/4" tall, Dated Christmas 1987. A heart-shaped green wreath decorated with red ribbon, berries and flowers frames the words "Ten Years Together." Tied with satin ribbon. **Artist:** LaDene Votruba

☐ Purchased 19＿＿＿　Pd $＿＿＿＿　MIB　NB　DB　BNT
☐ Want　Orig. Ret. $7.00　**NB** $16　**MIB** Sec. Mkt. **$22**

QX 441-9　THIMBLE SERIES: DRUMMER

Comments:　**Tenth in Series,** 2" tall. A brown bunny with a fluffy pom-pom tail plays his thimble drum. **Artist:** Bob Siedler

☐ Purchased 19＿＿＿　Pd $＿＿＿＿　MIB　NB　DB　BNT
☐ Want　Orig. Ret. $5.75　**NB** $21　**MIB** Sec. Mkt. **$30**

QX 454-7　THREE MEN IN A TUB

Comments:　Handcrafted, 3" tall. The butcher, the baker and the candlestick maker are all sitting in a small tub which says "Rub A Dub Dub." **Artist:** Donna Lee

☐ Purchased 19＿＿＿　Pd $＿＿＿＿　MIB　NB　DB　BNT
☐ Want　Orig. Ret. $8.00　**NB** $18　**MIB** Sec. Mkt. **$30**

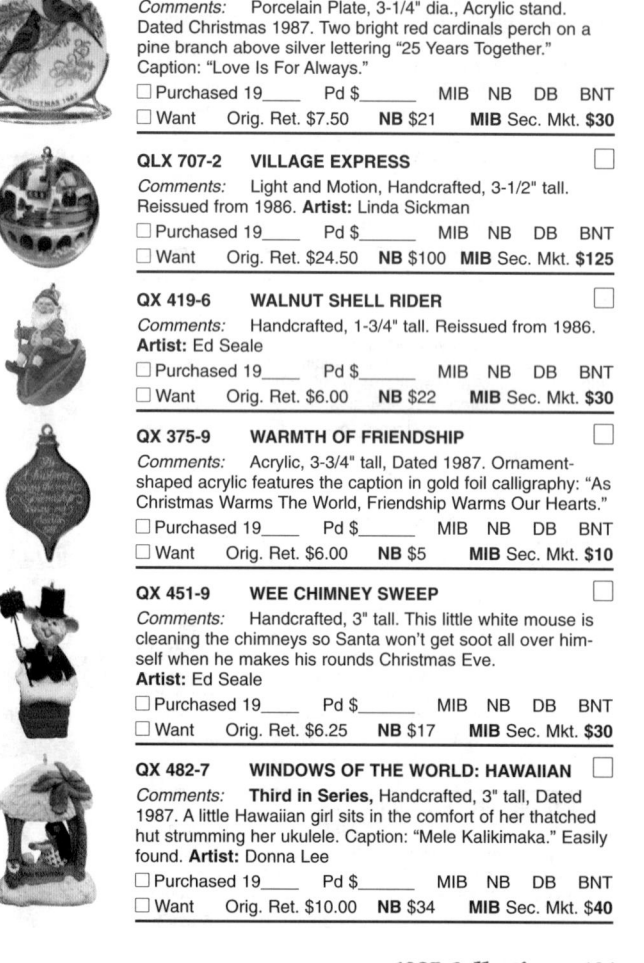

QX 280-7   TIME FOR FRIENDS

Comments: Red Glass Ball, 3" dia., Dated Christmas 1987. Two white mice decorate with a green holly garland. Caption: "When Good Friends Meet, Good Times Are Complete!" **Artist:** LaDene Votruba

☐ Purchased 19____   Pd $_____   MIB   NB   DB   BNT
☐ Want   Orig. Ret. $4.75   **NB** $15   **MIB** Sec. Mkt. **$23**

QX 484-9   TIN LOCOMOTIVE

Comments: Sixth in Series, Pressed Tin, 3-1/2" tall, Dated 1987. With red wheels that really roll and a brass bell that rings, this locomotive is a delight for collectors of all ages. **Artist:** Linda Sickman

☐ Purchased 19____   Pd $_____   MIB   NB   DB   BNT
☐ Want   Orig. Ret. $14.75   **NB** $50   **MIB** Sec. Mkt. **$65**

QLX 703-9   TRAIN STATION

Comments: Lighted, Handcrafted, 3-3/16" tall. The Merriville station is open for business. A mother and child are waiting for the next train to arrive and a ticket taker stands at his station. **Artist:** Donna Lee

☐ Purchased 19____   Pd $_____   MIB   NB   DB   BNT
☐ Want   Orig. Ret. $12.75   **NB** $38   **MIB** Sec. Mkt. **$50**

QX 459-7   TREETOP DREAMS

Comments: Handcrafted, 3" tall, Reissued in 1988. This little squirrel will find a pleasant surprise when he wakes. Santa has left an acorn in his green stocking. His bed is a vine wreath. **Artist:** Ed Seale

☐ Purchased 19____   Pd $_____   MIB   NB   DB   BNT
☐ Want   Orig. Ret. $6.75   **NB** $20   **MIB** Sec. Mkt. **$30**

QX 425-6   TREETOP TRIO/BLUEBIRDS

Comments: Handcrafted, 2" tall. Reissued from 1986. **Artist:** Donna Lee

☐ Purchased 19____   Pd $_____   MIB   NB   DB   BNT
☐ Want   Orig. Ret. $11.00   **NB** $18   **MIB** Sec. Mkt. **$30**

QX 370-9   TWELVE DAYS OF CHRISTMAS: FOUR COLLY BIRDS

Comments: **Fourth in Series,** Acrylic, 4" tall, Dated 1987. The diamond acrylic shape features four etched colly birds in the center, with gold foil captions. **Artist:** Sharon Pike

☐ Purchased 19____   Pd $_____   MIB   NB   DB   BNT
☐ Want   Orig. Ret. $6.50   **NB** $30   **MIB** Sec. Mkt. **$40**

QX 443-9   TWENTY-FIVE YEARS TOGETHER

Comments: Porcelain Plate, 3-1/4" dia., Acrylic stand. Dated Christmas 1987. Two bright red cardinals perch on a pine branch above silver lettering "25 Years Together." Caption: "Love Is For Always."

☐ Purchased 19____   Pd $_____   MIB   NB   DB   BNT
☐ Want   Orig. Ret. $7.50   **NB** $21   **MIB** Sec. Mkt. **$30**

QLX 707-2   VILLAGE EXPRESS

Comments: Light and Motion, Handcrafted, 3-1/2" tall. Reissued from 1986. **Artist:** Linda Sickman

☐ Purchased 19____   Pd $_____   MIB   NB   DB   BNT
☐ Want   Orig. Ret. $24.50   **NB** $100   **MIB** Sec. Mkt. **$125**

QX 419-6   WALNUT SHELL RIDER

Comments: Handcrafted, 1-3/4" tall. Reissued from 1986. **Artist:** Ed Seale

☐ Purchased 19____   Pd $_____   MIB   NB   DB   BNT
☐ Want   Orig. Ret. $6.00   **NB** $22   **MIB** Sec. Mkt. **$30**

QX 375-9   WARMTH OF FRIENDSHIP

Comments: Acrylic, 3-3/4" tall, Dated 1987. Ornament-shaped acrylic features the caption in gold foil calligraphy: "As Christmas Warms The World, Friendship Warms Our Hearts."

☐ Purchased 19____   Pd $_____   MIB   NB   DB   BNT
☐ Want   Orig. Ret. $6.00   **NB** $5   **MIB** Sec. Mkt. **$10**

QX 451-9   WEE CHIMNEY SWEEP

Comments: Handcrafted, 3" tall. This little white mouse is cleaning the chimneys so Santa won't get soot all over himself when he makes his rounds Christmas Eve. **Artist:** Ed Seale

☐ Purchased 19____   Pd $_____   MIB   NB   DB   BNT
☐ Want   Orig. Ret. $6.25   **NB** $17   **MIB** Sec. Mkt. **$30**

QX 482-7   WINDOWS OF THE WORLD: HAWAIIAN

Comments: **Third in Series,** Handcrafted, 3" tall, Dated 1987. A little Hawaiian girl sits in the comfort of her thatched hut strumming her ukulele. Caption: "Mele Kalikimaka." Easily found. **Artist:** Donna Lee

☐ Purchased 19____   Pd $_____   MIB   NB   DB   BNT
☐ Want   Orig. Ret. $10.00   **NB** $34   **MIB** Sec. Mkt. **$40**

QX 441-7   WOOD CHILDHOOD: HORSE ☐

Comments: **Fourth in Series,** Wood, 2-1/4" tall, Dated 1987. This little horse, with a plush mane and yarn tail, is standing on a cart with wheels that turn. He sports a hand painted red and green saddle. **Artist:** Bob Siedler

☐ Purchased 19____   Pd $_____   MIB   NB   DB   BNT
☐ Want   Orig. Ret. $7.50   **NB** $17   **MIB** Sec. Mkt. **$27**

QX 447-7   WORD OF LOVE ☐

Comments: Porcelain, 2-1/8" tall, Dated Christmas 1987. The word "Love" is sculpted into a contemporary design. A small red heart dangles inside the "o."

☐ Purchased 19____   Pd $_____   MIB   NB   DB   BNT
☐ Want   Orig. Ret. $8.00   **NB** $15   **MIB** Sec. Mkt. **$20**

QXC 580-9   WREATH OF MEMORIES
CHARTER CLUB MEMBERSHIP ORN. ☐

Comments: Handcrafted, 3-1/8" tall, Dated 1987. This detailed green wreath is decorated with Hallmark ornaments. Caption: "1987 Charter Member." Club logo is engraved in brass. **Artist:** Duane Unruh

☐ Purchased 19____   Pd $_____   MIB   NB   DB   BNT
☐ Want   Orig. Ret.: Gift to Charter Members.
    NB $40   **MIB** Sec. Mkt. **$65**

Gennie Alden's grandosn, Jaden, age seven months, thinks Barbie ornaments are super nice ... for now!

The Art & History of Ornaments

by Mark Leinweber, staff

Through the ages, folktales and folksongs have mentioned the use of evergreens for decorating. The Norsmen nailed boughs above their doors to protect their homes from evil spirits and carried them into their houses, to freshen the stale air and brighten their spirits during the long, cold, stuffy winters.

Pagan religions were prevalent during the early 7th century period of the Anglo-Saxons. Many pagan religions, the Druids for example, worshiped trees as gods. These Anglo-Saxon religious cults had a huge number of followers. Because of the competition created by these groups, Pope Gregory I instructed Augustine of Canterberry to incorporate any and all pagan customs in to the church if it would bring in more converts. The hanging of greens was one of the practices adopted at this time.

North European Thespians, in the early 1300s, strolled through the streets carrying heavy boughs of evergreen adorned with apples. The purpose of this "parade" was to advertise the religious plays they performed on the church steps. A production of Adam and Eve was traditionally enacted on December 24. The boughs represented the Garden of Eden.

The first written reference of a Christmas tree was in 1605, in Strasbourg. It was decorated with apples, gilded candies, paper roses and thin wafers. The tree was referred to as "Christbaum."

In the early 1800s, the Germans introduced the Christmas tree to America. German settlers in Pennsylvania decorated fir trees with home-baked cookies and cakes, cotton santas and silver paper.

Around 1870, the golden Victorian era of ornaments began. These trees were decorated with glass figures, crinkled gold and silver wire, beautiful heavy glass globes called kugels and with elegant paper ornaments called Dresdens. Another cherished ornament of the era was the Nuremburg Angel. Nuremburg Angels, named after their place of origin, wore a crinkled gold skirt, spun-glass wings and a face made of clay or bisque.

Ornaments have become very popular in the collectibles market. The themes of today's ornaments encompass nearly every aspect of human culture, from religion to cartoons and everything in between. They are a record of man's development and depict events and icons of our past, present and future.

From the first apples tied to an evergreen bough, the popularity and love of ornaments grows stronger year after year. Perhaps it's the memories that ornaments awaken in us that make them so popular; memories of warm houses filled with the smells of Christmas dinner, the warmth of sharing special times with parents, grandparents, children and relatives during the holiday season.

Part of the *magic* of ornaments may be the fact that they *are* put away, forgotten for a time, only to be brought back out like an old familiar friend. Ornaments make wonderful heirlooms for those very reasons. An ornament that hung each year on Grandma's tree will bring back fond memories every time you take it out to hang on your own tree.

Ornaments will, most likely, endure as long as mankind walks the earth. So whether you collect ornaments as art, or for spiritual reasons or nostalgia, you can be sure to find an ornament to satisfy your needs.

1988 Collection

QX 482-1   A "KISS"™ FROM SANTA
Comments: Handcrafted, 3-1/4" tall.
A "chocolate" Santa holds a Hershey's Kiss. His hat is red with a silvery trim. **Artist:** Duane Unruh
☐ Purchased 19 __   Pd $ __   MIB   NB   DB   BNT
☐ Want   Orig. Ret. $4.50   **NB** $22   **MIB** Sec. Mkt. **$30**

QX 488-1   AMERICANA DRUM
Comments: Tin, 2" dia., Dated 1988.
An American eagle and banner design is portrayed against a vivid blue background. Caption: "Merry Christmas U.S.A."
Artist: Linda Sickman
☐ Purchased 19 __   Pd $ __   MIB   NB   DB   BNT
☐ Want   Orig. Ret. $7.75   **NB** $20   **MIB** Sec. Mkt. **$25**

QX 408-4   ANGELIC MINSTREL: KEEPSAKE CLUB
Comments: Limited Edition 49,900, Wood Display Stand. Hand-Painted Fine Porcelain, 5" tall.
This blue gowned angel plays a golden lyre. Offered only to members of the Hallmark Keepsake Ornament Club. Some say this was overproduced for a Limited Edition. **Artist:** Donna Lee
☐ Purchased 19 __   Pd $ __   MIB   NB   DB   BNT
☐ Want   Orig. Ret. $29.50   **NB** $50   **MIB** Sec. Mkt. **$60**

QX 472-1   ARCTIC TENOR
Comments: Handcrafted, 1-3/4" tall.
This penguin is in great voice for his solo. He's wearing spats and a green bow tie and has his song book of "Arctic Arias" open.
Artist: Bob Siedler
☐ Purchased 19 __   Pd $ __   MIB   NB   DB   BNT
☐ Want   Orig. Ret. $4.00   **NB** $10   **MIB** Sec. Mkt. **$19**

QX 410-1   BABY REDBIRD
Comments: Handcrafted, 2-5/8" tall.
This baby resembles the cardinals who feast throughout the winter at bird feeders. **Artist:** Robert Chad
☐ Purchased 19 __   Pd $ __   MIB   NB   DB   BNT
☐ Want   Orig. Ret. $5.00   **NB** $15   **MIB** Sec. Mkt **$20**

QX 272-1   BABY'S FIRST CHRISTMAS: BOY
Comments: White Satin Ball, 2-7/8" dia., Dated 1988.
Caption: "From The Moment A New Baby Boy Arrives, He's The Love Of Your Heart, The Light In Your Eyes. Baby's First Christmas."
☐ Purchased 19 __   Pd $ __   MIB   NB   DB   BNT
☐ Want   Orig. Ret. $4.75   **NB** $18   **MIB** Sec. Mkt. **$25**

QX 272-4   BABY'S FIRST CHRISTMAS: GIRL
Comments: White Satin Ball, 2-7/8" dia., Dated 1988.
Caption: "A Sweet Baby Girl, So Tiny And New, Is A Bundle Of Joy And A Dream Come True. Baby's First Christmas."
☐ Purchased 19 __   Pd $ __   MIB   NB   DB   BNT
☐ Want   Orig. Ret. $4.75   **NB** $17   **MIB** Sec. Mkt. **$25**

QLX 718-4   BABY'S FIRST CHRISTMAS
Comments: Light and Motion, Handcrafted, 4" tall, Dated 1988.
A carousel of prancing horses under a blue and white canopy celebrates Baby's First Christmas. **Artist:** Ed Seale
☐ Purchased 19 __   Pd $ __   MIB   NB   DB   BNT
☐ Want   Orig. Ret. $24.00   **NB** $50   **MIB** Sec. Mkt. **$60**

QX 372-1   BABY'S FIRST CHRISTMAS
Comments: Acrylic, 4" tall, Dated 1988.
"Baby's First Christmas" in gold foil letters is framed by a heart made from two candy canes and is held by an intricately etched bunny. **Artist:** Sharon Pike
☐ Purchased 19 __   Pd $ __   MIB   NB   DB   BNT
☐ Want   Orig. Ret. $6.00   **NB** $18   **MIB** Sec. Mkt. **$23**

QX 470-1   BABY'S FIRST CHRISTMAS
Comments: Handcrafted, 3-5/8" tall, Dated 1988.
Baby's all wrapped up in white bunting and a green blanket trimmed with lace for a ride in a cute rocking horse trimmed in red and green. **Artist:** Ken Crow
☐ Purchased 19 __   Pd $ __   MIB   NB   DB   BNT
☐ Want   Orig. Ret. $9.75   **NB** $20   **MIB** Sec. Mkt. **$40**

QX 470-4   BABY'S FIRST CHRISTMAS PHOTOHOLDER
Comments: Fabric, 5" tall, Dated 1988.
Embroidered angels and holly decorate this heart-shaped photo holder. Caption: "Baby's First Christmas" and "A Baby Is A Gift Of Joy, A Gift Of Love At Christmas."
☐ Purchased 19 __   Pd $ __   MIB   NB   DB   BNT
☐ Want   Orig. Ret. $7.50   **NB** $21   **MIB** Sec. Mkt **$30**

QX 471-1   BABY'S SECOND CHRISTMAS
Comments: Handcrafted, 1-3/4" tall, Dated 1988.
A flocked bear enjoys pounding the blocks on a child's toy. "Baby's 2nd Christmas" on side. **Artist:** Sharon Pike
☐ Purchased 19 __   Pd $ __   MIB   NB   DB   BNT
☐ Want   Orig. Ret. $6.00   **NB** $20   **MIB** Sec. Mkt. **$33**

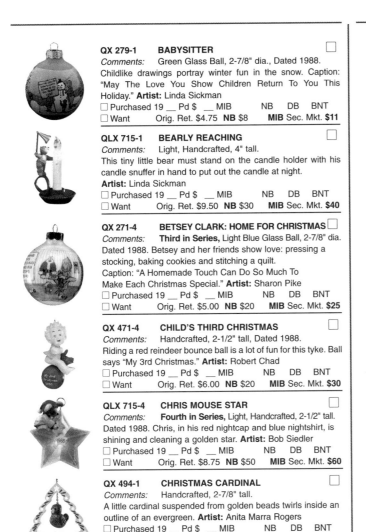

QX 279-1　　BABYSITTER ☐
Comments:　Green Glass Ball, 2-7/8" dia., Dated 1988.
Childlike drawings portray winter fun in the snow. Caption:
"May The Love You Show Children Return To You This
Holiday." **Artist:** Linda Sickman
☐ Purchased 19 __ Pd $ __ MIB　　　NB　DB　BNT
☐ Want　　Orig. Ret. $4.75 **NB** $8　　**MIB** Sec. Mkt. **$11**

QLX 715-1　　BEARLY REACHING ☐
Comments:　Light, Handcrafted, 4" tall.
This tiny little bear must stand on the candle holder with his
candle snuffer in hand to put out the candle at night.
Artist: Linda Sickman
☐ Purchased 19 __ Pd $ __ MIB　　　NB　DB　BNT
☐ Want　　Orig. Ret. $9.50 **NB** $30　　**MIB** Sec. Mkt. **$40**

QX 271-4　　BETSEY CLARK: HOME FOR CHRISTMAS ☐
Comments:　**Third in Series,** Light Blue Glass Ball, 2-7/8" dia.
Dated 1988. Betsey and her friends show love: pressing a
stocking, baking cookies and stitching a quilt.
Caption: "A Homemade Touch Can Do So Much To
Make Each Christmas Special." **Artist:** Sharon Pike
☐ Purchased 19 __ Pd $ __ MIB　　　NB　DB　BNT
☐ Want　　Orig. Ret. $5.00 **NB** $20　　**MIB** Sec. Mkt. **$25**

QX 471-4　　CHILD'S THIRD CHRISTMAS ☐
Comments:　Handcrafted, 2-1/2" tall, Dated 1988.
Riding a red reindeer bounce ball is a lot of fun for this tyke. Ball
says "My 3rd Christmas." **Artist:** Robert Chad
☐ Purchased 19 __ Pd $ __ MIB　　　NB　DB　BNT
☐ Want　　Orig. Ret. $6.00 **NB** $20　　**MIB** Sec. Mkt. **$30**

QLX 715-4　　CHRIS MOUSE STAR ☐
Comments:　**Fourth in Series,** Light, Handcrafted, 2-1/2" tall.
Dated 1988. Chris, in his red nightcap and blue nightshirt, is
shining and cleaning a golden star. **Artist:** Bob Siedler
☐ Purchased 19 __ Pd $ __ MIB　　　NB　DB　BNT
☐ Want　　Orig. Ret. $8.75 **NB** $50　　**MIB** Sec. Mkt. **$60**

QX 494-1　　CHRISTMAS CARDINAL ☐
Comments:　Handcrafted, 2-7/8" tall.
A little cardinal suspended from golden beads twirls inside an
outline of an evergreen. **Artist:** Anita Marra Rogers
☐ Purchased 19 __ Pd $ __ MIB　　　NB　DB　BNT
☐ Want　　Orig. Ret. $4.75 **NB** $15　　**MIB** Sec. Mkt. **$20**

QLX 716-1　　CHRISTMAS CLASSICS: ☐
　　　　　　NIGHT BEFORE CHRISTMAS
Comments:　**Third in Series.** Light, Handcrafted, 4-1/2" tall.
Dated 1988. While everyone sleeps snugly upstairs, Santa is
filling the stockings in the decorated living room downstairs. No
series number on this ornament. **Artist:** Donna Lee
☐ Purchased 19 __ Pd $ __ MIB　　　NB　DB　BNT
☐ Want　　Orig. Ret. $15.00 **NB** $25　　**MIB** Sec. Mkt. **$30**

QX 480-1　　CHRISTMAS CUCKOO ☐
Comments:　Handcrafted, 4-7/8" tall.
Tap the pendulum and watch for two surprises. The clock
changes from 12:00 to 3:00 and the little door opens to show a
blue bird inside. **Artist:** Ken Crow
☐ Purchased 19 __ Pd $ __ MIB　　　NB　DB　BNT
☐ Want　　Orig. Ret. $8.00 **NB** $30　　**MIB** Sec. Mkt. **$40**

QLX 717-1　　CHRISTMAS IS MAGIC ☐
Comments:　Light, Handcrafted, 3-1/4" tall.
Santa uses the light from a table lantern and his puppy's bones
to create a reindeer silhouette on the window. "Christmas Is
Magic!" **Artist:** Ken Crow
☐ Purchased 19 __ Pd $ __ MIB　　　NB　DB　BNT
☐ Want　　Orig. Ret. $12.00 **NB** $40　　**MIB** Sec. Mkt. **$55**

QX 407-1　　CHRISTMAS IS SHARING: KEEPSAKE CLUB ☐
Comments:　Limited Edition, 49,900, Hand Numbered.
Hand-Painted Bone China, 2-1/4" tall.
Two little rabbits sit in the arch of a tree bowed down with
the weight of the snowfall. **Artist:** Ed Seale
☐ Purchased 19 __ Pd $ __ MIB　　　NB　DB　BNT
☐ Want　　Orig. Ret. $17.50 **NB** $38　　**MIB** Sec. Mkt. **$50**

QX 372-4　　CHRISTMAS MEMORIES PHOTOHOLDER ☐
Comments:　Acrylic, 3-3/4" tall, Dated 1988.
This acrylic wreath is circled with silver foil snowflakes. Caption:
"Christmas Is More Than A Day In December... It's The Magic And
Love We'll Always Remember." **Artist:** Joyce Pattee
☐ Purchased 19 __ Pd $ __ MIB　　　NB　DB　BNT
☐ Want　　Orig. Ret. $6.50 **NB** $15　　**MIB** Sec. Mkt. **$25**

QLX 701-3　　CHRISTMAS MORNING ☐
Comments:　Light and Motion, Handcrafted, 4-5/16" tall.
Reissued from 1987.**Artist:** Ken Crow
☐ Purchased 19 __ Pd $ __ MIB　　　NB　DB　BNT
☐ Want　　Orig. Ret. $24.50 **NB** $40　　**MIB** Sec. Mkt. **$50**

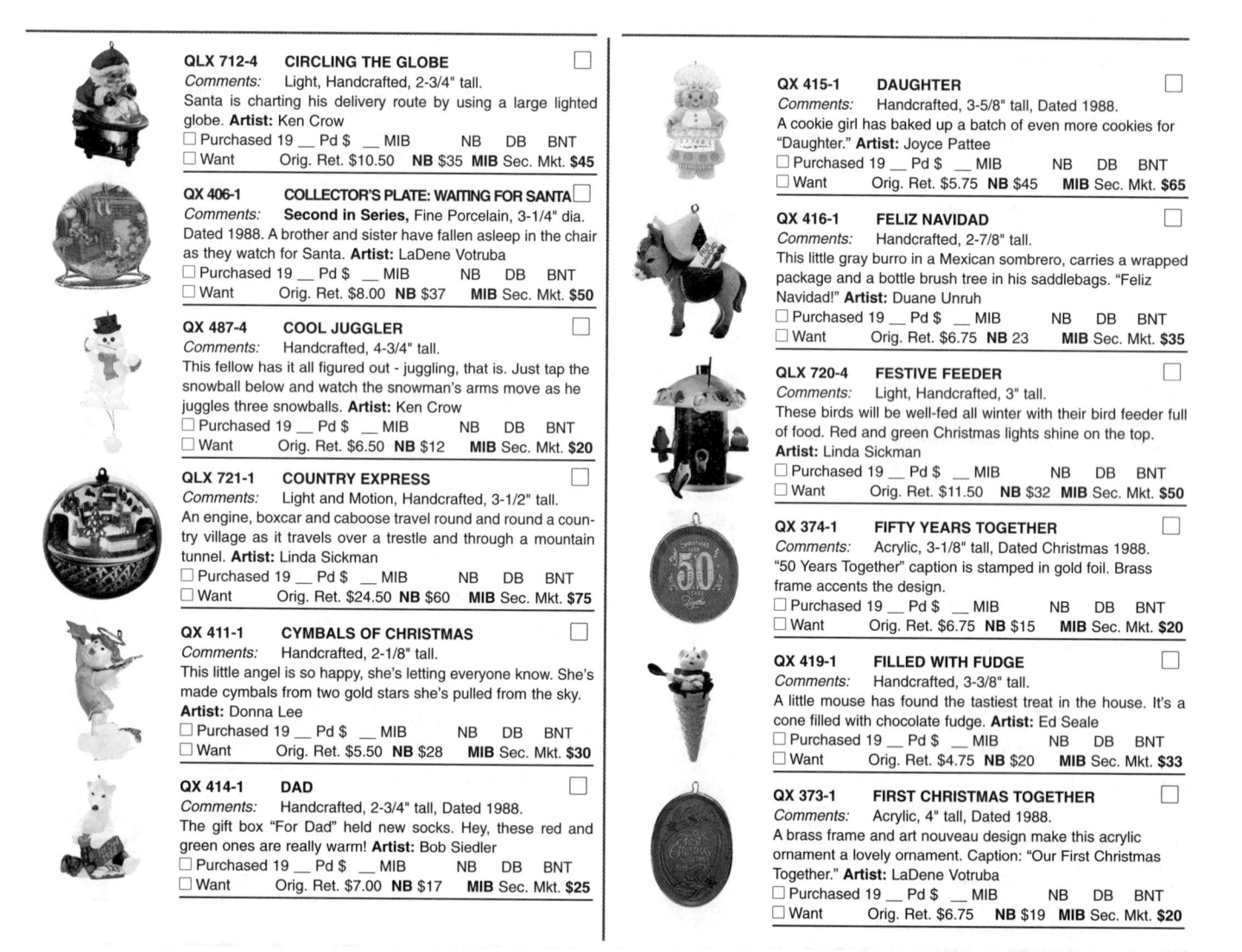

QLX 712-4   CIRCLING THE GLOBE ☐
Comments: Light, Handcrafted, 2-3/4" tall.
Santa is charting his delivery route by using a large lighted globe. **Artist:** Ken Crow
☐ Purchased 19 __ Pd $ __ MIB   NB   DB   BNT
☐ Want   Orig. Ret. $10.50 **NB** $35 **MIB** Sec. Mkt. **$45**

QX 406-1   COLLECTOR'S PLATE: WAITING FOR SANTA ☐
Comments: **Second in Series,** Fine Porcelain, 3-1/4" dia. Dated 1988. A brother and sister have fallen asleep in the chair as they watch for Santa. **Artist:** LaDene Votruba
☐ Purchased 19 __ Pd $ __ MIB   NB   DB   BNT
☐ Want   Orig. Ret. $8.00 **NB** $37   **MIB** Sec. Mkt. **$50**

QX 487-4   COOL JUGGLER ☐
Comments: Handcrafted, 4-3/4" tall.
This fellow has it all figured out - juggling, that is. Just tap the snowball below and watch the snowman's arms move as he juggles three snowballs. **Artist:** Ken Crow
☐ Purchased 19 __ Pd $ __ MIB   NB   DB   BNT
☐ Want   Orig. Ret. $6.50 **NB** $12   **MIB** Sec. Mkt. **$20**

QLX 721-1   COUNTRY EXPRESS ☐
Comments: Light and Motion, Handcrafted, 3-1/2" tall.
An engine, boxcar and caboose travel round and round a country village as it travels over a trestle and through a mountain tunnel. **Artist:** Linda Sickman
☐ Purchased 19 __ Pd $ __ MIB   NB   DB   BNT
☐ Want   Orig. Ret. $24.50 **NB** $60   **MIB** Sec. Mkt. **$75**

QX 411-1   CYMBALS OF CHRISTMAS ☐
Comments: Handcrafted, 2-1/8" tall.
This little angel is so happy, she's letting everyone know. She's made cymbals from two gold stars she's pulled from the sky. **Artist:** Donna Lee
☐ Purchased 19 __ Pd $ __ MIB   NB   DB   BNT
☐ Want   Orig. Ret. $5.50 **NB** $28   **MIB** Sec. Mkt. **$30**

QX 414-1   DAD ☐
Comments: Handcrafted, 2-3/4" tall, Dated 1988.
The gift box "For Dad" held new socks. Hey, these red and green ones are really warm! **Artist:** Bob Siedler
☐ Purchased 19 __ Pd $ __ MIB   NB   DB   BNT
☐ Want   Orig. Ret. $7.00 **NB** $17   **MIB** Sec. Mkt. **$25**

QX 415-1   DAUGHTER ☐
Comments: Handcrafted, 3-5/8" tall, Dated 1988.
A cookie girl has baked up a batch of even more cookies for "Daughter." **Artist:** Joyce Pattee
☐ Purchased 19 __ Pd $ __ MIB   NB   DB   BNT
☐ Want   Orig. Ret. $5.75 **NB** $45   **MIB** Sec. Mkt. **$65**

QX 416-1   FELIZ NAVIDAD ☐
Comments: Handcrafted, 2-7/8" tall.
This little gray burro in a Mexican sombrero, carries a wrapped package and a bottle brush tree in his saddlebags. "Feliz Navidad!" **Artist:** Duane Unruh
☐ Purchased 19 __ Pd $ __ MIB   NB   DB   BNT
☐ Want   Orig. Ret. $6.75 **NB** 23   **MIB** Sec. Mkt. **$35**

QLX 720-4   FESTIVE FEEDER ☐
Comments: Light, Handcrafted, 3" tall.
These birds will be well-fed all winter with their bird feeder full of food. Red and green Christmas lights shine on the top. **Artist:** Linda Sickman
☐ Purchased 19 __ Pd $ __ MIB   NB   DB   BNT
☐ Want   Orig. Ret. $11.50 **NB** $32 **MIB** Sec. Mkt. **$50**

QX 374-1   FIFTY YEARS TOGETHER ☐
Comments: Acrylic, 3-1/8" tall, Dated Christmas 1988.
"50 Years Together" caption is stamped in gold foil. Brass frame accents the design.
☐ Purchased 19 __ Pd $ __ MIB   NB   DB   BNT
☐ Want   Orig. Ret. $6.75 **NB** $15   **MIB** Sec. Mkt. **$20**

QX 419-1   FILLED WITH FUDGE ☐
Comments: Handcrafted, 3-3/8" tall.
A little mouse has found the tastiest treat in the house. It's a cone filled with chocolate fudge. **Artist:** Ed Seale
☐ Purchased 19 __ Pd $ __ MIB   NB   DB   BNT
☐ Want   Orig. Ret. $4.75 **NB** $20   **MIB** Sec. Mkt. **$33**

QX 373-1   FIRST CHRISTMAS TOGETHER ☐
Comments: Acrylic, 4" tall, Dated 1988.
A brass frame and art nouveau design make this acrylic ornament a lovely ornament. Caption: "Our First Christmas Together." **Artist:** LaDene Votruba
☐ Purchased 19 __ Pd $ __ MIB   NB   DB   BNT
☐ Want   Orig. Ret. $6.75 **NB** $19 **MIB** Sec. Mkt. **$20**

QX 274-1   FIRST CHRISTMAS TOGETHER ☐
Comments: Sparkling Glass Ball, 2-7/8" dia., Dated 1988.
Two cardinals against a snow-covered scene.
Caption: "Beauty Is Found In Many Things, But Most Of All In Love. Our First Christmas Together."
☐ Purchased 19 __ Pd $ __ MIB   NB   DB   BNT
☐ Wants   Orig. Ret. $4.75 **NB** $20   **MIB** Sec. Mkt. **$28**

QX 489-4   FIRST CHRISTMAS TOGETHER ☐
Comments: Handcrafted, 3-1/4" tall, Dated 1988.
Two bears with heart-shaped gifts behind their backs stand in the center of an open heart. Caption: "First Christmas Together." **Artist:** Sharon Pike
☐ Purchased 19 __ Pd $ __ MIB   NB   DB   BNT
☐ Want   Orig. Ret. $9.00 **NB** $25   **MIB** Sec. Mkt. **$40**

QLX 702-7   FIRST CHRISTMAS TOGETHER ☐
Comments: Lighted, Handcrafted, 3" tall, Dated 1988.
Two white mice sit in the center of a colorful candy wreath.
Caption: "Our First Christmas Together 1988."
☐ Purchased 19 __ Pd $ __ MIB   NB   DB   BNT
☐ Want   Orig. Ret. $12.00 **NB** $25 **MIB** Sec. Mkt. **$40**

QX 274-4   FIVE YEARS TOGETHER ☐
Comments: White Glass Ball, 2-7/8" dia.
Dated Christmas 1988. Five Christmas trees, composed of green and red hearts, circle the ball. Caption: "5 Years Together." **Artist:** Diana McGehee
☐ Purchased 19 __ Pd $ __ MIB   NB   DB   BNT
☐ Want   Orig. Ret. $4.75 **NB** $17   **MIB** Sec. Mkt. **$23**

QX 279-4   FROM OUR HOME TO YOURS ☐
Comments: Sparkling Glass Ball, 2-7/8" dia., Dated 1988.
Homes and happy snow-people are alternated around this sparkling ball. Caption: "Merry Christmas From Our Home To Yours." **Artist:** Joyce Pattee
☐ Purchased 19 __ Pd $ __ MIB   NB   DB   BNT
☐ Want   Orig. Ret. $4.75 **NB** $15   **MIB** Sec. Mkt. **$18**

QX 403-1   FROSTY FRIENDS ☐
Comments: **Ninth in Series,** Handcrafted, 3-3/8" tall.
Dated 1988. Our Arctic friends are having fun decorating the North Pole with red fabric ribbon. **Artist:** Ed Seale
☐ Purchased 19 __ Pd $ __ MIB   NB   DB   BNT
☐ Want   Orig. Ret. $8.75 **NB** $50   **MIB** Sec. Mkt. **$65**

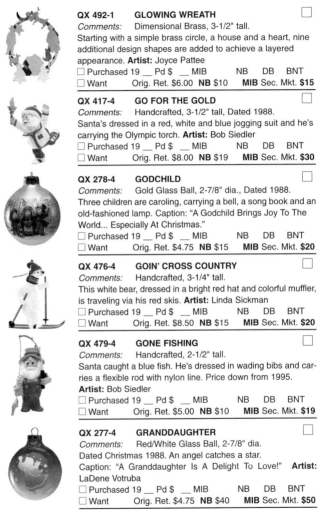

QX 492-1   GLOWING WREATH ☐
Comments: Dimensional Brass, 3-1/2" tall.
Starting with a simple brass circle, a house and a heart, nine additional design shapes are added to achieve a layered appearance. **Artist:** Joyce Pattee
☐ Purchased 19 __ Pd $ __ MIB   NB   DB   BNT
☐ Want   Orig. Ret. $6.00 **NB** $10   **MIB** Sec. Mkt. **$15**

QX 417-4   GO FOR THE GOLD ☐
Comments: Handcrafted, 3-1/2" tall, Dated 1988.
Santa's dressed in a red, white and blue jogging suit and he's carrying the Olympic torch. **Artist:** Bob Siedler
☐ Purchased 19 __ Pd $ __ MIB   NB   DB   BNT
☐ Want   Orig. Ret. $8.00 **NB** $19   **MIB** Sec. Mkt. **$30**

QX 278-4   GODCHILD ☐
Comments: Gold Glass Ball, 2-7/8" dia., Dated 1988.
Three children are caroling, carrying a bell, a song book and an old-fashioned lamp. Caption: "A Godchild Brings Joy To The World... Especially At Christmas."
☐ Purchased 19 __ Pd $ __ MIB   NB   DB   BNT
☐ Want   Orig. Ret. $4.75 **NB** $15   **MIB** Sec. Mkt. **$20**

QX 476-4   GOIN' CROSS COUNTRY ☐
Comments: Handcrafted, 3-1/4" tall.
This white bear, dressed in a bright red hat and colorful muffler, is traveling via his red skis. **Artist:** Linda Sickman
☐ Purchased 19 __ Pd $ __ MIB   NB   DB   BNT
☐ Want   Orig. Ret. $8.50 **NB** $15   **MIB** Sec. Mkt. **$20**

QX 479-4   GONE FISHING ☐
Comments: Handcrafted, 2-1/2" tall.
Santa caught a blue fish. He's dressed in wading bibs and carries a flexible rod with nylon line. Price down from 1995.
Artist: Bob Siedler
☐ Purchased 19 __ Pd $ __ MIB   NB   DB   BNT
☐ Want   Orig. Ret. $5.00 **NB** $10   **MIB** Sec. Mkt. **$19**

QX 277-4   GRANDDAUGHTER ☐
Comments: Red/White Glass Ball, 2-7/8" dia.
Dated Christmas 1988. An angel catches a star.
Caption: "A Granddaughter Is A Delight To Love!"   **Artist:** LaDene Votruba
☐ Purchased 19 __ Pd $ __ MIB   NB   DB   BNT
☐ Want   Orig. Ret. $4.75 **NB** $40   **MIB** Sec. Mkt. **$50**

QX 276-4   GRANDMOTHER

Comments: Gold Glass Ball, 2-7/8" dia., Dated 1988.
With the look of crewel embroidery, the caption is bordered with
the partridge and pear tree theme.
Caption: "Grandmother Makes Love A Christmas Tradition."
☐ Purchased 19 __ Pd $ __ MIB   NB   DB   BNT
☐ Want   Orig. Ret. $4.75 **NB** $12   **MIB** Sec. Mkt. **$19**

QX 277-1   GRANDPARENTS

Comments: Red Glass Ball, 2-7/8" dia., Dated Christmas 1988.
A cozy Christmas scene with a tree and a cat napping on a rug.
All depicted wiith the caption: "Grandparents Are The Heart Of
So Many Treasured Memories." **Artist:** Joyce Pattee
☐ Purchased 19 __ Pd $ __ MIB   NB   DB   BNT
☐ Want   Orig. Ret. $4.75 **NB** $10   **MIB** Sec. Mkt. **$19**

QX 278-1   GRANDSON

Comments: Green/White Glass Ball, 2-7/8" tall, Dated 1988.
Santa's catching snowflakes! Caption: "A Grandson Makes
Christmas Merry!" **Artist:** LaDene Votruba
☐ Purchased 19 __ Pd $ __ MIB   NB   DB   BNT
☐ Want   Orig. Ret. $4.75 **NB** $30   **MIB** Sec. Mkt. **$40**

QX 375-4   GRATITUDE

Comments: Acrylic, 3-3/8" tall, Dated 1988.
A snow-covered evergreen tree and snowflakes. Caption:
"Christmas Fills Our Hearts With Thoughts Of Those Who
Care." **Artist:** Joyce Pattee
☐ Purchased 19 __ Pd $ __ MIB   NB   DB   BNT
☐ Want   Orig. Ret. $6.00 **NB** $6   **MIB** Sec. Mkt. **$12.50**

QX 471-4   HAPPY HOLIDATA

Comments: Handcrafted, 1-1/2" tall.
Reissued from 1987. **Artist:** Bob Siedler
☐ Purchased 19 __ Pd $ __ MIB   NB   DB   BNT
☐ Want   Orig. Ret. $6.50 **NB** $20   **MIB** Sec. Mkt. **$30**

QLX 711-4   HEAVENLY GLOW

Comments: Light, Brass, 3" tall.
A delicately etched brass angel holds a Christmas star. Lighted
from within. **Artist:** Michele Pyda-Sevcik
☐ Purchased 19 __ Pd $ __ MIB   NB   DB   BNT
☐ Want   Orig. Ret. $11.75 **NB** $22   **MIB** Sec. Mkt. **$30**

QX 400-1   HERE COMES SANTA: KRINGLE KOACH

Comments: **Tenth in Series,** Handcrafted, 3-1/4" tall.
Dated 1988. Santa's delivering presents by way of the "Kringle
Koach." He's wearing a ten-gallon hat and carrying a teddy
bear passenger. **Artist:** Ken Crow
☐ Purchased 19 __ Pd $ __ MIB   NB   DB   BNT
☐ Want   Orig. Ret. $14.00 **NB** $38   **MIB** Sec. Mkt. **$50**

QX 422-1   HOE-HOE-HOE!

Comments: Handcrafted, 2-3/8" tall.
Santa's all ready to work in the garden. He's wearing a red
visor and green coveralls. **Artist:** Bob Siedler
☐ Purchased 19 __ Pd $ __ MIB   NB   DB   BNT
☐ Want   Orig. Ret. $5.00 **NB** $16   **MIB** Sec. Mkt. **$20**

QX 406-4   HOLIDAY HEIRLOOM: KEEPSAKE CLUB

Comments: **Second in Series,** Limited Edition 34,600.
Lead Crystal/Silver Plating, 3-1/2" tall, Dated 1988.
The second crystal bell has two angels in flight holding a silver-
plated star. The second in series was offered only to Club
Members. **Artist:** Duane Unruh
☐ Purchased 19 __ Pd $ __ MIB   NB   DB   BNT
☐ Want   Orig. Ret. $25.00 **NB** $21   **MIB** Sec. Mkt. **$35**

QX 423-1   HOLIDAY HERO

Comments: Handcrafted, 2-5/8" tall.
Whether on the field or off, S. Claus is number "1". He's ready
to pass the football for a win! **Artist:** Bob Siedler
☐ Purchased 19 __ Pd $ __ MIB   NB   DB   BNT
☐ Want   Orig. Ret. $5.00 **NB** $16   **MIB** Sec. Mkt. **$20**

QX 371-1   HOLIDAY WILDLIFE: PURPLE FINCH

Comments: **Seventh and Final in Series,** Wood, 2-1/2" dia.
Dated Christmas 1988. Caption: "Purple Finch, CARPODA-
CUSPURPUREUS, Seventh In A Series, Wildlife Collection."
☐ Purchased 19 __ Pd $ __ MIB   NB   DB   BNT
☐ Want   Orig. Ret. $7.75 **NB** $19   **MIB** Sec. Mkt. **$28**

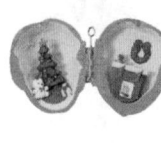

QX 469-7   IN A NUTSHELL

Comments: Handcrafted, 1-1/2" tall, Reissued from 1987.
Artist: Duane Unruh
☐ Purchased 19 __ Pd $ __ MIB   NB   DB   BNT
☐ Want   Orig. Ret. $5.50 **NB** $24   **MIB** Sec. Mkt. **$34**

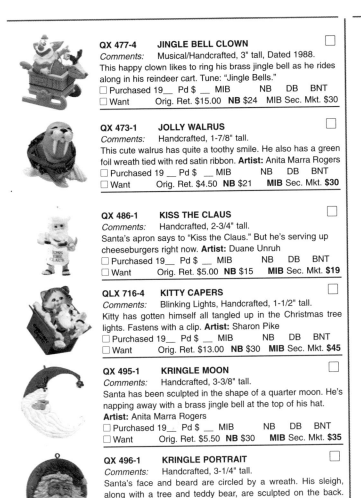

QX 477-4   JINGLE BELL CLOWN
Comments: Musical/Handcrafted, 3" tall, Dated 1988.
This happy clown likes to ring his brass jingle bell as he rides
along in his reindeer cart. Tune: "Jingle Bells."
☐ Purchased 19__ Pd $ __   MIB   NB   DB   BNT
☐ Want   Orig. Ret. $15.00 **NB** $24   MIB Sec. Mkt. **$30**

QX 473-1   JOLLY WALRUS
Comments: Handcrafted, 1-7/8" tall.
This cute walrus has quite a toothy smile. He also has a green
foil wreath tied with red satin ribbon. **Artist:** Anita Marra Rogers
☐ Purchased 19__ Pd $ __   MIB   NB   DB   BNT
☐ Want   Orig. Ret. $4.50 **NB** $21   **MIB** Sec. Mkt. **$30**

QX 486-1   KISS THE CLAUS
Comments: Handcrafted, 2-3/4" tall.
Santa's apron says to "Kiss the Claus." But he's serving up
cheeseburgers right now. **Artist:** Duane Unruh
☐ Purchased 19__ Pd $ __   MIB   NB   DB   BNT
☐ Want   Orig. Ret. $5.00 **NB** $15   **MIB** Sec. Mkt. **$19**

QLX 716-4   KITTY CAPERS
Comments: Blinking Lights, Handcrafted, 1-1/2" tall.
Kitty has gotten himself all tangled up in the Christmas tree
lights. Fastens with a clip. **Artist:** Sharon Pike
☐ Purchased 19__ Pd $ __   MIB   NB   DB   BNT
☐ Want   Orig. Ret. $13.00 **NB** $30   **MIB** Sec. Mkt. **$45**

QX 495-1   KRINGLE MOON
Comments: Handcrafted, 3-3/8" tall.
Santa has been sculpted in the shape of a quarter moon. He's
napping away with a brass jingle bell at the top of his hat.
Artist: Anita Marra Rogers
☐ Purchased 19__ Pd $ __   MIB   NB   DB   BNT
☐ Want   Orig. Ret. $5.50 **NB** $30   **MIB** Sec. Mkt. **$35**

QX 496-1   KRINGLE PORTRAIT
Comments: Handcrafted, 3-1/4" tall.
Santa's face and beard are circled by a wreath. His sleigh,
along with a tree and teddy bear, are sculpted on the back.
Some color differences have been noted.
☐ Purchased 19__ Pd $ __   MIB   NB   DB   BNT
☐ Want   Orig. Ret. $7.50 **NB** $30   **MIB** Sec. Mkt. **$40**

QX 495-4   KRINGLE TREE
Comments: Handcrafted, 3-3/8" tall.
Resembling an Old World carving is the Kringle Tree – it's
Santa in green, sculpted to look like a Christmas tree!
☐ Purchased 19__ Pd $ __   MIB   NB   DB   BNT
☐ Want   Orig. Ret. $6.50 **NB** $30   **MIB** Sec. Mkt. **$40**

QLX 701-7   KRINGLE'S TOY SHOP
Comments: Open House Ornament, Light/Motion, Handcrafted.
Reissued in 1989. Two children stand outside the large pic-
ture window and watch Santa's elves making the toys he will
deliver on Christmas Eve. **Artist:** Ed Seale
☐ Purchased 19__ Pd $ __   MIB   NB   DB   BNT
☐ Want   Orig. Ret. $24.50 **NB** $40   **MIB** Sec. Mkt. **$50**

QLX 718-1   LAST-MINUTE HUG
Comments: Light and Motion, Handcrafted, 3-1/2" tall.
As Santa heads out one door for his annual flight, Mrs. Claus
hurries out the other to give him one last hug.
Artist: Duane Unruh
☐ Purchased 19__ Pd $ __   MIB   NB   DB   BNT
☐ Want   Orig. Ret. $22.00 **NB** $40   **MIB** Sec. Mkt. **$50**

QX 408-1   LITTLE JACK HORNER
Comments: Handcrafted, 2-1/2" tall.
The nursery rhyme says, "He stuck in his thumb and pulled out
a plum." His name is on his hat. **Artist:** Bob Siedler
☐ Purchased 19__ Pd $ __   MIB   NB   DB   BNT
☐ Want   Orig. Ret. $8.00 **NB** $17   **MIB** Sec. Mkt. **$23**

QX 374-4   LOVE FILLS THE HEART
Comments: Acrylic, 3" tall.
Two birds perch on the border of holly leaves and berries.
Caption: "Love Fills The Heart Forever."
Artist: LaDene Votruba
☐ Purchased 19__ Pd $ __   MIB   NB   DB   BNT
☐ Want   Orig. Ret. $6.00 **NB** $15   **MIB** Sec. Mkt. **$25**

QX 275-4   LOVE GROWS
Comments: Chrome Glass Ball, 2-7/8" dia., Dated
Christmas 1988. To achieve a rich lacquered look, bright large
blossoms have been printed against a black background.
Caption: "Patiently, Joyfully, Beautifully, Love Grows."
☐ Purchased 19__ Pd $ __   MIB   NB   DB   BNT
☐ Want   Orig. Ret. $4.75 **NB** $21   **MIB** Sec. Mkt. **$33**

QX 486-4　LOVE SANTA ☐

Comments:　Handcrafted, 2-1/2" tall.
Santa is in great form as he volleys the tennis ball (pom-pom) back and forth. **Artist:** Bob Siedler

☐ Purchased 19__　Pd $ __　MIB　　　NB　　DB　　BNT
☐ Want　　　Orig. Ret. $5.00　**NB** $15　　**MIB** Sec. Mkt. **$20**

QX 493-4　LOVING BEAR ☐

Comments:　Handcrafted, 3-1/4" tall.
A teddy bear with his heart showing on his fur twirls inside a wreath of hearts. Handpainted. **Artist:** Anita Marra Rogers

☐ Purchased 19__　Pd $ __　MIB　　　NB　　DB　　BNT
☐ Want　　　Orig. Ret. $4.75　**NB** $11　　**MIB** Sec. Mkt. **$20**

QX 407-4　MARY'S ANGELS: BUTTERCUP ☐

Comments:　***FIRST IN SERIES***, 2-1/4" tall.
Redheaded Buttercup is dressed in yellow and is napping on a frosted acrylic cloud. Many sales reported in '96 used to obtain this lowered price from the preceding years. **Artist:** Robert Chad

☐ Purchased 19__　Pd $ __　MIB　　　NB　　DB　　BNT
☐ Want　　　Orig. Ret. $5.00　**NB** $35　　**MIB** Sec. Mkt. **$45**

QX 423-4　MERRY-MINT UNICORN ☐

Comments:　Hand-Painted Fine Porcelain, 3-3/4" tall.
This lovely white unicorn has a red and white striped horn and is balancing on a peppermint candy.
Artist: Anita Marra Rogers

☐ Purchased 19__　Pd $ __　MIB　　　NB　　DB　　BNT
☐ Want　　　Orig. Ret. $8.50　**NB** $20　　**MIB** Sec. Mkt. **$23**

QX 410-4　MIDNIGHT SNACK ☐

Comments:　Handcrafted, 2-1/2" tall.
Donuts make the perfect nighttime snack, and this little white mouse agrees as he nibbles away.
Artist: Bob Siedler

☐ Purchased 19__　Pd $ __　MIB　　　NB　　DB　　BNT
☐ Want　　　Orig. Ret. $6.00　**NB** $19　　**MIB** Sec. Mkt. **$23**

QX 403-4　MINIATURE CRECHE ☐

Comments:　**Fourth in Series**, Acrylic, 2-3/4" tall.
The Holy Family is depicted in frosted acrylic which has been set in a clear acrylic star. The edges of the star are faceted and painted gold. **Artist:** Duane Unruh

☐ Purchased 19__　Pd $ __　MIB　　　NB　　DB　　BNT
☐ Want　　　Orig. Ret. $8.50　**NB** $20　　**MIB** Sec. Mkt. **$35**

QX 468-7　MISTLETOAD ☐

Comments:　Handcrafted, 3-3/4" tall, Reissued from 1987.
Artist: Ken Crow

☐ Purchased 19__　Pd $ __　MIB　　　NB　　DB　　BNT
☐ Want　　　Orig. Ret. $7.00　**NB** $25　　**MIB** Sec. Mkt. **$30**

QLX 713-4　MOONLIT NAP ☐

Comments:　Light, Handcrafted, 2-3/4" tall.
A little angel, dressed in a blue gown and white wings, has hung his stocking on the tip of the brightly glowing moon awaiting Santa's visit. **Artist:** Robert Chad

☐ Purchased 19__　Pd $ __　MIB　　　NB　　DB　　BNT
☐ Want　　　Orig. Ret. $8.75　**NB** $21　　**MIB** Sec. Mkt. **$30**

QX 375-1　MOTHER ☐

Comments:　Acrylic, 3-3/4" tall, Dated 1988.
Heart shaped acrylic with gold foil heart outline and caption: "Mother Puts Love Inside Each Moment Of Christmas."

☐ Purchased 19__　Pd $ __　MIB　　　NB　　DB　　BNT
☐ Want　　　Orig. Ret. $6.50　**NB** $17　　**MIB** Sec. Mkt. **$21**

QX 414-4　MOTHER AND DAD ☐

Comments:　Fine Porcelain, 3" tall, Dated 1988.
A candle and holly design bring light to this bell. Caption: "Mother And Dad" and "You Give Christmas A Special Warmth And Glow." **Artist:** Joyce A. Lyle

☐ Purchased 19__　Pd $ __　MIB　　　NB　　DB　　BNT
☐ Want　　　Orig. Ret. $8.00　**NB** $14　　**MIB** Sec. Mkt. **$25**

QX 401-1　MR. AND MRS. CLAUS: SHALL WE DANCE? ☐

Comments:　**Third in Series**, Handcrafted, 4-1/4" tall.
Dated 1988. Santa always has time for a dance with his sweetheart. **Artist:** Duane Unruh

☐ Purchased 19__　Pd $ __　MIB　　　NB　　DB　　BNT
☐ Want　　　Orig. Ret. $13.00　**NB** $38　**MIB** Sec. Mkt. **$60**

QX 376-1　NEW HOME ☐

Comments:　Acrylic, 2-1/2" tall, Dated 1988.
Santa and his reindeer fly over a wintry home scene. Caption in gold foil: "A New Home Makes Christmas Merry And Bright."
Artist: LaDene Votruba

☐ Purchased 19__　Pd $ __　MIB　　　NB　　DB　　BNT
☐ Want　　　Orig. Ret. $6.00　**NB** $10　　**MIB** Sec. Mkt. **$20**

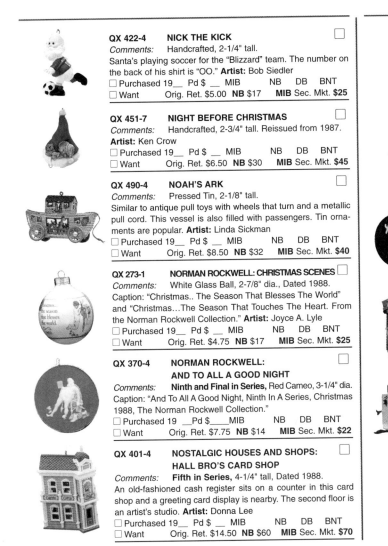

QX 422-4   NICK THE KICK
Comments: Handcrafted, 2-1/4" tall.
Santa's playing soccer for the "Blizzard" team. The number on the back of his shirt is "OO." **Artist:** Bob Siedler
☐ Purchased 19__ Pd $ __ MIB   NB   DB   BNT
☐ Want   Orig. Ret. $5.00 **NB** $17   **MIB** Sec. Mkt. **$25**

QX 451-7   NIGHT BEFORE CHRISTMAS
Comments: Handcrafted, 2-3/4" tall. Reissued from 1987.
Artist: Ken Crow
☐ Purchased 19__ Pd $ __ MIB   NB   DB   BNT
☐ Want   Orig. Ret. $6.50 **NB** $30   **MIB** Sec. Mkt. **$45**

QX 490-4   NOAH'S ARK
Comments: Pressed Tin, 2-1/8" tall.
Similar to antique pull toys with wheels that turn and a metallic pull cord. This vessel is also filled with passengers. Tin ornaments are popular. **Artist:** Linda Sickman
☐ Purchased 19__ Pd $ __ MIB   NB   DB   BNT
☐ Want   Orig. Ret. $8.50 **NB** $32   **MIB** Sec. Mkt. **$40**

QX 273-1   NORMAN ROCKWELL: CHRISTMAS SCENES
Comments: White Glass Ball, 2-7/8" dia., Dated 1988.
Caption: "Christmas.. The Season That Blesses The World" and "Christmas…The Season That Touches The Heart. From the Norman Rockwell Collection." **Artist:** Joyce A. Lyle
☐ Purchased 19__ Pd $ __ MIB   NB   DB   BNT
☐ Want   Orig. Ret. $4.75 **NB** $17   **MIB** Sec. Mkt. **$25**

QX 370-4   NORMAN ROCKWELL:
AND TO ALL A GOOD NIGHT
Comments: **Ninth and Final in Series,** Red Cameo, 3-1/4" dia.
Caption: "And To All A Good Night, Ninth In A Series, Christmas 1988, The Norman Rockwell Collection."
☐ Purchased 19 __Pd $____MIB   NB   DB   BNT
☐ Want   Orig. Ret. $7.75 **NB** $14   **MIB** Sec. Mkt. **$22**

QX 401-4   NOSTALGIC HOUSES AND SHOPS:
HALL BRO'S CARD SHOP
Comments: **Fifth in Series,** 4-1/4" tall, Dated 1988.
An old-fashioned cash register sits on a counter in this card shop and a greeting card display is nearby. The second floor is an artist's studio. **Artist:** Donna Lee
☐ Purchased 19__ Pd $ __ MIB   NB   DB   BNT
☐ Want   Orig. Ret. $14.50 **NB** $60   **MIB** Sec. Mkt. **$70**

QX 498-1   OLD-FASHIONED CHURCH
Comments: Wood, 4-1/2" tall.
In American country motif, this small white church boasts a steeple with a cross at the top. **Artist:** Linda Sickman
☐ Purchased 19__ Pd $ __ MIB   NB   DB   BNT
☐ Want   Orig. Ret. $4.00 **NB** $18   **MIB** Sec. Mkt. **$25**

QX 497-1   OLD-FASHIONED SCHOOLHOUSE
Comments: Wood, 3" tall.
The little red schoolhouse is reminiscent of early country with its flag and bell tower. **Artist:** Linda Sickman
☐ Purchased 19__ Pd $ __ MIB   NB   DB   BNT
☐ Want   Orig. Ret. $4.00 **NB** $15   **MIB** Sec. Mkt. **$23**

QX 481-4   OREO®
Comments: Handcrafted, 1-7/8" dia.
Cookie opens to show frosting inside. Santa's face is part of the frosting. "Ho Ho Ho!" **Artist:** Duane Unruh
☐ Purchased 19__ Pd $ __ MIB   NB   DB   BNT
☐ Want   Orig. Ret. $4.00 **NB** $16   **MIB** Sec. Mkt. **$20**

QXC 580-4   OUR CLUBHOUSE: KEEPSAKE CLUB
Comments: Handcrafted, 2-1/2" tall, Dated 1988.
"For Club Members Only" is a cute little clubhouse with a mouse inside. He's decorated the inside for Christmas. The Club logo is on the bottom. **Artist:** Bob Siedler
☐ Purchased 19__ Pd $ __ MIB   NB   DB   BNT
☐ Want   Price: Came with Club Membership of $_____
                NB $36   **MIB** Sec. Mkt. **$45**

QX 455-9   "OWLIDAY" WISH
Comments: Handcrafted, 2" tall. Reissued from 1987.
Artist: Sharon Pike
☐ Purchased 19__ Pd $ __ MIB   NB   DB   BNT
☐ Want   Orig. Ret. $6.50 **NB** $20   **MIB** Sec. Mkt. **$25**

QX 479-1   PAR FOR SANTA
Comments: Handcrafted, 2-5/8" tall.
Santa's waiting for the St. Nick Open to begin and he's ready to tee off in this golf design. **Artist:** Bob Siedler
☐ Purchased 19__ Pd $ __ MIB   NB   DB   BNT
☐ Want   Orig. Ret. $5.00 **NB** $15   **MIB** Sec. Mkt. **$20**

QLX 719-4   PARADE OF THE TOYS

Comments: Light and Motion, Handcrafted, 3-1/2" tall.
The toys are on parade. A toy soldier pulls a red wagon with a jack-in-the-box which pops up and down, a doll pushes a baby carriage and three ducks all circle a lighted Christmas tree.
Artist: Linda Sickman

☐ Purchased 19__   Pd $ __   MIB   NB   DB   BNT
☐ Want   Orig. Ret. $24.50 **NB** $42   **MIB** Sec. Mkt. **$55**

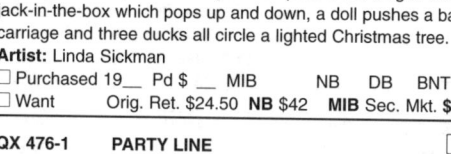

QX 476-1   PARTY LINE

Comments: Handcrafted, 1-3/4" tall.
Two little raccoons have solved their communication problems; they've created their own telephone from two miniature cans of "Campbell's Chicken Noodle Soup." Campbell's Collectibles are very popular. **Artist:** Sharon Pike

☐ Purchased 19__   Pd $ __   MIB   NB   DB   BNT
☐ Want   Orig. Ret. $8.75 **NB** $20   **MIB** Sec. Mkt. **$28**

QX 280-1   PEANUTS®

Comments: Blue Glass Ball, 2-7/8" dia., Dated Christmas 1988. Santa Snoopy flies across the sky on a sled loaded with gifts, and pulled by Woodstock and his friends.

☐ Purchased 19__   Pd $ __   MIB   NB   DB   BNT
☐ Want   Orig. Ret. $4.75 **NB** $40   **MIB** Sec. Mkt. **$50**

QX 487-1   PEEK-A-BOO KITTIES

Comments: Handcrafted, 5" tall.
While a kitten plays with a ball of yarn, two more peek out of the basket when the string is pulled. **Artist:** Ken Crow

☐ Purchased 19__   Pd $ __   MIB   NB   DB   BNT
☐ Want   Orig. Ret. $7.50 **NB** $18   **MIB** Sec. Mkt. **$23**

QX 478-4   POLAR BOWLER

Comments: Handcrafted, 2-1/4" tall.
Santa shows great form with his polished green bowling ball at the "North Pole Bowl." **Artist:** Bob Siedler

☐ Purchased 19__   Pd $ __   MIB   NB   DB   BNT
☐ Want   Orig. Ret. $5.00 **NB** $16   **MIB** Sec. Mkt. **$20**

QX 404-4   PORCELAIN BEAR

Comments: **Sixth in Series,** Fine Porcelain, 2-1/4" tall.
This year's cinnamon bear is thrilled with his gift! It's wrapped inside a red heart-shaped box with a green bow.
Artist: Sharon Pike

☐ Purchased 19__   Pd $ __   MIB   NB   DB   BNT
☐ Want   Orig. Ret. $8.00 **NB** $30   **MIB** Sec. Mkt. **$39**

QX 474-4   PURRFECT SNUGGLE

Comments: Handcrafted, 2" tall.
A gray and white striped kitten has found a new friend - a brown teddy bear with a holiday bow. **Artist:** Anita Marra Rogers

☐ Purchased 19__   Pd $ __   MIB   NB   DB   BNT
☐ Want   Orig. Ret. $6.25 **NB** $20   **MIB** Sec. Mkt. **$30**

QLX 712-1   RADIANT TREE

Comments: Light, Brass, 3-1/4" tall.
Ten cutout triangular panels form this brass tree which radiates light from all sides. **Artist:** Joyce A. Lyle

☐ Purchased 19__   Pd $ __   MIB   NB   DB   BNT
☐ Want   Orig. Ret. $11.75 **NB** $20   **MIB** Sec. Mkt. **$28**

QX 405-1   REINDEER CHAMPS: PRANCER

Comments: **Third in Series,** Handcrafted, 3-1/2" tall, Dated 1988.
"Prancer 88" is a basketball champion with his white sport shoes and shooting technique. **Artist:** Bob Siedler

☐ Purchased 19__   Pd $ __   MIB   NB   DB   BNT
☐ Want   Orig. Ret. $7.50 **NB** $20   **MIB** Sec. Mkt. **$35**

QX 452-7   REINDOGGY

Comments: Handcrafted, 2-3/4" tall, Reissued from 1987.
Artist: Bob Siedler

☐ Purchased 19__   Pd $ __   MIB   NB   DB   BNT
☐ Want   Orig. Ret. $5.75 **NB** $25   **MIB** Sec. Mkt. **$35**

QX 402-4   ROCKING HORSE

Comments: **Eighth in Series,** 3-1/4" wide, Dated 1988.
A dapple gray pony is accented with red, green and gold trappings, and is seated on bright red and green rockers. **Artist:** Linda Sickman

☐ Purchased 19__   Pd $ __   MIB   NB   DB   BNT
☐ Want   Orig. Ret. $10.75 **NB** $59   **MIB** Sec. Mkt. **$70**

QX 491-1   SAILING! SAILING!

Comments: Pressed Tin, 2-7/8" tall.
A red and white hoisted sail sets off this sailboat. A sailor enjoys the day as water laps against the sides of his boat.
Artist: Linda Sickman

☐ Purchased 19__   Pd $ __   MIB   NB   DB   BNT
☐ Want   Orig. Ret. $8.50 **NB** $16   **MIB** Sec. Mkt. **$25**

QLX 719-1　SANTA & SPARKY: ON WITH THE SHOW ☐
Comments:　**Third in Series,** Light and Motion, Handcrafted, 4" tall.
Dated 1988. Santa steps forward and waves his magic wand and presto! A penguin pops out of his hat!
☐ Purchased 19__　Pd $ __　MIB　　NB　DB　BNT
☐ Want　　Orig. Ret. $19.50　**NB** $39　**MIB** Sec. Mkt. **$45**

QX 483-4　SANTA FLAMINGO ☐
Comments:　Handcrafted, 5-1/2" tall.
This pink flamingo stands tall among others due to his long legs (which really move). He wears a red fabric Santa hat with furry white trim. **Artist:** Michele Pyda-Sevcik
☐ Purchased 19__　Pd $ __　MIB　　NB　DB　BNT
☐ Want　　Orig. Ret. $4.75　**NB** $35　**MIB** Sec. Mkt. **$40**

QX 492-4　SHINY SLEIGH ☐
Comments:　Dimensional Brass, 1-3/8" tall.
The multidimensional design of Santa and his reindeer has been achieved by bending and shaping one continuous piece of brass. **Artist:** Joyce Pattee
☐ Purchased 19__　Pd $ __　MIB　　NB　DB　BNT
☐ Want　　Orig. Ret. $5.75　**NB** $14　**MIB** Sec. Mkt. **$20**

QX 499-4　SISTER ☐
Comments:　Fine Porcelain Bell, 3" tall, Dated 1988.
A little girl places a star on the top of her Christmas tree. Caption: "Sisters Know So Many Ways To Brighten Up The Holidays!" **Artist:** LaDene Votruba
☐ Purchased 19__　Pd $ __　MIB　　NB　DB　BNT
☐ Want　　Orig. Ret. $8.00　**NB** $20　**MIB** Sec. Mkt. **$33**

QLX 720-1　SKATER'S WALTZ ☐
Comments:　Light and Motion, Handcrafted, 3-1/2" tall.
Two Victorian couples ice skate around snow covered evergreens and a lamppost. **Artist:** Duane Unruh
☐ Purchased 19__　Pd $ __　MIB　　NB　DB　BNT
☐ Want　　Orig. Ret. $24.50　**NB** $55　**MIB** Sec. Mkt. **$63**

QXC 580-1　SLEIGHFUL OF DREAMS: KEEPSAKE CLUB ☐
Comments:　Handcrafted, 2-1/8" tall, Dated 1988.
Designed to resemble an old-fashioned wooden sleigh, this creation features bas relief designs of favorite past Keepsake ornaments. **Artist:** Linda Sickman
☐ Purchased 19__　Pd $ __　MIB　　NB　DB　BNT
☐ Want　　Orig. Ret. $8.00　**NB** $50　**MIB** Sec. Mkt. **$75**

QX 472-4　SLIPPER SPANIEL ☐
Comments:　Handcrafted, 3" tall.
This little brown and white puppy has fallen asleep in a red flocked slipper. **Artist:** Ken Crow
☐ Purchased 19__　Pd $ __　MIB　　NB　DB　BNT
☐ Want　　Orig. Ret. $4.25　**NB** $15　**MIB** Sec. Mkt. **$20**

QX 474-1　SNOOPY® AND WOODSTOCK ☐
Comments:　Handcrafted, 2-3/8" tall.
These two friends have tucked themselves into a red and white knit stocking which includes a bone with a green bow.
Artist: Duane Unruh
☐ Purchased 19__　Pd $ __　MIB　　NB　DB　BNT
☐ Want　　Orig. Ret. $6.00　**NB** $33　**MIB** Sec. Mkt. **$47**

QX 475-1　SOFT LANDING ☐
Comments:　Handcrafted, 3" tall.
If Santa falls down on his ice skates, he won't get hurt — he's tied a green pillow to his waist. **Artist:** Robert Chad
☐ Purchased 19__　Pd $ __　MIB　　NB　DB　BNT
☐ Want　　Orig. Ret. $7.00　**NB** $20　**MIB** Sec. Mkt. **$25**

QX 415-4　SON ☐
Comments:　Handcrafted, 3-5/8" tall, Dated 1988.
Similar to the Daughter ornament, a cookie boy is carrying a cookie sheet full of more cookies. **Artist:** Joyce Pattee
☐ Purchased 19__　Pd $ __　MIB　　NB　DB　BNT
☐ Want　　Orig. Ret. $5.75　**NB** $31　**MIB** Sec. Mkt. **$40**

QLX 711-1　SONG OF CHRISTMAS ☐
Comments:　Light, Acrylic, 3-1/2" tall.
The beveled, faceted edge sets off the exquisite etched cardinal. Caption: "Song Of Christmas."
☐ Purchased 19__　Pd $ __　MIB　　NB　DB　BNT
☐ Want　　Orig. Ret. $8.50　**NB** $21　**MIB** Sec. Mkt. **$30**

QX 493-1　SPARKLING TREE ☐
Comments:　Dimensional Brass, 3-3/8" tall.
A brass Christmas tree is layered with brass silhouettes of a home, reindeer, doves, heart and star. There are also cutouts in the tree. **Artist:** Joyce Pattee
☐ Purchased 19__　Pd $ __　MIB　　NB　DB　BNT
☐ Want　　Orig. Ret. $6.00　**NB** $15　**MIB** Sec. Mkt. **$19**

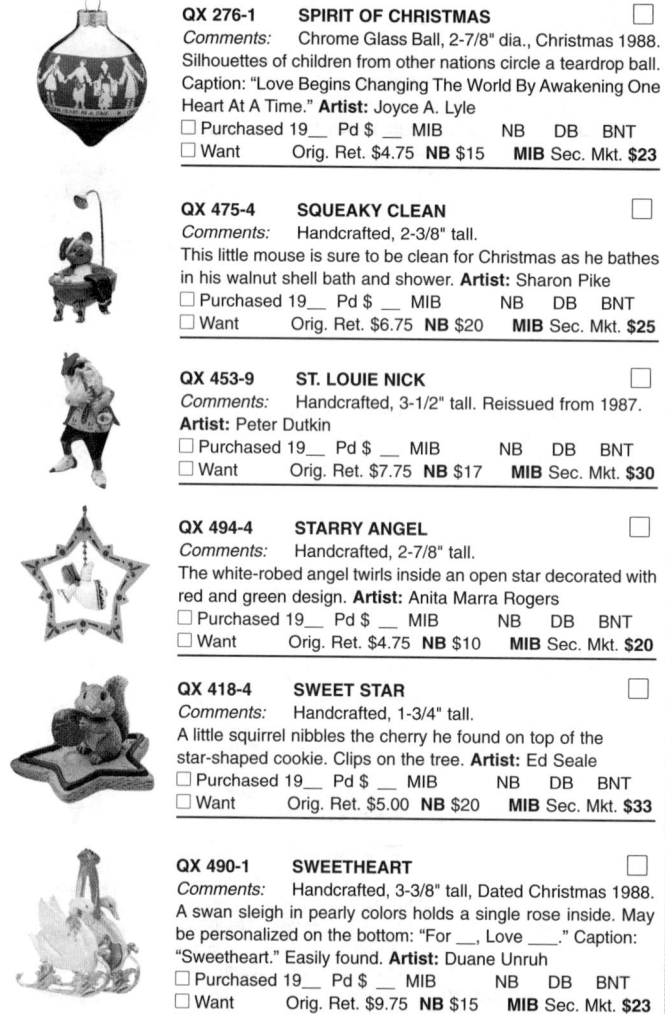

QX 276-1 SPIRIT OF CHRISTMAS ☐
Comments: Chrome Glass Ball, 2-7/8" dia., Christmas 1988.
Silhouettes of children from other nations circle a teardrop ball.
Caption: "Love Begins Changing The World By Awakening One
Heart At A Time." **Artist:** Joyce A. Lyle
☐ Purchased 19__ Pd $ __ MIB   NB   DB   BNT
☐ Want   Orig. Ret. $4.75 **NB** $15   **MIB** Sec. Mkt. **$23**

QX 475-4 SQUEAKY CLEAN ☐
Comments: Handcrafted, 2-3/8" tall.
This little mouse is sure to be clean for Christmas as he bathes
in his walnut shell bath and shower. **Artist:** Sharon Pike
☐ Purchased 19__ Pd $ __ MIB   NB   DB   BNT
☐ Want   Orig. Ret. $6.75 **NB** $20   **MIB** Sec. Mkt. **$25**

QX 453-9 ST. LOUIE NICK ☐
Comments: Handcrafted, 3-1/2" tall. Reissued from 1987.
Artist: Peter Dutkin
☐ Purchased 19__ Pd $ __ MIB   NB   DB   BNT
☐ Want   Orig. Ret. $7.75 **NB** $17   **MIB** Sec. Mkt. **$30**

QX 494-4 STARRY ANGEL ☐
Comments: Handcrafted, 2-7/8" tall.
The white-robed angel twirls inside an open star decorated with
red and green design. **Artist:** Anita Marra Rogers
☐ Purchased 19__ Pd $ __ MIB   NB   DB   BNT
☐ Want   Orig. Ret. $4.75 **NB** $10   **MIB** Sec. Mkt. **$20**

QX 418-4 SWEET STAR ☐
Comments: Handcrafted, 1-3/4" tall.
A little squirrel nibbles the cherry he found on top of the
star-shaped cookie. Clips on the tree. **Artist:** Ed Seale
☐ Purchased 19__ Pd $ __ MIB   NB   DB   BNT
☐ Want   Orig. Ret. $5.00 **NB** $20   **MIB** Sec. Mkt. **$33**

QX 490-1 SWEETHEART ☐
Comments: Handcrafted, 3-3/8" tall, Dated Christmas 1988.
A swan sleigh in pearly colors holds a single rose inside. May
be personalized on the bottom: "For __, Love ___." Caption:
"Sweetheart." Easily found. **Artist:** Duane Unruh
☐ Purchased 19__ Pd $ __ MIB   NB   DB   BNT
☐ Want   Orig. Ret. $9.75 **NB** $15   **MIB** Sec. Mkt. **$23**

QX 417-1 TEACHER ☐
Comments: Handcrafted, 2-1/4" tall, Dated 1988.
This flocked bunny has created a card for his favorite teacher
at Christmas. Caption: "For Teacher" and "Merry Christmas
1988." **Artist:** Sharon Pike
☐ Purchased 19__ Pd $ __ MIB   NB   DB   BNT
☐ Want   Orig. Ret. $6.25 **NB** $15   **MIB** Sec. Mkt. **$20**

QX 418-1 TEENY TASTER ☐
Comments: Handcrafted, 4-3/8" tall. Reissued in 1989.
Is anyone ready for a big red spoonful of batter? This cute little
chipmunk has some ready! **Artist:** Ed Seale
☐ Purchased 19__ Pd $ __ MIB   NB   DB   BNT
☐ Want   Orig. Ret. $4.75 **NB** $25   **MIB** Sec. Mkt. **$30**

QX 275-1 TEN YEARS TOGETHER ☐
Comments: White Glass Ball, 2-7/8" dia.
Dated Christmas 1988. A gentle snowfall gives a peaceful
appearance as two deer stand on a hill. Caption: "Love Warms
Every Moment, Brightens Every Day. Ten Years Together."
☐ Purchased 19__ Pd $ __ MIB   NB   DB   BNT
☐ Want   Orig. Ret. $4.75 **NB** $17   **MIB** Sec. Mkt. **$23**

QX 405-4 THIMBLE SNOWMAN ☐
Comments: **Eleventh in Series,** 2-3/8" tall.
The silvery thimble makes a perfect hat for this jolly snowman
with red scarf and green mittens. **Artist:** Bob Siedler
☐ Purchased 19__ Pd $ __ MIB   NB   DB   BNT
☐ Want   Orig. Ret. $5.75 **NB** $15   **MIB** Sec. Mkt. **$25**

QX 400-4 TIN LOCOMOTIVE ☐
Comments: **Seventh in Series,** Pressed Tin, 3" tall.
Dated 1988. This bright blue locomotive features a pierced tin
cowcatcher. **Artist:** Linda Sickman
☐ Purchased 19__ Pd $ __ MIB   NB   DB   BNT
☐ Want   Orig. Ret. $14.75 **NB** $45 **MIB** Sec. Mkt. **$60**

QX 473-4 TOWN CRIER, THE ☐
Comments: Handcrafted, 2-1/4" tall.
A Colonial-style rabbit rings his bell and makes his
announcement: "Hear Ye! Hear Ye! Christmas Joy Is Always
Near Ye!" **Artist:** Ed Seale
☐ Purchased 19__ Pd $ __ MIB   NB   DB   BNT
☐ Want   Orig. Ret. $5.50   **NB** $15 **MIB** Sec. Mkt. **$20**

QX 477-1   TRAVELS WITH SANTA

Comments: Handcrafted, 2" tall.
Santa's license plate proclaims "B MERRY" to all who pass him in his shiny travel trailer. Look through the picture window and you'll see his TV and bottlebrush Christmas tree.
Artist: Donna Lee

☐ Purchased 19__   Pd $ __   MIB   NB   DB   BNT
☐ Want   Orig. Ret. $10.00 **NB** $30   **MIB** Sec. Mkt. **$40**

QLX 710-4   TREE OF FRIENDSHIP

Comments: Lighted Acrylic, 4-1/4" tall.
This tree-shaped acrylic has beveled edges and etched snow–flakes and caption: "Friends Decorate The Holiday With Love."

☐ Purchased 19__   Pd $ __   MIB   NB   DB   BNT
☐ Want   Orig. Ret. $8.50 **NB** $16   **MIB** Sec. Mkt. **$25**

QX 459-7   TREETOP DREAMS

Comments: Handcrafted, 3" tall.
Reissued from 1987. **Artist:** Ed Seale

☐ Purchased 19__   Pd $ __   MIB   NB   DB   BNT
☐ Want   Orig. Ret. $6.75 **NB** $20   **MIB** Sec. Mkt. **$30**

QX 371-4   TWELVE DAYS OF CHRISTMAS: FIVE GOLDEN RINGS

Comments: **Fifth in Series,** Acrylic, 3" tall, Dated 1988.
With gold foil captions, a design of five rings is etched into this quatrefoil designed acrylic. **Artist:** Sharon Pike

☐ Purchased 19__   Pd $ __   MIB   NB   DB   BNT
☐ Want   Orig. Ret. $6.50 **NB** $22   **MIB** Sec. Mkt. **$30**

QX 373-4   TWENTY-FIVE YEARS TOGETHER

Comments: Acrylic, 3-1/8" tall, Dated Christmas 1988.
The caption, "25 Years Together" is stamped in silver foil on a silver bezeled acrylic ornament. **Artist:** Joyce Pattee

☐ Purchased 19__   Pd $ __   MIB   NB   DB   BNT
☐ Want   Orig. Ret. $6.75 **NB** $15   **MIB** Sec. Mkt. **$20**

QX 488-4   UNCLE SAM NUTCRACKER

Comments: Handcrafted, 5-1/4" tall, Dated 1988.
When you lift Uncle Sam's ponytail, his mouth moves in real nutcracker fashion. **Artist:** Donna Lee

☐ Purchased 19__   Pd $ __   MIB   NB   DB   BNT
☐ Want   Orig. Ret. $7.00 **NB** $15   **MIB** Sec. Mkt. **$20**

QX 409-1   VERY STRAWBEARY

Comments: Handcrafted, 2-1/4" tall.
This flocked teddy bear has a special treat - a strawberry snow-cone. Includes the artist's initials, "PDII."
Artist: Peter Dutkin

☐ Purchased 19__   Pd $ __   MIB   NB   DB   BNT
☐ Want   Orig. Ret. $4.75 **NB** $16   **MIB** Sec. Mkt. **$23**

QX 402-1   WINDOWS OF THE WORLD: FRENCH

Comments: **Fourth in Series,** Handcrafted, 3-1/2" tall.
Dated 1988. A little boy plays with his poodle near a fireplace waiting for Santa. A banner overhead proclaims "Joyeux Noel."
Artist: Donna Lee

☐ Purchased 19__   Pd $ __   MIB   NB   DB   BNT
☐ Want   Orig. Ret. $10.00 **NB** $25   **MIB** Sec. Mkt. **$35**

QX 478-1   WINTER FUN

Comments: Handcrafted, 2" tall.
Three children are racing downhill on a fast toboggan. One child faces backwards. **Artist:** Robert Chad

☐ Purchased 19__   Pd $ __   MIB   NB   DB   BNT
☐ Want   Orig. Ret. $8.50 **NB** $25   **MIB** Sec. Mkt. **$28**

QX 411-4   WONDERFUL SANTACYCLE, THE

Comments: Special Edition, Handcrafted, 4-1/4" tall.
Santa's fancy three-wheeler has replaced the normal seat and handlebars with a rocking horse! Includes golden spoked wheels. Easily found. **Artist:** Ed Seale

☐ Purchased 19__   Pd $ __   MIB   NB   DB   BNT
☐ Want   Orig. Ret. $22.50 **NB** $35   **MIB** Sec. Mkt. **$45**

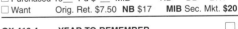

QX 404-1   WOOD CHILDHOOD: AIRPLANE

Comments: **Fifth in Series,** Wood, 1-5/8" tall, Dated 1988.
This toy wooden airplane is painted red and green and has a cord to pull it along. **Artist:** Peter Dutkin

☐ Purchased 19__   Pd $ __   MIB   NB   DB   BNT
☐ Want   Orig. Ret. $7.50 **NB** $17   **MIB** Sec. Mkt. **$20**

QX 416-4   YEAR TO REMEMBER

Comments: Ceramic, 3-3/4" tall, Dated 1988.
The year date has been designed in ivory ceramic and incorporates holly, berries and an oval frame. It is tied with a red satin ribbon.

☐ Purchased 19__   Pd $ __   MIB   NB   DB   BNT
☐ Want   Orig. Ret. $7.00 **NB** $19   **MIB** Sec. Mkt. **$25**

1988 Miniature Ornament Collection

QXM 574-4
BABY'S FIRST CHRISTMAS
2-1/2" tall, Dated 1988.
Artist: Donna Lee
☐ Purchased 19___ Pd $_____
MIB   NB   DB   BNT
☐ Want   Orig. Retail $5.00
NB $9   **MIB** Sec. Mkt. **$13**

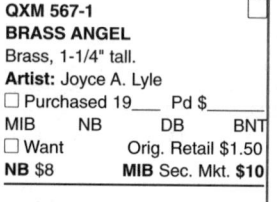

QXM 567-1
BRASS ANGEL
Brass, 1-1/4" tall.
Artist: Joyce A. Lyle
☐ Purchased 19___ Pd $_____
MIB   NB   DB   BNT
☐ Want   Orig. Retail $1.50
NB $8   **MIB** Sec. Mkt. **$10**

QXM 566-4
BRASS STAR
Brass, 1-1/4" tall.
Artist: Joyce A. Lyle
☐ Purchased 19___ Pd $_____
MIB   NB   DB   BNT
☐ Want   Orig. Retail $1.50
NB $7   **MIB** Sec. Mkt. **$13**

QXM 567-4
BRASS TREE
Brass, 1-1/4" tall.
Artist: Joyce A. Lyle
☐ Purchased 19___ Pd $_____
MIB   NB   DB   BNT
☐ Want   Orig. Retail $1.50
NB $8   **MIB** Sec. Mkt. **$10**

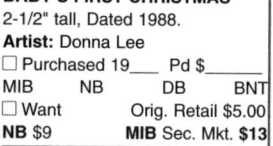

QXM 570-1 ☐
CANDY CANE ELF
7/8" tall. **Artist:** Bob Siedler
☐ Purchased 19___ Pd $_____
MIB   NB   DB   BNT
☐ Want   Orig. Retail $3.00
NB $15   **MIB** Sec. Mkt. **$20**

QXM 573-1 ☐
COUNTRY WREATH
1-1/2" tall. Reissued, 1989.
Artist: Anita Marra Rogers
☐ Purchased 19___ Pd $_____
MIB   NB   DB   BNT
☐ Want   Orig. Retail $4.00
NB $6   **MIB** Sec. Mkt. **$12**

QXM 574-1 ☐
FIRST CHRISTMAS TOGETHER
Wood/Straw Wreath, 1-3/4" tall,
Dated 1988. **Artist:** Diana McGehee
☐ Purchased 19___ Pd $_____
MIB   NB   DB   BNT
☐ Want   Orig. Retail $4.00
NB $7   **MIB** Sec. Mkt. **$13**

QXM 576-4 ☐
FRIENDS SHARE JOY
Faceted Acrylic, 1-1/4" tall.
Artist: Joyce Pattee
☐ Purchased 19___ Pd $_____
MIB   NB   DB   BNT
☐ Want   Orig. Retail $2.00
NB $9   **MIB** Sec. Mkt. **$15**

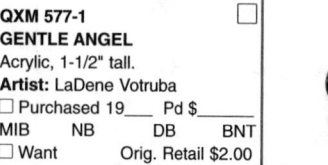

QXM 577-1 ☐
GENTLE ANGEL
Acrylic, 1-1/2" tall.
Artist: LaDene Votruba
☐ Purchased 19___ Pd $_____
MIB   NB   DB   BNT
☐ Want   Orig. Retail $2.00
NB $12   **MIB** Sec. Mkt. **$20**

QXM 561-4 ☐
HAPPY SANTA
Frosted Glass Ball, 3/4" dia.
Artist: Joyce Pattee
☐ Purchased 19___ Pd $_____
MIB   NB   DB   BNT
☐ Want   Orig. Retail $4.50
NB $12   **MIB** Sec. Mkt. **$20**

QXM 566-1 ☐
HEAVENLY GLOW TREE TOPPER
Brass. Reissued in 1989.
☐ Purchased 19___ Pd $_____
MIB   NB   DB   BNT
☐ Want   Orig. Retail $9.75
NB $11   **MIB** Sec. Mkt. **$20**

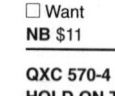

QXC 570-4 ☐
HOLD ON TIGHT:
KEEPSAKE CLUB
Artist: Bob Siedler, 15/16" tall.
☐ Purchased 19___ Pd $_____
MIB   NB   DB   BNT
☐ Want   Orig. Retail –
Free to Renewing Members
NB $60   **MIB** Sec. Mkt. **$75**

QXM 561-1 ☐
HOLY FAMILY
1-3/4" tall, Reissued in 1989.
Artist: Duane Unruh
☐ Purchased 19___ Pd $_____
MIB   NB   DB   BNT
☐ Want   Orig. Retail $8.50
NB $13   **MIB** Sec. Mkt. **$15**

QXM 572-1 ☐
JOLLY ST. NICK
Santa, 1-3/8" tall.
Artist: Duane Unruh
☐ Purchased 19___ Pd $_____
MIB   NB   DB   BNT
☐ Want   Orig. Retail $8.00
NB $20   **MIB** Sec. Mkt. **$27**

QXM 569-1
JOYOUS HEART
Wood, 1-1/8" tall.
Artist: Diana McGehee
☐ Purchased 19___ Pd $_____
MIB   NB   DB   BNT
☐ Want   Orig. Retail $3.50
NB $17   **MIB** Sec. Mkt. **$30**

QXM 568-1
FOLK ART LAMB
Wood, 1" tall. **Artist:** Joyce Pattee
☐ Purchased 19___ Pd $_____
MIB   NB   DB   BNT
☐ Want   Orig. Retail $2.75
NB $18   **MIB** Sec. Mkt. **$23**

QXM 568-4
FOLK ART REINDEER
Wood, 1-1/8" tall.
Artist: Joyce Pattee
☐ Purchased 19___ Pd $_____
MIB   NB   DB   BNT
☐ Want   Orig. Retail $3.00
NB $14   **MIB** Sec. Mkt. **$20**

QXM 562-1
KITTENS IN TOYLAND; TRAIN
FIRST IN SERIES, 3/4" tall.
Artist: Ken Crow
☐ Purchased 19___ Pd $_____
MIB   NB   DB   BNT
☐ Want   Orig. Retail $5.00
NB $15   **MIB** Sec. Mkt. **$25**

QXM 578-4
LITTLE DRUMMER BOY
1-1/4" tall.
Artist: Bob Siedler
☐ Purchased 19___ Pd $_____
MIB   NB   DB   BNT
☐ Want   Orig. Retail $4.50
NB $16   **MIB** Sec. Mkt. **$27**

QXM 577-4
LOVE IS FOREVER
Acrylic, 1" tall. **Artist:** Joyce Pattee
☐ Purchased 19___ Pd $_____
MIB   NB   DB   BNT
☐ Want   Orig. Retail $2.00
NB $8   **MIB** Sec. Mkt. **$15**

QXM 572-4
MOTHER
Heart, 1-1/4" tall, Dated 1988.
Artist: Sharon Pike
☐ Purchased 19___ Pd $_____
MIB   NB   DB   BNT
☐ Want   Orig. Retail $3.00
NB $8   **MIB** Sec. Mkt. **$13**

QXM 563-4
OLD ENGLISH VILLAGE:
FAMILY HOME; *FIRST IN*
SERIES, 1-1/4" tall, Dated 1988.
Artist: Donna Lee
☐ Purchased 19___ Pd $_____
MIB   NB   DB   BNT
☐ Want   Orig. Retail $8.50
NB $31   **MIB** Sec. Mkt. **$45**

QXM 563-1
PENGUIN PAL: GIFT
FIRST IN SERIES, 1" tall.
Artist: Bob Siedler
☐ Purchased 19___ Pd $_____
MIB   NB   DB   BNT
☐ Want   Orig. Retail $3.75
NB $15   **MIB** Sec. Mkt. **$25**

QXM 562-4
ROCKING HORSE: DAPPLED
FIRST IN SERIES, 1-1/8" tall,
Dated 1988.
Artist: Linda Sickman
☐ Purchased 19___ Pd $_____
MIB   NB   DB   BNT
☐ Want   Orig. Retail $4.50
NB $30   **MIB** Sec. Mkt. **$45**

QXM 560-1
SKATER'S WALTZ
1-3/8" tall. **Artist:** Duane Unruh
☐ Purchased 19___ Pd $_____
MIB   NB   DB   BNT
☐ Want   Orig. Retail $7.00
NB $15   **MIB** Sec. Mkt. **$20**

QXM 571-1
SNEAKER MOUSE
1/2" tall.
☐ Purchased 19___ Pd $_____
MIB   NB   DB   BNT
☐ Want   Orig. Retail $4.00
NB $15   **MIB** Sec. Mkt. **$20**

QXM 571-4
SNUGGLY SKATER
1-1/8" tall.
Artist: Bob Siedler
☐ Purchased 19___ Pd $_____
MIB   NB   DB   BNT
☐ Want   Orig. Retail $4.50
NB $16   **MIB** Sec. Mkt. **$28**

QXM 560-4
SWEET DREAMS
1-1/2" tall.
☐ Purchased 19___ Pd $_____
MIB   NB   DB   BNT
☐ Want   Orig. Retail $7.00
NB $17   **MIB** Sec. Mkt. **$23**

QXM 569-4
THREE LITTLE KITTIES
Willow, 15/16" tall, Reissued in
1989. **Artist:** Sharon Pike
☐ Purchased 19___ Pd $_____
MIB   NB   DB   BNT
☐ Want   Orig. Retail $6.00
NB $14   **MIB** Sec. Mkt. **$19**

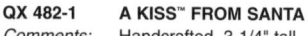

1989 Collection

QX 482-1   A KISS™ FROM SANTA ☐
Comments: Handcrafted, 3-1/4" tall.
Reissued from 1988. **Artist:** Duane Unruh
☐ Purchased 19 __ Pd $____MIB   NB   DB   BNT
☐ Want   Orig. Ret. $4.50 **NB** $22   **MIB** Sec. Mkt. **$30**

QLX 720-2   ANGEL MELODY ☐
Comments: Lighted Acrylic, 5-7/16" tall.
Etched and faceted to reflect the light, an angel in the center
joyfully plays her trumpet. **Artist:** LaDene Votruba
☐ Purchased 19 __ Pd $____MIB   NB   DB   BNT
☐ Want   Orig. Ret. $9.50 **NB** $16   **MIB** Sec. Mkt. **$25**

QLX 723-2   ANIMALS SPEAK, THE ☐
Comments: Lighted Panorama Ball, 3-5/8" tall.
The story of Christmas is illustrated. Caption: "The Animals
Rejoiced And Spoke, The Star Shone Bright Above, For On
This Day A Child Was Born To Touch The World With Love."
Artist: John Francis (Collin)
☐ Purchased 19 __ Pd $____MIB   NB   DB   BNT
☐ Want   Orig. Ret. $13.50 **NB** $100 **MIB** Sec. Mkt. **$125**

QX 452-5   BABY PARTRIDGE ☐
Comments: Handcrafted, 2-3/4" tall.
This sweet little bird attaches to your tree with a special clip.
Artist: John Francis (Collin)
☐ Purchased 19 __ Pd $____MIB   NB   DB   BNT
☐ Want   Orig. Ret. $6.75 **NB** $10   **MIB** Sec. Mkt. **$15**

QX 272-5   BABY'S FIRST CHRISTMAS: BOY ☐
Comments: Blue Satin Ball, 2-7/8" dia., Dated 1989.
Caption: "A New Baby Boy To Love. Baby's First Christmas."
Artist: LaDene Votruba
☐ Purchased 19 __ Pd $____MIB   NB   DB   BNT
☐ Want   Orig. Ret. $4.75 **NB** $13   **MIB** Sec. Mkt. **$24**

QX 272-2   BABY'S FIRST CHRISTMAS: GIRL ☐
Comments: Pink Satin Ball, 2-7/8" dia., Dated 1989.
Caption: "A New Baby Girl To Love. Baby's First Christmas."
Artist: LaDene Votruba
☐ Purchased 19 __ Pd $____MIB   NB   DB   BNT
☐ Want   Orig. Ret. $4.75 **NB** $12   **MIB** Sec. Mkt. **$23**

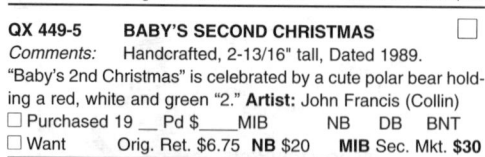
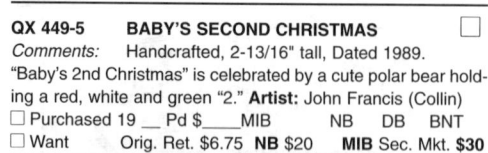
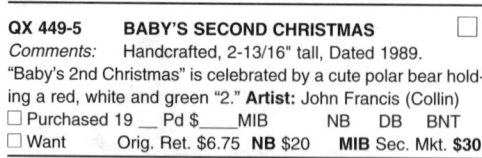

QX 381-5   BABY'S FIRST CHRISTMAS ☐
Comments: Acrylic, 3-7/16" tall, Dated 1989.
An etched reindeer holds a stocking full of toys for baby.
"Baby's First Christmas" in gold foil. **Artist:** John Francis (Collin)
☐ Purchased 19 __ Pd $____MIB   NB   DB   BNT
☐ Want   Orig. Ret. $6.75 **NB** $15   **MIB** Sec. Mkt. **$23**

QX 449-2   BABY'S FIRST CHRISTMAS ☐
Comments: Handcrafted, 2-5/8" tall, Dated 1989.
A flocked teddy bear wearing a green bow and red Santa cap holds a
candy cane "1." Hat says "Baby's 1st Christmas." **Artist:** Robert Chad
☐ Purchased 19 __ Pd $____MIB   NB   DB   BNT
☐ Want   Orig. Ret. $7.25 **NB** $70   **MIB** Sec. Mkt. **$80**

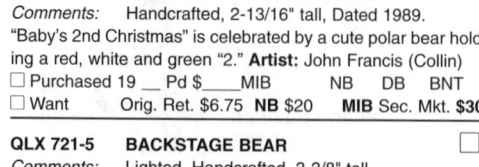

QLX 727-2   BABY'S FIRST CHRISTMAS ☐
Comments: Light, Motion and Music, Handcrafted, 4-1/2" tall.
Dated 1989. Mama mouse rocks baby's cradle as she rocks
back and forth. Caption: "Baby's First Christmas" and
"Christmas And Babies Fill A Home With Love." Plays "Brahms'
Lullaby." **Artist:** Ed Seale
☐ Purchased 19 __ Pd $____MIB   NB   DB   BNT
☐ Want   Orig. Ret. $30.00 **NB** $50   **MIB** Sec. Mkt. **$65**

QX 468-2   BABY'S FIRST CHRISTMAS PHOTOHOLDER ☐
Comments: Handcrafted, 3-3/4" tall, Dated 1989.
Caption: "A New Star On The Family Tree!" says it all!
Decorated with colorful toys. **Artist:** LaDene Votruba
☐ Purchased 19 __ Pd $____MIB   NB   DB   BNT
☐ Want   Orig. Ret. $6.25 **NB** $25   **MIB** Sec. Mkt. **$50**

QX 449-5   BABY'S SECOND CHRISTMAS ☐
Comments: Handcrafted, 2-13/16" tall, Dated 1989.
"Baby's 2nd Christmas" is celebrated by a cute polar bear hold-
ing a red, white and green "2." **Artist:** John Francis (Collin)
☐ Purchased 19 __ Pd $____MIB   NB   DB   BNT
☐ Want   Orig. Ret. $6.75 **NB** $20   **MIB** Sec. Mkt. **$30**

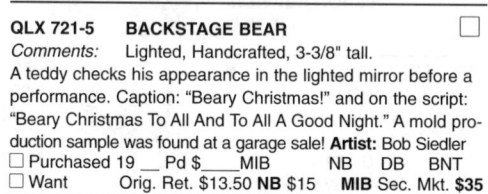

QLX 721-5   BACKSTAGE BEAR ☐
Comments: Lighted, Handcrafted, 3-3/8" tall.
A teddy checks his appearance in the lighted mirror before a
performance. Caption: "Beary Christmas!" and on the script:
"Beary Christmas To All And To All A Good Night." A mold pro-
duction sample was found at a garage sale! **Artist:** Bob Siedler
☐ Purchased 19 __ Pd $____MIB   NB   DB   BNT
☐ Want   Orig. Ret. $13.50 **NB** $15   **MIB** Sec. Mkt. **$35**

QX 489-5   BALANCING ELF
Comments: Handcrafted, 4-3/8" tall.
Look at this! Santa's elf holds two brass bells as he balances on one leg. **Artist:** Robert Chad
☐ Purchased 19 __ Pd $____MIB   NB   DB   BNT
☐ Want   Orig. Ret. $6.75 **NB** $17   **MIB** Sec. Mkt. **$23**

QX 454-2   BEAR-I-TONE
Comments: Handcrafted, 2-1/4" tall.
An adorable flocked bear plays a real metal triangle in the Christmas band. **Artist:** Bob Siedler
☐ Purchased 19 __ Pd $____MIB   NB   DB   BNT
☐ Want   Orig. Ret. $4.75 **NB** $15   **MIB** Sec. Mkt. **$20**

QX 230-2   BETSEY CLARK: HOME FOR CHRISTMAS
Comments: **Fourth in Series,** 2-7/8" dia., Dated 1989.
Betsey and her friends remember the animals outdoors at Christmas. Caption: "Fun And Friendship Are The Things The Christmas Season Always Brings!"
☐ Purchased 19 __ Pd $____MIB   NB   DB   BNT
☐ Want   Orig. Ret. $5.00 **NB** $25   **MIB** Sec. Mkt. **$37**

QX 445-2   BROTHER
Comments: Handcrafted, 3-1/4" tall, Dated 1989.
A puppy has jumped into this red and white high-top tennis shoe and is playing with the green laces. Caption: "Brother" and "No One Else Can Fill Your Shoes!" **Artist:** Joyce A. Lyle
☐ Purchased 19 __ Pd $____MIB   NB   DB   BNT
☐ Want   Orig. Ret. $7.25 **NB** $14   **MIB** Sec. Mkt. **$20**

QLX 724-5   BUSY BEAVER
Comments: Light, Handcrafted, 2-7/8" tall.
A beaver warms his paws over a fire in a barrel on a cold night. He's selling "Fresh Cut Trees." **Artist:** Donna Lee
☐ Purchased 19 __ Pd $____MIB   NB   DB   BNT
☐ Want   Orig. Ret. $17.50 **NB** $38   **MIB** Sec. Mkt. **$50**

QX 411-2   CACTUS COWBOY
Comments: Handcrafted, 3-1/2" tall, Dated 1989.
Not an easy ornament to locate. A smiling green cactus is wrapped up in red lights and wears a red cowboy hat. **Artist:** Peter Dutkin
☐ Purchased 19 __ Pd $____MIB   NB   DB   BNT
☐ Want   Orig. Ret. $6.75 **NB** $19   **MIB** Sec. Mkt. **$25**

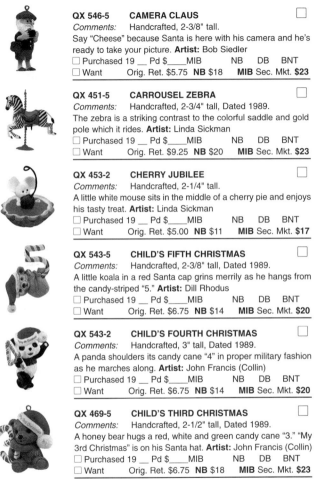

QX 546-5   CAMERA CLAUS
Comments: Handcrafted, 2-3/8" tall.
Say "Cheese" because Santa is here with his camera and he's ready to take your picture. **Artist:** Bob Siedler
☐ Purchased 19 __ Pd $____MIB   NB   DB   BNT
☐ Want   Orig. Ret. $5.75 **NB** $18   **MIB** Sec. Mkt. **$23**

QX 451-5   CARROUSEL ZEBRA
Comments: Handcrafted, 2-3/4" tall, Dated 1989.
The zebra is a striking contrast to the colorful saddle and gold pole which it rides. **Artist:** Linda Sickman
☐ Purchased 19 __ Pd $____MIB   NB   DB   BNT
☐ Want   Orig. Ret. $9.25 **NB** $20   **MIB** Sec. Mkt. **$23**

QX 453-2   CHERRY JUBILEE
Comments: Handcrafted, 2-1/4" tall.
A little white mouse sits in the middle of a cherry pie and enjoys his tasty treat. **Artist:** Linda Sickman
☐ Purchased 19 __ Pd $____MIB   NB   DB   BNT
☐ Want   Orig. Ret. $5.00 **NB** $11   **MIB** Sec. Mkt. **$17**

QX 543-5   CHILD'S FIFTH CHRISTMAS
Comments: Handcrafted, 2-3/8" tall, Dated 1989.
A little koala in a red Santa cap grins merrily as he hangs from the candy-striped "5." **Artist:** Dill Rhodus
☐ Purchased 19 __ Pd $____MIB   NB   DB   BNT
☐ Want   Orig. Ret. $6.75 **NB** $14   **MIB** Sec. Mkt. **$20**

QX 543-2   CHILD'S FOURTH CHRISTMAS
Comments: Handcrafted, 3" tall, Dated 1989.
A panda shoulders its candy cane "4" in proper military fashion as he marches along. **Artist:** John Francis (Collin)
☐ Purchased 19 __ Pd $____MIB   NB   DB   BNT
☐ Want   Orig. Ret. $6.75 **NB** $14   **MIB** Sec. Mkt. **$20**

QX 469-5   CHILD'S THIRD CHRISTMAS
Comments: Handcrafted, 2-1/2" tall, Dated 1989.
A honey bear hugs a red, white and green candy cane "3." "My 3rd Christmas" is on his Santa hat. **Artist:** John Francis (Collin)
☐ Purchased 19 __ Pd $____MIB   NB   DB   BNT
☐ Want   Orig. Ret. $6.75 **NB** $18   **MIB** Sec. Mkt. **$23**

QLX 722-5　CHRIS MOUSE COOKOUT ☐
Comments:　**Fifth in Series,** Handcrafted, 4-1/2" tall.
Dated 1989. Chris, dressed in a red nightcap and green night
shirt, toasts his marshmallow. **Artist:** Anita Marra Rogers
☐ Purchased 19 __ Pd $____MIB　　NB　DB　BNT
☐ Want　　Orig. Ret. $9.50 **NB** $39　**MIB** Sec. Mkt. **$45**

XPR 972-1　CHRISTMAS CARROUSEL HORSE ☐
　　　　　　COLLECTION: GINGER
Comments:　Special Offer, Handcrafted/Brass, 3-3/16" tall.
Dated 1989. Palomino with white mane and tail. Caption:
"Ginger, 4 In A Collection Of Four." **Artist:** Julia Lee
☐ Purchased 19 __ Pd $____MIB　　NB　DB　BNT
☐ Want　　Orig. Ret. $3.95 w/$10 Hallmark purchase.
　　　　　NB $10　　**MIB** Sec. Mkt. **$15**

XPR 972-2　CHRISTMAS CARROUSEL HORSE ☐
　　　　　　COLLECTION: HOLLY
Comments:　Special Offer, Handcrafted/Brass, 3-3/16" tall.
Dated 1989. Gray horse with red, gold and green saddle.
Caption: "Holly, 2 In A Collection Of Four." **Artist:** Julia Lee
☐ Purchased 19 __ Pd $____MIB　　NB　DB　BNT
☐ Want　　Orig. Ret. $3.95 w/$10 Hallmark purchase.
　　　　　NB $10　　**MIB** Sec. Mkt. **$15**

XPR 971-9　CHRISTMAS CARROUSEL HORSE ☐
　　　　　　COLLECTION: SNOW (MOST POPULAR)
Comments:　Special Offer, Handcrafted/Brass, 3-3/16" tall.
Dated 1989. White horse with golden mane and tail.
Caption: "Snow, 1 In A Collection Of Four." **Artist:** Julia Lee
☐ Purchased 19 __ Pd $____MIB　　NB　DB　BNT
☐ Want　　Orig. Ret. $3.95 w/$10 Hallmark purchase.
　　　　　NB $25　　**MIB** Sec. Mkt. **$30**

XPR 972-0　CHRISTMAS CARROUSEL HORSE ☐
　　　　　　COLLECTION: STAR
Comments:　Special Offer, Handcrafted/Brass, 3-3/16" tall.
Dated 1989. Brown horse with white mane and tail.
Caption: "Star, 3 In A Collection Of Four." **Artist:** Julia Lee
☐ Purchased 19 __ Pd $____MIB　　NB　DB　BNT
☐ Want　　Orig. Ret. $3.95 w/$10 Hallmark purchase.
　　　　　NB $10　　**MIB** Sec. Mkt. **$15**

XPR 972-3　CHRISTMAS CARROUSEL HORSE ☐
　　　　　　COLLECTION:CARROUSEL
　　　　　　DISPLAY STAND
Comments:　Special Offer, Handcrafted/Brass, 4-5/8" tall.
Dated 1989. Brass pole w/red and green ribbons in center.
Stand did not include horses.
☐ Purchased 19 __ Pd $____MIB　　NB　DB　BNT
☐ Want　　Orig. Ret. $1.00 w/any Hallmark purchase.
　　　　　NB $5　　**MIB** Sec. Mkt. **$10**

QLX 724-2　CHRISTMAS CLASSICS: ☐
　　　　　　LITTLE DRUMMER BOY
Comments:　**Fourth in Series,** Lighted, 3-1/4" tall, Dated 1989.
A little drummer boy kneels beside the manger to play his drum
for the Baby. **Artist:** Donna Lee
☐ Purchased 19 __ Pd $____MIB　　NB　DB　BNT
☐ Want　　Orig. Ret. $13.50 **NB** $33　**MIB** Sec. Mkt. **$43**

QXC 451-2　CHRISTMAS IS PEACEFUL: ☐
　　　　　　KEEPSAKE CLUB
Comments:　Limited Edition 49,900, Bone China, 2-1/2" tall.
Two owls are perched on a snowy branch of a tree. Trimmed
with gold. Hand numbered. **Artist:** Ed Seale
☐ Purchased 19 __ Pd $____MIB　　NB　DB　BNT
☐ Want　　Orig. Ret. $18.50 **NB** $29　**MIB** Sec. Mkt. **$45**

QX 544-5　CHRISTMAS KITTY ☐
Comments:　**FIRST IN SERIES,** Fine Porcelain, 3-3/16" tall.
This cute little kitty is wearing a light green dress with a red-
trimmed white collar and apron. She carries a basket of
poinsettias. Plentiful. **Artist:** Anita Marra Rogers
☐ Purchased 19 __ Pd $____MIB　　NB　DB　BNT
☐ Want　　Orig. Ret. $14.75 **NB** $25　**MIB** Sec. Mkt. **$33**

QX 488-5　CLAUS CONSTRUCTION ☐
Comments:　Handcrafted, 4-3/4" tall. Reissued in 1990.
Santa wears a personalized belt (Nick) and a hard hat as he
balances on the big metal beam. **Artist:** Ed Seale
☐ Purchased 19 __ Pd $____MIB　　NB　DB　BNT
☐ Want　　Orig. Ret. $7.75 **NB** $28　**MIB** Sec. Mkt. **$40**

QXC 428-5　COLLECT A DREAM: KEEPSAKE CLUB ☐
Comments:　Handcrafted, 1-3/4" tall, Dated 1989.
A mouse sleeps peacefully in his leafy hammock. His "Keepsake
Ornament Treasury" book lies open at his feet. Offered to
Keepsake Members only. Plentiful! **Artist:** Sharon Pike
☐ Purchased 19 __ Pd $____MIB　　NB　DB　BNT
☐ Want　　Orig. Ret. $9.00 **NB** $45　**MIB** Sec. Mkt. **$65**

QX 461-2　COLLECTOR'S PLATE: MORNING OF WONDER ☐
Comments:　**Third in Series,** Fine Porcelain, 3-1/4" dia.
Dated 1989. Christmas morning is always a delight for children
when they see their gifts. **Artist:** LaDene Votruba
☐ Purchased 19 __ Pd $____MIB　　NB　DB　BNT
☐ Want　　Orig. Ret. $8.25 **NB** $26　**MIB** Sec. Mkt. **$31**

QX 487-5 COOL SWING ☐
Comments: Handcrafted/Acrylic, 3-1/2" tall.
A penguin in a red stocking cap has fun swinging on his ice cube which says "Have A Cool Christmas." **Artist:** Ken Crow
☐ Purchased 19 __ Pd $____MIB   NB   DB   BNT
☐ Want   Orig. Ret. $6.25 **NB** $25   **MIB** Sec. Mkt. **$35**

QX 467-2 COUNTRY CAT ☐
Comments: Handcrafted, 2-1/4" tall.
This black and white fat cat is ready to ride. He's seated in an old-fashioned red wagon.**Artist:** Michele Pyda-Sevcik
☐ Purchased 19 __ Pd $____MIB   NB   DB   BNT
☐ Want   Orig. Ret. $6.25 **NB** $17   **MIB** Sec. Mkt. **$20**

QX 426-2 CRANBERRY BUNNY ☐
Comments: Handcrafted, 2-5/8" tall.
A cute, white, flocked bunny is wearing a green stocking hat and is stringing cranberries. **Artist:** Anita Marra Rogers
☐ Purchased 19 __ Pd $____MIB   NB   DB   BNT
☐ Want   Orig. Ret. $5.75 **NB** $13   **MIB** Sec. Mkt. **$18**

QX 435-2 CRAYOLA® CRAYON: BRIGHT JOURNEY ☐
Comments: **FIRST IN SERIES,** Handcrafted, 3" tall, Dated 1989.
Bear has built a raft with a sail made from a Crayola crayon box. Nice series... many first editions were bought up for secondary market. **Artist:** Linda Sickman
☐ Purchased 19 __ Pd $____MIB   NB   DB   BNT
☐ Want   Orig. Ret. $8.75 **NB** $42   **MIB** Sec. Mkt. **$50**

QX 441-2 DAD ☐
Comments: Handcrafted, 2-7/8" tall, Dated 1989.
Dad's red and white shorts are just a wee bit big. Captioned: "For Dad." **Artist:** Julia Lee
☐ Purchased 19 __ Pd $____MIB   NB   DB   BNT
☐ Want   Orig. Ret. $7.25 **NB** $10   **MIB** Sec. Mkt. **$15**

QX 443-2 DAUGHTER ☐
Comments: Handcrafted, 3" tall, Dated Christmas 1989.
This little wood-look doll is dressed in bright red and carries a hat box for "Daughter." **Artist:** Linda Sickman
☐ Purchased 19 __ Pd $____MIB   NB   DB   BNT
☐ Want   Orig. Ret. $6.25 **NB** $15   **MIB** Sec. Mkt. **$23**

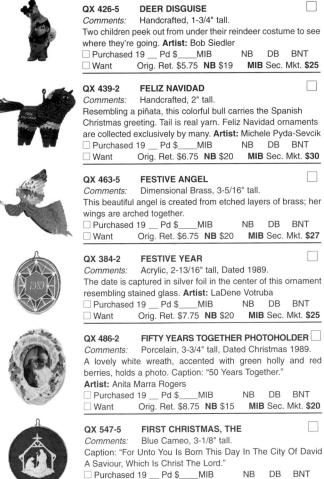

QX 426-5 DEER DISGUISE ☐
Comments: Handcrafted, 1-3/4" tall.
Two children peek out from under their reindeer costume to see where they're going. **Artist:** Bob Siedler
☐ Purchased 19 __ Pd $____MIB   NB   DB   BNT
☐ Want   Orig. Ret. $5.75 **NB** $19   **MIB** Sec. Mkt. **$25**

QX 439-2 FELIZ NAVIDAD ☐
Comments: Handcrafted, 2" tall.
Resembling a piñata, this colorful bull carries the Spanish Christmas greeting. Tail is real yarn. Feliz Navidad ornaments are collected exclusively by many. **Artist:** Michele Pyda-Sevcik
☐ Purchased 19 __ Pd $____MIB   NB   DB   BNT
☐ Want   Orig. Ret. $6.75 **NB** $20   **MIB** Sec. Mkt. **$30**

QX 463-5 FESTIVE ANGEL ☐
Comments: Dimensional Brass, 3-5/16" tall.
This beautiful angel is created from etched layers of brass; her wings are arched together.
☐ Purchased 19 __ Pd $____MIB   NB   DB   BNT
☐ Want   Orig. Ret. $6.75 **NB** $20   **MIB** Sec. Mkt. **$27**

QX 384-2 FESTIVE YEAR ☐
Comments: Acrylic, 2-13/16" tall, Dated 1989.
The date is captured in silver foil in the center of this ornament resembling stained glass. **Artist:** LaDene Votruba
☐ Purchased 19 __ Pd $____MIB   NB   DB   BNT
☐ Want   Orig. Ret. $7.75 **NB** $20   **MIB** Sec. Mkt. **$25**

QX 486-2 FIFTY YEARS TOGETHER PHOTOHOLDER ☐
Comments: Porcelain, 3-3/4" tall, Dated Christmas 1989.
A lovely white wreath, accented with green holly and red berries, holds a photo. Caption: "50 Years Together."
Artist: Anita Marra Rogers
☐ Purchased 19 __ Pd $____MIB   NB   DB   BNT
☐ Want   Orig. Ret. $8.75 **NB** $15   **MIB** Sec. Mkt. **$20**

QX 547-5 FIRST CHRISTMAS, THE ☐
Comments: Blue Cameo, 3-1/8" tall.
Caption: "For Unto You Is Born This Day In The City Of David A Saviour, Which Is Christ The Lord."
☐ Purchased 19 __ Pd $____MIB   NB   DB   BNT
☐ Want   Orig. Ret. $7.75 **NB** $10   **MIB** Sec. Mkt. **$18**

QX 383-2   FIRST CHRISTMAS TOGETHER ☐
Comments: Acrylic, 2-7/16" tall, Dated 1989.
Etched deer in the forest make a lovely ornament; gold foil
lettering "Our First Christmas." **Artist:** Dill Rhodus
☐ Purchased 19 __ Pd $____MIB   NB   DB   BNT
☐ Want   Orig. Ret. $6.75 **NB** $18   **MIB** Sec. Mkt. **$25**

QLX 734-2   FIRST CHRISTMAS TOGETHER ☐
Comments: Light, Handcrafted, 3-3/4" tall, Dated 1989.
The flickering light from the fireplace casts a warm glow for the
"First Christmas Together." **Artist:** Donna Lee
☐ Purchased 19 __ Pd $____MIB   NB   DB   BNT
☐ Want   Orig. Ret. $17.50 **NB** $30   **MIB** Sec. Mkt. **$45**

QX 485-2   FIRST CHRISTMAS TOGETHER ☐
Comments: Handcrafted, 3-1/2" tall, Dated 1989.
A heart-shaped wreath decorated with holly, berries and red
hearts makes the perfect support for a swing for these loving
chipmunks. **Artist:** Anita Marra Rogers
☐ Purchased 19 __ Pd $____MIB   NB   DB   BNT
☐ Want   Orig. Ret. $9.75 **NB** $18   **MIB** Sec. Mkt. **$25**

QX 273-2   FIRST CHRISTMAS TOGETHER ☐
Comments: White Glass Ball, 2-7/8" dia., Dated 1989.
Mr. Polar Bear holds a sprig of mistletoe over his sweetheart's
head as they rub noses. Caption: "Our First Christmas
Together" and "Tis The Season To Be Cuddly."
☐ Purchased 19 __ Pd $____MIB   NB   DB   BNT
☐ Want   Orig. Ret. $4.75 **NB** $17   **MIB** Sec. Mkt. **$25**

QX 273-5   FIVE YEARS TOGETHER ☐
Comments: Blue/Green Glass, 2-7/8" dia.
Dated Christmas 1989. Caption: "Five Years Together" and
"Love Makes The World A Beautiful Place To Be."
☐ Purchased 19 __ Pd $____MIB   NB   DB   BNT
☐ Want   Orig. Ret. $4.75 **NB** $15   **MIB** Sec. Mkt. **$23**

QLX 728-2   FOREST FROLICS ☐
Comments: *FIRST IN SERIES,* Light and Motion, Dated 1989.
Handcrafted, 4-7/16" tall. A candy cane in the center has a sign
that reads "Merry Christmas" while forest animals ski the trail
that circles it. **Artist:** Sharon Pike
☐ Purchased 19 __ Pd $____MIB   NB   DB   BNT
☐ Want   Orig. Ret. $24.50 **NB** $84   **MIB** Sec. Mkt. **$95**

QX 545-2   FORTY YEARS TOGETHER PHOTOHOLDER ☐
Comments: Porcelain, 3-3/4" tall, Dated Christmas 1989.
White wreath with green holly and red berries holds a couple's
favorite photo. Caption: "40 Years Together."
Artist: Anita Marra Rogers
☐ Purchased 19 __ Pd $____MIB   NB   DB   BNT
☐ Want   Orig. Ret. $8.75 **NB** $14   **MIB** Sec. Mkt. **$18**

QX 413-2   FRIENDSHIP TIME ☐
Comments: Handcrafted, 2-1/2" tall, Dated Christmas 1989.
Two delightful mice, in red and green, take time out to chat in a
teacup. Caption: "... Always Time For Friendship."
Artist: Julia Lee
☐ Purchased 19 __ Pd $____MIB   NB   DB   BNT
☐ Want   Orig. Ret. $9.75 **NB** $25   **MIB** Sec. Mkt. **$33**

QX 384-5   FROM OUR HOME TO YOURS ☐
Comments: Acrylic, 3-1/2" tall, Dated 1989.
A beautifully detailed mailbox full of gifts is etched onto oval
acrylic. Caption: "From Our Home To Yours At Christmas."
☐ Purchased 19 __ Pd $____MIB   NB   DB   BNT
☐ Want   Orig. Ret. $6.25 **NB** $8   **MIB** Sec. Mkt. **$16**

QX 457-2   FROSTY FRIENDS ☐
Comments: **Tenth in Series,** Handcrafted, 2-1/2" tall.
Dated 1989. The little Eskimo and his husky puppy are rushing
over the ice to deliver a gift. **Artist:** Ed Seale
☐ Purchased 19 __ Pd $____MIB   NB   DB   BNT
☐ Want   Orig. Ret. $9.25 **NB** $55   **MIB** Sec. Mkt. **$70**

QX 548-5   GENTLE FAWN ☐
Comments: Handcrafted, 2-5/16" tall.
This flocked fawn has large shiny eyes that tug at your heart.
He wears holly in his ribbon.
☐ Purchased 19 __ Pd $____MIB   NB   DB   BNT
☐ Want   Orig. Ret. $7.75 **NB** $15   **MIB** Sec. Mkt. **$20**

QX 386-2   GEORGE WASHINGTON BICENTENNIAL ☐
Comments: Acrylic, 3-9/16" tall, Dated 1989.
The likeness of George Washington is etched onto clear acrylic.
Caption: "1789-1989 American Bicentennial, George
Washington, First Presidential Inauguration."
☐ Purchased 19 __ Pd $____MIB   NB   DB   BNT
☐ Want   Orig. Ret. $6.25 **NB** $15   **MIB** Sec. Mkt. **$20**

QX 279-5   GIFT BRINGERS, THE: ST. NICHOLAS ☐
Comments: **FIRST IN SERIES,** White Glass Ball, 2-7/8" dia.
The tradition of St. Nicholas is captured on this ball.
Caption: "The Gift Bringers, St. Nicholas, Christmas 1989."
Artist: LaDene Votruba
☐ Purchased 19 __ Pd $____MIB   NB   DB   BNT
☐ Want   Orig. Ret. $5.00 **NB** $17   **MIB** Sec. Mkt. **$25**

QX 311-2   GODCHILD ☐
Comments: Acrylic, 2-3/4" tall, Dated 1989.
Gold foil stars and a gold foil halo and caption add to this
delightfully etched cherub who carries her message: "Merry
Christmas Godchild." **Artist:** John Francis (Collin)
☐ Purchased 19 __ Pd $____MIB   NB   DB   BNT
☐ Want   Orig. Ret. $6.25 **NB** $14   **MIB** Sec. Mkt. **$18**

QX 410-5   GOIN' SOUTH ☐
Comments: Handcrafted, 1-7/8" tall.
This little mouse has hitched a ride with a redbird and is head-
ed south for the winter. **Artist:** Ken Crow
☐ Purchased 19 __ Pd $____MIB   NB   DB   BNT
☐ Want   Orig. Ret. $4.25 **NB** $10   **MIB** Sec. Mkt. **$15**

QX 479-4   GONE FISHING ☐
Comments: Handcrafted, 2-1/2" tall.
Reissued from 1988. **Artist:** Bob Siedler
☐ Purchased 19 __ Pd $____MIB   NB   DB   BNT
☐ Want   Orig. Ret. $5.75 **NB** $10   **MIB** Sec. Mkt. **$19**

QX 464-2   GRACEFUL SWAN ☐
Comments: Dimensional Brass, 2-1/4" tall.
With its elaborate etching and detail, this swan is quite elegant
and graceful.
☐ Purchased 19 __ Pd $____MIB   NB   DB   BNT
☐ Want   Orig. Ret. $6.75 **NB** $15   **MIB** Sec. Mkt. **$20**

QX 278-2   GRANDDAUGHTER ☐
Comments: White and Green Glass Ball, 2-7/8" dia.
Dated 1989. The forest animals all have fun as they skate on a
frozen pond. Caption: "A Granddaughter Makes Christmastime
One Of The Best Times Of All!"
☐ Purchased 19 __ Pd $____MIB   NB   DB   BNT
☐ Want   Orig. Ret. $4.75 **NB** $24   **MIB** Sec. Mkt. **$33**

QX 382-2   GRANDDAUGHTER'S FIRST CHRISTMAS ☐
Comments: Acrylic, 4-1/4" tall, Dated 1989.
A kitten in a stocking cap likes to play in this etched stocking.
"Granddaughter's First Christmas" is stamped in gold foil.
Artist: John Francis (Collin)
☐ Purchased 19 __ Pd $____MIB   NB   DB   BNT
☐ Want   Orig. Ret. $6.75 **NB** $13   **MIB** Sec. Mkt. **$20**

QX 277-5   GRANDMOTHER ☐
Comments: Tan Glass Ball, 2-7/8" dia., Dated Christmas 1989.
A stencil-look garland of ribbon, pine cones and poinsettias
frames the caption: "A Grandmother Is Thought About Often...
And Always With Love." **Artist:** Joyce A. Lyle
☐ Purchased 19 __ Pd $____MIB   NB   DB   BNT
☐ Want   Orig. Ret. $4.75 **NB** $10   **MIB** Sec. Mkt. **$20**

QX 277-2   GRANDPARENTS ☐
Comments: Peach Glass Ball, 2-7/8" dia., Dated 1989.
The caption is printed against a frosty winter scene:
"Grandparents Make Christmas Welcome In Their Home And
In Their Hearts." **Artist:** Joyce A. Lyle
☐ Purchased 19 __ Pd $____MIB   NB   DB   BNT
☐ Want   Orig. Ret. $4.75 **NB** $10   **MIB** Sec. Mkt. **$20**

QX 278-5   GRANDSON ☐
Comments: Periwinkle Blue Glass, 2-7/8" dia., Dated 1989.
Santa climbs into a chimney; his bag of toys is nearby. Caption:
"A Grandson Brings Joy To Everyone... Just Like Christmas!"
☐ Purchased 19 __ Pd $____MIB   NB   DB   BNT
☐ Want   Orig. Ret. $4.75 **NB** $10   **MIB** Sec. Mkt. **$25**

QX 382-5   GRANDSON'S FIRST CHRISTMAS ☐
Comments: Acrylic, 4-1/4" tall, Dated 1989.
An etched puppy hides inside an acrylic stocking. "Grandson's
First Christmas" in gold. **Artist:** John Francis (Collin)
☐ Purchased 19 __ Pd $____MIB   NB   DB   BNT
☐ Want   Orig. Ret. $6.75 **NB** $12   **MIB** Sec. Mkt. **$18**

QX 385-2   GRATITUDE ☐
Comments: Acrylic, 2-3/4" dia., Dated 1989.
A green etched sprig of holly with a red ribbon is lovely on this
bezeled ornament. Caption: "Thankful Feelings Flow From
Heart To Heart At Christmas." **Artist:** LaDene Votruba
☐ Purchased 19 __ Pd $____MIB   NB   DB   BNT
☐ Want   Orig. Ret. $6.75 **NB** $8   **MIB** Sec. Mkt. **$14**

QX 418-5   GYM DANDY ☐
Comments: Handcrafted, 2-1/2" tall.
"Kringle's Gym" finds Santa in red and gray sweats working out with dumbbells. **Artist:** Bob Siedler
☐ Purchased 19 __ Pd $____MIB   NB   DB   BNT
☐ Want   Orig. Ret. $5.75 **NB** $15   **MIB** Sec. Mkt. **$20**

QX 430-5   HANG IN THERE ☐
Comments: Handcrafted, 3" tall.
A little mouse is hanging on to his red Santa cap, even though it's too big for him. He has a green ribbon tied to his leather tail. **Artist:** Ken Crow
☐ Purchased 19 __ Pd $____MIB   NB   DB   BNT
☐ Want   Orig. Ret. $5.25 **NB** $30   **MIB** Sec. Mkt. **$35**

QX 455-5   HARK! IT'S HERALD ☐
Comments: **FIRST IN SERIES,** Handcrafted, 2" tall, Dated 1989.
Herald, dressed in a green jacket and red hat, plays a Christmas tune on his xylophone. **Artist:** Ken Crow
☐ Purchased 19 __ Pd $____MIB   NB   DB   BNT
☐ Want   Orig. Ret. $6.75 **NB** $15   **MIB** Sec. Mkt. **$20**

QX 458-5 HERE COMES SANTA: CHRISTMAS CABOOSE ☐
Comments: **Eleventh in Series,** Handcrafted, 3-1/2" tall.
Dated 1989. This delightful caboose has movable wheels and shows Santa leaning out the window to wave at everyone as he passes. **Artist:** Ken Crow
☐ Purchased 19 __ Pd $____MIB   NB   DB   BNT
☐ Want   Orig. Ret. $14.75 **NB** $35   **MIB** Sec. Mkt. **$50**

QX 545-5   HERE'S THE PITCH ☐
Comments: Handcrafted, 2-3/8" tall.
Santa's playing the majors in his red baseball cap, cleated shoes and uniform. His name and number: "Santa 1." What else?! **Artist:** Bob Siedler
☐ Purchased 19 __ Pd $____MIB   NB   DB   BNT
☐ Want   Orig. Ret. $5.75 **NB** $15   **MIB** Sec. Mkt. **$20**

QLX 722-2   HOLIDAY BELL ☐
Comments: Lighted, Lead Crystal, 3-1/2" tall, Dated 1989.
With a specially designed brass cap, the many facets give this bell the look of hand-cut glass.
☐ Purchased 19 __ Pd $____MIB   NB   DB   BNT
☐ Want   Orig. Ret. $17.50 **NB** $10   **MIB** Sec. Mkt. **$20**

QXC 460-5   HOLIDAY HEIRLOOM: KEEPSAKE CLUB ☐
Comments: **Third and Final in Series,** Limited Edition 34,600.
Lead Crystal/Silver Plating, 2-1/2" tall, Dated 1989. A crystal bell hangs from a tree surrounded by old-fashioned toys. Offered only to Keepsake Club Members. **Artist:** Duane Unruh
☐ Purchased 19 __ Pd $____MIB   NB   DB   BNT
☐ Want   Orig. Ret. $25.00 **NB** $26   **MIB** Sec. Mkt. **$39**

QX 469-2   HOPPY HOLIDAYS ☐
Comments: Handcrafted, 2-3/4" tall, Dated 1989.
This little flocked bunny has hopped right into a shopping cart. He has two gifts in his red cart. **Artist:** Bob Siedler
☐ Purchased 19 __ Pd $____MIB   NB   DB   BNT
☐ Want   Orig. Ret. $7.75 **NB** $17   **MIB** Sec. Mkt. **$25**

QX 463-2   HORSE WEATHERVANE ☐
Comments: Handcrafted, 3" tall.
A white and brown horse, galloping into the wind, has been designed to resemble carved wood. **Artist:** Linda Sickman
☐ Purchased 19 __ Pd $____MIB   NB   DB   BNT
☐ Want   Orig. Ret. $5.75 **NB** $10   **MIB** Sec. Mkt. **$17**

QX 437-2   JOYFUL TRIO ☐
Comments: Handcrafted, 2-1/4" tall.
Holding a blue banner proclaiming "Joy To You," this delightful trio of angels sing out for peace and harmony.
Artist: John Francis (Collin)
☐ Purchased 19 __ Pd $____MIB   NB   DB   BNT
☐ Want   Orig. Ret. $9.75 **NB** $15   **MIB** Sec. Mkt. **$18**

QLX 729-5   JOYOUS CAROLERS ☐
Comments: Light, Motion and Music, Handcrafted, 4-11/16" tall.
Victorian carolers sing under a lamppost to the melody of a violin. Plays "We Wish You A Merry Christmas." **Artist:** Duane Unruh
☐ Purchased 19 __ Pd $____MIB   NB   DB   BNT
☐ Want   Orig. Ret. $30.00 **NB** $60   **MIB** Sec. Mkt. **$70**

QLX 701-7   KRINGLE'S TOY SHOP ☐
Comments: Light and Motion, Handcrafted, 3-5/8" tall.
Reissued from 1988.
Artist: Ed Seale
☐ Purchased 19 __ Pd $____MIB   NB   DB   BNT
☐ Want   Orig. Ret. $24.50 **NB** $40   **MIB** Sec. Mkt. **$50**

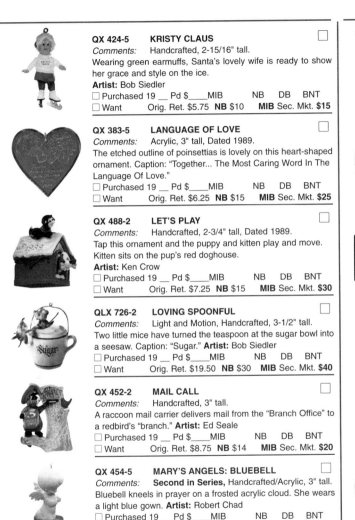

QX 424-5   KRISTY CLAUS ☐
Comments: Handcrafted, 2-15/16" tall.
Wearing green earmuffs, Santa's lovely wife is ready to show her grace and style on the ice.
Artist: Bob Siedler
☐ Purchased 19 __ Pd $____MIB   NB   DB   BNT
☐ Want   Orig. Ret. $5.75 **NB** $10   **MIB** Sec. Mkt. **$15**

QX 383-5   LANGUAGE OF LOVE ☐
Comments: Acrylic, 3" tall, Dated 1989.
The etched outline of poinsettias is lovely on this heart-shaped ornament. Caption: "Together... The Most Caring Word In The Language Of Love."
☐ Purchased 19 __ Pd $____MIB   NB   DB   BNT
☐ Want   Orig. Ret. $6.25 **NB** $15   **MIB** Sec. Mkt. **$25**

QX 488-2   LET'S PLAY ☐
Comments: Handcrafted, 2-3/4" tall, Dated 1989.
Tap this ornament and the puppy and kitten play and move. Kitten sits on the pup's red doghouse.
Artist: Ken Crow
☐ Purchased 19 __ Pd $____MIB   NB   DB   BNT
☐ Want   Orig. Ret. $7.25 **NB** $15   **MIB** Sec. Mkt. **$30**

QLX 726-2   LOVING SPOONFUL ☐
Comments: Light and Motion, Handcrafted, 3-1/2" tall.
Two little mice have turned the teaspoon at the sugar bowl into a seesaw. Caption: "Sugar." **Artist:** Bob Siedler
☐ Purchased 19 __ Pd $____MIB   NB   DB   BNT
☐ Want   Orig. Ret. $19.50 **NB** $30 **MIB** Sec. Mkt. **$40**

QX 452-2   MAIL CALL ☐
Comments: Handcrafted, 3" tall.
A raccoon mail carrier delivers mail from the "Branch Office" to a redbird's "branch." **Artist:** Ed Seale
☐ Purchased 19 __ Pd $____MIB   NB   DB   BNT
☐ Want   Orig. Ret. $8.75 **NB** $14   **MIB** Sec. Mkt. **$20**

QX 454-5   MARY'S ANGELS: BLUEBELL ☐
Comments: **Second in Series,** Handcrafted/Acrylic, 3" tall.
Bluebell kneels in prayer on a frosted acrylic cloud. She wears a light blue gown. **Artist:** Robert Chad
☐ Purchased 19 __ Pd $____MIB   NB   DB   BNT
☐ Want   Orig. Ret. $5.75 **NB** $85   **MIB** Sec. Mkt. **$95**

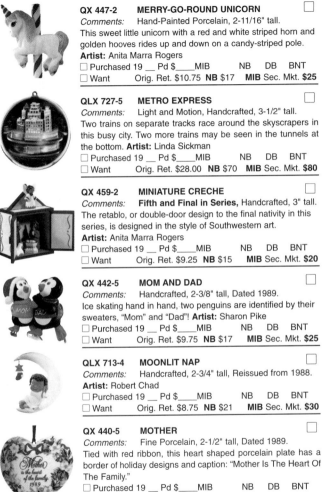

QX 447-2   MERRY-GO-ROUND UNICORN ☐
Comments: Hand-Painted Porcelain, 2-11/16" tall.
This sweet little unicorn with a red and white striped horn and golden hooves rides up and down on a candy-striped pole.
Artist: Anita Marra Rogers
☐ Purchased 19 __ Pd $____MIB   NB   DB   BNT
☐ Want   Orig. Ret. $10.75 **NB** $17   **MIB** Sec. Mkt. **$25**

QLX 727-5   METRO EXPRESS ☐
Comments: Light and Motion, Handcrafted, 3-1/2" tall.
Two trains on separate tracks race around the skyscrapers in this busy city. Two more trains may be seen in the tunnels at the bottom. **Artist:** Linda Sickman
☐ Purchased 19 __ Pd $____MIB   NB   DB   BNT
☐ Want   Orig. Ret. $28.00 **NB** $70   **MIB** Sec. Mkt. **$80**

QX 459-2   MINIATURE CRECHE ☐
Comments: **Fifth and Final in Series,** Handcrafted, 3" tall.
The retablo, or double-door design to the final nativity in this series, is designed in the style of Southwestern art.
Artist: Anita Marra Rogers
☐ Purchased 19 __ Pd $____MIB   NB   DB   BNT
☐ Want   Orig. Ret. $9.25 **NB** $15   **MIB** Sec. Mkt. **$20**

QX 442-5   MOM AND DAD ☐
Comments: Handcrafted, 2-3/8" tall, Dated 1989.
Ice skating hand in hand, two penguins are identified by their sweaters, "Mom" and "Dad"! **Artist:** Sharon Pike
☐ Purchased 19 __ Pd $____MIB   NB   DB   BNT
☐ Want   Orig. Ret. $9.75 **NB** $17   **MIB** Sec. Mkt. **$25**

QLX 713-4   MOONLIT NAP ☐
Comments: Handcrafted, 2-3/4" tall, Reissued from 1988.
Artist: Robert Chad
☐ Purchased 19 __ Pd $____MIB   NB   DB   BNT
☐ Want   Orig. Ret. $8.75 **NB** $21   **MIB** Sec. Mkt. **$30**

QX 440-5   MOTHER ☐
Comments: Fine Porcelain, 2-1/2" tall, Dated 1989.
Tied with red ribbon, this heart shaped porcelain plate has a border of holiday designs and caption: "Mother Is The Heart Of The Family."
☐ Purchased 19 __ Pd $____MIB   NB   DB   BNT
☐ Want   Orig. Ret. $9.75 **NB** $20   **MIB** Sec. Mkt. **$30**

QX 457-5   MR. AND MRS. CLAUS: HOLIDAY DUET ☐
Comments: **Fourth in Series,** Handcrafted, 3-1/4" tall.
Dated 1989. Santa and his wife sing "We Wish You A Merry
Christmas And A Happy New Year." **Artist:** Duane Unruh
☐ Purchased 19 __ Pd $____MIB   NB   DB   BNT
☐ Want   Orig. Ret. $13.25 **NB** $35   **MIB** Sec. Mkt. **$50**

QX 275-5   NEW HOME ☐
Comments: Lavender and White Glass Ball, 2-7/8" dia.
Dated Christmas 1989. A home is nestled among the trees in a
wintry landscape. Caption: "Love Is The Light In The Window
Of Your New Home." **Artist:** LaDene Votruba
☐ Purchased 19 __ Pd $____MIB   NB   DB   BNT
☐ Want   Orig. Ret. $4.75 **NB** $12   **MIB** Sec. Mkt. **$22**

QXC 448-3   NOELLE: KEEPSAKE CLUB ☐
Comments: Limited Edition 49,900, Fine Porcelain, 3-3/4" tall.
This elegant cat has a red bow with a jingle bell and sprig of
holly. Comes with wooden display stand. Available to Club
Members only. **Artist:** Duane Unruh
☐ Purchased 19 __ Pd $____MIB   NB   DB   BNT
☐ Want   Orig. Ret. $19.75 **NB** $50   **MIB** Sec. Mkt. **$60**

QX 276-2   NORMAN ROCKWELL ☐
Comments: Gold Glass Ball, 2-7/8" dia., Dated 1989.
"Norman Rockwell, Famous Holiday Covers From The
Saturday Evening Post" – "Santa's Seen In The Smiles The
Whole World Is Sharing, He's Found Where There's Friendship
And Loving And Caring." **Artist:** Joyce A. Lyle
☐ Purchased 19 __ Pd $____MIB   NB   DB   BNT
☐ Want   Orig. Ret. $4.75 **NB** $20   **MIB** Sec. Mkt. **$25**

QX 546-2   NORTH POLE JOGGER ☐
Comments: Handcrafted, 2-1/4" tall.
Santa's jogging suit reads "North Pole 1K." Santa jogs along
while he listens to his favorite music. **Artist:** Bob Siedler
☐ Purchased 19 __ Pd $____MIB   NB   DB   BNT
☐ Want   Orig. Ret. $5.75 **NB** $17   **MIB** Sec. Mkt. **$23**

QX 458-2   NOSTALGIC HOUSES AND SHOPS:
             U.S. POST OFFICE ☐
Comments: **Sixth in Series,** Handcrafted, 4-1/4" tall.
Dated 1989. Designed as a red brick building. The upstairs has
a furnished office. **Artist:** Donna Lee
☐ Purchased 19 __ Pd $____MIB   NB   DB   BNT
☐ Want   Orig. Ret. $14.25 **NB** $60   **MIB** Sec. Mkt. **$70**

QX 466-5   NOSTALGIC LAMB ☐
Comments: Handcrafted, 1-3/4" tall.
This lamb has been sculpted to show its curly wool. He rides in
a red wagon with wheels that turn. **Artist:** Michele Pyda-Sevcik
☐ Purchased 19 __ Pd $____MIB   NB   DB   BNT
☐ Want   Orig. Ret. $6.75 **NB** $13   **MIB** Sec. Mkt. **$15**

QX 465-5   NUTSHELL DREAMS ☐
Comments: Handcrafted, 1-1/2" tall.
A child sleeping in his bedroom dreams of the toys Santa will
leave; in another room, Santa motions quiet so as not to
wake the child. **Artist:** Robert Chad
☐ Purchased 19 __ Pd $____MIB   NB   DB   BNT
☐ Want   Orig. Ret. $5.75 **NB** $17   **MIB** Sec. Mkt. **$23**

QX 465-2   NUTSHELL HOLIDAY ☐
Comments: Handcrafted, 1-1/2" tall. Reissued in 1990.
Open this tiny nutshell and you will find a home decorated and
waiting for Santa's arrival.
Artist: Anita Marra Rogers
☐ Purchased 19 __ Pd $____MIB   NB   DB   BNT
☐ Want   Orig. Ret. $5.75 **NB** $17   **MIB** Sec. Mkt. **$27**

QX 487-2   NUTSHELL WORKSHOP ☐
Comments: Handcrafted, 1-1/2" tall.
Santa's elves keep busy building new toys in the tiny workshop
inside. **Artist:** Robert Chad
☐ Purchased 19 __ Pd $____MIB   NB   DB   BNT
☐ Want   Orig. Ret. $5.75 **NB** $17   **MIB** Sec. Mkt. **$23**

QX 434-5   OLD WORLD GNOME ☐
Comments: Handcrafted, 3-1/4" tall.
This friendly gnome has been created to resemble a European
wood carving.
☐ Purchased 19 __ Pd $____MIB   NB   DB   BNT
☐ Want   Orig. Ret. $7.75 **NB** $23   **MIB** Sec. Mkt. **$30**

QX 419-2   ON THE LINKS ☐
Comments: Handcrafted, 2-1/2" tall.
Santa's golf swing is perfect. He's wearing red slacks and
sunshade and a green shirt.
Artist: Bob Siedler
☐ Purchased 19 __ Pd $____MIB   NB   DB   BNT
☐ Want   Orig. Ret. $5.75 **NB** $15   **MIB** Sec. Mkt. **$23**

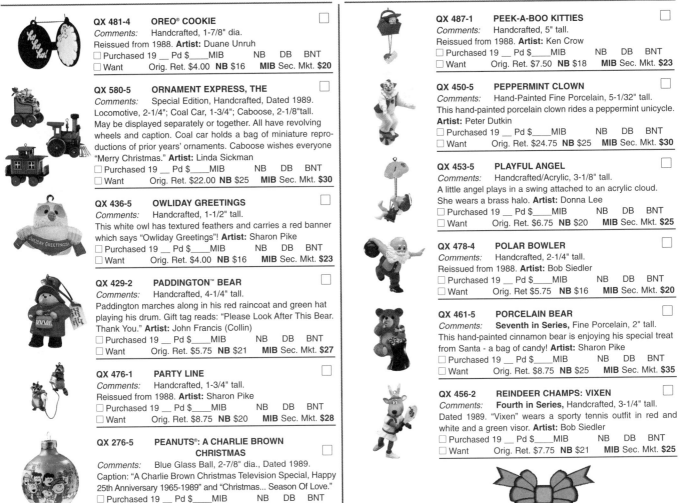

QX 481-4 OREO® COOKIE ☐
Comments: Handcrafted, 1-7/8" dia.
Reissued from 1988. **Artist:** Duane Unruh
☐ Purchased 19 __ Pd $____MIB NB DB BNT
☐ Want Orig. Ret. $4.00 **NB** $16 **MIB** Sec. Mkt. **$20**

QX 580-5 ORNAMENT EXPRESS, THE ☐
Comments: Special Edition, Handcrafted, Dated 1989.
Locomotive, 2-1/4"; Coal Car, 1-3/4"; Caboose, 2-1/8"tall.
May be displayed separately or together. All have revolving
wheels and caption. Coal car holds a bag of miniature repro-
ductions of prior years' ornaments. Caboose wishes everyone
"Merry Christmas." **Artist:** Linda Sickman
☐ Purchased 19 __ Pd $____MIB NB DB BNT
☐ Want Orig. Ret. $22.00 **NB** $25 **MIB** Sec. Mkt. **$30**

QX 436-5 OWLIDAY GREETINGS ☐
Comments: Handcrafted, 1-1/2" tall.
This white owl has textured feathers and carries a red banner
which says "Owliday Greetings"! **Artist:** Sharon Pike
☐ Purchased 19 __ Pd $____MIB NB DB BNT
☐ Want Orig. Ret. $4.00 **NB** $16 **MIB** Sec. Mkt. **$23**

QX 429-2 PADDINGTON™ BEAR ☐
Comments: Handcrafted, 4-1/4" tall.
Paddington marches along in his red raincoat and green hat
playing his drum. Gift tag reads: "Please Look After This Bear.
Thank You." **Artist:** John Francis (Collin)
☐ Purchased 19 __ Pd $____MIB NB DB BNT
☐ Want Orig. Ret. $5.75 **NB** $21 **MIB** Sec. Mkt. **$27**

QX 476-1 PARTY LINE ☐
Comments: Handcrafted, 1-3/4" tall.
Reissued from 1988. **Artist:** Sharon Pike
☐ Purchased 19 __ Pd $____MIB NB DB BNT
☐ Want Orig. Ret. $8.75 **NB** $20 **MIB** Sec. Mkt. **$28**

QX 276-5 PEANUTS®: A CHARLIE BROWN
CHRISTMAS ☐
Comments: Blue Glass Ball, 2-7/8" dia., Dated 1989.
Caption: "A Charlie Brown Christmas Television Special, Happy
25th Anniversary 1965-1989" and "Christmas... Season Of Love."
☐ Purchased 19 __ Pd $____MIB NB DB BNT
☐ Want Orig. Ret. $4.75 **NB** $30 **MIB** Sec. Mkt. **$40**

QX 487-1 PEEK-A-BOO KITTIES ☐
Comments: Handcrafted, 5" tall.
Reissued from 1988. **Artist:** Ken Crow
☐ Purchased 19 __ Pd $____MIB NB DB BNT
☐ Want Orig. Ret. $7.50 **NB** $18 **MIB** Sec. Mkt. **$23**

QX 450-5 PEPPERMINT CLOWN ☐
Comments: Hand-Painted Fine Porcelain, 5-1/32" tall.
This hand-painted porcelain clown rides a peppermint unicycle.
Artist: Peter Dutkin
☐ Purchased 19 __ Pd $____MIB NB DB BNT
☐ Want Orig. Ret. $24.75 **NB** $25 **MIB** Sec. Mkt. **$30**

QX 453-5 PLAYFUL ANGEL ☐
Comments: Handcrafted/Acrylic, 3-1/8" tall.
A little angel plays in a swing attached to an acrylic cloud.
She wears a brass halo. **Artist:** Donna Lee
☐ Purchased 19 __ Pd $____MIB NB DB BNT
☐ Want Orig. Ret. $6.75 **NB** $20 **MIB** Sec. Mkt. **$25**

QX 478-4 POLAR BOWLER ☐
Comments: Handcrafted, 2-1/4" tall.
Reissued from 1988. **Artist:** Bob Siedler
☐ Purchased 19 __ Pd $____MIB NB DB BNT
☐ Want Orig. Ret $5.75 **NB** $16 **MIB** Sec. Mkt. **$20**

QX 461-5 PORCELAIN BEAR ☐
Comments: **Seventh in Series,** Fine Porcelain, 2" tall.
This hand-painted cinnamon bear is enjoying his special treat
from Santa - a bag of candy! **Artist:** Sharon Pike
☐ Purchased 19 __ Pd $____MIB NB DB BNT
☐ Want Orig. Ret. $8.75 **NB** $25 **MIB** Sec. Mkt. **$35**

QX 456-2 REINDEER CHAMPS: VIXEN ☐
Comments: **Fourth in Series,** Handcrafted, 3-1/4" tall.
Dated 1989. "Vixen" wears a sporty tennis outfit in red and
white and a green visor. **Artist:** Bob Siedler
☐ Purchased 19 __ Pd $____MIB NB DB BNT
☐ Want Orig. Ret. $7.75 **NB** $21 **MIB** Sec. Mkt. **$25**

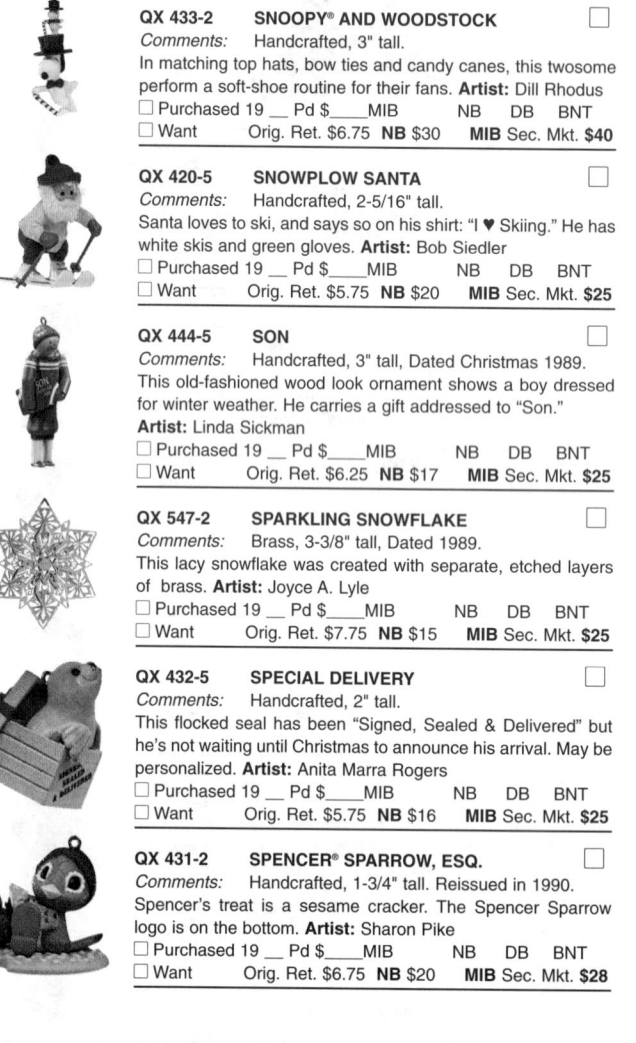

QX 462-2 ROCKING HORSE ☐
Comments: **Ninth in Series,** Handcrafted, 4" wide.
Dated 1989. A russet and black bay horse is fitted with brass
stirrups and red yarn rein. **Artist:** Linda Sickman
☐ Purchased 19 __ Pd $____MIB   NB   DB   BNT
☐ Want   Orig. Ret. $10.75 **NB** $60 **MIB** Sec. Mkt. **$70**

QX 407-2 RODNEY REINDEER ☐
Comments: Handcrafted, 5" tall, Dated 1989.
Rodney is checking the route for Christmas Eve on his
"Reindeer Route 89." He's made of a flexible material which
allows him to be bent into many positions. **Artist:** Bob Siedler
☐ Purchased 19 __ Pd $____MIB   NB   DB   BNT
☐ Want   Orig. Ret. $6.75 **NB** $10   **MIB** Sec. Mkt. **$15**

QX 467-5 ROOSTER WEATHERVANE ☐
Comments: Handcrafted, 3-1/2" tall.
With the design of American folk art, this bright, colorful rooster
is crowing good morning to everyone.
☐ Purchased 19 __ Pd $____MIB   NB   DB   BNT
☐ Want   Orig. Ret. $5.75 **NB** $10   **MIB** Sec. Mkt. **$18**

QLX 725-2 RUDOLPH THE RED-NOSED REINDEER ☐
Comments: Lighted, Handcrafted, 2-1/2" tall.
Rudolph's nose glows to light Santa's way, in addition to the
blinking lights on Santa's sleigh. **Artist:** Robert Chad
☐ Purchased 19 __ Pd $____MIB   NB   DB   BNT
☐ Want   Orig. Ret. $19.50 **NB** $60 **MIB** Sec. Mkt. **$70**

QX 415-2 SEA SANTA ☐
Comments: Handcrafted, 2-1/2" tall.
Santa's ready to do some diving for underwater treasure in his
scuba gear. Caption: "Sea Santa."
Artist: Bob Siedler
☐ Purchased 19 __ Pd $____MIB   NB   DB   BNT
☐ Want   Orig. Ret. $5.75 **NB** $20   **MIB** Sec. Mkt. **$30**

QX 279-2 SISTER ☐
Comments: Porcelain White Glass Ball, 2-7/8" dia.
Dated Christmas 1989. Caption: "Having A Sister Means
Happiness. Loving A Sister Means Joy."
☐ Purchased 19 __ Pd $____MIB   NB   DB   BNT
☐ Want   Orig. Ret. $4.75 **NB** $10   **MIB** Sec. Mkt. **$20**

QX 433-2 SNOOPY® AND WOODSTOCK ☐
Comments: Handcrafted, 3" tall.
In matching top hats, bow ties and candy canes, this twosome
perform a soft-shoe routine for their fans. **Artist:** Dill Rhodus
☐ Purchased 19 __ Pd $____MIB   NB   DB   BNT
☐ Want   Orig. Ret. $6.75 **NB** $30   **MIB** Sec. Mkt. **$40**

QX 420-5 SNOWPLOW SANTA ☐
Comments: Handcrafted, 2-5/16" tall.
Santa loves to ski, and says so on his shirt: "I ♥ Skiing." He has
white skis and green gloves. **Artist:** Bob Siedler
☐ Purchased 19 __ Pd $____MIB   NB   DB   BNT
☐ Want   Orig. Ret. $5.75 **NB** $20   **MIB** Sec. Mkt. **$25**

QX 444-5 SON ☐
Comments: Handcrafted, 3" tall, Dated Christmas 1989.
This old-fashioned wood look ornament shows a boy dressed
for winter weather. He carries a gift addressed to "Son."
Artist: Linda Sickman
☐ Purchased 19 __ Pd $____MIB   NB   DB   BNT
☐ Want   Orig. Ret. $6.25 **NB** $17   **MIB** Sec. Mkt. **$25**

QX 547-2 SPARKLING SNOWFLAKE ☐
Comments: Brass, 3-3/8" tall, Dated 1989.
This lacy snowflake was created with separate, etched layers
of brass. **Artist:** Joyce A. Lyle
☐ Purchased 19 __ Pd $____MIB   NB   DB   BNT
☐ Want   Orig. Ret. $7.75 **NB** $15   **MIB** Sec. Mkt. **$25**

QX 432-5 SPECIAL DELIVERY ☐
Comments: Handcrafted, 2" tall.
This flocked seal has been "Signed, Sealed & Delivered" but
he's not waiting until Christmas to announce his arrival. May be
personalized. **Artist:** Anita Marra Rogers
☐ Purchased 19 __ Pd $____MIB   NB   DB   BNT
☐ Want   Orig. Ret. $5.75 **NB** $16   **MIB** Sec. Mkt. **$25**

QX 431-2 SPENCER® SPARROW, ESQ. ☐
Comments: Handcrafted, 1-3/4" tall. Reissued in 1990.
Spencer's treat is a sesame cracker. The Spencer Sparrow
logo is on the bottom. **Artist:** Sharon Pike
☐ Purchased 19 __ Pd $____MIB   NB   DB   BNT
☐ Want   Orig. Ret. $6.75 **NB** $20   **MIB** Sec. Mkt. **$28**

QLX 728-5   SPIRIT OF ST. NICK ☐
Comments: Light and Motion, Handcrafted, 4" tall.
Early barnstorming days are recalled as Santa demonstrates his flying expertise. A banner reads "Spirit of St. Nick" and a message in the snow proclaims "Merry Christmas!"
Artist: Ed Seale
☐ Purchased 19 __ Pd $____MIB   NB   DB   BNT
☐ Want   Orig. Ret. $24.50 **NB** $60 **MIB** Sec. Mkt. **$75**

QX 456-5   STOCKING KITTEN ☐
Comments: Handcrafted, 2-3/4" tall. Reissued in 1990.
A sweet kitten is having fun playing in a bright red, flocked stocking with a green pom-pom. **Artist:** Sharon Pike
☐ Purchased 19 __ Pd $____MIB   NB   DB   BNT
☐ Want   Orig. Ret. $6.75 **NB** $17   **MIB** Sec. Mkt. **$23**

QX 438-5   SWEET MEMORIES PHOTOHOLDER ☐
Comments: Handcrafted, 3-1/16" tall, Dated 1989.
A candy-cane striped wreath is decorated with a large red fabric bow and green holly. Caption: "Christmas Is The Perfect Time For Making Sweet Memories."
☐ Purchased 19 __ Pd $____MIB   NB   DB   BNT
☐ Want   Orig. Ret. $6.75 **NB** $18   **MIB** Sec. Mkt. **$25**

QX 486-5   SWEETHEART ☐
Comments: Handcrafted, 4-5/8" wide, Dated 1989.
This red tandem bicycle has a gift in the basket that says "Merry Christmas Sweetheart." **Artist:** Linda Sickman
☐ Purchased 19 __ Pd $____MIB   NB   DB   BNT
☐ Want   Orig. Ret. $9.75 **NB** $30   **MIB** Sec. Mkt. **$33**

QX 412-5   TEACHER ☐
Comments: Handcrafted, 2-1/4" tall, Dated Christmas 1989.
This little mouse is a pleasant student. Inside his book he's written "For A Nice Teacher."
☐ Purchased 19 __ Pd $____MIB   NB   DB   BNT
☐ Want   Orig. Ret. $5.75 **NB** $10   **MIB** Sec. Mkt. **$15**
ERROR: The words on the book are turned around, facing the reader, rather than the mouse writing the words.
                            NB $21   **MIB** Sec. Mkt. **$25**

QX 418-1   TEENY TASTER ☐
Comments: Handcrafted, 4-3/8" tall.
Reissued from 1988. **Artist:** Ed Seale
☐ Purchased 19 __ Pd $____MIB   NB   DB   BNT
☐ Want   Orig. Ret. $4.75 **NB** $25   **MIB** Sec. Mkt. **$30**

QX 274-2   TEN YEARS TOGETHER ☐
Comments: White Glass Ball, 2-7/8" dia.
Dated Christmas 1989. A couple rides in a horse-drawn sleigh. Caption: "There's Joy In Each Season When There's Love In Our Hearts" and "Ten Years Together." **Artist:** Joyce A. Lyle
☐ Purchased 19 __ Pd $____MIB   NB   DB   BNT
☐ Want   Orig. Ret. $4.75 **NB** $20   **MIB** Sec. Mkt. **$30**

QX 455-2   THIMBLE SERIES: PUPPY ☐
Comments: **Twelfth and Final in Series,** Handcrafted, 1-3/4" tall.
This adorable puppy with a big red bow captures everyone's attention as he sits inside a thimble. **Artist:** Anita Marra Rogers
☐ Purchased 19 __ Pd $____MIB   NB   DB   BNT
☐ Want   Orig. Ret. $5.75 **NB** $19   **MIB** Sec. Mkt. **$27**

QX 460-2   TIN LOCOMOTIVE ☐
Comments: **Eighth and Final in Series,** Dated 1989.
Pressed Tin.
3-3/16" tall. The last locomotive in the series is also one of the most complex. A brass bell jingles as the wheels turn.
Artist: Linda Sickman
☐ Purchased 19 __ Pd $____MIB   NB   DB   BNT
☐ Want   Orig. Ret. $14.75 **NB** $50 **MIB** Sec. Mkt. **$60**

QLX 717-4   TINY TINKER ☐
Comments: Light and Motion, Handcrafted, 3" tall.
This little elf is burning the midnight oil to repair a shoe. A toy locomotive also waits for repair. **Artist:** Ken Crow
☐ Purchased 19 __ Pd $____MIB   NB   DB   BNT
☐ Want   Orig. Ret. $19.50 **NB** $50 **MIB** Sec. Mkt. **$60**

QX 409-2   TV BREAK ☐
Comments: Handcrafted, 3" tall.
Santa watches his favorite TV programs while relaxing in his hammock. **Artist:** Donna Lee
☐ Purchased 19 __ Pd $____MIB   NB   DB   BNT
☐ Want   Orig. Ret. $6.25 **NB** $10   **MIB** Sec. Mkt. **$15**

**QX 381-2   TWELVE DAYS OF CHRISTMAS:
                        SIX GEESE-A-LAYING** ☐
Comments: **Sixth in Series,** Acrylic, 3" tall, Dated 1989.
Six geese are etched into heart-shaped acrylic. Captions are printed in gold foil.
☐ Purchased 19 __ Pd $____MIB   NB   DB   BNT
☐ Want   Orig. Ret. $6.75 **NB** $15   **MIB** Sec. Mkt. **$20**

QX 485-5   TWENTY-FIVE YEARS TOGETHER PHOTOHOLDER

Comments: Porcelain, 3-3/4" tall, Dated Christmas 1989. A wreath decorated with holly and berries carries the silver caption: "25 Years Together." **Artist:** Anita Marra Rogers

☐ Purchased 19 __ Pd $____MIB   NB   DB   BNT
☐ Want   Orig. Ret. $8.75 **NB** $12   **MIB** Sec. Mkt. **$18**

QLX 723-5   UNICORN FANTASY

Comments: Lighted, Handcrafted, 4-1/2" tall. A shimmering unicorn prances inside a lighted, crystal gazebo. **Artist:** Dill Rhodus

☐ Purchased 19 __ Pd $____MIB   NB   DB   BNT
☐ Want   Orig. Ret. $9.50 **NB** $15   **MIB** Sec. Mkt. **$25**

QXC 580-2   VISIT FROM SANTA: KEEPSAKE CLUB

Comments: Handcrafted, 4" tall, Dated 1989. Santa with toys and "personalized" sled or "Merry Christmas." Sled was personalized with the name of the Club member. Personalized ornaments are selling for less than the Merry Christmas verse. **Artist:** Ken Crow

☐ Purchased 19 __ Pd $____MIB   NB   DB   BNT
☐ Want   Price: Came with Club Membership of $_____
                                        NB $45   **MIB** Sec. Mkt. **$60**

QX 489-2   WIGGLY SNOWMAN

Comments: Handcrafted, 4-3/4" tall. This pearly snowman wiggles and jiggles his head for you when you tap him. What fun! **Artist:** Dill Rhodus

☐ Purchased 19 __ Pd $____MIB   NB   DB   BNT
☐ Want   Orig. Ret. $6.75 **NB** $20   **MIB** Sec. Mkt. **$25**

QX 462-5   WINDOWS OF THE WORLD: GERMAN

Comments: **Fifth in Series,** Handcrafted, 3-3/4" tall. Dated 1989. Caption: "Frohliche Weihnachten." A little German boy sits near his Christmas tree in his Alpine cottage, playing his concertina. **Artist:** Donna Lee

☐ Purchased 19 __ Pd $____MIB   NB   DB   BNT
☐ Want   Orig. Ret. $10.75 **NB** $25   **MIB** Sec. Mkt. **$30**

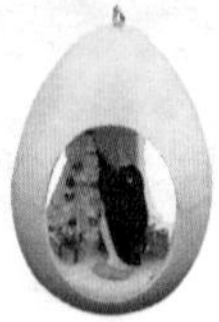

QX 427-2   WINTER SURPRISE

Comments: ***FIRST IN SERIES,*** Handcrafted, 3-1/4" tall. Dated 1989. Inside an egg-shaped peek-through ornament, two penguins decorate their white frosted Christmas tree with tiny ornaments. Series ended in 1992. Price up in '97.

☐ Purchased 19 __ Pd $____MIB   NB   DB   BNT
☐ Want   Orig. Ret. $10.75 **NB** $25   **MIB** Sec. Mkt. **$20**

QX 459-5   WOOD CHILDHOOD: TRUCK

Comments: **Sixth and Final in Series,** Wood, 2" tall. Dated 1989. This truck is hauling a cargo of Christmas trees as it rolls along on movable wheels.

☐ Purchased 19 __ Pd $____MIB   NB   DB   BNT
☐ Want   Orig. Ret. $7.75 **NB** $18   **MIB** Sec. Mkt. **$25**

QX 274-5   WORLD OF LOVE

Comments: Silver Blue Glass Ball, 2-7/8" dia., Dated 1989. Children from around the world enjoy the holiday season. Caption: "Christmas Is Here, And The Sound Of Love Echoes All Over The World."

☐ Purchased 19 __ Pd $____MIB   NB   DB   BNT
☐ Want   Orig. Ret. $4.75 **NB** $25   **MIB** Sec. Mkt. **$35**

There must be an easier way for me to deliver all these Collectors' Bulletins™!

Tell them to subscribe to the Colletors' Bulletin™!

1989 Miniature Ornament Collection

QXM 568-2
ACORN SQUIRREL
1-3/8" tall, Reissued in 1990.
Artist: Sharon Pike
☐ Purchased 19___ Pd $_____
MIB   NB   DB   BNT
☐ Want   Orig. Retail $4.50
NB $8   **MIB** SEC. MKT. **$12**

QXM 573-2
BABY'S FIRST CHRISTMAS
Acrylic, 1-3/8" tall, Dated '89.
Artist: Sharon Pike
☐ Purchased 19___ Pd $_____
MIB   NB   DB   BNT
☐ Want   Orig. Retail $6.00
NB $8   **MIB** SEC. MKT. **$12**

QXM 572-5
BRASS PARTRIDGE
Etched Brass, 1-1/4" dia.
Artist: Joyce A. Lyle
☐ Purchased 19___ Pd $_____
MIB   NB   DB   BNT
☐ Want   Orig. Retail $3.00
NB $6   **MIB** SEC. MKT. **$12**

QXM 570-2
BRASS SNOWFLAKE
Dimensional Brass, 1-3/8" tall.
Artist: Joyce A. Lyle
☐ Purchased 19___ Pd $_____
MIB   NB   DB   BNT
☐ Want   Orig. Retail $4.50
NB $8   **MIB** SEC. MKT. **$14**

QXM 577-5
BUNNY HUG
Etched, Faceted Acrylic, 1-1/4"
tall. **Artist:** LaDene Votruba
☐ Purchased 19___ Pd $_____
MIB   NB   DB   BNT
☐ Want   Orig. Retail $3.00
NB $6   **MIB** SEC. MKT. **$11**

QXM 573-5
COZY SKATER
1-3/8" tall, Reissued in 1990.
Artist: Joyce A. Lyle
☐ Purchased 19___ Pd $_____
MIB   NB   DB   BNT
☐ Want   Orig. Retail $4.50
NB $9   **MIB** SEC. MKT. **$13**

QXM 573-1
COUNTRY WREATH
1-1/2" tall. **Artist:** Anita Marra
Rogers. Reissued from 1988.
☐ Purchased 19___ Pd $_____
MIB   NB   DB   BNT
☐ Want   Orig. Retail $4.50
NB $6   **MIB** SEC. MKT. **$12**

QXM 564-2
FIRST CHRISTMAS TOGETHER
Ceramic, 1-3/8" tall, Dated 1989.
Artist: LaDene Votruba
☐ Purchased 19___ Pd $_____
MIB   NB   DB   BNT
☐ Want   Orig. Retail $8.50
NB $9   **MIB** SEC. MKT. **$12**

QXM 569-2
FOLK ART BUNNY
1" tall. **Artist:** Joyce Pattee
☐ Purchased 19___ Pd $_____
MIB   NB   DB   BNT
☐ Want   Orig. Retail $4.50
NB $6   **MIB** SEC. MKT. **$10**

QXM 566-2
HAPPY BLUEBIRD
7/8" tall, Reissued in 1990.
Artist: Anita Marra Rogers
☐ Purchased 19___ Pd $_____
MIB   NB   DB   BNT
☐ Want   Orig. Retail $4.50
NB $11   **MIB** SEC. MKT. **$15**

QXM 566-1
HEAVENLY GLOW TREE TOPPER
Reissued from 1988.
☐ Purchased 19___ Pd $_____
MIB   NB   DB   BNT
☐ Want   Orig. Retail $9.75
NB $11   **MIB** SEC. MKT. **$20**

QXM 577-2
HOLIDAY DEER
Faceted Acrylic Teardrop, 1-1/2"
tall. **Artist:** LaDene Votruba
☐ Purchased 19___ Pd $_____
MIB   NB   DB   BNT
☐ Want   Orig. Retail $3.00
NB $6   **MIB** SEC. MKT. **$11**

QXM 561-1
HOLY FAMILY
1-3/4" tall. **Artist:** Duane Unruh
Reissued from 1988.
☐ Purchased 19___ Pd $_____
MIB   NB   DB   BNT
☐ Want   Orig. Retail $8.50
NB $13   **MIB** SEC. MKT. **$15**

QXM 561-2
KITTENS IN TOYLAND:
SCOOTER
Second in Series, 1" tall.
Artist: Ken Crow
☐ Purchased 19___ Pd $_____
MIB   NB   DB   BNT
☐ Want   Orig. Retail $4.50
NB $14   **MIB** SEC. MKT. **$21**

QXM 572-2
KITTY CART
Wood, 1-1/8" tall.
Artist: Joyce Pattee
☐ Purchased 19___ Pd $_____
MIB   NB   DB   BNT
☐ Want   Orig. Retail $3.00
NB $6   **MIB** SEC. MKT. **$8**

QXM 562-5
KRINGLES, THE: GIFT
FIRST IN SERIES,
1-1/8" tall.
Artist: Anita Marra Rogers
☐ Purchased 19___ Pd $_____
MIB   NB   DB   BNT
☐ Want   Orig. Retail $6.00
NB $24   **MIB** SEC. MKT. **$33**

QXM 567-5
LITTLE SOLDIER
1-3/8" tall, Reissued in 1990.
Artist: Linda Sickman
☐ Purchased 19___ Pd $_____
MIB   NB   DB   BNT
☐ Want   Orig. Retail $4.50
NB $6   **MIB** SEC. MKT. **$10**

QXM 562-2
LITTLE STAR BRINGER
Blue Angel, 1-1/4" tall, Dated 1989.
Artist: Joyce A. Lyle
☐ Purchased 19___ Pd $_____
MIB   NB   DB   BNT
☐ Want   Orig. Retail $6.00
NB $10   **MIB** SEC. MKT. **$20**

QXM 574-5
LOAD OF CHEER
7/8" tall, Dated 1989.
Artist: Dill Rhodus
☐ Purchased 19___ Pd $_____
MIB   NB   DB   BNT
☐ Want   Orig. Retail $6.00
NB $10   **MIB** SEC. MKT. **$20**

QXM 563-5
LOVEBIRDS
Brass, 1-1/8" tall.
Artist: Sharon Pike
☐ Purchased 19___ Pd $_____
MIB   NB   DB   BNT
☐ Want   Orig. Retail $6.00
NB $9   **MIB** SEC. MKT. **$15**

QXM 575-5
MERRY SEAL
Hand Painted Porcelain, 7/8" tall.
Artist: John Francis (Collin)
☐ Purchased 19___ Pd $_____
MIB   NB   DB   BNT
☐ Want   Orig. Retail $6.00
NB $9   **MIB** SEC. MKT. **$15**

QXM 564-5
MOTHER
Blue Cameo, Chrome Bezel,
1-1/4" dia., Dated 1989.
☐ Purchased 19___ Pd $_____
MIB   NB   DB   BNT
☐ Want   Orig. Retail $6.00
NB $10   **MIB** SEC. MKT. **$15**

QXM 576-2
NOEL R.R.: LOCOMOTIVE
FIRST IN SERIES, 1" tall, Dated
1989. **Artist:** Linda Sickman
☐ Purchased 19___ Pd $_____
MIB   NB   DB   BNT
☐ Want   Orig. Retail $8.50
NB $30   **MIB** SEC. MKT. **$43**

QXM 561-5
OLD ENGLISH VILLAGE:
SWEET SHOP
Second in Series, 1-1/4" tall,
Dated 1989.
Artist: Julia Lee
☐ Purchased 19___ Pd $_____
MIB   NB   DB   BNT
☐ Want   Orig. Retail $8.50
NB $15   **MIB** SEC. MKT. **$20**

QXM 569-5
OLD WORLD SANTA
1-3/8" tall. Reissued in 1990.
Artist: Bob Siedler
☐ Purchased 19___ Pd $_____
MIB   NB   DB   BNT
☐ Want   Orig. Retail $3.00
NB $5   **MIB** SEC. MKT. **$10**

QXM 560-2
PENGUIN PAL: CANDY CANE
Second in Series, Acrylic,
1-3/8" tall.
☐ Purchased 19___ Pd $_____
MIB   NB   DB   BNT
☐ Want   Orig. Retail $4.50
NB $15   **MIB** SEC. MKT. **$20**

QXM 573-4
PINECONE BASKET
7/8" tall. **Artist:** Dill Rhodus
☐ Purchased 19___ Pd $_____
MIB   NB   DB   BNT
☐ Want   Orig. Retail $4.50
NB $5   **MIB** SEC. MKT. **$7**

QXM 571-5
PUPPY CART
Wood, 1-1/4" tall.
Artist: Linda Sickman
☐ Purchased 19___ Pd $_____
MIB   NB   DB   BNT
☐ Want   Orig. Retail $3.00
NB $5   **MIB** SEC. MKT. **$9**

QXM 578-2
REJOICE
Faceted Acrylic, 1" tall.
Artist: LaDene Votruba
☐ Purchased 19___ Pd $_____
MIB   NB   DB   BNT
☐ Want   Orig. Retail $3.00
NB $5   **MIB** SEC. MKT. **$10**

QXM 560-5
ROCKING HORSE: PALOMINO
Second in Series, 1-1/8" tall,
Dated 1989. **Artist:** Linda
Sickman
☐ Purchased 19___ Pd $_____
MIB   NB   DB   BNT
☐ Want   Orig. Retail $4.50
NB $20   **MIB** SEC. MKT. **$30**

QXM 571-2
ROLY-POLY PIG
7/8" tall, Reissued in 1990.
Artist: Sharon Pike
☐ Purchased 19___ Pd $_____
MIB   NB   DB   BNT
☐ Want   Orig. Retail $3.00
NB $11   **MIB** SEC. MKT. **$18**

QXM 570-5
ROLY-POLY RAM
7/8" tall.
☐ Purchased 19___ Pd $_____
MIB   NB   DB   BNT
☐ Want   Orig. Retail $3.00
NB $6   **MIB** SEC. MKT. **$14**

QXM 563-2
SANTA'S MAGIC RIDE
Special Edition, 1-3/16" tall.
Artist: Anita Marra Rogers
☐ Purchased 19___ Pd $_____
MIB   NB   DB   BNT
☐ Want   Orig. Retail $8.50
NB $15   **MIB** SEC. MKT. **$20**

QXM 566-5
SANTA'S ROADSTER
15/16" tall, Dated 1989. **Artist:**
Ken Crow
☐ Purchased 19___ Pd $_____
MIB   NB   DB   BNT
☐ Want   Orig. Retail $6.00
NB $10   **MIB** SEC. MKT. **$15**

QXM 568-5
SCRIMSHAW REINDEER
15/16" tall.
Artist: LaDene Votruba
☐ Purchased 19___ Pd $_____
MIB   NB   DB   BNT
☐ Want   Orig. Retail $4.50
NB $6   **MIB** SEC. MKT. **$10**

QXM 576-5
SHARING A RIDE
1-1/4" tall.
Artist: Peter Dutkin
☐ Purchased 19___ Pd $_____
MIB   NB   DB   BNT
☐ Want   Orig. Retail $8.50
NB $10   **MIB** SEC. MKT. **$17**

QXC 581-2
**SITTING PURRTY: KEEPSAKE
CLUB**
1-1/4" tall, Dated 1989. **Artist:**
Peter Dutkin
☐ Purchased 19___ Pd $_____
MIB   NB   DB   BNT
☐ Want   Orig. Retail –
          Free to Club Members
NB $30   **MIB** SEC. MKT. **$45**

QXM 575-2
SLOW MOTION
1" tall. **Artist:** Bob Siedler
☐ Purchased 19___ Pd $_____
MIB   NB   DB   BNT
☐ Want   Orig. Retail $6.00
NB $8   **MIB** SEC. MKT. **$17**

QXM 565-2
SPECIAL FRIEND
Willow, 1-3/8" tall, Dated 1989.
☐ Purchased 19___ Pd $_____
MIB   NB   DB   BNT
☐ Want   Orig. Retail $4.50
NB $8   **MIB** SEC. MKT. **$14**

QXM 565-5
STARLIT MOUSE
1-3/16" tall, Dated 1989.
Artist: Dill Rhodus
☐ Purchased 19___ Pd $_____
MIB   NB   DB   BNT
☐ Want   Orig. Retail $4.50
NB $10   **MIB** SEC. MKT. **$17**

QXM 567-2
STOCKING PAL
1" tall, Reissued in 1990.
Artist: Julia Lee
☐ Purchased 19___ Pd $_____
MIB   NB   DB   BNT
☐ Want   Orig. Retail $4.50
NB $7   **MIB** SEC. MKT. **$10**

QXM 574-2
STROLLIN' SNOWMAN
Hand Painted Fine Porcelain,
1-1/4" tall. **Artist:** Bob Siedler
☐ Purchased 19___ Pd $_____
MIB   NB   DB   BNT
☐ Want   Orig. Retail $4.50
NB $8   **MIB** SEC. MKT. **$10**

QXM 569-4
THREE LITTLE KITTIES
15/16" tall **Artist:** Sharon Pike
Reissued from 1988.
☐ Purchased 19___ Pd $_____
MIB   NB   DB   BNT
☐ Want   Orig. Retail $6.00
NB $14   **MIB** SEC. MKT. **$19**

1990 Collection

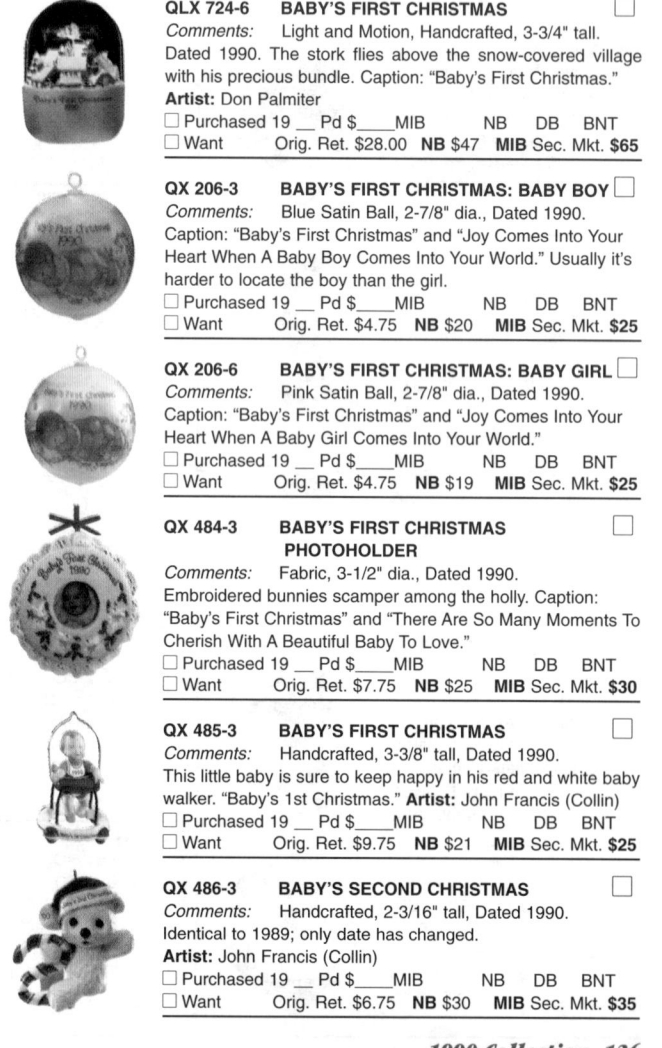

QX 317-3   ACROSS THE MILES
Comments: Acrylic, 3-1/2" tall.
Etched into this oval acrylic, a happy raccoon carries a large poinsettia. Caption: "Christmas Smiles Across The Miles."
Artist: LaDene Votruba
☐ Purchased 19 __ Pd $____MIB   NB   DB   BNT
☐ Want   Orig. Ret. $6.75 **NB** $7   **MIB** Sec. Mkt. **$10**

QX 474-6   ANGEL KITTY
Comments: Handcrafted, 2-9/16" tall, Dated 1990.
The artist used her own cat as the model for this ornament, dressed in a blue dress and slippers with sparkling net wings, a brass halo and brass star wand. **Artist:** Michele Pyda-Sevcik
☐ Purchased 19 __ Pd $____MIB   NB   DB   BNT
☐ Want   Orig. Ret. $8.75 **NB** $17   **MIB** Sec. Mkt. **$25**

QXC 445-3   ARMFUL OF JOY: KEEPSAKE CLUB
Comments: Handcrafted, 2-13/16" tall, Dated 1990.
This wide-eyed elf has quite a job. He's trying to balance a stack of colorful gifts. Top box is labeled "1990 Membership Kit." Club logo is on the elf's shopping bag. Available to Club Members only. **Artist:** John Francis (Collin)
☐ Purchased 19 __ Pd $____MIB   NB   DB   BNT
☐ Want   Orig. Ret. $9.75 **NB** $30   **MIB** Sec. Mkt. **$45**

QX 548-6   BABY UNICORN
Comments: Fine Porcelain, 2" tall.
This iridescent unicorn watches from large, dark eyes. His horn and hooves are painted gold. **Artist:** Anita Marra Rogers
☐ Purchased 19 __ Pd $____MIB   NB   DB   BNT
☐ Want   Orig. Ret. $9.75 **NB** $20   **MIB** Sec. Mkt. **$25**

QX 303-6   BABY'S FIRST CHRISTMAS
Comments: Acrylic, 4-7/32" tall, Dated 1990.
A fluffy etched puppy takes a ride in a hot air balloon. Caption: "Baby's First Christmas." **Artist:** Anita Marra Rogers
☐ Purchased 19 __ Pd $____MIB   NB   DB   BNT
☐ Want   Orig. Ret. $6.75 **NB** $17   **MIB** Sec. Mkt. **$23**

QX 485-6   BABY'S FIRST CHRISTMAS
Comments: Handcrafted, 2-3/8" tall, Dated 1990.
A baby bear dreams sweetly, with candy cane in hand, on a green leaf. "Baby's First Christmas." **Artist:** John Francis (Collin)
☐ Purchased 19 __ Pd $____MIB   NB   DB   BNT
☐ Want   Orig. Ret. $7.75 **NB** $31   **MIB** Sec. Mkt. **$40**

QLX 724-6   BABY'S FIRST CHRISTMAS
Comments: Light and Motion, Handcrafted, 3-3/4" tall.
Dated 1990. The stork flies above the snow-covered village with his precious bundle. Caption: "Baby's First Christmas."
Artist: Don Palmiter
☐ Purchased 19 __ Pd $____MIB   NB   DB   BNT
☐ Want   Orig. Ret. $28.00 **NB** $47   **MIB** Sec. Mkt. **$65**

QX 206-3   BABY'S FIRST CHRISTMAS: BABY BOY
Comments: Blue Satin Ball, 2-7/8" dia., Dated 1990.
Caption: "Baby's First Christmas" and "Joy Comes Into Your Heart When A Baby Boy Comes Into Your World." Usually it's harder to locate the boy than the girl.
☐ Purchased 19 __ Pd $____MIB   NB   DB   BNT
☐ Want   Orig. Ret. $4.75 **NB** $20   **MIB** Sec. Mkt. **$25**

QX 206-6   BABY'S FIRST CHRISTMAS: BABY GIRL
Comments: Pink Satin Ball, 2-7/8" dia., Dated 1990.
Caption: "Baby's First Christmas" and "Joy Comes Into Your Heart When A Baby Girl Comes Into Your World."
☐ Purchased 19 __ Pd $____MIB   NB   DB   BNT
☐ Want   Orig. Ret. $4.75 **NB** $19   **MIB** Sec. Mkt. **$25**

**QX 484-3   BABY'S FIRST CHRISTMAS
         PHOTOHOLDER**
Comments: Fabric, 3-1/2" dia., Dated 1990.
Embroidered bunnies scamper among the holly. Caption: "Baby's First Christmas" and "There Are So Many Moments To Cherish With A Beautiful Baby To Love."
☐ Purchased 19 __ Pd $____MIB   NB   DB   BNT
☐ Want   Orig. Ret. $7.75 **NB** $25   **MIB** Sec. Mkt. **$30**

QX 485-3   BABY'S FIRST CHRISTMAS
Comments: Handcrafted, 3-3/8" tall, Dated 1990.
This little baby is sure to keep happy in his red and white baby walker. "Baby's 1st Christmas." **Artist:** John Francis (Collin)
☐ Purchased 19 __ Pd $____MIB   NB   DB   BNT
☐ Want   Orig. Ret. $9.75 **NB** $21   **MIB** Sec. Mkt. **$25**

QX 486-3   BABY'S SECOND CHRISTMAS
Comments: Handcrafted, 2-3/16" tall, Dated 1990.
Identical to 1989; only date has changed.
Artist: John Francis (Collin)
☐ Purchased 19 __ Pd $____MIB   NB   DB   BNT
☐ Want   Orig. Ret. $6.75 **NB** $30   **MIB** Sec. Mkt. **$35**

QX 548-3 BEARBACK RIDER ☐
Comments: Handcrafted, 3-1/4" tall, Dated 1990.
A perky penguin with a red hat is riding "bear-back" on a polar bear on red and white rockers. **Artist:** Ken Crow
☐ Purchased 19 __ Pd $____MIB   NB   DB   BNT
☐ Want   Orig. Ret. $9.75 **NB** $25   **MIB** Sec. Mkt. **$30**

QX 473-3 BEARY GOOD DEAL ☐
Comments: Handcrafted, 2" tall.
This cute flocked bear is playing with "Santa" cards, and he must have a good hand by the smile on his face.
Artist: Bob Siedler
☐ Purchased 19 __ Pd $____MIB   NB   DB   BNT
☐ Want   Orig. Ret. $6.75 **NB** $10   **MIB** Sec. Mkt. **$15**

QLX 732-6 BEARY SHORT NAP ☐
Comments: Lighted, Handcrafted, 2-3/8" tall, Dated 1990.
Tomorrow is Dec. 25, so this Santa bear cannot nap too long. A little mouse also naps in a drawer of his desk.
Artist: Bob Siedler
☐ Purchased 19 __ Pd $____MIB   NB   DB   BNT
☐ Want   Orig. Ret. $10.00 **NB** $26 **MIB** Sec. Mkt. **$33**

QX 203-3 BETSEY CLARK–HOME FOR CHRISTMAS ☐
Comments: **Fifth in Series**, Pink Glass Ball, 2-7/8" dia.
Dated 1990. Betsey's children are making holiday music.
Caption: "Merry Christmas" and "Tis The Season When Hearts Are Singing!"
☐ Purchased 19 __ Pd $____MIB   NB   DB   BNT
☐ Want   Orig. Ret. $5.00 **NB** $20   **MIB** Sec. Mkt. **$25**

QX 519-6 BILLBOARD BUNNY ☐
Comments: Handcrafted, 2-3/8" tall.
The Easter Bunny is wearing a bright red sandwich board proclaiming his thoughts about the Christmas season:
"Bah Hum Bug" and "Ban Fruit Cake." **Artist:** Julia Lee
☐ Purchased 19 __ Pd $____MIB   NB   DB   BNT
☐ Want   Orig. Ret. $7.75 **NB** $21   **MIB** Sec. Mkt. **$23**

QLX 736-3 BLESSINGS OF LOVE ☐
Comments: Lighted Panorama Ball, 4-3/4" tall.
The barn animals watch the Baby Jesus sleeping in the manger. Caption: "His Humble Birth Blessed All The Earth With Love And Joy Forever."
☐ Purchased 19 __ Pd $____MIB   NB   DB   BNT
☐ Want   Orig. Ret. $14.00 **NB** $40 **MIB** Sec. Mkt. **$50**

QX 504-3 BORN TO DANCE ☐
Comments: Handcrafted, 2-9/16" tall.
This little ballerina mouse is wearing a pink lacy tutu and is very flexible. She may be bent into various dance positions.
Artist: Sharon Pike
☐ Purchased 19 __ Pd $____MIB   NB   DB   BNT
☐ Want   Orig. Ret. $7.75 **NB** $20   **MIB** Sec. Mkt. **$25**

QX 449-3 BROTHER ☐
Comments: Handcrafted, 2-3/16" tall, Dated 1990.
The baseball glove claims "M.V.B. Most Valuable Brother" and the puppy sitting in the middle of the glove thinks so, too.
Artist: Bob Siedler
☐ Purchased 19 __ Pd $____MIB   NB   DB   BNT
☐ Want   Orig. Ret. $5.75 **NB** $11 **MIB** Sec. Mkt. **$15**

QX 316-6 CHILD CARE GIVER ☐
Comments: Acrylic, 3" tall, Dated Christmas 1990.
Etched onto this quatrefoil shaped ornament is a teddy bear hugging a bunny. Gold foil caption: "A Special Person Like You Is Every Child's Dream."
☐ Purchased 19 __ Pd $____MIB   NB   DB   BNT
☐ Want   Orig. Ret. $6.75 **NB** $10 **MIB** Sec. Mkt. **$14**

QX 487-6 CHILD'S FIFTH CHRISTMAS ☐
Comments: Handcrafted, 2-3/8" tall, Dated 1990.
Identical to 1989; only the date has changed.
Artist: Dill Rhodus
☐ Purchased 19 __ Pd $____MIB   NB   DB   BNT
☐ Want   Orig. Ret. $6.75 **NB** $14 **MIB** Sec. Mkt. **$20**

QX 487-3 CHILD'S FOURTH CHRISTMAS ☐
Comments: Handcrafted, 3" tall, Dated 1990.
Identical to 1989; only the date has changed.
Artist: John Francis (Collin)
☐ Purchased 19 __Pd $____MIB   NB   DB   BNT
☐ Want   Orig. Ret. $6.75 **NB** $14 **MIB** Sec. Mkt. **$20**

QX 486-6 CHILD'S THIRD CHRISTMAS ☐
Comments: Handcrafted, 2-1/2" tall, Dated 1990.
Identical to 1989; only the date has changed.
Artist: John Francis (Collin)
☐ Purchased 19 __ Pd $____MIB   NB   DB   BNT
☐ Want   Orig. Ret. $6.75 **NB** $20 **MIB** Sec. Mkt. **$25**

QLX 724-3   CHILDREN'S EXPRESS
Comments: Light and Motion, Handcrafted, 3-3/4" tall.
Two children have fun playing with a train set. The little boy
swings his legs and moves his head back and forth as he
watches the train. **Artist:** Linda Sickman
☐ Purchased 19 __ Pd $____MIB   NB   DB   BNT
☐ Want   Orig. Ret. $28.00 **NB** $63   **MIB** Sec. Mkt. **$80**

QX 436-6   CHIMING IN
Comments: Handcrafted/Brass, 5" tall, Dated 1990.
A little squirrel is standing on top of the chimes waiting for his
cue to ring the chimes with his candy cane mallet.
Artist: Sharon Pike
☐ Purchased 19 __ Pd $____MIB   NB   DB   BNT
☐ Want   Orig. Ret. $9.75 **NB** $16   **MIB** Sec. Mkt. **$25**

QLX 729-6   CHRIS MOUSE WREATH
Comments: **Sixth in Series**, Handcrafted, 4-1/2" tall.
Dated 1990. Chris lights the candle inside a lovely green
wreath decorated with gold ball ornaments.
Artist: Anita Marra Rogers
☐ Purchased 19 __ Pd $____MIB   NB   DB   BNT
☐ Want   Orig. Ret. $10.00 **NB** $39   **MIB** Sec. Mkt. **$50**

**QLX 730-3   CHRISTMAS CLASSICS:
THE LITTLEST ANGEL**
Comments: **Fifth in Series**, Lighted, 4-1/2" tall.
Dated 1990. The Littlest Angel kneels in awe as his gift to the
Child is transformed into the Star of Bethlehem. Caption: "The
Littlest Angel." **Artist:** John Francis (Collin)
☐ Purchased 19 __ Pd $____MIB   NB   DB   BNT
☐ Want   Orig. Ret. $14.00 **NB** $37 **MIB** Sec. Mkt. **$50**

QX 437-3   CHRISTMAS CROC
Comments: Handcrafted, 1-1/18" tall.
This bright green crocodile wears a Christmas red smile and a
fabric muffler to match. Twist the tip of his tail and he'll open his
mouth for you. **Artist:** Michele Pyda-Sevcik
☐ Purchased 19 __ Pd $____MIB   NB   DB   BNT
☐ Want   Orig. Ret. $7.75 **NB** $19   **MIB** Sec. Mkt. **$25**

QX 450-6   CHRISTMAS KITTY
Comments: **Second in Series**, Fine Porcelain, 3" tall.
This hand-painted grey kitten is lovely in her pale blue and
white coat, hat and muff with sprigs of holly.
Artist: Anita Marra Rogers
☐ Purchased 19 __ Pd $____MIB   NB   DB   BNT
☐ Want   Orig. Ret. $14.75 **NB** $23   **MIB** Sec. Mkt. **$31**

QXC 476-6   CHRISTMAS LIMITED: KEEPSAKE CLUB
Comments: Limited Edition 38,700, Wood Display Stand.
Cast Metal, 2-5/8" tall. This blue and red, brass-trimmed
locomotive has a brass bell that rings and wheels that turn.
Available to Members only. **Artist:** Linda Sickman
☐ Purchased 19 __ Pd $____MIB   NB   DB   BNT
☐ Want   Orig. Ret. $19.75 **NB** $95 **MIB** Sec. Mkt. **$125**

QLX 727-6   CHRISTMAS MEMORIES
Comments: Light and Motion, Handcrafted, 4-1/4" tall.
A Clydesdale horse pulls a family in a sleigh as they bring home
their Christmas tree. Caption: "The Joy Is In Remembering..."
Artist: Duane Unruh
☐ Purchased 19 __ Pd $____MIB   NB   DB   BNT
☐ Want   Orig. Ret. $25.00 **NB** $40   **MIB** Sec. Mkt. **$50**

QX 524-6   CHRISTMAS PARTRIDGE
Comments: Dimensional Brass, 3-1/4" tall.
A delicately etched partridge dangles inside the silhouette of a
pear with large etched leaves. **Artist:** Linda Sickman
☐ Purchased 19 __ Pd $____MIB   NB   DB   BNT
☐ Want   Orig. Ret. $7.75 **NB** $12   **MIB** Sec. Mkt. **$15**

QX 488-5   CLAUS CONSTRUCTION
Comments: Handcrafted, 4-3/4" tall.
Reissued from 1989. **Artist:** Ed Seale
☐ Purchased 19 __ Pd $____MIB   NB   DB   BNT
☐ Want   Orig. Ret. $7.75 **NB** $28   **MIB** Sec. Mkt. **$40**

QXC 445-6   CLUB HOLLOW: KEEPSAKE CLUB
Comments: Handcrafted, 1-7/8" tall, Dated 1990.
This feathered owl is reading "Whoo's Whoo" in the "Courier
1990," snug inside his snow-capped home. "Collectors Club +
Me" is carved in the back of the tree. Club logo on the bottom.
Artist: Ken Crow
☐ Purchased 19 __ Pd $____MIB   NB   DB   BNT
☐ Want   Price: Came with Club Membership of $_____
                                                        NB $25   **MIB** Sec. Mkt. **$35**

**QX 443-6   COLLECTOR'S PLATE:
COOKIES FOR SANTA**
Comments: **Fourth in Series**, Fine Porcelain, 3-1/4" dia.
Dated 1990. Two children have set out a plate of cookies and
are writing their wish list for Santa. Caption "Cookies For
Santa" on back. **Artist:** LaDene Votruba
☐ Purchased 19 __ Pd $____MIB   NB   DB   BNT
☐ Want   Orig. Ret. $8.75 **NB** $30   **MIB** Sec. Mkt. **$35**

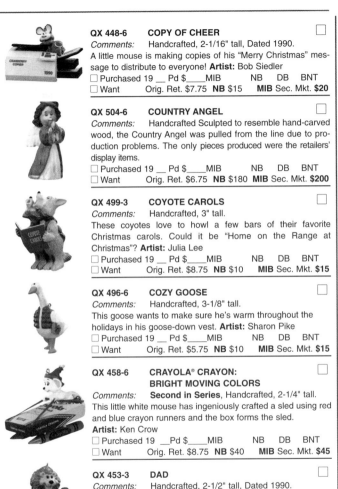

QX 448-6   COPY OF CHEER ☐
Comments: Handcrafted, 2-1/16" tall, Dated 1990.
A little mouse is making copies of his "Merry Christmas" message to distribute to everyone! **Artist:** Bob Siedler
☐ Purchased 19 __ Pd $____MIB   NB   DB   BNT
☐ Want   Orig. Ret. $7.75 **NB** $15   **MIB** Sec. Mkt. **$20**

QX 504-6   COUNTRY ANGEL ☐
Comments: Handcrafted Sculpted to resemble hand-carved wood, the Country Angel was pulled from the line due to production problems. The only pieces produced were the retailers' display items.
☐ Purchased 19 __ Pd $____MIB   NB   DB   BNT
☐ Want   Orig. Ret. $6.75 **NB** $180 **MIB** Sec. Mkt. **$200**

QX 499-3   COYOTE CAROLS ☐
Comments: Handcrafted, 3" tall.
These coyotes love to howl a few bars of their favorite Christmas carols. Could it be "Home on the Range at Christmas"? **Artist:** Julia Lee
☐ Purchased 19 __ Pd $____MIB   NB   DB   BNT
☐ Want   Orig. Ret. $8.75 **NB** $10   **MIB** Sec. Mkt. **$15**

QX 496-6   COZY GOOSE ☐
Comments: Handcrafted, 3-1/8" tall.
This goose wants to make sure he's warm throughout the holidays in his goose-down vest. **Artist:** Sharon Pike
☐ Purchased 19 __ Pd $____MIB   NB   DB   BNT
☐ Want   Orig. Ret. $5.75 **NB** $10   **MIB** Sec. Mkt. **$15**

QX 458-6   CRAYOLA® CRAYON:
BRIGHT MOVING COLORS ☐
Comments: **Second in Series**, Handcrafted, 2-1/4" tall.
This little white mouse has ingeniously crafted a sled using red and blue crayon runners and the box forms the sled.
Artist: Ken Crow
☐ Purchased 19 __Pd $____MIB   NB   DB   BNT
☐ Want   Orig. Ret. $8.75 **NB** $40   **MIB** Sec. Mkt. **$45**

QX 453-3   DAD ☐
Comments: Handcrafted, 2-1/2" tall, Dated 1990.
Dad is one happy king, whether of forest or home in his oversized sweater. **Artist:** Julia Lee
☐ Purchased 19 __ Pd $____MIB   NB   DB   BNT
☐ Want   Orig. Ret. $6.75 **NB** $10   **MIB** Sec. Mkt. **$15**

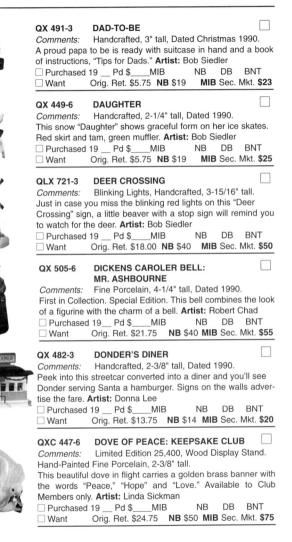

QX 491-3   DAD-TO-BE ☐
Comments: Handcrafted, 3" tall, Dated Christmas 1990.
A proud papa to be is ready with suitcase in hand and a book of instructions, "Tips for Dads." **Artist:** Bob Siedler
☐ Purchased 19 __ Pd $____MIB   NB   DB   BNT
☐ Want   Orig. Ret. $5.75 **NB** $19   **MIB** Sec. Mkt. **$23**

QX 449-6   DAUGHTER ☐
Comments: Handcrafted, 2-1/4" tall, Dated 1990.
This snow "Daughter" shows graceful form on her ice skates. Red skirt and tam, green muffler. **Artist:** Bob Siedler
☐ Purchased 19 __ Pd $____MIB   NB   DB   BNT
☐ Want   Orig. Ret. $5.75 **NB** $19   **MIB** Sec. Mkt. **$25**

QLX 721-3   DEER CROSSING ☐
Comments: Blinking Lights, Handcrafted, 3-15/16" tall.
Just in case you miss the blinking red lights on this "Deer Crossing" sign, a little beaver with a stop sign will remind you to watch for the deer. **Artist:** Bob Siedler
☐ Purchased 19 __ Pd $____MIB   NB   DB   BNT
☐ Want   Orig. Ret. $18.00 **NB** $40   **MIB** Sec. Mkt. **$50**

QX 505-6   DICKENS CAROLER BELL:
MR. ASHBOURNE ☐
Comments: Fine Porcelain, 4-1/4" tall, Dated 1990.
First in Collection. Special Edition. This bell combines the look of a figurine with the charm of a bell. **Artist:** Robert Chad
☐ Purchased 19__ Pd $____MIB   NB   DB   BNT
☐ Want   Orig. Ret. $21.75 **NB** $40 **MIB** Sec. Mkt. **$55**

QX 482-3   DONDER'S DINER ☐
Comments: Handcrafted, 2-3/8" tall, Dated 1990.
Peek into this streetcar converted into a diner and you'll see Donder serving Santa a hamburger. Signs on the walls advertise the fare. **Artist:** Donna Lee
☐ Purchased 19 __ Pd $____MIB   NB   DB   BNT
☐ Want   Orig. Ret. $13.75 **NB** $14 **MIB** Sec. Mkt. **$20**

QXC 447-6   DOVE OF PEACE: KEEPSAKE CLUB ☐
Comments: Limited Edition 25,400, Wood Display Stand. Hand-Painted Fine Porcelain, 2-3/8" tall.
This beautiful dove in flight carries a golden brass banner with the words "Peace," "Hope" and "Love." Available to Club Members only. **Artist:** Linda Sickman
☐ Purchased 19 __ Pd $____MIB   NB   DB   BNT
☐ Want   Orig. Ret. $24.75 **NB** $50 **MIB** Sec. Mkt. **$75**

QLX 735-6 ELF OF THE YEAR ☐
Comments: Lighted, Handcrafted, 2-15/16" tall, Dated 1990.
This little elf, all dressed in green, holds a glowing red 1990 outlined in gold. Artist: Patricia Andrews
☐ Purchased 19 __ Pd $____ MIB   NB   DB   BNT
☐ Want   Orig. Ret. $10.00 **NB** $20   **MIB** Sec. Mkt. **$25**

QLX 726-5 ELFIN WHITTLER ☐
Comments: Light and Motion, Handcrafted, 3-1/8" tall.
Listen carefully and you can hear a tapping sound as this busy little elf carves a statue of Santa. A teddy bear has been whittled on the reverse side of the same stump. **Artist:** Ken Crow
☐ Purchased 19 __ Pd $____ MIB   NB   DB   BNT
☐ Want   Orig. Ret. $20.00 **NB** $40   **MIB** Sec. Mkt. **$55**

QX 446-6 FABULOUS DECADE ☐
Comments: **FIRST IN SERIES**, Handcrafted/Brass, 1-3/8" tall. Dated 1990. A frisky squirrel holds up a brass 1990 to usher in the decade. Popular Series! Artist: Ed Seale
☐ Purchased 19 __ Pd $____ MIB   NB   DB   BNT
☐ Want   Orig. Ret. $7.75 **NB** $25   **MIB** Sec. Mkt. **$30**

QX 517-3 FELIZ NAVIDAD ☐
Comments: Handcrafted, 3" tall, Dated 1990.
A little white mouse's serape shows the year as this fellow peeks out of a bright red chili pepper. His sombrero wishes everyone "Feliz Navidad."
☐ Purchased 19 __ Pd $____ MIB   NB   DB   BNT
☐ Want   Orig. Ret. $6.75 **NB** $15   **MIB** Sec. Mkt. **$20**

QX 490-6 FIFTY YEARS TOGETHER ☐
Comments: Faceted Glass, 2-9/16" tall.
Dated Christmas 1990. Gold foil lettering is lovely on this heart-shaped faceted glass ornament. Caption: "50 Years Together." **Artist:** Joyce Pattee
☐ Purchased 19 __ Pd $____ MIB   NB   DB   BNT
☐ Want   Orig. Ret. $9.75 **NB** $13   **MIB** Sec. Mkt. **$20**

QLX 725-5 FIRST CHRISTMAS TOGETHER ☐
Comments: Lighted, Handcrafted, 3-5/8" tall, Dated 1990.
When the porch light turns off, a light inside the house turns on, silhouetting a couple in the picture window. "Our First Christmas Together" **Artist:** Donna Lee
☐ Purchased 19 __ Pd $____ MIB   NB   DB   BNT
☐ Want   Orig. Ret. $18.00 **NB** $47   **MIB** Sec. Mkt. **$50**

QX 488-6 FIRST CHRISTMAS TOGETHER PHOTOHOLDER ☐
Comments: Fabric, 3-1/4" tall, Dated 1990.
Caption: "First Christmas Together" and "Loving Memories Are Celebrations Of The Heart." **Artist:** LaDene Votruba
☐ Purchased 19 __ Pd $____ MIB   NB   DB   BNT
☐ Want   Orig. Ret. $7.75 **NB** $15   **MIB** Sec. Mkt. **$20**

QX 213-6 FIRST CHRISTMAS TOGETHER ☐
Comments: Light Gold Glass Ball, 2-7/8" dia., Dated 1990.
Inside a cozy living room, a raccoon couple trim their tree. "Our First Christmas Together" and "Love Decorates Our Lives With Joy!" **Artist:** LaDene Votruba
☐ Purchased 19 __ Pd $____ MIB   NB   DB   BNT
☐ Want   Orig. Ret. $4.75 **NB** $16   **MIB** Sec. Mkt. **$27**

QX 314-6 FIRST CHRISTMAS TOGETHER ☐
Comments: Acrylic, 2-3/4" tall, Dated 1990.
Two etched doves and a heart-shaped holly wreath are set off with gold foil caption: "Our First Christmas Together." **Artist:** LaDene Votruba
☐ Purchased 19 __ Pd $____ MIB   NB   DB   BNT
☐ Want   Orig. Ret. $6.75 **NB** $15   **MIB** Sec. Mkt. **$25**

QX 488-3 FIRST CHRISTMAS TOGETHER ☐
Comments: Handcrafted, 1-9/16" tall, Dated 1990.
Two happy foxes snuggle together inside a cozy, snow-covered log. Caption: "Our First Christmas Together" and "Isn't Love Wonderful!" **Artist:** Michele Pyda-Sevcik
☐ Purchased 19 __ Pd $____ MIB   NB   DB   BNT
☐ Want   Orig. Ret. $9.75 **NB** $28   **MIB** Sec. Mkt. **$30**

QX 210-3 FIVE YEARS TOGETHER ☐
Comments: Light Silver Glass Ball, 2-7/8" dia.
Dated Christmas 1990. Two deer prance around this teardrop ball. Caption: "5 Years Together" and "Loves Makes You Happy!" **Artist:** LaDene Votruba
☐ Purchased 19 __ Pd $____ MIB   NB   DB   BNT
☐ Want   Orig. Ret. $4.75 **NB** $15   **MIB** Sec. Mkt. **$25**

QLX 723-6 FOREST FROLICS ☐
Comments: **Second in Series**, Light and Motion, Dated 1990. Handcrafted, 4-1/2" tall. The forest friends have gathered together for fun and play. Caption: "Merry Christmas 1990." Artist: Sharon Pike
☐ Purchased 19 __ Pd $____ MIB   NB   DB   BNT
☐ Want   Orig. Ret. $25.00 **NB** $54   **MIB** Sec. Mkt. **$60**

QX 490-3 FORTY YEARS TOGETHER ☐
Comments: Faceted Glass, 2-9/16" tall.
Dated Christmas 1990. The caption in this heart-shaped glass
ornament is in red foil. "40 Years Together."
Artist: Joyce Pattee
☐ Purchased 19 __ Pd $____MIB   NB   DB   BNT
☐ Want   Orig. Ret. $9.75 **NB** $15   **MIB** Sec. Mkt. **$20**

QX 414-3 FRIENDSHIP KITTEN ☐
Comments: Handcrafted, 2-3/8" tall, Dated 1990.
A white kitten seals a Hallmark card addressed "To a Special
Friend" and has added his own greeting, "Merry Christmas."
Artist: Dill Rhodus
☐ Purchased 19 __ Pd $____MIB   NB   DB   BNT
☐ Want   Orig. Ret. $6.75 **NB** $17   **MIB** Sec. Mkt. **$20**

QX 216-6 FROM OUR HOME TO YOURS ☐
Comments: Periwinkle Blue Glass Ball, 2-7/8" dia.
Dated Christmas 1990. A needlepoint design shows two homes
and a white picket fence. Caption: "From Our Home To Yours."
☐ Purchased 19 __ Pd $____MIB   NB   DB   BNT
☐ Want   Orig. Ret. $4.75 **NB** $10   **MIB** Sec. Mkt. **$20**

QX 439-6 FROSTY FRIENDS ☐
Comments: **Eleventh in Series**, Handcrafted, 2-1/2" tall.
Dated 1990. The little Eskimo and a flocked seal are having lots
of fun sliding on the ice. **Artist:** Ed Seale
☐ Purchased 19 __ Pd $____MIB   NB   DB   BNT
☐ Want   Orig. Ret. $9.75 **NB** $27   **MIB** Sec. Mkt. **$40**

QX 230-3 GARFIELD ☐
Comments: Blue Chrome Glass Ball, 2-7/8" dia.
Dated 1990. Garfield cuts a neat design on the ice with his ice
skates.Caption: "Merry Christmas" and "Oh Yeah – Happy New Year,
Too!"
☐ Purchased 19 __ Pd $____MIB   NB   DB   BNT
☐ Want   Orig. Ret. $4.75 **NB** $20   **MIB** Sec. Mkt. **$25**

QX 475-6 GENTLE DREAMERS ☐
Comments: Handcrafted, 1-7/16" tall.
Nestled together in the center of a large red poinsettia are two
sleeping flocked bunnies. Clip-on orn. **Artist:** John Francis (Collin)
☐ Purchased 19 __ Pd $____MIB   NB   DB   BNT
☐ Want   Orig. Ret. $8.75 **NB** $25   **MIB** Sec. Mkt. **$30**

QX 280-3 GIFT BRINGERS, THE: ST. LUCIA ☐
Comments: **Second in Series**, White Glass Ball, 2-7/9" dia.
St. Lucia welcomes the Christmas season in a white robe and
a crown of candles. Caption: "The Gift Bringers, St. Lucia,
Christmas 1990." **Artist:** LaDene Votruba
☐ Purchased 19 __ Pd $____MIB   NB   DB   BNT
☐ Want   Orig. Ret. $5.00 **NB** $17   **MIB** Sec. Mkt. **$25**

QX 503-3 GINGERBREAD ELF ☐
Comments: Handcrafted, 3-11/16" tall, Dated 1990.
A rosy cheeked gingerbread baker with a flowing white beard
and sparkling chef's hat has baked two reindeer cookies, now
on a silver tray.
☐ Purchased 19 __ Pd $____MIB   NB   DB   BNT
☐ Want   Orig. Ret. $5.75 **NB** $15   **MIB** Sec. Mkt. **$20**

QX 317-6 GODCHILD ☐
Comments: Acrylic, 2-5/8" tall, Dated 1990.
A happy, waving koala slides down the hill on his toboggan.
Caption: "Merry Christmas, Godchild." **Artist:** John Francis (Collin)
☐ Purchased 19 __ Pd $____MIB   NB   DB   BNT
☐ Want   Orig. Ret. $6.75 **NB** $15   **MIB** Sec. Mkt. **$20**

QX 496-3 GOLF'S MY BAG ☐
Comments: Handcrafted, 3-3/4" tall.
You can surely tell which clubs are Santa's by his specially
designed reindeer head covers for his clubs. Bag is inscribed
"Golf's My Bag! Santa." **Artist:** Julia Lee
☐ Purchased 19 __ Pd $____MIB   NB   DB   BNT
☐ Want   Orig. Ret. $7.75 **NB** $24   **MIB** Sec. Mkt. **$30**

QX 523-6 GOOSE CART ☐
Comments: Handcrafted, 1-3/4" tall.
Riding in a green cart which says "Welcome Christmas" is this
goose with a red bow around its neck.
☐ Purchased 19 __ Pd $____MIB   NB   DB   BNT
☐ Want   Orig. Ret. $7.75 **NB** $12   **MIB** Sec. Mkt. **$16**

QX 228-6 GRANDDAUGHTER ☐
Comments: Pink Glass Ball, 2-7/8" dia.
Dated Christmas 1990. Caption: "Granddaughter – Happiness
Happens Wherever She Goes!" **Artist:** Joyce A. Lyle
☐ Purchased 19 __ Pd $____MIB   NB   DB   BNT
☐ Want   Orig. Ret. $4.75 **NB** $18   **MIB** Sec. Mkt. **$25**

QX 310-6　GRANDDAUGHTER'S FIRST CHRISTMAS ☐
Comments:　Acrylic, 3-9/16" tall, Dated 1990.
A little mouse of frosted, textured acrylic is sitting inside a hat box. Pink foil lettering announces "Granddaughter's First Christmas." **Artist:** John Francis (Collin)
☐ Purchased 19 __ Pd $____MIB　　NB　DB　BNT
☐ Want　　Orig. Ret. $6.75 **NB** $15　　**MIB** Sec. Mkt. **$23**

QX 223-6　GRANDMOTHER ☐
Comments:　Blue/White Glass Ball, 2-7/8" dia.
Dated Christmas 1990. A little mouse writes a message: "Grandmother... You're Wonderful!" on a tall wooden fence. **Artist:** LaDene Votruba
☐ Purchased 19 __ Pd $____MIB　　NB　DB　BNT
☐ Want　　Orig. Ret. $4.75 **NB** $10　　**MIB** Sec. Mkt. **$20**

QX 225-3　GRANDPARENTS ☐
Comments:　Kelly Green Glass Ball, 2-7/8" dia., Dated 1990.
Garland of evergreen, holly, candy canes, poinsettia and ribbon frame two messages: "Grandparents And Christmas... Two Beautiful Ways To Say Love" and "Season's Greetings."
☐ Purchased 19 __ Pd $____MIB　　NB　DB　BNT
☐ Want　　Orig. Ret. $4.75 **NB** $10　　**MIB** Sec. Mkt. **$20**

QX 229-3　GRANDSON ☐
Comments:　Porcelain White Glass Ball, 2-7/8" dia.
Dated 1990. Five white bears are having loads of Christmas fun! Caption: "For You" and "A Grandson Fills Christmas With Cheer!" **Artist:** LaDene Votruba
☐ Purchased 19 __ Pd $____MIB　　NB　DB　BNT
☐ Want　　Orig. Ret. $4.75 **NB** $15　　**MIB** Sec. Mkt. **$30**

QX 306-3　GRANDSON'S FIRST CHRISTMAS ☐
Comments:　Acrylic, 3-21/32" tall, Dated 1990.
A baby lamb is snuggled inside a clear box. "Grandson's First Christmas" in blue foil letters. **Artist:** John Francis (Collin)
☐ Purchased 19 __ Pd $____MIB　　NB　DB　BNT
☐ Want　　Orig. Ret. $6.75 **NB** $10　　**MIB** Sec. Mkt. **$15**

QX 465-6　GREATEST STORY ☐
Comments:　***FIRST IN SERIES***, Bisque Porcelain/Brass, 3-3/4" tall. Dated 1990. A porcelain nativity dangles inside a lacy brass snowflake. Artist: LaDene Votruba
☐ Purchased 19 __ Pd $____MIB　　NB　DB　BNT
☐ Want　　Orig. Ret. $12.75 **NB** $20　　**MIB** Sec. Mkt. **$25**

QX 471-3　HANG IN THERE ☐
Comments:　Handcrafted, 2-1/4" tall.
A charming little raccoon in his green cap is hanging on tightly to a branch, so as not to miss anything. **Artist:** Ed Seale
☐ Purchased 19 __ Pd $____MIB　　NB　DB　BNT
☐ Want　　Orig. Ret. $6.75 **NB** $12　　**MIB** Sec. Mkt. **$23**

QX 464-5　HAPPY VOICES ☐
Comments:　Wood, 3-1/8" tall.
A shadow box provides a perfect setting for two carolers and their dog. Caption: "Happy Voices Fill The Air!"
Artist: LaDene Votruba
☐ Purchased 19 __ Pd $____MIB　　NB　DB　BNT
☐ Want　　Orig. Ret. $6.75 **NB** $12　　**MIB** Sec. Mkt. **$15**

QX 476-3　HAPPY WOODCUTTER ☐
Comments:　Handcrafted, 2" tall, Dated 1990.
This little fellow with the big toothy smile has cut a Christmas tree for his home... with a chain saw. **Artist:** Julia Lee
☐ Purchased 19 __ Pd $____MIB　　NB　DB　BNT
☐ Want　　Orig. Ret. $9.75 **NB** $10　　**MIB** Sec. Mkt. **$18**

QX 446-3　HARK! IT'S HERALD ☐
Comments:　**Second in Series**, Handcrafted, 2-1/8" tall.
Dated 1990. Herald is ready to celebrate the holidays with his new bass drum. **Artist:** Ken Crow
☐ Purchased 19 __ Pd $____MIB　　NB　DB　BNT
☐ Want　　Orig. Ret. $6.75 **NB** $17　　**MIB** Sec. Mkt. **$25**

QX 472-6　HEART OF CHRISTMAS ☐
Comments:　***FIRST IN SERIES***, Handcrafted, 2" tall, Dated 1990.This double-hinged heart opens to reveal Santa filling the stockings. One child watches from behind the Christmas tree and another from the stairs. "Keep The Magic Of Christmas In Your Heart." **Artist**: Ed Seale
☐ Purchased 19 __ Pd $____MIB　　NB　DB　BNT
☐ Want　　Orig. Ret. $13.75 **NB** $65　　**MIB** Sec. Mkt. **$80**

QX 492-3　HERE COMES SANTA: FESTIVE SURREY ☐
Comments:　**Twelfth in Series**, Handcrafted, 3-1/8" tall.
Dated 1990. Santa's surrey has wheels that revolve and is decorated with a wreath on the back of the seat. A bag of toys is at Santa's feet. **Artist:** Linda Sickman
☐ Purchased 19 __ Pd $____MIB　　NB　DB　BNT
☐ Want　　Orig. Ret. $14.75 **NB** $35　　**MIB** Sec. Mkt. **$45**

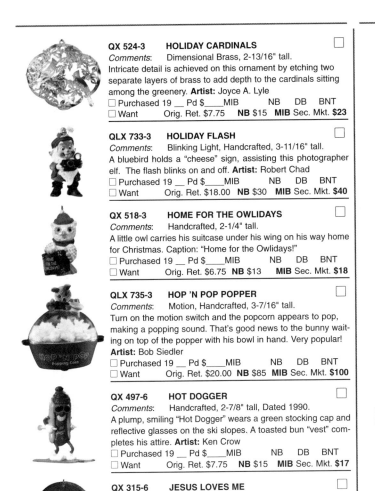

QX 524-3   HOLIDAY CARDINALS   ☐
Comments: Dimensional Brass, 2-13/16" tall.
Intricate detail is achieved on this ornament by etching two separate layers of brass to add depth to the cardinals sitting among the greenery. **Artist:** Joyce A. Lyle
☐ Purchased 19 __ Pd $____MIB   NB   DB   BNT
☐ Want   Orig. Ret. $7.75 **NB** $15 **MIB** Sec. Mkt. **$23**

QLX 733-3   HOLIDAY FLASH   ☐
Comments: Blinking Light, Handcrafted, 3-11/16" tall.
A bluebird holds a "cheese" sign, assisting this photographer elf. The flash blinks on and off. **Artist:** Robert Chad
☐ Purchased 19 __ Pd $____MIB   NB   DB   BNT
☐ Want   Orig. Ret. $18.00 **NB** $30 **MIB** Sec. Mkt. **$40**

QX 518-3   HOME FOR THE OWLIDAYS   ☐
Comments: Handcrafted, 2-1/4" tall.
A little owl carries his suitcase under his wing on his way home for Christmas. Caption: "Home for the Owlidays!"
☐ Purchased 19 __ Pd $____MIB   NB   DB   BNT
☐ Want   Orig. Ret. $6.75 **NB** $13   **MIB** Sec. Mkt. **$18**

QLX 735-3   HOP 'N POP POPPER   ☐
Comments: Motion, Handcrafted, 3-7/16" tall.
Turn on the motion switch and the popcorn appears to pop, making a popping sound. That's good news to the bunny waiting on top of the popper with his bowl in hand. Very popular! **Artist:** Bob Siedler
☐ Purchased 19 __ Pd $____MIB   NB   DB   BNT
☐ Want   Orig. Ret. $20.00 **NB** $85 **MIB** Sec. Mkt. **$100**

QX 497-6   HOT DOGGER   ☐
Comments: Handcrafted, 2-7/8" tall, Dated 1990.
A plump, smiling "Hot Dogger" wears a green stocking cap and reflective glasses on the ski slopes. A toasted bun "vest" completes his attire. **Artist:** Ken Crow
☐ Purchased 19 __ Pd $____MIB   NB   DB   BNT
☐ Want   Orig. Ret. $7.75 **NB** $15 **MIB** Sec. Mkt. **$17**

QX 315-6   JESUS LOVES ME   ☐
Comments: Acrylic, 2-3/4" dia.
A happy bunny shows his joy in this etched frosted design. Caption: "Jesus Loves Me." **Artist:** Joyce Pattee
☐ Purchased 19 __ Pd $____MIB   NB   DB   BNT
☐ Want   Orig. Ret. $6.75 **NB** $10 **MIB** Sec. Mkt. **$15**

QX 468-3   JOLLY DOLPHIN   ☐
Comments: Handcrafted, 3" tall.
A happy dolphin performs tricks for the holiday season as he jumps through a wreath decorated with ribbons.
Artist: Anita Marra Rogers
☐ Purchased 19 __ Pd $____MIB   NB   DB   BNT
☐ Want   Orig. Ret. $6.75 **NB** $20   **MIB** Sec. Mkt. **$40**

QX 550-3   JOY IS IN THE AIR   ☐
Comments: Handcrafted, 2-5/8" tall, Dated 1990.
Santa parachutes to earth to deliver some toys to the boys and girls. Caption: "Joy Is In The Air!" **Artist:** Ken Crow
☐ Purchased 19 __ Pd $____MIB   NB   DB   BNT
☐ Want   Orig. Ret. $7.75 **NB** $20   **MIB** Sec. Mkt. **$25**

QX 410-6   KING KLAUS   ☐
Comments: Handcrafted, 4-5/8" tall.
Santa waves a Christmas greeting from the top of the Empire State Building. **Artist:** Ed Seale
☐ Purchased 19 __ Pd $____MIB   NB   DB   BNT
☐ Want   Orig. Ret. $7.75 **NB** $15   **MIB** Sec. Mkt. **$23**

QX 471-6   KITTY'S BEST PAL   ☐
Comments: Handcrafted, 2-3/8" tall, Dated 1990.
This adorable kitten, nestled in a dated Christmas stocking, snuggles against Santa's cheek.**Artist:** John Francis (Collin)
☐ Purchased 19 __ Pd $____MIB   NB   DB   BNT
☐ Want   Orig. Ret. $6.75 **NB** $10   **MIB** Sec. Mkt. **$15**

QLX 722-6   LETTER TO SANTA   ☐
Comments: Light, Handcrafted, 2-1/2" tall.
A pajama-clad child sends his letter to Santa by way of the computer! His message: "Dear Santa, I've Been Very, Very, Very Good!" **Artist:** Anita Marra Rogers
☐ Purchased 19 __ Pd $____MIB   NB   DB   BNT
☐ Want   Orig. Ret. $14.00 **NB** $30   **MIB** Sec. Mkt. **$40**

QX 523-3   LITTLE DRUMMER BOY   ☐
Comments: Handcrafted, 2-3/8" tall, Dated 1990.
This little fellow will march straight into your heart as he beats his dated drum. **Artist:** Duane Unruh
☐ Purchased 19 __ Pd $____MIB   NB   DB   BNT
☐ Want   Orig. Ret. $7.75 **NB** $15   **MIB** Sec. Mkt. **$20**

QX 470-3   LONG WINTER'S NAP

Comments: Handcrafted, 1-3/8" tall, Dated 1990.
A dachshund wearing a Santa cap sleeps soundly in an open-ended gift box. He fastens to the tree with a special clip.
Artist: Anita Marra Rogers

☐ Purchased 19 __ Pd $____MIB   NB   DB   BNT
☐ Want   Orig. Ret. $6.75 **NB** $15   **MIB** Sec. Mkt. **$25**

QX 547-6   LOVABLE DEARS

Comments: Handcrafted, 2-5/16" tall.
A little girl, dressed in a bright red coat and blue muffler, shares a hug with her pet fawn. **Artist**: Duane Unruh

☐ Purchased 19 __ Pd $____MIB   NB   DB   BNT
☐ Want   Orig. Ret. $8.75 **NB** $15   **MIB** Sec. Mkt. **$19**

QX 442-3   MARY'S ANGELS: ROSEBUD

Comments: **Third in Serie**s, Handcrafted and Acrylic, 3-1/8" tall. Rosebud, in a pink gown and with wings spread, holds a candle for all to see. She stands on a frosted acrylic cloud.
Artist: Robert Chad

☐ Purchased 19 __ Pd $____MIB   NB   DB   BNT
☐ Want   Orig. Ret. $5.75 **NB** $30   **MIB** Sec. Mkt **$40**

QX 444-6   MEOW MART

Comments: Handcrafted, 1-1/4" tall.
What does it take to make a playful kitten happy? Only a sack from the "Meow Mart" and a ball of red yarn! **Artist**: Sharon Pike

☐ Purchased 19 __ Pd $____MIB   NB   DB   BNT
☐ Want   Orig. Ret. $7.75 **NB** $20   **MIB** Sec. Mkt. **$30**

QX 473-6   MERRY OLDE SANTA

Comments: **FIRST IN SERIES**, Handcrafted, 4-3/4" tall. Dated 1990. An old-fashioned German Santa has toys tucked into his pockets and carries a small Christmas tree in his hand.
Artist: Ed Seale

☐ Purchased 19 __ Pd $____MIB   NB   DB   BNT
☐ Want   Orig. Ret. $14.75 **NB** $60 **MIB** Sec. Mkt. **$78**

QX 459-3   MOM AND DAD

Comments: Handcrafted, 2-1/2" tall, Dated 1990.
These smiling bears are mailing a Hallmark card in their mailbox, which is sitting on a tree stump. Mailbox reads "Mom And Dad." **Artist**: Robert Chad

☐ Purchased 19 __ Pd $____MIB   NB   DB   BNT
☐ Want   Orig. Ret. $8.75 **NB** $20   **MIB** Sec. Mkt. **$30**

QX 491-6   MOM-TO-BE

Comments: Handcrafted, 2-7/8" tall, Dated Christmas 1990. First to debut for Mom-To-Be. This Momma bunny is happily awaiting a new little bundle. **Artist**: Bob Siedler

☐ Purchased 19 __ Pd $____MIB   NB   DB   BNT
☐ Want   Orig. Ret. $5.75 **NB** $25   **MIB** Sec. Mkt. **$33**

QX 493-3   MOOY CHRISTMAS

Comments: Handcrafted, 2-1/16" tall.
This little holstein wears a bright red scarf with its Christmas greeting: "Mooy Christmas."

☐ Purchased 19 __ Pd $____MIB   NB   DB   BNT
☐ Want   Orig. Ret. $6.75 **NB** $17   **MIB** Sec. Mkt. **$30**

QX 453-6   MOTHER

Comments: Ceramic w/Bisque Finish, 2-7/8" dia., Dated 1990.Delicate filigree lettering confirms that "Mother Is Love." Tied with red ribbon. **Artist**: LaDene Votruba

☐ Purchased 19 __ Pd $____MIB   NB   DB   BNT
☐ Want   Orig. Ret. $8.75 **NB** $25   **MIB** Sec. Mkt. **$30**

QX 475-3   MOUSEBOAT

Comments: Handcrafted, 3" tall, Dated 1990.
A whimsical sailor mouse is headed out to sea in his walnut shell boat. The sail contains the signature of the artist, "Seale" and the date. **Artist**: Ed Seale

☐ Purchased 19 __ Pd $____MIB   NB   DB   BNT
☐ Want   Orig. Ret. $7.75 **NB** $16   **MIB** Sec. Mkt. **$20**

QX 439-3   MR. AND MRS. CLAUS: POPCORN PARTY

Comments: **Fifth in Serie**s, Handcrafted, 3" tall, Dated 1990. Santa and his Mrs. have popped a big pan of popcorn and are busy stringing it to put on their Christmas tree.
Artist: Duane Unruh

☐ Purchased 19 __ Pd $____MIB   NB   DB   BNT
☐ Want   Orig. Ret. $13.75 **NB** $60 **MIB** Sec. Mkt. **$80**

QLX 726-3   MRS. SANTA'S KITCHEN

Comments: Light and Motion, Handcrafted, 4-3/4" tall. Dated 1990. Mrs. Santa's special recipe gingerbread cookies dance around her kitchen. Caption: "Christmas Cookies Dance And Play To Celebrate The Holiday!" **Artist**: Dill Rhodus

☐ Purchased 19 __ Pd $____MIB   NB   DB   BNT
☐ Want   Orig. Ret. $25.00 **NB** $80 **MIB** Sec. Mkt. **$90**

QX 434-3   NEW HOME ☐
Comments: Handcrafted, 2-11/16" tall, Dated 1990.
A three-dimensional effect has been added to this heart to portray a home, tree and snowman. Caption: "There's No Place Like… A New Home!" **Artist:** Michele Pyda-Sevcik
☐ Purchased 19 __ Pd $____MIB   NB   DB   BNT
☐ Want   Orig. Ret. $6.75 **NB** $25   **MIB** Sec. Mkt. **$30**

QX 229-6   NORMAN ROCKWELL ART ☐
Comments: Light Gold Glass Ball, 2-7/8" dia., Christmas 1990.
"Norman Rockwell, Famous Holiday Covers From The Saturday Evening Post." "Merrie Christmas, Post Cover: Dec. 17, 1938." "God Bless Us Everyone, Said Tiny Tim" "Post Cover: Dec. 15, 1934." "Merrie Christmas, Post Cover: Dec. 8, 1928."
Artist: Joyce A. Lyle
☐ Purchased 19 __ Pd $____MIB   NB   DB   BNT
☐ Want   Orig. Ret. $4.75 **NB** $15   **MIB** Sec. Mkt. **$25**

QX 469-6   NOSTALGIC HOUSES AND SHOPS: ☐
**   HOLIDAY HOME**
Comments: **Seventh in Series**, Handcrafted, 3-7/8" tall.
Dated 1990. A decorated bottlebrush tree shows through the picture window of a furnished living room.
Artist: Donna Lee
☐ Purchased 19 __ Pd $____MIB   NB   DB   BNT
☐ Want   Orig. Ret. $14.75 **NB** $70   **MIB** Sec. Mkt. **$80**

QX 519-3   NUTSHELL CHAT ☐
Comments: Handcrafted, 1-7/16" tall.
Inside a walnut shell, a child telephones Santa and tells him what he wants for Christmas. Santa listens from the other half of the shell as he rests in his chair.
☐ Purchased 19 __ Pd $____MIB   NB   DB   BNT
☐ Want   Orig. Ret. $6.75 **NB** $10   **MIB** Sec. Mkt. **$15**

QX 465-2   NUTSHELL HOLIDAY ☐
Comments: Handcrafted, 1-1/2" tall, Reissued from 1989.
Artist: Anita Marra Rogers
☐ Purchased 19 __ Pd $____MIB   NB   DB   BNT
☐ Want   Orig. Ret. $5.75 **NB** $10   **MIB** Sec. Mkt. **$15**

QLX 721-2   PARTRIDGES IN A PEAR ☐
Comments: Lighted, Dimensional Brass, 3-3/4" tall.
An exquisite brass pear features a filigree partridge in each section of the ornament. **Artist:** Joyce A. Lyle
☐ Purchased 19 __ Pd $____MIB   NB   DB   BNT
☐ Want   Orig. Ret. $14.00 **NB** $20   **MIB** Sec. Mkt. **$25**

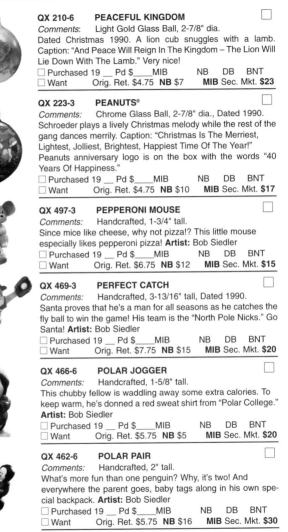

QX 210-6   PEACEFUL KINGDOM ☐
Comments: Light Gold Glass Ball, 2-7/8" dia.
Dated Christmas 1990. A lion cub snuggles with a lamb.
Caption: "And Peace Will Reign In The Kingdom – The Lion Will Lie Down With The Lamb." Very nice!
☐ Purchased 19 __ Pd $____MIB   NB   DB   BNT
☐ Want   Orig. Ret. $4.75 **NB** $7   **MIB** Sec. Mkt. **$23**

QX 223-3   PEANUTS® ☐
Comments: Chrome Glass Ball, 2-7/8" dia., Dated 1990.
Schroeder plays a lively Christmas melody while the rest of the gang dances merrily. Caption: "Christmas Is The Merriest, Lightest, Jolliest, Brightest, Happiest Time Of The Year!" Peanuts anniversary logo is on the box with the words "40 Years Of Happiness."
☐ Purchased 19 __ Pd $____MIB   NB   DB   BNT
☐ Want   Orig. Ret. $4.75 **NB** $10   **MIB** Sec. Mkt. **$17**

QX 497-3   PEPPERONI MOUSE ☐
Comments: Handcrafted, 1-3/4" tall.
Since mice like cheese, why not pizza!? This little mouse especially likes pepperoni pizza! **Artist:** Bob Siedler
☐ Purchased 19 __ Pd $____MIB   NB   DB   BNT
☐ Want   Orig. Ret. $6.75 **NB** $12   **MIB** Sec. Mkt. **$15**

QX 469-3   PERFECT CATCH ☐
Comments: Handcrafted, 3-13/16" tall, Dated 1990.
Santa proves that he's a man for all seasons as he catches the fly ball to win the game! His team is the "North Pole Nicks." Go Santa! **Artist:** Bob Siedler
☐ Purchased 19 __ Pd $____MIB   NB   DB   BNT
☐ Want   Orig. Ret. $7.75 **NB** $15   **MIB** Sec. Mkt. **$20**

QX 466-6   POLAR JOGGER ☐
Comments: Handcrafted, 1-5/8" tall.
This chubby fellow is waddling away some extra calories. To keep warm, he's donned a red sweat shirt from "Polar College."
Artist: Bob Siedler
☐ Purchased 19 __ Pd $____MIB   NB   DB   BNT
☐ Want   Orig. Ret. $5.75 **NB** $5   **MIB** Sec. Mkt. **$20**

QX 462-6   POLAR PAIR ☐
Comments: Handcrafted, 2" tall.
What's more fun than one penguin? Why, it's two! And everywhere the parent goes, baby tags along in his own special backpack. **Artist:** Bob Siedler
☐ Purchased 19 __ Pd $____MIB   NB   DB   BNT
☐ Want   Orig. Ret. $5.75 **NB** $16   **MIB** Sec. Mkt. **$30**

QX 515-6 POLAR SPORT ☐
Comments: Handcrafted 1-3/4" tall.
Our dapper penguin draws looks from everyone around wearing a scarf and beret and driving his red convertible sports car.
Artist: Bob Siedler

☐ Purchased 19 __ Pd $____MIB NB DB BNT
☐ Want Orig. Ret. $7.75 **NB** $18 **MIB** Sec. Mkt. **$25**

QX 516-6 POLAR TV ☐
Comments: Handcrafted 1-5/8" tall.
Life can be great! This penguin relaxes on a shimmery iceberg and sips a cool drink as he watches the "Polar News" on television. **Artist:** Bob Siedler

☐ Purchased 19 __ Pd $____MIB NB DB BNT
☐ Want Orig. Ret. $7.75 **NB** $17 **MIB** Sec. Mkt. **$20**

QX 466-3 POLAR V.I.P. ☐
Comments: Handcrafted, 2" tall.
This fellow must be a "Very Important Penguin." He carries a briefcase and cordless phone to keep in touch with his clientele. **Artist:** Bob Siedler

☐ Purchased 19 __ Pd $____MIB NB DB BNT
☐ Want Orig. Ret. $5.75 **NB** $17 **MIB** Sec. Mkt. **$20**

QX 463-3 POLAR VIDEO ☐
Comments: Handcrafted, 2" tall.
Go ahead and behave naturally... our perky penguin is going to capture all the holiday fun on his new camcorder. **Artist:** Bob Siedler

☐ Purchased 19 __ Pd $____MIB NB DB BNT
☐ Want Orig. Ret. $5.75 **NB** $5 **MIB** Sec. Mkt. **$10**

QX 498-6 POOLSIDE WALRUS ☐
Comments: Handcrafted, 1-3/4" tall.
What fun! This walrus wears a red swimming suit and sits on his reindeer float. **Artist:** Julia Lee

☐ Purchased 19 __ Pd $____MIB NB DB BNT
☐ Want Orig. Ret. $7.75 **NB** $15 **MIB** Sec. Mkt. **$27**

QX 442-6 PORCELAIN BEAR ☐
Comments: **Eighth and Final in Series**, Fine Porcelain, 1-9/16" tall. The final cinnamon bear finishes his holiday decorating by placing a star on the top of his tree.

☐ Purchased 19 __ Pd $____MIB NB DB BNT
☐ Want Orig. Ret. $8.75 **NB** $15 **MIB** Sec. Mkt. **$20**

QX 443-3 REINDEER CHAMPS: COMET ☐
Comments: **Fifth in Series**, Handcrafted, 3-3/16" tall.
Dated 1990. Comet scores again! He's wearing a sporty soccer uniform of red and green and is set to kick the soccer ball.
Artist: Bob Siedler

☐ Purchased 19 __ Pd $____MIB NB DB BNT
☐ Want Orig. Ret. $7.75 **NB** $25 **MIB** Sec. Mkt. **$30**

QX 464-6 ROCKING HORSE ☐
Comments: **Tenth in Series**, Handcrafted, 4" wide.
Dated 1990. **Scarce.** This Appaloosa has a festive look with a red and green saddle and matching rockers.
Artist: Linda Sickman

☐ Purchased 19 __ Pd $____MIB NB DB BNT
☐ Want Orig. Ret. $10.75 **NB** $90 **MIB** Sec. Mkt. **$100**

QX 468-6 S. CLAUS TAXI ☐
Comments: Handcrafted, 2" tall, Dated 12-25-1990.
Santa's taxi is in constant demand. He has a teddy bear passenger in the front seat. The taxi's wheels revolve. License: "Santa." **Artist:** Peter Dutkin

☐ Purchased 19 __ Pd $____MIB NB DB BNT
☐ Want Orig. Ret. $11.75 **NB** $25 **MIB** Sec. Mkt. **$30**

QX 498-3 SANTA SCHNOZ ☐
Comments: Handcrafted, 2-1/2" tall.
Santa sports a phony pair of glasses, mustache and schnoz! He's hiding a gift behind his back. **Artist:** Ken Crow

☐ Purchased 19 __ Pd $____MIB NB DB BNT
☐ Want Orig. Ret. $6.75 **NB** $30 **MIB** Sec. Mkt. **$40**

QLX 725-6 SANTA'S HO-HO-HOEDOWN ☐
Comments: Light and Motion, Handcrafted, 4-3/8" tall.
"Ho-Ho-Ho! Doe-See-Doe! Grab Your Partner – And 'Round We Go!" calls Santa as four reindeer couples twirl around at the barn dance. **Artist:** Ken Crow

☐ Purchased 19 __ Pd $____MIB NB DB BNT
☐ Want Orig. Ret. $25.00 **NB** $70 **MIB** Sec. Mkt. **$90**

QX 227-3 SISTER ☐
Comments: Porcelain White Glass Ball, 2-7/8" dia., Dated 1990. Large colorful poinsettias add charm. Caption: "A Sister Adds Her Own Special Touch To The Beauty And Joy Of Christmas."

☐ Purchased 19 __ Pd $____MIB NB DB BNT
☐ Want Orig. Ret. $4.75 **NB** $16 **MIB** Sec. Mkt. **$23**

QX 472-3   SNOOPY® AND WOODSTOCK ☐
Comments: Handcrafted, 2-1/4" tall.
Snoopy and Woodstock share a special hug between friends.
The slogan "40 Years Of Happiness" appears on the ornament
box. **Artist:** Dill Rhodus
☐ Purchased 19 __ Pd $____MIB   NB   DB   BNT
☐ Want   Orig. Ret. $6.75 **NB** $25   **MIB** Sec. Mkt. **$30**

QX 451-6   SON ☐
Comments: Handcrafted, 1-7/8" tall, Dated 1990.
A warmly dressed "snowboy" loves to play hockey. His cap
reads "Son" and his jersey announces the year.
Artist: Bob Siedler
☐ Purchased 19 __ Pd $____MIB   NB   DB   BNT
☐ Want   Orig. Ret. $5.75 **NB** $20   **MIB** Sec. Mkt. **$30**

QLX 725-3   SONG & DANCE ☐
Comments: Motion and Music, Handcrafted, 4-1/8" tall.
A mouse couple spins around and around on a record as it plays
"Jingle Bells" on the old phonograph. Caption: "Love And
Christmas... Two Reasons To Celebrate!"**Artist:** Anita Marra Rogers
☐ Purchased 19 __ Pd $____MIB   NB   DB   BNT
☐ Want   Orig. Ret. $20.00 **NB** $75   **MIB** Sec. Mkt. **$95**

QX 431-2   SPENCER® SPARROW, ESQ. ☐
Comments: Handcrafted, 1-3/4" tall, Reissued from 1989.
Artist: Sharon Pike
☐ Purchased 19 __ Pd $____MIB   NB   DB   BNT
☐ Want   Orig. Ret. $6.75 **NB** $20   **MIB** Sec. Mkt. **$28**

QX 549-6   SPOON RIDER ☐
Comments: Handcrafted, 2-1/2" tall.
A couple of mischievous elves are ready to go sledding – in a
teaspoon. Where's the snow? **Artist:** Patricia Andrews
☐ Purchased 19 __ Pd $____MIB   NB   DB   BNT
☐ Want   Orig. Ret. $9.75 **NB** $10   **MIB** Sec. Mkt. **$15**

QLX 730-6   STARLIGHT ANGEL ☐
Comments: Lighted, Handcrafted, 2-3/4" tall.
A sweet angel wearing a blue robe and shiny brass halo is
carrying a bag full of bright, shiny stars.
Artist: Anita Marra Rogers
☐ Purchased 19 __ Pd $____MIB   NB   DB   BNT
☐ Want   Orig. Ret. $14.00 **NB** $35   **MIB** Sec. Mkt. **$40**

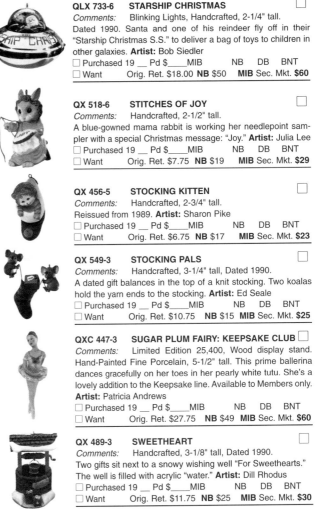

QLX 733-6   STARSHIP CHRISTMAS ☐
Comments: Blinking Lights, Handcrafted, 2-1/4" tall.
Dated 1990. Santa and one of his reindeer fly off in their
"Starship Christmas S.S." to deliver a bag of toys to children in
other galaxies. **Artist:** Bob Siedler
☐ Purchased 19 __ Pd $____MIB   NB   DB   BNT
☐ Want   Orig. Ret. $18.00 **NB** $50   **MIB** Sec. Mkt. **$60**

QX 518-6   STITCHES OF JOY ☐
Comments: Handcrafted, 2-1/2" tall.
A blue-gowned mama rabbit is working her needlepoint sam-
pler with a special Christmas message: "Joy." **Artist:** Julia Lee
☐ Purchased 19 __ Pd $____MIB   NB   DB   BNT
☐ Want   Orig. Ret. $7.75 **NB** $19   **MIB** Sec. Mkt. **$29**

QX 456-5   STOCKING KITTEN ☐
Comments: Handcrafted, 2-3/4" tall.
Reissued from 1989. **Artist:** Sharon Pike
☐ Purchased 19 __ Pd $____MIB   NB   DB   BNT
☐ Want   Orig. Ret. $6.75 **NB** $17   **MIB** Sec. Mkt. **$23**

QX 549-3   STOCKING PALS ☐
Comments: Handcrafted, 3-1/4" tall, Dated 1990.
A dated gift balances in the top of a knit stocking. Two koalas
hold the yarn ends to the stocking. **Artist:** Ed Seale
☐ Purchased 19 __ Pd $____MIB   NB   DB   BNT
☐ Want   Orig. Ret. $10.75 **NB** $15 **MIB** Sec. Mkt. **$25**

QXC 447-3   SUGAR PLUM FAIRY: KEEPSAKE CLUB ☐
Comments: Limited Edition 25,400, Wood display stand.
Hand-Painted Fine Porcelain, 5-1/2" tall. This prime ballerina
dances gracefully on her toes in her pearly white tutu. She's a
lovely addition to the Keepsake line. Available to Members only.
Artist: Patricia Andrews
☐ Purchased 19 __ Pd $____MIB   NB   DB   BNT
☐ Want   Orig. Ret. $27.75 **NB** $49 **MIB** Sec. Mkt. **$60**

QX 489-3   SWEETHEART ☐
Comments: Handcrafted, 3-1/8" tall, Dated 1990.
Two gifts sit next to a snowy wishing well "For Sweethearts."
The well is filled with acrylic "water." **Artist:** Dill Rhodus
☐ Purchased 19 __ Pd $____MIB   NB   DB   BNT
☐ Want   Orig. Ret. $11.75 **NB** $25 **MIB** Sec. Mkt. **$30**

QX 448-3　　TEACHER ☐

Comments:　　Handcrafted, 2-3/8" tall, Dated Dec. 25, 1990.
An adorable chipmunk points to the lessons he has learned,
along with a message, "We ♥ Teacher." **Artist:** Ed Seale

☐ Purchased 19 __ Pd $____MIB　　NB　　DB　　BNT
☐ Want　　Orig. Ret. $7.75　**NB** $10　　**MIB** Sec. Mkt. **$17**

QX 215-3　　TEN YEARS TOGETHER ☐

Comments:　　White Glass Ball, 2-7/8" dia.
Dated Christmas 1990. Red Birds enjoy an early winter snow-
fall. Caption: "Love Wraps The World In Wonder. 10 Years
Together." **Artist:** Joyce A. Lyle

☐ Purchased 19 __ Pd $____MIB　　NB　　DB　　BNT
☐ Want　　Orig. Ret. $4.75　**NB** $16　　**MIB** Sec. Mkt. **$22**

QX 499-6　　THREE LITTLE PIGGIES ☐

Comments:　　Handcrafted, 2-5/8" tall.
A red and blue five-toed stocking holds these happy chaps in
their colorful nightcaps. **Artist:** Ken Crow

☐ Purchased 19 __ Pd $____MIB　　NB　　DB　　BNT
☐ Want　　Orig. Ret. $7.75　**NB** $15　　**MIB** Sec. Mkt. **$20**

QX 213-3　　TIME FOR LOVE: CARDINALS ☐

Comments:　　Light Gold Glass Ball, 2-7/8" dia., Dated 1990.A
pair of cardinals perch on evergreen and holly branches.
Caption: "Christmas Is A Beautiful Time To Be In Love."
Artist: Joyce A. Lyle

☐ Purchased 19 __ Pd $____MIB　　NB　　DB　　BNT
☐ Want　　Orig. Ret. $4.75　**NB** $15　　**MIB** Sec. Mkt. **$25**

QX 303-3　　TWELVE DAYS OF CHRISTMAS:
**　　　　　　　SEVEN SWANS A-SWIMMING** ☐

Comments:　　**Seventh in Series**, Acrylic, 3-3/8" tall.
Dated 1990. An etched swan swims on this acrylic teardrop, sym-
bolic of the gifts given on the seventh day. Captions in gold foil.

☐ Purchased 19 __ Pd $____MIB　　NB　　DB　　BNT
☐ Want　　Orig. Ret. $6.75　**NB** $27　　**MIB** Sec. Mkt. **$32**

QX 489-6　　TWENTY-FIVE YEARS TOGETHER ☐

Comments:　　Faceted Glass, 2-9/16" tall, Dated Christmas
1990. The faceted glass heart has a silver caption: "25 Years
Together". **Artist**: Joyce Pattee

☐ Purchased 19 __ Pd $____MIB　　NB　　DB　　BNT
☐ Want　　Orig. Ret. $9.75　**NB** $15　　**MIB** Sec. Mkt. **$20**

QX 492-6　　TWO PEAS IN A POD ☐

Comments:　　Handcrafted, 3-3/4" tall.
This pea pod houses two smiling peas who are looking through
an opening in the pod. Tied with red satin ribbon.
Artist: Patricia Andrews

☐ Purchased 19 __ Pd $____MIB　　NB　　DB　　BNT
☐ Want　　Orig. Ret. $4.75　**NB** $14　　**MIB** Sec. Mkt. **$20**

QX 477-3　　WELCOME, SANTA ☐

Comments:　　Handcrafted, 2-5/8" tall.
Press the candle and Santa starts up the chimney. Caption:
"Welcome Santa" and "With A Wink And A Grin And A Big 'Ho, Ho
Ho,' Santa Drops In With A Christmas Hello!" **Artist:** Ken Crow

☐ Purchased 19 __ Pd $____MIB　　NB　　DB　　BNT
☐ Want　　Orig. Ret. $11.75　**NB** $20　　**MIB** Sec. Mkt. **$25**

QX 463-6　　WINDOWS OF THE WORLD: IRISH ☐

Comments:　　**Sixth and Final in Series**, Handcrafted, 3" tall.
Dated 1990. An Irish child leans out her window to see a lep-
rechaun holding a gift. The caption "Nollaig Shona" means
Merry Christmas. **Artist:** Donna Lee

☐ Purchased 19 __ Pd $____MIB　　NB　　DB　　BNT
☐ Want　　Orig. Ret. $10.75　**NB** $35　　**MIB** Sec. Mkt. **$40**

QX 444-3　　WINTER SURPRISE ☐

Comments:　　**Second in Series**, Handcrafted, 3-1/4" tall.
Dated 1990. Two penguins ice skate on a frozen lake. The
scene is completed by two bottle brush trees and a glittering
blue sky. **Artist:** John Francis (Collin)

☐ Purchased 19 __ Pd $____MIB　　NB　　DB　　BNT
☐ Want　　Orig. Ret. $10.75　**NB** $15　　**MIB** Sec. Mkt. **$20**

Angels we have heard on high!

1990 Miniature Ornament Collection

QXM 568-2
ACORN SQUIRREL
1-3/8" tall. **Artist:** Sharon Pike
Reissued from 1989.
☐ Purchased 19___ Pd $_____
MIB   NB   DB   BNT
☐ Want   Orig. Retail $4.50
NB $8   **MIB** Sec. Mkt. **$12**

QXM 568-6
ACORN WREATH
1-1/4" tall. **Artist:** Ken Crow
☐ Purchased 19___ Pd $_____
MIB   NB   DB   BNT
☐ Want   Orig. Retail $6.00
NB $8   **MIB** Sec. Mkt. **$12**

QXM 565-6
AIR SANTA
1/2" tall, Dated 1990.
☐ Purchased 19___ Pd $_____
MIB   NB   DB   BNT
☐ Want   Orig. Retail $4.50
NB $8   **MIB** Sec. Mkt. **$12.50**

QXM 570-3
BABY'S FIRST CHRISTMAS
Cradle, 1-1/8" tall, Dated 1990.
Artist: John Francis (Collin)
☐ Purchased 19___ Pd $_____
MIB   NB   DB   BNT
☐ Want   Orig. Retail $8.50
NB $15   **MIB** Sec. Mkt. **$20**

QXM 569-6
BASKET BUDDY
1-3/16" tall.
Artist: Anita Marra Rogers
☐ Purchased 19___ Pd $_____
MIB   NB   DB   BNT
☐ Want   Orig. Retail $6.00
NB $10   **MIB** Sec. Mkt. **$15**

QXM 563-3
BEAR HUG
15/16" tall. **Artist:** Don Palmiter
☐ Purchased 19___ Pd $_____
MIB   NB   DB   BNT
☐ Want   Orig. Retail $6.00
NB $7   **MIB** Sec. Mkt. **$14**

QXM 577-6
BRASS BOUQUET
Antiqued Brass Medallion, 1-1/4"
tall. **Artist:** Joyce A. Lyle
☐ Purchased 19___ Pd $_____
MIB   NB   DB   BNT
☐ Want   Orig. Retail $6.00
NB $5   **MIB** Sec. Mkt. **$6.50**

QXM 579-3
BRASS HORN
Etched, Pierced Brass, 3/4" tall,
Dated 1990.
☐ Purchased 19___ Pd $_____
MIB   NB   DB   BNT
☐ Want   Orig. Retail $3.00
NB $4   **MIB** Sec. Mkt. **$7**

QXM 579-6
BRASS PEACE
Filigree Brass, 1-1/4" tall.
☐ Purchased 19___ Pd $_____
MIB   NB   DB   BNT
☐ Want   Orig. Retail $3.00
NB $4   **MIB** Sec. Mkt. **$7**

QXM 578-6
BRASS SANTA   Etched,
Pierced Brass, 1-1/4" tall, Dated
1990. **Artist:** Joyce Pattee
☐ Purchased 19___ Pd $_____
MIB   NB   DB   BNT
☐ Want   Orig. Retail $3.00
NB $5   **MIB** Sec. Mkt. **$9**

QXM 583-3
BRASS YEAR
Etched Brass, 3/4" tall, Dated
1990.
☐ Purchased 19___ Pd $_____
MIB   NB   DB   BNT
☐ Want   Orig. Retail $3.00
NB $5   **MIB** Sec. Mkt. **$8**

QXM 567-3
BUSY CARVER
3/4" tall, Dated 1990.
Artist: Ken Crow
☐ Purchased 19___ Pd $_____
MIB   NB   DB   BNT
☐ Want   Orig. Retail $4.50
NB $7   **MIB** Sec. Mkt. **$6**

QXM 563-6
CHRISTMAS DOVE
1-1/16" tall. **Artist:** Bob Siedler
☐ Purchased 19___ Pd $_____
MIB   NB   DB   BNT
☐ Want   Orig. Retail $4.50
NB $8   **MIB** Sec. Mkt. **$15**

QXM 553-3
CLOISONNÉ POINSETTIA
Precious Edition,
Cloisonné/Brass, 1" dia.
Artist: LaDene Votruba
☐ Purchased 19___ Pd $_____
MIB   NB   DB   BNT
☐ Want   Orig. Retail $10.50
NB $10   **MIB** Sec. Mkt. **$13**

QXM 569-3
COUNTRY HEART
1-3/8" tall.
Artist: Anita Marra Rogers
☐ Purchased 19___ Pd $_____
MIB   NB   DB   BNT
☐ Want   Orig. Retail $4.50
NB $5   **MIB** Sec. Mkt. **$10**

QXM 573-5
COZY SKATER
1-3/8" tall. **Artist:** Joyce A. Lyle.
Reissued from 1989.
☐ Purchased 19___ Pd $_____
MIB   NB   DB   BNT
☐ Want   Orig. Retail $4.50
NB $9   **MIB** Sec. Mkt. **$13**

QXC 560-3
CROWN PRINCE: KEEPSAKE CLUB
1-3/8" tall, Dated 1990.
Artist: Anita Marra Rogers
☐ Purchased 19___ Pd $_____
MIB   NB   DB   BNT
☐ Want   Orig. Retail --- Gift to all Club Members
NB $24   **MIB** Sec. Mkt. **$35**

QXM 578-3
FESTIVE ANGEL TREE TOPPER
Glass/Brass.
☐ Purchased 19___ Pd $_____
MIB   NB   DB   BNT
☐ Want   Orig. Retail $9.75
NB $44   **MIB** Sec. Mkt. **$50**

QXM 553-6
FIRST CHRISTMAS TOGETHER
Hand-Painted Fine Porcelain,
1" tall, Dated 1990.
Artist: Patricia Andrews
☐ Purchased 19___ Pd $_____
MIB   NB   DB   BNT
☐ Want   Orig. Retail $6.00
NB $7   **MIB** Sec. Mkt. **$15**

QXM 568-3
GOING SLEDDING
13/16" tall. **Artist:** Julia Lee
☐ Purchased 19___ Pd $_____
MIB   NB   DB   BNT
☐ Want   Orig. Retail $4.50
NB $10   **MIB** Sec. Mkt. **$15**

QXM 572-3
GRANDCHILD'S FIRST CHRISTMAS, 1990
High Chair, 1-1/4" tall.
Artist: Bob Siedler
☐ Purchased 19___ Pd $_____
MIB   NB   DB   BNT
☐ Want   Orig. Retail $6.00
NB $7   **MIB** Sec. Mkt. **$12**

QXM 566-2
HAPPY BLUEBIRD
7/8" tall. **Artist:** Anita Marra
Rogers, Reissued from 1989.
☐ Purchased 19___ Pd $_____
MIB   NB   DB   BNT
☐ Want   Orig. Retail $4.50
NB $11   **MIB** Sec. Mkt. **$15**

QXM 552-6
HOLIDAY CARDINAL
Faceted, Etched Acrylic, 1-1/2"
tall. **Artist:** John Francis (Collin)
☐ Purchased 19___ Pd $_____
MIB   NB   DB   BNT
☐ Want   Orig. Retail $3.00
NB $4   **MIB** Sec. Mkt. **$10**

QXM 573-6
KITTENS IN TOYLAND: SAILBOAT
Third in Series, 13/16" tall.
Artist: Ken Crow
☐ Purchased 19___ Pd $_____
MIB   NB   DB   BNT
☐ Want   Orig. Retail $4.50
NB $14   **MIB** Sec. Mrk. **$20**

QXM 575-3
KRINGLES, THE
Second in Series, 1" tall.
Artist: Anita Marra Rogers
☐ Purchased 19___ Pd $_____
MIB   NB   DB   BNT
☐ Want   Orig. Retail $6.00
NB $23   **MIB** Sec. Mkt. **$30**

QXM 567-6
LION & LAMB,
1-1/8" tall, Wood.
Artist: Linda Sickman
☐ Purchased 19___ Pd $_____
MIB   NB   DB   BNT
☐ Want   Orig. Retail $4.50
NB $5   **MIB** Sec. Mkt. **$10**

XPR 972-3
LITTLE FROSTY FRIENDS: LITTLE BEAR
1" tall, Dated 1990.
Artist: Bob Siedler
☐ Purchased 19___ Pd $_____
MIB   NB   DB   BNT
☐ Want   Orig. Retail $2.95
w/$5 purchase
NB $5   **MIB** Sec. Mkt. **$10**

XPR 972-0
LITTLE FROSTY FRIENDS: LITTLE FROSTY
1-7/16" tall, Dated 1990.
Artist: Bob Siedler
☐ Purchased 19___ Pd $_____
MIB   NB   DB   BNT
☐ Want   Orig. Retail $2.95
w/$5 purchase
NB $5   **MIB** Sec. Mkt. **$10**

XPR 972-2
LITTLE FROSTY FRIENDS: LITTLE HUSKY
1-1/8" tall, Dated 1990.
Artist: Ed Seale
☐ Purchased 19___ Pd $_____
MIB   NB   DB   BNT
☐ Want   Orig. Retail $2.95
w/$5 purchase
NB $4   **MIB** Sec. Mkt. **$9.50**

XPR 972-1
LITTLE FROSTY FRIENDS: LITTLE SEAL
1-1/8" tall, Dated 1990.
Artist: Julia Lee
☐ Purchased 19___ Pd $_____
MIB   NB   DB   BNT
☐ Want   Orig. Retail $2.95
w/$5 purchase
NB $4   **MIB** Sec. Mkt. **$9**

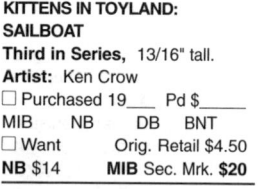
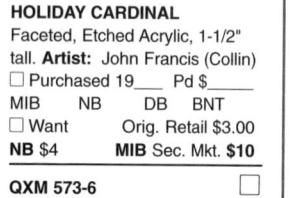

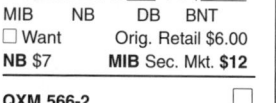

XPR 972-4
LITTLE FROSTY FRIENDS: MEMORY WREATH
5" dia., Dated 1990.
Artist: Donna Lee
☐ Purchased 19___ Pd $_____
MIB   NB   DB   BNT
☐ Want   Orig. Retail $2.95
w/ purch.
NB $5   **MIB** Sec. Mkt. **$10**

QXM 567-5
LITTLE SOLDIER
1-3/8" tall. **Artist:** Linda Sickman, Reissued from 1989.
☐ Purchased 19___ Pd $_____
MIB   NB   DB   BNT
☐ Want   Orig. Retail $4.50
NB $6   **MIB** Sec. Mkt. **$10**

QXM 552-3
LOVING HEARTS
Faceted Acrylic, 1-1/4" tall.
☐ Purchased 19___ Pd $_____
MIB   NB   DB   BNT
☐ Want   Orig. Retail $3.00
NB $4   **MIB** Sec. Mkt. **$10**

QXM 564-3
MADONNA AND CHILD
1-1/4" tall.
Artist: Anita Marra Rogers
☐ Purchased 19___ Pd $_____
MIB   NB   DB   BNT
☐ Want   Orig. Retail $6.00
NB $10   **MIB** Sec. Mkt. **$12**

QXM 571-6
MOTHER
Rose Cameo, 1-1/8", Dated 1990.
Artist: Joyce A. Lyle
☐ Purchased 19___ Pd $_____
MIB   NB   DB   BNT
☐ Want   Orig. Retail $4.50
NB $10   **MIB** Sec. Mkt. **$18**

QXM 570-6
NATIVITY
1-3/8" tall, Dated 1990.
Artist: Duane Unruh
☐ Purchased 19___ Pd $_____
MIB   NB   DB   BNT
☐ Want   Orig. Retail $4.50
NB $15   **MIB** Sec. Mkt. **$20**

QXM 573-3
NATURE'S ANGELS: BUNNY
FIRST IN SERIES, 1-1/4" tall.
Artist: Ed Seale
☐ Purchased 19___ Pd $_____
MIB   NB   DB   BNT
☐ Want   Orig. Retail $4.50
NB $15   **MIB** Sec. Mkt. **$26**

QXM 575-6
NOEL R.R.: COAL CAR
Second in Series, 3/4" tall, Dated 1990.
Artist: Linda Sickman
☐ Purchased 19___ Pd $_____
MIB   NB   DB   BNT
☐ Want   Orig. Retail $8.50
NB $28   **MIB** Sec. Mkt. **$34**

QXM 576-3
OLD ENGLISH VILLAGE: SCHOOL
Third in Series, 1-1/8" tall, Dated 1990. **Artist:** Julia Lee
☐ Purchased 19___ Pd $_____
MIB   NB   DB   BNT
☐ Want   Orig. Retail $8.50
NB $18   **MIB** Sec. Mkt. **$25**

QXM 569-5
OLD WORLD SANTA
1-3/8" tall. **Artist:** Bob Siedler, Reissued from 1989.
☐ Purchased 19___ Pd $_____
MIB   NB   DB   BNT
☐ Want   Orig. Retail $3.00
NB $5   **MIB** Sec. Mkt. **$10**

QXM 561-6
PANDA'S SURPRISE
7/8" tall, Dated 1990.
Artist: John Francis (Collin)
☐ Purchased 19___ Pd $_____
MIB   NB   DB   BNT
☐ Want   Orig. Retail $4.50
NB $7   **MIB** Sec. Mkt. **$14**

QXM 574-6
PENGUIN PAL
Third in Series, 7/8" tall.
☐ Purchased 19___ Pd $_____
MIB   NB   DB   BNT
☐ Want   Orig. Retail $4.50
NB $15   **MIB** Sec. Mkt. **$20**

QXM 551-6
PERFECT FIT
15/16" tall, Dated 1990.
Artist: Robert Chad
☐ Purchased 19___ Pd $_____
MIB   NB   DB   BNT
☐ Want   Orig. Retail $4.50
NB $9   **MIB** Sec. Mkt. **$13**

QXM 566-6
PUPPY LOVE
1" tall. **Artist:** Don Palmiter
☐ Purchased 19___ Pd $_____
MIB   NB   DB   BNT
☐ Want   Orig. Retail $6.00
NB $6   **MIB** Sec. Mkt. **$12**

QXM 574-3
ROCKING HORSE: PINTO
Third in Series, 1-1/8" tall, Dated 1990.
Artist: Linda Sickman
☐ Purchased 19___ Pd $_____
MIB   NB   DB   BNT
☐ Want   Orig. Retail $4.50
NB $20   **MIB** Sec. Mkt. **$25**

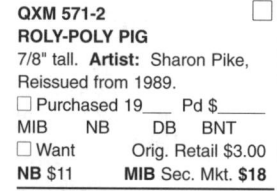
QXM 571-2
ROLY-POLY PIG
7/8" tall. **Artist:** Sharon Pike,
Reissued from 1989.
☐ Purchased 19___ Pd $_____
MIB   NB   DB   BNT
☐ Want   Orig. Retail $3.00
NB $11   **MIB** Sec. Mkt. **$18**

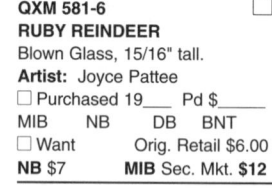
QXM 581-6
RUBY REINDEER
Blown Glass, 15/16" tall.
Artist: Joyce Pattee
☐ Purchased 19___ Pd $_____
MIB   NB   DB   BNT
☐ Want   Orig. Retail $6.00
NB $7   **MIB** Sec. Mkt. **$12**

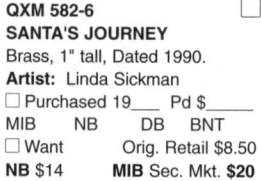
QXM 582-6
SANTA'S JOURNEY
Brass, 1" tall, Dated 1990.
Artist: Linda Sickman
☐ Purchased 19___ Pd $_____
MIB   NB   DB   BNT
☐ Want   Orig. Retail $8.50
NB $14   **MIB** Sec. Mkt. **$20**

QXM 576-6
SANTA'S STREETCAR
1-1/4" wide, Dated 1990.
Artist: Donna Lee
☐ Purchased 19___ Pd $_____
MIB   NB   DB   BNT
☐ Want   Orig. Retail $8.50
NB $15   **MIB** Sec. Mkt. **$20**

QXM 577-3
SNOW ANGEL
1-1/8" tall. **Artist:** Julia Lee
☐ Purchased 19___ Pd $_____
MIB   NB   DB   BNT
☐ Want   Orig. Retail $6.00
NB $11   **MIB** Sec. Mkt. **$15**

QXM 572-6
SPECIAL FRIENDS
15/16" tall.
Artist: Sharon Pike
☐ Purchased 19___ Pd $_____
MIB   NB   DB   BNT
☐ Want   Orig. Retail $6.00
NB $9   **MIB** Sec. Mkt. **$14**

QXM 562-3
STAMP COLLECTOR
7/8" tall. Dated Christmas 1990.
Artist: Ken Crow
☐ Purchased 19___ Pd $_____
MIB   NB   DB   BNT
☐ Want   Orig. Retail $4.50
NB $7   **MIB** Sec. Mkt. **$10**

QXM 560-6
STRINGING ALONG
1-1/8" tall.
Artist: Ed Seale
☐ Purchased 19___ Pd $_____
MIB   NB   DB   BNT
☐ Want   Orig. Retail $8.50
NB $14   **MIB** Sec. Mkt. **$18**

QXM 567-2
STOCKING PAL
1" tall. **Artist:** Julia Lee,
Reissued from 1989.
☐ Purchased 19___ Pd $_____
MIB   NB   DB   BNT
☐ Want   Orig. Retail $4.50
NB $7   **MIB** Sec. Mkt. **$10**

QXM 566-3
SWEET SLUMBER
9/16" tall.
Artist: Bob Siedler
☐ Purchased 19___ Pd $_____
MIB   NB   DB   BNT
☐ Want   Orig. Retail $4.50
NB $7   **MIB** Sec. Mkt. **$10**

QXM 565-3
TEACHER
7/8" tall, Dated 1990.
Artist: Sharon Pike
☐ Purchased 19___ Pd $_____
MIB   NB   DB   BNT
☐ Want   Orig. Retail $4.50
NB $7   **MIB** Sec. Mkt. **$10**

QXM 554-3
THIMBLE BELLS
FIRST IN SERIES, Fine
Porcelain, 1-1/8" tall, Dated 1990.
Artist: Michele Pyda-Sevcik
☐ Purchased 19___ Pd $_____
MIB   NB   DB   BNT
☐ Want   Orig. Retail $6.00
NB $12   **MIB** Sec. Mkt. **$18**

QXM 564-6
TYPE OF JOY
11/16" tall.
Artist: Robert Chad
☐ Purchased 19___ Pd $_____
MIB   NB   DB   BNT
☐ Want   Orig. Retail $4.50
NB $5   **MIB** Sec. Mkt. **$10**

QXM 571-3
WARM MEMORIES
1-1/8" tall, Dated 1990.
Artist: Ed Seale
☐ Purchased 19___ Pd $_____
MIB   NB   DB   BNT
☐ Want   Orig. Retail $4.50
NB $8   **MIB** Sec. Mkt. **$11**

QXM 584-3
WEE NUTCRACKER
1-1/4" tall, Dated 1990.
Artist: Bob Siedler
☐ Purchased 19___ Pd $_____
MIB   NB   DB   BNT
☐ Want   Orig. Retail $8.50
NB $10   **MIB** Sec. Mkt. **$15**

1991 Collection

QX 488-7 A CHILD'S CHRISTMAS ☐
Comments: Handcrafted, 2-3/8" tall, Dated 1991.
A wide-eyed child with his old-fashioned
wood-style blocks is seated on a braided rug captioned "A
Child's Christmas." **Artist:** John Francis (Collin)
☐ Purchased 19 __Pd $____MIB   NB   DB   BNT
☐ Want   Orig. Ret. $9.75   **NB** $12   **MIB** Sec. Mkt. **$18**

QX 499-7 A CHRISTMAS CAROL COLLECTION: ☐
BOB CRATCHIT
Comments: Hand-Painted Fine Porcelain, 3-15/16" tall.
Caption: "Bob Cratchit 1991." Holding a Ledger and quill pen,
Bob Cratchit wears the dress of a Victorian bookkeeper.
Artist: Duane Unruh
☐ Purchased 19 __Pd $____MIB   NB   DB   BNT
☐ Want   Orig. Ret. $13.75   **NB** $22   **MIB** Sec. Mkt. **$36**

QX 498-9 A CHRISTMAS CAROL COLLECTION: ☐
EBENEZER SCROOGE
Comments: Hand-Painted Fine Porcelain, 4-1/16" tall.
Caption: "Ebenezer Scrooge 1991." A content, smiling Scrooge
has found the real source of happiness in giving to others.
Artist: Duane Unruh
☐ Purchased 19 __Pd $____MIB   NB   DB   BNT
☐ Want   Orig. Ret. $13.75   **NB** $30   **MIB** Sec. Mkt. **$46**

QX 479-9 A CHRISTMAS CAROL COLLECTION: ☐
MERRY CAROLERS
Comments: Hand-Painted Fine Porcelain, 4-1/8" tall.
Caption: "Merry Carolers 1991." A man and woman sing the
story of Christmas. Caption on pages: "Joy To The World! The
Lord Is Come." **Artist:** Duane Unruh
☐ Purchased 19 __Pd $____MIB   NB   DB   BNT
☐ Want   Orig. Ret. $29.75   **NB** $73   **MIB** Sec. Mkt. **$90**

QX 499-9 A CHRISTMAS CAROL COLLECTION: ☐
MRS. CRATCHIT
Comments: Hand-Painted Fine Porcelain, 3-7/8" tall.
Caption: "Mrs. Cratchit 1991." In a ruffled dress, Mrs. Cratchit
serves a Christmas turkey provided by a generous Scrooge.
Artist: Duane Unruh
☐ Purchased 19 __Pd $____MIB   NB   DB   BNT
☐ Want   Orig. Ret. $13.75   **NB** $27   **MIB** Sec. Mkt. **$33**

QX 503-7 A CHRISTMAS CAROL COLLECTION: ☐
TINY TIM
Comments: Hand-Painted Fine Porcelain, 2-1/8" tall.
Caption: "Tiny Tim 1991." The child sits on a wooden bench with
his crutches nearby. **Artist:** Duane Unruh
☐ Purchased 19 __Pd $____MIB   NB   DB   BNT
☐ Want   Orig. Ret. $10.75   **NB** $30   **MIB** Sec. Mkt. **$40**

QX 315-7 ACROSS THE MILES ☐
Comments: Acrylic, 2-5/8" tall, Dated 1991.
Sparkling acrylic, framed in brass, is etched with holly leaves
and ribbons. "There's No Such Thing As Far Away When
Christmas Draws Us Close." **Artist:** Joyce Lyle
☐ Purchased 19 __Pd $____MIB   NB   DB   BNT
☐ Want   Orig. Ret. $6.75   **NB** $8   **MIB** Sec. Mkt. **$15**

QX 532-9 ALL STAR ☐
Comments: Handcrafted, 2-1/8" tall, Dated 1991.
This two-toned turtle is "All Star '91" as shown by his umpire's
cap and his catcher's mitt. **Artist:** Bob Siedler
☐ Purchased 19 __Pd $____MIB   NB   DB   BNT
☐ Want   Orig. Ret. $6.75   **NB** $5   **MIB** Sec. Mkt. **$10**

QLX 711-7 ARCTIC DOME ☐
Comments: Light and Motion, Handcrafted, 2-15/16" tall.
Dated 1991. Santa and his North Stars reindeer are playing the
polar bear South Paws. The lines move back and forth across the
field and Santa spins away from the defenders. **Artist:** Ken Crow
☐ Purchased 19 __Pd $____MIB   NB   DB   BNT
☐ Want   Orig. Ret. $25.00   **NB** $40   **MIB** Sec. Mkt. **$55**

QX 510-7 BABY'S FIRST CHRISTMAS ☐
Comments: Silver-Plated, 2-5/8" tall, Dated 1991.
An intricately sculpted bear peeks out of the top of a baby
bootie. A silver tag detaches for engraving and personalization.
Artist: John Francis (Collin)
☐ Purchased 19 __Pd $____MIB   NB   DB   BNT
☐ Want   Orig. Ret. $17.75   **NB** $42   **MIB** Sec. Mkt. **$50**

QLX 724-7 BABY'S FIRST CHRISTMAS ☐
Comments: Lighted, Handcrafted, 4-1/2" tall, Dated 1991.
Santa takes time from his busy schedule. Plays "Rock-A-Bye-
Baby." Caption: "Baby's First Christmas" and "Rock-A-Bye-
Baby." **Artist:** Ed Seale
☐ Purchased 19 __Pd $____MIB   NB   DB   BNT
☐ Want   Orig. Ret. $30.00   **NB** $89   **MIB** Sec. Mkt. **$100**

QX 488-9 BABY'S FIRST CHRISTMAS ☐
Comments: Handcrafted, 2-1/2" tall, Dated 1991.
This adorable teddy hugs his big candy cane "1." His flocked cap says "Baby's First Christmas." **Artist:** John Francis (Collin)
☐ Purchased 19 __Pd $____MIB   NB   DB   BNT
☐ Want   Orig. Ret. $7.75   **NB** $27 **MIB** Sec. Mkt. **$34**

QX 221-7   BABY'S FIRST CHRISTMAS: BABY BOY ☐
Comments: Blue Satin Ball, 2-7/8" dia., Dated 1991.
Caption: "A Baby Boy's World... Soft With Lullabies, Sweet With Hugs, Bright With Wonder, Warm With Love. Baby's First Christmas." **Artist:** Mary Hamilton
☐ Purchased 19 __Pd $____MIB   NB   DB   BNT
☐ Want   Orig. Ret. $4.75   **NB** $18 **MIB** Sec. Mkt. **$20**

QX 222-7   BABY'S FIRST CHRISTMAS: BABY GIRL ☐
Comments: Pink Satin Ball, 2-7/8" dia., Dated 1991.
Caption: "A Baby Girl's World... Soft With Lullabies, Sweet With Hugs, Bright With Wonder, Warm With Love. Baby's First Christmas." **Artist:** Mary Hamilton
☐ Purchased 19 __Pd $____MIB   NB   DB   BNT
☐ Want   Orig. Ret. $4.75   **NB** $15 **MIB** Sec. Mkt. **$20**

QX 486-9   BABY'S FIRST CHRISTMAS
PHOTOHOLDER ☐
Comments: Fabric, 4-3/8" dia., Dated 1991.
Embroidered teddy bears and holly frame baby's photo. Caption: "Baby's First Christmas" and "The Cutest Grins, The Brightest Eyes, Always Come In Baby Size." **Artist:** LaDene Votruba
☐ Purchased 19 __Pd $____MIB   NB   DB   BNT
☐ Want   Orig. Ret. $7.75   **NB** $24 **MIB** Sec. Mkt. **$30**

QX 489-7   BABY'S SECOND CHRISTMAS ☐
Comments: Handcrafted, 2-3/16" tall, Dated 1991.
Identical to 1989; only the date has changed.
Artist: John Francis (Collin)
☐ Purchased 19 __Pd $____MIB   NB   DB   BNT
☐ Want   Orig. Ret. $6.75   **NB** $22 **MIB** Sec. Mkt. **$30**

QX 537-7   BASKET BELL PLAYERS ☐
Comments: Handcrafted and Wicker, 2" tall, Dated 1991.
Two adorable kittens are having fun playing with the shiny brass bell tied to the handle of their basket. **Artist:** Ed Seale
☐ Purchased 19 __Pd $____MIB   NB   DB   BNT
☐ Want   Orig. Ret. $7.75   **NB** $20 **MIB** Sec. Mkt. **$28**

QXC 725-9   BEARY ARTISTIC: KEEPSAKE CLUB ☐
Comments: Lighted, Handcrafted and Acrylic, 2-1/2" tall.
This little bear is carving the word "JOY" from a chunk of "ice." The "O" contains the logo for the Keepsake Ornament® Club. Club Members only. **Artist:** Bob Siedler
☐ Purchased 19 __Pd $____MIB   NB   DB   BNT
☐ Want   Orig. Ret. $10.00   **NB** $30 **MIB** Sec. Mkt. **$40**

QX 210-9   BETSEY CLARK: HOME FOR CHRISTMAS ☐
Comments: **Sixth and Final in Series,** Dated 1991.
Light Blue Glass Ball, 2-7/8" dia. Betsey and her friends love the snow! Caption: "Getting Favorite Friends Together Is Extra Fun In Frosty Weather!" The box notes a new series will begin in 1992.
☐ Purchased 19 __Pd $____MIB   NB   DB   BNT
☐ Want   Orig. Ret. $5.00   **NB** $25 **MIB** Sec. Mkt. **$30**

QX 532-7   BIG CHEESE, THE ☐
Comments: Handcrafted, 1-7/8" tall.
Dated Merry Christmas 1991. "The Big Cheese" has stuffed himself with Swiss cheese and has curled up in the hole he has nibbled. **Artist:** Bob Siedler
☐ Purchased 19 __Pd $____MIB   NB   DB   BNT
☐ Want   Orig. Ret. $6.75   **NB** $14 **MIB** Sec. Mkt. **$20**

QLX 724-9   BRINGING HOME THE TREE ☐
Comments: Light and Motion, Handcrafted, 4-3/8" tall.
Dated 1991. A man and child emerge from the forest with their tree. The door to the home swings open and they go inside, their dog following closely behind. Caption: "Merry Christmas."
Artist: Duane Unruh
☐ Purchased 19 __Pd $____MIB   NB   DB   BNT
☐ Want   Orig. Ret. $28.00   **NB** $55 **MIB** Sec. Mkt. **$70**

QX 547-9   BROTHER ☐
Comments: Handcrafted, 2-3/4" tall, Dated 1991.
Designed especially for a "Superstar Brother" is a puppy hanging onto the rim of the basketball hoop. **Artist:** Bob Siedler
☐ Purchased 19 __Pd $____MIB   NB   DB   BNT
☐ Want   Orig. Ret. $6.75   **NB** $14 **MIB** Sec. Mkt. **$20**

QX 490-9   CHILD'S FIFTH CHRISTMAS ☐
Comments: Handcrafted, 2-3/8" tall, Dated 1991.
Identical to 1989; only the date has changed. **Artist:** Dill Rhodus
☐ Purchased 19 __Pd $____MIB   NB   DB   BNT
☐ Want   Orig. Ret. $6.75   **NB** $14 **MIB** Sec. Mkt. **$20**

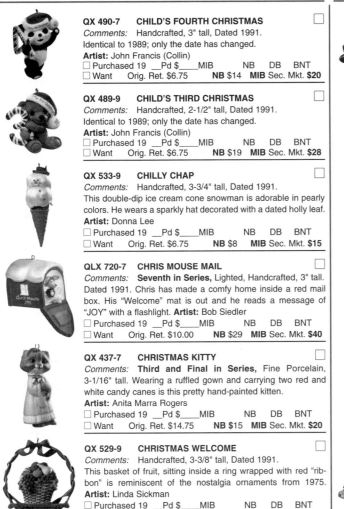

QX 490-7   CHILD'S FOURTH CHRISTMAS ☐
Comments: Handcrafted, 3" tall, Dated 1991.
Identical to 1989; only the date has changed.
Artist: John Francis (Collin)
☐ Purchased 19 __Pd $____MIB   NB   DB   BNT
☐ Want   Orig. Ret. $6.75   **NB** $14   **MIB** Sec. Mkt. **$20**

QX 489-9   CHILD'S THIRD CHRISTMAS ☐
Comments: Handcrafted, 2-1/2" tall, Dated 1991.
Identical to 1989; only the date has changed.
Artist: John Francis (Collin)
☐ Purchased 19 __Pd $____MIB   NB   DB   BNT
☐ Want   Orig. Ret. $6.75   **NB** $19   **MIB** Sec. Mkt. **$28**

QX 533-9   CHILLY CHAP ☐
Comments: Handcrafted, 3-3/4" tall, Dated 1991.
This double-dip ice cream cone snowman is adorable in pearly
colors. He wears a sparkly hat decorated with a dated holly leaf.
Artist: Donna Lee
☐ Purchased 19 __Pd $____MIB   NB   DB   BNT
☐ Want   Orig. Ret. $6.75   **NB** $8   **MIB** Sec. Mkt. **$15**

QLX 720-7   CHRIS MOUSE MAIL ☐
Comments: **Seventh in Series,** Lighted, Handcrafted, 3" tall.
Dated 1991. Chris has made a comfy home inside a red mail
box. His "Welcome" mat is out and he reads a message of
"JOY" with a flashlight. **Artist:** Bob Siedler
☐ Purchased 19 __Pd $____MIB   NB   DB   BNT
☐ Want   Orig. Ret. $10.00   **NB** $29   **MIB** Sec. Mkt. **$40**

QX 437-7   CHRISTMAS KITTY ☐
Comments: **Third and Final in Series,** Fine Porcelain,
3-1/16" tall. Wearing a ruffled gown and carrying two red and
white candy canes is this pretty hand-painted kitten.
Artist: Anita Marra Rogers
☐ Purchased 19 __Pd $____MIB   NB   DB   BNT
☐ Want   Orig. Ret. $14.75   **NB** $15   **MIB** Sec. Mkt. **$20**

QX 529-9   CHRISTMAS WELCOME ☐
Comments: Handcrafted, 3-3/8" tall, Dated 1991.
This basket of fruit, sitting inside a ring wrapped with red "rib-
bon" is reminiscent of the nostalgia ornaments from 1975.
Artist: Linda Sickman
☐ Purchased 19 __Pd $____MIB   NB   DB   BNT
☐ Want   Orig. Ret. $9.75   **NB** $15   **MIB** Sec. Mkt. **$25**

QX 431-9   CLASSIC AMERICAN CARS: 1957 CORVETTE ☐
Comments: **FIRST IN SERIES,** Handcrafted, 1-5/16" tall.
Dated 1991. Very popular. Some are found with green
Christmas tree, some with brown. No difference in value
between the two. **Artist:** Don Palmiter
☐ Purchased 19 __Pd $____MIB   NB   DB   BNT
☐ Want   Orig. Ret. $12.75   **NB** $150
                                  MIB Sec. Mkt. **$175 - $195**

XPR 973-3   CLAUS & CO. R.R. ORNAMENTS: CABOOSE ☐
Comments: Handcrafted, Dated 1991.
Santa waves happily to one and all as the train passes through.
Artist: Don Palmiter
☐ Purchased 19 __Pd $____MIB   NB   DB   BNT
☐ Want   Orig. Ret. $3.95 w/$5 Hallmark purchase.
                              NB $5   **MIB** Sec. Mkt. **$10**

XPR 973-1   CLAUS & CO. R.R. ORNAMENTS: GIFT CAR ☐
Comments: Handcrafted, Dated 1991. **Artist:** Don Palmiter
This coal car carries an overflowing load of brightly wrapped gifts.
☐ Purchased 19 __Pd $____MIB   NB   DB   BNT
☐ Want   Orig. Ret. $3.95 w/$5 Hallmark purchase.
                              NB $5   **MIB** Sec. Mkt. **$15**

**XPR 973-0   CLAUS & CO. R.R. ORNAMENTS:
                LOCOMOTIVE** ☐
Comments: Handcrafted, Dated 1991. **Artist:** Don Palmiter
☐ Purchased 19 __Pd $____MIB   NB   DB   BNT
☐ Want   Orig. Ret. $3.95 w/$5 Hallmark purchase.
                              NB $29   **MIB** Sec. Mkt. **$40**

**XPR 973-2   CLAUS & CO. R.R. ORNAMENTS:
                PASSENGER CAR** ☐
Comments: Handcrafted, Dated 1991. **Artist:** Don Palmiter
☐ Purchased 19 __Pd $____MIB   NB   DB   BNT
☐ Want   Orig. Ret. $3.95 w/$5 Hallmark purchase.
                              NB $5   **MIB** Sec. Mkt. **$10**

XPR 973-4   CLAUS & CO. R.R. ORNAMENTS: TRESTLE ☐
Comments: Handcrafted, Dated 1991. **Artist:** Don Palmiter
Holds four ornament cars in the series. Train cars not included.
☐ Purchased 19 __Pd $____MIB   NB   DB   BNT
☐ Want   Orig. Ret. $2.95 w/any Hallmark purchase
                              NB $5   **MIB** Sec. Mkt. **$10**

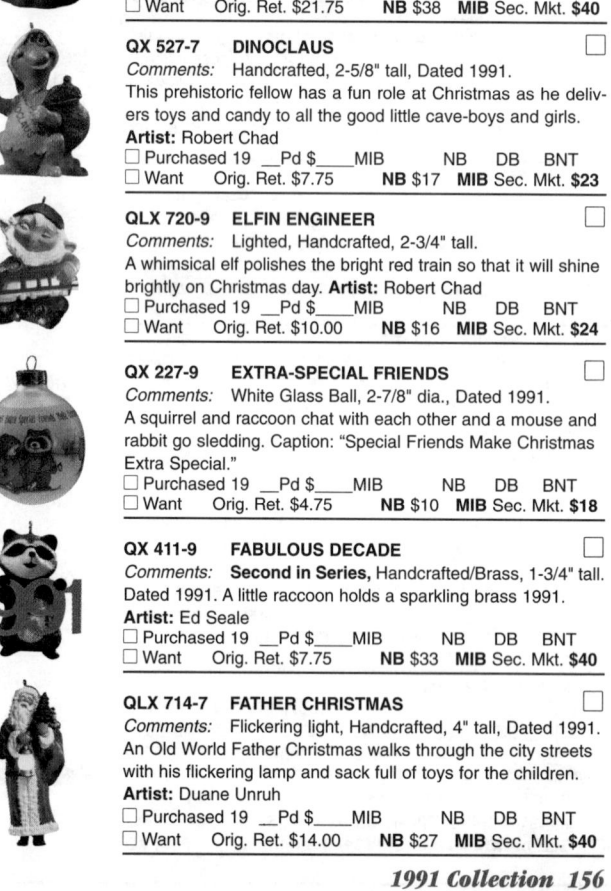

QX 436-9   COLLECTOR'S PLATE: LET IT SNOW ☐
Comments: **Fifth in Series,** Fine Porcelain, 3-1/4" dia.
Dated 1991. Two children and their dog have fun on a snowy
day, building a snowman. **Artist:** LaDene Votruba
☐ Purchased 19 __Pd $____MIB   NB   DB   BNT
☐ Want   Orig. Ret. $8.75   **NB** $21   **MIB** Sec. Mkt. **$30**

QX 421-9   CRAYOLA® CRAYON: ☐
          BRIGHT VIBRANT CAROLS
Comments: **Third in Series,** Handcrafted, 3-1/4" tall.
Dated 1991. A red teddy bear is seated at a pipe organ created
from an open box of crayons. The sheet music is titled "Bright
Vibrant Carols" and the words... "Jingle Bears! Jingle Bears!"
Artist: Ken Crow
☐ Purchased 19 __Pd $____MIB   NB   DB   BNT
☐ Want   Orig. Ret. $9.75   **NB** $29   **MIB** Sec. Mkt. **$40**

QX 519-9   CUDDLY LAMB ☐
Comments: Handcrafted, 1-7/8" tall.
Detailed texturing and white flocking give this lamb the look and
feel of wool. **Artist:** Anita Marra Rogers
☐ Purchased 19 __Pd $____MIB   NB   DB   BNT
☐ Want   Orig. Ret. $6.75   **NB** $15   **MIB** Sec. Mkt. **$20**

QX 512-7   DAD ☐
Comments: Handcrafted, 2-1/4" tall, Dated Dad 1991.
A white polar bear dad, with wrench in hand, reads that it is
"Easy To Assemble!" Unfortunately, the instruction sheet
appears to be complex. **Artist:** Julia Lee
☐ Purchased 19 __Pd $____MIB   NB   DB   BNT
☐ Want   Orig. Ret. $7.75   **NB** $13   **MIB** Sec. Mkt. **$18**

QX 487-9   DAD-TO-BE ☐
Comments: Handcrafted, 2-3/8" tall, Dated Christmas 1991.
This kangaroo papa-to-be proudly announces the fact on his
shirt. **Artist:** Julia Lee
☐ Purchased 19 __Pd $____MIB   NB   DB   BNT
☐Want   Orig. Ret. $5.75   **NB** $10   **MIB** Sec. Mkt. **$18**

QX 547-7   DAUGHTER ☐
Comments: Handcrafted, 3-1/16" tall, Dated Daughter 1991.
A little white mouse with a red hair bow snuggles peacefully in
a pink slipper. **Artist:** Bob Siedler
☐ Purchased 19 __Pd $____MIB   NB   DB   BNT
☐ Want   Orig. Ret. $5.75   **NB** $35   **MIB** Sec. Mkt. **$40**

QX 503-9   DICKENS CAROLER BELL: ☐
          MRS. BEAUMONT
Comments: **Second in Series,** Special Edition, Dated 1991.
Hand-Painted Fine Porcelain, 4-1/4" tall. This lovely Victorian
lady is beautifully detailed and holds an open song book.
Artist: Robert Chad
☐ Purchased 19 __Pd $____MIB   NB   DB   BNT
☐ Want   Orig. Ret. $21.75   **NB** $38   **MIB** Sec. Mkt. **$40**

QX 527-7   DINOCLAUS ☐
Comments: Handcrafted, 2-5/8" tall, Dated 1991.
This prehistoric fellow has a fun role at Christmas as he deliv-
ers toys and candy to all the good little cave-boys and girls.
Artist: Robert Chad
☐ Purchased 19 __Pd $____MIB   NB   DB   BNT
☐ Want   Orig. Ret. $7.75   **NB** $17   **MIB** Sec. Mkt. **$23**

QLX 720-9   ELFIN ENGINEER ☐
Comments: Lighted, Handcrafted, 2-3/4" tall.
A whimsical elf polishes the bright red train so that it will shine
brightly on Christmas day. **Artist:** Robert Chad
☐ Purchased 19 __Pd $____MIB   NB   DB   BNT
☐ Want   Orig. Ret. $10.00   **NB** $16   **MIB** Sec. Mkt. **$24**

QX 227-9   EXTRA-SPECIAL FRIENDS ☐
Comments: White Glass Ball, 2-7/8" dia., Dated 1991.
A squirrel and raccoon chat with each other and a mouse and
rabbit go sledding. Caption: "Special Friends Make Christmas
Extra Special."
☐ Purchased 19 __Pd $____MIB   NB   DB   BNT
☐ Want   Orig. Ret. $4.75   **NB** $10   **MIB** Sec. Mkt. **$18**

QX 411-9   FABULOUS DECADE ☐
Comments: **Second in Series,** Handcrafted/Brass, 1-3/4" tall.
Dated 1991. A little raccoon holds a sparkling brass 1991.
Artist: Ed Seale
☐ Purchased 19 __Pd $____MIB   NB   DB   BNT
☐ Want   Orig. Ret. $7.75   **NB** $33   **MIB** Sec. Mkt. **$40**

QLX 714-7   FATHER CHRISTMAS ☐
Comments: Flickering light, Handcrafted, 4" tall, Dated 1991.
An Old World Father Christmas walks through the city streets
with his flickering lamp and sack full of toys for the children.
Artist: Duane Unruh
☐ Purchased 19 __Pd $____MIB   NB   DB   BNT
☐ Want   Orig. Ret. $14.00   **NB** $27   **MIB** Sec. Mkt. **$40**

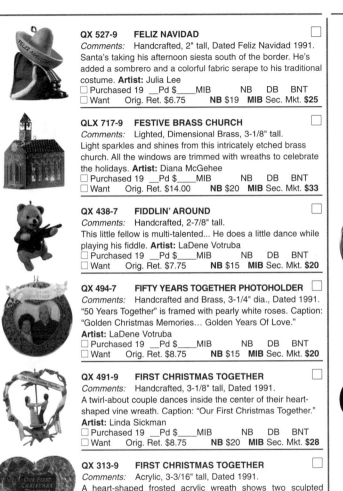

QX 527-9 FELIZ NAVIDAD
Comments: Handcrafted, 2" tall, Dated Feliz Navidad 1991. Santa's taking his afternoon siesta south of the border. He's added a sombrero and a colorful fabric serape to his traditional costume. **Artist:** Julia Lee
☐ Purchased 19 __Pd $____MIB   NB   DB   BNT
☐ Want   Orig. Ret. $6.75   **NB** $19 **MIB** Sec. Mkt. **$25**

QLX 717-9 FESTIVE BRASS CHURCH
Comments: Lighted, Dimensional Brass, 3-1/8" tall. Light sparkles and shines from this intricately etched brass church. All the windows are trimmed with wreaths to celebrate the holidays. **Artist:** Diana McGehee
☐ Purchased 19 __Pd $____MIB   NB   DB   BNT
☐ Want   Orig. Ret. $14.00   **NB** $20 **MIB** Sec. Mkt. **$33**

QX 438-7 FIDDLIN' AROUND
Comments: Handcrafted, 2-7/8" tall. This little fellow is multi-talented... He does a little dance while playing his fiddle. **Artist:** LaDene Votruba
☐ Purchased 19 __Pd $____MIB   NB   DB   BNT
☐ Want   Orig. Ret. $7.75   **NB** $15 **MIB** Sec. Mkt. **$20**

QX 494-7 FIFTY YEARS TOGETHER PHOTOHOLDER
Comments: Handcrafted and Brass, 3-1/4" dia., Dated 1991. "50 Years Together" is framed with pearly white roses. Caption: "Golden Christmas Memories… Golden Years Of Love."
Artist: LaDene Votruba
☐ Purchased 19 __Pd $____MIB   NB   DB   BNT
☐ Want   Orig. Ret. $8.75   **NB** $15 **MIB** Sec. Mkt. **$20**

QX 491-9 FIRST CHRISTMAS TOGETHER
Comments: Handcrafted, 3-1/8" tall, Dated 1991. A twirl-about couple dances inside the center of their heart-shaped vine wreath. Caption: "Our First Christmas Together."
Artist: Linda Sickman
☐ Purchased 19 __Pd $____MIB   NB   DB   BNT
☐ Want   Orig. Ret. $8.75   **NB** $20 **MIB** Sec. Mkt. **$28**

QX 313-9 FIRST CHRISTMAS TOGETHER
Comments: Acrylic, 3-3/16" tall, Dated 1991. A heart-shaped frosted acrylic wreath shows two sculpted doves and the caption in gold foil: "Our First Christmas Together." **Artist:** Sharon Pike
☐ Purchased 19 __Pd $____MIB   NB   DB   BNT
☐ Want   Orig. Ret. $6.75   **NB** $12 **MIB** Sec. Mkt. **$25**

QX 222-9 FIRST CHRISTMAS TOGETHER
Comments: White Glass Ball, 2-7/8" dia., Dated 1991. A romantic Victorian couple is ice skating. Caption: "Our First Christmas Together" and "Christmas Is For Sharing With The Special One You Love."
☐ Purchased 19 __Pd $____MIB   NB   DB   BNT
☐ Want   Orig. Ret. $4.75   **NB** $10 **MIB** Sec. Mkt. **$20**

QLX 713-7 FIRST CHRISTMAS TOGETHER
Comments: Light and Motion, Handcrafted, 4-1/8" tall. Dated 1991. A large red heart proclaims "Our First Christmas Together" as a loving teddy bear couple snuggle in a swan-shaped car at the "Tunnel of Love." **Artist:** Linda Sickman
☐ Purchased 19 __Pd $____MIB   NB   DB   BNT
☐ Want   Orig. Ret. $25.00   **NB** $45 **MIB** Sec. Mkt. **$60**

QX 491-7 FIRST CHRISTMAS TOGETHER PHOTOHOLDER
Comments: Handcrafted and Brass, 3-1/4" dia., Dated 1991. "1st Christmas Together" written on a banner is carried by two ivory doves. Caption: "Of Life's Many Treasures, The Most Beautiful Is Love." **Artist:** LaDene Votruba
☐ Purchased 19 __Pd $____MIB   NB   DB   BNT
☐ Want   Orig. Ret. $8.75   **NB** $24 **MIB** Sec. Mkt. **$30**

QX 492-7 FIVE YEARS TOGETHER
Comments: Faceted Glass, 2-9/16" tall, Dated 1991. Caption in red foil.
☐ Purchased 19 __Pd $____MIB   NB   DB   BNT
☐ Want   Orig. Ret. $7.75   **NB** $10 **MIB** Sec. Mkt. **$20**

QXC 315-9 FIVE YEARS TOGETHER: KEEPSAKE CLUB CHARTER MEMBER
Comments: Acrylic, 3" tall, Dated 1991. A red quatrefoil with gold lettering has the Keepsake Ornament® Club logo and "Charter Member, Five Years Together."
☐ Purchased 19 __Pd $____MIB   NB   DB   BNT
☐ Want   Price: Free Gift to Charter Members
       NB $25 **MIB** Sec. Mkt. **$45**

QX 535-9 FOLK ART REINDEER
Comments: Hand Painted Wood and Brass, 2-5/16" tall. Dated 1991. This hand-carved, hand-painted reindeer is wearing a collar with the date in brass. No two ornaments will be exactly alike. **Artist:** LaDene Votruba
☐ Purchased 19 __Pd $____MIB   NB   DB   BNT
☐ Want   Orig. Ret. $8.75   **NB** $15 **MIB** Sec. Mkt. **$20**

QLX 721-9   FOREST FROLICS
Comments: **Third in Series,** Light and Motion, Dated 1991.
Handcrafted, 4-1/2" tall. As the "stage" revolves, it appears that
each member of the ice show is skating in a circle. Caption:
"Merry Christmas." **Artist:** Sharon Pike
☐ Purchased 19 __Pd $____MIB   NB   DB   BNT
☐ Want   Orig. Ret. $25.00   **NB** $59   **MIB** Sec. Mkt. **$70**

QX 493-9   FORTY YEARS TOGETHER
Comments: Faceted Glass, 2-9/16" tall, Dated 1991.
Identical to 1990 with date change.
☐ Purchased 19 __Pd $____MIB   NB   DB   BNT
☐ Want   Orig. Ret. $7.75   **NB** $12   **MIB** Sec. Mkt. **$20**

QX 528-9   FRIENDS ARE FUN
Comments: Handcrafted, 2-15/16" tall.
Dated Christmas 1991. Give one of these bunnies a push on
the teeter-totter and they move up and down; the package
moves back and forth. Caption: "Friends Are For Fun!"
Artist: Ken Crow
☐ Purchased 19 __Pd $____MIB   NB   DB   BNT
☐ Want   Orig. Ret. $9.75   **NB** $15   **MIB** Sec. Mkt. **$25**

QLX 716-9   FRIENDSHIP TREE
Comments: Lighted, Handcrafted, 3-1/8" tall, Dated 1991.
Sharing homes in the same snow-covered tree makes it easy to
exchange gifts. **Artist:** Peter Dutkin
☐ Purchased 19 __Pd $____MIB   NB   DB   BNT
☐ Want   Orig. Ret. $10.00   **NB** $14   **MIB** Sec. Mkt. **$25**

QX 228-7   FROM OUR HOME TO YOURS
Comments: Midnight Blue and White Glass Ball, 2-7/8" dia.
Dated Christmas 1991. A bright red cardinal delivers a message
of JOY from the bears to the mice. Caption: "From Our Home
To Yours." **Artist:** LaDene Votruba
☐ Purchased 19 __Pd $____MIB   NB   DB   BNT
☐ Want   Orig. Ret. $4.75   **NB** $18   **MIB** Sec. Mkt. **$23**

QX 432-7   FROSTY FRIENDS
Comments: **Twelfth in Series,** Handcrafted and Acrylic, 1-
7/8" tall. Dated 1991. Ice hockey is fun when you have a little
penguin friend to play with you. **Artist:** Sharon Pike
☐ Purchased 19 __Pd $____MIB   NB   DB   BNT
☐ Want   Orig. Ret. $9.75   **NB** $29   **MIB** Sec. Mkt. **$40**

QXC 477-9   GALLOPING INTO CHRISTMAS:
              KEEPSAKE™ CLUB
Comments: Limited Edition 28,400, Wood Display Stand.
Pressed Tin, 3" tall. A carefully painted and detailed Santa on
horseback rolls along on wheels that move. Available to
Members Only. **Artist:** Linda Sickman
☐ Purchased 19 __Pd $____MIB   NB   DB   BNT
☐ Want   Orig. Ret. $19.75   **NB** $100   **MIB** Sec. Mkt. **$125**

QX 517-7   GARFIELD
Comments: Handcrafted, 3-3/4" tall, Dated 1991.
Garfield is an angel in his brass halo and white wings. He sits
on a dated star. **Artist:** Dill Rhodus
☐ Purchased 19 __Pd $____MIB   NB   DB   BNT
☐ Want   Orig. Ret. $7.75   **NB** $18   **MIB** Sec. Mkt. **$30**

QX 211-7   GIFT BRINGERS, THE: CHRISTKINDL
Comments: **Third in Series,** White Glass Ball, 2-7/8" dia.
Christmas 1991. Symbolizing the Christ Child, Christkindl trav-
els through the countryside on a tiny deer delivering gifts.
Artist: LaDene Votruba
☐ Purchased 19 __Pd $____MIB   NB   DB   BNT
☐ Want   Orig. Ret. $5.00   **NB** $17   **MIB** Sec. Mkt. **$25**

QX 531-9   GIFT OF JOY
Comments: Brass, Chrome and Copper, 4" tall, Christmas
1991. A brass "J," chrome "O" and copper "Y" in die-cut design spell
JOY on all four sides. Each letter revolves. **Artist:** Diana McGehee
☐ Purchased 19 __Pd $____MIB   NB   DB   BNT
☐ Want   Orig. Ret. $8.75   **NB** $16   **MIB** Sec. Mkt. **$25**

QX 548-9   GODCHILD
Comments: Handcrafted, 2-1/16" tall, Dated 1991.
A little angel in white playing her trumpet, is suspended from a
golden banner which reads: "Merry Christmas, Godchild!"
Artist: Ron Bishop
☐ Purchased 19 __Pd $____MIB   NB   DB   BNT
☐ Want   Orig. Ret. $6.75   **NB** $10   **MIB** Sec. Mkt. **$20**

QX 229-9   GRANDDAUGHTER
Comments: Porcelain White Glass Ball, 2-7/8" dia.
Dated Christmas 1991. Knit-look bunnies prance on a pink
background. Caption: "A Granddaughter Is A Special Joy!"
Artist: Michele Pyda-Sevcik
☐ Purchased 19 __Pd $____MIB   NB   DB   BNT
☐ Want   Orig. Ret. $4.75   **NB** $18   **MIB** Sec. Mkt. **$30**

QX 511-9 GRANDDAUGHTER'S FIRST CHRISTMAS ☐
Comments: Handcrafted, 4-1/4" tall, Dated 1991.
A little bear dressed in a pink frock holds a chain of raised letters that spell "Granddaughter." Pink foil caption on her hat says, "My First Christmas." **Artist:** Robert Chad
☐ Purchased 19 __Pd $____MIB   NB   DB   BNT
☐ Want   Orig. Ret. $6.75   **NB** $20   **MIB** Sec. Mkt. **$25**

QX 230-7 GRANDMOTHER ☐
Comments: Light Gold Glass Ball, 2-7/8" dia.
Dated Christmas 1991. Christmas flowers and greenery frame the caption: "A Grandmother Grows Ever More Loving... Ever More Loved."
☐ Purchased 19 __Pd $____MIB   NB   DB   BNT
☐ Want   Orig. Ret. $4.75   **NB** $17   **MIB** Sec. Mkt. **$20**

QX 230-9 GRANDPARENTS ☐
Comments: White Glass Ball, 2-7/8" dia.
Dated Christmas 1991. A wintry village scene. Caption: "Grandparents Add So Many Beautiful Pages To Your Album Of Memories." **Artist:** Michele Pyda-Sevcik
☐ Purchased 19 __Pd $____MIB   NB   DB   BNT
☐ Want   Orig. Ret. $4.75   **NB** $12   **MIB** Sec. Mkt. **$17**

QX 229-7 GRANDSON ☐
Comments: Porcelain White Glass Ball, 2-7/8" dia.
Dated 1991. Resembling hand-knit sweaters, prancing reindeer frame the caption: "A Grandson Makes Christmas Even More Wonderful!" **Artist:** Michele Pyda-Sevcik
☐ Purchased 19 __Pd $____MIB   NB   DB   BNT
☐ Want   Orig. Ret. $4.75   **NB** $15   **MIB** Sec. Mkt. **$25**

QX 511-7 GRANDSON'S FIRST CHRISTMAS ☐
Comments: Handcrafted, 4-1/4" tall, Dated 1991.
Similar to the Granddaughter ornament, this bear is dressed in blue, holding the letters "Grandson." "My First Christmas" is lettered in blue foil. **Artist:** Robert Chad
☐ Purchased 19 __Pd $____MIB   NB   DB   BNT
☐ Want   Orig. Ret. $6.75   **NB** $15   **MIB** Sec. Mkt. **$27**

QX 412-9 GREATEST STORY ☐
Comments: **Second in Series,** Dated 1991.
Fine Bisque Porcelain and Brass, 3-3/4" tall. The shepherds stare in awe at the Star of Bethlehem. **Artist:** LaDene Votruba
☐ Purchased 19 __Pd $____MIB   NB   DB   BNT
☐ Want   Orig. Ret. $12.75   **NB** $18   **MIB** Sec. Mkt. **$27**

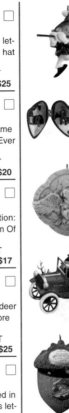

QX 437-9 HARK! IT'S HERALD ☐
Comments: **Third in Series,** Handcrafted, 2" tall, Dated 1991.This year, Herald has decided to try his musical talents with a golden fife. **Artist:** Anita Marra Rogers
☐ Purchased 19 __Pd $____MIB   NB   DB   BNT
☐ Want   Orig. Ret. $6.75   **NB** $16   **MIB** Sec. Mkt. **$20**

QX 435-7 HEART OF CHRISTMAS ☐
Comments: **Second in Series,** Handcrafted, 2" tall.
Dated 1991. A father and son are "bringing home the tree." Mother waves as they near home. Opens locket-style. **Artist:** Ed Seale
☐ Purchased 19 __Pd $____MIB   NB   DB   BNT
☐ Want   Orig. Ret. $13.75   **NB** $23   **MIB** Sec. Mkt. **$27**

QX 436-7 HEAVENLY ANGELS ☐
Comments: **FIRST IN SERIES,** Handcrafted, 3-1/16" tall.
Dated Christmas 1991. A bas relief, baroque style angel has been carved and antiqued. **Artist:** Joyce A. Lyle
☐ Purchased 19 __Pd $____MIB   NB   DB   BNT
☐ Want   Orig. Ret. $7.75   **NB** $12   **MIB** Sec. Mkt. **$18**

QX 434-9 HERE COMES SANTA: SANTA'S ANTIQUE CAR ☐
Comments: **Thirteenth in Series,** Handcrafted, 2-1/4" tall.
Dated 1991. Santa's riding into Christmas in an antique car with a hood ornament resembling reindeer antlers! License plate says "SANTA." **Artist:** Linda Sickman
☐ Purchased 19 __Pd $____MIB   NB   DB   BNT
☐ Want   Orig. Ret. $14.75   **NB** $47   **MIB** Sec. Mkt. **$60**

QXC 476-9 HIDDEN TREASURE/LI'L KEEPER: KEEPSAKE CLUB ☐
Comments: Handcrafted: Acorn 2-1/8 tall; Squirrel 7/8" tall.
Dated 1991. This be-ribboned acorn has a key that turns to reveal more surprises inside. **Artist:** Ken Crow
☐ Purchased 19 __Pd $____MIB   NB   DB   BNT
☐ Want   Price: Came with Club Membership of $20.00
                               NB $26   **MIB** Sec. Mkt. **$38**

QLX 717-7 HOLIDAY GLOW ☐
Comments: Lighted Panorama Ball, 3-3/4" tall.
A puppy and kitten look inside a home decorated for Christmas. Light fills the room inside and highlights the decorations on the tree. **Artist:** Sharon Pike
☐ Purchased 19 __Pd $____MIB   NB   DB   BNT
☐ Want   Orig. Ret. $14.00   **NB** $20   **MIB** Sec. Mkt. **$30**

QX 410-9　HOOKED ON SANTA
Comments:　Handcrafted, 4" tall.
Santa's hooked a big one this time... himself! His hook has gotten caught in his green waders. **Artist:** Julia Lee
☐ Purchased 19 __Pd $____MIB　　NB　DB　BNT
☐ Want　　Orig. Ret. $7.75　　**NB $20**　**MIB** Sec. Mkt. **$25**

QLX 723-7　IT'S A WONDERFUL LIFE
Comments:　Blinking Lights, Handcrafted, 3-3/16" tall.
Dated 1991. A nostalgic movie theater is now showing a classic, It's A Wonderful Life. The marquee proclaims "Happy Holidays" and on a poster: "Coming Soon: A Christmas Carol."
Artist: Donna Lee
☐ Purchased 19 __Pd $____MIB　　NB　DB　BNT
☐ Want　　Orig. Ret. $20.00　　**NB $65**　**MIB** Sec. Mkt. **$80**

QX 314-7　JESUS LOVES ME
Comments:　Blue Cameo, 2-3/4" dia., Christmas 1991.
A baby squirrel kneels beside his bed to say his nighttime prayers. Caption: "Jesus Loves Me." **Artist:** Dill Rhodus
☐ Purchased 19 __Pd $____MIB　　NB　DB　BNT
☐ Want　　Orig. Ret. $7.75　　**NB $12**　**MIB** Sec. Mkt. **$18**

QLX 732-3　JINGLE BEARS
Comments:　Light, Music and Motion, Handcrafted, 4-3/8" tall.
Papa bear plays the tune "Jingle Bells" and mama sways from side to side. Caption: "Happy Family Memories Make The Season Bright." **Artist:** Julia Lee
☐ Purchased 19 __Pd $____MIB　　NB　DB　BNT
☐ Want　　Orig. Ret. $25.00　　**NB $46**　**MIB** Sec. Mkt. **$58**

QX 541-9　JOLLY WOLLY SANTA
Comments:　Handcrafted, 3-3/4" tall, Dated 1991.
With his sack of toys and jingle bells, this whimsical Santa is ready for Christmas. **Artist:** Linda Sickman
☐ Purchased 19 __Pd $____MIB　　NB　DB　BNT
☐ Want　　Orig. Ret. $7.75　　**NB $17**　**MIB** Sec. Mkt. **$23**

QX 542-7　JOLLY WOLLY SNOWMAN
Comments:　Handcrafted, 3-3/4" tall, Dated 1991.
A well-rounded fellow, for sure! The snowman design lithographed on this tin container has a corncob pipe and eyes made out of coal. **Artist:** Linda Sickman
☐ Purchased 19 __Pd $____MIB　　NB　DB　BNT
☐ Want　　Orig. Ret. $7.75　　**NB $17**　**MIB** Sec. Mkt. **$23**

QX 542-9　JOLLY WOLLY SOLDIER
Comments:　Pressed Tin, 3-3/4" tall, Dated 1991.
This tin soldier, dressed in his elaborate red and blue uniform, keeps everyone in step with the beat of his drum.
Artist: Linda Sickman
☐ Purchased 19 __Pd $____MIB　　NB　DB　BNT
☐ Want　　Orig. Ret. $7.75　　**NB $15**　**MIB** Sec. Mkt. **$20**

QX 536-9　JOYOUS MEMORIES PHOTOHOLDER
Comments:　Hand-Painted, Handcrafted, 3-3/8" dia.
Dated 1991. A bas-relief holly design, sculpted and painted white on white, frames a favorite photograph. Caption: "Each Joy Of Christmas Becomes A Precious Memory."
Artist: LaDene Votruba
☐ Purchased 19 __Pd $____MIB　　NB　DB　BNT
☐ Want　　Orig. Ret. $6.75　　**NB $16**　**MIB** Sec. Mkt. **$28**

QLX 711-9　KRINGLE'S BUMPER CARS
Comments:　Blinking Lights and Motion, Handcrafted, 3-3/4" tall. Santa, one of his elves and a reindeer have a bit of fun playing in the bumper cars. **Artist:** Linda Sickman
☐ Purchased 19 __Pd $____MIB　　NB　DB　BNT
☐ Want　　Orig. Ret. $25.00　　**NB $45**　**MIB** Sec. Mkt. **$55**

QX 223-7　MARY ENGELBREIT
Comments:　Porcelain White Glass Ball, 2-7/8" dia.
Dated Christmas 1991. Santa leads a parade of elves, dove, bunny and reindeer. More Engelbreit products debuting may influence her ornament prices.
☐ Purchased 19 __Pd $____MIB　　NB　DB　BNT
☐ Want　　Orig. Ret. $4.75　　**NB $19**　**MIB** Sec. Mkt. **$30**

QX 427-9　MARY'S ANGELS: IRIS
Comments:　**Fourth in Series,** Handcrafted and Acrylic, 2" tall.
Iris sleeps comfortably on her frosted acrylic cloud. She's wearing a lavender dress. This is a popular series.
Artist: Robert Chad
☐ Purchased 19 __Pd $____MIB　　NB　DB　BNT
☐ Want　　Orig. Ret. $6.75　　**NB $22**　**MIB** Sec. Mkt. **$40**

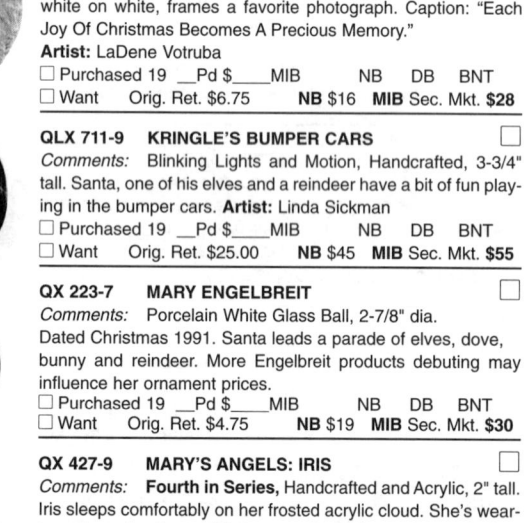

QX 538-9　MATCHBOX MEMORIES: EVERGREEN INN
Comments:　Handcrafted, 1-7/16" tall, Dated 1991.
The proprietor of this country inn looks surprisingly like Santa! Caption: "Evergreen Inn 1991" **Artist:** Ed Seale
☐ Purchased 19 __Pd $____MIB　　NB　DB　BNT
☐ Want　　Orig. Ret. $8.75　　**NB $10**　**MIB** Sec. Mkt. **$15**

QX 539-9   MATCHBOX MEMORIES: HOLIDAY CAFE ☐
Comments: Handcrafted, 1-7/16" tall, Dated 1991.
A couple sit at a table by the window and hold hands. Lettering on the "window" is reversed. **Artist:** Ed Seale
☐ Purchased 19 __Pd $____MIB   NB   DB   BNT
☐ Want   Orig. Ret. $8.75   **NB** $10   **MIB** Sec. Mkt. **$15**

QX 539-7   MATCHBOX MEMORIES: SANTA'S STUDIO ☐
Comments: Handcrafted, 1-7/16" tall, Dated 1991.
Santa chisels and sculpts a likeness of one of his elves. Statue has the appearance of marble. **Artist:** Ed Seale
☐ Purchased 19 __Pd $____MIB   NB   DB   BNT
☐ Want   Orig. Ret. $8.75   **NB** $10   **MIB** Sec. Mkt. **$15**

QX 435-9   MERRY OLDE SANTA ☐
Comments: **Second in Series,** Handcrafted, 4" tall.
Dated 1991. This Old World Santa carries a walking stick with a brass bell to announce his arrival. He wears a long red coat.
Artist: Julia Lee
☐ Purchased 19 __Pd $____MIB   NB   DB   BNT
☐ Want   Orig. Ret. $14.75   **NB** $69   **MIB** Sec. Mkt. **$83**

QLX 714-9   MOLE FAMILY HOME ☐
Comments: Flickering Light, Handcrafted, 3-3/8" tall.
Dated 1991. All that may be seen above ground is a snow-covered tree stump and red door, but underground mother bakes cookies while father and child read a story. **Artist:** Julia Lee
☐ Purchased 19 __Pd $____MIB   NB   DB   BNT
☐ Want   Orig. Ret. $20.00   **NB** $39   **MIB** Sec. Mkt. **$50**

QX 546-7   MOM AND DAD ☐
Comments: Handcrafted, 3-5/8" tall, Dated 1991.
Two raccoons are snuggling together in a real knit stocking. The stocking carries the caption: "Mom And Dad."
☐ Purchased 19 __Pd $____MIB   NB   DB   BNT
☐ Want   Orig. Ret. $9.75   **NB** $15   **MIB** Sec. Mkt. **$24**

QX 487-7   MOM-TO-BE ☐
Comments: Handcrafted, 2-3/8" tall, Dated Christmas 1991.
The lady kangaroo carries a wrapped gift in her pouch. Her sweat shirt reads "Mom-To-Be." **Artist:** Julia Lee
☐ Purchased 19 __Pd $____MIB   NB   DB   BNT
☐ Want   Orig. Ret. $5.75   **NB** $21   **MIB** Sec. Mkt. **$27**

QX 545-7   MOTHER ☐
Comments: Fine Porcelain, Hand-Formed Tin, 3-1/8" tall.
This porcelain pendant is hung by a tin "ribbon." Caption: "Having You For A Mother Is The Nicest Gift Of All" and "Mother, Christmas 1991."
☐ Purchased 19 __Pd $____MIB   NB   DB   BNT
☐ Want   Orig. Ret. $9.75   **NB** $29   **MIB** Sec. Mkt. **$35**

QX 433-9   MR. AND MRS. CLAUS: CHECKING HIS LIST ☐
Comments: **Sixth in Series,** Handcrafted, 3" tall, Dated 1991.
Mrs. Santa holds the list while Santa checks the items and makes sure everything is ready to go. **Artist:** Duane Unruh
☐ Purchased 19 __Pd $____MIB   NB   DB   BNT
☐ Want   Orig. Ret. $13.75   **NB** $34   **MIB** Sec. Mkt. **$50**

QX 544-9   NEW HOME ☐
Comments: Handcrafted, 2-1/4" tall, Dated 1991.
A bright red cardinal perches on the stand outside his bird-house. Caption: "New Home" and "Home... The Place Where Happiness Lives!" **Artist:** Ron Bishop
☐ Purchased 19 __Pd $____MIB   NB   DB   BNT
☐ Want   Orig. Ret. $6.75   **NB** $25   **MIB** Sec. Mkt. **$30**

QX 530-7   NIGHT BEFORE CHRISTMAS ☐
Comments: Handcrafted, 3-1/4" tall, Dated 1991.
Santa turns around and around on a chimney top. Let's see... which house is next? **Artist:** Linda Sickman
☐ Purchased 19 __Pd $____MIB   NB   DB   BNT
☐ Want   Orig. Ret. $9.75   **NB** $16   **MIB** Sec. Mkt. **$25**

QX 486-7   NOAH'S ARK ☐
Comments: Handcrafted, 3" tall, Dated 1991.
Caption: "Joy•Love•Hope•Peace" and "Noah's Ark." When the knob on the side of the ark is turned, the animals move their heads and Noah raises his arm. **Artist:** Ken Crow
☐ Purchased 19 __Pd $____MIB   NB   DB   BNT
☐ Want   Orig. Ret. $13.75   **NB** $40   **MIB** Sec. Mkt. **$50**

QX 225-9   NORMAN ROCKWELL ART ☐
Comments: Lt. Gold Glass Ball, 2-7/8" dia., Christmas 1991.
Caption: "Santa's Wee Helpers Work All Through The Year, But They're Specially Busy As Christmas Draws Near With Last Minute Touches To Finish The Toys And Make Them All Ready For Good Girls and Boys!" **Artist:** Joyce A. Lyle
☐ Purchased 19 __Pd $____MIB   NB   DB   BNT
☐ Want   Orig. Ret. $5.00   **NB** $18   **MIB** Sec. Mkt. **$30**

QX 413-9 NOSTALGIC HOUSES AND SHOPS: FIRE STATION
Comments: **Eighth in Series,** Handcrafted, 4" tall.
Dated 1991. Awaiting the return of the fireman at "Fire Co. 1991" are an old-time fire engine, Christmas tree and two dalmatians. **Artist:** Donna Lee
☐ Purchased 19 __Pd $____MIB NB DB BNT
☐ Want Orig. Ret. $14.75 **NB** $50 **MIB** Sec. Mkt. **$70**

QX 535-7 NOTES OF CHEER
Comments: Handcrafted, 1-3/4" tall, Dated 1991.
This flocked brown bear seems to be asking "any requests?" as he plays his special keyboard. **Artist:** Bob Siedler
☐ Purchased 19 __Pd $____MIB NB DB BNT
☐ Want Orig. Ret. $5.75 **NB** $11 **MIB** Sec. Mkt. **$15**

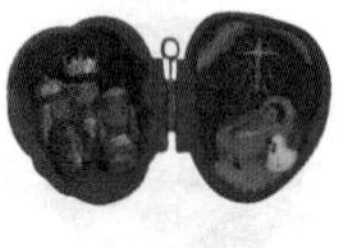

QX 517-6 NUTSHELL NATIVITY
Comments: Handcrafted, 1-7/16" tall.
The three kings (left) kneel before the Baby in the manger (right) and present their gifts. **Artist:** Anita Macra Rogers
☐ Purchased 19 __Pd $____MIB NB DB BNT
☐ Want Orig. Ret. $6.75 **NB** $20 **MIB** Sec. Mkt. **$27**

QX 483-3 NUTTY SQUIRREL
Comments: Handcrafted, 1-3/4" tall.
The detailed sculpting on this little fellow makes him a prize. He Is delivering an acorn tied with a bright red handcrafted bow. **Artist:** Sharon Pike
☐ Purchased 19 __Pd $____MIB NB DB BNT
☐ Want Orig. Ret. $5.75 **NB** $10 **MIB** Sec. Mkt. **$15**

QX 431-7 OLD FASHIONED SLED
Comments: Handcrafted, 1-5/16" tall, Dated 1991.
This authentically detailed sled pictures winter scenery. Tiny gold bells are on the front of the Bentwood-style runners. **Artist:** Linda Sickman
☐ Purchased 19 __Pd $____MIB NB DB BNT
☐ Want Orig. Ret. $8.75 **NB** $11 **MIB** Sec. Mkt. **$19**

QX 534-7 ON A ROLL
Comments: Handcrafted, 5" tall, Merry Christmas 1991.
A little mouse swings on a strand of green fabric ribbon, scissors in hand. The red spool fastens to the tree with a wishbone hanger. **Artist:** Ken Crow
☐ Purchased 19 __Pd $____MIB NB DB BNT
☐ Want Orig. Ret. $6.75 **NB** $15 **MIB** Sec. Mkt. **$22**

QX 529-7 PARTRIDGE IN A PEAR TREE
Comments: Handcrafted, 3-5/16" tall, Dated 1991.
This ornament of a partridge sitting in the top of a pear tree has the look of carved wood. **Artist:** Linda Sickman
☐ Purchased 19 __Pd $____MIB NB DB BNT
☐ Want Orig. Ret. $9.75 **NB** $15 **MIB** Sec. Mkt. **$21**

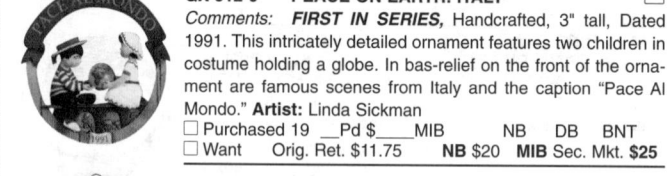

QX 512-9 PEACE ON EARTH: ITALY
Comments: **FIRST IN SERIES,** Handcrafted, 3" tall, Dated 1991. This intricately detailed ornament features two children in costume holding a globe. In bas-relief on the front of the ornament are famous scenes from Italy and the caption "Pace Al Mondo." **Artist:** Linda Sickman
☐ Purchased 19 __Pd $____MIB NB DB BNT
☐ Want Orig. Ret. $11.75 **NB** $20 **MIB** Sec. Mkt. **$25**

QX 225-7 PEANUTS®
Comments: Chrome Glass Ball, 2-7/8" dia., Dated 1991.
The gang decorates Snoopy's doghouse.
Caption: "It's The Time Of The Year For Sharing Good Cheer!"
☐ Purchased 19 __Pd $____MIB NB DB BNT
☐ Want Orig. Ret. $5.00 **NB** $18 **MIB** Sec. Mkt. **$25**

QLX 722-9 PEANUTS®
Comments: **FIRST IN SERIES,** Flickering Light, Handcrafted, 3" tall. Dated 1991. Snoopy and Woodstock wait for Santa – inside the stocking on the fireplace. The mantel holds a plate of cookies "For Santa." **Artist:** Dill Rhodus
☐ Purchased 19 __Pd $____MIB NB DB BNT
☐ Want Orig. Ret. $18.00 **NB** $65 **MIB** Sec. Mkt. **$75**

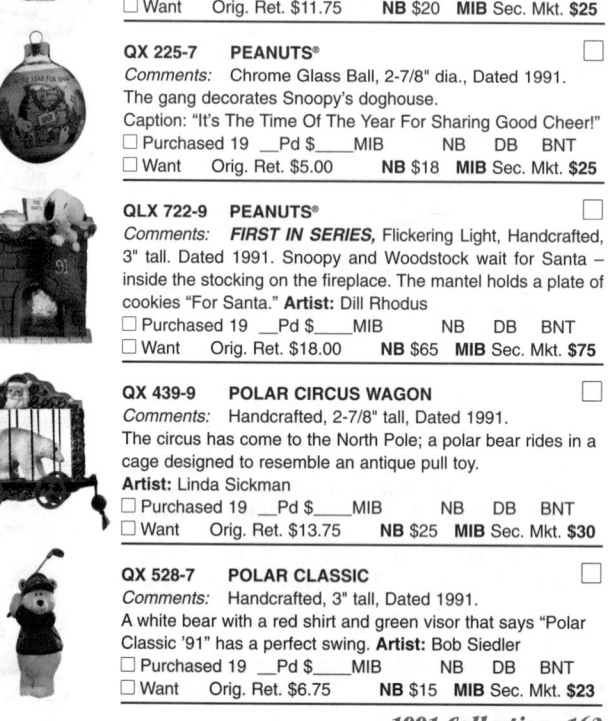

QX 439-9 POLAR CIRCUS WAGON
Comments: Handcrafted, 2-7/8" tall, Dated 1991.
The circus has come to the North Pole; a polar bear rides in a cage designed to resemble an antique pull toy.
Artist: Linda Sickman
☐ Purchased 19 __Pd $____MIB NB DB BNT
☐ Want Orig. Ret. $13.75 **NB** $25 **MIB** Sec. Mkt. **$30**

QX 528-7 POLAR CLASSIC
Comments: Handcrafted, 3" tall, Dated 1991.
A white bear with a red shirt and green visor that says "Polar Classic '91" has a perfect swing. **Artist:** Bob Siedler
☐ Purchased 19 __Pd $____MIB NB DB BNT
☐ Want Orig. Ret. $6.75 **NB** $15 **MIB** Sec. Mkt. **$23**

QX 537-9   PUPPY LOVE
Comments: ***FIRST IN SERIES,*** Handcrafted and Brass.
3-1/8" tall, Dated 1991. A golden cocker spaniel rides a candy cane. He wears a brass identification tag on a red ribbon around his neck. **Artist:** Anita Marra Rogers
☐ Purchased 19 __Pd $____MIB   NB   DB   BNT
☐ Want   Orig. Ret. $7.75   **NB** $40   **MIB** Sec. Mkt. **$60**

QX 434-7   REINDEER CHAMPS: CUPID
Comments: **Sixth in Series,** Handcrafted, 3-1/8" tall.
Dated 1991. Cupid serves on the volleyball court with style and grace. Hisr name is on his shirt. **Artist:** Bob Siedler
☐ Purchased 19 __Pd $____MIB   NB   DB   BNT
☐ Want   Orig. Ret. $7.75   **NB** $20   **MIB** Sec. Mkt. **$30**

QX 414-7   ROCKING HORSE
Comments: **Eleventh in Series,** Handcrafted, 4" wide.
Dated 1991. A buckskin wears a patterned saddle that resembles hand-tooled leather with shiny brass stirrups. His mane and tail are black. **Artist:** Linda Sickman
☐ Purchased 19 __Pd $____MIB   NB   DB   BNT
☐ Want   Orig. Ret. $10.75   **NB** $45   **MIB** Sec. Mkt. **$60**

QLX 727-3   SALVATION ARMY BAND
Comments: Light, Motion and Music, Handcrafted, 4-5/8" tall.
Standing on a brick street beneath a lighted lamp, a band plays "Joy To The World." Includes the familiar kettle and sign: "The Salvation Army®, Sharing Is Caring." **Artist:** Duane Unruh
☐ Purchased 19 __Pd $____MIB   NB   DB   BNT
☐ Want   Orig. Ret. $30.00   **NB** $60   **M IB** Sec. Mkt. **$80**

QX 438-9   SANTA SAILOR
Comments: Handcrafted and Metal, 3-3/8" tall, Dated 1991.
Santa's dressed in nautical dress blues and stands with his pack of toys on a metal anchor. **Artist:** Ed Seale
☐ Purchased 19 __Pd $____MIB   NB   DB   BNT
☐ Want   Orig. Ret. $9.75   **NB** $20   **MIB** Sec. Mkt. **$25**

QLX 716-7   SANTA SPECIAL
Comments: Light, Motion and Sound, Handcrafted, 3-1/8" tall.
This locomotive looks, acts and sounds like a real train. The headlight is lighted; it whistles and chugs. The wheels and drive rods turn. Engineer Santa waves. Reissued in 1992.
Artist: Ed Seale
☐ Purchased 19 __Pd $____MIB   NB   DB   BNT
☐ Want   Orig. Ret. $40.00   **NB** $65   **MIB** Sec. Mkt. **$80**

QLX 715-9   SANTA'S HOT LINE
Comments: Blinking Lights, Handcrafted, 3-7/8" tall.
Dated 1991. A busy elf answers calls on this old-fashioned switchboard and adds to his list: "Sara - Train, Paul - Puppy." **Artist:** Ken Crow
☐ Purchased 19 __Pd $____MIB   NB   DB   BNT
☐ Want   Orig. Ret. $18.00   **NB** $35   **MIB** Sec. Mkt. **$43**

QX 523-7   SANTA'S PREMIERE: GOLD CROWN ORNAMENT
Comments: Hand-Painted Fine Porcelain, 3-1/4" tall.
Dated 1991. The handle of this gold-rimmed porcelain bell is a finely crafted Santa in a long red coat. Caption: "Hallmark Keepsake Ornament™ Premiere, Gold Crown Exclusive."
☐ Purchased 19 __Pd $____MIB   NB   DB   BNT
☐ Want   Orig. Ret. $10.75   **NB** $25   **MIB** Sec. Mkt. **$30**

QXC 479-7   SECRETS FOR SANTA: KEEPSAKE CLUB
Comments: Limited Edition 28,700, Wood Display Stand.
Hand-Painted, Handcrafted, 3-1/2" tall. A child seated on Santa's lap whispers a wish in his ear. Available to Club Members only. **Artist:** Anita Marra Rogers
☐ Purchased 19 __Pd $____MIB   NB   DB   BNT
☐ Want   Orig. Ret. $23.75   **NB** $40   **MIB** Sec. Mkt. **$50**

QX 548-7   SISTER
Comments: Handcrafted, 3-3/4" tall, Dated 1991.
This cookie angel has been lavishly decorated with pearly "icing" to serve up a lovely treat for "Sister," as noted on the star she is holding. **Artist:** Joyce A. Lyle
☐ Purchased 19 __Pd $____MIB   NB   DB   BNT
☐ Want   Orig. Ret. $6.75   **NB** $16   **MIB** Sec. Mkt. **$20**

QX 544-7   SKI LIFT BUNNY
Comments: Handcrafted, 2-3/4" tall, Dated 1991.
With a white pom-pom tail, this colorfully dressed bunny loves to ride the ski lift. **Artist:** Julia Lee
☐ Purchased 19 __Pd $____MIB   NB   DB   BNT
☐ Want   Orig. Ret. $6.75   **NB** $15   **MIB** Sec. Mkt. **$23**

QLX 726-6   SKI TRIP
Comments: Light and Motion, Handcrafted, 4-1/4" tall.
In this snow-covered village, skiers ride the ski lift to the top of the hill then glide down the slopes. Lights shine through the lodge's windows. **Artist:** Ed Seale
☐ Purchased 19 __Pd $____MIB   NB   DB   BNT
☐ Want   Orig. Ret. $28.00   **NB** $55   **MIB** Sec. Mkt. **$60**

QX 519-7   SNOOPY® AND WOODSTOCK
Comments: Handcrafted, 2-1/8" tall, Dated 1991.
Snoopy and Woodstock enjoy a Christmas meal of pepperoni
pizza and root beer. **Artist:** Dill Rhodus
☐ Purchased 19 __Pd $____MIB   NB   DB   BNT
☐ Want   Orig. Ret. $6.75   **NB** $30 **MIB** Sec. Mkt. **$40**

QX 526-9   SNOWY OWL
Comments: Handcrafted, 3" tall.
The distinctive markings for this wide-eyed owl make it very
impressive as well as beautiful. **Artist:** Linda Sickman
☐ Purchased 19 __Pd $____MIB   NB   DB   BNT
☐ Want   Orig. Ret. $7.75   **NB** $15 **MIB** Sec. Mkt. **$20**

QX 546-9   SON
Comments: Handcrafted, 3-3/16" tall, Dated Son 1991.
This flocked red slipper holds a flocked white mouse that is fast
asleep on a green pillow. **Artist:** Bob Siedler
☐ Purchased 19 __Pd $____MIB   NB   DB   BNT
☐ Want   Orig. Ret. $5.75   **NB** $18 **MIB** Sec. Mkt. **$23**

QLX 715-7   SPARKLING ANGEL
Comments: Blinking Lights, Handcrafted, 3-13/16" tall.
The stars on this little angel's glittering gold tinsel garland twin-
kle off and on. **Artist:** Robert Chad
☐ Purchased 19 __Pd $____MIB   NB   DB   BNT
☐ Want   Orig. Ret. $18.00   **NB** $30 **MIB** Sec. Mkt. **$38**

QLX 719-9   STAR TREK: STARSHIP ENTERPRISE
Comments: Blinking Lights, Handcrafted, 1-5/8" tall.
Dated 1991. Commemorating the 25th anniversary of the tele-
vision series Star Trek. Many Star Trek collectors were unaware
of its debut. Production was much less than '92's Shuttlecraft
Galileo, which was abundant. **Artist:** Lynn Norton
☐ Purchased 19 __Pd $____MIB   NB   DB   BNT
☐ Want   Orig. Ret. $20.00 **Lights Not Working** $200
                                     NB $350 **MIB** Sec. Mkt. **$400**

QX 536-7   SWEET TALK
Comments: Handcrafted, 2-1/8" tall.
A little girl's love for her pony is evident... aren't candy canes
just as good for ponies as sugar cubes? **Artist:** Duane Unruh
☐ Purchased 19 __Pd $____MIB   NB   DB   BNT
☐ Want   Orig. Ret. $8.75   **NB** $30 **MIB** Sec. Mkt. **$40**

QX 495-7   SWEETHEART
Comments: Fine Porcelain, 2-1/2" tall, Dated 1991.
An old-fashioned sleigh ride has been reproduced on a heart-
shaped porcelain ornament. Caption: "Merry Christmas, Sweet-
heart" and "Gently Comes The Season Of Love."
☐ Purchased 19 __Pd $____MIB   NB   DB   BNT
☐ Want   Orig. Ret. $9.75   **NB** $20 **MIB** Sec. Mkt. **$30**

QX 228-9   TEACHER
Comments: Porcelain White Glass Ball, 2-7/8" dia.
Dated Christmas 1991. This ornament has the look of a child's
drawing. "For My Teacher" is written on this ornament and it pic-
tures a tree with gifts and wreath. **Artist:** Anita Marra Rogers
☐ Purchased 19 __Pd $____MIB   NB   DB   BNT
☐ Want   Orig. Ret. $4.75   **NB** $7 **MIB** Sec. Mkt. **$12**

QX 492-9   TEN YEARS TOGETHER
Comments: Faceted Glass, 2-9/16" tall, Dated 1991.
Caption in red foil.
☐ Purchased 19 __Pd $____MIB   NB   DB   BNT
☐ Want   Orig. Ret. $7.75   **NB** $15 **MIB** Sec. Mkt. **$23**

**QX 533-7   TENDER TOUCHES COLLECTION:
FANFARE BEAR**
Comments: Hand-Painted and Handcrafted, 2-7/16" tall.
Dated 1991. The "Little Drummer Bear" plays his drum with real
wooden drumsticks. **Artist:** Ed Seale
☐ Purchased 19 __Pd $____MIB   NB   DB   BNT
☐ Want   Orig. Ret. $8.75   **NB** $14 **MIB** Sec. Mkt. **$20**

**QX 496-9   TENDER TOUCHES COLLECTION:
GLEE CLUB BEARS**
Comments: Hand-Painted and Handcrafted, 2" tall, Dated
1991. Three brown bears in ivory choir robes sing carols from
their "Deck the Halls" song book. **Artist:** Ed Seale
☐ Purchased 19 __Pd $____MIB   NB   DB   BNT
☐ Want   Orig. Ret. $8.75   **NB** $17 **MIB** Sec. Mkt. **$20**

**QX 495-9   TENDER TOUCHES COLLECTION:
LOOK OUT BELOW**
Comments: Hand-Painted and Handcrafted, 1-3/4" tall.
Dated 1991. A little gray mouse waves to his friends as he sleds
down the hill. **Artist:** Ed Seale
☐ Purchased 19 __Pd $____MIB   NB   DB   BNT
☐ Want   Orig. Ret. $8.75   **NB** $15 **MIB** Sec. Mkt. **$20**

**QX 498-7   TENDER TOUCHES COLLECTION:
                LOVING STITCHES**
Comments: Hand-Painted and Handcrafted, 2-1/4" tall.
Dated 1991. A darling chipmunk rocks in her high-back rocking
chair and stitches a heart sampler for a special friend.
Artist: Ed Seale
☐ Purchased 19 __Pd $____MIB   NB   DB   BNT
☐ Want   Orig. Ret. $8.75   **NB** $20 **MIB** Sec. Mkt. **$25**

**QX 497-7   TENDER TOUCHES COLLECTION:
                PLUM DELIGHTFUL**
Comments: Hand-Painted, Handcrafted, 2-1/4" tall.
Dated 1991. Mrs. Raccoon has prepared a delicious plum
pudding to serve her Christmas guests. Her white lace apron
has a dated heart. **Artist:** Ed Seale
☐ Purchased 19 __Pd $____MIB   NB   DB   BNT
☐ Want   Orig. Ret. $8.75   **NB** $15 **MIB** Sec. Mkt. **$20**

**QX 497--9   TENDER TOUCHES COLLECTION:
                 SNOW TWINS**
Comments: Hand-Painted and Handcrafted, 2-1/8" tall.
Dated 1991. Don't all snowmen have long ears and a carrot for a
nose? The little fellow in the red suit thinks so. **Artist:** Ed Seale
☐ Purchased 19 __Pd $____MIB   NB   DB   BNT
☐ Want   Orig. Ret. $8.75   **NB** $15 **MIB** Sec. Mkt. **$20**

**QX 496-7   TENDER TOUCHES COLLECTION:
                YULE LOGGER**
Comments: Hand-Painted and Handcrafted, 2" tall, Dated
1991.This adorable beaver in his red sweater, jeans and yellow
muffler, has gnawed his own tree. **Artist:** Ed Seale
☐ Purchased 19 __Pd $____MIB   NB   DB   BNT
☐ Want   Orig. Ret. $8.75   **NB** $18 **MIB** Sec. Mkt. **$22**

QX 530-9   TERRIFIC TEACHER
Comments: Handcrafted, 2-1/4" tall, Dated Christmas 1991.
This cute little owl has a special rubber stamp created for his
Terrific Teacher. **Artist:** Linda Sickman
☐ Purchased 19 __Pd $____MIB   NB   DB   BNT
☐ Want   Orig. Ret. $6.75   **NB** $11 **MIB** Sec. Mkt. **$17**

QLX 712-9   TOYLAND TOWER
Comments: Motion, Handcrafted, 3-13/16" tall.
A teddy bear sits and beats a drum at the gate entrance as a
colorful soldier guards the tower. **Artist:** Ken Crow
☐ Purchased 19 __Pd $____MIB   NB   DB   BNT
☐ Want   Orig. Ret. $20.00   **NB** $37 **MIB** Sec. Mkt. **$45**

QX 439-7   TRAMP AND LADDIE
Comments: Handcrafted, 2-11/16" tall.
Laddie doesn't want anything to happen to his kitten friend, so
he carries it safely in a basket. **Artist:** John Francis (Collin)
☐ Purchased 19 __Pd $____MIB   NB   DB   BNT
☐ Want   Orig. Ret. $7.75   **NB** $30 **MIB** Sec. Mkt. **$40**

**QX 308-9   TWELVE DAYS OF CHRISTMAS:
                EIGHT MAIDS A-MILKING**
Comments: **Eighth in Series,** Acrylic, 3-7/8" tall, Dated 1991.
A sweet maiden milks her cow which is wearing a holly garland
and bell.
☐ Purchased 19 __Pd $____MIB   NB   DB   BNT
☐ Want   Orig. Ret. $6.75   **NB** $26 **MIB** Sec. Mkt. **$30**

**QX 493-7   TWENTY-FIVE YEARS TOGETHER
                PHOTOHOLDER**
Comments: Handcrafted and Chrome, 3-1/4" dia., Dated
1991. Caption is on a blue banner with swans: "25 Years
Together" and "Silver Christmas Memories... Silver Years Of
Love." **Artist:** LaDene Votruba
☐ Purchased 19 __Pd $____MIB   NB   DB   BNT
☐ Want   Orig. Ret. $8.75   **NB** $12 **MIB** Sec. Mkt. **$20**

QX 494-9   UNDER THE MISTLETOE
Comments: Handcrafted, 2-3/8" tall, Dated 1991.
A little tan rabbit holds a sprig of mistletoe and sneaks a kiss
from his sweetheart. **Artist:** Sharon Pike
☐ Purchased 19 __Pd $____MIB   NB   DB   BNT
☐ Want   Orig. Ret. $8.75   **NB** $16 **MIB** Sec. Mkt. **$20**

QX 504-7   UP 'N' DOWN JOURNEY
Comments: Handcrafted, 3-3/8" tall, Dated Merry Christmas
1991. Tap the sleigh and Santa rocks back and forth, waving to
everyone, while the reindeer prances. **Artist:** Ken Crow
☐ Purchased 19 __Pd $____MIB   NB   DB   BNT
☐ Want   Orig. Ret. $9.75   **NB** $18 **MIB** Sec. Mkt. **$28**

**QX 557-9   WINNIE-THE-POOH COLLECTION:
                CHRISTOPHER ROBIN**
Comments: Handcrafted, 4-3/4" tall.
Christopher Robin is wearing red shoes and scarf and is bring-
ing home the Christmas tree. **Artist:** Bob Siedler
☐ Purchased 19 __Pd $____MIB   NB   DB   BNT
☐ Want   Orig. Ret. $9.75   **NB** $22 **MIB** Sec. Mkt. **$35**

QX 561-7   WINNIE-THE-POOH COLLECTION:
KANGA AND ROO
Comments: Handcrafted, 3-1/4" tall.
Mother Kanga shows baby Roo a string of cranberries to
decorate the Christmas tree. **Artist:** Bob Siedler
☐ Purchased 19 __ Pd $____MIB   NB   DB   BNT
☐ Want   Orig. Ret. $9.75   **NB** $40   **MIB** Sec. Mkt. **$50**

QX 557-7   WINNIE-THE-POOH COLLECTION:
PIGLET AND EEYORE
Comments: Handcrafted, 2-3/4" tall.
Piglet rides bravely on Eeyore's back, carrying a red ornament
for the tree. Eeyore wears a pink ribbon tied on his tail.
Artist: Bob Siedler
☐ Purchased 19 __ Pd $____MIB   NB   DB   BNT
☐ Want   Orig. Ret. $9.75   **NB** $40   **MIB** Sec. Mkt. **$50**

QX 560-7   WINNIE-THE-POOH COLLECTION: RABBIT
Comments: Handcrafted, 3" tall.
Rabbit brings a red translucent star to add to the Christmas
tree. It is for the very top. **Artist:** Bob Siedler
☐ Purchased 19 __ Pd $____MIB   NB   DB   BNT
☐ Want   Orig. Ret. $9.75   **NB** $25   **MIB** Sec. Mkt. **$30**

QX 560-9   WINNIE-THE-POOH COLLECTION: TIGGER
Comments: Handcrafted, 3-1/2" tall.
Tigger springs into Christmas carrying a brightly wrapped gift.
He's proof that "tiggers" truly are wonderful things.
Artist: Bob Siedler
☐ Purchased 19 __ Pd $____MIB   NB   DB   BNT
☐ Want   Orig. Ret. $9.75   **NB** $85   **MIB** Sec. Mkt. **$110**

QX 556-9   WINNIE-THE-POOH COLLECTION:
WINNIE-THE-POOH
Comments: Handcrafted, 3" tall.
Pooh's idea of the perfect gift is a jar of "Hunny" tied with a big
red bow. **Artist:** Bob Siedler
☐ Purchased 19 __ Pd $____MIB   NB   DB   BNT
☐ Want   Orig. Ret. $9.75   **NB** $40   **MIB** Sec. Mkt. **$55**

QX 427-7   WINTER SURPRISE
Comments: **Third in Series,** Handcrafted, 3-1/4" tall.
Dated 1991. A penguin trio sings from "Polar Carols 1991" as
they stand beside a snow-covered tree. **Artist:** Joyce A. Lyle
☐ Purchased 19 __ Pd $____MIB   NB   DB   BNT
☐ Want   Orig. Ret. $10.75   **NB** $19   **MIB** Sec. Mkt. **$23**

Specialty Ornaments

QX 524-9   FLAG OF LIBERTY
Comments: Handcrafted, 3-5/16" tall, Dated 1991.
A pearlized yellow banner carries the caption: "God Bless
America 1991" on this commemorative ornament of Desert
Shield/Desert Storm. For each ornament sold, Hallmark donat-
ed $1.00 to the American Red Cross. The first shipment in June
was very limited, but Hallmark began shipping the ornaments
again in August. **Artist:** Donna Lee
☐ Purchased 19 __ Pd $____MIB   NB   DB   BNT
☐ Want   Orig. Retail $6.75 **NB** $16   **MIB** Sec. Mkt. **$20**

Convention Ornaments

KANSAS CITY SANTA: SPECIAL EDITION
Comments: Silver-Plated, Dated "K.C. 1991."
This special edition Santa was given as a parting gift to all who
attended the 1991 Keepsake Ornament Convention in June.
Santa holds a plate with the Club logo.
☐ Purchased 19 __ Pd $____MIB   NB   DB   BNT
☐ Want   Orig. Retail Gift _____   **MIB** Sec. Mkt.**$800**

A Frosty Friends Display created by
Constance T. of Wisconsin.

1991
Miniature Ornament Collection

QXM 586-9
ALL ABOARD
1" tall, Dated 1991.
Artist: Robert Chad
☐ Purchased 19___ Pd $_____
MIB NB DB BNT
☐ Want Orig. Retail $4.50
NB $12 **MIB** Sec. Mkt. **$18**

QXM 579-9
BABY'S FIRST CHRISTMAS, 1991
Carriage, 1" tall.
Artist: John Francis (Collin)
☐ Purchased 19___ Pd $_____
MIB NB DB BNT
☐ Want Orig. Retail $6.00
NB $13 **MIB** Sec. Mkt. **$23**

QXM 597-7
BRASS BELLS
Etched, Pierced Brass, 1-1/4" tall,
Dated 1991. **Artist:** Patricia Andrews
☐ Purchased 19___ Pd $_____
MIB NB DB BNT
☐ Want Orig. Retail $3.00
NB $6 **MIB** Sec. Mkt. **$10**

QXM 597-9
BRASS CHURCH
Etched Brass, 1-1/4" tall, Dated 1991.
☐ Purchased 19___ Pd $_____
MIB NB DB BNT
☐ Want Orig. Retail $3.00
NB $7 **MIB** Sec. Mkt. **$10**

QXM 598-7
BRASS SOLDIER
Etched Brass, 1-1/4" tall, Dated 1991.
☐ Purchased 19___ Pd $_____
MIB NB DB BNT
☐ Want Orig. Retail $3.00
NB $7 **MIB** Sec. Mkt. **$10**

QXM 587-7
BRIGHT BOXERS
1" tall, Dated 1991.
Artist: Dill Rhodus
☐ Purchased 19___ Pd $_____
MIB NB DB BNT
☐ Want Orig. Retail $4.50
NB $15 **MIB** Sec. Mkt. **$18**

QXM 593-9
BUSY BEAR
Wood, 1-7/16" tall.
Artist: Dill Rhodus
☐ Purchased 19___ Pd $_____
MIB NB DB BNT
☐ Want Orig. Retail $4.50
NB $8 **MIB** Sec. Mkt. **$13**

QXM 595-7
CARDINAL CAMEO
1-7/16" tall, Dated "Season's
Greetings 1991." **Artist:** Joyce A. Lyle
☐ Purchased 19___ Pd $_____
MIB NB DB BNT
☐ Want Orig. Retail $6.00
NB $11 **MIB** Sec. Mkt. **$18**

QXM 594-9
CARING SHEPHERD
Painted Porcelain, 1-1/16" tall.
Artist: John Francis (Collin)
☐ Purchased 19___ Pd $_____
MIB NB DB BNT
☐ Want Orig. Retail $6.00
NB $11 **MIB** Sec. Mkt. **$18**

QXM 586-7
COOL 'N' SWEET
Fine Porcelain, 1-3/16" tall, Dated
1991. **Artist:** Sharon Pike
☐ Purchased 19___ Pd $_____
MIB NB DB BNT
☐ Want Orig. Retail $4.50
NB $15 **MIB** Sec. Mkt. **$20**

QXM 599-9
COUNTRY SLEIGH
Enamel, 1" tall, Dated 1991.
Artist: LaDene Votruba
☐ Purchased 19___ Pd $_____
MIB NB DB BNT
☐ Want Orig. Retail $4.50
NB $9 **MIB** Sec. Mkt. **$15**

QXM 585-7
COURIER TURTLE
1-1/8" tall. **Artist:** Sharon Pike
☐ Purchased 19___ Pd $_____
MIB NB DB BNT
☐ Want Orig. Retail $4.50
NB $5 **MIB** Sec. Mkt. **$10**

QXM 591-7
FANCY WREATH
1-1/16" tall.
Artist: Joyce A. Lyle
☐ Purchased 19___ Pd $_____
MIB NB DB BNT
☐ Want Orig. Retail $4.50
NB $10 **MIB** Sec. Mkt. **$15**

QXM 588-7
FELIZ NAVIDAD
Straw, 1" tall, Dated 1991.
Artist: Anita Marra Rogers
☐ Purchased 19___ Pd $_____
MIB NB DB BNT
☐ Want Orig. Retail $6.00
NB $10 **MIB** Sec. Mkt. **$17**

QXM 581-9
FIRST CHRISTMAS TOGETHER
Brass, 1-1/8" tall, Dated 1991.
Artist: Duane Unruh
☐ Purchased 19___ Pd $_____
MIB NB DB BNT
☐ Want Orig. Retail $6.00
NB $11 **MIB** Sec. Mkt. **$18**

QXM 585-9
FLY BY
7/8" tall, Dated 1991.
Artist: Ken Crow
☐ Purchased 19___ Pd $_____
MIB NB DB BNT
☐ Want   Orig. Retail $4.50
NB $10   **MIB** Sec. Mkt. **$18**

QXM 594-7
FRIENDLY FAWN
1-1/8" tall, Dated 1991.
Artist: Julia Lee
☐ Purchased 19___ Pd $_____
MIB NB DB BNT
☐ Want   Orig. Retail $6.00
NB $9   **MIB** Sec. Mkt. **$17**

QXM 569-7
GRANDCHILD'S FIRST CHRISTMAS
Hand-Painted Fine Porcelain, 1-1/16", Dated 1991.
Artist: Anita Marra Rogers
☐ Purchased 19___ Pd $_____
MIB NB DB BNT
☐ Want   Orig. Retail $4.50
NB $9   **MIB** Sec. Mkt. **$15**

QXM 568-7
HEAVENLY MINSTREL
1-3/16" tall.
Artist: Donna Lee
☐ Purchased 19___ Pd $_____
MIB NB DB BNT
☐ Want   Orig. Retail $9.75
NB $20   **MIB** Sec. Mkt. **$23**

QXM 599-7
HOLIDAY SNOWFLAKE
Etched, Faceted Acrylic, 1-15/32" tall, 1991. **Artist:** Dill Rhodus
☐ Purchased 19___ Pd $_____
MIB NB DB BNT
☐ Want   Orig. Retail $3.00
NB $8   **MIB** Sec. Mkt. **$13**

QXM 568-9
KEY TO LOVE
1" tall, Dated "Love 1991."
Artist: Ken Crow
☐ Purchased 19___ Pd $_____
MIB NB DB BNT
☐ Want   Orig. Retail $4.50
NB $11   **MIB** Sec. Mkt. **$17**

QXM 563-9
KITTENS IN TOYLAND: AIRPLANE
Fourth in Series, 7/8" tall.
Artist: Ken Crow
☐ Purchased 19___ Pd $_____
MIB NB DB BNT
☐ Want   Orig. Retail $4.50
NB $13   **MIB** Sec. Mkt. **$20**

QXM 587-9
KITTY IN A MITTY
1" tall, Dated 1991.
Artist: Patricia Andrews
☐ Purchased 19___ Pd $_____
MIB NB DB BNT
☐ Want   Orig. Retail $4.50
NB $8   **MIB** Sec. Mkt. **$13**

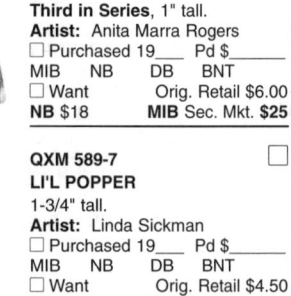

QXM 564-7
KRINGLES, THE: PLATE OF COOKIES
Third in Series, 1" tall.
Artist: Anita Marra Rogers
☐ Purchased 19___ Pd $_____
MIB NB DB BNT
☐ Want   Orig. Retail $6.00
NB $18   **MIB** Sec. Mkt. **$25**

QXM 589-7
LI'L POPPER
1-3/4" tall.
Artist: Linda Sickman
☐ Purchased 19___ Pd $_____
MIB NB DB BNT
☐ Want   Orig. Retail $4.50
NB $12   **MIB** Sec. Mkt. **$18**

QXM 595-9
LOVE IS BORN
Porcelain, 1-1/16" dia., Dated 1991. **Artist:** LaDene Votruba
☐ Purchased 19___ Pd $_____
MIB NB DB BNT
☐ Want   Orig. Retail $6.00
NB $12   **MIB** Sec. Mkt. **$20**

QXM 567-7
LULU & FAMILY
7/8" tall.
Artist: Anita Marra Rogers
☐ Purchased 19___ Pd $_____
MIB NB DB BNT
☐ Want   Orig. Retail $6.00
NB $11   **MIB** Sec. Mkt. **$15**

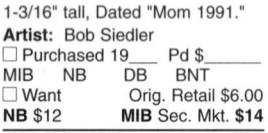

QXM 569-9
MOM
1-3/16" tall, Dated "Mom 1991."
Artist: Bob Siedler
☐ Purchased 19___ Pd $_____
MIB NB DB BNT
☐ Want   Orig. Retail $6.00
NB $12   **MIB** Sec. Mkt. **$14**

QXM 592-7
N. POLE BUDDY
1" tall, Dated 1991.
Artist: Don Palmiter
☐ Purchased 19___ Pd $_____
MIB NB DB BNT
☐ Want   Orig. Retail $4.50
NB $10   **MIB** Sec. Mkt. **$20**

QXM 565-7
NATURE'S ANGELS: PUPPY
Second in Series,
Brass, 1-1/8" tall,
Artist: Sharon Pike
☐ Purchased 19___ Pd $_____
MIB NB DB BNT
☐ Want   Orig. Retail $4.50
NB $14   **MIB** Sec. Mkt. **$23**

QXM 598-9
NOEL
Faceted Acrylic, 3-1/32" tall,
Dated 1991. **Artist:** Linda
Sickman
☐ Purchased 19___ Pd $_____
MIB   NB   DB   BNT
☐ Want   Orig. Retail $3.00
NB $9   **MIB** Sec. Mkt. **$13**

QXM 564-9
NOEL R.R.: PASSENGER CAR
Third in Series, 13/16" tall,
Dated 1991.
Artist: Linda Sickman
☐ Purchased 19___ Pd $_____
MIB   NB   DB   BNT
☐ Want   Orig. Retail $8.50
NB $44   **MIB** Sec. Mkt. **$50**

QXM 562-7
OLD ENGLISH VILLAGE:
COUNTRY INN
Fourth in Series,
1-1/8" tall, Dated 1991.
Artist: Julia Lee.
☐ Purchased 19___ Pd $_____
MIB   NB   DB   BNT
☐ Want   Orig. Retail $8.50
NB $24   **MIB** Sec. Mkt. **$30**

QXM 562-9
PENGUIN PAL
Fourth & Final in Series,
Artist: Bob Siedler, 3/4" tall
☐ Purchased 19___ Pd $_____
MIB   NB   DB   BNT
☐ Want   Orig. Retail $4.50
NB $10   **MIB** Sec. Mkt. **$15**

QXM 566-9
RING-A-DING ELF
Brass, 1-1/4" tall, Dated 1991.
Artist: Robert Chad
☐ Purchased 19___ Pd $_____
MIB   NB   DB   BNT
☐ Want   Orig. Retail $8.50
NB $14   **MIB** Sec. Mkt. **$20**

QXM 563-7
ROCKING HORSE: GREY ARABIAN
Fourth in Series, 1-1/8" tall,
Dated 1991. Popular Series!
Artist: Linda Sickman
☐ Purchased 19___ Pd $_____
MIB   NB   DB   BNT
☐ Want   Orig. Retail $4.50
NB $25   **MIB** Sec. Mkt. **$30**

QXM 590-9
SEASIDE OTTER
7/8" tall. **Artist:** Bob Siedler
☐ Purchased 19___ Pd $_____
MIB   NB   DB   BNT
☐ Want   Orig. Retail $4.50
NB $8   **MIB** Sec. Mkt. **$13**

QXM 567-9
SILVERY SANTA
Edition, Silver-Plated, 1-1/8" tall,
Dated 1991. **Artist:** Julia Lee
☐ Purchased 19___ Pd $_____
MIB   NB   DB   BNT
☐ Want   Orig. Retail $9.75
NB $16   **MIB** Sec. Mkt. **$24**

QXM 579-7
SPECIAL FRIENDS
Wicker, 13/16" tall, Dated 1991.
Artist: Julia Lee
☐ Purchased 19___ Pd $_____
MIB   NB   DB   BNT
☐ Want   Orig. Retail $8.50
NB $14   **MIB** Sec. Mkt. **$20**

QXM 565-9
THIMBLE BELLS
Series, 1-1/8" tall, Dated 1991.
Artist: Michele Pyda-Sevcik
☐ Purchased 19___ Pd $_____
MIB   NB   DB   BNT
☐ Want   Orig. Retail $18
NB $18   **MIB** Sec. Mkt. **$27**

QXM 582-7
TINY TEA PARTY SET

Fine Porcelain, Dated 1991. Other mini sets not
porcelain. These porcelain ornaments were "first of
their kind." They were not bought up on the
secondary market due to the inital retail. Following
sets were artplas, not porcelain. The second issue
was over-ordered and plentiful. Hope to see these
mini sets continue for years to come! Bring back the
porcelain! More! More!
Artist: Ed Seale
Cookie Plate, 11/16" tall. Teacup Lounger, 5/8" tall.
Teacup Taster, 13/16" tall. Teapot, 1" tall.
Creamer, 1-3/16" tall. Sugar Bowl, 15/16" tall.
☐ Purchased 19___ Pd $_____
MIB   NB   DB   BNT
☐ WantOrig. Retail $29.00
NB $125   **MIB** Sec. Mkt. **$170-175**

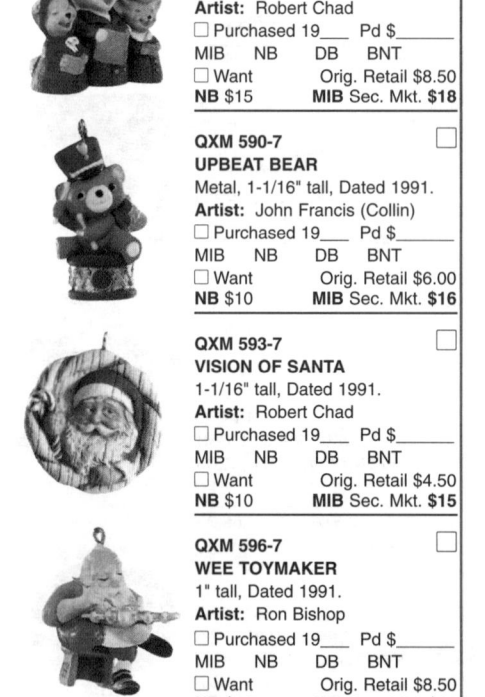

QXM 588-9
TOP HATTER
1" tall, Dated 1991.
Artist: Ed Seale
☐ Purchased 19___ Pd $_____
MIB   NB   DB   BNT
☐ Want   Orig. Retail $6.00
NB $12   **MIB** Sec. Mkt. **$18**

QXM 589-9
TREELAND TRIO
7/8" tall, Dated 1991.
Artist: Robert Chad
☐ Purchased 19___ Pd $_____
MIB   NB   DB   BNT
☐ Want   Orig. Retail $8.50
NB $15   **MIB** Sec. Mkt. **$18**

QXM 590-7
UPBEAT BEAR
Metal, 1-1/16" tall, Dated 1991.
Artist: John Francis (Collin)
☐ Purchased 19___ Pd $_____
MIB   NB   DB   BNT
☐ Want   Orig. Retail $6.00
NB $10   **MIB** Sec. Mkt. **$16**

QXM 593-7
VISION OF SANTA
1-1/16" tall, Dated 1991.
Artist: Robert Chad
☐ Purchased 19___ Pd $_____
MIB   NB   DB   BNT
☐ Want   Orig. Retail $4.50
NB $10   **MIB** Sec. Mkt. **$15**

QXM 596-7
WEE TOYMAKER
1" tall, Dated 1991.
Artist: Ron Bishop
☐ Purchased 19___ Pd $_____
MIB   NB   DB   BNT
☐ Want   Orig. Retail $8.50
NB $10   **MIB** Sec. Mkt. **$16**

QXM 566-7
WOODLAND BABIES
FIRST IN SERIES, 1" tall.
Artist: Ken Crow
☐ Purchased 19___ Pd $_____
MIB   NB   DB   BNT
☐ Want   Orig. Retail $6.00
NB $15   **MIB** Sec. Mkt. **$18**

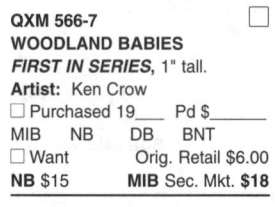

"My mother said while she's at work to use my initiative if I need money, so I'm selling some of her ornaments."

1991
Easter Ornament Collection

QEO 518-9
BABY'S FIRST EASTER
Hand-Painted/ 1-1/2" tall,
Dated 1991.
☐ Purchased 19___ Pd $_____
MIB   NB   DB   BNT
☐ Want   Original Retail $8.75
NB $20   **MIB** Sec. Mkt. **$30**

QEO 517-9
DAUGHTER
Hand-Painted, 1-1/2" tall.
☐ Purchased 19___ Pd $_____
MIB   NB   DB   BNT
☐ Want   Original Retail $5.75
NB $20   **MIB** Sec. Mkt. **$30**

QEO 513-7
EASTER MEMORIES PHOTOHOLDER
Fabric, 2-1/2" tall, Dated 1991.
☐ Purchased 19___ Pd $_____
MIB   NB   DB   BNT
☐ Want   Original Retail $7.75
NB $14   **MIB** Sec. Mkt. **$17**

QEO 514-9
FULL OF LOVE
Hand-Painted, 2" tall, Dated 1991.
☐ Purchased 19___ Pd $_____
MIB   NB   DB   BNT
☐ Want   Original Retail $7.75
NB $30   **MIB** Sec. Mkt. **$50**

QEO 515-9
GENTLE LAMB
Hand-Painted, 2" tall, Dated 1991.
☐ Purchased 19___ Pd $_____
MIB   NB   DB   BNT
☐ Want   Original Retail $6.75
NB $15   **MIB** Sec. Mkt. **$20**

QEO 517-7
GRANDCHILD
Hand-Painted, 2-1/2" tall,
Dated 1991.
☐ Purchased 19___ Pd $_____
MIB   NB   DB   BNT
☐ Want   Original Retail $6.75
NB $15   **MIB** Sec. Mkt. **$20**

QEO 514-7
LI'L DIPPER
Hand-Painted, 2-1/2" tall.
☐ Purchased 19___ Pd $_____
MIB   NB   DB   BNT
☐ Want   Original Retail $6.75
NB $15   **MIB** Sec. Mkt. **$23**

QEO 513-9
LILY EGG
Hand-Painted Fine Porcelain, 2"
tall, Dated 1991.
☐ Purchased 19___ Pd $_____
MIB   NB   DB   BNT
☐ Want   Original Retail $9.75
NB $15   **MIB** Sec. Mkt. **$23**

QEO 518-7
SON
Hand-Painted, 1-1/2" tall.
☐ Purchased 19___ Pd $_____
MIB   NB   DB   BNT
☐ Want   Original Retail $5.75
NB $15   **MIB** Sec. Mkt. **$25**

QEO 516-9
SPIRIT OF EASTER
Hand-Painted, 2" tall, Dated 1991.
☐ Purchased 19___ Pd $_____
MIB   NB   DB   BNT
☐ Want   Original Retail $7.75
NB $18   **MIB** Sec. Mkt. **$33**

QEO 516-7
SPRINGTIME STROLL
Hand-Painted, 2-1/2" tall,
Dated 1991.
☐ Purchased 19___ Pd $_____
MIB   NB   DB   BNT
☐ Want   Original Retail $6.75
NB $15   **MIB** Sec. Mkt. **$25**

1992 Collection

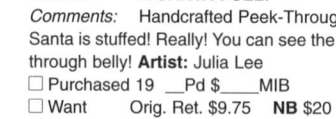

QX 457-4 A CHILD'S CHRISTMAS
Comments: Handcrafted, 2-3/4" tall, Dated 1992.
A teddy bear sleeps peacefully on a rocking lamb's back. May be personalized six ways with inserts for Niece, Nephew, Grand-daughter, Grandson, Great-Grandchild or A Child's Christmas. **Artist:** John Francis (Collin)
☐ Purchased 19 __Pd $____MIB   NB   DB   BNT
☐ Want   Orig. Ret. $9.75   **NB** $12   **MIB** Sec. Mkt. $17

QX 599-1 A SANTA-FULL!
Comments: Handcrafted Peek-Through, 3" tall, Dated 1992.
Santa is stuffed! Really! You can see the cookies inside his see-through belly! **Artist:** Julia Lee
☐ Purchased 19 __Pd $____MIB   NB   DB   BNT
☐ Want   Orig. Ret. $9.75   **NB** $20   **MIB** Sec. Mkt. $40

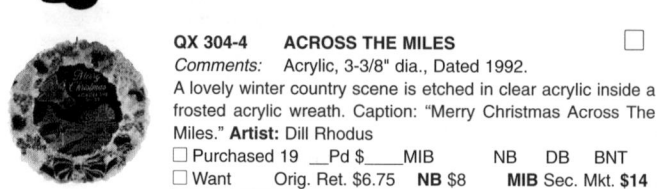

QX 304-4 ACROSS THE MILES
Comments: Acrylic, 3-3/8" dia., Dated 1992.
A lovely winter country scene is etched in clear acrylic inside a frosted acrylic wreath. Caption: "Merry Christmas Across The Miles." **Artist:** Dill Rhodus
☐ Purchased 19 __Pd $____MIB   NB   DB   BNT
☐ Want   Orig. Ret. $6.75   **NB** $8   **MIB** Sec. Mkt. $14

QLX 723-9 ANGEL OF LIGHT
Comments: Lighted Tree Topper, 10-1/4" tall.
This delicate angel, in a flowing gown of blue and white, carries a brightly lit acrylic star.
☐ Purchased 19 __Pd $____MIB   NB   DB   BNT
☐ Want   Orig. Ret. $30.00   **NB** $30   **MIB** Sec. Mkt. $34

QX 485-1 ANNIVERSARY YEAR PHOTOHOLDER
Comments: Brass and Chrome, Dated 1992.
Caption: "Loving Moments Together. Loving Memories Forever." Personalize to mark the 5th, 10th, 25th, 30th, 35th, 40th or 50th anniversary. **Artist:** Duane Unruh
☐ Purchased 19 __Pd $____MIB   NB   DB   BNT
☐ Want   Orig. Ret. $9.75   **NB** $19   **MIB** Sec. Mkt. $27

QX 464-4 BABY'S FIRST CHRISTMAS
Comments: Handcrafted, 2-1/8" tall, Dated 1992.
This cute light brown bear holds a red, white and green striped candy cane "1" in celebration of its first Christmas. **Artist:** John Francis (Collin)
☐ Purchased 19 __Pd $____MIB   NB   DB   BNT
☐ Want   Orig. Ret. $7.75   **NB** $19   **MIB** Sec. Mkt. $28

QX 458-1 BABY'S FIRST CHRISTMAS
Comments: Hand-Painted Fine Porcelain, 3-1/2" tall, Dated 1992.
A tiny baby sleeps soundly in a wicker-look basket tied with pale green ribbon. **Artist:** Patricia Andrews
☐ Purchased 19 __Pd $____MIB   NB   DB   BNT
☐ Want   Orig. Ret. $18.75 **NB** $22   **MIB** Sec. Mkt. $40

QLX 728-1 BABY'S FIRST CHRISTMAS
Comments: Light and Music, Handcrafted, 3-7/16" tall.
Dated 1992. Baby sleeps soundly in this white, lace-trimmed crib. Plays "Silent Night." **Artist:** Ken Crow
☐ Purchased 19 __Pd $____MIB   NB   DB   BNT
☐ Want   Orig. Ret. $22.00 **NB** $65   **MIB** Sec. Mkt. $80

QX 219-1 BABY'S FIRST CHRISTMAS - BABY BOY
Comments: Blue Satin Ball, 2-7/8" dia., Dated 1992.
Forest animals decorate a Christmas tree. Caption: "To Love, Spoil, Play With, Adore – That's What Baby Boys Are For!" **Artist:** LaDene Votruba
☐ Purchased 19 __Pd $____MIB   NB   DB   BNT
☐ Want   Orig. Ret. $4.75   **NB** $13   **MIB** Sec. Mkt. $20

QX 220-4 BABY'S FIRST CHRISTMAS - BABY GIRL
Comments: Pink Satin Ball, 2-7/8" dia., Dated 1992.
Forest animals decorate a Christmas tree. Caption: "To Love, Spoil, Play With, Adore – That's What Baby Girls Are For!" **Artist:** LaDene Votruba
☐ Purchased 19 __Pd $____MIB   NB   DB   BNT
☐ Want   Orig. Ret. $4.75   **NB** $13   **MIB** Sec. Mkt. $20

QX 464-1 BABY'S FIRST CHRISTMAS
PHOTOHOLDER
Comments: Embroidered Fabric, 3-3/16" tall, Dated 1992.
White eyelet lace and embroidered designs frame baby's photo. Caption: "With Every Small Discovery, Baby Makes A Merry Memory." **Artist:** LaDene Votruba
☐ Purchased 19 __Pd $____MIB   NB   DB   BNT
☐ Want   Orig. Ret. $7.75   **NB** $19   **MIB** Sec. Mkt. $25

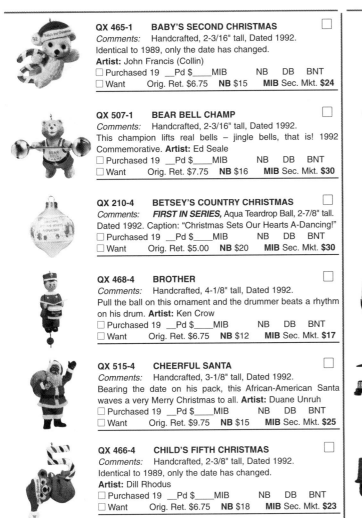

QX 465-1 BABY'S SECOND CHRISTMAS ☐
Comments: Handcrafted, 2-3/16" tall, Dated 1992.
Identical to 1989, only the date has changed.
Artist: John Francis (Collin)
☐ Purchased 19 __Pd $____MIB   NB   DB   BNT
☐ Want   Orig. Ret. $6.75   **NB** $15   **MIB** Sec. Mkt. **$24**

QX 507-1 BEAR BELL CHAMP ☐
Comments: Handcrafted, 2-3/16" tall, Dated 1992.
This champion lifts real bells – jingle bells, that is! 1992
Commemorative. **Artist:** Ed Seale
☐ Purchased 19 __Pd $____MIB   NB   DB   BNT
☐ Want   Orig. Ret. $7.75   **NB** $16   **MIB** Sec. Mkt. **$30**

QX 210-4 BETSEY'S COUNTRY CHRISTMAS ☐
Comments: **FIRST IN SERIES,** Aqua Teardrop Ball, 2-7/8" tall.
Dated 1992. Caption: "Christmas Sets Our Hearts A-Dancing!"
☐ Purchased 19 __Pd $____MIB   NB   DB   BNT
☐ Want   Orig. Ret. $5.00   **NB** $20   **MIB** Sec. Mkt. **$30**

QX 468-4 BROTHER ☐
Comments: Handcrafted, 4-1/8" tall, Dated 1992.
Pull the ball on this ornament and the drummer beats a rhythm
on his drum. **Artist:** Ken Crow
☐ Purchased 19 __Pd $____MIB   NB   DB   BNT
☐ Want   Orig. Ret. $6.75   **NB** $12   **MIB** Sec. Mkt. **$17**

QX 515-4 CHEERFUL SANTA ☐
Comments: Handcrafted, 3-1/8" tall, Dated 1992.
Bearing the date on his pack, this African-American Santa
waves a very Merry Christmas to all. **Artist:** Duane Unruh
☐ Purchased 19 __Pd $____MIB   NB   DB   BNT
☐ Want   Orig. Ret. $9.75   **NB** $15   **MIB** Sec. Mkt. **$25**

QX 466-4 CHILD'S FIFTH CHRISTMAS ☐
Comments: Handcrafted, 2-3/8" tall, Dated 1992.
Identical to 1989, only the date has changed.
Artist: Dill Rhodus
☐ Purchased 19 __Pd $____MIB   NB   DB   BNT
☐ Want   Orig. Ret. $6.75   **NB** $18   **MIB** Sec. Mkt. **$23**

QX 466-1 CHILD'S FOURTH CHRISTMAS ☐
Comments: Handcrafted, 3" tall, Dated 1992.
Identical to 1989, only the date has changed.
Artist: John Francis (Collin)
☐ Purchased 19 __Pd $____MIB   NB   DB   BNT
☐ Want   Orig. Ret. $6.75   **NB** $18   **MIB** Sec. Mkt. **$25**

QX 465-4 CHILD'S THIRD CHRISTMAS ☐
Comments: Handcrafted, 2-1/2" tall, Dated 1992.
Identical to 1989, only the date has changed.
Artist: John Francis (Collin)
☐ Purchased 19 __Pd $____MIB   NB   DB   BNT
☐ Want   Orig. Ret. $6.75   **NB** $14   **MIB** Sec. Mkt. **$23**

QLX 707-4 CHRIS MOUSE TALES ☐
Comments: **Eighth in Series,** Light, Handcrafted, 3-9/16" tall.
Dated 1992. Chris Mouse opens the shutters of his brightly lit
shoe-house. A "Chris Mouse Tales" story book forms the roof for
his "house." **Artist:** Anita Marra Rogers
☐ Purchased 19 __Pd $____MIB   NB   DB   BNT
☐ Want   Orig. Ret. $12.00   **NB** $22   **MIB** Sec. Mkt. **$30**

QLX 727-1 CHRISTMAS PARADE ☐
Comments: Light and Motion, Handcrafted, 3-3/8" tall, Dated 1992.
It's Christmas time in the city as evidenced by the decorations
atop the skyscrapers and the parade marching 'round the city.
Artist: Linda Sickman
☐ Purchased 19 __Pd $____MIB   NB   DB   BNT
☐ Want   Orig. Ret. $30.00   **NB** $49   **MIB** Sec. Mkt. **$60**

QX 532-1 CHRISTMAS SKY LINE COLLECTION: ☐
CABOOSE
Comments: Die Cast Metal, 2" tall, Dated 1992.
The traditional red caboose brings up the tail of the Christmas
Sky Line Collection. May be displayed hanging or standing.
Artist: Linda Sickman
☐ Purchased 19 __Pd $____MIB   NB   DB   BNT
☐ Want   Orig. Ret. $9.75   **NB** $15   **MIB** Sec. Mkt. **$20**

QX 540-1 CHRISTMAS SKY LINE COLLECTION: ☐
COAL CAR
Comments: Die Cast Metal, 1-7/8" tall, Dated 1992.
"Christmas Sky Line" proudly proclaims the name of the line on
the side of the coal car. **Artist:** Linda Sickman
☐ Purchased 19 __Pd $____MIB   NB   DB   BNT
☐ Want   Orig. Ret. $9.75   **NB** $15   **MIB** Sec. Mkt. **$20**

QX 531-1 CHRISTMAS SKY LINE COLLECTION: LOCOMOTIVE ☐

Comments: Die Cast Metal, 1-3/4" tall, Dated 1992.
This cheery locomotive is bright blue with red wheels and a red cabin. **Artist:** Linda Sickman
☐ Purchased 19 __Pd $____MIB   NB   DB   BNT
☐ Want   Orig. Ret. $9.75 **NB** $45   **MIB** Sec. Mkt. **$55**

QX 531-4 CHRISTMAS SKY LINE COLLECTION: STOCK CAR ☐

Comments: Die Cast Metal, 1-7/8" tall, Dated 1992.
The stock car is painted a bright yellow with black stripes. **Artist:** Linda Sickman
☐ Purchased 19 __Pd $____MIB   NB   DB   BNT
☐ Want   Orig. Ret. $9.75 **NB** $15   **MIB** Sec. Mkt. **$20**

QXC 546-4 CHRISTMAS TREASURES: KEEPSAKE CLUB ☐

Comments: Limited Edition 15,500, Handcrafted, Dated 1992.
Chest 1-3/16" tall. A chest of Christmas Treasures holds three dated miniature ornaments: an ice skate, a horse on wheels, and a Santa jack-in-the box. **Artist:** Robert Chad
☐ Purchased 19 __Pd $____MIB   NB   DB   BNT
☐ Want   Orig. Ret. $22.00 **NB** $110   **MIB** Sec. Mkt. **$125-150**

QX 428-4 CLASSIC AMERICAN CARS: 1966 MUSTANG ☐

Comments: **Second in Series,** Handcrafted, 1-1/4" tall.
Dated 1992. White mustang convertible with a " tree" and gift-wrapped packages. **Artist:** Don Palmiter
☐ Purchased 19 __Pd $____MIB   NB   DB   BNT
☐ Want   Orig. Ret. $12.75 **NB** $32   **MIB** Sec. Mkt. **$50**

QX 446-1 COLLECTOR'S PLATE: SWEET HOLIDAY HARMONY ☐

Comments: **Sixth and Final in Series** Porcelain, 3-1/4" dia.
Dated 1992. Includes Acrylic Display Stand. This brother and sister duet becomes a trio when their puppy joins his voice with theirs. **Artist:** LaDene Votruba
☐ Purchased 19 __Pd $____MIB   NB   DB   BNT
☐ Want   Orig. Ret. $8.75 **NB** $15   **MIB** Sec. Mkt. **$25**

QLX 726-4 CONTINENTAL EXPRESS ☐

Comments: Light and Motion, Handcrafted, 3-3/4" tall.
Dated 1992. Two trains circle a village going in opposite directions. **Artist:** Linda Sickman
☐ Purchased 19 __Pd $____MIB   NB   DB   BNT
☐ Want   Orig. Ret. $32.00 **NB** $65   **MIB** Sec. Mkt. **$75**

QX 547-4 COOL FLIERS ☐

Comments: Handcrafted, 3-1/2" tall, Dated 1992.
These two can really swing! A snowman and snow woman on trapezes may be hung on separate branches; their hands interlock to complete their act. **Artist:** Julia Lee
☐ Purchased 19 __Pd $____MIB   NB   DB   BNT
☐ Want   Orig. Ret. $10.75 **NB** $18   **MIB** Sec. Mkt. **$25**

QX 426-4 CRAYOLA® CRAYON: BRIGHT BLAZING COLORS ☐

Comments: **Fourth in Series,** Handcrafted, 2-1/8" tall,
Dated 1992. A dalmatian, wearing a bright red fireman's helmet, races to the rescue. **Artist:** Ken Crow
☐ Purchased 19 __Pd $____MIB   NB   DB   BNT
☐ Want   Orig. Ret. $9.75 **NB** $21   **MIB** Sec. Mkt. **$33**

QX 467-4 DAD ☐

Comments: Handcrafted, 2-5/16" tall, Dated 1992.
It's official! "Dad's A Winner!" Dad naps comfortably in his recliner with a smile on his face, as the newspaper declares that it's been a "Banner Year For Dad!" **Artist:** Bob Siedler
☐ Purchased 19 __Pd $____MIB   NB   DB   BNT
☐ Want   Orig. Ret. $7.75 **NB** $19   **MIB** Sec. Mkt. **$23**

QX 461-1 DAD-TO-BE ☐

Comments: Handcrafted, 2-3/8" tall, Dated 1992.
Dad rooster crows out the good news – he'll be a father soon! **Artist:** Julia Lee
☐ Purchased 19 __Pd $____MIB   NB   DB   BNT
☐ Want   Orig. Ret. $6.75 **NB** $14   **MIB** Sec. Mkt. **$18**

QLX 726-1 DANCING NUTCRACKER, THE ☐

Comments: Light, Motion and Music, Handcrafted, 3-1/4" tall,
Dated 1992. As the music plays the "Overture to Tchaikovsky's Nutcracker," the Nutcracker dances for you. "Wide" range of reported sales on this one. **Artist:** LaDene Votruba
☐ Purchased 19 __Pd $____MIB   NB   DB   BNT
☐ Want   Orig. Ret. $30.00 **NB** $45   **MIB** Sec. Mkt. **$60**

QX 503-1 DAUGHTER ☐

Comments: Handcrafted, 2-1/8" tall, Dated 1992.
This girl squirrel is flying high in her pink and silver airplane. Wearing a turquoise sweater, she waves happily.
Artist: John Francis (Collin)
☐ Purchased 19 __Pd $____MIB   NB   DB   BNT
☐ Want   Orig. Ret. $6.75 **NB** $16   **MIB** Sec. Mkt. **$28**

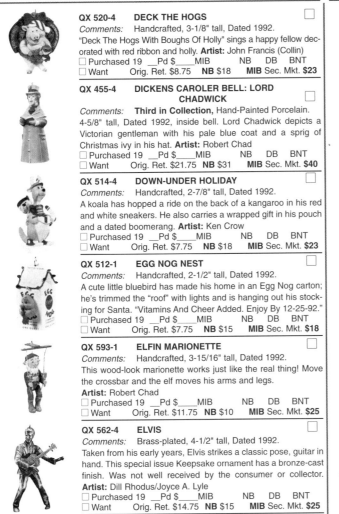

QX 520-4　DECK THE HOGS
Comments:　Handcrafted, 3-1/8" tall, Dated 1992.
"Deck The Hogs With Boughs Of Holly" sings a happy fellow decorated with red ribbon and holly. **Artist:** John Francis (Collin)
☐ Purchased 19 __Pd $____MIB　　NB　DB　BNT
☐ Want　　Orig. Ret. $8.75　**NB** $18　**MIB** Sec. Mkt. **$23**

QX 455-4　DICKENS CAROLER BELL: LORD CHADWICK
Comments:　**Third in Collection,** Hand-Painted Porcelain.
4-5/8" tall, Dated 1992, inside bell. Lord Chadwick depicts a Victorian gentleman with his pale blue coat and a sprig of Christmas ivy in his hat. **Artist:** Robert Chad
☐ Purchased 19 __Pd $____MIB　　NB　DB　BNT
☐ Want　　Orig. Ret. $21.75　**NB** $31　**MIB** Sec. Mkt. **$40**

QX 514-4　DOWN-UNDER HOLIDAY
Comments:　Handcrafted, 2-7/8" tall, Dated 1992.
A koala has hopped a ride on the back of a kangaroo in his red and white sneakers. He also carries a wrapped gift in his pouch and a dated boomerang. **Artist:** Ken Crow
☐ Purchased 19 __Pd $____MIB　　NB　DB　BNT
☐ Want　　Orig. Ret. $7.75　**NB** $18　**MIB** Sec. Mkt. **$23**

QX 512-1　EGG NOG NEST
Comments:　Handcrafted, 2-1/2" tall, Dated 1992.
A cute little bluebird has made his home in an Egg Nog carton; he's trimmed the "roof" with lights and is hanging out his stocking for Santa. "Vitamins And Cheer Added. Enjoy By 12-25-92."
☐ Purchased 19 __Pd $____MIB　　NB　DB　BNT
☐ Want　　Orig. Ret. $7.75　**NB** $15　**MIB** Sec. Mkt. **$18**

QX 593-1　ELFIN MARIONETTE
Comments:　Handcrafted, 3-15/16" tall, Dated 1992.
This wood-look marionette works just like the real thing! Move the crossbar and the elf moves his arms and legs.
Artist: Robert Chad
☐ Purchased 19 __Pd $____MIB　　NB　DB　BNT
☐ Want　　Orig. Ret. $11.75　**NB** $10　**MIB** Sec. Mkt. **$25**

QX 562-4　ELVIS
Comments:　Brass-plated, 4-1/2" tall, Dated 1992.
Taken from his early years, Elvis strikes a classic pose, guitar in hand. This special issue Keepsake ornament has a bronze-cast finish. Was not well received by the consumer or collector.
Artist: Dill Rhodus/Joyce A. Lyle
☐ Purchased 19 __Pd $____MIB　　NB　DB　BNT
☐ Want　　Orig. Ret. $14.75　**NB** $15　**MIB** Sec. Mkt. **$25**

QLX 727-4　ENCHANTED CLOCK
Comments:　Light and Motion, Handcrafted, 3-15/16" tall.
Caption: "When This Enchanted Clock Strikes Twelve Each Starry Christmas Eve, The Magic Toys Will Dance And Play, If Only You Believe." Several found below retail. **Artist:** Ken Crow
☐ Purchased 19 __Pd $____MIB　　NB　DB　BNT
☐ Want　　Orig. Ret. $30.00　**NB** $45　**MIB** Sec. Mkt. **$60**

QX 424-4　FABULOUS DECADE
Comments:　**Third in Series,** 1-7/8" tall, Handcrafted and Brass.
Dated 1992. A light brown bear with a red neck ribbon holds a shiny brass "1992." **Artist:** Ed Seale
☐ Purchased 19 __Pd $____MIB　　NB　DB　BNT
☐ Want　　Orig. Ret. $7.75　**NB** $30　**MIB** Sec. Mkt. **$40**

QLX 709-1　FEATHERED FRIENDS
Comments:　Light, Handcrafted, 1-15/16" tall, Dated 1992.
A favorite pastime for many during the winter months is to watch the birds at outdoor feeders. **Artist:** Linda Sickman
☐ Purchased 19 __Pd $____MIB　　NB　DB　BNT
☐ Want　　Orig. Ret. $14.00　**NB** $25　**MIB** Sec. Mkt. **$30**

QX 518-1　FELIZ NAVIDAD
Comments:　Handcrafted, 2-7/8" tall, Dated 1992.
A merry mouse rides his guitar and wishes everyone "Feliz Navidad"... Merry Christmas! **Artist:** Patricia Andrews
☐ Purchased 19 __Pd $____MIB　　NB　DB　BNT
☐ Want　　Orig. Ret. $6.75　**NB** $19　**MIB** Sec. Mkt. **$20**

QX 301-1　FIRST CHRISTMAS TOGETHER, OUR
Comments:　Acrylic, 3" tall, Dated 1992.
Red hearts and gold foil lettering decorate this clear acrylic heart. Caption: "Our First Christmas Together 1992." **Artist:** LaDene Votruba
☐ Purchased 19 __Pd $____MIB　　NB　DB　BNT
☐ Want　　Orig. Ret. $6.75　**NB** $17　**MIB** Sec. Mkt. **$20**

QX 506-1　FIRST CHRISTMAS TOGETHER, OUR
Comments:　Handcrafted, 2-7/8" tall, Dated 1992.
Two little mice share a sugar heart inside a silvery sugar bowl. Caption: "Our First Christmas Together 1992." **Artist:** Julia Lee
☐ Purchased 19 __Pd $____MIB　　NB　DB　BNT
☐ Want　　Orig. Ret. $9.75　**NB** $15　**MIB** Sec. Mkt. **$20**

QX 469-4 FIRST CHRISTMAS TOGETHER PHOTOHOLDER ☐

Comments: Handcrafted, 3-1/2" tall, Dated 1992. Slide your favorite photo into the shutter-framed window of this snow-capped home. Captions: "Our First Christmas Together" and "Home Is Where The Heart Is." **Artist:** Ed Seale

☐ Purchased 19 __Pd $____MIB   NB   DB   BNT
☐ Want   Orig. Ret. $8.75 **NB** $12   **MIB** Sec. Mkt. **$24**

QX 518-4 FOR MY GRANDMA PHOTOHOLDER ☐

Comments: Embroidered Fabric, 3-1/8" tall, Dated 1992. Hearts and holly decorate this heart-shaped ivory photo holder for Grandma. Caption: "Merry Christmas – With Love And Kisses From XOXO."

☐ Purchased 19 __Pd $____MIB   NB   DB   BNT
☐ Want   Orig. Ret. $7.75 **NB** $10   **MIB** Sec. Mkt. **$15**

QX 484-4 FOR THE ONE I LOVE ☐

Comments: Hand-Painted Fine Porcelain, 2-3/8" tall, Dated 1992. This ivory heart is filled with lovely pink roses in full bloom. Captions: "For The One I Love" and "Having Your Love Makes Christmas Perfect 1992." **Artist:** Joyce A. Lyle

☐ Purchased 19 __Pd $____MIB   NB   DB   BNT
☐ Want   Orig. Ret. $9.75 **NB** $14   **MIB** Sec. Mkt. **$22**

QLX 725-4 FOREST FROLICS ☐

Comments: **Fourth in Series,** Handcrafted, 4-1/8" tall, Dated 1992. Light and Motion. Forest friends have fun together on a seesaw which moves up and down. **Artist:** Sharon Pike

☐ Purchased 19 __Pd $____MIB   NB   DB   BNT
☐ Want   Orig. Ret. $28.00 **NB** $43   **MIB** Sec. Mkt. **$65**

QX 504-1 FRIENDLY GREETINGS ☐

Comments: Handcrafted, 2-5/16" tall, Dated 1992. A yellow and white kitten shares "A Friendly Christmas Greeting." Caption: "Friendship – Tis The Reason To Be Jolly!" Add your own message inside the card as well. **Artist:** Robert Chad

☐ Purchased 19 __Pd $____MIB   NB   DB   BNT
☐ Want   Orig. Ret. $7.75 **NB** $12   **MIB** Sec. Mkt. **$16**

QX 503-4 FRIENDSHIP LINE ☐

Comments: Handcrafted, 4-1/2" tall, Dated 1992. Two chipmunks converse gaily on a red telephone receiver. **Artist:** Ed Seale

☐ Purchased 19 __Pd $____MIB   NB   DB   BNT
☐ Want   Orig. Ret. $9.75 **NB** $16   **MIB** Sec. Mkt. **$30**

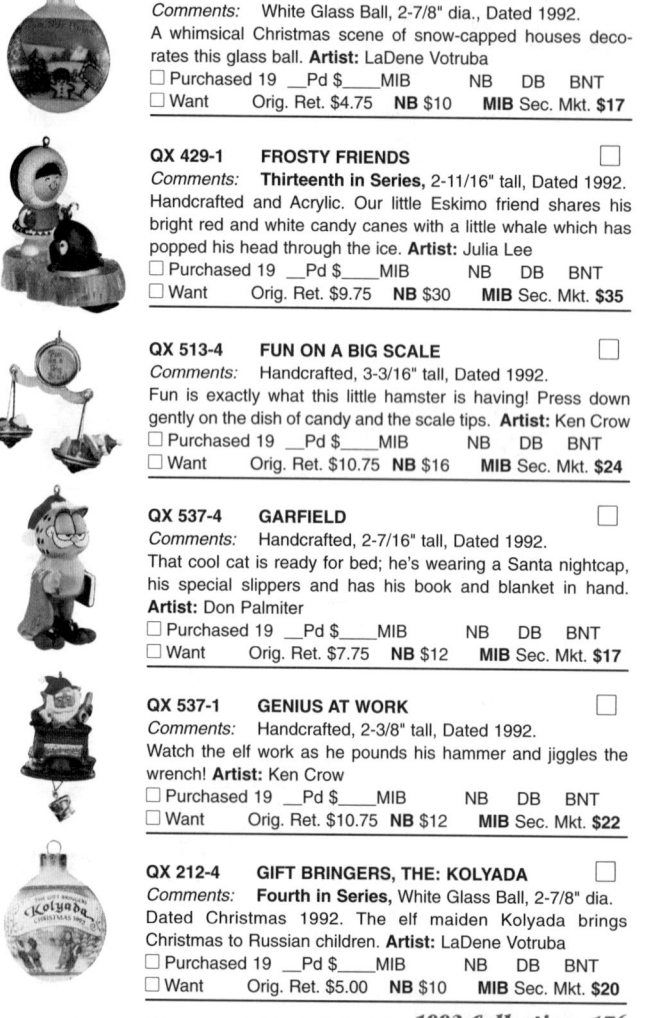

QX 213-1 FROM OUR HOME TO YOURS ☐

Comments: White Glass Ball, 2-7/8" dia., Dated 1992. A whimsical Christmas scene of snow-capped houses decorates this glass ball. **Artist:** LaDene Votruba

☐ Purchased 19 __Pd $____MIB   NB   DB   BNT
☐ Want   Orig. Ret. $4.75 **NB** $10   **MIB** Sec. Mkt. **$17**

QX 429-1 FROSTY FRIENDS ☐

Comments: **Thirteenth in Series,** 2-11/16" tall, Dated 1992. Handcrafted and Acrylic. Our little Eskimo friend shares his bright red and white candy canes with a little whale which has popped his head through the ice. **Artist:** Julia Lee

☐ Purchased 19 __Pd $____MIB   NB   DB   BNT
☐ Want   Orig. Ret. $9.75 **NB** $30   **MIB** Sec. Mkt. **$35**

QX 513-4 FUN ON A BIG SCALE ☐

Comments: Handcrafted, 3-3/16" tall, Dated 1992. Fun is exactly what this little hamster is having! Press down gently on the dish of candy and the scale tips. **Artist:** Ken Crow

☐ Purchased 19 __Pd $____MIB   NB   DB   BNT
☐ Want   Orig. Ret. $10.75 **NB** $16   **MIB** Sec. Mkt. **$24**

QX 537-4 GARFIELD ☐

Comments: Handcrafted, 2-7/16" tall, Dated 1992. That cool cat is ready for bed; he's wearing a Santa nightcap, his special slippers and has his book and blanket in hand. **Artist:** Don Palmiter

☐ Purchased 19 __Pd $____MIB   NB   DB   BNT
☐ Want   Orig. Ret. $7.75 **NB** $12   **MIB** Sec. Mkt. **$17**

QX 537-1 GENIUS AT WORK ☐

Comments: Handcrafted, 2-3/8" tall, Dated 1992. Watch the elf work as he pounds his hammer and jiggles the wrench! **Artist:** Ken Crow

☐ Purchased 19 __Pd $____MIB   NB   DB   BNT
☐ Want   Orig. Ret. $10.75 **NB** $12   **MIB** Sec. Mkt. **$22**

QX 212-4 GIFT BRINGERS, THE: KOLYADA ☐

Comments: **Fourth in Series,** White Glass Ball, 2-7/8" dia. Dated Christmas 1992. The elf maiden Kolyada brings Christmas to Russian children. **Artist:** LaDene Votruba

☐ Purchased 19 __Pd $____MIB   NB   DB   BNT
☐ Want   Orig. Ret. $5.00 **NB** $10   **MIB** Sec. Mkt. **$20**

QX 594-1   GODCHILD ☐
Comments: Handcrafted, 1-5/8" tall, Dated 1992.
The love of the Godparent and Godchild for each other is portrayed on the faces of these sheep. **Artist:** Duane Unruh
☐ Purchased 19 __Pd $____MIB   NB   DB   BNT
☐ Want   Orig. Ret. $6.75   **NB** $12   **MIB** Sec. Mkt. **$20**

QX 598-4   GOLF'S A BALL ☐
Comments: Handcrafted, 3-1/2" tall, Dated 1992.
This cheery snowman is fashioned from golf balls and has golf clubs for arms. **Artist:** Lee Schuler
☐ Purchased 19 __Pd $____MIB   NB   DB   BNT
☐ Want   Orig. Ret. $6.75   **NB** $21   **MIB** Sec. Mkt. **$30**

QX 517-1   GONE WISHIN' ☐
Comments: Handcrafted, 1-11/16" tall, Dated 1992.
While Santa naps in his silver motorboat, he has hooked a green package on his line. **Artist:** Donna Lee
☐ Purchased 19 __Pd $____MIB   NB   DB   BNT
☐ Want   Orig. Ret. $8.75   **NB** $15   **MIB** Sec. Mkt. **$20**

QLX 724-4   GOOD SLEDDING AHEAD ☐
Comments: Light and Motion, Handcrafted, 3-9/16" tall, Dated 1992. A dog follows closely behind as the children sled 'round and 'round their house. **Artist:** Don Palmiter
☐ Purchased 19 __Pd $____MIB   NB   DB   BNT
☐ Want   Orig. Ret. $28.00 **NB** $38   **MIB** Sec. Mkt. **$58**

QX 560-4   GRANDDAUGHTER ☐
Comments: Handcrafted, 1-3/4" tall, Dated 1992.
A little mouse, with pink frock and a bow on her head, naps in the core of the red apple she has been nibbling. Caption: "Grand-daughter, You're The Apple Of My Eye." **Artist:** Ed Seale
☐ Purchased 19 __Pd $____MIB   NB   DB   BNT
☐ Want   Orig. Ret. $6.75   **NB** $19   **MIB** Sec. Mkt. **$25**

QX 463-4   GRANDDAUGHTER'S
            FIRST CHRISTMAS ☐
Comments: Handcrafted, 2-3/16" tall, Dated 1992.
This little girl cub loves the toys and ice skates tucked inside her Christmas bag. **Artist:** Bob Siedler
☐ Purchased 19 __Pd $____MIB   NB   DB   BNT
☐ Want   Orig. Ret. $6.75   **NB** $10   **MIB** Sec. Mkt. **$17**

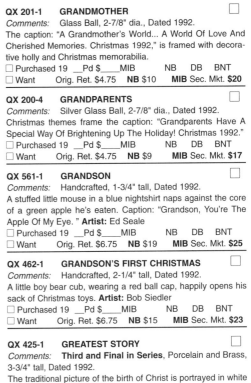

QX 201-1   GRANDMOTHER ☐
Comments: Glass Ball, 2-7/8" dia., Dated 1992.
The caption: "A Grandmother's World... A World Of Love And Cherished Memories. Christmas 1992," is framed with decorative holly and Christmas memorabilia.
☐ Purchased 19 __Pd $____MIB   NB   DB   BNT
☐ Want   Orig. Ret. $4.75   **NB** $10   **MIB** Sec. Mkt. **$20**

QX 200-4   GRANDPARENTS ☐
Comments: Silver Glass Ball, 2-7/8" dia., Dated 1992.
Christmas themes frame the caption: "Grandparents Have A Special Way Of Brightening Up The Holiday! Christmas 1992."
☐ Purchased 19 __Pd $____MIB   NB   DB   BNT
☐ Want   Orig. Ret. $4.75   **NB** $9   **MIB** Sec. Mkt. **$17**

QX 561-1   GRANDSON ☐
Comments: Handcrafted, 1-3/4" tall, Dated 1992.
A stuffed little mouse in a blue nightshirt naps against the core of a green apple he's eaten. Caption: "Grandson, You're The Apple Of My Eye. " **Artist:** Ed Seale
☐ Purchased 19 __Pd $____MIB   NB   DB   BNT
☐ Want   Orig. Ret. $6.75   **NB** $19   **MIB** Sec. Mkt. **$25**

QX 462-1   GRANDSON'S FIRST CHRISTMAS ☐
Comments: Handcrafted, 2-1/4" tall, Dated 1992.
A little boy bear cub, wearing a red ball cap, happily opens his sack of Christmas toys. **Artist:** Bob Siedler
☐ Purchased 19 __Pd $____MIB   NB   DB   BNT
☐ Want   Orig. Ret. $6.75   **NB** $15   **MIB** Sec. Mkt. **$23**

QX 425-1   GREATEST STORY ☐
Comments: **Third and Final in Series**, Porcelain and Brass, 3-3/4" tall, Dated 1992.
The traditional picture of the birth of Christ is portrayed in white porcelain. **Artist:** LaDene Votruba
☐ Purchased 19 __Pd $____MIB   NB   DB   BNT
☐ Want   Orig. Ret. $12.75 **NB** $19   **MIB** Sec. Mkt. **$25**

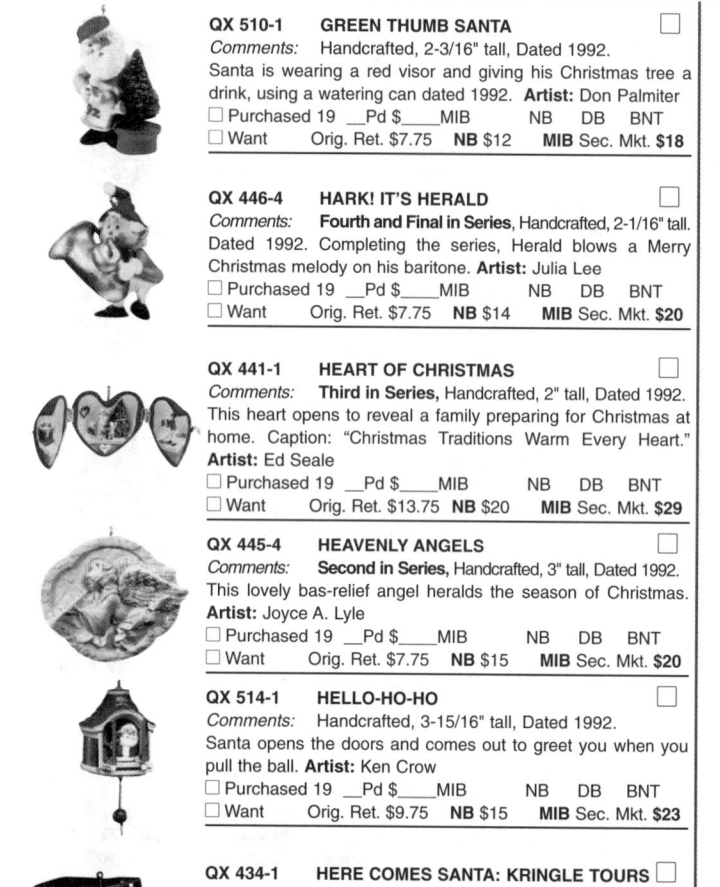

QX 510-1   GREEN THUMB SANTA ☐
Comments: Handcrafted, 2-3/16" tall, Dated 1992.
Santa is wearing a red visor and giving his Christmas tree a drink, using a watering can dated 1992. **Artist:** Don Palmiter
☐ Purchased 19 __Pd $____MIB   NB   DB   BNT
☐ Want   Orig. Ret. $7.75   **NB** $12   **MIB** Sec. Mkt. **$18**

QX 446-4   HARK! IT'S HERALD ☐
Comments: **Fourth and Final in Series,** Handcrafted, 2-1/16" tall. Dated 1992. Completing the series, Herald blows a Merry Christmas melody on his baritone. **Artist:** Julia Lee
☐ Purchased 19 __Pd $____MIB   NB   DB   BNT
☐ Want   Orig. Ret. $7.75   **NB** $14   **MIB** Sec. Mkt. **$20**

QX 441-1   HEART OF CHRISTMAS ☐
Comments: **Third in Series,** Handcrafted, 2" tall, Dated 1992. This heart opens to reveal a family preparing for Christmas at home. Caption: "Christmas Traditions Warm Every Heart." **Artist:** Ed Seale
☐ Purchased 19 __Pd $____MIB   NB   DB   BNT
☐ Want   Orig. Ret. $13.75   **NB** $20   **MIB** Sec. Mkt. **$29**

QX 445-4   HEAVENLY ANGELS ☐
Comments: **Second in Series,** Handcrafted, 3" tall, Dated 1992. This lovely bas-relief angel heralds the season of Christmas. **Artist:** Joyce A. Lyle
☐ Purchased 19 __Pd $____MIB   NB   DB   BNT
☐ Want   Orig. Ret. $7.75   **NB** $15   **MIB** Sec. Mkt. **$20**

QX 514-1   HELLO-HO-HO ☐
Comments: Handcrafted, 3-15/16" tall, Dated 1992.
Santa opens the doors and comes out to greet you when you pull the ball. **Artist:** Ken Crow
☐ Purchased 19 __Pd $____MIB   NB   DB   BNT
☐ Want   Orig. Ret. $9.75   **NB** $15   **MIB** Sec. Mkt. **$23**

QX 434-1   HERE COMES SANTA: KRINGLE TOURS ☐
Comments: **Fourteenth in Series,** Handcrafted, 2-5/8" tall. Dated 1992. Santa makes the perfect tour guide as he leads the Christmas tour. This is the longest-running Keepsake Ornament series. **Artist:** Linda Sickman
☐ Purchased 19 __Pd $____MIB   NB   DB   BNT
☐ Want   Orig. Ret. $14.75   **NB** $30   **MIB** Sec. Mkt. **$45**

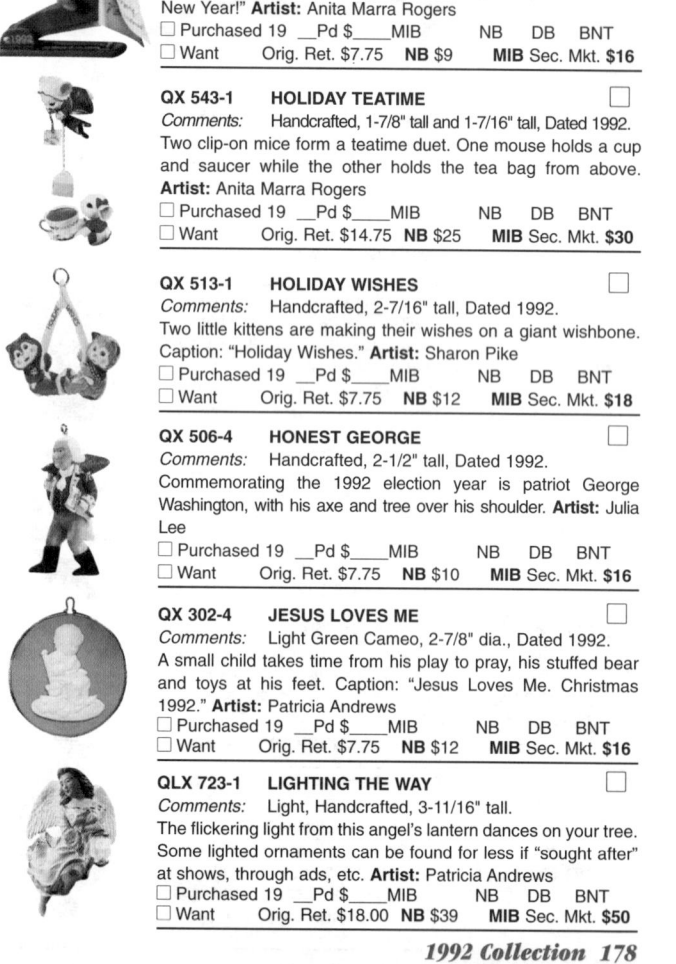

QX 504-4   HOLIDAY MEMO ☐
Comments: Handcrafted, 2-7/16" tall, Dated 1992.
This cute Christmas critter, astride a stapler, holds a message, "MEMO: Have A Very Merry Christmas... (inside) And A Terrific New Year!" **Artist:** Anita Marra Rogers
☐ Purchased 19 __Pd $____MIB   NB   DB   BNT
☐ Want   Orig. Ret. $7.75   **NB** $9   **MIB** Sec. Mkt. **$16**

QX 543-1   HOLIDAY TEATIME ☐
Comments: Handcrafted, 1-7/8" tall and 1-7/16" tall, Dated 1992. Two clip-on mice form a teatime duet. One mouse holds a cup and saucer while the other holds the tea bag from above. **Artist:** Anita Marra Rogers
☐ Purchased 19 __Pd $____MIB   NB   DB   BNT
☐ Want   Orig. Ret. $14.75   **NB** $25   **MIB** Sec. Mkt. **$30**

QX 513-1   HOLIDAY WISHES ☐
Comments: Handcrafted, 2-7/16" tall, Dated 1992.
Two little kittens are making their wishes on a giant wishbone. Caption: "Holiday Wishes." **Artist:** Sharon Pike
☐ Purchased 19 __Pd $____MIB   NB   DB   BNT
☐ Want   Orig. Ret. $7.75   **NB** $12   **MIB** Sec. Mkt. **$18**

QX 506-4   HONEST GEORGE ☐
Comments: Handcrafted, 2-1/2" tall, Dated 1992.
Commemorating the 1992 election year is patriot George Washington, with his axe and tree over his shoulder. **Artist:** Julia Lee
☐ Purchased 19 __Pd $____MIB   NB   DB   BNT
☐ Want   Orig. Ret. $7.75   **NB** $10   **MIB** Sec. Mkt. **$16**

QX 302-4   JESUS LOVES ME ☐
Comments: Light Green Cameo, 2-7/8" dia., Dated 1992.
A small child takes time from his play to pray, his stuffed bear and toys at his feet. Caption: "Jesus Loves Me. Christmas 1992." **Artist:** Patricia Andrews
☐ Purchased 19 __Pd $____MIB   NB   DB   BNT
☐ Want   Orig. Ret. $7.75   **NB** $12   **MIB** Sec. Mkt. **$16**

QLX 723-1   LIGHTING THE WAY ☐
Comments: Light, Handcrafted, 3-11/16" tall.
The flickering light from this angel's lantern dances on your tree. Some lighted ornaments can be found for less if "sought after" at shows, through ads, etc. **Artist:** Patricia Andrews
☐ Purchased 19 __Pd $____MIB   NB   DB   BNT
☐ Want   Orig. Ret. $18.00   **NB** $39   **MIB** Sec. Mkt. **$50**

QLX 709-4   LOOK! IT'S SANTA

Comments: Lighted, Handcrafted, 4-1/16" tall, Dated 1992. Excited children peer around their Christmas tree to catch a glimpse of Santa; they know he's there because they see his shadow on the wall. **Artist:** Donna Lee

☐ Purchased 19   __Pd $____MIB   NB   DB   BNT
☐ Want   Orig. Ret. $14.00 **NB** $30   **MIB** Sec. Mkt. **$50**

QX 484-1   LOVE TO SKATE

Comments: Handcrafted, 2-5/8" tall, Dated Christmas 1992. This bear couple have eyes only for each other as they skate into the Christmas season. **Artist:** Anita Marra Rogers

☐ Purchased 19   __Pd $____MIB   NB   DB   BNT
☐ Want   Orig. Ret. $8.75 **NB** $14   **MIB** Sec. Mkt. **$20**

QX 515-1   LOVING SHEPHERD

Comments: Handcrafted, 2-13/16" tall, Dated 1992. A content, happy lamb looks with joy to his shepherd, confident of his love and care. **Artist:** Patricia Andrews

☐ Purchased 19   __Pd $____MIB   NB   DB   BNT
☐ Want   Orig. Ret. $7.75 **NB** $12   **MIB** Sec. Mkt. **$17**

QX 427-4   MARY'S ANGELS: LILY

Comments: **Fifth in Series,** Acrylic, Handcrafted, 2-7/16" tall. Lily yawns widely and wipes her eyes as she sits sleepy-eyed on her frosted acrylic cloud. This is a popular series. **Artist:** Robert Chad

☐ Purchased 19   __Pd $____MIB   NB   DB   BNT
☐ Want   Orig. Ret. $6.75 **NB** $40   **MIB** Sec. Mkt. **$50**

QX 516-1   MEMORIES TO CHERISH PHOTOHOLDER

Comments: Fine Porcelain, 3-5/8" tall, Dated 1992. Frame a favorite photo in this lovely hand-painted fine porcelain ornament. "Merry Christmas 1992." **Artist:** Patricia Andrews

☐ Purchased 19   __Pd $____MIB   NB   DB   BNT
☐ Want   Orig. Ret. $10.75 **NB** $14   **MIB** Sec. Mkt. **$22**

QX 441-4   MERRY OLDE SANTA

Comments: **Third in Series,** Handcrafted, 4-1/8" tall, Dated 1992. While a teddy sits nearby on a toy drum, Santa is filling a red stocking with a horn. **Artist:** Duane Unruh

☐ Purchased 19   __Pd $____MIB   NB   DB   BNT
☐ Want   Orig. Ret. $14.75 **NB** $30   **MIB** Sec. Mkt. **$40**

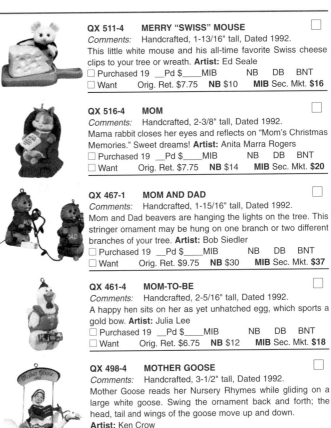

QX 511-4   MERRY "SWISS" MOUSE

Comments: Handcrafted, 1-13/16" tall, Dated 1992. This little white mouse and his all-time favorite Swiss cheese clips to your tree or wreath. **Artist:** Ed Seale

☐ Purchased 19   __Pd $____MIB   NB   DB   BNT
☐ Want   Orig. Ret. $7.75 **NB** $10   **MIB** Sec. Mkt. **$16**

QX 516-4   MOM

Comments: Handcrafted, 2-3/8" tall, Dated 1992. Mama rabbit closes her eyes and reflects on "Mom's Christmas Memories." Sweet dreams! **Artist:** Anita Marra Rogers

☐ Purchased 19   __Pd $____MIB   NB   DB   BNT
☐ Want   Orig. Ret. $7.75 **NB** $14   **MIB** Sec. Mkt. **$20**

QX 467-1   MOM AND DAD

Comments: Handcrafted, 1-15/16" tall, Dated 1992. Mom and Dad beavers are hanging the lights on the tree. This stringer ornament may be hung on one branch or two different branches of your tree. **Artist:** Bob Siedler

☐ Purchased 19   __Pd $____MIB   NB   DB   BNT
☐ Want   Orig. Ret. $9.75 **NB** $30   **MIB** Sec. Mkt. **$37**

QX 461-4   MOM-TO-BE

Comments: Handcrafted, 2-5/16" tall, Dated 1992. A happy hen sits on her as yet unhatched egg, which sports a gold bow. **Artist:** Julia Lee

☐ Purchased 19   __Pd $____MIB   NB   DB   BNT
☐ Want   Orig. Ret. $6.75 **NB** $12   **MIB** Sec. Mkt. **$18**

QX 498-4   MOTHER GOOSE

Comments: Handcrafted, 3-1/2" tall, Dated 1992. Mother Goose reads her Nursery Rhymes while gliding on a large white goose. Swing the ornament back and forth; the head, tail and wings of the goose move up and down. **Artist:** Ken Crow

☐ Purchased 19   __Pd $____MIB   NB   DB   BNT
☐ Want   Orig. Ret. $13.75 **NB** $23   **MIB** Sec. Mkt. **$30**

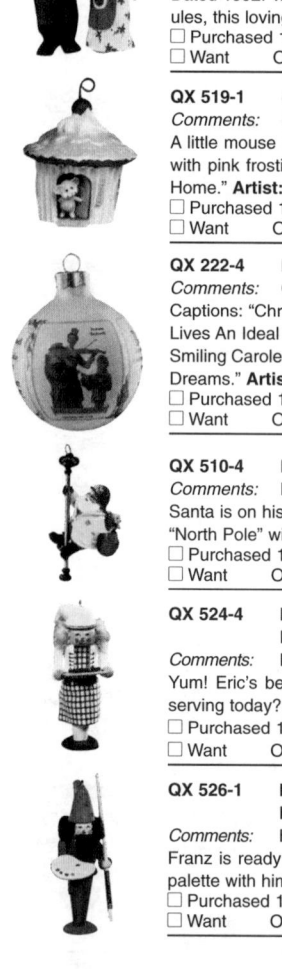

QX 429-4   MR. AND MRS. CLAUS:
GIFT EXCHANGE ☐
Comments: **Seventh in Series,** Handcrafted, 3-1/8" tall.
Dated 1992. Taking time out from their busy Christmas sched-
ules, this loving couple exchanges gifts. **Artist:** Duane Unruh
☐ Purchased 19 __Pd $____MIB   NB   DB   BNT
☐ Want   Orig. Ret. $14.75 **NB** $31   **MIB** Sec. Mkt. **$45**

QX 519-1   NEW HOME ☐
Comments: Handcrafted, 2-1/2" tall, Dated 1992.
A little mouse looks out the door of his cupcake home, topped
with pink frosting "snow" and a cherry. Caption: "Home Sweet
Home." **Artist:** Sharon Pike
☐ Purchased 19 __Pd $____MIB   NB   DB   BNT
☐ Want   Orig. Ret. $8.75 **NB** $15   **MIB** Sec. Mkt. **$18**

QX 222-4   NORMAN ROCKWELL ART ☐
Comments: Glass Ball, 2-7/8" dia., Dated 1992.
Captions: "Christmas Sing Merrily" and "In Each Of Our Hearts
Lives An Ideal Christmas... A Season Of Snow-Covered Trees,
Smiling Carolers, And Santa Claus, A Season Of Memories And
Dreams." **Artist:** Joyce A. Lyle
☐ Purchased 19 __Pd $____MIB   NB   DB   BNT
☐ Want   Orig. Ret. $5.00 **NB** $14   **MIB** Sec. Mkt. **$25**

QX 510-4   NORTH POLE FIRE FIGHTER ☐
Comments: Handcrafted, 3-3/4" tall, Dated 1992.
Santa is on his way to rescue Christmas as he slides down the
"North Pole" with his pack on his back. **Artist:** Ed Seale
☐ Purchased 19 __Pd $____MIB   NB   DB   BNT
☐ Want   Orig. Ret. $9.75 **NB** $19   **MIB** Sec. Mkt. **$23**

QX 524-4   NORTH POLE NUTCRACKERS:
ERIC THE BAKER ☐
Comments: Handcrafted, 4-3/8" tall, Dated on Bottom – 1992.
Yum! Eric's been in the kitchen again. What tasty treat is he
serving today? **Artist:** Linda Sickman
☐ Purchased 19 __Pd $____MIB   NB   DB   BNT
☐ Want   Orig. Ret. $8.75 **NB** $14   **MIB** Sec. Mkt. **$23**

QX 526-1   NORTH POLE NUTCRACKERS:
FRANZ THE ARTIST ☐
Comments: Handcrafted, 4-5/8" tall, Dated on Bottom - 1992.
Franz is ready to paint your portrait! He carries his brush and
palette with him. **Artist:** Linda Sickman
☐ Purchased 19 __Pd $____MIB   NB   DB   BNT
☐ Want   Orig. Ret. $8.75 **NB** $16   **MIB** Sec. Mkt. **$25**

QX 526-4   NORTH POLE NUTCRACKERS:
FRIEDA THE ANIMALS' FRIEND ☐
Comments: Handcrafted, 4-3/8" tall, Dated on Bottom - 1992.
The animals know of Frieda's love for them and they happily
come to her. **Artist:** Linda Sickman
☐ Purchased 19 __Pd $____MIB   NB   DB   BNT
☐ Want   Orig. Ret. $8.75 **NB** $20   **MIB** Sec. Mkt. **$27**

QX 528-1   NORTH POLE NUTCRACKERS:
LUDWIG THE MUSICIAN ☐
Comments: Handcrafted, 4-7/8" tall, Dated on Bottom - 1992.
Ludwig's talents are readily seen by his sheet music and
French Horn. **Artist:** Linda Sickman
☐ Purchased 19 __Pd $____MIB   NB   DB   BNT
☐ Want   Orig. Ret. $8.75 **NB** $18   **MIB** Sec. Mkt. **$23**

QX 525-1   NORTH POLE NUTCRACKERS:
MAX THE TAILOR ☐
Comments: Handcrafted, 4-3/8" tall, Dated on Bottom - 1992.
Max comes complete with needle and thread to stitch a torn
teddy bear. **Artist:** Linda Sickman
☐ Purchased 19 __Pd $____MIB   NB   DB   BNT
☐ Want   Orig. Ret. $8.75 **NB** $18   **MIB** Sec. Mkt. **$23**

QX 525-4   NORTH POLE NUTCRACKERS:
OTTO THE CARPENTER ☐
Comments: Handcrafted, 4-3/8" tall, Dated on Bottom - 1992.
Otto is ready for business with his mallet in one hand and his
masterpiece in the other. **Artist:** Linda Sickman
☐ Purchased 19 __Pd $____MIB   NB   DB   BNT
☐ Want   Orig. Ret. $8.75 **NB** $18   **MIB** Sec. Mkt. **$23**

QX 425-4   NOSTALGIC HOUSES AND SHOPS:
FIVE-AND-TEN-CENT STORE ☐
Comments: **Ninth in Series,** Handcrafted, 3-5/8" tall, Dated
1992. This old-fashioned shop recreates yesteryear, down to
the bubble gum machine in front of the store. **Artist:** Donna Lee
☐ Purchased 19 __Pd $____MIB   NB   DB   BNT
☐ Want   Orig. Ret. $14.75 **NB** $35   **MIB** Sec. Mkt. **$45**

QLX 708-1   NUT, SWEET NUT
Comments: Light, Handcrafted, 2-1/16" tall, Dated 1992.
A cute little chipmunk peeks through the door of his snow-covered walnut home. **Artist:** Ken Crow
☐ Purchased 19 __Pd $____MIB   NB   DB   BNT
☐ Want   Orig. Ret. $10.00 **NB** $17   **MIB** Sec. Mkt. **$23**

QX 541-1   O CHRISTMAS TREE
Comments: Porcelain Bell, Dated 1992.
A Christmas tree sits atop this Hallmark Keepsake Premiere Bell. **Artist:** LaDene Votruba
☐ Purchased 19 __Pd $____MIB   NB   DB   BNT
☐ Want   Orig. Ret. $10.75 **NB** $20   **MIB** Sec. Mkt. **$25**

QLX 722-1   OUR FIRST CHRISTMAS
Comments: Light, Panorama Ball, 3-5/8" tall, Dated 1992.
The view inside this blue panorama ball reveals a couple enjoying a cozy, flickering fireplace. Caption: "Christmas Is A Magic Time Of Sweet, Romantic Moments."
Artist: Robert Chad
☐ Purchased 19 __Pd $____MIB   NB   DB   BNT
☐ Want   Orig. Ret. $20.00 **NB** $31   **MIB** Sec. Mkt. **$43**

QX 561-4   OWL
Comments: Handcrafted, 2-7/8" tall.
Owl is getting ready for Christmas with his string of colored lights. An addition to the Winnie-the-Pooh collection.
Artist: Bob Siedler
☐ Purchased 19 __Pd $____MIB   NB   DB   BNT
☐ Want   Orig. Ret. $9.75 **NB** $15   **MIB** Sec. Mkt. **$20**

QX 454-4   OWLIVER
Comments: **FIRST IN SERIES,** Handcrafted, 2-1/16" tall.
Dated 1992. Owliver reads from a book. This first in series ornament is still not showing an increase on the secondary market.
Artist: Bob Siedler
☐ Purchased 19 __Pd $____MIB   NB   DB   BNT
☐ Want   Orig. Ret. $7.75 **NB** $13   **MIB** Sec. Mkt. **$18**

QX 523-4   PARTRIDGE IN A PEAR TREE
Comments: Handcrafted, 4-1/8" tall, Dated 1992.
The pear at the top of this tree, planted in a gift box, opens to reveal an embarrassed partridge in his boxer shorts. Tree trunk is dated. **Artist:** Bob Siedler
☐ Purchased 19 __Pd $____MIB   NB   DB   BNT
☐ Want   Orig. Ret. $8.75 **NB** $14   **MIB** Sec. Mkt. **$20**

QX 517-4   PEACE ON EARTH: SPAIN
Comments: **Second in Series,** Handcrafted, 3" dia., Dated 1992.
Two Spanish children wish to all "Paz Sobre La Tierra."
Artist: Linda Sickman
☐ Purchased 19 __Pd $____MIB   NB   DB   BNT
☐ Want   Orig. Ret. $11.75 **NB** $13   **MIB** Sec. Mkt. **$23**

QX 224-4   PEANUTS®
Comments: Chrome Ball, 2-7/8" dia., Christmas 1992.
Charlie Brown, Lucy and the rest of the Peanuts gang act out the Nativity. Caption: "... Behold, I Bring You Good Tidings Of Great Joy, Which Shall Be To All People."
☐ Purchased 19 __Pd $____MIB   NB   DB   BNT
☐ Want   Orig. Ret. $5.00 **NB** $30   **MIB** Sec. Mkt. **$40**

QLX 721-4   PEANUTS®
Comments: **Second in Series,** Handcrafted, 3-15/16" tall.
Dated 1992. Lights blink merrily on the wreath as Snoopy and Woodstock sit cozily on the roof of Snoopy's doghouse.
Caption: "Happy Holidays." **Artist:** Dill Rhodus
☐ Purchased 19 __Pd $____MIB   NB   DB   BNT
☐ Want   Orig. Ret. $18.00 **NB** $33   **MIB** Sec. Mkt. **$50**

QX 529-1   PLEASE PAUSE HERE
Comments: Handcrafted, 4" tall, Dated 1992.
Santa's note reads, "Dear Santa, Please Pause Here. Your PAL." Santa holds his Coca-Cola and does just that. Clips onto a tree branch or garland. **Artist:** Donna Lee
☐ Purchased 19 __Pd $____MIB   NB   DB   BNT
☐ Want   Orig. Ret. $14.75 **NB** $17   **MIB** Sec. Mkt. **$30**

QX 491-4   POLAR POST

Comments: Handcrafted, 2-7/8" tall, Dated 1992.
This polar mail carrier, dressed in a red scarf, holds a real working compass to help find the North Pole. **Artist:** Ed Seale
☐ Purchased 19 __Pd $____MIB   NB   DB   BNT
☐ Want   Orig. Ret. $8.75 **NB** $15   **MIB** Sec. Mkt. **$20**

QX 448-4   PUPPY LOVE

Comments: **Second in Series,** 2-5/8" tall, Handcrafted Brass. Dated 1992. A gray and white terrier wags a Merry Christmas from his wicker basket. **Artist:** Anita Marra Rogers
☐ Purchased 19 __Pd $____MIB   NB   DB   BNT
☐ Want   Orig. Ret. $7.75 **NB** $30   **MIB** Sec. Mkt. **$40**

QX 509-4   RAPID DELIVERY

Comments: Handcrafted, 1-7/8" tall, Dated 1992.
The Christmas deliveries must be made... so this cute little elf braves the rapids in his blue raft. **Artist:** Don Palmiter
☐ Purchased 19 __Pd $____MIB   NB   DB   BNT
☐ Want   Orig. Ret. $8.75 **NB** $20   **MIB** Sec. Mkt. **$25**

QX 528-4   REINDEER CHAMPS: DONDER

Comments: **Seventh in Series,** Handcrafted, 3-1/16" tall. Dated 1992. Donder is ready to strike out the opposing team. He's wearing his team colors: white with red socks and a green shirt. **Artist:** Bob Siedler
☐ Purchased 19 __Pd $____MIB   NB   DB   BNT
☐ Want   Orig. Ret. $8.75 **NB** $30   **MIB** Sec. Mkt. **$35**

QX 426-1   ROCKING HORSE

Comments: **Twelfth in Series,** Handcrafted, 3" tall, Dated 1992. This brown horse wears a lacy white saddle blanket with a green saddle trimmed in red. **Artist:** Linda Sickman
☐ Purchased 19 __Pd $____MIB   NB   DB   BNT
☐ Want   Orig. Ret. $10.75 **NB** $30   **MIB** Sec. Mkt. **$45**

QXC 508-1   RODNEY TAKES FLIGHT:

KEEPSAKE CLUB

Comments: Handcrafted, 1-3/4" tall, Dated 1992.
Rodney is off and flying! Captions: "Rodney's Flight School Holiday Special" and "FLY WITH RODNEY Club Members Welcome." **Artist:** Donna Lee
☐ Purchased 19 __Pd $____MIB   NB   DB   BNT
☐ Want   Orig. Ret. Came with Club Membership of $20.00
                            NB $17   **MIB** Sec. Mkt. **$23**

QX 507-4   SANTA MARIA

Comments: Handcrafted, 3-1/8" tall, Dated 1992.
Santa spies land as he stands aboard the Santa Maria, commemorating the 500th anniversary of Columbus' arrival in America. Plenty out there on the secondary market!
Artist: Ken Crow
☐ Purchased 19 __Pd $____MIB   NB   DB   BNT
☐ Want   Orig. Ret. $12.75 **NB** $25   **MIB** Sec. Mkt. **$30**

XPR 973-5   SANTA & HIS REINDEER COLLECTION:
              DASHER & DANCER (SLEIGH ON PAGE 183)

Comments: Handcrafted, 3-15/64" tall.
Dasher and Dancer lead the way to Hallmark's Christmas Open House Promotional ornaments. **Artist:** Ken Crow
☐ Purchased 19 __Pd $____MIB   NB   DB   BNT
☐ Want   Orig. Ret. $4.95 with any $5 Hallmark purchase
                            NB $40   **MIB** Sec. Mkt. **$50**

XPR 973-6   SANTA & HIS REINDEER COLLECTION:
              PRANCER & VIXEN

Comments: Handcrafted, 3-15/64" tall.
Artist: Ken Crow
☐ Purchased 19 __Pd $____MIB   NB   DB   BNT
☐ Want   Orig. Ret. $4.95 with any $5 Hallmark purchase
                            NB $12   **MIB** Sec. Mkt. **$20**

XPR 973-7   SANTA & HIS REINDEER COLLECTION:
              COMET & CUPID

Comments: Handcrafted, 3-3/64" tall.
Artist: Ken Crow
☐ Purchased 19 __Pd $____MIB   NB   DB   BNT
☐ Want   Orig. Ret. $4.95 with any $5 Hallmark purchase
                            NB $12   **MIB** Sec. Mkt. **$20**

XPR 973-8   SANTA & HIS REINDEER COLLECTION:
              DONDER & BLITZEN

Comments: Handcrafted, 3-5/32" tall.
Artist: Ken Crow
☐ Purchased 19 __Pd $____MIB   NB   DB   BNT
☐ Want   Orig. Ret. $4.95 with any $5 Hallmark purchase
                            NB $30   **MIB** Sec. Mkt. **$40**

XPR 973-9   SANTA & HIS REINDEER COLLECTION: ☐
SANTA & SLEIGH
Comments: Handcrafted, 2-9/16" tall, Dated 1992.
Santa and his sleigh complete the collection. All ornaments in
this set link together. **Artist:** Ken Crow
☐ Purchased 19 __Pd $____MIB   NB   DB   BNT
☐ Want   Orig. Ret. $4.95 with any $5 Hallmark purchase
                              NB $20   **MIB** Sec. Mkt. **$30**

QLX 716-7   SANTA SPECIAL ☐
Comments: Light, Motion and Sound, Handcrafted, 3-1/8" tall.
Reissued from 1991. **Artist:** Ed Seale
☐ Purchased 19 __Pd $____MIB   NB   DB   BNT
☐ Want   Orig. Ret. $40.00 **NB** $65   **MIB** Sec. Mkt. **$80**

QLX 732-1   SANTA SUB ☐
Comments: Blinking Lights, Handcrafted, 2-3/4" tall, Dated 1992.
Santa's safe in the USS Peppermint, red and white striped sub-
marine. **Artist:** Ken Crow
☐ Purchased 19 __Pd $____MIB   NB   DB   BNT
☐ Want   Orig. Ret. $18.00 **NB** $30   **MIB** Sec. Mkt. **$40**

QLX 724-1   SANTA'S ANSWERING MACHINE ☐
Comments: Voice, Sound and Blinking Light, 1-7/8" tall.
Dated 1992. Santa's not in, but when you press the button you
will hear his Christmas message to you, along with the jingling
of bells. **Artist:** Julia Lee
☐ Purchased 19 __Pd $____MIB   NB   DB   BNT
☐ Want   Orig. Ret. $22.00 **NB** $37   **MIB** Sec. Mkt. **$45**

QXC 729-1   SANTA'S CLUB LIST: KEEPSAKE CLUB ☐
Comments: Members Only, Light, Handcrafted, 2-1/8" tall.
Dressed as Santa, a small raccoon holds a lighted candle and
reads from "Santa's Club List." **Artist:** Ed Seale
☐ Purchased 19 __Pd $____MIB   NB   DB   BNT
☐ Want   Orig. Ret. $15.00 **NB** $30   **MIB** Sec. Mkt. **$40**

QX 543-4   SANTA'S HOOK SHOT ☐
Comments: Handcrafted, 2" tall, Dated 1992.
Santa's "Hooked on Christmas!" Set of two ornaments includes
Santa, wearing a green dated jersey and red shorts and a clip-
on basketball hoop with basketball. **Artist:** Ed Seale
☐ Purchased 19 __Pd $____MIB   NB   DB   BNT
☐ Want   Orig. Ret. $12.75 **NB** $22   **MIB** Sec. Mkt. **$29**

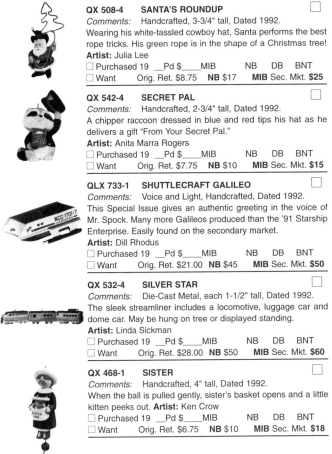

QX 508-4   SANTA'S ROUNDUP ☐
Comments: Handcrafted, 3-3/4" tall, Dated 1992.
Wearing his white-tassled cowboy hat, Santa performs the best
rope tricks. His green rope is in the shape of a Christmas tree!
Artist: Julia Lee
☐ Purchased 19 __Pd $____MIB   NB   DB   BNT
☐ Want   Orig. Ret. $8.75 **NB** $17   **MIB** Sec. Mkt. **$25**

QX 542-4   SECRET PAL ☐
Comments: Handcrafted, 2-3/4" tall, Dated 1992.
A chipper raccoon dressed in blue and red tips his hat as he
delivers a gift "From Your Secret Pal."
Artist: Anita Marra Rogers
☐ Purchased 19 __Pd $____MIB   NB   DB   BNT
☐ Want   Orig. Ret. $7.75 **NB** $10   **MIB** Sec. Mkt. **$15**

QLX 733-1   SHUTTLECRAFT GALILEO ☐
Comments: Voice and Light, Handcrafted, Dated 1992.
This Special Issue gives an authentic greeting in the voice of
Mr. Spock. Many more Galileos produced than the '91 Starship
Enterprise. Easily found on the secondary market.
Artist: Dill Rhodus
☐ Purchased 19 __Pd $____MIB   NB   DB   BNT
☐ Want   Orig. Ret. $21.00 **NB** $45   **MIB** Sec. Mkt. **$50**

QX 532-4   SILVER STAR ☐
Comments: Die-Cast Metal, each 1-1/2" tall, Dated 1992.
The sleek streamliner includes a locomotive, luggage car and
dome car. May be hung on tree or displayed standing.
Artist: Linda Sickman
☐ Purchased 19 __Pd $____MIB   NB   DB   BNT
☐ Want   Orig. Ret. $28.00 **NB** $50   **MIB** Sec. Mkt. **$60**

QX 468-1   SISTER ☐
Comments: Handcrafted, 4" tall, Dated 1992.
When the ball is pulled gently, sister's basket opens and a little
kitten peeks out. **Artist:** Ken Crow
☐ Purchased 19 __Pd $____MIB   NB   DB   BNT
☐ Want   Orig. Ret. $6.75 **NB** $10   **MIB** Sec. Mkt. **$18**

Family happiness is homemade.

QX 521-4 SKIING 'ROUND ☐
Comments: Handcrafted, 3-5/8" tall, Dated 1992.
This fellow has gotten himself all bound up in the middle of a
snowball. **Artist:** Julia Lee
☐ Purchased 19 __Pd $____MIB   NB   DB   BNT
☐ Want   Orig. Ret. $8.75   **NB** $15   **MIB** Sec. Mkt. **$20**

QX 595-4 SNOOPY® AND WOODSTOCK ☐
Comments: Handcrafted, 2-3/4" tall, Dated 1992.
Woodstock enjoys a flight hanging onto the tip of Snoopy's hat
as he glides along on his ice skates. These two friends are hav-
ing lots of fun! **Artist:** Anita Marra Rogers
☐ Purchased 19 __Pd $____MIB   NB   DB   BNT
☐ Want   Orig. Ret. $8.75   **NB** $30   **MIB** Sec. Mkt. **$40**

QX 502-4 SON ☐
Comments: Handcrafted, 2" tall, Dated 1992.
This daring boy squirrel, clad in a red sweater and flying gog-
gles, waves Merry Christmas from his blue and silver plane.
Artist: John Francis (Collin)
☐ Purchased 19 __Pd $____MIB   NB   DB   BNT
☐ Want   Orig. Ret. $6.75   **NB** $20   **MIB** Sec. Mkt. **$27**

QX 541-4 SPECIAL CAT PHOTOHOLDER ☐
Comments: Handcrafted, 4-1/8" tall, Dated 1992.
A little mouse takes advantage of the fact that the owner here is
only a photo of the family cat. **Artist:** Robert Chad
☐ Purchased 19 __Pd $____MIB   NB   DB   BNT
☐ Want   Orig. Ret. $7.75   **NB** $10   **MIB** Sec. Mkt. **$17**

QX 542-1 SPECIAL DOG PHOTOHOLDER ☐
Comments: Handcrafted, 4-13/16" tall, Dated 1992.
This cheery red doghouse is trimmed with Christmas lights and
a bright star. **Artist:** Robert Chad
☐ Purchased 19 __Pd $____MIB   NB   DB   BNT
☐ Want   Orig. Ret. $7.75   **NB** $12   **MIB** Sec. Mkt. **$20**

QX 523-1 SPIRIT OF CHRISTMAS STRESS ☐
Comments: Handcrafted, 3-1/2" tall.
Handling all the details of what to buy for Christmas can occa-
sionally be stressful, as depicted by this Shoebox Greetings
character. **Artist:** Robert Chad
☐ Purchased 19 __Pd $____MIB   NB   DB   BNT
☐ Want   Orig. Ret. $8.75   **NB** $14   **MIB** Sec. Mkt. **$20**

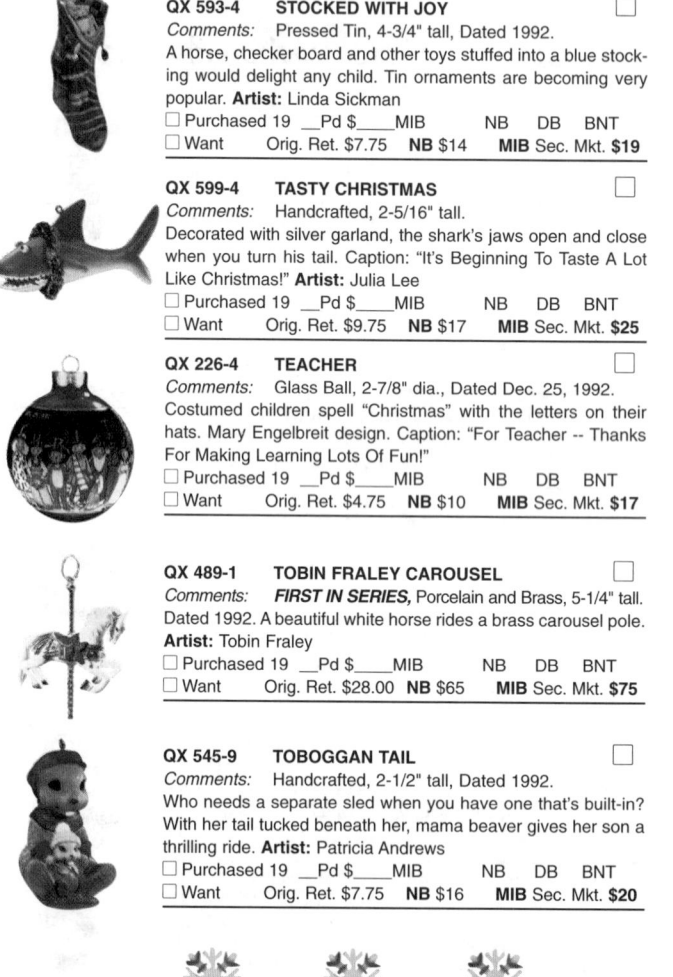

QX 593-4 STOCKED WITH JOY ☐
Comments: Pressed Tin, 4-3/4" tall, Dated 1992.
A horse, checker board and other toys stuffed into a blue stock-
ing would delight any child. Tin ornaments are becoming very
popular. **Artist:** Linda Sickman
☐ Purchased 19 __Pd $____MIB   NB   DB   BNT
☐ Want   Orig. Ret. $7.75   **NB** $14   **MIB** Sec. Mkt. **$19**

QX 599-4 TASTY CHRISTMAS ☐
Comments: Handcrafted, 2-5/16" tall.
Decorated with silver garland, the shark's jaws open and close
when you turn his tail. Caption: "It's Beginning To Taste A Lot
Like Christmas!" **Artist:** Julia Lee
☐ Purchased 19 __Pd $____MIB   NB   DB   BNT
☐ Want   Orig. Ret. $9.75   **NB** $17   **MIB** Sec. Mkt. **$25**

QX 226-4 TEACHER ☐
Comments: Glass Ball, 2-7/8" dia., Dated Dec. 25, 1992.
Costumed children spell "Christmas" with the letters on their
hats. Mary Engelbreit design. Caption: "For Teacher -- Thanks
For Making Learning Lots Of Fun!"
☐ Purchased 19 __Pd $____MIB   NB   DB   BNT
☐ Want   Orig. Ret. $4.75   **NB** $10   **MIB** Sec. Mkt. **$17**

QX 489-1 TOBIN FRALEY CAROUSEL ☐
Comments: **FIRST IN SERIES,** Porcelain and Brass, 5-1/4" tall.
Dated 1992. A beautiful white horse rides a brass carousel pole.
Artist: Tobin Fraley
☐ Purchased 19 __Pd $____MIB   NB   DB   BNT
☐ Want   Orig. Ret. $28.00 **NB** $65   **MIB** Sec. Mkt. **$75**

QX 545-9 TOBOGGAN TAIL ☐
Comments: Handcrafted, 2-1/2" tall, Dated 1992.
Who needs a separate sled when you have one that's built-in?
With her tail tucked beneath her, mama beaver gives her son a
thrilling ride. **Artist:** Patricia Andrews
☐ Purchased 19 __Pd $____MIB   NB   DB   BNT
☐ Want   Orig. Ret. $7.75   **NB** $16   **MIB** Sec. Mkt. **$20**

QX 509-1   TREAD BEAR ☐
Comments: Handcrafted, 2-1/4" tall, Dated 1992.
Swinging happily in his tire swing, this little white bear is dressed warmly in his red scarf. Caption: "Bear Paws 1992 Road Gripper." **Artist:** Ed Seale
☐ Purchased 19 __Pd $____MIB   NB   DB   BNT
☐ Want   Orig. Ret. $8.75 **NB** $20   **MIB** Sec. Mkt. **$25**

QX 499-1   TURTLE DREAMS ☐
Comments: Handcrafted, 1-13/16" tall, Dated 1992.
Open the shell and find this little fellow all tucked in, complete with a red stocking cap! Caption: "Don't Open Till Christmas."
Artist: Julia Lee
☐ Purchased 19 __Pd $____MIB   NB   DB   BNT
☐ Want   Orig. Ret. $8.75 **NB** $20   **MIB** Sec. Mkt. **$28**

QX 303-1   TWELVE DAYS OF CHRISTMAS: ☐
             NINE LADIES DANCING
Comments: **Ninth in Series,** Acrylic, 3" tall, Dated 1992.
A lovely maiden with holly decorations on her skirt dances on a quatrefoil shaped acrylic. This series needs a scarce one!
Artist: Michele Pyda-Sevcik
☐ Purchased 19 __Pd $____MIB   NB   DB   BNT
☐ Want   Orig. Ret. $6.75 **NB** $20   **MIB** Sec. Mkt. **$25**

QX 500-1   UNCLE ART'S ICE CREAM ☐
Comments: Handcrafted, 3-1/4" tall, Dated 1992.
A cute little mouse seems to be having fun turning the crank on this old fashioned ice cream maker. **Artist:** Bob Siedler
☐ Purchased 19 __Pd $____MIB   NB   DB   BNT
☐ Want   Orig. Ret. $8.75 **NB** $15   **MIB** Sec. Mkt. **$20**

QLX 732-4   UNDER CONSTRUCTION ☐
Comments: Light, Handcrafted, 3-1/2" tall, Dated 1992.
A little beaver flashes his red light to warn that you're nearing the tree-trimming zone. Caption: "Caution, Tree-Trimming Zone, 1992 Branch Under Construction." **Artist:** Don Palmiter
☐ Purchased 19 __Pd $____MIB   NB   DB   BNT
☐ Want   Orig. Ret. $18.00 **NB** $35   **MIB** Sec. Mkt. **$43**

QX 505-1   V.P. OF IMPORTANT STUFF ☐
Comments: Handcrafted, 2-1/16" tall, Dated 1992.
A penguin eats his donut from inside a white coffee cup. Caption in green print. **Artist:** Bob Siedler
☐ Purchased 19 __Pd $____MIB   NB   DB   BNT
☐ Want   Orig. Ret. $6.75 **NB** $10   **MIB** Sec. Mkt. **$15**

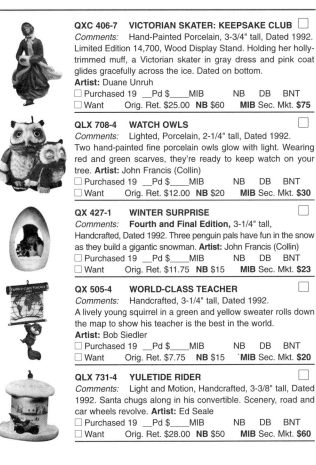

QXC 406-7   VICTORIAN SKATER: KEEPSAKE CLUB ☐
Comments: Hand-Painted Porcelain, 3-3/4" tall, Dated 1992.
Limited Edition 14,700, Wood Display Stand. Holding her holly-trimmed muff, a Victorian skater in gray dress and pink coat glides gracefully across the ice. Dated on bottom.
Artist: Duane Unruh
☐ Purchased 19 __Pd $____MIB   NB   DB   BNT
☐ Want   Orig. Ret. $25.00 **NB** $60   **MIB** Sec. Mkt. **$75**

QLX 708-4   WATCH OWLS ☐
Comments: Lighted, Porcelain, 2-1/4" tall, Dated 1992.
Two hand-painted fine porcelain owls glow with light. Wearing red and green scarves, they're ready to keep watch on your tree. **Artist:** John Francis (Collin)
☐ Purchased 19 __Pd $____MIB   NB   DB   BNT
☐ Want   Orig. Ret. $12.00 **NB** $20   **MIB** Sec. Mkt. **$30**

QX 427-1   WINTER SURPRISE ☐
Comments: **Fourth and Final Edition,** 3-1/4" tall,
Handcrafted, Dated 1992. Three penguin pals have fun in the snow as they build a gigantic snowman. **Artist:** John Francis (Collin)
☐ Purchased 19 __Pd $____MIB   NB   DB   BNT
☐ Want   Orig. Ret. $11.75 **NB** $15   **MIB** Sec. Mkt. **$23**

QX 505-4   WORLD-CLASS TEACHER ☐
Comments: Handcrafted, 3-1/4" tall, Dated 1992.
A lively young squirrel in a green and yellow sweater rolls down the map to show his teacher is the best in the world.
Artist: Bob Siedler
☐ Purchased 19 __Pd $____MIB   NB   DB   BNT
☐ Want   Orig. Ret. $7.75 **NB** $15   `**MIB** Sec. Mkt. **$20**

QLX 731-4   YULETIDE RIDER ☐
Comments: Light and Motion, Handcrafted, 3-3/8" tall, Dated 1992. Santa chugs along in his convertible. Scenery, road and car wheels revolve. **Artist:** Ed Seale
☐ Purchased 19 __Pd $____MIB   NB   DB   BNT
☐ Want   Orig. Ret. $28.00 **NB** $50   **MIB** Sec. Mkt. **$60**

1992 Miniature Ornament Collection

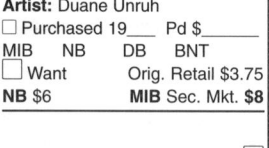

QXM 551-1
A+ TEACHER
1-1/8" tall, **Dated** 1992.
Artist: Duane Unruh
☐ Purchased 19___ Pd $_____
MIB   NB   DB   BNT
☐ Want   Orig. Retail $3.75
NB $6   **MIB** Sec. Mkt. **$8**

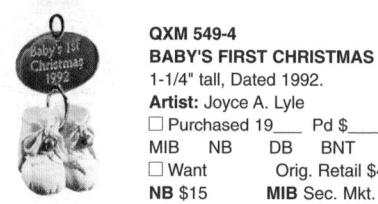

QXM 552-4
ANGELIC HARPIST
1-1/4" tall. **Artist:** Joyce A. Lyle
☐ Purchased 19___ Pd $_____
MIB   NB   DB   BNT
☐ Want   Orig. Retail $4.50
NB $10   **MIB** Sec. Mkt. **$15**

QXM 549-4
BABY'S FIRST CHRISTMAS
1-1/4" tall, Dated 1992.
Artist: Joyce A. Lyle
☐ Purchased 19___ Pd $_____
MIB   NB   DB   BNT
☐ Want   Orig. Retail $4.50
NB $15   **MIB** Sec. Mkt. **$20**

QXM 554-4
BEARYMORES, THE
FIRST IN SERIES, 1-1/8" tall,
Dated 1992.
Artist: Anita Marra Rogers
☐ Purchased 19___ Pd $_____
MIB   NB   DB   BNT
☐ Want   Orig. Retail $5.75
NB $15   **MIB** Sec. Mkt. **$18**

QXM 548-4
BLACK-CAPPED CHICKADEE
1-3/8" tall, Dated 1992.
Artist: John Francis (Collin)
☐ Purchased 19___ Pd $_____
MIB   NB   DB   BNT
☐ Want   Orig. Retail $3.00
NB $9   **MIB** Sec. Mkt. **$15**

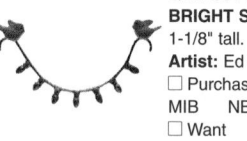

QXM 584-1
BRIGHT STRINGERS
1-1/8" tall.
Artist: Ed Seale
☐ Purchased 19___ Pd $_____
MIB   NB   DB   BNT
☐ Want   Orig. Retail $3.75
NB $10   **MIB** Sec. Mkt. **$15**

QXM 581-4
BUCK-A-ROO
1-1/8" tall, Dated 1993.
Artist: Ken Crow
☐ Purchased 19___ Pd $_____
MIB   NB   DB   BNT
☐ Want   Orig. Retail $4.50
NB $12   **MIB** Sec. Mkt. **$17**

QXC 519-4
CHIPMUNK PARCEL SERVICE:
KEEPSAKE CLUB
Dated 1992.
Artist: Ed Seale
☐ Purchased 19___ Pd $_____
MIB   NB   DB   BNT
☐ Want   Early Renewal Gift to
Keepsake Orn. Club Members
NB $6   **MIB** Sec. Mkt. **$10**

QXM 581-1
CHRISTMAS BONUS
1-3/16" tall, Dated 1992.
Artist: Don Palmiter
☐ Purchased 19___ Pd $_____
MIB   NB   DB   BNT
☐ Want   Orig. Retail $3.00
NB $5   **MIB** Sec. Mkt. **$9**

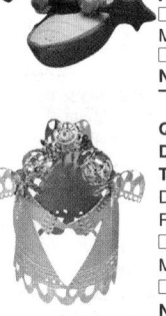

QXM 584-4
CHRISTMAS COPTER
7/8" tall, Dated 1992.
Artist: John Francis (Collin)
☐ Purchased 19___ Pd $_____
MIB   NB   DB   BNT
☐ Want   Orig. Retail $5.75
NB $10   **MIB** Sec. Mkt. **$15**

QXM 588-4
COCA-COLA SANTA
1-3/16" tall.
Artist: Duane Unruh
☐ Purchased 19___ Pd $_____
MIB   NB   DB   BNT
☐ Want   Orig. Retail $5.75
NB $11   **MIB** Sec. Mkt. **$18**

QXM 556-1
COOL UNCLE SAM
1" tall, Dated 1992.
Election Year Commemorative,
Artist: Julia Lee
☐ Purchased 19___ Pd $_____
MIB   NB   DB   BNT
☐ Want   Orig. Retail $3.00
NB $12   **MIB** Sec. Mkt. **$18**

QXM 555-1
COZY KAYAK
3/4" tall, Dated 1992.
Artist: Julia Lee
☐ Purchased 19___ Pd $_____
MIB   NB   DB   BNT
☐ Want   Orig. Retail $3.75
NB $10   **MIB** Sec. Mkt. **$14**

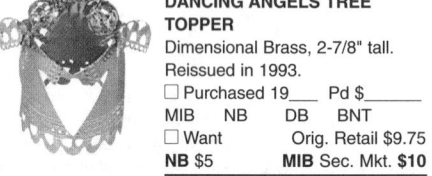

QXM 589-1
DANCING ANGELS TREE
TOPPER
Dimensional Brass, 2-7/8" tall.
Reissued in 1993.
☐ Purchased 19___ Pd $_____
MIB   NB   DB   BNT
☐ Want   Orig. Retail $9.75
NB $5   **MIB** Sec. Mkt. **$10**

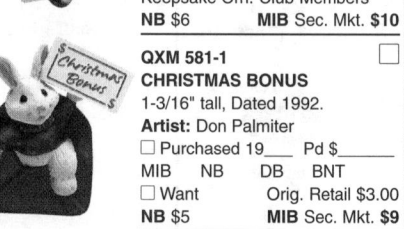

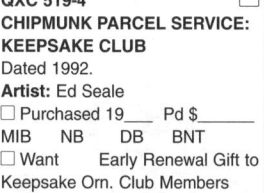

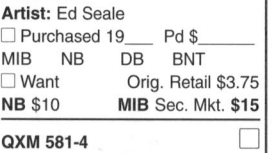

QXM 530-1
FAST FINISH
7/8" tall, Dated1992.
Artist: Dill Rhodus
☐ Purchased 19___ Pd $_____
MIB NB DB BNT
☐ Want   Orig. Retail $3.75
NB $7   **MIB** Sec. Mkt. **$13**

QXM 548-1
FEEDING TIME
1" tall, Dated 1992.
Artist: Ken Crow
☐ Purchased 19___ Pd $_____
MIB NB DB BNT
☐ Want   Orig. Retail $5.75
NB $10   **MIB** Sec. Mkt. **$15**

QXM 587-4
FRIENDLY TIN SOLDIER
Pressed Tin, 1-1/16" tall.
Artist: Linda Sickman
☐ Purchased 19___ Pd $_____
MIB NB DB BNT
☐ Want   Orig. Retail $4.50
NB $13   **MIB** Sec. Mkt. **$18**

QXM 552-1
FRIENDS ARE TOPS
1-1/8" tall, Dated 1992.
Artist: Ken Crow
☐ Purchased 19___ Pd $_____
MIB NB DB BNT
☐ Want   Orig. Retail $4.50
NB $7   **MIB** Sec. Mkt. **$12**

QXM 592-4
GERBIL, INC.
7/8" tall, Dated 1992.
Artist: Bob Siedler
☐ Purchased 19___ Pd $_____
MIB NB DB BNT
☐ Want   Orig. Retail $3.75
NB $6   **MIB** Sec. Mkt. **$11**

QXM 587-1
GOING PLACES
1" tall, Dated 1992.
Artist: Patricia Andrews
☐ Purchased 19___ Pd $_____
MIB NB DB BNT
☐ Want   Orig. Retail $3.75
NB $7   **MIB** Sec. Mkt. **$10**

QXM 550-1
GRANDCHILD'S FIRST CHRISTMAS
1-1/4" tall, Dated1992.
Artist: John Francis (Collin)
☐ Purchased 19___ Pd $_____
MIB NB DB BNT
☐ Want   Orig. Retail $5.75
NB $9   **MIB** Sec. Mkt. **$15**

QXM 551-4
GRANDMA
1-1/8" tall, Dated 1992.
Artist: Duane Unruh
☐ Purchased 19___ Pd $_____
MIB NB DB BNT
☐ Want   Orig. Retail $4.50
NB $10   **MIB** Sec. Mkt. **$15**

QXM 547-1
HARMONY TRIO
Three, 1-1/8" tall, Dated1992.
Artist: LaDene Votruba
☐ Purchased 19___ Pd $_____
MIB NB DB BNT
☐ Want   Orig. Retail $11.75
NB $15   **MIB** Sec. Mkt. **$20**

QXM 586-1
HICKORY, DICKORY, DOCK
1-3/16" tall, Dated 1992.
Artist: Robert Chad
☐ Purchased 19___ Pd $_____
MIB NB DB BNT
☐ Want   Orig. Retail $3.75
NB $8   **MIB** Sec. Mkt. **$13**

QXM 536-4
HOLIDAY HOLLY
Precious Edition, 22k Gold Plated,
1-1/8" tall, Dated 1992.
☐ Purchased 19___ Pd $_____
MIB NB DB BNT
☐ Want   Orig. Retail $9.75
NB $15   **MIB** Sec. Mkt. **$20**

QXM 583-4
HOLIDAY SPLASH
1" tall, Dated 1992.
Artist: John Francis (Collin)
☐ Purchased 19___ Pd $_____
MIB NB DB BNT
☐ Want   Orig. Retail $5.75
NB $7   **MIB** Sec. Mkt. **$13**

QXM 583-1
HOOP IT UP
1" tall, Dated 1992.
Artist: Ken Crow
☐ Purchased 19___ Pd $_____
MIB NB DB BNT
☐ Want   Orig. Retail $4.50
NB $7   **MIB** Sec. Mkt. **$13**

QXM 588-1
INSIDE STORY
3/4" tall, Dated 1992.
Artist: Ed Seale
☐ Purchased 19___ Pd $_____
MIB NB DB BNT
☐ Want   Orig. Retail $7.25
NB $15   **MIB** Sec. Mkt. **$20**

QXM 539-1
**KITTENS IN TOYLAND: POGO
STICK, Fifth and Final in
Series** 1-3/16" tall.
Artist: Ken Crow
☐ Purchased 19___ Pd $_____
MIB NB DB BNT
☐ Want   Orig. Retail $4.50
NB $15   **MIB** Sec. Mkt. **$18**

QXM 538-1
KRINGLES, THE
Fourth in Series, 1" tall.
Artist: Anita Marra Rogers
☐ Purchased 19___ Pd $_____
MIB NB DB BNT
☐ Want   Orig. Retail $6.00
NB $17   **MIB** Sec. Mkt. **$23**

QXM 586-4
LITTLE TOWN OF BETHLEHEM
1" dia., Dated 1992.
Artist: Linda Sickman
☐ Purchased 19___ Pd $_____
MIB NB DB BNT
☐ Want   Orig. Retail $3.00
NB $17   **MIB** Sec. Mkt. **$23**

QXM 585-4
MINTED FOR SANTA
Copper, 1" dia., Dated 1992.
Artist: Duane Unruh
☐ Purchased 19___ Pd $_____
MIB NB DB BNT
☐ Want   Orig. Retail $3.75
NB $10   **MIB** Sec. Mkt. **$15**

QXM 550-4
MOM
1-3/16" tall, Dated 1992.
Artist: Patricia Andrews
☐ Purchased 19___ Pd $_____
MIB NB DB BNT
☐ Want   Orig. Retail $4.50
NB $10   **MIB** Sec. Mkt. **$15**

QXM 545-1
NATURE'S ANGELS
Third in Series, 1" tall.
Artist: Sharon Pike
☐ Purchased 19___ Pd $_____
MIB NB DB BNT
☐ Want   Orig. Retail $4.50
NB $15   **MIB** Sec. Mkt. **$20**

QXM 554-1
NIGHT BEFORE CHRISTMAS, THE: HOUSE
Tin Display House, 8" tall x 5-1/2" wide; Rocker w/Mouse, 1-1/8" tall.
Artists: LaDene Votruba and Duane Unruh
☐ Purchased 19___ Pd $_____
MIB NB DB BNT
☐ Want   Orig. Retail $13.75
NB $25   **MIB** Sec. Mkt. **$30**

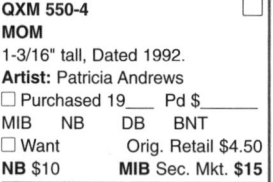

QXM 544-1
NOEL R.R.: BOX CAR
Fourth in Series, 13/16" tall, Dated 1992. **Artist:** Linda Sickman
☐ Purchased 19___ Pd $_____
MIB NB DB BNT
☐ Want   Orig. Retail $7.00
NB $10   **MIB** Sec. Mkt. **$15**

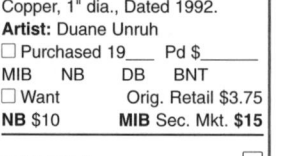

QXM 538-4
OLD ENGLISH VILLAGE: CHURCH
Fifth in Series, 1-5/16" tall, Dated 1992. **Artist:** Julia Lee
☐ Purchased 19___ Pd $_____
MIB NB DB BNT
☐ Want   Orig. Retail $7.00
NB $25   **MIB** Sec. Mkt. **$35**

QXM 557-1
PERFECT BALANCE
1-1/4" tall, Dated 1992.
Artist: Anita Marra Rogers
☐ Purchased 19___ Pd $_____
MIB NB DB BNT
☐ Want   Orig. Retail $3.00
NB $8   **MIB** Sec. Mkt. **$13**

QXM 553-4
POLAR POLKA
1-13/16" tall, Dated 1992.
Artist: Ed Seale
☐ Purchased 19___ Pd $_____
MIB NB DB BNT
☐ Want   Orig. Retail $4.50
NB $10   **MIB** Sec. Mkt. **$15**

QXM 557-4
PUPPET SHOW
1" tall, Dated 1992.
Artist: Bob Siedler
☐ Purchased 19___ Pd $_____
MIB NB DB BNT
☐ Want   Orig. Retail $3.00
NB $8   **MIB** Sec. Mkt. **$13**

QXM 545-4
ROCKING HORSE: BROWN HORSE
Fifth in Series, 1-1/8" tall, Dated 1992. **Artist:** Linda Sickman
☐ Purchased 19___ Pd $_____
MIB NB DB BNT
☐ Want   Orig. Retail $4.50
NB $15   **MIB** Sec. Mkt. **$23**

QXM 579-4
SEW, SEW TINY
Dated 1992. Not Porcelain.
Artist: Ed Seale
A. Basket Break, 1-1/8" tall
D. Cutting Edge, 7/8" tall
B. Threaded Thru, 1-1/4" tall
E. Buttoned Up, 3/4" tall
C. Pinned On, 1-1/8" tall
F. Thimble Full, 13/16" tall
☐ Purchased 19___ Pd $_____
MIB NB DB BNT
☐ Want   Orig. Retail $29.00
NB $38   **MIB** Sec. Mkt. **$45**

QXM 582-1
SKI FOR TWO
15/16" tall, Dated 1992.
Artist: Patricia Andrews
☐ Purchased 19___ Pd $_____
MIB   NB   DB   BNT
☐ Want   Orig. Retail $4.50
NB $10   **MIB** Sec. Mkt. **$15**

QXM 556-4
SNOWSHOE BUNNY
1-1/16" tall.
Artist: LaDene Votruba
☐ Purchased 19___ Pd $_____
MIB   NB   DB   BNT
☐ Want   Orig. Retail $3.75
NB $8   **MIB** Sec. Mkt. **$15**

QXM 555-4
SNUG KITTY
1" tall, Dated 1992.
Artist: Sharon Pike
☐ Purchased 19___ Pd $_____
MIB   NB   DB   BNT
☐ Want   Orig. Retail $3.75
NB $8   **MIB** Sec. Mkt. **$13**

QXM 592-1
SPUNKY MONKEY
1-3/8" tall, Dated 1992.
Artist: Robert Chad
☐ Purchased 19___ Pd $_____
MIB   NB   DB   BNT
☐ Want   Orig. Retail $3.00
NB $10   **MIB** Sec. Mkt. **$15**

QXM 546-1
THIMBLE BELLS
Third in Series, Porcelain, 1-1/8" tall,
Dated 1992. **Artist:** Joyce A. Lyle
☐ Purchased 19___ Pd $_____
MIB   NB   DB   BNT
☐ Want   Orig. Retail $6.00
NB $17   **MIB** Sec. Mkt. **$23**

QXM 585-1
VISIONS OF ACORNS
1-3/16" tall, Dated 1992.
Artist: Patricia Andrews
☐ Purchased 19___ Pd $_____
MIB   NB   DB   BNT
☐ Want   Orig. Retail $4.50
NB $10   **MIB** Sec. Mkt. **$15**

QXM 553-1
WEE THREE KINGS
1-3/16" tall, Dated 1991.
Artist: Don Palmiter
☐ Purchased 19___ Pd $_____
MIB   NB   DB   BNT
☐ Want   Orig. Retail $5.75
NB $13   **MIB** Sec. Mkt. **$23**

QXM 544-4
WOODLAND BABIES
Second in Series, 1" tall, Dated
1992. **Artist:** Don Palmiter
☐ Purchased 19___ Pd $_____
MIB   NB   DB   BNT
☐ Want   Orig. Retail $6.00
NB $11   **MIB** Sec. Mkt. **$15**

1992
Easter Ornament Collection

QEO 927-1
BABY'S FIRST EASTER
3" tall, Dated 1992.
Artist: John Francis (Collin)
☐ Purchased 19___ Pd $_____
MIB   NB   DB   BNT
☐ Want   Original Retail $6.75
NB $18   **MIB** Sec. Mkt. **$23**

QEO 935-4
BELLE BUNNY
Porcelain, 3" tall, Dated 1992.
Artist: LaDene Votruba
☐ Purchased 19___ Pd $_____
MIB   NB   DB   BNT
☐ Want   Original Retail $9.75
NB $15   **MIB** Sec. Mkt. **$20**

QEO 929-1
BLESS YOU
3" tall.
Artist: John Francis (Collin)
☐ Purchased 19___ Pd $_____
MIB   NB   DB   BNT
☐ Want   Original Retail $6.75
NB $10   **MIB** Sec. Mkt. **$25**

QEO 936-4
COSMIC RABBIT
3" tall, Dated 1992.
Artist: Bob Siedler
☐ Purchased 19___ Pd $_____
MIB   NB   DB   BNT
☐ Want   Original Retail $7.75
NB $10   **MIB** Sec. Mkt. **$20**

QEO 930-4
CRAYOLA® BUNNY
3" tall, Dated 1992.
Artist: Anita Marra Rogers
☐ Purchased 19___ Pd $_____
MIB   NB   DB   BNT
☐ Want   Original Retail $7.75
NB $25   **MIB** Sec. Mkt. **$33**

QEO 935-1
CULTIVATED GARDENER
3" tall, Caption: "Carrots 1992."
Artist: Bob Siedler
☐ Purchased 19___ Pd $_____
MIB   NB   DB   BNT
☐ Want   Original Retail $5.75
NB $8   **MIB** Sec. Mkt. **$15**

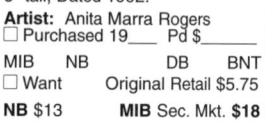

QEO 928-4
DAUGHTER
3" tall, Dated 1992.
Artist: Anita Marra Rogers
☐ Purchased 19___ Pd $_____
MIB   NB   DB   BNT
☐ Want   Original Retail $5.75
NB $13   **MIB** Sec. Mkt. **$18**

QEO 930-1
EASTER PARADE
FIRST IN SERIES, 3" tall, Dated
1992. **Artist:** Ken Crow
☐ Purchased 19___ Pd $_____
MIB   NB   DB   BNT
☐ Want   Original Retail $6.75
NB $20   **MIB** Sec. Mkt. **$30**

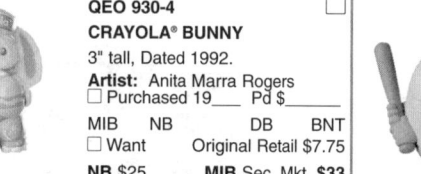

QEO 934-1
EGGS IN SPORTS
FIRST IN SERIES, 3" tall,
Caption: "Grade A's '92." Series
ended in 1994.
Artist: Bob Siedler
☐ Purchased 19___ Pd $_____
MIB   NB   DB   BNT
☐ Want   Original Retail $6.75
NB $20   **MIB** Sec. Mkt. **$35**

QEO 936-1
EGGSPERT PAINTER
3" tall, Dated 1992.
Artist: Bob Siedler
☐ Purchased 19___ Pd $_____
MIB   NB   DB   BNT
☐ Want   Original Retail $6.75
NB $15   **MIB** Sec. Mkt. **$24**

QEO 933-1
EVERYTHING'S DUCKY!
3" tall, Dated 1992.
Artist: Sharon Pike
☐ Purchased 19___ Pd $_____
MIB   NB   DB   BNT
☐ Want   Original Retail $6.75
NB $14   **MIB** Sec. Mkt. **$20**

QEO 927-4
GRANDCHILD
3" tall. **Artist:** Ken Crow
☐ Purchased 19___ Pd $_____
MIB   NB   DB   BNT
☐ Want   Original Retail $6.75
NB $15   **MIB** Sec. Mkt. **$20**

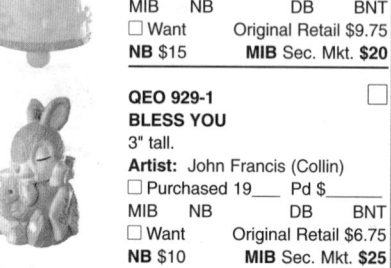
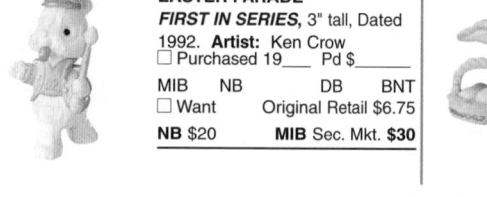

QEO 933-4
JOY BEARER
Dated 1992.
Artist: Don Palmiter
☐ Purchased 19___ Pd $_____
MIB   NB   DB   BNT
☐ Want   Original Retail $8.75
NB $20   **MIB** Sec. Mkt. **$25**

QEO 931-4
PROMISE OF EASTER
Porcelain, 3" tall, Dated 1992.
Caption: "God's love shines
everywhere."
Artist: Joyce A. Lyle
☐ Purchased 19___ Pd $_____
MIB   NB   DB   BNT
☐ Want   Original Retail $8.75
NB $15   **MIB** Sec. Mkt. **$20**

QEO 932-4
ROCKING BUNNY
Nickel-Plated, 3" tall. Caption:
"Happy Easter 1992."
Artist: LaDene Votruba
☐ Purchased 19___ Pd $_____
MIB   NB   DB   BNT
☐ Want   Original Retail $9.75
NB $17   **MIB** Sec. Mkt. **$23**

QEO 929-4
SOMEBUNNY LOVES YOU
3" tall.
Artist: John Francis (Collin)
☐ Purchased 19___ Pd $_____
MIB   NB   DB   BNT
☐ Want   Original Retail $6.75
NB $25   **MIB** Sec. Mkt. **$30**

QEO 928-1
SON
3" tall, Dated 1992.
Artist: Anita Marra Rogers
☐ Purchased 19___ Pd $_____
MIB   NB   DB   BNT
☐ Want   Original Retail $5.75
NB $10   **MIB** Sec. Mkt. **$20**

QEO 932-1
SPRINGTIME EGG
3" tall, Dated 1992.
Artist: Julia Lee
☐ Purchased 19___ Pd $_____
MIB   NB   DB   BNT
☐ Want   Original Retail $8.75
NB $15   **MIB** Sec. Mkt. **$20**

QEO 934-4
SUNNY WISHER
3" tall. **Artist:** Sharon Pike,
Caption: "Sunny Easter Wishes."
☐ Purchased 19___ Pd $_____
MIB   NB   DB   BNT
☐ Want   Original Retail $5.75
NB $10   **MIB** Sec. Mkt. **$18**

QEO 931-1
WARM MEMORIES
Fabric Photoholder, 4" tall, Dated
1992. Caption: "Easter brings
warm memories."
Artist: LaDene Votruba.
☐ Purchased 19___ Pd $_____
MIB   NB   DB   BNT
☐ Want   Original Retail $7.75
NB $12   **MIB** Sec. Mkt. **$16**

1993 Collection

QX 568-2 20TH ANNIVERSARY: FROSTY FRIENDS ☐

Comments: Handcrafted, 2-1/2" tall, Dated 1993. Frosty and his penguin pal decorate their igloo for a Merry Christmas. This anniversary edition complements the Frosty Friends Series. **Artist:** Ed Seale

☐ Purchased 19____   Pd $_____   MIB NB DB BNT
☐ Want   Orig. Ret. $20.00   **NB** $39   **MIB** Sec. Mkt. **$50**

QX 530-2 20TH ANNIVERSARY: GLOWING PEWTER WREATH ☐

Comments: Fine Pewter, 3-11/16" tall, Dated 1993. Images of Santa, musical instruments, a star and a dated stocking are part of the design on this pewter wreath. Seek and ye shall find for even less. **Artist:** Duane Unruh

☐ Purchased 19____   Pd $_____   MIB NB DB BNT
☐ Want   Orig. Ret. $18.75   **NB** $28   **MIB** Sec. Mkt. **$35**

QX 567-5 20TH ANNIVERSARY: SHOPPING WITH SANTA ☐

Comments: Handcrafted, 3-1/2" tall, Dated 1993. Santa drives into Christmas in this vintage car. Let's go Hallmarking! This ornament complements the Here Comes Santa series. **Artist:** Linda Sickman

☐ Purchased 19____   Pd $_____   MIB NB DB BNT
☐ Want   Orig. Ret. $24.00   **NB** $41   **MIB** Sec. Mkt. **$50**

QX 561-2 20TH ANNIVERSARY: TANNENBAUM'S DEPT. STORE ☐

Comments: Handcrafted, 4-15/16" tall, Dated 1993. Tannenbaum's three-story shop complements the Nostalgic Houses and Shops Series. **Artist:** Donna Lee

☐ Purchased 19____   Pd $_____   MIB NB DB BNT
☐ Want   Orig. Ret. $26.00   **NB** $45   **MIB** Sec. Mkt. **$55**

QX 588-2 A CHILD'S CHRISTMAS ☐

Comments: Handcrafted, 2-5/16" tall, Dated 1993. A light brown teddy has popped out of a brightly striped gift box to wish happy holidays. May be personalized for Niece, Nephew, Granddaughter, Grandson, Great-Grandchild or A Child's Christmas. **Artist:** John Francis (Collin)

☐ Purchased 19____   Pd $_____   MIB NB DB BNT
☐ Want   Orig. Ret. $9.75   **NB** $12   **MIB** Sec. Mkt. **$20**

QX 591-2 ACROSS THE MILES ☐

Comments: Handcrafted, 1-11/16" tall, Dated 1993. This white bear is sprawled on the ice reading a journal from "Across the Miles." **Artist:** John Francis (Collin)

☐ Purchased 19____   Pd $_____   MIB NB DB BNT
☐ Want   Orig. Ret. $8.75   **NB** $17   **MIB** Sec. Mkt. **$20**

QX 597-2 ANNIVERSARY YEAR PHOTOHOLDER ☐

Comments: Brass and Chrome, 3-13/16" tall, Dated 1993. This ornate photo holder may be personalized eight ways to mark anniversaries for 5, 10, 25, 30, 35, 40, 50 and 60 years. **Artist:** Joyce A. Lyle

☐ Purchased 19____   Pd $_____   MIB NB DB BNT
☐ Want   Orig. Ret. $9.75   **NB** $11   **MIB** Sec. Mkt. **$20**

QX 590-2 APPLE FOR TEACHER ☐

Comments: Handcrafted, 2-3/8" tall, Dated 1993. Open the apple and view two mice students at their desks and a chalkboard which may be personalized. Caption: "A Is For Apple, A+ Is For Teacher." **Artist:** Ed Seale

☐ Purchased 19____   Pd $_____   MIB NB DB BNT
☐ Want   Orig. Ret. $7.75   **NB** $8   **MIB** Sec. Mkt. **$17**

QX 551-2 BABY'S FIRST CHRISTMAS ☐

Comments: Silver plated, 3-1/16" tall, Dated 1993. This silver-plated baby rattle is all tied up in a red bow and comes with a silver tag which may be engraved for personalization. **Artist:** Don Palmiter

☐ Purchased 19____   Pd $_____   MIB NB DB BNT
☐ Want   Orig. Ret. $18.75   **NB** $20   **MIB** Sec. Mkt. **$37**

QX 551-5 BABY'S FIRST CHRISTMAS ☐

Comments: Handcrafted, 3-3/16" tall, Dated 1993. An adorable baby squirrel plays merrily in its walnut shell "swing." **Artist:** Patricia Andrews

☐ Purchased 19____   Pd $_____   MIB NB DB BNT
☐ Want   Orig. Ret. $10.75   **NB** $16   **MIB** Sec. Mkt. **$25**

QX 552-2 BABY'S FIRST CHRISTMAS PHOTOHOLDER ☐

Comments: Handcrafted, 4-3/4" dia., Dated 1993. Christmas and baby designs adorn this "quilted" lace-trimmed photoholder. Caption: "Christmas And Babies Fill A Home With Special Joys." **Artist:** Anita Marra Rogers

☐ Purchased 19____   Pd $_____   MIB NB DB BNT
☐ Want   Orig. Ret. $7.75   **NB** $13.75 **MIB** Sec. Mkt. **$25**

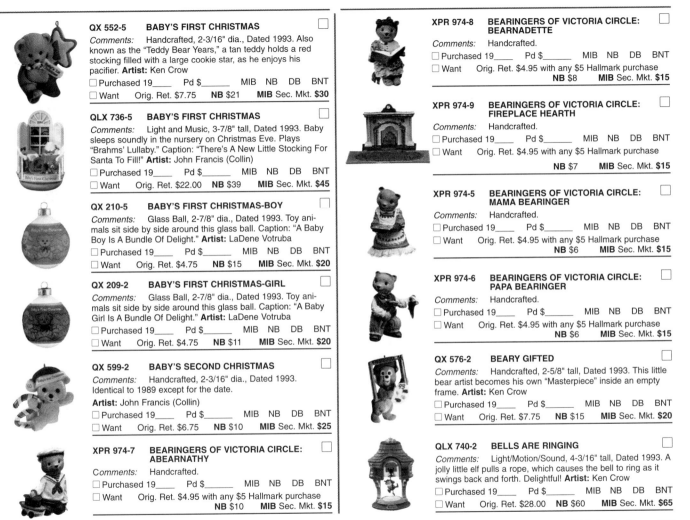

QX 552-5   BABY'S FIRST CHRISTMAS

Comments: Handcrafted, 2-3/16" dia., Dated 1993. Also known as the "Teddy Bear Years," a tan teddy holds a red stocking filled with a large cookie star, as he enjoys his pacifier. **Artist:** Ken Crow

☐ Purchased 19____   Pd $_____   MIB   NB   DB   BNT
☐ Want   Orig. Ret. $7.75   **NB** $21   **MIB** Sec. Mkt. **$30**

QLX 736-5   BABY'S FIRST CHRISTMAS

Comments: Light and Music, 3-7/8" tall, Dated 1993. Baby sleeps soundly in the nursery on Christmas Eve. Plays "Brahms' Lullaby." Caption: "There's A New Little Stocking For Santa To Fill!" **Artist:** John Francis (Collin)

☐ Purchased 19____   Pd $_____   MIB   NB   DB   BNT
☐ Want   Orig. Ret. $22.00   **NB** $39   **MIB** Sec. Mkt. **$45**

QX 210-5   BABY'S FIRST CHRISTMAS-BOY

Comments: Glass Ball, 2-7/8" dia., Dated 1993. Toy animals sit side by side around this glass ball. Caption: "A Baby Boy Is A Bundle Of Delight." **Artist:** LaDene Votruba

☐ Purchased 19____   Pd $_____   MIB   NB   DB   BNT
☐ Want   Orig. Ret. $4.75   **NB** $15   **MIB** Sec. Mkt. **$20**

QX 209-2   BABY'S FIRST CHRISTMAS-GIRL

Comments: Glass Ball, 2-7/8" dia., Dated 1993. Toy animals sit side by side around this glass ball. Caption: "A Baby Girl Is A Bundle Of Delight." **Artist:** LaDene Votruba

☐ Purchased 19____   Pd $_____   MIB   NB   DB   BNT
☐ Want   Orig. Ret. $4.75   **NB** $11   **MIB** Sec. Mkt. **$20**

QX 599-2   BABY'S SECOND CHRISTMAS

Comments: Handcrafted, 2-3/16" dia., Dated 1993. Identical to 1989 except for the date.

Artist: John Francis (Collin)

☐ Purchased 19____   Pd $_____   MIB   NB   DB   BNT
☐ Want   Orig. Ret. $6.75   **NB** $10   **MIB** Sec. Mkt. **$25**

XPR 974-7   BEARINGERS OF VICTORIA CIRCLE: ABEARNATHY

Comments: Handcrafted.

☐ Purchased 19____   Pd $_____   MIB   NB   DB   BNT
☐ Want   Orig. Ret. $4.95 with any $5 Hallmark purchase
NB $10   **MIB** Sec. Mkt. **$15**

XPR 974-8   BEARINGERS OF VICTORIA CIRCLE: BEARNADETTE

Comments: Handcrafted.

☐ Purchased 19____   Pd $_____   MIB   NB   DB   BNT
☐ Want   Orig. Ret. $4.95 with any $5 Hallmark purchase
NB $8   **MIB** Sec. Mkt. **$15**

XPR 974-9   BEARINGERS OF VICTORIA CIRCLE: FIREPLACE HEARTH

Comments: Handcrafted.

☐ Purchased 19____   Pd $_____   MIB   NB   DB   BNT
☐ Want   Orig. Ret. $4.95 with any $5 Hallmark purchase
NB $7   **MIB** Sec. Mkt. **$15**

XPR 974-5   BEARINGERS OF VICTORIA CIRCLE: MAMA BEARINGER

Comments: Handcrafted.

☐ Purchased 19____   Pd $_____   MIB   NB   DB   BNT
☐ Want   Orig. Ret. $4.95 with any $5 Hallmark purchase
NB $6   **MIB** Sec. Mkt. **$15**

XPR 974-6   BEARINGERS OF VICTORIA CIRCLE: PAPA BEARINGER

Comments: Handcrafted.

☐ Purchased 19____   Pd $_____   MIB   NB   DB   BNT
☐ Want   Orig. Ret. $4.95 with any $5 Hallmark purchase
NB $6   **MIB** Sec. Mkt. **$15**

QX 576-2   BEARY GIFTED

Comments: Handcrafted, 2-5/8" tall, Dated 1993. This little bear artist becomes his own "Masterpiece" inside an empty frame. **Artist:** Ken Crow

☐ Purchased 19____   Pd $_____   MIB   NB   DB   BNT
☐ Want   Orig. Ret. $7.75   **NB** $15   **MIB** Sec. Mkt. **$20**

QLX 740-2   BELLS ARE RINGING

Comments: Light/Motion/Sound, 4-3/16" tall, Dated 1993. A jolly little elf pulls a rope, which causes the bell to ring as it swings back and forth. Delightful! **Artist:** Ken Crow

☐ Purchased 19____   Pd $_____   MIB   NB   DB   BNT
☐ Want   Orig. Ret. $28.00   **NB** $60   **MIB** Sec. Mkt. **$65**

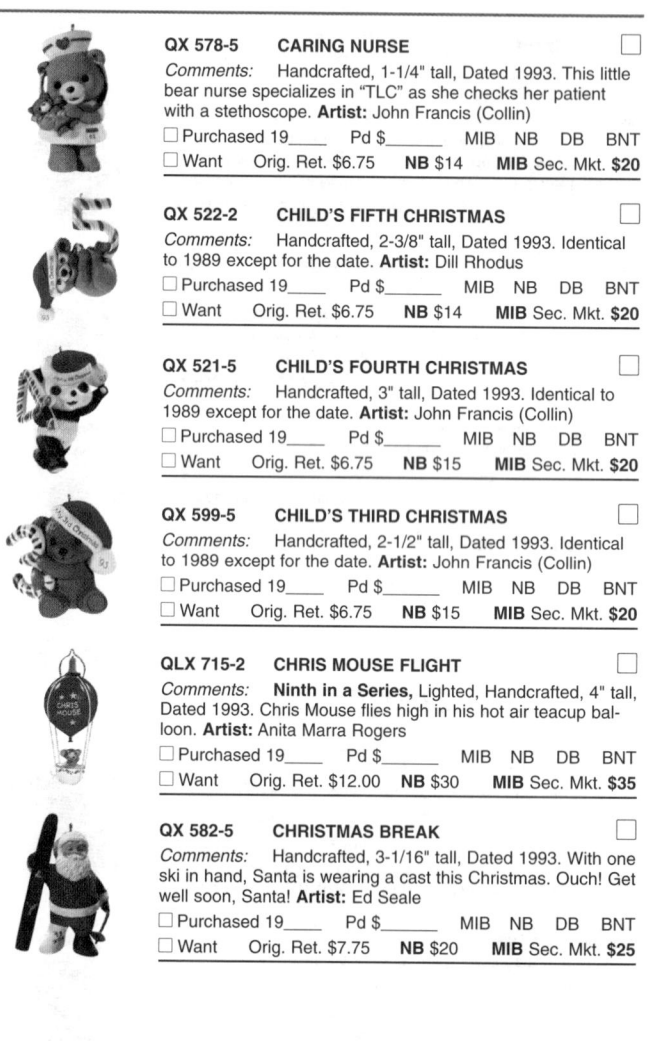

QX 206-2 BETSEY'S COUNTRY CHRISTMAS ☐

Comments: **Second in Series,** Teardrop Ball, 2-7/8" tall, Dated 1993. Caption: "Happy Is The Memory Of Bringing Home The Christmas Tree!"

☐ Purchased 19____ Pd $_____ MIB NB DB BNT
☐ Want Orig. Ret. $5.00 **NB** $14 **MIB** Sec. Mkt. **$20**

QX 584-2 BIG ON GARDENING ☐

Comments: Handcrafted, 2-1/2" tall, Dated 1993. This cute little elephant in a red gardening apron is holding a red potted flower and gardening tools. **Artist:** LaDene Votruba

☐ Purchased 19____ Pd $_____ MIB NB DB BNT
☐ Want Orig. Ret. $9.75 **NB** $15 **MIB** Sec. Mkt. **$20**

QX 535-2 BIG ROLLER ☐

Comments: Handcrafted, 3-1/16" tall, Dated 1993. This little creature, dressed for winter, runs on a nickel-plated exercise wheel that really spins. **Artist:** Bob Siedler

☐ Purchased 19____ Pd $_____ MIB NB DB BNT
☐ Want Orig. Ret. $8.75 **NB** $12 **MIB** Sec. Mkt. **$19**

QX 525-2 BIRD WATCHER ☐

Comments: Handcrafted, 2-7/16" tall, Dated 1993. All set with his sneakers, camera and binoculars, a bluebird has its eyes on Santa and his reindeer. **Artist:** Julia Lee

☐ Purchased 19____ Pd $_____ MIB NB DB BNT
☐ Want Orig. Ret. $9.75 **NB** $7 **MIB** Sec. Mkt. **$10**

QX 556-5 BOWLING FOR ZZZS ☐

Comments: Handcrafted, 1-13/16" tall, Dated 1993. A little mouse naps under a hand towel captioned "Santa Claus Lanes," which is tucked inside a bowling bag. **Artist:** John Francis (Collin)

☐ Purchased 19____ Pd $_____ MIB NB DB BNT
☐ Want Orig. Ret. $7.75 **NB** $15 **MIB** Sec. Mkt. **$20**

QX 554-2 BROTHER ☐

Comments: Handcrafted, 2-3/8" tall, Dated 1993. Sporting a red, white and green football helmet, this pup is sure to score big! **Artist:** Anita Marra Rogers

☐ Purchased 19____ Pd $_____ MIB NB DB BNT
☐ Want Orig. Ret. $6.75 **NB** $10 **MIB** Sec. Mkt. **$15**

QX 578-5 CARING NURSE ☐

Comments: Handcrafted, 1-1/4" tall, Dated 1993. This little bear nurse specializes in "TLC" as she checks her patient with a stethoscope. **Artist:** John Francis (Collin)

☐ Purchased 19____ Pd $_____ MIB NB DB BNT
☐ Want Orig. Ret. $6.75 **NB** $14 **MIB** Sec. Mkt. **$20**

QX 522-2 CHILD'S FIFTH CHRISTMAS ☐

Comments: Handcrafted, 2-3/8" tall, Dated 1993. Identical to 1989 except for the date. **Artist:** Dill Rhodus

☐ Purchased 19____ Pd $_____ MIB NB DB BNT
☐ Want Orig. Ret. $6.75 **NB** $14 **MIB** Sec. Mkt. **$20**

QX 521-5 CHILD'S FOURTH CHRISTMAS ☐

Comments: Handcrafted, 3" tall, Dated 1993. Identical to 1989 except for the date. **Artist:** John Francis (Collin)

☐ Purchased 19____ Pd $_____ MIB NB DB BNT
☐ Want Orig. Ret. $6.75 **NB** $15 **MIB** Sec. Mkt. **$20**

QX 599-5 CHILD'S THIRD CHRISTMAS ☐

Comments: Handcrafted, 2-1/2" tall, Dated 1993. Identical to 1989 except for the date. **Artist:** John Francis (Collin)

☐ Purchased 19____ Pd $_____ MIB NB DB BNT
☐ Want Orig. Ret. $6.75 **NB** $15 **MIB** Sec. Mkt. **$20**

QLX 715-2 CHRIS MOUSE FLIGHT ☐

Comments: **Ninth in a Series,** Lighted, Handcrafted, 4" tall, Dated 1993. Chris Mouse flies high in his hot air teacup balloon. **Artist:** Anita Marra Rogers

☐ Purchased 19____ Pd $_____ MIB NB DB BNT
☐ Want Orig. Ret. $12.00 **NB** $30 **MIB** Sec. Mkt. **$35**

QX 582-5 CHRISTMAS BREAK ☐

Comments: Handcrafted, 3-1/16" tall, Dated 1993. With one ski in hand, Santa is wearing a cast this Christmas. Ouch! Get well soon, Santa! **Artist:** Ed Seale

☐ Purchased 19____ Pd $_____ MIB NB DB BNT
☐ Want Orig. Ret. $7.75 **NB** $20 **MIB** Sec. Mkt. **$25**

QX 527-5   CLASSIC AMERICAN CARS: 1956 FORD THUNDERBIRD

Comments: **Third in Series,** Handcrafted, 2-5/16" tall, Dated 1993. This T-bird is guaranteed to delight car collectors of all ages! **Artist:** Don Palmiter

☐ Purchased 19_____   Pd $_____   MIB   NB   DB   BNT
☐ Want   Orig. Ret. $12.75   **NB** $30   **MIB** Sec. Mkt. **$40**

QX 566-2   CLEVER COOKIE

Comments: Handcrafted, Tin, 3-1/8" tall, Dated 1993. Clever is the right word, as this gingerbread cookie girl decides to leave her cutter frame. **Artist:** Linda Sickman

☐ Purchased 19_____   Pd $_____   MIB   NB   DB   BNT
☐ Want   Orig. Ret. $7.75   **NB** $25   **MIB** Sec. Mkt. **$30**

QX 593-5   COACH

Comments: Handcrafted, 2-1/2" tall, Dated 1993. A new commemorative ornament to the line, this penguin, wearing a red cap, holds onto his clipboard as he blows a silver whistle. **Artist:** Don Palmiter

☐ Purchased 19_____   Pd $_____   MIB   NB   DB   BNT
☐ Want   Orig. Ret. $6.75   **NB** $10   **MIB** Sec. Mkt. **$16**

QX 442-2   CRAYOLA® CRAYON: BRIGHT SHINING CASTLE

Comments: **Fifth in Series,** Handcrafted, 3-5/8" tall, Dated 1993. A bear trumpet player welcomes everyone to his colorful castle. **Artist:** Ken Crow

☐ Purchased 19_____   Pd $_____   MIB   NB   DB   BNT
☐ Want   Orig. Ret. $10.75   **NB** $25   **MIB** Sec. Mkt. **$30**

QX 528-5   CURLY 'N KINGLY

Comments: Handcrafted, 4-1/8" tall, Dated 1993. A lion and a lamb work together to ring the bell and wish you a Merry Christmas. **Artist:** Ken Crow

☐ Purchased 19_____   Pd $_____   MIB   NB   DB   BNT
☐ Want   Orig. Ret. $10.75   **NB** $20   **MIB** Sec. Mkt. **$25**

QX 585-5   DAD

Comments: Handcrafted, 2-5/8" tall, Dated 1993. Dad is all set to make something special in his workshop with his saw and his tool belt. **Artist:** Julia Lee

☐ Purchased 19_____   Pd $_____   MIB   NB   DB   BNT
☐ Want   Orig. Ret. $7.75   **NB** $12   **MIB** Sec. Mkt. **$18**

QX 553-2   DAD-TO-BE

Comments: Handcrafted, 2-1/8" tall, Dated 1993. "Dad-To-Bee," wearing a red and white cap, is buzzing to his honey with a bouquet of flowers. **Artist:** Julia Lee

☐ Purchased 19_____   Pd $_____   MIB   NB   DB   BNT
☐ Want   Orig. Ret. $6.75   **NB** $12   **MIB** Sec. Mkt. **$15**

QX 587-2   DAUGHTER

Comments: Handcrafted, 4-7/16" tall, Dated 1993. This giraffe with bendable neck and legs is wearing a sweater and ice skates. **Artist:** LaDene Votruba

☐ Purchased 19_____   Pd $_____   MIB   NB   DB   BNT
☐ Want   Orig. Ret. $6.75   **NB** $20   **MIB** Sec. Mkt. **$22**

QX 550-5   DICKENS CAROLER BELL: LADY DAPHNE

Comments: **Fourth and Final in Collection,** Porcelain Bell. 4-1/4" tall, Dated 1993. Lady Daphne is ready for caroling in her red and white coat, hat and songbook in hand. **Artist:** Robert Chad

☐ Purchased 19_____   Pd $_____   MIB   NB   DB   BNT
☐ Want   Orig. Ret. $21.75   **NB** $25   **MIB** Sec. Mkt. **$30**

QLX 717-2   DOG'S BEST FRIEND

Comments: Lighted, 3" tall. A black and white pooch adorns a fire hydrant with Christmas lights and an acrylic star. **Artist:** Julia Lee

☐ Purchased 19_____   Pd $_____   MIB   NB   DB   BNT
☐ Want   Orig. Ret. $12.00   **NB** $20   **MIB** Sec. Mkt. **$28**

QLX 737-2   DOLLHOUSE DREAMS

Comments: Lighted, 3-5/16" tall, Dated 1993. A little girl plays with her dollhouse which is complete with a flickering fire in the hearth and lights which blink on upstairs. **Artist:** Ken Crow

☐ Purchased 19_____   Pd $_____   MIB   NB   DB   BNT
☐ Want   Orig. Ret. $22.00   **NB** $45   **MIB** Sec. Mkt. **$50**

QX 557-5   DUNKIN' ROO

Comments: Handcrafted, 3-7/8" tall, Dated 1993. Wearing red tennis shoes and a green shirt, this kangaroo is sure to get his ball into the basket. **Artist:** Bob Siedler

☐ Purchased 19_____   Pd $_____   MIB   NB   DB   BNT
☐ Want   Orig. Ret. $7.75   **NB** $12   **MIB** Sec. Mkt. **$17**

QX 447-5 FABULOUS DECADE

Comments: **Fourth in Series,** Handcrafted and Brass. 1-13/16" tall, Dated 1993. A perky skunk carries a brass "1993" by its tail. **Artist:** Sharon Pike

☐ Purchased 19____   Pd $_____   MIB   NB   DB   BNT
☐ Want   Orig. Ret. $7.75   **NB** $15   **MIB** Sec. Mkt. **$20**

QX 578-2 FAITHFUL FIRE FIGHTER

Comments: Handcrafted, 2-3/4" tall. A little Dalmatian, in a fireman's hat and yellow raincoat, is ready to go with a water hose in paw. **Artist:** LaDene Votruba

☐ Purchased 19____   Pd $_____   MIB   NB   DB   BNT
☐ Want   Orig. Ret. $7.75   **NB** $15   **MIB** Sec. Mkt. **$20**

QX 536-5 FELIZ NAVIDAD

Comments: Handcrafted Brass, 2-15/16" tall, Dated 1993. A monk stands at the entrance of a Spanish mission, complete with a gold bell in the tower. **Artist:** Donna Lee

☐ Purchased 19____   Pd $_____   MIB   NB   DB   BNT
☐ Want   Orig. Ret. $8.75   **NB** $15   **MIB** Sec. Mkt. **$23**

QX 557-2 FILLS THE BILL

Comments: Handcrafted, 3-7/8" tall, Dated 1993. Pole in hand, a pelican sitting at "Pier 93" is casting his fishing line for a Christmas nibble. **Artist:** Bob Siedler

☐ Purchased 19____   Pd $_____   MIB   NB   DB   BNT
☐ Want   Orig. Ret. $8.75   **NB** $15   **MIB** Sec. Mkt. **$18**

QLX 716-5 FOREST FROLICS

Comments: **Fifth in a Series,** Light/Motion, Handcrafted, 4-3/16" tall, Dated 1993. Woodland animals scamper around a snow coated tree adorned with a lighted gold star. **Artist:** Sharon Pike

☐ Purchased 19____   Pd $_____   MIB   NB   DB   BNT
☐ Want   Orig. Ret. $25.00   **NB** $45   **MIB** Sec. Mkt. **$53**

QX 414-2 FROSTY FRIENDS

Comments: **Fourteenth in Series,** Handcrafted, 2-7/8" tall, Dated 1993. Frosty's little husky puppy snuggles into his icy doghouse. **Artist:** Julia Lee

☐ Purchased 19____   Pd $_____   MIB   NB   DB   BNT
☐ Want   Orig. Ret. $9.75   **NB** $30   **MIB** Sec. Mkt. **$40**

QXC 544-2 GENTLE TIDINGS: KEEPSAKE CLUB

Comments: Hand-painted Porcelain, 4-9/16" dia., Dated 1993. A delicate porcelain angel cradles a lamb in her arms. Available to Club Members only. **Artist:** Patricia Andrews

☐ Purchased 19____   Pd $_____   MIB   NB   DB   BNT
☐ Want   Orig. Ret. $25.00   **NB** $37   **MIB** Sec. Mkt. **$48**

QX 206-5 GIFT BRINGERS, THE: THE MAGI

Comments: **Fifth and Final in Series,** Glass Ball. 2-7/8" dia., Dated 1993. Three wise men from the East bring their gifts of gold, frankincense and myrrh to the Baby Jesus. **Artist:** LaDene Votruba

☐ Purchased 19____   Pd $_____   MIB   NB   DB   BNT
☐ Want   Orig. Ret. $5.00   **NB** $15   **MIB** Sec. Mkt. **$20**

QX 587-5 GODCHILD

Comments: Handcrafted, 2" tall, Dated 1993. A small child kneels in prayer by his pillow which reads, "Bless You, Godchild 1993." **Artist:** Robert Chad

☐ Purchased 19____   Pd $_____   MIB   NB   DB   BNT
☐ Want   Orig. Ret. $8.75   **NB** $15   **MIB** Sec. Mkt. **$23**

QX 555-2 GRANDCHILD'S FIRST CHRISTMAS

Comments: Handcrafted, 1-7/8" tall, Dated 1993. With the wonder of its first Christmas, this adorable baby raccoon's eyes are aglow. **Artist:** John Francis (Collin)

☐ Purchased 19____   Pd $_____   MIB   NB   DB   BNT
☐ Want   Orig. Ret. $6.75   **NB** $12   **MIB** Sec. Mkt. **$15**

QX 563-5 GRANDDAUGHTER

Comments: Handcrafted, 3-5/8" tall, Dated 1993. A little koala girl with a pink bow in her hair, waves hello from her stand on a red telephone. **Artist:** Robert Chad

☐ Purchased 19____   Pd $_____   MIB   NB   DB   BNT
☐ Want   Orig. Ret. $6.75   **NB** $15   **MIB** Sec. Mkt. **$23**

QX 566-5 GRANDMOTHER

Comments: Handcrafted, 2-9/16" tall, Dated 1993. A card reading "Grandmother 1993" sits atop a lovely basket filled with poinsettias. **Artist:** Patricia Andrews

☐ Purchased 19____   Pd $_____   MIB   NB   DB   BNT
☐ Want   Orig. Ret. $6.75   **NB** $15   **MIB** Sec. Mkt. **$20**

QX 208-5 GRANDPARENTS

Comments: Glass Ball, 2-7/8" Dia., Dated 1993. Christmas flowers and green bands against a white sleeve are graced with the words: "The Christmas Traditions, Loving And Giving Are Kept By Grandparents All Year, 1993."
Artist: LaDene Votruba

☐ Purchased 19____ Pd $_____ MIB NB DB BNT
☐ Want Orig. Ret. $4.75 **NB** $12 **MIB** Sec. Mkt. **$18**

QX 563-2 GRANDSON

Comments: Handcrafted, 3-11/16" tall, Dated 1993. An active koala bear, dressed in a bright red shirt with matching cap, waves and swings on a green telephone receiver.
Artist: Robert Chad

☐ Purchased 19____ Pd $_____ MIB NB DB BNT
☐ Want Orig. Ret. $6.75 **NB** $15 **MIB** Sec. Mkt. **$22**

QX 540-2 GREAT CONNECTIONS

Comments: Handcrafted, 3-5/8" tall, Dated 1993. Two little redbirds, with their blue and green ski hats, are busy making a paper chain garland for the tree. (Set of two hang-together ornaments.) **Artist:** Anita Marra Rogers

☐ Purchased 19____ Pd $_____ MIB NB DB BNT
☐ Want Orig. Ret. $10.75 **NB** $20 **MIB** Sec. Mkt. **$25**

QX 536-2 HE IS BORN

Comments: Handcrafted, 3-9/16" tall, Dated Christmas 1993. A touching Nativity scene is engraved on this bisque-look ornament. Caption: "For Unto Us A Child Is Born... Isaiah 9:6." **Artist:** Joyce A. Lyle

☐ Purchased 19____ Pd $_____ MIB NB DB BNT
☐ Want Orig. Ret. $9.75 **NB** $30 **MIB** Sec. Mkt. **$40**

QX 448-2 HEART OF CHRISTMAS

Comments: **Fourth in Series,** Handcrafted, 2" tall, Dated 1993. Open this Christmas heart and view the lovely wintry landscape inside. Caption: "Christmas Brings A Gentle Peace That Enters Every Heart." **Artist:** Ed Seale

☐ Purchased 19____ Pd $_____ MIB NB DB BNT
☐ Want Orig. Ret. $14.75 **NB** $25 **MIB** Sec. Mkt. **$30**

QX 494-5 HEAVENLY ANGELS

Comments: **Third and Final in Series,** Handcrafted, 3" tall, Dated 1993. An angel cradles a dove in her hands.
Artist: Joyce A. Lyle

☐ Purchased 19____ Pd $_____ MIB NB DB BNT
☐ Want Orig. Ret. $7.75 **NB** $15 **MIB** Sec. Mkt. **$20**

QX 410-2 HERE COMES SANTA: HAPPY HAUL-IDAYS

Comments: **Fifteenth in Series,** Handcrafted, 2-7/8" tall, Dated 1993. Santa is delivering toys rather than hauling things away in his truck. **Artist:** Linda Sickman

☐ Purchased 19____ Pd $_____ MIB NB DB BNT
☐ Want Orig. Ret. $14.75 **NB** $35 **MIB** Sec. Mkt. **$40**

QX 533-2 HIGH TOP-PURR

Comments: Handcrafted, 2-3/16" tall, Dated 1993. Tucked inside a red sneaker is a little brown kitten that enjoys playing with the shoe strings. **Artist:** Ed Seale

☐ Purchased 19____ Pd $_____ MIB NB DB BNT
☐ Want Orig. Ret. $8.75 **NB** $18 **MIB** Sec. Mkt. **$25**

QX 572-5 HOLIDAY BARBIE™

Comments: **FIRST IN SERIES,** Handcrafted, 3-1/2" tall, Dated 1993. Patterned after 1993 Holiday Barbie doll.
Artist: Patricia Andrews

☐ Purchased 19____ Pd $_____ MIB NB DB BNT
☐ Want Orig. Ret. $14.75 **NB** $140 **MIB** Sec. Mkt. **$170**

QX 562-2 HOLIDAY FLIERS: TIN AIRPLANE

Comments: Handcrafted, 1-5/16" tall, Dated 1993. Santa pilots a red and gray airplane with a message to all, "Season's Greetings." **Artist:** Linda Sickman

☐ Purchased 19____ Pd $_____ MIB NB DB BNT
☐ Want Orig. Ret. $7.75 **NB** $19 **MIB** Sec. Mkt. **$30**

QX 562-5 HOLIDAY FLIERS: TIN BLIMP

Comments: Handcrafted, 1-11/16" tall, Dated 1993. "Happy Holidays 1993" are wished to all on the sides of his holiday decorated blimp. **Artist:** Linda Sickman

☐ Purchased 19____ Pd $_____ MIB NB DB BNT
☐ Want Orig. Ret. $7.75 **NB** $11 **MIB** Sec. Mkt. **$17**

QX 561-5 HOLIDAY FLIERS: TIN HOT AIR BALLOON

Comments: Handcrafted, 2-5/8" tall, Dated 1993. A golden colored hot air balloon, decorated with holly and red bows, wishes everyone a "Merry Christmas." **Artist:** Linda Sickman

☐ Purchased 19____ Pd $_____ MIB NB DB BNT
☐ Want Orig. Ret. $7.75 **NB** $15 **MIB** Sec. Mkt. **$20**

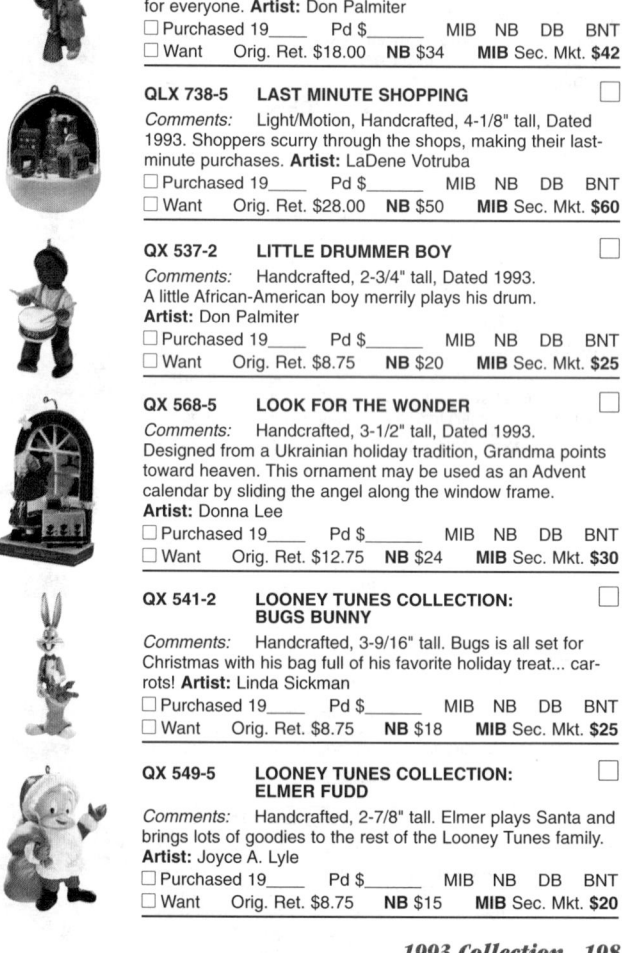

QX 556-2   HOME FOR CHRISTMAS

Comments: Handcrafted, 1-3/4" tall, Dated 1993. A little ball player slides to home plate. Cute! **Artist:** Bob Siedler

☐ Purchased 19___   Pd $_____   MIB   NB   DB   BNT
☐ Want   Orig. Ret. $7.75   **NB** $15   **MIB** Sec. Mkt. **$18**

QLX 739-5   HOME ON THE RANGE

Comments: Light/Motion/Music, Handcrafted, 4-1/8" tall, Dated 1993. Plays "Home On The Range." Santa's rocking horse is hitched to one cactus, and Christmas lights and star adorn another "Christmas Cactus." Santa and horse rock. **Artist:** Linda Sickman

☐ Purchased 19___   Pd $_____   MIB   NB   DB   BNT
☐ Want   Orig. Ret. $32.00   **NB** $60   **MIB** Sec. Mkt. **$75**

QX 525-5   HOWLING GOOD TIME

Comments: Handcrafted, 3" tall, Dated 1993. In a Texan mood, Santa dons his cowboy hat and sings a duet with his good pal, a brown dog. **Artist:** Anita Marra Rogers

☐ Purchased 19___   Pd $_____   MIB   NB   DB   BNT
☐ Want   Orig. Ret. $9.75   **NB** $15   **MIB** Sec. Mkt. **$23**

QX 583-5   ICICLE BICYCLE

Comments: Handcrafted, 2-1/2" tall, Dated 1993. A snowman races his cool cycle with wheels that really turn. **Artist:** Julia Lee

☐ Purchased 19___   Pd $_____   MIB   NB   DB   BNT
☐ Want   Orig. Ret. $9.75   **NB** $15   **MIB** Sec. Mkt. **$20**

QXC 527-2   IT'S IN THE MAIL: KEEPSAKE CLUB

Comments: Handcrafted, 2-5/8" tall, Dated 1993. A little "Post Mouse" is sending you a copy of the "Collector's Courier," but only if you are a member of the Keepsake Ornament Club! **Artist:** Ed Seale

☐ Purchased 19___   Pd $_____   MIB   NB   DB   BNT
☐ Want   Orig. Ret. Comes w/Membership
   NB $15   **MIB** Sec. Mkt. **$23**

QX 529-5   JULIANNE AND TEDDY

Comments: Handcrafted and Fabric, 2-3/4" tall, Dated 1993. This Special Edition ornament is a dark-haired Victorian child with her favorite teddy. **Artist:** Duane Unruh

☐ Purchased 19___   Pd $_____   MIB   NB   DB   BNT
☐ Want   Orig. Ret. $21.75   **NB** $40   **MIB** Sec. Mkt. **$55**

QLX 719-2   LAMPLIGHTER, THE

Comments: Lighted, 4-3/16" tall, Dated 1993. A little bear lights an old-fashioned street lantern to make Christmas bright for everyone. **Artist:** Don Palmiter

☐ Purchased 19___   Pd $_____   MIB   NB   DB   BNT
☐ Want   Orig. Ret. $18.00   **NB** $34   **MIB** Sec. Mkt. **$42**

QLX 738-5   LAST MINUTE SHOPPING

Comments: Light/Motion, Handcrafted, 4-1/8" tall, Dated 1993. Shoppers scurry through the shops, making their last-minute purchases. **Artist:** LaDene Votruba

☐ Purchased 19___   Pd $_____   MIB   NB   DB   BNT
☐ Want   Orig. Ret. $28.00   **NB** $50   **MIB** Sec. Mkt. **$60**

QX 537-2   LITTLE DRUMMER BOY

Comments: Handcrafted, 2-3/4" tall, Dated 1993. A little African-American boy merrily plays his drum. **Artist:** Don Palmiter

☐ Purchased 19___   Pd $_____   MIB   NB   DB   BNT
☐ Want   Orig. Ret. $8.75   **NB** $20   **MIB** Sec. Mkt. **$25**

QX 568-5   LOOK FOR THE WONDER

Comments: Handcrafted, 3-1/2" tall, Dated 1993. Designed from a Ukrainian holiday tradition, Grandma points toward heaven. This ornament may be used as an Advent calendar by sliding the angel along the window frame. **Artist:** Donna Lee

☐ Purchased 19___   Pd $_____   MIB   NB   DB   BNT
☐ Want   Orig. Ret. $12.75   **NB** $24   **MIB** Sec. Mkt. **$30**

QX 541-2   LOONEY TUNES COLLECTION: BUGS BUNNY

Comments: Handcrafted, 3-9/16" tall. Bugs is all set for Christmas with his bag full of his favorite holiday treat... carrots! **Artist:** Linda Sickman

☐ Purchased 19___   Pd $_____   MIB   NB   DB   BNT
☐ Want   Orig. Ret. $8.75   **NB** $18   **MIB** Sec. Mkt. **$25**

QX 549-5   LOONEY TUNES COLLECTION: ELMER FUDD

Comments: Handcrafted, 2-7/8" tall. Elmer plays Santa and brings lots of goodies to the rest of the Looney Tunes family. **Artist:** Joyce A. Lyle

☐ Purchased 19___   Pd $_____   MIB   NB   DB   BNT
☐ Want   Orig. Ret. $8.75   **NB** $15   **MIB** Sec. Mkt. **$20**

QX 565-2   LOONEY TUNES COLLECTION: PORKY PIG ☐

Comments: Handcrafted, 2-9/18" tall. Santa's coming! Porky is ready for bed dressed in his nightshirt and slippers, but he's getting Santa's treats ready first! **Artist:** Patricia Andrews

☐ Purchased 19____   Pd $_____   MIB   NB   DB   BNT
☐ Want   Orig. Ret. $8.75   **NB** $15   **MIB** Sec. Mkt. **$20**

QX 540-5   LOONEY TUNES COLLECTION: SYLVESTER AND TWEETY ☐

Comments: Handcrafted, 3-9/16" tall. Sylvester and Tweety get into the spirit of Christmas. Tweety is wearing a red Santa cap and Sylvester is sporting antlers and sleigh bells. **Artist:** Don Palmiter

☐ Purchased 19____   Pd $_____   MIB   NB   DB   BNT
☐ Want   Orig. Ret. $9.75   **NB** $25   **MIB** Sec. Mkt. **$30**

QX 574-5   LOU RANKIN POLAR BEAR ☐

Comments: Handcrafted, 3-15/16" tall. This unique bear is sculpted after the style of artist Lou Rankin. **Artist:** Dill Rhodus

☐ Purchased 19____   Pd $_____   MIB   NB   DB   BNT
☐ Want   Orig. Ret. $9.75   **NB** $25   **MIB** Sec. Mkt. **$30**

QX 532-5   MAKIN' MUSIC ☐

Comments: Handcrafted and Brass, 2" tall. A little mouse plays his violin as he stands atop a brass music staff. **Artist:** Ed Seale

☐ Purchased 19____   Pd $_____   MIB   NB   DB   BNT
☐ Want   Orig. Ret. $9.75   **NB** $15   **MIB** Sec. Mkt. **$20**

QX 577-5   MAKING WAVES ☐

Comments: Handcrafted, 2-1/2" tall, Dated 1993. Santa and one of his reindeer are racing into Christmas in a speedboat. **Artist:** Don Palmiter

☐ Purchased 19____   Pd $_____   MIB   NB   DB   BNT
☐ Want   Orig. Ret. $9.75   **NB** $20   **MIB** Sec. Mkt. **$27**

QX 207-5   MARY ENGELBREIT ☐

Comments: Glass Ball, 2-7/8" dia., Dated 1993. Christmas morning is a delight for all children, as depicted on this ball ornament. Caption: "Christmas Morning 1993." ©1993 Mary Engelbreit

☐ Purchased 19____   Pd $_____   MIB   NB   DB   BNT
☐ Want   Orig. Ret. $5.00   **NB** $10   **MIB** Sec. Mkt. **$18**

QX 428-2   MARY'S ANGELS: IVY ☐

Comments: **Sixth in Series,** Handcrafted, 2-3/8" tall. Many collectors have reported finding the box with Joy instead of Ivy; this is because of hard-to-read script writing. The box is not misprinted. **Artist:** Robert Chad

☐ Purchased 19____   Pd $_____   MIB   NB   DB   BNT
☐ Want   Orig. Ret. $6.75   **NB** $20   **MIB** Sec. Mkt. **$28**

QX 538-5   MAXINE ☐

Comments: Handcrafted, 3-7/16" tall. Maxine has a style all her own, with a Santa coat and beard and bunny slippers on her feet. **Artist:** Linda Sickman

☐ Purchased 19____   Pd $_____   MIB   NB   DB   BNT
☐ Want   Orig. Ret. $8.75   **NB** $25   **MIB** Sec. Mkt. **$35**

QX 484-2   MERRY OLDE SANTA ☐

Comments: **Fourth in Series,** Handcrafted, 4-5/16" tall, Dated 1993. Santa announces his arrival with the golden bell he rings, his pack on his back and a pair of ice skates for a lucky boy or girl. **Artist:** Anita Marra Rogers

☐ Purchased 19____   Pd $_____   MIB   NB   DB   BNT
☐ Want   Orig. Ret. $14.75   **NB** $30   **MIB** Sec. Mkt. **$40**

QLX 747-6   MESSAGES OF CHRISTMAS ☐

Comments: Special Issue, Handcrafted, Recordable, 4-1/2" tall, Dated 1993. Collectors were able to record their own Christmas message on this ornament. **Artist:** Bob Siedler

☐ Purchased 19____   Pd $_____   MIB   NB   DB   BNT
☐ Want   Orig. Ret. $35.00   **NB** $40   **MIB** Sec. Mkt. **$58**

QX 585-2   MOM ☐

Comments: Handcrafted, 2-5/8" tall, Dated 1993. Mom is ready to go shopping. **Artist:** Julia Lee

☐ Purchased 19____   Pd $_____   MIB   NB   DB   BNT
☐ Want   Orig. Ret. $7.75   **NB** $15   **MIB** Sec. Mkt. **$20**

QX 584-5   MOM AND DAD ☐

Comments: Handcrafted, 2-11/16" tall, Dated 1993. Two lovable red foxes open their gift. Love their slippers! **Artist:** Don Palmiter

☐ Purchased 19____   Pd $_____   MIB   NB   DB   BNT
☐ Want   Orig. Ret. $9.75   **NB** $15   **MIB** Sec. Mkt. **$20**

QX 553-5   MOM-TO-BE

Comments: Handcrafted, 2-1/8" tall, Dated 1993. Mama bee is preparing for her new little one – she's bringing in the honey pot. **Artist:** Julia Lee

☐ Purchased 19____   Pd $_____   MIB   NB   DB   BNT
☐ Want   Orig. Ret. $6.75   **NB** $12   **MIB** Sec. Mkt. **$18**

QX 528-2   MOTHER GOOSE: HUMPTY DUMPTY

Comments: **FIRST IN SERIES,** Handcrafted, 2-1/2" tall, Dated 1993. Inspired by the nursery rhyme Humpty Dumpty. **Artists:** Ed Seale/LaDene Votruba

☐ Purchased 19____   Pd $_____   MIB   NB   DB   BNT
☐ Want   Orig. Ret. $13.75   **NB** $40   **MIB** Sec. Mkt. **$45**

QX 420-2   MR. AND MRS. CLAUS: A FITTING MOMENT

Comments: **Eighth in Series,** Handcrafted, 3-1/8" tall, Dated 1993. Does Santa's suit still fit? Mrs. Claus is checking to see if alterations are needed. **Artist:** John Francis (Collin)

☐ Purchased 19____   Pd $_____   MIB   NB   DB   BNT
☐ Want   Orig. Ret. $14.75   **NB** $35   **MIB** Sec. Mkt. **$45**

QX 573-5   NEPHEW

Comments: Handcrafted, 2-1/2" tall, Dated 1993. This little fella is ready for a western Christmas.
Artist: Anita Marra Rogers

☐ Purchased 19____   Pd $_____   MIB   NB   DB   BNT
☐ Want   Orig. Ret. $6.75   **NB** $10   **MIB** Sec. Mkt. **$15**

QX 590-5   NEW HOME

Comments: Enamel on Metal, 3-5/16" tall, Dated 1993. The top portion of this unique key is a house! What a novel ornament. Caption: "A New Home Opens The Door To Memories And Love." **Artist:** Don Palmiter

☐ Purchased 19____   Pd $_____   MIB   NB   DB   BNT
☐ Want   Orig. Ret. $7.75   **NB** $40   **MIB** Sec. Mkt. **$50**

QX 573-2   NIECE

Comments: Handcrafted, 2-1/2" tall, Dated 1993. All set for Christmas, this little gal wears a red hat and boots, and has a dated gold star. **Artist:** Anita Marra Rogers

☐ Purchased 19____   Pd $_____   MIB   NB   DB   BNT
☐ Want   Orig. Ret. $6.75   **NB** $10   **MIB** Sec. Mkt. **$15**

QLX 739-2   NORTH POLE MERRYTHON

Comments: Light and Motion, 4-1/8" tall, Dated 1993. Santa and his reindeer run around the North Pole on this lighted ornament. Caption: "Go Santa 1993." **Artist:** Ed Seale

☐ Purchased 19____   Pd $_____   MIB   NB   DB   BNT
☐ Want   Orig. Ret. $25.00   **NB** $40   **MIB** Sec. Mkt. **$50**

QX 417-5   NOSTALGIC HOUSES AND SHOPS: COZY HOME

Comments: **Tenth in Series,** Handcrafted, 3-13/16" tall, Dated 1993. What a lovely home! A veranda covers the old-fashioned porch and welcomes all inside. **Artist:** Donna Lee

☐ Purchased 19____   Pd $_____   MIB   NB   DB   BNT
☐ Want   Orig. Ret. $14.75   **NB** $45   **MIB** Sec. Mkt. **$53**

QX 526-5   ON HER TOES

Comments: Handcrafted, 3-15/16" tall. A young ballerina in pastel pink twirls on one toe. **Artist:** Patricia Andrews

☐ Purchased 19____   Pd $_____   MIB   NB   DB   BNT
☐ Want   Orig. Ret. $8.75   **NB** $15   **MIB** Sec. Mkt. **$20**

QX 534-2   ONE ELF-MARCHING BAND

Comments: Handcrafted, 2-7/8" tall, Dated 1993. A bell in one hand and baton in the other, the elf beats the drum and claps the cymbals on his back when the cord is pulled. **Artist:** Robert Chad

☐ Purchased 19____   Pd $_____   MIB   NB   DB   BNT
☐ Want   Orig. Ret. $12.75   **NB** $20   **MIB** Sec. Mkt. **$28**

QX 594-2   OUR CHRISTMAS TOGETHER

Comments: Handcrafted, 4-13/16" tall, Dated 1993. Two cats cuddle together on a swing built for two. A Christmas wreath decorates the back of the swing.
Artist: Donna Lee

☐ Purchased 19____   Pd $_____   MIB   NB   DB   BNT
☐ Want   Orig. Ret. $10.75   **NB** $18   **MIB** Sec. Mkt. **$23**

QX 589-2   OUR FAMILY PHOTOHOLDER

Comments: Handcrafted, 4-9/16" tall, Dated 1993. Insert your favorite photo in the picture window of this "house." Caption: "Happy Holidays 1993" **Artist:** Duane Unruh

☐ Purchased 19____   Pd $_____   MIB   NB   DB   BNT
☐ Want   Orig. Ret. $7.75   **NB** $12   **MIB** Sec. Mkt. **$20**

QX 595-5   OUR FIRST CHRISTMAS TOGETHER

Comments: **Brass and Silver Plated,** 3-1/4" tall, Dated 1993. A silver-plated man and woman dance and spin in the center of a brass heart etched with holly and "Our First Christmas 1993." **Artist:** Anita Marra Rogers

☐ Purchased 19_____   Pd $_____   MIB   NB   DB   BNT
☐ Want   Orig. Ret. $18.75   **NB** $29   **MIB** Sec. Mkt. **$38**

QX 564-2   OUR FIRST CHRISTMAS TOGETHER

Comments: Handcrafted, 2-3/16" tall, Dated 1993. A raccoon couple celebrate their first Christmas around their Christmas tree. **Artist:** Joyce A. Lyle

☐ Purchased 19_____   Pd $_____   MIB   NB   DB   BNT
☐ Want   Orig. Ret. $9.75   **NB** $10   **MIB** Sec. Mkt. **$15**

QLX 735-5   OUR FIRST CHRISTMAS TOGETHER

Comments: Lighted, 2-3/4" tall, Dated 1993. A couple sit side by side in front of a flickering fire inside this peek-through ball. **Artist:** Robert Chad

☐ Purchased 19_____   Pd $_____   MIB   NB   DB   BNT
☐ Want   Orig. Ret. $20.00   **NB** $40   **MIB** Sec. Mkt. **$43**

QX 595-2   OUR FIRST CHRISTMAS TOGETHER PHOTOHOLDER

Comments: Handcrafted, 3-5/8" tall, Dated 1993. Red hearts adorn an oval green wreath for this photo frame. Caption: "Love Is The Heart's Most Cherished Treasure." **Artist:** Duane Unruh

☐ Purchased 19_____   Pd $_____   MIB   NB   DB   BNT
☐ Want   Orig. Ret. $8.75   **NB** $15   **MIB** Sec. Mkt. **$18**

QX 301-5   OUR FIRST CHRISTMAS TOGETHER

Comments: Acrylic, 3-3/8" tall, Dated 1993. Two frosted swans snuggle together inside a frosted heart frame. **Artist:** Patricia Andrews

☐ Purchased 19_____   Pd $_____   MIB   NB   DB   BNT
☐ Want   Orig. Ret. $6.75   **NB** $12   **MIB** Sec. Mkt. **$18**

QX 542-5   OWLIVER

Comments: **Second in Series,** Handcrafted, 2-3/8" tall, Dated 1993. Owliver naps on a tree stump while a little squirrel delivers a present. **Artist:** Bob Siedler

☐ Purchased 19_____   Pd $_____   MIB   NB   DB   BNT
☐ Want   Orig. Ret. $7.75   **NB** $12   **MIB** Sec. Mkt. **$18**

QX 524-2   PEACE ON EARTH: POLAND

Comments: **Third and Final in Series,** Handcrafted, 3" dia., Dated 1993. Children in native dress portray a message for all mankind; one of peace. Caption: "Pokój Ludziom Dobrej Wol." **Artist:** Linda Sickman

☐ Purchased 19_____   Pd $_____   MIB   NB   DB   BNT
☐ Want   Orig. Ret. $11.75   **NB** $20   **MIB** Sec. Mkt. **$25**

QLX 715-5   PEANUTS®

Comments: **Third in Series,** Blinking Lights, Handcrafted. 3-1/2" tall, Dated 1993. Snoopy and Woodstock admire their Christmas tree; its lights blink off and on. **Artist:** Dill Rhodus

☐ Purchased 19_____   Pd $_____   MIB   NB   DB   BNT
☐ Want   Orig. Ret. $18.00   **NB** $40   **MIB** Sec. Mkt. **$50**

QX 207-2   PEANUTS®

Comments: Glass Ball, 2-7/8" dia., Dated 1993. The Peanuts characters are wishing you a Merry Christmas in Spanish, German, Italian, French and English.

☐ Purchased 19_____   Pd $_____   MIB   NB   DB   BNT
☐ Want   Orig. Ret. $5.00   **NB** $25   **MIB** Sec. Mkt. **$30**

QX 531-5   PEANUTS® GANG

Comments: *FIRST IN SERIES,* Handcrafted, 2-3/8" tall, Dated 1993. Charlie Brown has a twin! It's a "snow boy" he built himself! **Artist:** Dill Rhodus

☐ Purchased 19_____   Pd $_____   MIB   NB   DB   BNT
☐ Want   Orig. Ret. $9.75   **NB** $55   **MIB** Sec. Mkt. **$65**

QX 524-5   PEEK-A-BOO TREE

Comments: Handcrafted, 4-3/16" tall, Dated 1993. Little animals peek in and out of the tree when you turn the pinecone knob. **Artist:** Ken Crow

☐ Purchased 19_____   Pd $_____   MIB   NB   DB   BNT
☐ Want   Orig. Ret. $10.75   **NB** $16   **MIB** Sec. Mkt. **$24**

QX 532-2   PEEP INSIDE

Comments: Handcrafted, 2-7/16" tall, Dated 1993. A birdhouse opens to reveal Mama's babies inside on the nest, waiting for their Christmas dinner. **Artist:** Donna Lee

☐ Purchased 19_____   Pd $_____   MIB   NB   DB   BNT
☐ Want   Orig. Ret. $13.75   **NB** $17   **MIB** Sec. Mkt. **$28**

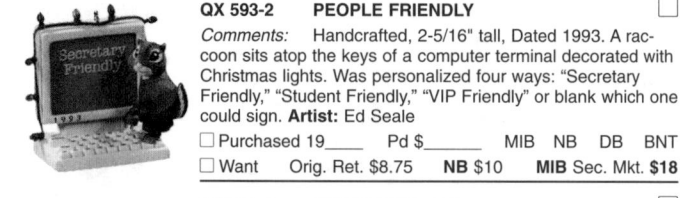

QX 593-2　　PEOPLE FRIENDLY ☐

Comments:　Handcrafted, 2-5/16" tall, Dated 1993. A raccoon sits atop the keys of a computer terminal decorated with Christmas lights. Was personalized four ways: "Secretary Friendly," "Student Friendly," "VIP Friendly" or blank which one could sign. **Artist:** Ed Seale

☐ Purchased 19＿＿＿　Pd $＿＿＿＿　MIB　NB　DB　BNT
☐ Want　Orig. Ret. $8.75　**NB** $10　**MIB** Sec. Mkt. **$18**

QX 577-2　　PERFECT MATCH ☐

Comments:　Handcrafted, 3-1/3" tall, Dated 1993. A little bear sits between two yellow tennis balls in a canister captioned "Perfect Match Tennis Balls '93." **Artist:** Bob Siedler

☐ Purchased 19＿＿＿　Pd $＿＿＿＿　MIB　NB　DB　BNT
☐ Want　Orig. Ret. $8.75　**NB** $15　**MIB** Sec. Mkt. **$20**

QX 575-5　　PINK PANTHER, THE ☐

Comments:　Handcrafted, 3" tall, Dated 1993. Dressed as Santa and carrying his pack on his back, the Pink Panther prepares to climb down the chimney. **Artist:** Don Palmiter

☐ Purchased 19＿＿＿　Pd $＿＿＿＿　MIB　NB　DB　BNT
☐ Want　Orig. Ret. $12.75　**NB** $24　**MIB** Sec. Mkt. **$29**

QX 574-2　　PLAYFUL PALS: COCA-COLA SANTA ☐

Comments:　Handcrafted, 3-7/8" tall, Dated 1993. A little black French poodle sits up and begs for Santa's cookie. The gift-wrapped doghouse is dated. **Artist:** Anita Marra Rogers

☐ Purchased 19＿＿＿　Pd $＿＿＿＿　MIB　NB　DB　BNT
☐ Want　Orig. Ret. $14.75　**NB** $20　**MIB** Sec. Mkt. **$30**

QX 539-2　　POPPING GOOD TIMES ☐

Comments:　Handcrafted, 2" tall, Dated 1993. Two individual mice, one with a bag of popcorn and the other with a popcorn popper, create a set of hang-together ornaments. **Artist:** Robert Chad

☐ Purchased 19＿＿＿　Pd $＿＿＿＿　MIB　NB　DB　BNT
☐ Want　Orig. Ret. $14.75　**NB** $25　**MIB** Sec. Mkt. **$30**

QX 504-5　　PUPPY LOVE ☐

Comments:　**Third in Series,** Handcrafted, 1-9/16" tall, Dated 1993. A golden retriever is enjoying a speedy trip downhill on a toboggan. **Artist:** Anita Marra Rogers

☐ Purchased 19＿＿＿　Pd $＿＿＿＿　MIB　NB　DB　BNT
☐ Want　Orig. Ret. $7.75　**NB** $25　**MIB** Sec. Mkt. **$30**

QX 579-5　　PUTT-PUTT PENGUIN ☐

Comments:　Handcrafted, 3" tall, Dated 1993. A perky penguin in a blue hat rides to the next hole in his red golf cart. The words "Putt-Putt" are on both sides of the cart. **Artist:** Julia Lee

☐ Purchased 19＿＿＿　Pd $＿＿＿＿　MIB　NB　DB　BNT
☐ Want　Orig. Ret. $9.75　**NB** $15　**MIB** Sec. Mkt. **$24**

QX 579-2　　QUICK AS A FOX ☐

Comments:　Handcrafted, 2-5/8" tall, Dated 1993. This little postal fox handles his deliveries with speed and ingenuity. He has fastened his package to a pair of ice skate blades and rides his way into Christmas. **Artist:** Ken Crow

☐ Purchased 19＿＿＿　Pd $＿＿＿＿　MIB　NB　DB　BNT
☐ Want　Orig. Ret. $8.75　**NB** $14　**MIB** Sec. Mkt. **$18**

QLX 736-2　　RADIO NEWS FLASH ☐

Comments:　Light and Sound, 3-3/16" tall, Dated 1993. A kitten listens to the sounds of Christmas on this holly trimmed old-fashioned radio. Caption: "Christmas Is In The Air!" **Artist:** Donna Lee

☐ Purchased 19＿＿＿　Pd $＿＿＿＿　MIB　NB　DB　BNT
☐ Want　Orig. Ret. $22.00　**NB** $45　**MIB** Sec. Mkt. **$50**

QLX 718-5　　RAIDING THE FRIDGE ☐

Comments:　Lighted, 3-7/16" tall, Dated 1993. Santa's catching a late-night snack. The refrigerator light is on because he has the door open. Caption: "Cold Milk And Cool Cookies For Santa!" **Artist:** Anita Marra Rogers

☐ Purchased 19＿＿＿　Pd $＿＿＿＿　MIB　NB　DB　BNT
☐ Want　Orig. Ret. $16.00　**NB** $29　**MIB** Sec. Mkt. **$35**

QX 512-4　　READY FOR FUN ☐

Comments:　Handcrafted, Tin, 3-1/8" tall, Dated 1993. A gingerbread cookie boy moves out of his cookie cutter frame so that he might join in the Christmas festivities. **Artist:** Joyce A. Lyle

☐ Purchased 19＿＿＿　Pd $＿＿＿＿　MIB　NB　DB　BNT
☐ Want　Orig. Ret. $7.75　**NB** $11　**MIB** Sec. Mkt. **$18**

QX 433-1　　REINDEER CHAMPS: BLITZEN ☐

Comments:　**Eighth and Final in Series,** Handcrafted. 3-1/8" tall, Dated 1993. Blitzen scores again! Santa's reindeer team wins this football game! **Artist:** Bob Siedler

☐ Purchased 19＿＿＿　Pd $＿＿＿＿　MIB　NB　DB　BNT
☐ Want　Orig. Ret. $8.75　**NB** $25　**MIB** Sec. Mkt. **$30**

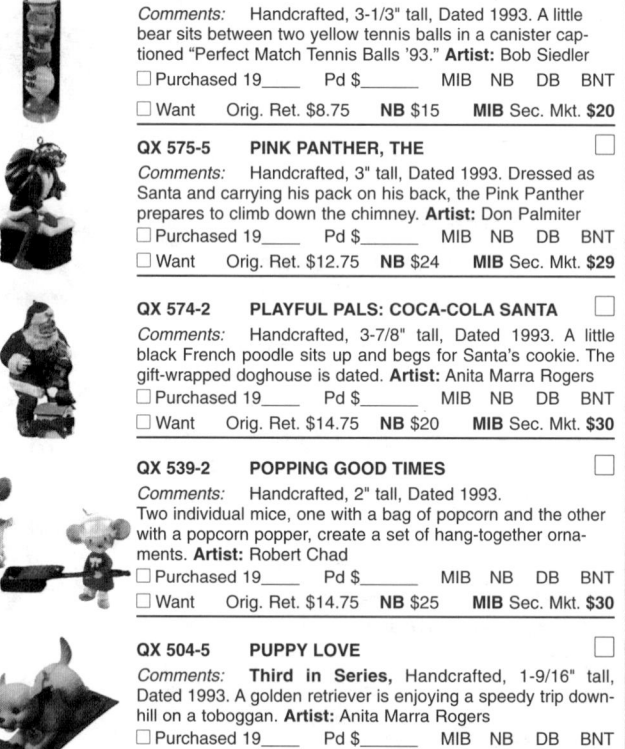

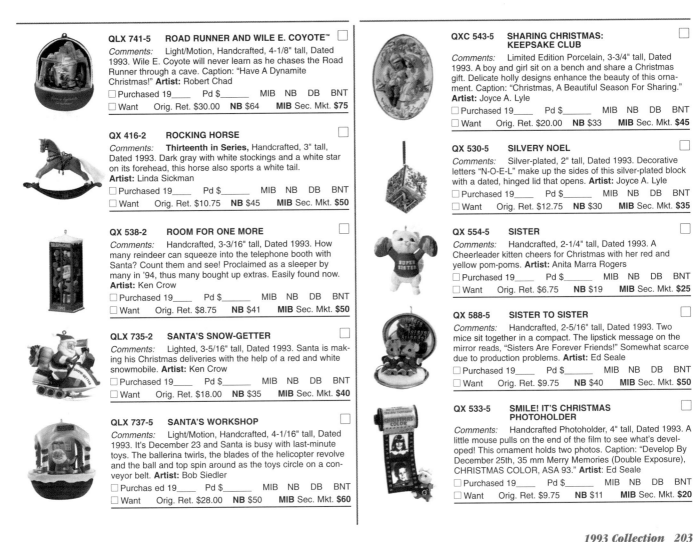

QLX 741-5   ROAD RUNNER AND WILE E. COYOTE™
Comments: Light/Motion, Handcrafted, 4-1/8" tall, Dated
1993. Wile E. Coyote will never learn as he chases the Road
Runner through a cave. Caption: "Have A Dynamite
Christmas!" **Artist:** Robert Chad

☐ Purchased 19____   Pd $_____   MIB NB DB BNT
☐ Want   Orig. Ret. $30.00   **NB** $64   **MIB** Sec. Mkt. **$75**

QX 416-2   ROCKING HORSE
Comments: **Thirteenth in Series,** Handcrafted, 3" tall,
Dated 1993. Dark gray with white stockings and a white star
on its forehead, this horse also sports a white tail.
Artist: Linda Sickman

☐ Purchased 19____   Pd $_____   MIB NB DB BNT
☐ Want   Orig. Ret. $10.75   **NB** $45   **MIB** Sec. Mkt. **$50**

QX 538-2   ROOM FOR ONE MORE
Comments: Handcrafted, 3-3/16" tall, Dated 1993. How
many reindeer can squeeze into the telephone booth with
Santa? Count them and see! Proclaimed as a sleeper by
many in '94, thus many bought up extras. Easily found now.
Artist: Ken Crow

☐ Purchased 19____   Pd $_____   MIB NB DB BNT
☐ Want   Orig. Ret. $8.75   **NB** $41   **MIB** Sec. Mkt. **$50**

QLX 735-2   SANTA'S SNOW-GETTER
Comments: Lighted, 3-5/16" tall, Dated 1993. Santa is making his Christmas deliveries with the help of a red and white
snowmobile. **Artist:** Ken Crow

☐ Purchased 19____   Pd $_____   MIB NB DB BNT
☐ Want   Orig. Ret. $18.00   **NB** $35   **MIB** Sec. Mkt. **$40**

QLX 737-5   SANTA'S WORKSHOP
Comments: Light/Motion, Handcrafted, 4-1/16" tall, Dated
1993. It's December 23 and Santa is busy with last-minute
toys. The ballerina twirls, the blades of the helicopter revolve
and the ball and top spin around as the toys circle on a con-
veyor belt. **Artist:** Bob Siedler

☐ Purchas ed 19____   Pd $_____   MIB NB DB BNT
☐ Want   Orig. Ret. $28.00   **NB** $50   **MIB** Sec. Mkt. **$60**

**QXC 543-5   SHARING CHRISTMAS:
KEEPSAKE CLUB**
Comments: Limited Edition Porcelain, 3-3/4" tall, Dated
1993. A boy and girl sit on a bench and share a Christmas
gift. Delicate holly designs enhance the beauty of this ornament. Caption: "Christmas, A Beautiful Season For Sharing."
Artist: Joyce A. Lyle

☐ Purchased 19____   Pd $_____   MIB NB DB BNT
☐ Want   Orig. Ret. $20.00   **NB** $33   **MIB** Sec. Mkt. **$45**

QX 530-5   SILVERY NOEL
Comments: Silver-plated, 2" tall, Dated 1993. Decorative
letters "N-O-E-L" make up the sides of this silver-plated block
with a dated, hinged lid that opens. **Artist:** Joyce A. Lyle

☐ Purchased 19____   Pd $_____   MIB NB DB BNT
☐ Want   Orig. Ret. $12.75   **NB** $30   **MIB** Sec. Mkt. **$35**

QX 554-5   SISTER
Comments: Handcrafted, 2-1/4" tall, Dated 1993. A
Cheerleader kitten cheers for Christmas with her red and
yellow pom-poms. **Artist:** Anita Marra Rogers

☐ Purchased 19____   Pd $_____   MIB NB DB BNT
☐ Want   Orig. Ret. $6.75   **NB** $19   **MIB** Sec. Mkt. **$25**

QX 588-5   SISTER TO SISTER
Comments: Handcrafted, 2-5/16" tall, Dated 1993. Two
mice sit together in a compact. The lipstick message on the
mirror reads, "Sisters Are Forever Friends!" Somewhat scarce
due to production problems. **Artist:** Ed Seale

☐ Purchased 19____   Pd $_____   MIB NB DB BNT
☐ Want   Orig. Ret. $9.75   **NB** $40   **MIB** Sec. Mkt. **$50**

**QX 533-5   SMILE! IT'S CHRISTMAS
PHOTOHOLDER**
Comments: Handcrafted Photoholder, 4" tall, Dated 1993. A
little mouse pulls on the end of the film to see what's devel-
oped! This ornament holds two photos. Caption: "Develop By
December 25th, 35 mm Merry Memories (Double Exposure),
CHRISTMAS COLOR, ASA 93." **Artist:** Ed Seale

☐ Purchased 19____   Pd $_____   MIB NB DB BNT
☐ Want   Orig. Ret. $9.75   **NB** $11   **MIB** Sec. Mkt. **$20**

QX 535-5   SNOW BEAR ANGEL

Comments: Handcrafted, 2-3/4" dia., Dated 1993. Making angels in the snow is fun! Even this bear enjoys it. Pull the snowball and the bear will move his arms and legs. Caption: "This Little Bear Has Christmas Fun By Making Angels, One By One!" Remember when we were kids? We did this too!
Artist: Julia Lee

☐ Purchased 19____   Pd $_____   MIB   NB   DB   BNT
☐ Want   Orig. Ret. $7.75   **NB** $10   **MIB** Sec. Mkt. **$18**

QX 576-5   SNOWBIRD

Comments: Handcrafted, 2-5/8" tall, Dated 1993. This bird is ready for some Christmas sights. He's wearing his sunglasses and tennis shoes, with his gift and camera in hand.
Artist: Julia Lee

☐ Purchased 19____   Pd $_____   MIB   NB   DB   BNT
☐ Want   Orig. Ret. $7.75   **NB** $15   **MIB** Sec. Mkt. **$20**

QX 531-2   SNOWY HIDEAWAY

Comments: Handcrafted, 3" dia., Dated 1993. A little red fox sits quietly in a snow-covered wreath.
Artist: John Francis (Collin)

☐ Purchased 19____   Pd $_____   MIB   NB   DB   BNT
☐ Want   Orig. Ret. $9.75   **NB** $15   **MIB** Sec. Mkt. **$20**

QX 586-5   SON

Comments: Handcrafted, 4-7/16" tall, Dated 1993. Bendable neck and legs are a special feature of this giraffe wearing a red turtleneck sweater and blue ice skates. **Artist:** LaDene Votruba

☐ Purchased 19____   Pd $_____   MIB   NB   DB   BNT
☐ Want   Orig. Ret. $6.75   **NB** $15   **MIB** Sec. Mkt. **$23**

QLX 740-5   SONG OF THE CHIMES

Comments: Light and Motion, 4-1/8" tall, Dated 1993. Brass doves are set in motion by the heat of the "candle." Chimes ring as the doves circle the star. **Artist:** Patricia Andrews

☐ Purchased 19____   Pd $_____   MIB   NB   DB   BNT
☐ Want   Orig. Ret. $25.00   **NB** $45   **MIB** Sec. Mkt. **$55**

QX 523-5   SPECIAL CAT PHOTOHOLDER

Comments: Handcrafted, Brass, 4-1/8" tall, Dated 1993. Insert a photo of your "Classy Cat" into this photo frame designed as a cat collar. A golden bell signals that Christmas time is near. **Artist:** LaDene Votruba

☐ Purchased 19____   Pd $_____   MIB   NB   DB   BNT
☐ Want   Orig. Ret. $7.75   **NB** $10   **MIB** Sec. Mkt. **$16**

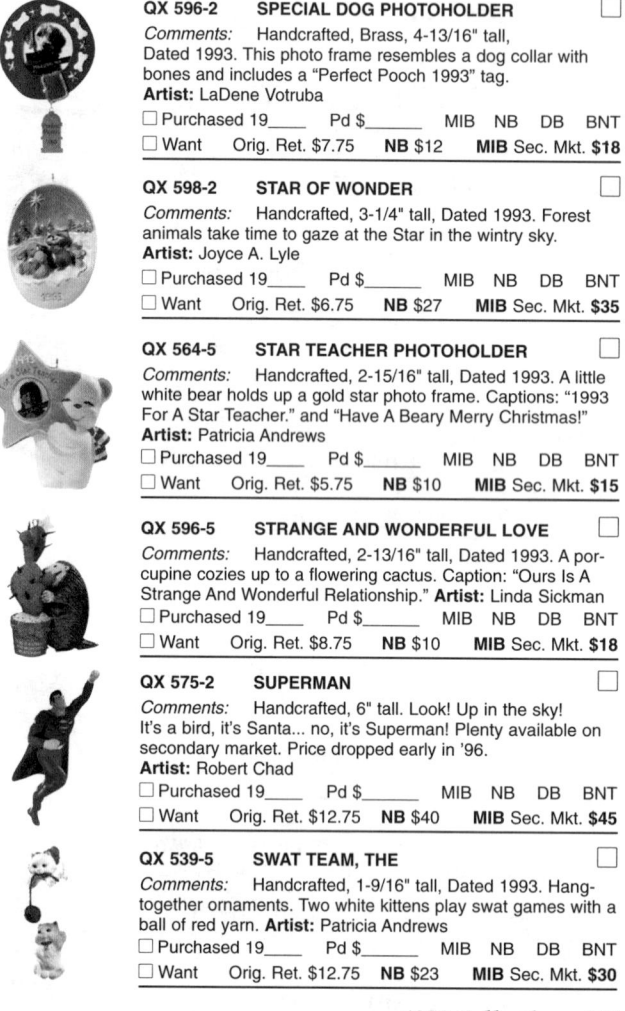

QX 596-2   SPECIAL DOG PHOTOHOLDER

Comments: Handcrafted, Brass, 4-13/16" tall, Dated 1993. This photo frame resembles a dog collar with bones and includes a "Perfect Pooch 1993" tag.
Artist: LaDene Votruba

☐ Purchased 19____   Pd $_____   MIB   NB   DB   BNT
☐ Want   Orig. Ret. $7.75   **NB** $12   **MIB** Sec. Mkt. **$18**

QX 598-2   STAR OF WONDER

Comments: Handcrafted, 3-1/4" tall, Dated 1993. Forest animals take time to gaze at the Star in the wintry sky.
Artist: Joyce A. Lyle

☐ Purchased 19____   Pd $_____   MIB   NB   DB   BNT
☐ Want   Orig. Ret. $6.75   **NB** $27   **MIB** Sec. Mkt. **$35**

QX 564-5   STAR TEACHER PHOTOHOLDER

Comments: Handcrafted, 2-15/16" tall, Dated 1993. A little white bear holds up a gold star photo frame. Captions: "1993 For A Star Teacher." and "Have A Beary Merry Christmas!"
Artist: Patricia Andrews

☐ Purchased 19____   Pd $_____   MIB   NB   DB   BNT
☐ Want   Orig. Ret. $5.75   **NB** $10   **MIB** Sec. Mkt. **$15**

QX 596-5   STRANGE AND WONDERFUL LOVE

Comments: Handcrafted, 2-13/16" tall, Dated 1993. A porcupine cozies up to a flowering cactus. Caption: "Ours Is A Strange And Wonderful Relationship." **Artist:** Linda Sickman

☐ Purchased 19____   Pd $_____   MIB   NB   DB   BNT
☐ Want   Orig. Ret. $8.75   **NB** $10   **MIB** Sec. Mkt. **$18**

QX 575-2   SUPERMAN

Comments: Handcrafted, 6" tall. Look! Up in the sky! It's a bird, it's Santa... no, it's Superman! Plenty available on secondary market. Price dropped early in '96.
Artist: Robert Chad

☐ Purchased 19____   Pd $_____   MIB   NB   DB   BNT
☐ Want   Orig. Ret. $12.75   **NB** $40   **MIB** Sec. Mkt. **$45**

QX 539-5   SWAT TEAM, THE

Comments: Handcrafted, 1-9/16" tall, Dated 1993. Hang-together ornaments. Two white kittens play swat games with a ball of red yarn. **Artist:** Patricia Andrews

☐ Purchased 19____   Pd $_____   MIB   NB   DB   BNT
☐ Want   Orig. Ret. $12.75   **NB** $23   **MIB** Sec. Mkt. **$30**

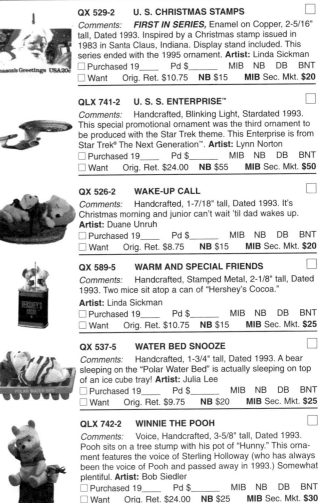

QX 534-5   THAT'S ENTERTAINMENT ☐
Comments: Handcrafted, 2-15/16" tall, Dated 1993. Watch as Santa pulls a rabbit out of his hat! **Artist:** Bob Siedler
☐ Purchased 19____   Pd $_____   MIB NB DB BNT
☐ Want   Orig. Ret. $8.75   **NB** $15   **MIB** Sec. Mkt. **$20**

QX 555-5   TO MY GRANDMA ☐
Comments: Handcrafted, 3-5/16" tall, Dated 1993. A red note pad doubles as a photo holder. May be personalized. Captions: "To My Grandma XOXO, 1993 XOXO" and "I May Be Little, But I Love You Great Big!" **Artist:** Donna Lee
☐ Purchased 19____   Pd $_____   MIB NB DB BNT
☐ Want   Orig. Ret. $7.75   **NB** $14   **MIB** Sec. Mkt. **$18**

QX 550-2   TOBIN FRALEY CARROUSEL ☐
Comments: **Second in Series,** Porcelain and Brass, 5-1/4" tall, Dated 1993. A white horse decorated in Christmas finery gallops into Christmas. Secondary market buyers bought less of this ornament than the first, so this is the reason for the higher value. (Supply and demand.)
☐ Purchased 19____   Pd $_____   MIB NB DB BNT
☐ Want   Orig. Ret. $28.00   **NB** $57   **MIB** Sec. Mkt. **$60**

QX 592-5   TOP BANANA ☐
Comments: Handcrafted, 2-7/16" tall, Dated 1993. This perky little monkey, dressed in a Santa suit and sitting on top of a bunch of bananas, is sure to perk up anyone's Christmas. **Artist:** Anita Marra Rogers
☐ Purchased 19____   Pd $_____   MIB NB DB BNT
☐ Want   Orig. Ret. $7.75   **NB** $14   **MIB** Sec. Mkt. **$20**

QXC 543-2   TRIMMED WITH MEMORIES: ☐
KEEPSAKE CLUB ANNIVERSARY EDITION
Comments: Handcrafted, 3-7/8" tall, Dated 1993 and 1973. A blue spruce is decorated with small gold replicas of Keepsake ornaments, as well as candles and garland. **Artist:** Linda Sickman
☐ Purchased 19____   Pd $_____   MIB NB DB BNT
☐ Want   Orig. Ret. $12.00   **NB** $35   **MIB** Sec. Mkt. **$40**

QX 301-2   TWELVE DAYS OF CHRISTMAS: ☐
TEN LORDS A-LEAPING
Comments: **Tenth in Series,** Acrylic, 3" tall, Dated 1993. One of the ten lords leaps among holly leaves on this heart-shaped acrylic ornament. **Artist:** Robert Chad
☐ Purchased 19____   Pd $_____   MIB NB DB BNT
☐ Want   Orig. Ret. $6.75   **NB** $20   **MIB** Sec. Mkt. **$25**

QX 529-2   U. S. CHRISTMAS STAMPS ☐
Comments: **FIRST IN SERIES,** Enamel on Copper, 2-5/16" tall, Dated 1993. Inspired by a Christmas stamp issued in 1983 in Santa Claus, Indiana. Display stand included. This series ended with the 1995 ornament. **Artist:** Linda Sickman
☐ Purchased 19____   Pd $_____   MIB NB DB BNT
☐ Want   Orig. Ret. $10.75   **NB** $15   **MIB** Sec. Mkt. **$20**

QLX 741-2   U. S. S. ENTERPRISE™ ☐
Comments: Handcrafted, Blinking Light, Stardated 1993. This special promotional ornament was the third ornament to be produced with the Star Trek theme. This Enterprise is from Star Trek® The Next Generation™. **Artist:** Lynn Norton
☐ Purchased 19____   Pd $_____   MIB NB DB BNT
☐ Want   Orig. Ret. $24.00   **NB** $55   **MIB** Sec. Mkt. **$50**

QX 526-2   WAKE-UP CALL ☐
Comments: Handcrafted, 1-7/18" tall, Dated 1993. It's Christmas morning and junior can't wait 'til dad wakes up. **Artist:** Duane Unruh
☐ Purchased 19____   Pd $_____   MIB NB DB BNT
☐ Want   Orig. Ret. $8.75   **NB** $15   **MIB** Sec. Mkt. **$20**

QX 589-5   WARM AND SPECIAL FRIENDS ☐
Comments: Handcrafted, Stamped Metal, 2-1/8" tall, Dated 1993. Two mice sit atop a can of "Hershey's Cocoa." **Artist:** Linda Sickman
☐ Purchased 19____   Pd $_____   MIB NB DB BNT
☐ Want   Orig. Ret. $10.75   **NB** $15   **MIB** Sec. Mkt. **$25**

QX 537-5   WATER BED SNOOZE ☐
Comments: Handcrafted, 1-3/4" tall, Dated 1993. A bear sleeping on the "Polar Water Bed" is actually sleeping on top of an ice cube tray! **Artist:** Julia Lee
☐ Purchased 19____   Pd $_____   MIB NB DB BNT
☐ Want   Orig. Ret. $9.75   **NB** $20   **MIB** Sec. Mkt. **$25**

QLX 742-2   WINNIE THE POOH ☐
Comments: Voice, Handcrafted, 3-5/8" tall, Dated 1993. Pooh sits on a tree stump with his pot of "Hunny." This orna-ment features the voice of Sterling Holloway (who has always been the voice of Pooh and passed away in 1993.) Somewhat plentiful. **Artist:** Bob Siedler
☐ Purchased 19____   Pd $_____   MIB NB DB BNT
☐ Want   Orig. Ret. $24.00   **NB** $25   **MIB** Sec. Mkt. **$30**

QX 571-2   WINNIE THE POOH COLLECTION:
                        EEYORE   ☐

Comments: Handcrafted, 2" tall. Hang on, Eeyore!
Artist: Bob Siedler

☐ Purchased 19_____   Pd $_____   MIB   NB   DB   BNT
☐ Want   Orig. Ret. $9.75   **NB** $15   **MIB** Sec. Mkt. **$20**

QX 567-2   WINNIE THE POOH COLLECTION:
                        KANGA AND ROO   ☐

Comments: Handcrafted, 3-3/8" tall. Roo peeks out from
Kanga's pouch for a better view. **Artist:** Bob Siedler

☐ Purchased 19_____   Pd $_____   MIB   NB   DB   BNT
☐ Want   Orig. Ret. $9.75   **NB** $14   **MIB** Sec. Mkt. **$18**

QX 569-5   WINNIE THE POOH COLLECTION: OWL ☐

Comments: Handcrafted, 3-5/8" tall. Owl stays warm in
winter by strapping a hot water bottle to his stomach.
Artist: Bob Siedler

☐ Purchased 19_____   Pd $_____   MIB   NB   DB   BNT
☐ Want   Orig. Ret. $9.75   **NB** $12   **MIB** Sec. Mkt. **$15**

QX 570-2   WINNIE THE POOH COLLECTION:
                        RABBIT   ☐

Comments: Handcrafted, 3-1/2" tall. Rabbit finds that frying
pans make great snowshoes! **Artist:** Bob Siedler

☐ Purchased 19_____   Pd $_____   MIB   NB   DB   BNT
☐ Want   Orig. Ret. $9.75   **NB** $12   **MIB** Sec. Mkt. **$15**

QX 570-5   WINNIE THE POOH COLLECTION:
                        TIGGER AND PIGLET   ☐

Comments: Handcrafted, 3-3/4" tall. As Tigger glides on his
ice skates, Piglet grabs a ride on his tail. **Artist:** Bob Siedler

☐ Purchased 19_____   Pd $_____   MIB   NB   DB   BNT
☐ Want   Orig. Ret. $9.75   **NB** $25   **MIB** Sec. Mkt. **$30**

QX 571-5   WINNIE THE POOH COLLECTION:
                        WINNIE THE POOH   ☐

Comments: Handcrafted, 3-3/8" tall. Pooh is an expert
skier! **Artist:** Bob Siedler

☐ Purchased 19_____   Pd $_____   MIB   NB   DB   BNT
☐ Want   Orig. Ret. $9.75   **NB** $20   **MIB** Sec. Mkt. **$25**

QXC 569-2   YOU'RE ALWAYS WELCOME ☐

Comments: Handcrafted, 2-1/2" tall, Dated 1993. A Tender
Touches bear puts out her special "Welcome 1993" door mat.
The Tender Touches logo and Keepsake Ornament Premiere
is on the base of this ornament. Plentiful in '94 and '95!
Artist: Ed Seale

☐ Purchased 19_____   Pd $_____   MIB   NB   DB   BNT
☐ Want   Orig. Ret. $9.75   **NB** $49   **MIB** Sec. Mkt. **$60**

Hallmark Keepsake Personalized Ornaments

These ornaments may not escalate in value on the secondary market unless, perhaps, they are personalized with a well-known name or saying. No sales on these have been reported or found advertised.

QP 603-5   BABY BLOCK PHOTOHOLDER ☐

Comments: Handcrafted Photoholder, 2-13/16" tall. A baby
bear shaking its green rattle sits atop a baby block which is
also a photo holder. May be personalized with a name or special message. Was special ordered through Hallmark.
Reissued in 1994. **Artist:** John Francis (Collin)

☐ Purchased 19_____   Pd $_____   MIB   NB   DB   BNT
☐ Want   Orig. Ret. $14.75   **MIB** Sec. Mkt. **N.E.**

QP 605-2   COOL SNOWMAN ☐

Comments: White Glass Ball, 2-7/8" diam. Personalization
is in the caption area above the snowman's head.

☐ Purchased 19_____   Pd $_____   MIB   NB   DB   BNT
☐ Want   Orig. Ret. $8.75   **MIB** Sec. Mkt. **N.E.**

QP 602-5   FESTIVE ALBUM PHOTOHOLDER ☐

Comments: Handcrafted Photoholder, 7-7/16" tall. This
engraved photo album holds your favorite photo inside. A little
mouse swings from a ribbon. Reissued in 1994. Similiar to the '95
(July Premiere) artists' photo ornament. **Artist:** LaDene Votruba

☐ Purchased 19_____   Pd $_____   MIB   NB   DB   BNT
☐ Want   Orig. Ret. $12.75   **MIB** Sec. Mkt. **N.E.**

QP 604-2   FILLED WITH COOKIES ☐

Comments: Handcrafted, 2-1/8" tall. An acorn-designed
cookie jar is being raided by a little squirrel. Shh! Don't tell!
Reissued in '95. **Artist:** Anita Marra Rogers

☐ Purchased 19_____   Pd $_____   MIB   NB   DB   BNT
☐ Want   Orig. Ret. $12.75   **MIB** Sec. Mkt. **N.E.**

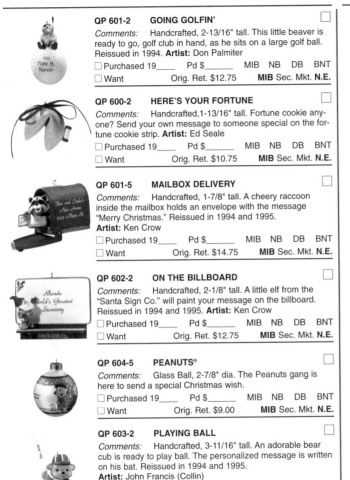

QP 601-2   GOING GOLFIN'

Comments: Handcrafted, 2-13/16" tall. This little beaver is ready to go, golf club in hand, as he sits on a large golf ball. Reissued in 1994. **Artist:** Don Palmiter

☐ Purchased 19____   Pd $_____   MIB   NB   DB   BNT
☐ Want   Orig. Ret. $12.75   **MIB** Sec. Mkt. **N.E.**

QP 600-2   HERE'S YOUR FORTUNE

Comments: Handcrafted,1-13/16" tall. Fortune cookie anyone? Send your own message to someone special on the fortune cookie strip. **Artist:** Ed Seale

☐ Purchased 19____   Pd $_____   MIB   NB   DB   BNT
☐ Want   Orig. Ret. $10.75   **MIB** Sec. Mkt. **N.E.**

QP 601-5   MAILBOX DELIVERY

Comments: Handcrafted, 1-7/8" tall. A cheery raccoon inside the mailbox holds an envelope with the message "Merry Christmas." Reissued in 1994 and 1995. **Artist:** Ken Crow

☐ Purchased 19____   Pd $_____   MIB   NB   DB   BNT
☐ Want   Orig. Ret. $14.75   **MIB** Sec. Mkt. **N.E.**

QP 602-2   ON THE BILLBOARD

Comments: Handcrafted, 2-1/8" tall. A little elf from the "Santa Sign Co." will paint your message on the billboard. Reissued in 1994 and 1995. **Artist:** Ken Crow

☐ Purchased 19____   Pd $_____   MIB   NB   DB   BNT
☐ Want   Orig. Ret. $12.75   **MIB** Sec. Mkt. **N.E.**

QP 604-5   PEANUTS®

Comments: Glass Ball, 2-7/8" dia. The Peanuts gang is here to send a special Christmas wish.

☐ Purchased 19____   Pd $_____   MIB   NB   DB   BNT
☐ Want   Orig. Ret. $9.00   **MIB** Sec. Mkt. **N.E.**

QP 603-2   PLAYING BALL

Comments: Handcrafted, 3-11/16" tall. An adorable bear cub is ready to play ball. The personalized message is written on his bat. Reissued in 1994 and 1995. **Artist:** John Francis (Collin)

☐ Purchased 19____   Pd $_____   MIB   NB   DB   BNT
☐ Want   Orig. Ret. $12.75   **MIB** Sec. Mkt. **N.E.**

QP 605-5   REINDEER IN THE SKY

Comments: Glass Ball, 2-7/8" dia. Santa's reindeer hold a conversation of your design!

☐ Purchased 19____   Pd $_____   MIB   NB   DB   BNT
☐ Want   Orig. Ret. $8.75   **MIB** Sec. Mkt. **N.E.**

QP 600-5   SANTA SAYS

Comments: Handcrafted, 2-15/16" tall. What does Santa say? Pull the cord and the message pops out of the pack on his back. Reissued in 1994. **Artist:** Ed Seale

☐ Purchased 19____   Pd $_____   MIB   NB   DB   BNT
☐ Want   Orig. Ret. $12.75   **MIB** Sec. Mkt. **N.E.**

Hallmark Keepsake Showcase Ornaments

Found at Gold Crown Stores only
Folk Art Americana

QK 105-2   ANGEL IN FLIGHT

Comments: Wood Look, 3-1/4" tall, Dated 1993. This angel appears to be hand-chiseled in wood. **Artist:** Linda Sickman

☐ Purchased 19____   Pd $_____   MIB   NB   DB   BNT
☐ Want   Orig. Ret. $15.75   **NB** $40   **MIB** Sec. Mkt. **$50**

QK 105-5   POLAR BEAR ADVENTURE

Comments: Wood Look, 2-15/16" tall, Dated 1993. A small elf brings home the tree. **Artist:** Linda Sickman

☐ Purchased 19____   Pd $_____   MIB   NB   DB   BNT
☐ Want   Orig. Ret. $15.00   **NB** $55   **MIB** Sec. Mkt. **$60**

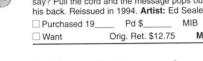

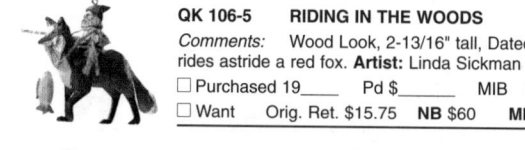

QK 106-5   RIDING IN THE WOODS ☐

Comments: Wood Look, 2-13/16" tall, Dated 1993. An elf rides astride a red fox. **Artist:** Linda Sickman

☐ Purchased 19____   Pd $_____   MIB   NB   DB   BNT
☐ Want   Orig. Ret. $15.75   **NB** $60   **MIB** Sec. Mkt. **$70**

QK 104-5   RIDING THE WIND ☐

Comments: Wood Look, 2-1/16" tall, Dated 1993. An elf flies on the back of a white goose. **Artist:** Linda Sickman

☐ Purchased 19____   Pd $_____   MIB   NB   DB   BNT
☐ Want   Orig. Ret. $15.75   **NB** $50   **MIB** Sec. Mkt. **$65**

QK 107-2   SANTA CLAUS ☐

Comments: Wood Look, 4-5/8" tall, Dated 1993. Santa delivers lots of toys to children. Santa collectors love him! **Artist:** Linda Sickman

☐ Purchased 19____   Pd $_____   MIB   NB   DB   BNT
☐ Want   Orig. Ret. $16.75   **NB** $200   **MIB** Sec. Mkt. **$225**

Holiday Enchantment

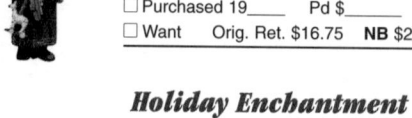

QK 103-2   ANGELIC MESSENGERS ☐

Comments: Porcelain, 3-1/2" tall, Dated 1993. Angels descend from heaven to relate the good news that Christ has been born in Bethlehem. **Artist:** LaDene Votruba

☐ Purchased 19____   Pd $_____   MIB   NB   DB   BNT
☐ Want   Orig. Ret. $13.75   **NB** $25   **MIB** Sec. Mkt. **$30**

QK 104-2   BRINGING HOME THE TREE ☐

Comments: Porcelain, 2-13/16" tall, Dated 1993. A couple emerges from the woods pulling their Christmas tree on a sled. **Artist:** Robert Chad

☐ Purchased 19____   Pd $_____   MIB   NB   DB   BNT
☐ Want   Orig. Ret. $13.75   **NB** $30   **MIB** Sec. Mkt. **$35**

QK 101-2   JOURNEY TO THE FOREST ☐

Comments: Porcelain, 4-1/2" tall, Dated 1993. Santa goes into the forest to check on his reindeer.

☐ Purchased 19____   Pd $_____   MIB   NB   DB   BNT
☐ Want   Orig. Ret. $13.75   **NB** $27   **MIB** Sec. Mkt. **$32.50**

QK 102-5   MAGI, THE ☐

Comments: Porcelain, 3-3/4" tall, Dated 1993. The wise men follow the star to Bethlehem to find the Christ Child. Caption: "We Three Kings Of Orient Are, Bearing Gifts We Traverse Afar, Field And Fountain, Moor And Mountain, Following Yonder Star."

☐ Purchased 19____   Pd $_____   MIB   NB   DB   BNT
☐ Want   Orig. Ret. $13.75   **NB** $25   **MIB** Sec. Mkt. **$30**

QK 100-5   VISIONS OF SUGARPLUMS ☐

Comments: Fine Porcelain, 3-1/2" dia., Dated 1993. A child dreams of Christmas treats and toys on Christmas Eve. Caption: "The Children Were Nestled All Snug In Their Beds, While Visions Of Sugarplums Danced In Their Heads." **Artist:** LaDene Votruba

☐ Purchased 19____   Pd $_____   MIB   NB   DB   BNT
☐ Want   Orig. Ret. $13.75   **NB** $26   **MIB** Sec. Mkt. **$35**

Old-World Silver

QK 107-5   SILVER DOVE OF PEACE ☐

Comments: Silver-Plated, 3-3/16" tall, Dated 1993. A dove of peace is intricately engraved in European style on the sides of this silver ornament. Caption: "Silver Dove Of Peace." **Artist:** Don Palmiter

☐ Purchased 19____   Pd $_____   MIB   NB   DB   BNT
☐ Want   Orig. Ret. $24.75   **NB** $26   **MIB** Sec. Mkt. **$35**

QK 109-2   SILVER SANTA ☐

Comments: Silver-Plated, 3-5/16" tall, Dated 1993. A design of Santa's head circles the sides of this ornament. **Artist:** Duane Unruh

☐ Purchased 19____   Pd $_____   MIB   NB   DB   BNT
☐ Want   Orig. Ret. $24.75   **NB** $25   **MIB** Sec. Mkt. **$30**

QK 108-2   SILVER SLEIGH ☐

Comments: Silver-Plated, 3-1/8" tall, Dated 1993. Detailed engraving on this ornament portrays a sleigh. **Artist:** Don Palmiter

☐ Purchased 19____   Pd $_____   MIB   NB   DB   BNT
☐ Want   Orig. Ret. $24.75   **NB** $26   **MIB** Sec. Mkt. **$35**

QK 108-5   SILVER STAR AND HOLLY ☐

Comments: Silver-Plated, 3-1/16" tall, Dated 1993. Lavishly engraved stars and holly decorate this unique Christmas ornament. **Artist:** Don Palmiter

☐ Purchased 19____   Pd $_____   MIB   NB   DB   BNT
☐ Want   Orig. Ret. $24.75   **NB** $26   **MIB** Sec. Mkt. **$35**

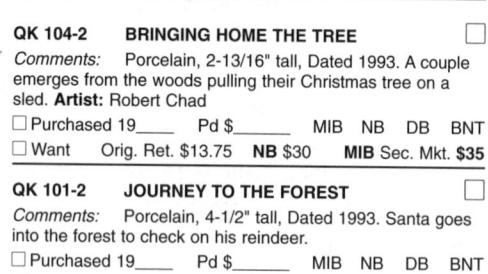

Portraits in Bisque

QK 115-2   CHRISTMAS FEAST

Comments: Porcelain Bisque, 3-1/2" tall, Dated 1993. Two little girls look on as mother carries the roasted turkey to the table. **Artist:** Sharon Pike

☐ Purchased 19____   Pd $_____   MIB NB DB BNT
☐ Want   Orig. Ret. $15.75 **NB** $17   **MIB** Sec. Mkt. **$24**

QK 114-2   JOY OF SHARING

Comments: Porcelain Bisque, 3-1/2" tall, Dated 1993. Two friends exchange Christmas gifts during this season of giving.

☐ Purchased 19____   Pd $_____   MIB NB DB BNT
☐ Want   Orig. Ret. $15.75 **NB** $18   **MIB** Sec. Mkt. **$24**

QK 114-5   MISTLETOE KISS

Comments: Porcelain Bisque, 3-5/6" tall. A gentleman prepares to kiss his favorite lady as he holds a sprig of mistletoe over her head. **Artist:** Sharon Pike

☐ Purchased 19____   Pd $_____   MIB NB DB BNT
☐ Want   Orig. Ret. $15.75 **NB** $15   **MIB** Sec. Mkt. **$20**

QK 116-2   NORMAN ROCKWELL: JOLLY POSTMAN

Comments: Porcelain Bisque, 3-1/4" tall. Children crowd around a happy postman who is delivering the Christmas mail. **Artist:** Peter Dutkin

☐ Purchased 19____   Pd $_____   MIB NB DB BNT
☐ Want   Orig. Ret. $15.75 **NB** $20   **MIB** Sec. Mkt. **$25**

QK 115-5   NORMAN ROCKWELL: FILLING THE STOCKINGS

Comments: Porcelain Bisque, 3-9/16" tall. Santa is busy with his chores on Christmas Eve. **Artist:** Peter Dutkin

☐ Purchased 19____   Pd $_____   MIB NB DB BNT
☐ Want   Orig. Ret. $15.75 **NB** $20   **MIB** Sec. Mkt. **$25**

Convention Ornaments

KANSAS CITY ANGEL: SPECIAL EDITION

Comments: Silver-Plated, Dated "K.C. 1993." This special edition Angel was given as a parting gift to all who attended the 1993 Keepsake Ornament Conventions in June and September.

☐ Purchased 19____   Pd $_____   MIB NB DB BNT
☐ Want   **NB** $380   **MIB** Sec. Mkt. **$395**

Keepsake Signature Collection

SANTA'S FAVORITE STOP

Comments: Handcrafted, Dated 1993 with removable Santa ornament. Sculpted by 14 artists, this tabletop was available only at Hallmark stores hosting special 1993 Artist's Appearances; only 200 per event were available. **Artists:** Removable Santa, Ken Crow; Stocking Holder Snowman, Patricia Andrews; Elf on Mantel, Robert Chad; Hearth/Puppy, John Francis (Collin); Cat, Julia Lee; Victorian Doll, Joyce A. Lyle; Santa's Bag, Don Palmiter; Fireplace, Dill Rhodus; Cookies and Milk for Santa/Garland, Anita Marra Rogers; Stocking Holder Teddy Bear, Ed Seale; Toy Train/Kindling Box, Linda Sickman; Stocking Holder Mouse, Bob Siedler; Clock on the Mantel, Duane Unruh; and Teddy Bear, LaDene Votruba.

☐ Purchased 19____   Pd $_____   MIB NB DB BNT
☐ Want   Orig. Ret. $55 with $25 purchase of Keepsake Ornaments
   MIB Sec. Mkt. **$375** if signed by all

The Van Gogh family tree

After much careful research, it has been discovered that the artist Vincent Van Gogh had many relatives.

Among them were:

His obnoxious brother ...Please Gogh

His dizzy aunt...Verti Gogh

The brother who worked at a convenience store ...Stopn Gogh

The grandfather from Yugoslavia ... U Gogh

The brother who bleached his clothes ... Hue Gogh

The cousin from Illinois... Chica Gogh

His magician uncle ... Wherediddy Gogh

The bird lover uncle ... Flamin Gogh

His nephew psychoanalyst ... E Gogh

The fruit loving cousin ... Man Gogh

1993 Miniature Ornament Collection

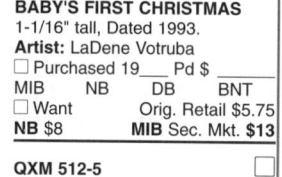

QXM 514-5
BABY'S FIRST CHRISTMAS
1-1/16" tall, Dated 1993.
Artist: LaDene Votruba
☐ Purchased 19___ Pd $ _____
MIB   NB   DB   BNT
☐ Want   Orig. Retail $5.75
NB $8   **MIB** Sec. Mkt. **$13**

QXM 512-5
BEARYMORES, THE
Second in Series,
1-1/8" tall, Dated 1993.
Artist: Anita Marra Rogers
☐ Purchased 19___ Pd $ _____
MIB   NB   DB   BNT
☐ Want   Orig. Retail $5.75
NB $15   **MIB** Sec. Mkt. **$19**

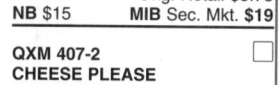

QXM 407-2
CHEESE PLEASE
1-1/4" tall, Dated 1993.
Artist: Bob Siedler
☐ Purchased 19___ Pd $ _____
MIB   NB   DB   BNT
☐ Want   Orig. Retail $3.75
NB $7   **MIB** Sec. Mkt. **$10**

QXM 408-5
CHRISTMAS CASTLE
1-1/8" tall, Dated 1993.
Artist: Ed Seale
☐ Purchased 19___ Pd $ _____
MIB   NB   DB   BNT
☐ Want   Orig. Retail $5.75
NB $8   **MIB** Sec. Mkt. **$13**

QXM 401-2
CLOISONNÉ SNOWFLAKE
Precious Edition. Cloisonné/
Brass, 1" dia. Being used as
earrings and necklaces. *Very
Popular!* **Artist:** LaDene Votruba
☐ Purchased 19___ Pd $ _____
MIB   NB   DB   BNT
☐ Want   Orig. Retail $9.75
NB $15   **MIB** Sec. Mkt. **$20**

QXM 406-2
COUNTRY FIDDLING
1" tall, Dated 1993.
Artist: John Francis (Collin)
☐ Purchased 19___ Pd $ _____
MIB   NB   DB   BNT
☐ Want   Orig. Retail $3.75
NB $8   **MIB** Sec. Mkt. **$13**

QXM 401-5
CRYSTAL ANGEL
Full lead crystal and gold-plated,
1" tall, Dated 1993. Being used
as a necklace! Another debuted
in '96 being "green."
Artist: Don Palmiter
☐ Purchased 19___ Pd $ _____
MIB   NB   DB   BNT
☐ Want   Orig. Retail $9.75
NB $30   **MIB** Sec. Mkt. **$40**

QXM 589-1
DANCING ANGELS TREE-
TOPPER
Dimensional brass 2-7/8" tall.
Reissued from 1992.
☐ Purchased 19___ Pd $ _____
MIB   NB   DB   BNT
☐ Want   Orig. Retail $9.75
NB $10   **MIB** Sec. Mkt. **$12**

QXM 407-5
EARS TO PALS
1-3/16" tall, Dated 1993.
Artist: Patricia Andrews
☐ Purchased 19___ Pd $ _____
MIB   NB   DB   BNT
☐ Want   Orig. Retail $3.75
NB $5   **MIB** Sec. Mkt. **$9**

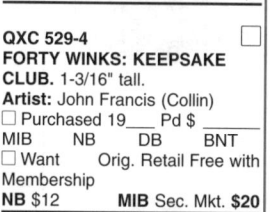

QXC 529-4
FORTY WINKS: KEEPSAKE
CLUB. 1-3/16" tall.
Artist: John Francis (Collin)
☐ Purchased 19___ Pd $ _____
MIB   NB   DB   BNT
☐ Want   Orig. Retail Free with
Membership
NB $12   **MIB** Sec. Mkt. **$20**

QXM 516-2
GRANDMA
1" tall, Dated 1993.
Artist: Ed Seale
☐ Purchased 19___ Pd $ _____
MIB   NB   DB   BNT
☐ Want   Orig. Retail $4.50
NB $6   **MIB** Sec. Mkt. **$13**

QXM 405-5
I DREAM OF SANTA
1-1/8" tall, Dated 1993.
Artist: Linda Sickman
☐ Purchased 19___ Pd $ _____
MIB   NB   DB   BNT
☐ Want   Orig. Retail $3.75
NB $8   **MIB** Sec. Mkt. **$14**

QXM 404-5
INTO THE WOODS
1" tall, Dated 1993.
Artist: Ed Seale
☐ Purchased 19___ Pd $ _____
MIB   NB   DB   BNT
☐ Want   Orig. Retail $3.75
NB $5   **MIB** Sec. Mkt. **$9**

QXM 513-5
KRINGLES, THE: WREATH
Fifth and Final in Series, 1" tall.
Artist: Anita Marra Rogers
☐ Purchased 19___ Pd $ _____
MIB   NB   DB   BNT
☐ Want   Orig. Retail $5.75
NB $8   **MIB** Sec. Mkt. **$16**

QXM 412-2
LEARNING TO SKATE
1-1/8" tall. **Artist:** Robert Chad
☐ Purchased 19___ Pd $ _____
MIB   NB   DB   BNT
☐ Want   Orig. Retail $3.00
NB $7   **MIB** Sec. Mkt. **$10**

QXM411-5
LIGHTING A PATH
1-1/16" tall. **Artist:** Robert Chad
☐ Purchased 19___ Pd $ _____
MIB   NB   DB   BNT
☐ Want   Orig. Retail $3.00
NB $6   **MIB** Sec. Mkt. **$10**

QXM 400-5
MARCH OF THE TEDDY BEARS
FIRST IN SERIES, 1-7/16" tall,
Dated 1993. **Artist:** Duane Unruh
☐ Purchased 19___ Pd $ _____
MIB   NB   DB   BNT
☐ Want   Orig. Retail $4.50
NB $13   **MIB** Sec. Mkt. **$17**

QXM 404-2
MERRY MASCOT
1-3/8" tall, Dated 1993.
Artist: Bob Siedler
☐ Purchased 19___ Pd $ _____
MIB   NB   DB   BNT
☐ Want   Orig. Retail $3.75
NB $6   **MIB** Sec. Mkt. **$10**

QXM 515-5
MOM
1-1/8" tall, Dated 1993.
Artist: Patricia Andrews
☐ Purchased 19___ Pd $ _____
MIB   NB   DB   BNT
☐ Want   Orig. Retail $4.50
NB $10   **MIB** Sec. Mkt. **$15**

QXM 409-2
MONKEY MELODY
Stringer ornament, 15/16" tall,
Dated 1993.
Artist: Linda Sickman
☐ Purchased 19___ Pd $ _____
MIB   NB   DB   BNT
☐ Want   Orig. Retail $5.75
NB $10   **MIB** Sec. Mkt. **$16**

QXM 512-2
NATURE'S ANGELS
Fourth in Series,
1-1/8" tall, Dated 1993.
Artist: Patricia Andrews
☐ Purchased 19___ Pd $ _____
MIB   NB   DB   BNT
☐ Want   Orig. Retail $4.50
NB $15   **MIB** Sec. Mkt. **$20**

QXM 511-5
**NIGHT BEFORE CHRISTMAS,
THE: BED**
Second in Series, 1-1/8" tall,
Dated 1993.
Artist: LaDene Votruba
☐ Purchased 19___ Pd $ _____
MIB   NB   DB   BNT
☐ Want   Orig. Retail $4.50
NB $16   **MIB** Sec. Mkt. **$23**

QXM 510-5
NOEL R.R.: FLATBED CAR
Fifth in Series, 1-1/8" tall, Dated
1993. **Artist:** Linda Sickman
☐ Purchased 19___ Pd $ _____
MIB   NB   DB   BNT
☐ Want   Orig. Retail $7.00
NB $14   **MIB** Sec. Mkt. **$25**

QXM 410-5
NORTH POLE FIRE TRUCK
5/8" tall, Dated 1993.
Artist: Don Palmiter
☐ Purchased 19___ Pd $ _____
MIB   NB   DB   BNT
☐ Want   Orig. Retail $4.75
NB $10   **MIB** Sec. Mkt. **$15**

QXM 513-2
**OLD ENGLISH VILLAGE:
TOY SHOP**
Sixth in Series, 1-3/16" tall,
Dated 1993. **Artist:** Julia Lee
☐ Purchased 19___ Pd $ _____
MIB   NB   DB   BNT
☐ Want   Orig. Retail $7.00
NB $15   **MIB** Sec. Mkt. **$22**

QXM 400-2
ON THE ROAD
FIRST IN SERIES, Pressed Tin,
7/16" tall, Dated 1993.
Artist: Linda Sickman
☐ Purchased 19___ Pd $ _____
MIB   NB   DB   BNT
☐ Want   Orig. Retail $5.75
NB $14   **MIB** Sec. Mkt. **$22**

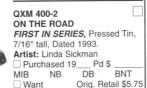

QXM 405-2
PEAR-SHAPED TONES
1" tall, Dated 1993.
Artist: Joyce A. Lyle
☐ Purchased 19___ Pd $ _____
MIB   NB   DB   BNT
☐ Want   Orig. Retail $3.75
NB $5   **MIB** Sec. Mkt. **$9**

QXM 409-5
PULL OUT A PLUM
5/8" tall, Dated 1993.
Artist: John Francis (Collin)
☐ Purchased 19___ Pd $ _____
MIB   NB   DB   BNT
☐ Want   Orig. Retail $5.75
NB $8   **MIB** Sec. Mkt. **$15**

QXM 411-2
REFRESHING FLIGHT
7/8" tall. **Artist:** Robert Chad
☐ Purchased 19___ Pd $ _____
MIB   NB   DB   BNT
☐ Want   Orig. Retail $5.75
NB $10   **MIB** Sec. Mkt. **$15**

QXM 545-2
**REVOLVING TREE BASE:
HOLIDAY EXPRESS**
Train circles on track.
Free miniature tree w/purchase.
Reissued in1994 and 1995.
☐ Purchased 19___ Pd $ _____
MIB   NB   DB   BNT
☐ Want   Orig. Retail $50
NB $60   **MIB** Sec. Mkt. **$74**

QXM 511-2
**ROCKING HORSE:
APPALOOSA**
Sixth in Series, 1-1/8" tall, Dated
1993. **Artist:** Linda Sickman
☐ Purchased 19___ Pd $ _____
MIB   NB   DB   BNT
☐ Want   Orig. Retail $4.50
NB $11   **MIB** Sec. Mkt. **$15**

QXM 402-5
'ROUND THE MOUNTAIN
1-11/16" tall, Dated 1993.
Artist: Ken Crow
☐ Purchased 19___ Pd $ _____
MIB   NB   DB   BNT
☐ Want   Orig. Retail $7.25
NB $10   **MIB** Sec. Mkt. **$18**

QXM 517-2
SECRET PAL
New Commemorative, 1" tall,
Dated 1993.
Artist: Anita Marra Rogers
☐ Purchased 19___ Pd $ _____
MIB   NB   DB   BNT
☐ Want   Orig. Retail $3.75
NB $6   **MIB** Sec. Mkt. **$10**

QXM 518-2
SNUGGLE BIRDS
1-9/16" tall, Dated 1993.
Artist: Patricia Andrews
☐ Purchased 19___ Pd $ _____
MIB   NB   DB   BNT
☐ Want   Orig. Retail $5.75
NB $10   **MIB** Sec. Mkt. **$15**

GQXM 516-5
SPECIAL FRIENDS
1" tall, Dated 1993.
Artist: John Francis (Collin)
☐ Purchased 19___ Pd $ _____
MIB   NB   DB   BNT
☐ Want   Orig. Retail $4.50
NB $7   **MIB** Sec. Mkt. **$12**

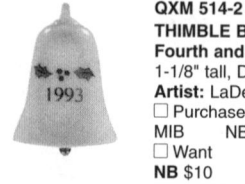

QXM 514-2
THIMBLE BELLS
Fourth and Final in Series,
1-1/8" tall, Dated 1993.
Artist: LaDene Votruba
☐ Purchased 19___ Pd $ _____
MIB   NB   DB   BNT
☐ Want   Orig. Retail $5.76
NB $10   **MIB** Sec. Mkt. **$15**

QXM 403-2
TINY GREEN THUMBS
Set of Six, Dated 1993.
Artist: Ed Seale
Here We Grow, 1-1/4" tall.
Teeny Clips, 1-1/8" tall.
Li'l Sprinkler, 13/16" tall.
Ever Green, 13/16" tall.
Keep on Hoein', 11/16" tall.
Just Resting, 11/16" tall.
☐ Purchased 19___ Pd $ _____
MIB   NB   DB   BNT
☐ Want   Orig. Retail $29.00
NB $40   **MIB** Sec. Mkt. **$50**

QXM 402-2
VISIONS OF SUGARPLUMS
Pewter, 1-3/8" tall, Dated 1993.
Artist: Don Palmiter
☐ Purchased 19___ Pd $ _____
MIB   NB   DB   BNT
☐ Want   Orig. Retail $7.25
NB $9   **MIB** Sec. Mkt. **$17**

QXM 510-2
WOODLAND BABIES
Third and Final in Series,
1-1/8" tall, Dated 1993.
Artist: John Francis (Collin)
☐ Purchased 19___ Pd $ _____
MIB   NB   DB   BNT
☐ Want   Orig. Retail $5.75
NB $8   **MIB** Sec. Mkt. **$16**

Happy John's Hallmark Sponsor

*"I hope you were only kidding
when you said you weren't going
to sponsor our Club anymore!"*

1993 Easter Ornament Collection

QEO 834-5
BABY'S FIRST EASTER
1-1/4" tall, Dated 1993.
Artist: Don Palmiter
☐ Purchased 19___ Pd $ _____
MIB   NB   DB   BNT
☐ Want   Orig. Retail $6.75
NB $8   **MIB** Sec. Mkt. **$16**

QEO 840-5
BACKYARD BUNNY
2" tall, Dated 1993.
Artist: Linda Sickman
☐ Purchased 19___ Pd $ _____
MIB   NB   DB   BNT
☐ Want   Orig. Retail $6.75
NB $9   **MIB** Sec. Mkt. **$17**

QEO 840-2
BARROW OF GIGGLES
1-7/8" tall, Dated 1993.
Artist: Patricia Andrews
☐ Purchased 19___ Pd $ _____
MIB   NB   DB   BNT
☐ Want   Orig. Retail $8.75
NB $10   **MIB** Sec. Mkt. **$20**

QEO 836-2
BEAUTIFUL MEMORIES
Photoholder, 2-1/2" tall.
Caption: "1993 Beautiful Easter
Memories."**Artist:** Duane Unruh.
☐ Purchased 19___ Pd $ _____
MIB   NB   DB   BNT
☐ Want   Orig. Retail $6.75
NB $8   **MIB** Sec. Mkt. **$14**

QEO 839-2
BEST-DRESSED TURTLE
1-7/8" tall. **Artist:** Julia Lee
☐ Purchased 19___ Pd $ _____
MIB   NB   DB   BNT
☐ Want   Orig. Retail $5.75
NB $8   **MIB** Sec. Mkt. **$15**

QEO 837-5
CHICKS-ON-A-TWIRL
Twirl-About, 3" tall, Dated 1993.
Artist: Joyce A. Lyle
☐ Purchased 19___ Pd $ _____
MIB   NB   DB   BNT
☐ Want   Orig. Retail $7.75
NB $9   **MIB** Sec. Mkt. **$18**

QEO 834-2
DAUGHTER
2-1/2" tall, Dated 1993.
Artist: Patricia Andrews
☐ Purchased 19___ Pd $ _____
MIB   NB   DB   BNT
☐ Want   Orig. Retail $5.75
NB $9   **MIB** Sec. Mkt. **$17**

QEO 832-5
EASTER PARADE
Second in Series, 2-7/8" tall,
Dated 1993. **Artist:** Julia Lee
☐ Purchased 19___ Pd $ _____
MIB   NB   DB   BNT
☐ Want   Orig. Retail $6.75
NB $10   **MIB** Sec. Mkt. **$20**

QEO 833-2
EGGS IN SPORTS
Second in Series, 2" tall.
Caption: "Tennis 93 Ace"
Artist: Bob Siedler
☐ Purchased 19___ Pd $ _____
MIB   NB   DB   BNT
☐ Want   Orig. Retail $6.75
NB $10   **MIB** Sec. Mkt. **$20**

QEO 835-2
GRANDCHILD
1-7/8" tall, Dated 1993.
Artist: Bob Siedler
☐ Purchased 19___ Pd $ _____
MIB   NB   DB   BNT
☐ Want   Orig. Retail $6.75
NB $10   **MIB** Sec. Mkt. **$20**

QEO 831-2
LI'L PEEPER
1-7/8" tall. **Artist:** Julia Lee
☐ Purchased 19___ Pd $ _____
MIB   NB   DB   BNT
☐ Want   Orig. Retail $7.75
NB $16   **MIB** Sec. Mkt. **$23**

QEO 831-5
LOP-EARED BUNNY
7/8" tall. **Artist:** Linda Sickman
☐ Purchased 19___ Pd $ _____
MIB   NB   DB   BNT
☐ Want   Orig. Retail $5.75
NB $15   **MIB** Sec. Mkt. **$20**

QEO 837-2
LOVELY LAMB
Porcelain, 3" tall, Dated 1993.
Artist: LaDene Votruba
☐ Purchased 19___ Pd $ _____
MIB   NB   DB   BNT
☐ Want   Orig. Retail $9.75
NB $16   **MIB** Sec. Mkt. **$23**

QEO 839-5
MAYPOLE STROLL
2" - 2-1/2" tall. Basket, 4-1/4" tall.
Dollie Duck, Ricky Rabbit and
Chester Chipmunk,
Artists: John Francis (Collin) and
Robert Chad
☐ Purchased 19___ Pd $ _____
MIB   NB   DB   BNT
☐ Want   Orig. Retail $28.00
NB $40   **MIB** Sec. Mkt. **$55**

QEO 838-2
NUTTY EGGS
1-7/8" tall. **Artist:** Julia Lee
☐ Purchased 19___ Pd $ _____
MIB   NB   DB   BNT
☐ Want   Orig. Retail $6.75
NB $10   **MIB** Sec. Mkt. **$15**

QEO 836-5
RADIANT WINDOW
3-1/4" tall. **Artist:** Duane Unruh
☐ Purchased 19___ Pd $ _____
MIB　　NB　　DB　　BNT
☐ Want　　Orig. Retail $7.75
NB $10　　**MIB** Sec. Mkt. **$18**

QEO 833-5
SON
2-1/2" tall, Dated 1993.
Artist: Patricia Andrews
☐ Purchased 19___ Pd $ _____
MIB　　NB　　DB　　BNT
☐ Want　　Orig. Retail $5.75
NB $9　　**MIB** Sec. Mkt. **$17**

QEO 832-2
SPRINGTIME BONNETS
FIRST IN SERIES, 2-1/4" tall,
Dated 1993. Very popular.
Artist: Donna Lee
☐ Purchased 19___ Pd $ _____
MIB　　NB　　DB　　BNT
☐ Want　　Orig. Retail $7.75
NB $25　　**MIB** Sec. Mkt. **$30**

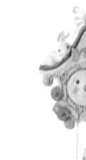

QEO 838-5
TIME FOR EASTER
3-1/2" tall. Caption: "1993 Time
for Easter Fun!"
Artist: Robert Chad
☐ Purchased 19___ Pd $ _____
MIB　　NB　　DB　　BNT
☐ Want　　Orig. Retail $8.75
NB $15　　**MIB** Sec. Mkt. **$20**

A Crafty Idea!

Items Needed:
- 1996 Hallmark Language of Flowers Pansy ornament
- 1 - 8" x 10" Victorian Style Oval Frame
- 1 - 12" x 14" Press-On Peel & Stick Mounting Board (found in framing section of most craft stores)
- 12" x 14" Blue or Lavender Cotton Fabric
- 1 Pkg. SIMPLY STITCHES Item #RE200-C Ribbon Embroidery Appliques (found at House of Fabrics Stores - Craft Section cost $11.49) or handmade silk ribbon roses & leaves to decorate.
- 2 white Velcro Peel & Stick mounting disks - small - 3/4" in diameter
- Aleene's Thick Designer Tacky Glue

To make the *Pansy* Display Frame: Disassemble the Oval Frame and use the paper insert inside the frame as a guide to cut an oval shape out of the Press-On mounting board. Make sure the oval fits exactly inside the frame and lays flat. If your frame came with glass, you will not need it for this project. Peel off the waxy paper on the mounting board to reveal the sticky surface, and carefully line up the fabric backing and press it onto the sticky board, smoothing it out so that it lays completely flat against the board. Trim away all of the excess fabric around the edges of the board and insert it back into the frame. Replace the backboard and easel section back into the frame.

Arrange the ribbon embroidery appliques on the fabric surface at the top and bottom of the frame. Add the *Pansy* angel and position all the items so that you are happy with the layout. Then, carefully place several dots of tacky glue on to the back of each embroidery section with a toothpick and glue down to the fabric surface. Use pins to hold in place until the glue dries.

Cut the Velcro disks in half and adhere them to places on the *Pansy* ornament that will touch the fabric background. The angel is not flat, so you will have to find the exact points where it touches the fabric and adhere the Velcro in place on both the ornament and fabric background. Use the lavender ribbon included with the "Pansy" angel to hang her from the ribbon embroidery at the top of the frame. With the ends of the ribbon, you can form a bow at the top and then pin or glue the ribbon in place. The angel will stay in place with the Velcro. Hang or display the *Pansy* ornament frame where you can enjoy it year 'round!

Designed by Club Treasurer, Vicki Cavaz – June 1997
Cable Car Ornament Collectors' Club　　San Francisco/Bay Area

1994 Collection

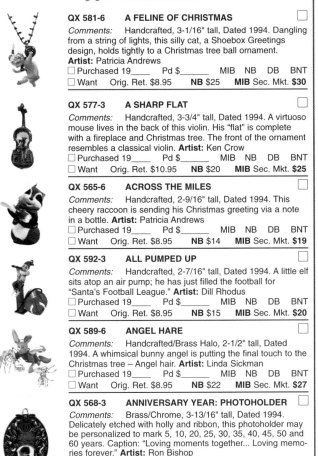

QX 581-6   A FELINE OF CHRISTMAS

Comments: Handcrafted, 3-1/16" tall, Dated 1994. Dangling from a string of lights, this silly cat, a Shoebox Greetings design, holds tightly to a Christmas tree ball ornament.
Artist: Patricia Andrews
☐ Purchased 19____   Pd $_____   MIB NB DB BNT
☐ Want   Orig. Ret. $8.95   **NB** $25   **MIB** Sec. Mkt. **$30**

QX 577-3   A SHARP FLAT

Comments: Handcrafted, 3-3/4" tall, Dated 1994. A virtuoso mouse lives in the back of this violin. His "flat" is complete with a fireplace and Christmas tree. The front of the ornament resembles a classical violin. **Artist:** Ken Crow
☐ Purchased 19____   Pd $_____   MIB NB DB BNT
☐ Want   Orig. Ret. $10.95   **NB** $20   **MIB** Sec. Mkt. **$25**

QX 565-6   ACROSS THE MILES

Comments: Handcrafted, 2-9/16" tall, Dated 1994. This cheery raccoon is sending his Christmas greeting via a note in a bottle. **Artist:** Patricia Andrews
☐ Purchased 19____   Pd $_____   MIB NB DB BNT
☐ Want   Orig. Ret. $8.95   **NB** $14   **MIB** Sec. Mkt. **$19**

QX 592-3   ALL PUMPED UP

Comments: Handcrafted, 2-7/16" tall, Dated 1994. A little elf sits atop an air pump; he has just filled the football for "Santa's Football League." **Artist:** Dill Rhodus
☐ Purchased 19____   Pd $_____   MIB NB DB BNT
☐ Want   Orig. Ret. $8.95   **NB** $15   **MIB** Sec. Mkt. **$20**

QX 589-6   ANGEL HARE

Comments: Handcrafted/Brass Halo, 2-1/2" tall, Dated 1994. A whimsical bunny angel is putting the final touch to the Christmas tree – Angel hair. **Artist:** Linda Sickman
☐ Purchased 19____   Pd $_____   MIB NB DB BNT
☐ Want   Orig. Ret. $8.95   **NB** $22   **MIB** Sec. Mkt. **$27**

QX 568-3   ANNIVERSARY YEAR: PHOTOHOLDER

Comments: Brass/Chrome, 3-13/16" tall, Dated 1994. Delicately etched with holly and ribbon, this photoholder may be personalized to mark 5, 10, 20, 25, 30, 35, 40, 45, 50 and 60 years. Caption: "Loving moments together... Loving memories forever." **Artist:** Ron Bishop
☐ Purchased 19____   Pd $_____   MIB NB DB BNT
☐ Want   Orig. Ret. $10.95   **NB** $15   **MIB** Sec. Mkt. **$20**

QLX 738-3   AWAY IN A MANGER

Comments: Light, Handcrafted, 3-7/16" tall, Dated 1994. The star of Bethlehem is aglow and casts its light on Baby Jesus lying in his manger bed. Caption: "Away in a manger, no crib for a bed. The little Lord Jesus laid down his sweet head." **Artist:** Joyce Lyle
☐ Purchased 19____   Pd $_____   MIB NB DB BNT
☐ Want   Orig. Ret. $16.00   **NB** $35   **MIB** Sec. Mkt. **$40**

QX 563-3   BABY'S FIRST CHRISTMAS

Comments: Porcelain/Brass, 2-9/16" tall, Dated 1994. A brass tag, bell and green satin ribbon grace porcelain "knitted" booties. **Artist:** Duane Unruh
☐ Purchased 19____   Pd $_____   MIB NB DB BNT
☐ Want   Orig. Ret. $18.95   **NB** $20   **MIB** Sec. Mkt. **$40**

QX 574-3   BABY'S FIRST CHRISTMAS

Comments: Handcrafted, 1-7/8" tall, Dated 1994. Pull the safety pin to open the baby block; shh... a baby teddy is sound asleep inside. **Artist:** Ed Seale
☐ Purchased 19____   Pd $_____   MIB NB DB BNT
☐ Want   Orig. Ret. $12.95   **NB** $25   **MIB** Sec. Mkt. **$30**

QLX 746-6   BABY'S FIRST CHRISTMAS

Comments: Light and Music, Handcrafted, 2-11/16" tall, Dated 1994. Mama and Papa squirrels check on their tiny infant, sound asleep in his cradle. Plays "Rock-a-Bye Baby." **Artist:** John Francis (Collin)
☐ Purchased 19____   Pd $_____   MIB NB DB BNT
☐ Want   Orig. Ret. $20.00   **NB** $30   **MIB** Sec. Mkt. **$35**

QX 571-3   BABY'S FIRST CHRISTMAS:
TEDDY BEAR YEARS COLLECTION

Comments: Handcrafted, 2-3/16" tall, Dated 1994. Baby celebrates his first Christmas with a stocking and star-shaped Christmas cookie. Design is repeated from 1993.
Artist: Ken Crow
☐ Purchased 19____   Pd $_____   MIB NB DB BNT
☐ Want   Orig. Ret. $7.95   **NB** $25   **MIB** Sec. Mkt. **$30**

QX 243-6   BABY'S FIRST CHRISTMAS: BABY BOY

Comments: Glass Ball, 2-7/8" dia., Dated 1994. As Santa peeks through the window, a baby boy is bouncing in his crib. Caption: "Santa's excited for he'll soon get to meet a new baby boy who's precious and sweet."
☐ Purchased 19____   Pd $_____   MIB NB DB BNT
☐ Want   Orig. Ret. $5.00   **NB** $13   **MIB** Sec. Mkt. **$18**

QX 243-3   BABY'S FIRST CHRISTMAS: BABY GIRL ☐

Comments: Glass Ball, 2-7/8" dia., Dated 1994. Santa peeks through a window and watches a baby girl in her crib. Caption: "Santa's excited for he'll soon get to meet a new baby girl who's precious and sweet."

☐ Purchased 19_____   Pd $_____   MIB   NB   DB   BNT
☐ Want   Orig. Ret. $5.00   **NB** $14   **MIB** Sec. Mkt. **$19**

QX 563-6   BABY'S FIRST CHRISTMAS PHOTOHOLDER ☐

Comments: Handcrafted, 3-5/16" tall, Dated 1994. Baby's photo is framed appropriately with stars, a teddy bear and rocking horse. Caption: "There's a new little star on your horizon." **Artist:** LaDene Votruba

☐ Purchased 19_____   Pd $_____   MIB   NB   DB   BNT
☐ Want   Orig. Ret. $7.95   **NB** $13   **MIB** Sec. Mkt. **$18**

QX 571-6   BABY'S SECOND CHRISTMAS: TEDDY BEAR YEARS COLLECTION ☐

Comments: Handcrafted, 2-3/8" tall, Dated 1994. This teddy wears a red and white bow tie and holds a green Christmas stocking with a tree-shaped cookie. **Artist:** Ken Crow

☐ Purchased 19_____   Pd $_____   MIB   NB   DB   BNT
☐ Want   Orig. Ret. 7.95   **NB** $23   **MIB** Sec. Mkt. **$25**

QX 500-6   BARBIE™ ☐

Comments: ***FIRST IN SERIES,*** Handcrafted, 4-7/16" tall. Dated 1994. Barbie is back in her original black and white swimsuit, marking the 35th anniversary of her debut in 1959.

☐ Purchased 19_____   Pd $_____   MIB   NB   DB   BNT
☐ Want   Orig. Ret. $14.95   **NB** $35   **MIB** Sec. Mkt. **$40**

QLX 750-6   BARNEY™ ☐

Comments: Light and Motion, Handcrafted, 4-1/8" tall, Dated 1994. Barney and his rabbit friend sled around a snowman. Caption: "Sledding is simply Stu-u-u-pendous."

☐ Purchased 19_____   Pd $_____   MIB   NB   DB   BNT
☐ Want   Orig. Ret. $24.00   **NB** $45   **MIB** Sec. Mkt. **$50**

QX 596-6   BARNEY™ ☐

Comments: Handcrafted, 3-15/16" tall, Dated 1994. A favorite of many small children, this popular purple dinosaur skates into Christmas wearing a Santa cap.

☐ Purchased 19_____   Pd $_____   MIB   NB   DB   BNT
☐ Want   Orig. Ret. $9.95   **NB** $20   **MIB** Sec. Mkt. **$25**

QX 532-3   BASEBALL HEROES: BABE RUTH ☐

Comments: ***FIRST IN SERIES,*** Handcrafted, 3-3/8" Dia., Dated 1994. Caption: "714 Career Home Runs, 60 Home Runs in 1927; .342 Lifetime Batting Average; Inducted into Hall of Fame 1936." This new series features baseball greats, the first of which is "The Babe." **Artist:** Dill Rhodus

☐ Purchased 19_____   Pd $_____   MIB   NB   DB   BNT
☐ Want   Orig. Ret. $12.95   **NB** $50   **MIB** Sec. Mkt. **$55**

QX 585-3   BATMAN ☐

Comments: Handcrafted, 5-11/16" tall, Dated 1994. Batman swings from the Batarang. The size is complementary to Superman, which was issued in 1993. **Artist:** Robert Chad

☐ Purchased 19_____   Pd $_____   MIB   NB   DB   BNT
☐ Want   Orig. Ret. $12.95   **NB** $25   **MIB** Sec. Mkt. **$30**

QX 537-3   BEATLES GIFT SET ☐

Comments: Handcrafted, Dated 1994. Set includes four ornaments plus microphones, stage and drum set. An abundance is waiting to be sold on the secondary market! **Artist:** Anita Marra Rogers

A. Paul McCartney, 4-9/16"   F. Drum Set, 2-3/4"
B. John Lennon, 4-1/2"   G. Floor Tom-Tom, 2-13/16"
C. George Harrison, 4-9/16"   H. Top Hat Cymbal, 2-7/16"
D. Ringo Starr, 3-3/4"   I. Stage, 2-3/16"
E. Stand with Two Microphones, 3-15/16"

☐ Purchased 19_____   Pd $_____   MIB   NB   DB   BNT
☐ Want   Orig. Ret. $48.00   **NB** $95   **MIB** Sec. Mkt. **$100**

QX 240-3   BETSEY'S COUNTRY CHRISTMAS ☐

Comments: **Third and Final in Series,** Teardrop Ball, 2-7/8" dia., Dated 1994. Betsey and her friends gather together to decorate the house for the Christmas holidays. Caption: "It's the simple joys, the simple pleasures, the heart remembers and dearly treasures."

☐ Purchased 19_____   Pd $_____   MIB   NB   DB   BNT
☐ Want   Orig. Ret. $5.00   **NB** $13   **MIB** Sec. Mkt. **$18**

QX 587-3   BIG SHOT ☐

Comments: Handcrafted, 2-7/8" tall, Dated 1994. This little fellow actually spins the basketball on his finger! **Artist:** Bob Siedler

☐ Purchased 19_____   Pd $_____   MIB   NB   DB   BNT
☐ Want   Orig. Ret. $7.95   **NB** $14   **MIB** Sec. Mkt. **$19**

QX 551-6   BROTHER ☐

Comments: Handcrafted, 1-15/16" tall, Dated 1994. "Super Terrific Brother" zips around town in his sports car.
Artist: Sharon Pike

☐ Purchased 19____   Pd $_____   MIB NB DB BNT
☐ Want   Orig. Ret. $6.95   **NB** $13   **MIB** Sec. Mkt. **$17**

QX 587-6   BUSY BATTER ☐

Comments: Handcrafted, 2-5/8" tall, Dated 1994. The "Wood Sox" are up to bat. Someone pitch the ball to this busy beaver before he chews his bat to pieces! **Artist:** Bob Siedler

☐ Purchased 19____   Pd $_____   MIB NB DB BNT
☐ Want   Orig. Ret. $7.95   **NB** $15   **MIB** Sec. Mkt. **$20**

QLX 737-6   CANDY CANE LOOKOUT ☐

Comments: Light and Voice, Handcrafted, 4-1/4" tall, Dated 1994. A penguin at the top of the lighthouse keeps a lookout while Santa, Mrs. Claus and another penguin sing carols below. **Artist:** John Francis (Collin)

☐ Purchased 19____   Pd $_____   MIB NB DB BNT
☐ Want   Orig. Ret. $18.00   **NB** $65   **MIB** Sec. Mkt. **$70**

QX 577-6   CANDY CAPER ☐

Comments: Handcrafted, 2-11/16" tall, Dated 1994. A glass jar full of peppermint candies is just too irresistible!
Artist: Patricia Andrews

☐ Purchased 19____   Pd $_____   MIB NB DB BNT
☐ Want   Orig. Ret. $8.95   **NB** $15   **MIB** Sec. Mkt. **$20**

QX 582-3   CARING DOCTOR ☐

Comments: Handcrafted, 2-5/16" tall, Dated 1994. The doctor dates the cast on his cookie patient.
Artist: Anita Marra Rogers

☐ Purchased 19____   Pd $_____   MIB NB DB BNT
☐ Want   Orig. Ret. $8.95   **NB** $15   **MIB** Sec. Mkt. **$20**

QX 531-3   CAT NAPS ☐

Comments: ***FIRST IN SERIES,*** Handcrafted, 1-15/16" tall. Dated 1994. Kitty naps in her very own cookie jar. Not all First in series increase in value quickly. **Artist:** Dill Rhodus

☐ Purchased 19____   Pd $_____   MIB NB DB BNT
☐ Want   Orig. Ret. $7.75   **NB** $45   **MIB** Sec. Mkt. **$50**

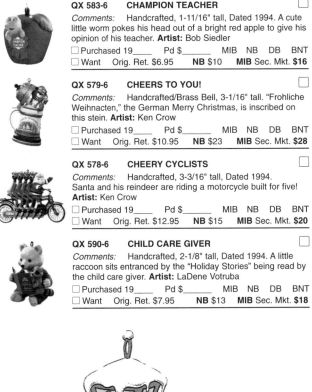

QX 583-6   CHAMPION TEACHER ☐

Comments: Handcrafted, 1-11/16" tall, Dated 1994. A cute little worm pokes his head out of a bright red apple to give his opinion of his teacher. **Artist:** Bob Siedler

☐ Purchased 19____   Pd $_____   MIB NB DB BNT
☐ Want   Orig. Ret. $6.95   **NB** $10   **MIB** Sec. Mkt. **$16**

QX 579-6   CHEERS TO YOU! ☐

Comments: Handcrafted/Brass Bell, 3-1/16" tall. "Frohliche Weihnacten," the German Merry Christmas, is inscribed on this stein. **Artist:** Ken Crow

☐ Purchased 19____   Pd $_____   MIB NB DB BNT
☐ Want   Orig. Ret. $10.95   **NB** $23   **MIB** Sec. Mkt. **$28**

QX 578-6   CHEERY CYCLISTS ☐

Comments: Handcrafted, 3-3/16" tall, Dated 1994. Santa and his reindeer are riding a motorcycle built for five!
Artist: Ken Crow

☐ Purchased 19____   Pd $_____   MIB NB DB BNT
☐ Want   Orig. Ret. $12.95   **NB** $15   **MIB** Sec. Mkt. **$20**

QX 590-6   CHILD CARE GIVER ☐

Comments: Handcrafted, 2-1/8" tall, Dated 1994. A little raccoon sits entranced by the "Holiday Stories" being read by the child care giver. **Artist:** LaDene Votruba

☐ Purchased 19____   Pd $_____   MIB NB DB BNT
☐ Want   Orig. Ret. $7.95   **NB** $13   **MIB** Sec. Mkt. **$18**

QX 573-3 CHILD'S FIFTH CHRISTMAS: TEDDY BEAR YEARS COLLECTION

Comments: Handcrafted, 2-3/8" tall, Dated 1994. Design is repeated from 1993. **Artist:** Dill Rhodus

☐ Purchased 19____ Pd $_____ MIB NB DB BNT
☐ Want Orig. Ret. $6.95 **NB** $17 **MIB** Sec. Mkt. **$22**

QX 572-6 CHILD'S FOURTH CHRISTMAS: TEDDY BEAR YEARS COLLECTION

Comments: Handcrafted, 3" tall, Dated 1994. Design is repeated from 1993. **Artist:** John Francis (Collin)

☐ Purchased 19____ Pd $_____ MIB NB DB BNT
☐ Want Orig. Ret. $6.95 **NB** $20 **MIB** Sec. Mkt. **$23**

QX 572-3 CHILD'S THIRD CHRISTMAS: TEDDY BEAR YEARS COLLECTION

Comments: Handcrafted, 2-1/2" tall, Dated 1994. Design is repeated from 1993. **Artist:** John Francis (Collin)

☐ Purchased 19____ Pd $_____ MIB NB DB BNT
☐ Want Orig. Ret. $6.95 **NB** $20 **MIB** Sec. Mkt. **$24**

QLX 739-3 CHRIS MOUSE JELLY

Comments: **Tenth in Series,** Lighted, Handcrafted, 2-13/16" tall, Dated 1994. Chris Mouse dips into "Lite Jelly From the Kitchen of Chris Mouse" to add a bread and jelly sandwich to his evening cheese snack. **Artist:** Anita Marra Rogers

☐ Purchased 19____ Pd $_____ MIB NB DB BNT
☐ Want Orig. Ret. $12.00 **NB** $25 **MIB** Sec. Mkt. **$30**

QX 542-2 CLASSIC AMERICAN CARS: 1957 CHEVROLET BEL AIR

Comments: Fourth in Series, Handcrafted, 1-3/8" tall, Dated 1994. A well-liked addition to a very popular series. **Artist:** Don Palmiter

☐ Purchased 19____ Pd $_____ MIB NB DB BNT
☐ Want Orig. Ret. $12.95 **NB** $25 **MIB** Sec. Mkt. **$30**

QX 593-3 COACH

Comments: Handcrafted, 3-1/8" tall, Dated 1994. A happy coach is ready to go with his gym bag and whistle.

Artist: Duane Unruh

☐ Purchased 19____ Pd $_____ MIB NB DB BNT
☐ Want Orig. Ret. $7.95 **NB** $10 **MIB** Sec. Mkt. **$17**

QX 539-6 COCK-A-DOODLE CHRISTMAS

Comments: Handcrafted, 3-3/16" tall, Dated 1994. A rooster crows his Christmas greeting from atop a pony. **Artist:** LaDene Votruba

☐ Purchased 19____ Pd $_____ MIB NB DB BNT
☐ Want Orig. Ret. $8.95 **NB** $25 **MIB** Sec. Mkt. **$30**

QX 589-3 COLORS OF JOY

Comments: Handcrafted, 2-3/16" tall, Dated 1994. A little mouse stands in a tray of paints and adds his holiday sentiment to the cover. **Artist:** Ed Seale

☐ Purchased 19____ Pd $_____ MIB NB DB BNT
☐ Want Orig. Ret. $7.95 **NB** $11 **MIB** Sec. Mkt. **$17**

QLX 742-6 CONVERSATIONS WITH SANTA

Comments: Motion and Voice, Handcrafted, 3-1/8" tall, Dated 1994. Santa's mouth moves as he speaks one of four messages. **Artist:** Ed Seale

☐ Purchased 19____ Pd $_____ MIB NB DB BNT
☐ Want Orig. Ret. $28.00 **NB** $55 **MIB** Sec. Mkt. **$60**

QLX 741-6 COUNTRY SHOWTIME

Comments: Blinking Lights and Motion, Handcrafted 4-3/8" tall. Dated 1994. This jointed "wooden" Santa dances at center stage. **Artist:** Linda Sickman

☐ Purchased 19____ Pd $_____ MIB NB DB BNT
☐ Want Orig. Ret. $22.00 **NB** $40 **MIB** Sec. Mkt. **$45**

QX 527-3 CRAYOLA® CRAYON: BRIGHT PLAYFUL COLORS

Comments: **Sixth in Series,** Handcrafted, 3-3/8" tall, Dated 1994. A Teddy Bear swings on his colorful playground set while waiting for Santa. Popular series. **Artist:** Ken Crow

☐ Purchased 19____ Pd $_____ MIB NB DB BNT
☐ Want Orig. Ret. $10.95 **NB** $25 **MIB** Sec. Mkt. **$30**

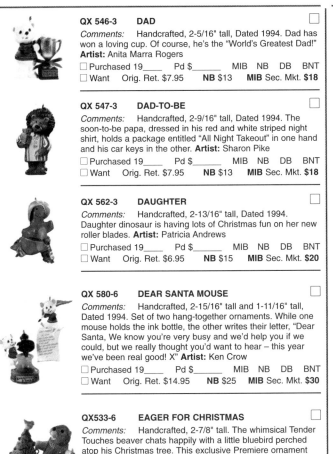

QX 546-3 DAD

Comments: Handcrafted, 2-5/16" tall, Dated 1994. Dad has won a loving cup. Of course, he's the "World's Greatest Dad!" **Artist:** Anita Marra Rogers

☐ Purchased 19_____ Pd $_____ MIB NB DB BNT
☐ Want Orig. Ret. $7.95 **NB** $13 **MIB** Sec. Mkt. **$18**

QX 547-3 DAD-TO-BE

Comments: Handcrafted, 2-9/16" tall, Dated 1994. The soon-to-be papa, dressed in his red and white striped night shirt, holds a package entitled "All Night Takeout" in one hand and his car keys in the other. **Artist:** Sharon Pike

☐ Purchased 19_____ Pd $_____ MIB NB DB BNT
☐ Want Orig. Ret. $7.95 **NB** $13 **MIB** Sec. Mkt. **$18**

QX 562-3 DAUGHTER

Comments: Handcrafted, 2-13/16" tall, Dated 1994. Daughter dinosaur is having lots of Christmas fun on her new roller blades. **Artist:** Patricia Andrews

☐ Purchased 19_____ Pd $_____ MIB NB DB BNT
☐ Want Orig. Ret. $6.95 **NB** $15 **MIB** Sec. Mkt. **$20**

QX 580-6 DEAR SANTA MOUSE

Comments: Handcrafted, 2-15/16" tall and 1-11/16" tall, Dated 1994. Set of two hang-together ornaments. While one mouse holds the ink bottle, the other writes their letter, "Dear Santa, We know you're very busy and we'd help you if we could, but we really thought you'd want to hear – this year we've been real good! X" **Artist:** Ken Crow

☐ Purchased 19_____ Pd $_____ MIB NB DB BNT
☐ Want Orig. Ret. $14.95 **NB** $25 **MIB** Sec. Mkt. **$30**

QX533-6 EAGER FOR CHRISTMAS

Comments: Handcrafted, 2-7/8" tall. The whimsical Tender Touches beaver chats happily with a little bluebird perched atop his Christmas tree. This exclusive Premiere ornament was available for purchase during the Keepsake Ornament Premiere in July, 1994. **Artist:** Ed Seale

☐ Purchased 19_____ Pd $_____ MIB NB DB BNT
☐ Want Orig. Ret. $15.00 **NB** $23 **MIB** Sec. Mkt. **$28**

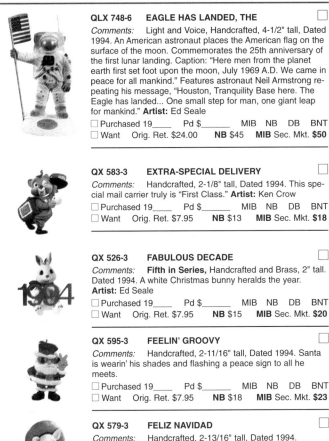

QLX 748-6 EAGLE HAS LANDED, THE

Comments: Light and Voice, Handcrafted, 4-1/2" tall, Dated 1994. An American astronaut places the American flag on the surface of the moon. Commemorates the 25th anniversary of the first lunar landing. Caption: "Here men from the planet earth first set foot upon the moon, July 1969 A.D. We came in peace for all mankind." Features astronaut Neil Armstrong repeating his message, "Houston, Tranquility Base here. The Eagle has landed... One small step for man, one giant leap for mankind." **Artist:** Ed Seale

☐ Purchased 19_____ Pd $_____ MIB NB DB BNT
☐ Want Orig. Ret. $24.00 **NB** $45 **MIB** Sec. Mkt. **$50**

QX 583-3 EXTRA-SPECIAL DELIVERY

Comments: Handcrafted, 2-1/8" tall, Dated 1994. This special mail carrier truly is "First Class." **Artist:** Ken Crow

☐ Purchased 19_____ Pd $_____ MIB NB DB BNT
☐ Want Orig. Ret. $7.95 **NB** $13 **MIB** Sec. Mkt. **$18**

QX 526-3 FABULOUS DECADE

Comments: **Fifth in Series,** Handcrafted and Brass, 2" tall. Dated 1994. A white Christmas bunny heralds the year. **Artist:** Ed Seale

☐ Purchased 19_____ Pd $_____ MIB NB DB BNT
☐ Want Orig. Ret. $7.95 **NB** $15 **MIB** Sec. Mkt. **$20**

QX 595-3 FEELIN' GROOVY

Comments: Handcrafted, 2-11/16" tall, Dated 1994. Santa is wearin' his shades and flashing a peace sign to all he meets.

☐ Purchased 19_____ Pd $_____ MIB NB DB BNT
☐ Want Orig. Ret. $7.95 **NB** $18 **MIB** Sec. Mkt. **$23**

QX 579-3 FELIZ NAVIDAD

Comments: Handcrafted, 2-13/16" tall, Dated 1994. A little Spanish Chihuahua in his sombrero awakens from his siesta and pops up from a gaily painted Mexican pot. **Artist:** Anita Marra Rogers

☐ Purchased 19_____ Pd $_____ MIB NB DB BNT
☐ Want Orig. Ret. $8.95 **NB** $18 **MIB** Sec. Mkt. **$23**

QLX 743-3   FELIZ NAVIDAD

Comments: Motion and Music, Handcrafted, 3-1/8" tall, Dated 1994. A boy taps the bell-shaped piñata with a stick and the children dance around the sombrero. Plays "Feliz Navidad." **Artist:** Linda Crow

☐ Purchased 19____   Pd $_____   MIB   NB   DB   BNT
☐ Want   Orig. Ret. $28.00   **NB** $70   **MIB** Sec. Mkt. **$75**

QX 584-6   FOLLOW THE SUN

Comments: Handcrafted, 3-13/16" tall, Dated 1994. Riding a reindeer and sleigh weather vane, this bird is following "Route 94" to "Lake Wannagothere." **Artist:** Ken Crow

☐ Purchased 19____   Pd $_____   MIB   NB   DB   BNT
☐ Want   Orig. Ret. $8.95   **NB** $15   **MIB** Sec. Mkt. **$20**

QX 561-3   FOR MY GRANDMA: PHOTOHOLDER

Comments: Handcrafted, 3-9/16" tall, Dated 1994. Grandma will be delighted with this brightly decorated Christmas tree photoholder. Caption: "1994 I Love you! From _____" **Artist:** Donna Lee

☐ Purchased 19____   Pd $_____   MIB   NB   DB   BNT
☐ Want   Orig. Ret. $6.95   **NB** $11   **MIB** Sec. Mkt. **$16**

QLX 743-6   FOREST FROLICS

Comments: **Sixth in Series,** Light/Motion, Handcrafted, 4-1/8" tall, Dated 1994. The forest animals play happily around the Christmas tree. **Artist:** Sharon Pike

☐ Purchased 19____   Pd $_____   MIB   NB   DB   BNT
☐ Want   Orig. Ret. $28.00   **NB** $55   **MIB** Sec. Mkt. **$60**

QX 500-3   FRED AND BARNEY: THE FLINTSTONES®

Comments: Handcrafted, 2-5/8" tall, Dated 1994. The ever-popular duo are headed out in their Stone Age car. **Artist:** Dill Rhodus

☐ Purchased 19____   Pd $_____   MIB   NB   DB   BNT
☐ Want   Orig. Ret. $14.95   **NB** $28   **MIB** Sec. Mkt. **$33**

QX 568-6   FRIENDLY PUSH

Comments: Handcrafted, 3-1/8" tall, Dated 1994. As one little brown mouse sits inside an ice skate, another little gray mouse gives a friendly little push. **Artist:** Bob Seidler

☐ Purchased 19____   Pd $_____   MIB   NB   DB   BNT
☐ Want   Orig. Ret. $8.95   **NB** $15   **MIB** Sec. Mkt. **$20**

QX 476-6   FRIENDSHIP SUNDAE

Comments: Handcrafted, 3-1/4" tall, Dated 1994. These two white mice must love lots of Hershey's chocolate on their ice cream! Yum, yum! **Artist:** Linda Sickman

☐ Purchased 19____   Pd $_____   MIB   NB   DB   BNT
☐ Want   Orig. Ret. $10.95   **NB** $15   **MIB** Sec. Mkt. **$20**

QX 529-3   FROSTY FRIENDS

Comments: **Fifteenth in Series,** Handcrafted, 2-1/8" tall. Dated 1994. Little Eskimo holds a wreath while his polar bear friend jumps through. **Artist:** Ed Seale

☐ Purchased 19____   Pd $_____   MIB   NB   DB   BNT
☐ Want   Orig. Ret. $9.95   **NB** $32   **MIB** Sec. Mkt. **$37**

QX 598-6   GARDEN ELVES COLLECTION: DAISY DAYS

Comments: Handcrafted, 2-7/8" tall. Summer daisies always brighten up a room, and this blonde haired lass is bringing some home to share. **Artist:** Robert Chad

☐ Purchased 19____   Pd $_____   MIB   NB   DB   BNT
☐ Want   Orig. Ret. $9.95   **NB** $20   **MIB** Sec. Mkt. **$25**

QX 599-3   GARDEN ELVES COLLECTION: HARVEST JOY

Comments: Handcrafted, 2-13/16" tall. This little lad is bringing home the bounty of a good autumn harvest. **Artist:** Robert Chad

☐ Purchased 19____   Pd $_____   MIB   NB   DB   BNT
☐ Want   Orig. Ret. $9.95   **NB** $20   **MIB** Sec. Mkt. **$25**

QX 598-3   GARDEN ELVES COLLECTION: TULIP TIME

Comments: Handcrafted, 2-5/16" tall. A pot full of red tulips testifies to this young lady's green thumb. She represents Spring. **Artist:** Robert Chad

☐ Purchased 19____   Pd $_____   MIB   NB   DB   BNT
☐ Want   Orig. Ret. $9.95   **NB** $20   **MIB** Sec. Mkt. **$25**

QX 597-6   GARDEN ELVES COLLECTION: YULETIDE CHEER

Comments: Handcrafted, 2-13/16" tall. This little lad is getting ready for Christmas. He has a miniature tree in one hand and a holly leaf in the other. **Artist:** Robert Chad

☐ Purchased 19____   Pd $_____   MIB   NB   DB   BNT
☐ Want   Orig. Ret. $9.95   **NB** $20   **MIB** Sec. Mkt. **$25**

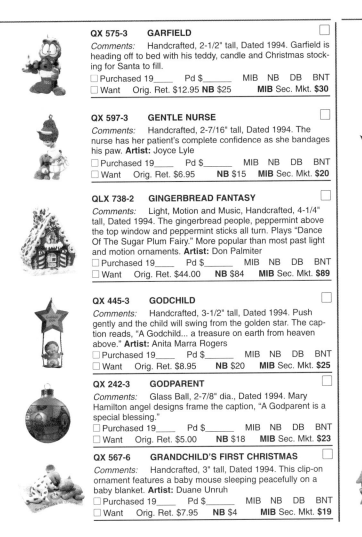

QX 575-3 GARFIELD

Comments: Handcrafted, 2-1/2" tall, Dated 1994. Garfield is heading off to bed with his teddy, candle and Christmas stocking for Santa to fill.

☐ Purchased 19____   Pd $_____   MIB NB DB BNT
☐ Want   Orig. Ret. $12.95 **NB** $25   **MIB** Sec. Mkt. **$30**

QX 597-3 GENTLE NURSE

Comments: Handcrafted, 2-7/16" tall, Dated 1994. The nurse has her patient's complete confidence as she bandages his paw. **Artist:** Joyce Lyle

☐ Purchased 19____   Pd $_____   MIB NB DB BNT
☐ Want   Orig. Ret. $6.95   **NB** $15   **MIB** Sec. Mkt. **$20**

QLX 738-2 GINGERBREAD FANTASY

Comments: Light, Motion and Music, Handcrafted, 4-1/4" tall, Dated 1994. The gingerbread people, peppermint above the top window and peppermint sticks all turn. Plays "Dance Of The Sugar Plum Fairy." More popular than most past light and motion ornaments. **Artist:** Don Palmiter

☐ Purchased 19____   Pd $_____   MIB NB DB BNT
☐ Want   Orig. Ret. $44.00   **NB** $84   **MIB** Sec. Mkt. **$89**

QX 445-3 GODCHILD

Comments: Handcrafted, 3-1/2" tall, Dated 1994. Push gently and the child will swing from the golden star. The caption reads, "A Godchild... a treasure on earth from heaven above." **Artist:** Anita Marra Rogers

☐ Purchased 19____   Pd $_____   MIB NB DB BNT
☐ Want   Orig. Ret. $8.95   **NB** $20   **MIB** Sec. Mkt. **$25**

QX 242-3 GODPARENT

Comments: Glass Ball, 2-7/8" dia., Dated 1994. Mary Hamilton angel designs frame the caption, "A Godparent is a special blessing."

☐ Purchased 19____   Pd $_____   MIB NB DB BNT
☐ Want   Orig. Ret. $5.00   **NB** $18   **MIB** Sec. Mkt. **$23**

QX 567-6 GRANDCHILD'S FIRST CHRISTMAS

Comments: Handcrafted, 3" tall, Dated 1994. This clip-on ornament features a baby mouse sleeping peacefully on a baby blanket. **Artist:** Duane Unruh

☐ Purchased 19____   Pd $_____   MIB NB DB BNT
☐ Want   Orig. Ret. $7.95   **NB** $4   **MIB** Sec. Mkt. **$19**

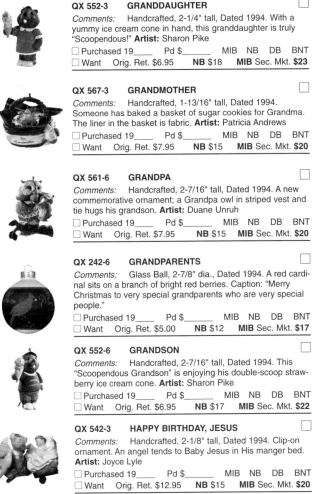

QX 552-3 GRANDDAUGHTER

Comments: Handcrafted, 2-1/4" tall, Dated 1994. With a yummy ice cream cone in hand, this granddaughter is truly "Scoopendous!" **Artist:** Sharon Pike

☐ Purchased 19____   Pd $_____   MIB NB DB BNT
☐ Want   Orig. Ret. $6.95   **NB** $18   **MIB** Sec. Mkt. **$23**

QX 567-3 GRANDMOTHER

Comments: Handcrafted, 1-13/16" tall, Dated 1994. Someone has baked a basket of sugar cookies for Grandma. The liner in the basket is fabric. **Artist:** Patricia Andrews

☐ Purchased 19____   Pd $_____   MIB NB DB BNT
☐ Want   Orig. Ret. $7.95   **NB** $15   **MIB** Sec. Mkt. **$20**

QX 561-6 GRANDPA

Comments: Handcrafted, 2-7/16" tall, Dated 1994. A new commemorative ornament; a Grandpa owl in striped vest and tie hugs his grandson. **Artist:** Duane Unruh

☐ Purchased 19____   Pd $_____   MIB NB DB BNT
☐ Want   Orig. Ret. $7.95   **NB** $15   **MIB** Sec. Mkt. **$20**

QX 242-6 GRANDPARENTS

Comments: Glass Ball, 2-7/8" dia., Dated 1994. A red cardinal sits on a branch of bright red berries. Caption: "Merry Christmas to very special grandparents who are very special people."

☐ Purchased 19____   Pd $_____   MIB NB DB BNT
☐ Want   Orig. Ret. $5.00   **NB** $12   **MIB** Sec. Mkt. **$17**

QX 552-6 GRANDSON

Comments: Handcrafted, 2-7/16" tall, Dated 1994. This "Scoopendous Grandson" is enjoying his double-scoop strawberry ice cream cone. **Artist:** Sharon Pike

☐ Purchased 19____   Pd $_____   MIB NB DB BNT
☐ Want   Orig. Ret. $6.95   **NB** $17   **MIB** Sec. Mkt. **$22**

QX 542-3 HAPPY BIRTHDAY, JESUS

Comments: Handcrafted, 2-1/8" tall, Dated 1994. Clip-on ornament. An angel tends to Baby Jesus in His manger bed. **Artist:** Joyce Lyle

☐ Purchased 19____   Pd $_____   MIB NB DB BNT
☐ Want   Orig. Ret. $12.95   **NB** $15   **MIB** Sec. Mkt. **$20**

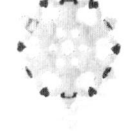

QX 526-6   HEART OF CHRISTMAS ☐

Comments: **Fifth and Final in Series,** Handcrafted, 2" tall, Dated 1994. It's Christmas and Mama has a feast in store for her family. **Artist:** Ed Seale

☐ Purchased 19___   Pd $_____   MIB   NB   DB   BNT
☐ Want   Orig. Ret. $14.95   **NB** $25   **MIB** Sec. Mkt. **$30**

QX 440-6   HEARTS IN HARMONY ☐

Comments: Porcelain, 3" tall, Dated 1994. Boys and girls of different nationalities join hearts in unity to form a unique snowflake pattern. **Artist:** Patricia Andrews

☐ Purchased 19___   Pd $_____   MIB   NB   DB   BNT
☐ Want   Orig. Ret. $10.95   **NB** $17   **MIB** Sec. Mkt. **$23**

QX 553-6   HELPFUL SHEPHERD ☐

Comments: Handcrafted/Brass Staff, 2-11/16" tall. A shepherd carries his lamb across his shoulders. **Artist:** Robert Chad

☐ Purchased 19___   Pd $_____   MIB   NB   DB   BNT
☐ Want   Orig. Ret. $8.95   **NB** $15   **MIB** Sec. Mkt. **$20**

QX 529-6   HERE COMES SANTA: MAKIN' TRACTOR TRACKS ☐

Comments: **Sixteenth in Series,** Handcrafted, 2-11/16" tall. Dated 1994. Santa plows the "back forty" with his "Reindeer" tractor. This piece is somewhat scarce. **Artist:** Linda Sickman

☐ Purchased 19___   Pd $_____   MIB   NB   DB   BNT
☐ Want   Orig. Ret. $14.95   **NB** $55   **MIB** Sec. Mkt. **$60**

QX 521-6   HOLIDAY BARBIE™ ☐

Comments: **Second in Series,** Handcrafted, 3-3/8" tall, Dated 1994. Barbie glitters in her gold and ivory gown. She coordinated with the Holiday Barbie Doll which was offered in 1994 and the 1995 Hallmark stocking hanger. **Artist:** —

☐ Purchased 19___   Pd $_____   MIB   NB   DB   BNT
☐ Want   Orig. Ret. $14.95   **NB** $45   **MIB** Sec. Mkt. **$60**

QX 582-6   HOLIDAY PATROL ☐

Comments: Handcrafted, 2-1/2" tall, Dated 1994. "Stop for Christmas" is the message of this policeman. **Artist:** Dill Rhodus

☐ Purchased 19___   Pd $_____   MIB   NB   DB   BNT
☐ Want   Orig. Ret. $8.95   **NB** $15   **MIB** Sec. Mkt. **$20**

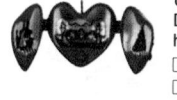

QXC 482-3   HOLIDAY PURSUIT: KEEPSAKE CLUB ☐

Comments: Handcrafted, 2-7/8" tall, Dated 1994. Super sleuth Keepsake Bear is hot on the trail of the 1994 ornaments. **Artist:** John Francis (Collin)

☐ Purchased 19___   Pd $_____   MIB   NB   DB   BNT
☐ Want   Orig. Ret.: Came with Club Membership
NB $20   **MIB** Sec. Mkt. **$24**

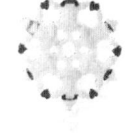

QX 594-6   ICE SHOW ☐

Comments: Handcrafted, 2-7/8" tall, Dated 1994. A little redbird does amazing tricks skating atop an ice cube. Many of the ice cubes are found with bubbles in them. A perfect cube with no bubble has a projected value of $45. **Artist:** Patricia Andrews

☐ Purchased 19___   Pd $_____   MIB   NB   DB   BNT
☐ Want   Orig. Ret. $7.95   **NB** $15   **MIB** Sec. Mkt. **$20**

QX 576-3   IN THE PINK ☐

Comments: Handcrafted, 2-3/4" tall, Dated 1994. A pink flamingo lounges in the shade of a palm tree, sipping his drink. **Artist:** Patricia Andrews

☐ Purchased 19___   Pd $_____   MIB   NB   DB   BNT
☐ Want   Orig. Ret. $9.95   **NB** $19   **MIB** Sec. Mkt. **$24**

QX 585-6   IT'S A STRIKE ☐

Comments: Handcrafted, 2-13/16" tall, Dated 1994. This monkey will have a perfect score if he continues to bowl strikes at "Santa Claus Lanes." **Artist:** Bob Siedler

☐ Purchased 19___   Pd $_____   MIB   NB   DB   BNT
☐ Want   Orig. Ret. $8.95   **NB** $15   **MIB** Sec. Mkt. **$20**

QX 578-3   JINGLE BELL BAND ☐

Comments: Handcrafted, 4" tall, Dated 1994. Our musical mice in the band play the bells – jingle bells, that is! **Artist:** Ken Crow

☐ Purchased 19___   Pd $_____   MIB   NB   DB   BNT
☐ Want   Orig. Ret. $10.95 **NB** $25   **MIB** Sec. Mkt. **$30**

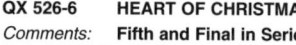

QXC 483-3   JOLLY HOLLY SANTA: KEEPSAKE CLUB ☐

Comments: Handcrafted/Hand Painted, 3-1/8" tall, Dated 1994, Limited Edition, 16,398 pieces produced, Wood Display Stand. This Santa depicts the essence of a Victorian Christmas with a bag full of toys for all the girls and boys. **Artist:** Joyce A. Lyle

☐ Purchased 19___   Pd $_____   MIB   NB   DB   BNT
☐ Want   Orig. Ret. $22.00   **NB** $45   **MIB** Sec. Mkt. **$50**

QX 447-3   JOYOUS SONG

Comments: Handcrafted, 3-9/16" tall, Dated 1994. An African-American girl in a red choir robe sings a happy melody. **Artist:** Patricia Andrews

☐ Purchased 19___   Pd $_____   MIB   NB   DB   BNT
☐ Want   Orig. Ret. $8.95   **NB** $15   **MIB** Sec. Mkt. **$20**

QX 575-6   JUMP-ALONG JACKALOPE

Comments: Handcrafted, 3-7/16" tall, Dated 1994. The elusive jackalope has been captured in a Keepsake ornament. **Artist:** John Francis (Collin)

☐ Purchased 19___   Pd $_____   MIB   NB   DB   BNT
☐ Want   Orig. Ret. $8.95   **NB** $14   **MIB** Sec. Mkt. **$19**

QX 541-3   KEEP ON MOWIN'

Comments: Handcrafted, 3-1/8" tall, Dated 1994. Santa, in t-shirt, shorts and sandals, pushes a mower; the wheels and blades of the mower turn freely. **Artist:** Bob Siedler

☐ Purchased 19___   Pd $_____   MIB   NB   DB   BNT
☐ Want   Orig. Ret. $8.95   **NB** $15   **MIB** Sec. Mkt. **$20**

QX 591-6   KICKIN' ROO

Comments: Handcrafted, 2-11/16" tall, Dated 1994. A little Roo in his red and white jersey is a big hit on the soccer field. **Artist:** Bob Siedler

☐ Purchased 19___   Pd $_____   MIB   NB   DB   BNT
☐ Want   Orig. Ret. $7.95   **NB** $15   **MIB** Sec. Mkt. **$20**

QX 542-6   KIDDIE CAR CLASSICS: MURRAY® CHAMPION

Comments: **FIRST IN SERIES,** Die Cast Metal, 1-7/8" tall, Dated 1994. This ornament series is similar to the larger Hallmark Kiddie Car Classics. There was a first in series Murray Champion in the mini line in 1995. Very popular! **Artist:** Don Palmiter

☐ Purchased 19___   Pd $_____   MIB   NB   DB   BNT
☐ Want   Orig. Ret. $13.95   **NB** $60   MIB Sec. Mkt. **$65**

QX 541-6   KITTY'S CATAMARAN

Comments: Handcrafted, 4-9/16" tall, Dated 1994. Kitty is taking his sailboat, the "Cat's Meow," out for a holiday ride. **Artist:** Ed Seale

☐ Purchased 19___   Pd $_____   MIB   NB   DB   BNT
☐ Want   Orig. Ret. $10.95   **NB** $10   **MIB** Sec. Mkt. **$15**

QLX 741-3   KRINGLE TROLLEY

Comments: Light, Handcrafted, 3-5/16" tall, Dated 1994. Santa's picking up travelers on the "Kringle Christmas Trolley" up and down the "Jingle Bell Lane Snow Express." **Artist:** Ken Crow

☐ Purchased 19___   Pd $_____   MIB   NB   DB   BNT
☐ Want   Orig. Ret. $20.00   **NB** $45   **MIB** Sec. Mkt. **$50**

QX 588-6   KRINGLE'S KAYAK

Comments: Handcrafted, 1-13/16" tall, Dated 1994. Some of Santa's deliveries cannot be reached by sleigh, so he takes a kayak. **Artist:** Ed Seale

☐ Purchased 19___   Pd $_____   MIB   NB   DB   BNT
☐ Want   Orig. Ret. $7.95   **NB** $17   **MIB** Sec. Mkt. **$22**

QX 540-6   LION KING, THE: MUFASA AND SIMBA

Comments: Handcrafted, 3" tall. Father and son enjoy their time together, playing and learning about life in the wild.

☐ Purchased 19___   Pd $_____   MIB   NB   DB   BNT
☐ Want   Orig. Ret. $14.95   **NB** $15   **MIB** Sec. Mkt. **$25**

QX 530-3   LION KING, THE: SIMBA AND NALA

Comments: Handcrafted, 2" tall, 2-3/8" tall. Set of two hang-together ornaments. The young lion prince and his best friend, Nala, love to play together.

☐ Purchased 19___   Pd $_____   MIB   NB   DB   BNT
☐ Want   Orig. Ret. $12.95   **NB** $20   **MIB** Sec. Mkt. **$25**

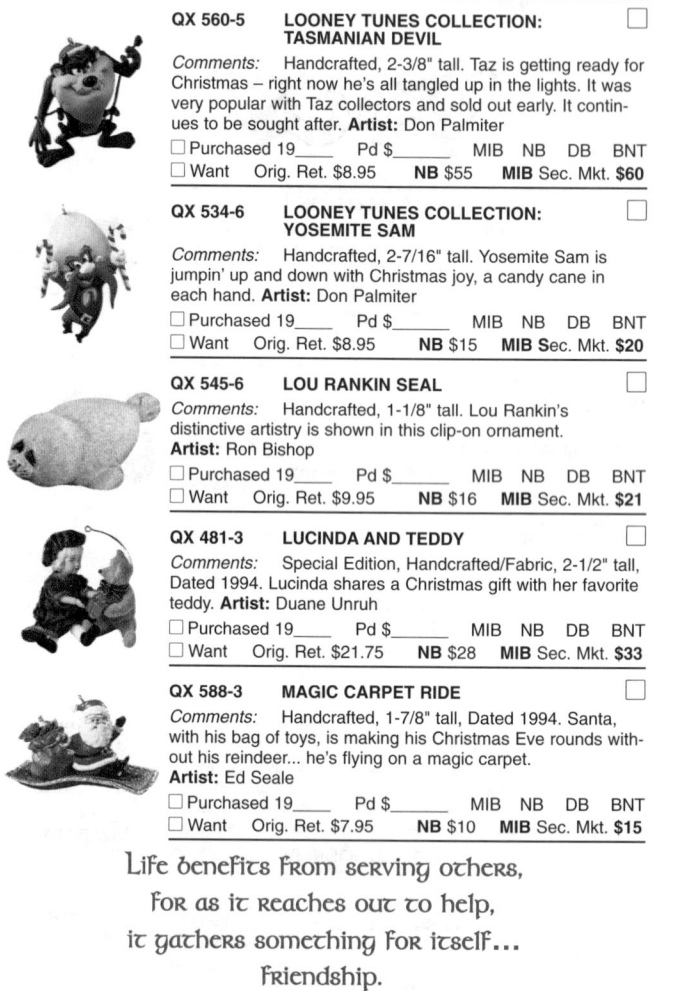

QLX 751-3   LION KING, THE: SIMBA, SARABI AND MUFASA

Comments: Light and Music, Handcrafted, 4-1/4" tall. Mufasa's family is complete with the birth of the new prince, Simba. Plays "Circle of Life." This was recalled because of defective sound. **Artist:** Ken Crow

☐ Purchased 19___   Pd $_____   MIB NB DB BNT
☐ Want   Orig. Ret. $32.00   **NB** $45   **MIB** Sec. Mkt. **$50**

QLX 751-6   LION KING, THE: SIMBA, SARABI AND MUFASA

Comments: Lighted, Handcrafted, 4-1/4" tall. Mufasa's family is complete with the birth of the new prince. No Music. **Artist:** Ken Crow

☐ Purchased 19___   Pd $_____   MIB NB DB BNT
☐ Want   Orig. Ret. $20.00   **NB** $25   **MIB** Sec. Mkt. **$30**

QX 536-6   LION KING, THE: TIMON AND PUMBAA

Comments: Handcrafted, 2-1/4" tall. The warthog and his little friend frolic without a care in the world.

☐ Purchased 19___   Pd $_____   MIB NB DB BNT
☐ Want   Orig. Ret. $8.95   **NB** $15   **MIB** Sec. Mkt. **$20**

QX 541-5   LOONEY TUNES COLLECTION: DAFFY DUCK

Comments: Handcrafted, 3" tall. Daffy is trying out an angel robe and wings. His halo is brass. **Artist:** Don Palmiter

☐ Purchased 19___   Pd $_____   MIB NB DB BNT
☐ Want   Orig. Ret. $8.95   **NB** $20   **MIB** Sec. Mkt. **$25**

QX 560-2   LOONEY TUNES COLLECTION: ROAD RUNNER AND WILE E. COYOTE

Comments: Handcrafted, 3-1/2" tall. The crafty coyote has a special gift for the road runner. Watch out! There's a wire attached! **Artist:** Robert Chad

☐ Purchased 19___   Pd $_____   MIB NB DB BNT
☐ Want   Orig. Ret. $12.95   **NB** $23   **MIB** Sec. Mkt. **$28**

QX 534-3   LOONEY TUNES COLLECTION: SPEEDY GONZALES

Comments: Handcrafted, 1-5/8" tall. Speedy is hoping to get even more zip... on his red skis. **Artist:** Don Palmiter

☐ Purchased 19___   Pd $_____   MIB NB DB BNT
☐ Want   Orig. Ret. $8.95   **NB** $20   **MIB** Sec. Mkt. **$25**

QX 560-5   LOONEY TUNES COLLECTION: TASMANIAN DEVIL

Comments: Handcrafted, 2-3/8" tall. Taz is getting ready for Christmas – right now he's all tangled up in the lights. It was very popular with Taz collectors and sold out early. It continues to be sought after. **Artist:** Don Palmiter

☐ Purchased 19___   Pd $_____   MIB NB DB BNT
☐ Want   Orig. Ret. $8.95   **NB** $55   **MIB** Sec. Mkt. **$60**

QX 534-6   LOONEY TUNES COLLECTION: YOSEMITE SAM

Comments: Handcrafted, 2-7/16" tall. Yosemite Sam is jumpin' up and down with Christmas joy, a candy cane in each hand. **Artist:** Don Palmiter

☐ Purchased 19___   Pd $_____   MIB NB DB BNT
☐ Want   Orig. Ret. $8.95   **NB** $15   **MIB** Sec. Mkt. **$20**

QX 545-6   LOU RANKIN SEAL

Comments: Handcrafted, 1-1/8" tall. Lou Rankin's distinctive artistry is shown in this clip-on ornament. **Artist:** Ron Bishop

☐ Purchased 19___   Pd $_____   MIB NB DB BNT
☐ Want   Orig. Ret. $9.95   **NB** $16   **MIB** Sec. Mkt. **$21**

QX 481-3   LUCINDA AND TEDDY

Comments: Special Edition, Handcrafted/Fabric, 2-1/2" tall, Dated 1994. Lucinda shares a Christmas gift with her favorite teddy. **Artist:** Duane Unruh

☐ Purchased 19___   Pd $_____   MIB NB DB BNT
☐ Want   Orig. Ret. $21.75   **NB** $28   **MIB** Sec. Mkt. **$33**

QX 588-3   MAGIC CARPET RIDE

Comments: Handcrafted, 1-7/8" tall, Dated 1994. Santa, with his bag of toys, is making his Christmas Eve rounds without his reindeer... he's flying on a magic carpet. **Artist:** Ed Seale

☐ Purchased 19___   Pd $_____   MIB NB DB BNT
☐ Want   Orig. Ret. $7.95   **NB** $10   **MIB** Sec. Mkt. **$15**

Life benefits from serving others,
for as it reaches out to help,
it gathers something for itself...
friendship.

QXC 483-6 MAJESTIC DEER: KEEPSAKE CLUB

Comments: Limited Edition, 27,180 pieces produced. Wood Display Stand, Hand-Painted Fine Porcelain/Pewter, 3-3/4" tall. A white deer with pewter horns leaps gracefully among the branches of your tree. Available to Club Members only. **Artist:** Duane Unruh

☐ Purchased 19____   Pd $_____   MIB NB DB BNT
☐ Want   Orig. Ret. $25.00   **NB** $45   **MIB** Sec. Mkt. **$50**

QX 540-3 MAKING IT BRIGHT

Comments: Handcrafted, 3-5/16" tall, Dated 1994. A squirrel paints his name on the side of a silver mail box.
Artist: Dill Rhodus

☐ Purchased 19____   Pd $_____   MIB NB DB BNT
☐ Want   Orig. Ret. $8.95   **NB** $15   **MIB** Sec. Mkt. **$20**

QX 241-6 MARY ENGELBREIT

Comments: Glass Ball, 2-7/8" dia., Dated 1994. Snowmen circle the ball along with the caption, "Let It Snow."

☐ Purchased 19____   Pd $_____   MIB NB DB BNT
☐ Want   Orig. Ret. $5.00   **NB** $15   **MIB** Sec. Mkt. **$20**

QX 527-6 MARY'S ANGELS: JASMINE

Comments: **Seventh in Series**, Handcrafted, 2-7/8" tall. A sweet angel dangles a star from her perch atop a cloud.
Artist: Robert Chad

☐ Purchased 19____   Pd $_____   MIB NB DB BNT
☐ Want   Orig. Ret. $6.95   **NB** $17   **MIB** Sec. Mkt. **$22**

QLX 750-3 MAXINE

Comments: Blinking lights, Handcrafted, 4" tall, Dated 1994. Maxine has gotten her Christmas lights out and is preparing to decorate for the holidays. **Artist:** Linda Sickman

☐ Purchased 19____   Pd $_____   MIB NB DB BNT
☐ Want   Orig. Ret. $20.00   **NB** $45   **MIB** Sec. Mkt. **$50**

QX 591-3 MERRY FISHMAS

Comments: Handcrafted, 2-1/8" tall, Dated 1994. This little fellow is feeding the line from his bobber through the eye of the brass hook. **Artist:** Don Palmiter

☐ Purchased 19____   Pd $_____   MIB NB DB BNT
☐ Want   Orig. Ret. $8.95   **NB** $18   **MIB** Sec. Mkt. **$23**

QX 525-6 MERRY OLDE SANTA

Comments: **Fifth in Series**, Handcrafted, 4-3/16" tall, Dated 1994. Santa makes his travels with a lantern, wreath and tree. **Artist:** Robert Chad

☐ Purchased 19____   Pd $_____   MIB NB DB BNT
☐ Want   Orig. Ret. $14.95   **NB** $28   **MIB** Sec. Mkt. **$33**

QX 599-6 MISTLETOE SURPRISE

Comments: Handcrafted, 1-15/16" tall and 1-9/16" tall, Dated 1994. Set of two hang-together ornaments. A little mouse hangs overhead with mistletoe, setting the stage for a surprise kiss below. **Artist:** Ed Seale

☐ Purchased 19____   Pd $_____   MIB NB DB BNT
☐ Want   Orig. Ret. $12.95   **NB** $28   **MIB** Sec. Mkt. **$33**

QX 546-6 MOM

Comments: Handcrafted, 2-5/16" tall, Dated 1994. The "Most Outstanding Mom" now has a trophy to prove it!
Artist: Anita Marra Rogers

☐ Purchased 19____   Pd $_____   MIB NB DB BNT
☐ Want   Orig. Ret. $7.95   **NB** $13   **MIB** Sec. Mkt. **$18**

QX 566-6 MOM AND DAD

Comments: Handcrafted, 2-15/16" tall, Dated 1994. I see Mommy kissing Daddy, all dressed up like Santa Claus.
Artist: Bob Siedler

☐ Purchased 19____   Pd $_____   MIB NB DB BNT
☐ Want   Orig. Ret. $9.95   **NB** $20   **MIB** Sec. Mkt. **$25**

QX 550-6 MOM-TO-BE

Comments: Handcrafted, 2-1/2" tall, Dated 1994. Midnight cravings never seem to be satisfied, as the soon–to–be Mama lion is finding herself a late-night snack.
Artist: Sharon Pike

☐ Purchased 19____   Pd $_____   MIB NB DB BNT
☐ Want   Orig. Ret. $7.95   **NB** $13   **MIB** Sec. Mkt. **$18**

QX 521-3 MOTHER GOOSE: HEY DIDDLE, DIDDLE

Comments: **Second in Series**, Handcrafted, 2-1/2" tall, Dated 1994. This hasn't been a widely popular series so far. Caption: "Hey diddle, diddle, the cat and the fiddle, the cow jumped over the moon." **Artist:** Ed Seale

☐ Purchased 19____   Pd $_____   MIB NB DB BNT
☐ Want   Orig. Ret. $13.95   **NB** $35   **MIB** Sec. Mkt. **$40**

QX 528-3 MR. AND MRS. CLAUS: A HANDWARMING PRESENT

Comments: **Ninth in Series,** Handcrafted, 3-1/4" tall. Dated 1994. "To Santa." Santa receives a pair of mittens from a loving Mrs. Claus. **Artist:** Duane Unruh

☐ Purchased 19____ Pd $_____ MIB NB DB BNT
☐ Want Orig. Ret. $14.95 **NB** $35 **MIB** Sec. Mkt. **$40**

QX 554-6 NEPHEW

Comments: Handcrafted, 1-13/16" tall, Dated 1994. Santa comes to wish nephew a very merry Christmas. **Artist:** John Francis (Collin)

☐ Purchased 19____ Pd $_____ MIB NB DB BNT
☐ Want Orig. Ret. $7.95 **NB** $12 **MIB** Sec. Mkt. **$17**

QX 566-3 NEW HOME

Comments: Handcrafted, 2-5/16" tall, Dated 1994. The residents of this acorn home are ready for the holidays as seen by the window box of poinsettias and the wreath on the door. A plaque on the home says, "New Home 1994."
Artist: Patricia Andrews

☐ Purchased 19____ Pd $_____ MIB NB DB BNT
☐ Want Orig. Ret. $8.95 **NB** $15 **MIB** Sec. Mkt. **$20**

QX 554-3 NIECE

Comments: Handcrafted, 1-1/2" tall, Dated 1994. Mrs. Santa is bringing a special doll to her niece in a cart pulled by a happy reindeer. **Artist:** John Francis (Collin)

☐ Purchased 19____ Pd $_____ MIB NB DB BNT
☐ Want Orig. Ret. $7.95 **NB** $12 **MIB** Sec. Mkt. **$17**

QX 241-3 NORMAN ROCKWELL ART

Comments: Glass Ball, 2-7/8" dia., Dated 1994. Captions: "Post Cover December 29, 1956" and "Christmas 1994." Norman Rockwell "Bottom Drawer." A famous cover from *The Saturday Evening Post.* **Artist:** Joyce Lyle

☐ Purchased 19____ Pd $_____ MIB NB DB BNT
☐ Want Orig. Ret. $5.00 **NB** $15 **MIB** Sec. Mkt. **$20**

QX 528-6 NOSTALGIC HOUSES AND SHOPS: NEIGHBORHOOD DRUGSTORE

Comments: **Eleventh in Series,** Handcrafted, 4-1/16" tall. Dated 1994. A pharmacy and soda fountain are part of this drugstore. **Artist:** Donna Lee

☐ Purchased 19____ Pd $_____ MIB NB DB BNT
☐ Want Orig. Ret. $14.95 **NB** $35 **MIB** Sec. Mkt. **$40**

QXC 485-3 ON CLOUD NINE: KEEPSAKE CLUB

Comments: Handcrafted, 2-1/16" tall, Dated 1994. A little angel relaxes on a cloud. Available to Club Members only. **Artist:** Donna Lee

☐ Purchased 19____ Pd $_____ MIB NB DB BNT
☐ Want Orig. Ret. $12.00 **NB** $25 **MIB** Sec. Mkt. **$30**

QX 569-6 OPEN-AND-SHUT HOLIDAY

Comments: Handcrafted, 3-5/16" tall, Dated 1994. What better gift for a business associate. The file drawer opens to find a Christmas surprise inside. **Artist:** Bob Siedler

☐ Purchased 19____ Pd $_____ MIB NB DB BNT
☐ Want Orig. Ret. $9.95 **NB** $10 **MIB** Sec. Mkt. **$15**

QX 481-6 OUR CHRISTMAS TOGETHER

Comments: Handcrafted, 2-3/8" tall, Dated 1994. A pair of flocked redbirds cuddle together. Their nest of holly leaves clips to the tree. **Artist:** Anita Marra Rogers

☐ Purchased 19____ Pd $_____ MIB NB DB BNT
☐ Want Orig. Ret. $9.95 **NB** $10 **MIB** Sec. Mkt. **$15**

QX 557-6 OUR FAMILY: PHOTOHOLDER

Comments: Handcrafted, 3-5/8" dia., Dated 1994. White poinsettias, gold bells and a red bow on a bright green wreath form a frame for a favorite family photograph. Caption: "The wonderful meaning of Christmas is found in the circle of family love." **Artist:** Patricia Andrews

☐ Purchased 19____ Pd $_____ MIB NB DB BNT
☐ Want Orig. Ret. $7.95 **NB** $15 **MIB** Sec. Mkt. **$20**

QX 570-6 OUR FIRST CHRISTMAS TOGETHER

Comments: Handcrafted/Brass, 3-1/8" tall, Dated 1994. Two bears go for a ride in a sleigh with brass runners. They keep warm and cozy with their fabric hats and scarves. **Artist:** Patricia Andrews

☐ Purchased 19____ Pd $_____ MIB NB DB BNT
☐ Want Orig. Ret. $18.95 **NB** $35 **MIB** Sec. Mkt. **$40**

QX 564-3 OUR FIRST CHRISTMAS TOGETHER

Comments: Acrylic, 2-5/16" tall, Dated 1994. A couple shares a kiss as well as gifts. **Artist:** Ron Bishop

☐ Purchased 19____ Pd $_____ MIB NB DB BNT
☐ Want Orig. Ret. $9.95 **NB** $20 **MIB** Sec. Mkt. **$25**

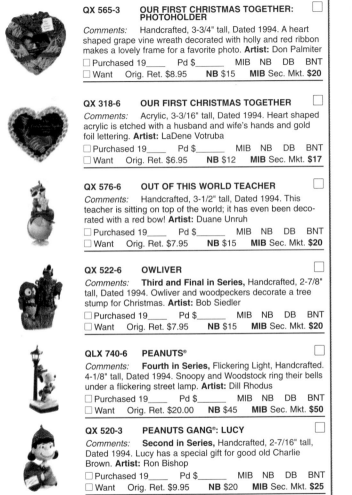

QX 565-3   OUR FIRST CHRISTMAS TOGETHER: PHOTOHOLDER ☐

Comments: Handcrafted, 3-3/4" tall, Dated 1994. A heart shaped grape vine wreath decorated with holly and red ribbon makes a lovely frame for a favorite photo. **Artist:** Don Palmiter

☐ Purchased 19____   Pd $_____   MIB   NB   DB   BNT
☐ Want   Orig. Ret. $8.95   **NB** $15   **MIB** Sec. Mkt. **$20**

QX 318-6   OUR FIRST CHRISTMAS TOGETHER ☐

Comments: Acrylic, 3-3/16" tall, Dated 1994. Heart shaped acrylic is etched with a husband and wife's hands and gold foil lettering. **Artist:** LaDene Votruba

☐ Purchased 19____   Pd $_____   MIB   NB   DB   BNT
☐ Want   Orig. Ret. $6.95   **NB** $12   **MIB** Sec. Mkt. **$17**

QX 576-6   OUT OF THIS WORLD TEACHER ☐

Comments: Handcrafted, 3-1/2" tall, Dated 1994. This teacher is sitting on top of the world; it has even been decorated with a red bow! **Artist:** Duane Unruh

☐ Purchased 19____   Pd $_____   MIB   NB   DB   BNT
☐ Want   Orig. Ret. $7.95   **NB** $15   **MIB** Sec. Mkt. **$20**

QX 522-6   OWLIVER ☐

Comments: **Third and Final in Series,** Handcrafted, 2-7/8" tall, Dated 1994. Owliver and woodpeckers decorate a tree stump for Christmas. **Artist:** Bob Siedler

☐ Purchased 19____   Pd $_____   MIB   NB   DB   BNT
☐ Want   Orig. Ret. $7.95   **NB** $15   **MIB** Sec. Mkt. **$20**

QLX 740-6   PEANUTS® ☐

Comments: **Fourth in Series,** Flickering Light, Handcrafted. 4-1/8" tall, Dated 1994. Snoopy and Woodstock ring their bells under a flickering street lamp. **Artist:** Dill Rhodus

☐ Purchased 19____   Pd $_____   MIB   NB   DB   BNT
☐ Want   Orig. Ret. $20.00   **NB** $45   **MIB** Sec. Mkt. **$50**

QX 520-3   PEANUTS GANG®: LUCY ☐

Comments: **Second in Series,** Handcrafted, 2-7/16" tall, Dated 1994. Lucy has a special gift for good old Charlie Brown. **Artist:** Ron Bishop

☐ Purchased 19____   Pd $_____   MIB   NB   DB   BNT
☐ Want   Orig. Ret. $9.95   **NB** $20   **MIB** Sec. Mkt. **$25**

QLX 742-3   PEEKABOO PUP ☐

Comments: Motion, Handcrafted, 3-7/8" tall, Dated 1994. The lid on the basket is opening... who is it? It's a cute little pup playing his favorite game! **Artist:** Anita Marra Rogers

☐ Purchased 19____   Pd $_____   MIB   NB   DB   BNT
☐ Want   Orig. Ret. $20.00   **NB** $38   **MIB** Sec. Mkt. **$43**

QX 586-3   PRACTICE MAKES PERFECT ☐

Comments: Handcrafted, 2-5/16" tall, Dated 1994. It takes a lot of practice to perfect a tennis game but this little pup is willing to work at it. **Artist:** Don Palmiter

☐ Purchased 19____   Pd $_____   MIB   NB   DB   BNT
☐ Want   Orig. Ret. $8.95   **NB** $15   **MIB** Sec. Mkt. **$20**

QX 525-3   PUPPY LOVE ☐

Comments: **Fourth in Series,** Handcrafted with Brass Tag. 2-5/16" tall, Dated 1994. A white puppy is entangled in garland. **Artist:** Anita Marra Rogers

☐ Purchased 19____   Pd $_____   MIB   NB   DB   BNT
☐ Want   Orig. Ret. $7.95   **NB** $20   **MIB** Sec. Mkt. **$25**

QX 584-3   RED HOT HOLIDAY ☐

Comments: Handcrafted, 2-5/8" tall, Dated 1994. This would be a great gift for the fireman in your life. He comes prepared with his red fire chief's cap and fire extinguisher. **Artist:** Anita Marra Rogers

☐ Purchased 19____   Pd $_____   MIB   NB   DB   BNT
☐ Want   Orig. Ret. $7.95   **NB** $15   **MIB** Sec. Mkt. **$20**

QX 592-6   REINDEER PRO ☐

Comments: Handcrafted, 3-3/16" tall, Dated 1994. This reindeer golfer is set to play, rain or shine. **Artist:** Dill Rhodus

☐ Purchased 19____   Pd $_____   MIB   NB   DB   BNT
☐ Want   Orig. Ret. $7.95   **NB** $15   **MIB** Sec. Mkt. **$20**

QX 535-6   RELAXING MOMENT ☐

Comments: Handcrafted, 2-9/16" tall, Dated 1994. Santa's taking a break with his favorite beverage, Coca-Cola, as a fawn sleeps by his chair. **Artist:** John Francis (Collin)

☐ Purchased 19____   Pd $_____   MIB   NB   DB   BNT
☐ Want   Orig. Ret. $14.95   **NB** $27   **MIB** Sec. Mkt. **$32**

QLX 740-3　ROCK CANDY MINER ☐

Comments:　Flickering Light, Handcrafted, 2-5/8" tall, Dated 1994. This little gopher is pleased with his progress. He's mined a cart full of sweet candy from the Rock Candy Mine. **Artist:** Bob Siedler

☐ Purchased 19____　Pd $_____　MIB　NB　DB　BNT
☐ Want　Orig. Ret. $20.00　**NB** $35　**MIB** Sec. Mkt. **$40**

QX 501-6　ROCKING HORSE ☐

Comments:　**Fourteenth in Series,** Handcrafted, 3" tall, Dated 1994. Dark brown with white stockings and brown tail. **Artist:** Linda Sickman

☐ Purchased 19____　Pd $_____　MIB　NB　DB　BNT
☐ Want　Orig. Ret. $10.95　**NB** $25　**MIB** Sec. Mkt. **$30**

QX 545-3　SANTA'S LEGO® SLEIGH ☐

Comments:　Handcrafted, 1-13/16" tall, Dated 1994. Santa is making his Christmas deliveries this year in a sleigh built from LEGO® blocks! Another Lego® ornament debuted in '95! **Artist:** Ken Crow

☐ Purchased 19____　Pd $_____　MIB　NB　DB　BNT
☐ Want　Orig. Ret. $10.95　**NB** $17　**MIB** Sec. Mkt. **$22**

QLX 747-3　SANTA'S SING-ALONG ☐

Comments:　Light and Music, Handcrafted, 3-15/16" tall, Dated 1994. Caption: "Sing Along with Santa." Santa is announcing his arrival with his calliope. Plays "Santa Claus Is Coming To Town." **Artist:** Ken Crow

☐ Purchased 19____　Pd $_____　MIB　NB　DB　BNT
☐ Want　Orig. Ret. $24.00　**NB** $43　**MIB** Sec. Mkt. **$48**

XPR 945-0　SARAH, PLAIN AND TALL COLLECTION, THE: COUNTRY CHURCH, THE ☐

Comments:　Handcrafted, 5" tall, Dated 1994. This white-framed, shake-shingled church was where Sarah and Jacob danced for the first time and later married.

☐ Purchased 19____　Pd $_____　MIB　NB　DB　BNT
☐ Want　Orig. Ret. $7.95 with any Hallmark Purchase
　　　　　　NB $18　**MIB** Sec. Mkt. **$33**

XPR 945-2　SARAH, PLAIN AND TALL COLLECTION, THE: HAYS TRAIN STATION, THE ☐

Comments:　Handcrafted, 5" tall, Dated 1994. Sarah arrived from Maine by train. Here at the old train station she met Jacob Witting.

☐ Purchased 19____　Pd $_____　MIB　NB　DB　BNT
☐ Want　Orig. Ret. $7.95 with any Hallmark Purchase
　　　　　　NB $18　**MIB** Sec. Mkt. **$23**

XPR 945-1　SARAH, PLAIN AND TALL COLLECTION, THE: MRS. PARKLEY'S GENERAL STORE ☐

Comments:　Handcrafted, 5" tall, Dated 1994. People met here at the General Store and heard the latest news as they purchased food, dry goods and other provisions.

☐ Purchased 19____　Pd $_____　MIB　NB　DB　BNT
☐ Want　Orig. Ret. $7.95 with any Hallmark Purchase
　　　　　　NB $15　**MIB** Sec. Mkt. **$20**

XPR 945-4　SARAH, PLAIN AND TALL COLLECTION, THE: SARAH'S MAINE HOME ☐

Comments:　Handcrafted, 5" tall, Dated 1994. Sarah lived here, off the coast of Maine, with her maiden aunts - Mattie, Harriet and Lou.

☐ Purchased 19____　Pd $_____　MIB　NB　DB　BNT
☐ Want　Orig. Ret. $7.95 with any Hallmark Purchase
　　　　　　NB $13　**MIB** Sec. Mkt. **$18**

XPR 945-3　SARAH, PLAIN AND TALL COLLECTION, THE: SARAH'S PRAIRIE HOME ☐

Comments:　Handcrafted, 5" tall, Dated 1994. Sarah, a mail order bride, came to Kansas to live here with Jacob and his children, Anna and Caleb.

☐ Purchased 19____　Pd $_____　MIB　NB　DB　BNT
☐ Want　Orig. Ret. $7.95 with any Hallmark Purchase
　　　　　　NB $15　**MIB** Sec. Mkt. **$20**

QX 573-6　SECRET SANTA ☐

Comments:　Handcrafted, 2-5/8" tall, Dated 1994. Who is that masked puppy with reindeer antlers? Why, it's your pal, Secret Santa! We've had several reports of ornaments being found with the caption, "From Your Secret Pal." **Artist:** Duane Unruh

☐ Purchased 19____　Pd $_____　MIB　NB　DB　BNT
☐ Want　Orig. Ret. $7.95　**NB** $18　**MIB** Sec. Mkt. **$23**

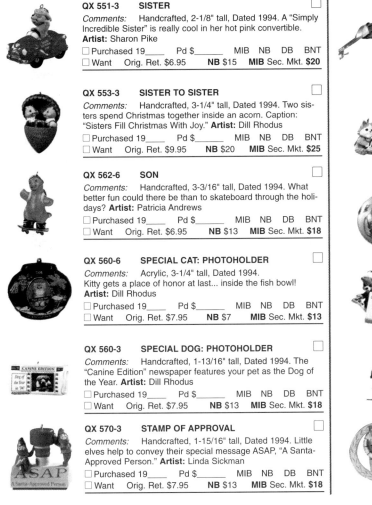

QX 551-3   SISTER   ☐

Comments: Handcrafted, 2-1/8" tall, Dated 1994. A "Simply Incredible Sister" is really cool in her hot pink convertible.
Artist: Sharon Pike

☐ Purchased 19____   Pd $_____   MIB   NB   DB   BNT
☐ Want   Orig. Ret. $6.95   **NB** $15   **MIB** Sec. Mkt. **$20**

QX 553-3   SISTER TO SISTER   ☐

Comments: Handcrafted, 3-1/4" tall, Dated 1994. Two sisters spend Christmas together inside an acorn. Caption: "Sisters Fill Christmas With Joy." **Artist:** Dill Rhodus

☐ Purchased 19____   Pd $_____   MIB   NB   DB   BNT
☐ Want   Orig. Ret. $9.95   **NB** $20   **MIB** Sec. Mkt. **$25**

QX 562-6   SON   ☐

Comments: Handcrafted, 3-3/16" tall, Dated 1994. What better fun could there be than to skateboard through the holidays? **Artist:** Patricia Andrews

☐ Purchased 19____   Pd $_____   MIB   NB   DB   BNT
☐ Want   Orig. Ret. $6.95   **NB** $13   **MIB** Sec. Mkt. **$18**

QX 560-6   SPECIAL CAT: PHOTOHOLDER   ☐

Comments: Acrylic, 3-1/4" tall, Dated 1994. Kitty gets a place of honor at last... inside the fish bowl!
Artist: Dill Rhodus

☐ Purchased 19____   Pd $_____   MIB   NB   DB   BNT
☐ Want   Orig. Ret. $7.95   **NB** $7   **MIB** Sec. Mkt. **$13**

QX 560-3   SPECIAL DOG: PHOTOHOLDER   ☐

Comments: Handcrafted, 1-13/16" tall, Dated 1994. The "Canine Edition" newspaper features your pet as the Dog of the Year. **Artist:** Dill Rhodus

☐ Purchased 19____   Pd $_____   MIB   NB   DB   BNT
☐ Want   Orig. Ret. $7.95   **NB** $13   **MIB** Sec. Mkt. **$18**

QX 570-3   STAMP OF APPROVAL   ☐

Comments: Handcrafted, 1-15/16" tall, Dated 1994. Little elves help to convey their special message ASAP, "A Santa-Approved Person." **Artist:** Linda Sickman

☐ Purchased 19____   Pd $_____   MIB   NB   DB   BNT
☐ Want   Orig. Ret. $7.95   **NB** $13   **MIB** Sec. Mkt. **$18**

QLX 738-6   STAR TREK®: THE NEXT GENERATION KLINGON BIRD OF PREY™   ☐

Comments: Flickering and Glowing Lights, Handcrafted. 2-1/8" tall, Stardated 1994. The Klingon battle cruiser joins the line-up of space craft from The Next Generation.
Artist: Lynn Norton

☐ Purchased 19____   Pd $_____   MIB   NB   DB   BNT
☐ Want   Orig. Ret. $24.00   **NB** $35   **MIB** Sec. Mkt. **$40**

QX 580-3   SWEET GREETING   ☐

Comments: Handcrafted, 1-1/2" tall and 1-3/4" tall, Dated 1994. Set of two hang-together ornaments. Busy kittens decorate a sugar cookie greeting for the tree. **Artist:** Don Palmiter

☐ Purchased 19____   Pd $_____   MIB   NB   DB   BNT
☐ Want   Orig. Ret. $10.95   **NB** $18   **MIB** Sec. Mkt. **$23**

QX 244-3   TALE OF PETER RABBIT, THE: BEATRIX POTTER   ☐

Comments: Glass Ball, 2-7/8" dia., Dated 1994. Caption: "Once upon a time there were four little rabbits and their names were Flopsy, Mopsy, Cotton-tail and Peter."

☐ Purchased 19____   Pd $_____   MIB   NB   DB   BNT
☐ Want   Orig. Ret. $5.00   **NB** $18   **MIB** Sec. Mkt. **$23**

QX 569-3   THICK 'N' THIN   ☐

Comments: Handcrafted, 2" tall, Clip-on orn., Dated 1994. Two bears share a pizza. Caption: "Friends Stand by You Through Thick and Thin!" **Artist:** Anita Marra Rogers

☐ Purchased 19____   Pd $_____   MIB   NB   DB   BNT
☐ Want   Orig. Ret. $10.95   **NB** $18   **MIB** Sec. Mkt. **$23**

QX 586-6   THRILL A MINUTE   ☐

Comments: Handcrafted, 3-11/16" tall, Dated 1994. This skier is in for a thrill, no matter which direction he travels! His destinations include "Look Out, Earth's Edge" and "No Way."
Artist: Bob Siedler

☐ Purchased 19____   Pd $_____   MIB   NB   DB   BNT
☐ Want   Orig. Ret. $8.95   **NB** $15   **MIB** Sec. Mkt. **$20**

QX 581-3   TIME OF PEACE   ☐

Comments: Handcrafted, 2-9/16" tall, Dated 1994. A lion and lamb stand together in an engraved oval which proclaims "Peace." This ornament resembles hand-carved wood.
Artist: Patricia Andrews

☐ Purchased 19____   Pd $_____   MIB   NB   DB   BNT
☐ Want   Orig. Ret. $7.95   **NB** $12   **MIB** Sec. Mkt. **$17**

QX 522-3 TOBIN FRALEY CAROUSEL ☐

Comments: **Third in Series,** Porcelain and Brass, 5-1/4" tall. Dated 1994. Collectors have questioned the fact that all the horses in this series are white. **Artist:** Tobin Fraley

☐ Purchased 19___ Pd $_____ MIB NB DB BNT
☐ Want Orig. Ret. $28.00 **NB** $55 **MIB** Sec. Mkt. **$60**

QLX 749-6 TOBIN FRALEY HOLIDAY CAROUSEL ☐

Comments: **FIRST IN SERIES,** Light and Music, Handcrafted. 4-15/16" tall, Dated 1994. A nostalgic carousel is decorated with Santa faces. Plays "Skater's Waltz."

Artist: Duane Unruh

☐ Purchased 19___ Pd $_____ MIB NB DB BNT
☐ Want Orig. Ret. $32.00 **NB** $70 **MIB** Sec. Mkt. **$75**

QX 564-6 TOU CAN LOVE ☐

Comments: Handcrafted, 3" tall, Dated 1994. A pair of gaily colored toucans stand together on a gift. Caption: "Tou-Can make Christmas more fun!" **Artist:** Anita Marra Rogers

☐ Purchased 19___ Pd $_____ MIB NB DB BNT
☐ Want Orig. Ret. $8.95 **NB** $15 **MIB** Sec. Mkt. **$20**

QX 318-3 TWELVE DAYS OF CHRISTMAS: ELEVEN PIPERS PIPING ☐

Comments: **Eleventh in Series,** Acrylic, 3-3/8" tall, Dated 1994. A Scotsman in his kilt plays his bagpipe, adding to the Christmas merriment.

☐ Purchased 19___ Pd $_____ MIB NB DB BNT
☐ Want Orig. Ret. $6.95 **NB** $15 **MIB** Sec. Mkt. **$20**

QX 520-6 U.S. CHRISTMAS STAMPS ☐

Comments: **Second in Series,** Enamel on Copper, 2-5/16" tall, Dated 1994. Caption: "Christmas 1994 Children Trimming Tree. Designer: Dollie Tingle Date of Issuance: Oct. 28, 1982; Place of Issuance: Snow, OK." This series ended with the '95 ornament.

☐ Purchased 19___ Pd $_____ MIB NB DB BNT
☐ Want Orig. Ret. $10.95 **NB** $15 **MIB** Sec. Mkt. **$20**

QLX 744-3 VERY MERRY MINUTES ☐

Comments: Light and Motion, Handcrafted, 4-5/16" tall, Dated 1994. One little mouse sleeps atop the clock as another swings playfully on the pendulum. **Artist:** LaDene Votruba

☐ Purchased 19___ Pd $_____ MIB NB DB BNT
☐ Want Orig. Ret. $24.00 **NB** $43 **MIB** Sec. Mkt. **$48**

QLX 746-3 WHITE CHRISTMAS ☐

Comments: Flickering Light/Music, Handcrafted, 3-3/16" tall. Dated 1994. The world may be covered in white but all is warm and cozy inside. Plays "White Christmas."
Artist: Donna Lee

☐ Purchased 19___ Pd $_____ MIB NB DB BNT
☐ Want Orig. Ret. $28.00 **NB** $40 **MIB** Sec. Mkt. **$45**

QX 574-6 WINNIE THE POOH AND TIGGER ☐

Comments: Handcrafted, 2-1/2" tall. A very excitable, bouncy Tigger has just jumped on Winnie the Pooh, putting him on his back. **Artist:** Bob Siedler

☐ Purchased 19___ Pd $_____ MIB NB DB BNT
☐ Want Orig. Ret. $12.95 **NB** $28 **MIB** Sec. Mkt. **$33**

QLX 749-3 WINNIE THE POOH PARADE ☐

Comments: Motion and Music, Handcrafted, 4-1/8" tall, Dated 1994. Pooh twirls as the gang parades around him; Tigger spins on his tail. Plays "Winnie the Pooh Theme."
Artist: Ken Crow

☐ Purchased 19___ Pd $_____ MIB NB DB BNT
☐ Want Orig. Ret. $32.00 **NB** $60 **MIB** Sec. Mkt. **$65**

QX 544-6 WIZARD OF OZ COLLECTION, THE: COWARDLY LION, THE ☐

Comments: Handcrafted, 3-9/16" tall. The Cowardly Lion searches for courage with his tail in his hands. This ornament is highly sought after. **Artist:** Patricia Andrews

☐ Purchased 19___ Pd $_____ MIB NB DB BNT
☐ Want Orig. Ret. $9.95 **NB** $35 **MIB** Sec. Mkt. **$40**

QX 543-3 WIZARD OF OZ COLLECTION, THE: DOROTHY AND TOTO ☐

Comments: Handcrafted, 3-9/16" tall. Dorothy carries Toto in her arm as she skips down the yellow brick road. This ornament is highly sought after. **Artist:** Joyce Lyle

☐ Purchased 19___ Pd $_____ MIB NB DB BNT
☐ Want Orig. Ret. $10.95 **NB** $65 **MIB** Sec. Mkt. **$70**

QX 543-6 WIZARD OF OZ COLLECTION, THE: SCARECROW ☐

Comments: Handcrafted, 3-7/8" tall. Scarecrow looks as if he has been plucked from the fence post. This ornament is highly sought after. **Artist:** Duane Unruh

☐ Purchased 19___ Pd $_____ MIB NB DB BNT
☐ Want Orig. Ret. $9.95 **NB** $35 **MIB** Sec. Mkt. **$40**

QX 544-3   WIZARD OF OZ COLLECTION, THE: TIN MAN ☐

Comments: Handcrafted, 3-13/16" tall. The tin man is reproduced in great detail; he even has his trusty axe. This ornament is highly sought after. **Artist:** Duane Unruh

☐ Purchased 19_____   Pd $_____   MIB   NB   DB   BNT
☐ Want   Orig. Ret. $9.95   **NB** $35   **MIB** Sec. Mkt. **$40**

QX 531-6   YULETIDE CENTRAL: LOCOMOTIVE ☐

Comments: **FIRST IN SERIES,** Pressed Tin, 2-9/16" tall. Dated 1994. This series will feature different train components and not just locomotives, such as the Tin Locomotive series of the past. **Artist:** Linda Sickman

☐ Purchased 19_____   Pd $_____   MIB   NB   DB   BNT
☐ Want   Orig. Ret. $18.95   **NB** $45   **MIB** Sec. Mkt. **$50**

Hallmark Keepsake Personalized Ornaments

No sales found on these ornaments. Any ornament with personal message is unlikely to bring a significant secondary market price.

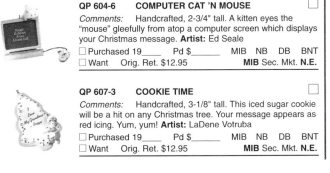

QP 603-5   BABY BLOCK ☐

Comments: Handcrafted Photoholder, 2-13/16" tall. Reissued from 1993. **Artist:** John Francis (Collin)

☐ Purchased 19_____   Pd $_____   MIB   NB   DB   BNT
☐ Want   Orig. Ret. $14.95   **MIB** Sec. Mkt. **N.E.**

QP 604-6   COMPUTER CAT 'N MOUSE ☐

Comments: Handcrafted, 2-3/4" tall. A kitten eyes the "mouse" gleefully from atop a computer screen which displays your Christmas message. **Artist:** Ed Seale

☐ Purchased 19_____   Pd $_____   MIB   NB   DB   BNT
☐ Want   Orig. Ret. $12.95   **MIB** Sec. Mkt. **N.E.**

QP 607-3   COOKIE TIME ☐

Comments: Handcrafted, 3-1/8" tall. This iced sugar cookie will be a hit on any Christmas tree. Your message appears as red icing. Yum, yum! **Artist:** LaDene Votruba

☐ Purchased 19_____   Pd $_____   MIB   NB   DB   BNT
☐ Want   Orig. Ret. $12.95   **MIB** Sec. Mkt. **N.E.**

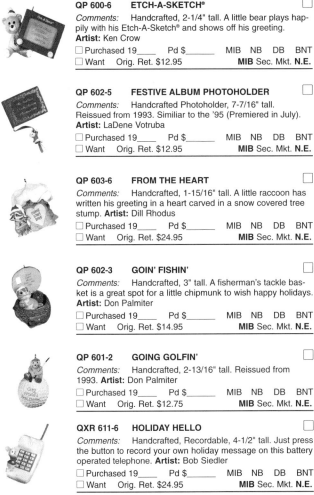

QP 600-6   ETCH-A-SKETCH® ☐

Comments: Handcrafted, 2-1/4" tall. A little bear plays happily with his Etch-A-Sketch® and shows off his greeting. **Artist:** Ken Crow

☐ Purchased 19_____   Pd $_____   MIB   NB   DB   BNT
☐ Want   Orig. Ret. $12.95   **MIB** Sec. Mkt. **N.E.**

QP 602-5   FESTIVE ALBUM PHOTOHOLDER ☐

Comments: Handcrafted Photoholder, 7-7/16" tall. Reissued from 1993. Similiar to the '95 (Premiered in July). **Artist:** LaDene Votruba

☐ Purchased 19_____   Pd $_____   MIB   NB   DB   BNT
☐ Want   Orig. Ret. $12.95   **MIB** Sec. Mkt. **N.E.**

QP 603-6   FROM THE HEART ☐

Comments: Handcrafted, 1-15/16" tall. A little raccoon has written his greeting in a heart carved in a snow covered tree stump. **Artist:** Dill Rhodus

☐ Purchased 19_____   Pd $_____   MIB   NB   DB   BNT
☐ Want   Orig. Ret. $24.95   **MIB** Sec. Mkt. **N.E.**

QP 602-3   GOIN' FISHIN' ☐

Comments: Handcrafted, 3" tall. A fisherman's tackle basket is a great spot for a little chipmunk to wish happy holidays. **Artist:** Don Palmiter

☐ Purchased 19_____   Pd $_____   MIB   NB   DB   BNT
☐ Want   Orig. Ret. $14.95   **MIB** Sec. Mkt. **N.E.**

QP 601-2   GOING GOLFIN' ☐

Comments: Handcrafted, 2-13/16" tall. Reissued from 1993. **Artist:** Don Palmiter

☐ Purchased 19_____   Pd $_____   MIB   NB   DB   BNT
☐ Want   Orig. Ret. $12.75   **MIB** Sec. Mkt. **N.E.**

QXR 611-6   HOLIDAY HELLO ☐

Comments: Handcrafted, Recordable, 4-1/2" tall. Just press the button to record your own holiday message on this battery operated telephone. **Artist:** Bob Siedler

☐ Purchased 19_____   Pd $_____   MIB   NB   DB   BNT
☐ Want   Orig. Ret. $24.95   **MIB** Sec. Mkt. **N.E.**

QP 601-5   MAILBOX DELIVERY

Comments: Handcrafted, 1-7/8" tall. Introduced in 1993, reissued in '94 and '95. **Artist:** Ken Crow

☐ Purchased 19____   Pd $_____   MIB NB DB BNT
☐ Want   Orig. Ret. $14.95   **MIB** Sec. Mkt. **N.E.**

QP 606-6   NOVEL IDEA

Comments: Handcrafted, 2-7/16" tall. A little mouse points out a special message written in the pages of a red book. **Artist:** LaDene Votruba

☐ Purchased 19____   Pd $_____   MIB NB DB BNT
☐ Want   Orig. Ret. $12.95   **MIB** Sec. Mkt. **N.E.**

QP 602-2   ON THE BILLBOARD

Comments: Handcrafted, 2-1/8" tall. Introduced in 1993, reissued in '94 and '95. **Artist:** Ken Crow

☐ Purchased 19____   Pd $_____   MIB NB DB BNT
☐ Want   Orig. Ret. $12.95   **MIB** Sec. Mkt. **N.E.**

QP 603-2   PLAYING BALL

Comments: Handcrafted, 3-11/16" tall. Introduced in 1993, reissued in '94 and '95. **Artist:** John Francis (Collin)

☐ Purchased 19____   Pd $_____   MIB NB DB BNT
☐ Want   Orig. Ret. $12.95   **MIB** Sec. Mkt. **N.E.**

QP 605-6   REINDEER ROOTERS

Comments: Handcrafted, 2-15/16" tall. Four happy reindeer, with a megaphone and waving banner, will help to send your Christmas greeting. In my opinion, this ornament, with a cute saying that complements the '94 Cheery Cyclists ornament (found on page 217) may obtain a secondary value faster. Reissued in '95. **Artist:** Ken Crow

☐ Purchased 19____   Pd $_____   MIB NB DB BNT
☐ Want   Orig. Ret. $12.95   **MIB** Sec. Mkt. **N.E.**

QP 600-5   SANTA SAYS

Comments: Handcrafted, 2-15/16" tall. Introduced in 1993, reissued in '94. **Artist:** Ed Seale

☐ Purchased 19____   Pd $_____   MIB NB DB BNT
☐ Want   Orig. Ret. $14.95   **MIB** Sec. Mkt. **N.E.**

Hallmark Keepsake Showcase Ornaments
Christmas Lights

QK 112-3   HOME FOR THE HOLIDAYS

Comments: Porcelain Bisque, Lighted, 4-1/16" tall, Dated 1994. Smoke rises from a snow covered cottage and light glows through the windows. **Artist:** Don Palmiter

☐ Purchased 19____   Pd $_____   MIB NB DB BNT
☐ Want   Orig. Ret. $15.75   **MIB** Sec. Mkt. **N.E.**

QK 111-6   MOONBEAMS

Comments: Porcelain Bisque, Lighted, 4-5/16" tall, Dated 1994. A star with a moon cut-out dangles from the top of a quarter moon. Light streams from the pin-hole design of this sleepy moon. **Artist:** Patricia Andrews

☐ Purchased 19____   Pd $_____   MIB NB DB BNT
☐ Want   Orig. Ret. $15.75   **MIB** Sec. Mkt. **N.E.**

QK 112-6   MOTHER AND CHILD

Comments: Porcelain Bisque, Lighted, 3-1/2" tall, Dated 1994. A bright shining star stands above the Madonna, attending to her Holy Child. **Artist:** Anita Marra Rogers

☐ Purchased 19____   Pd $_____   MIB NB DB BNT
☐ Want   Orig. Ret. $15.75   **MIB** Sec. Mkt. **N.E.**

QK 110-6   PEACEFUL VILLAGE

Comments: Porcelain Bisque, Lighted, 2-13/16" tall, Dated 1994. Soft light illuminates the church in this snow covered village. Includes gold ribbon. **Artist:** Robert Chad

☐ Purchased 19____   Pd $_____   MIB NB DB BNT
☐ Want   Orig. Ret. $15.75   **MIB** Sec. Mkt. **N.E.**

A husband is a man who expects his wife to be perfect and to understand why he isn't.

Folk Art Americana

QK 118-3 CATCHING 40 WINKS ☐

Comments: Wood Look, 1-7/8" tall, Dated 1994. An elf settles down for a quick snooze among the brightly wrapped packages. **Artist:** Linda Sickman

☐ Purchased 19____   Pd $_____   MIB NB DB BNT
☐ Want   Orig. Ret. $16.75   **NB** $17   **MIB** Sec. Mkt. **$20**

QK 116-6 GOING TO TOWN ☐

Comments: Wood Look, 2-7/16" tall, Dated 1994. Pouches filled with grain, an elf heads to market with his best "pack pig." **Artist:** Linda Sickman

☐ Purchased 19____   Pd $_____   MIB NB DB BNT
☐ Want   Orig. Ret. $15.75   **NB** $16   **MIB** Sec. Mkt. **$20**

QK 117-3 RACING THROUGH THE SNOW ☐

Comments: Wood Look, 3-1/16" tall, Dated 1994. An elf races through the winter landscape astride a rooster on snowshoes. **Artist:** Linda Sickman

☐ Purchased 19____   Pd $_____   MIB NB DB BNT
☐ Want   Orig. Ret. $15.75   **NB** $20   **MIB** Sec. Mkt. **$25**

QK 119-3 RARIN' TO GO ☐

Comments: Wood Look, 2-11/16" tall, Dated 1994. Hang on tight! This elf is in store for a quick hop through the forest atop a long-eared rabbit. **Artist:** Linda Sickman

☐ Purchased 19____   Pd $_____   MIB NB DB BNT
☐ Want   Orig. Ret. $15.75   **NB** $16   **MIB** Sec. Mkt. **$20**

QK 117-6 ROUNDUP TIME ☐

Comments: Wood Look, 2-11/16" tall, Dated 1994. Wrapped gifts have been tied to this fellow's unique transportation... a cow. Let's get "moo...ving;" Christmas is just around the corner. **Artist:** Linda Sickman

☐ Purchased 19____   Pd $_____   MIB NB DB BNT
☐ Want   Orig. Ret. $16.75   **NB** $20   **MIB** Sec. Mkt. **$25**

Holiday Favorites

QK 105-3 DAPPER SNOWMAN ☐

Comments: Crackled Porcelain, 3-5/8" tall, Dated 1994. This dapper fellow is highlighted with blue accents and a striped candy cane. **Artist:** LaDene Votruba

☐ Purchased 19____   Pd $_____   MIB NB DB BNT
☐ Want   Orig. Ret. $13.75   **NB** $15   **MIB** Sec. Mkt. **$20**

QK 103-3 GRACEFUL FAWN ☐

Comments: Crackled Porcelain, 2-11/16" tall, Dated 1994. Delicately painted blue leaves circle the fawn's neck. Includes blue ribbon. **Artist:** LaDene Votruba

I Purchased 19____   Pd $_____   MIB NB DB BNT
☐ Want   Orig. Ret. $11.75   **NB** $13   **MIB** Sec. Mkt. **$18**

QK 104-6 JOLLY SANTA ☐

Comments: Crackled Porcelain, 3-11/16" tall, Dated 1994. Santa is chuckling a happy "ho, ho, ho!" He's wearing red striped mittens and is holding a miniature tree. Includes red ribbon. **Artist:** LaDene Votruba

☐ Purchased 19____   Pd $_____   MIB NB DB BNT
☐ Want   Orig. Ret. $13.75   **NB** $25   **MIB** Sec. Mkt. **$30**

QK 103-6 JOYFUL LAMB ☐

Comments: Crackled Porcelain, 2-5/16" tall, Dated 1994. A green garland graces the neck of a serene lamb. Includes green ribbon. **Artist:** LaDene Votruba

☐ Purchased 19____   Pd $_____   MIB NB DB BNT
☐ Want   Orig. Ret. $11.75   **NB** $17   **MIB** Sec. Mkt. **$22**

QK 104-3 PEACEFUL DOVE ☐

Comments: Crackled Porcelain, 3-5/8" tall, Dated 1994. Trimmed in blue, this graceful dove will add a touch of grace to any tree. Includes blue ribbon. **Artist:** LaDene Votruba

☐ Purchased 19____   Pd $_____   MIB NB DB BNT
☐ Want   Orig. Ret. $11.75   **NB** $12   **MIB** Sec. Mkt. **$15**

Old-World Silver - 1994

QK 102-6 **SILVER BELLS** ☐

Comments: Silver-Plated, 3-3/16" tall, Dated 1994. Silver bells ring out the joy of Christmas, depicted in a filigree design. **Artist:** Duane Unruh

☐ Purchased 19____   Pd $_____   MIB NB DB BNT
☐ Want   Orig. Ret. $24.75   **MIB** Sec. Mkt. **$25**

QK 102-3 **SILVER BOWS** ☐

Comments: Silver-Plated, 3-5/16" tall, Dated 1994. Delicate bows add a touch of beauty to this intricate Old World ornament. **Artist:** Don Palmiter

☐ Purchased 19____   Pd $_____   MIB NB DB BNT
☐ Want   Orig. Ret. $24.75   **MIB** Sec. Mkt. **$25**

QK 100-6 **SILVER POINSETTIA** ☐

Comments: Silver-Plated, 3-1/8" tall, Dated 1994. A finely detailed poinsettia provides the focal point for this diamond shaped ornament. **Artist:** Duane Unruh

☐ Purchased 19____   Pd $_____   MIB NB DB BNT
☐ Want   Orig. Ret. $24.75   **MIB** Sec. Mkt. **$25**

QK 101-6 **SILVER SNOWFLAKE** ☐

Comments: Silver-Plated, 3-1/16" tall, Dated 1994. Intricate snowflake designs circle the ornament. **Artist:** Duane Unruh

☐ Purchased 19____   Pd $_____   MIB NB DB BNT
☐ Want   Orig. Ret. $24.75   **MIB** Sec. Mkt. **$25**

Specialty Ornament

CRAYOLA® CRAYON ORNAMENT ☐

Comments: Handcrafted. Came as free gift in tin box of Crayola Crayons.

☐ Purchased 19____   Pd $_____   MIB NB DB BNT
☐ Want   Orig. Ret. $57.99-$9.99 (depending on location of purchase without tin box $5-$10)   **MIB** Sec. Mkt. **$10**

COLLECTOR'S SURVIVAL KIT – PREMIERE '94 ☐

Comments: Handcrafted, Dated 1994. Given as a free gift during premiere week.

☐ Purchased 19____   Pd $_____   MIB NB DB BNT
☐ Want   **MIB** Sec. Mkt. **$12.50**

Hallmark Expo Ornaments
Expo 1994

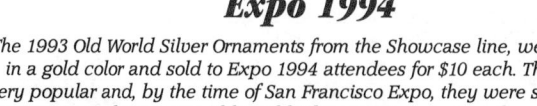

The 1993 Old World Silver Ornaments from the Showcase line, were finished in a gold color and sold to Expo 1994 attendees for $10 each. These were very popular and, by the time of San Francisco Expo, they were sold out. The 1994 Bows and Poinsettia Old World Silver Ornaments were then also dipped in a gold colored finish and sold to lucky Expo attendees.

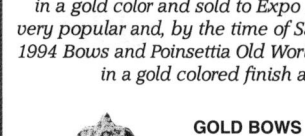

GOLD BOWS ☐

Comments: 1994 Old World Silver ornament dipped in a gold colored finish with attached ribbon that said "Expo '94."

☐ Purchased 19____   Pd $_____   MIB NB DB BNT
☐ Want Orig. Ret. $10.00   **MIB** Sec. Mkt. **$20**

GOLD DOVE OF PEACE ☐

Comments: 1993 Old World Silver ornament dipped in a gold colored finish with attached ribbon that said "Expo '94."

☐ Purchased 19____   Pd $_____   MIB NB DB BNT
☐ Want Orig. Ret. $10.00   **MIB** Sec. Mkt. **$20**

GOLD POINSETTIA ☐

Comments: 1994 Old World Silver ornament dipped in a gold colored finish with attached ribbon that said "Expo '94."

☐ Purchased 19____   Pd $_____   MIB NB DB BNT
☐ Want   Orig. Ret. $10.00   **MIB** Sec. Mkt. **$22**

GOLD SANTA ☐

Comments: 1993 Old World Silver ornament dipped in a gold colored finish with attached ribbon that said "Expo '94."

☐ Purchased 19____   Pd $_____   MIB NB DB BNT
☐ Want   Orig. Ret. $10.00   **MIB** Sec. Mkt. **$25**

GOLD STAR AND HOLLY ☐

Comments: 1993 Old World Silver ornament dipped in a gold colored finish with attached ribbon that said "Expo '94."

☐ Purchased 19____   Pd $_____   MIB NB DB BNT
☐ Want   Orig. Ret. $10.00   **MIB** Sec. Mkt. **$20**

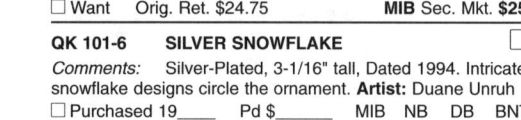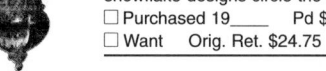

QXC 484-3   MRS. CLAUS' CUPBOARD ☐

Comments: Handcrafted, Dated 1994. Only available at eight 1994 Hallmark Expos held across the USA. Mrs. Claus' Cupboard is filled with delightful surprises... miniature copies of favorite Keepsake ornaments such as: Cheerful Santa, Noah's Ark, the 1993 Folk Art Polar Bear Adventure, a Nativity and more!

☐ Purchased 19_____ Pd $_____   MIB NB DB BNT
☐ Want   Orig. Ret. $55 with $25 purchase of
              Keepsake Ornaments   **MIB** Sec. Mkt. **$300**

CIRCLE OF FRIENDSHIP ☐

Comments: Handcrafted, Dated 1993. A Members Only ornament in 1993, this was also given away through special drawings at Expo '94s. This has been the most asked about ornament of the Expo prizes.

☐ Purchased 19_____ Pd $_____   MIB NB DB BNT
☐ Want   Orig. Ret. w/membership 1993 or drawing
              MIB Sec. Mkt. **$125**

Expo 1994 Prizes

Available at the '94 Expo were several gifts
given to fortunate attendees who entered different drawings.
Gifts given included:
a signed Star Trek ornament,
a '94 Looney Tunes set,
complete set of all mini ornaments from '94,
a signed Mary Engelbreit ball and an original signed artist sketch.

Also available by special drawings;
the '93 Circle of Friendship (a Member's Only ornament in '93);
Red '94 First Edition
Murray Champion ornament
(five given away per each Expo);
and the Red '94 Chevy which could have been signed by Don Palmiter
at the two Expos he attended.

Collector Pins

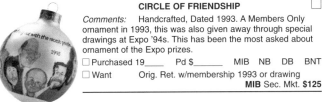

Keepsake Round-Up Club
Bay City, TX

Hallmark Collectors' Club
Casa De Navidad,
Albuquerque, NM

**Illini Hallmark
Collectors' Club**
IL.

**Arkansas Keepsake
Collectors' Club**
AK.

**1996
Artist On Tour Pin**

**Pony Express
Hallmark Collectors**
St. Joseph, MO

**Ozarks Ornament
Collectors Club**
MO

**Hallmark Harvesters,
Tuscola County**

1994 Miniature Ornament Collection

QXM 407-3
A MERRY FLIGHT
1" tall, Dated 1994. Turn dial with thumb and Santa circles the village. **Artist:** Ken Crow
☐ Purchased 19___ Pd $ _____
MIB   NB   DB   BNT
☐ Want   Orig. Retail $5.75
NB $8   **MIB** Sec. Mkt. **$13**

QXM 400-3
BABY'S FIRST CHRISTMAS
1-1/4" tall, Dated 1994.
Artist: Joyce Lyle
☐ Purchased 19___ Pd $ _____
MIB   NB   DB   BNT
☐ Want   Orig. Retail $5.75
NB $9   **MIB** Sec. Mkt. **$14**

QXM 403-3
BAKING TINY TREATS
Set of Six, Dated 1994. Merry Mixer, 1-1/8" tall, Standin' By, 3/4" tall;Just Dozin', 1/2" tal; Rollin' Along, 13/16" tall; Scoop, 11/16" tall,Official Taster, 9/16" tall.
Artist: Ed Seale
☐ Purchased 19___ Pd $_____
MIB   NB   DB   BNT
☐ WantOrig. Retail $29.00
NB $55   **MIB** Sec. Mkt. **$60**

QXM 407-6
BEARY PERFECT TREE
1-3/16" tall, Dated 1994.
Artist: Ron Bishop
☐ Purchased 19___ Pd $ _____
MIB   NB   DB   BNT
☐ Want   Orig. Retail $4.75
NB $12   **MIB** Sec. Mkt. **$17**

QXM 513-3
BEARYMORES, THE
Third and Final in Series,
1-1/8" tall, Dated 1994.
Artist: Anita Marra Rogers
☐ Purchased 19___ Pd $ _____
MIB   NB   DB   BNT
☐ Want   Orig. Retail $5.75
NB $12   **MIB** Sec. Mkt. **$17**

QXM 515-3
CENTURIES OF SANTA
FIRST IN SERIES,
1-1/4" tall, Dated 1994.
Artist: Linda Sickman
☐ Purchased 19___ Pd $ _____
MIB   NB   DB   BNT
☐ Want   Orig. Retail $6.00
NB $20   **MIB** Sec. Mkt. **$25**

QXM 406-3
CORNY ELF
1" tall. **Artist:** Dill Rhodus
☐ Purchased 19___ Pd $ _____
MIB   NB   DB   BNT
☐ Want   Orig. Retail $4.50
NB $7   **MIB** Sec. Mkt. **$12**

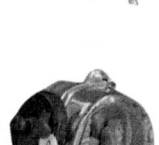

QXM 410-3
CUTE AS A BUTTON
13/16" tall, Dated 1994.
Artist: Ken Crow
☐ Purchased 19___ Pd $ _____
MIB   NB   DB   BNT
☐ Want   Orig. Retail $3.75
NB $10   **MIB** Sec. Mkt. **$15**

QXM 589-1
DANCING ANGELS
TREE-TOPPER
Dimensional Brass, 2-7/8" tall, Reissued from 1992.
☐ Purchased 19___ Pd $ _____
MIB   NB   DB   BNT
☐ Want   Orig. Retail $9.75
NB $6   **MIB** Sec. Mkt. **$12**

QXM 402-6
DAZZLING REINDEER
Precious Edition, Pewter, 1-3/8" tall. **Artist:** LaDene Votruba
☐ Purchased 19___ Pd $ _____
MIB   NB   DB   BNT
☐ Want   Orig. Retail $9.75
NB $15   **MIB** Sec. Mkt. **$20**

QXM 401-6
FRIENDS NEED HUGS
13/16" tall, Dated 1994.
Artist: Joyce Lyle
☐ Purchased 19___ Pd $ _____
MIB   NB   DB   BNT
☐ Want   Orig. Retail $4.50
NB $10   **MIB** Sec. Mkt. **$15**

QXM 405-6
GRACEFUL CARROUSEL
HORSE
Pewter, 1-1/4" tall, Dated 1994.
☐ Purchased 19___ Pd $ _____
MIB   NB   DB   BNT
☐ Want   Orig. Retail $7.75
NB $13   **MIB** Sec. Mkt. **$18**

QXM 516-6
HAVE A COOKIE
7/8" tall, Dated 1994, Artist's Favorite. **Artist:** Donna Lee
☐ Purchased 19___ Pd $ _____
MIB   NB   DB   BNT
☐ Want   Orig. Retail $5.75
NB $10   **MIB** Sec. Mkt. **$15**

QXM 400-6
HEARTS A-SAIL
15/16" tall, Dated 1994.
Artist: Ron Bishop
☐ Purchased 19___ Pd $ _____
MIB   NB   DB   BNT
☐ Want   Orig. Retail $5.75
NB $8   **MIB** Sec. Mkt. **$13**

QXM 545-2
HOLIDAY EXPRESS:
REVOLVING TREE BASE
4-1/4" tall. Reissued from 1993.
Train circles track. Miniature tree
sold separately.
☐ Purchased 19___ Pd $ _____
MIB   NB   DB   BNT
☐ Want   Orig. Retail $50.00
NB $65   **MIB** Sec. Mkt. **$70**

QXM 405-3
JOLLY VISITOR
1" tall, Dated 1994.
Artist: Linda Sickman
☐ Purchased 19___ Pd $ _____
MIB   NB   DB   BNT
☐ Want   Orig. Retail $5.75
NB $10   **MIB** Sec. Mkt. **$15**

QXM 409-3
JOLLY WOLLY SNOWMAN
1" tall, Dated 1994. Snowman
wobbles when tapped gently.
Artist: LaDene Votruba
☐ Purchased 19___ Pd $ _____
MIB   NB   DB   BNT
☐ Want   Orig. Retail $3.75
NB $8   **MIB** Sec. Mkt. **$13**

QXM 403-6
JOURNEY TO BETHLEHEM
1-1/4" tall. **Artist:** Joyce Lyle
☐ Purchased 19___ Pd $ _____
MIB   NB   DB   BNT
☐ Want   Orig. Retail $5.75
NB $9   **MIB** Sec. Mkt. **$18**

QXM 408-6
JUST MY SIZE
1-5/16" tall, Dated 1994.
Artist: Ron Bishop
☐ Purchased 19___ Pd $ _____
MIB   NB   DB   BNT
☐ Want   Orig. Retail $3.75
NB $8   **MIB** Sec. Mkt. **$10**

QXM 404-3
LOVE WAS BORN
1-3/16" tall, Dated 1994.
Artist: Linda Sickman
☐ Purchased 19___ Pd $ _____
MIB   NB   DB   BNT
☐ Want   Orig. Retail $4.50
NB $8   **MIB** Sec. Mkt. **$15**

QXM 510-6
MARCH OF THE TEDDY BEARS
Second in Series, 1-3/16" tall,
Dated 1994. **Artist:** Duane Unruh
☐ Purchased 19___ Pd $ _____
MIB   NB   DB   BNT
☐ Want   Orig. Retail $4.50
NB $9   **MIB** Sec. Mkt. **$20**

QXM 406-6
MELODIC CHERUB
1-5/16" tall, Dated 1994.
Artist: Anita Marra Rogers
☐ Purchased 19___ Pd $ _____
MIB   NB   DB   BNT
☐ Want   Orig. Retail $3.75
NB $8   **MIB** Sec. Mkt. **$10**

QXM 401-3
MOM
1" tall, Dated 1994.
Artist: Anita Marra Rogers
☐ Purchased 19___ Pd $ _____
MIB   NB   DB   BNT
☐ Want   Orig. Retail $4.50
NB $5   **MIB** Sec. Mkt. **$14**

QXM 512-6
NATURE'S ANGELS
Fifth in Series, 1-3/16" tall.
Artist: LaDene Votruba
☐ Purchased 19___ Pd $ _____
MIB   NB   DB   BNT
☐ Want   Orig. Retail $4.50
NB $8   **MIB** Sec. Mkt. **$12**

QXM 512-3
NIGHT BEFORE CHRISTMAS,
THE: FATHER
Third in Series, 1-3/16" tall,
Dated 1994. **Artist:** Duane Unruh
☐ Purchased 19___ Pd $ _____
MIB   NB   DB   BNT
☐ Want   Orig. Retail $4.50
NB $11   **MIB** Sec. Mkt. **$15**

QXM 410-6
NOAH'S ARK
Special Edition, Three piece set. Ark, 3-1/8" tall: bears,
5/8" tall: seals, 5/8" tall. Deck lifts off and ladder lowers.
Merry Walruses and Playful Penguins were added in '95.
African Elephants from '96 complemented the set,
although not a part of the series. **Artist:** Linda Sickman
☐ Purchased 19___ Pd $__
MIB   NB   DB   BNT
☐ Want   Orig. Retail $24.50
NB $44   **MIB** Sec. Mkt. **$60**

QXM 511-3
NOEL R.R.: STOCK CAR
Sixth in Series, 13/16" tall,
Dated 1994. Doors slide open
and closed.
Artist: Linda Sickman
☐ Purchased 19___ Pd $ _____
MIB   NB   DB   BNT
☐ Want   Orig. Retail $7.00
NB $15   **MIB** Sec. Mkt. **$22**

QXM 514-6
NUTCRACKER GUILD
FIRST IN SERIES, 1-3/16" tall,
Dated 1994. Opens and closes
like real nutcrackers.
Artist: Linda Sickman
☐ Purchased 19___ Pd $ _____
MIB   NB   DB   BNT
☐ Want   Orig. Retail $5.75
NB $10   **MIB** Sec. Mkt. **$23**

QXM 514-3
**OLD ENGLISH VILLAGE:
HAT SHOP**
Seventh in Series, 7/8" tall,
Dated 1994.
Artist: Patricia Andrews
☐ Purchased 19___ Pd $ _____
MIB   NB   DB   BNT
☐ Want   Orig. Retail $7.00
NB $10   **MIB** Sec. Mkt. **$17**

QXM 510-3
ON THE ROAD
Second in Series, Pressed Tin,
7/16" tall, Dated 1994. Wheels
turn. Pressed tin ornaments do
well on the secondary market.
Artist: Linda Sickman
☐ Purchased 19___ Pd $ _____
MIB   NB   DB   BNT
☐ Want   Orig. Retail $5.75
NB $10   **MIB** Sec. Mkt. **$17**

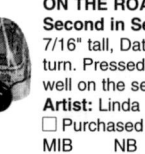

QXM 515-6
POUR SOME MORE
1-9/16" tall. Caption: "Enjoy
Coca-Cola®" **Artist:** Robert Chad
☐ Purchased 19___ Pd $ _____
MIB   NB   DB   BNT
☐ Want   Orig. Retail $5.75
NB $6   **MIB** Sec. Mkt. **$13**

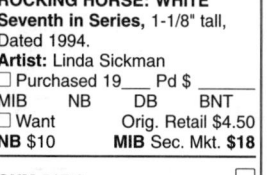

QXM 511-6
ROCKING HORSE: WHITE
Seventh in Series, 1-1/8" tall,
Dated 1994.
Artist: Linda Sickman
☐ Purchased 19___ Pd $ _____
MIB   NB   DB   BNT
☐ Want   Orig. Retail $4.50
NB $10   **MIB** Sec. Mkt. **$18**

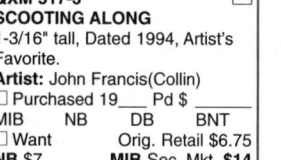

QXM 517-3
SCOOTING ALONG
1-3/16" tall, Dated 1994, Artist's
Favorite.
Artist: John Francis(Collin)
☐ Purchased 19___ Pd $ _____
MIB   NB   DB   BNT
☐ Want   Orig. Retail $6.75
NB $7   **MIB** Sec. Mkt. **$14**

QXC 480-6
**SWEET BOUQUET: KEEPSAKE
COLLECTOR'S CLUB**
1-3/16" dia. Caption: "Santa's
Club Soda."
☐ Purchased 19___ Pd $ _____
MIB   NB   DB   BNT
☐ Want   Orig. Retail Included
               with Membership Kit
NB $15   **MIB** Sec. Mkt. **$25**

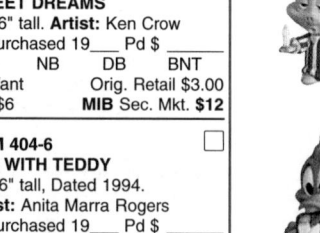

QXM 409-6
SWEET DREAMS
11/16" tall. **Artist:** Ken Crow
☐ Purchased 19___ Pd $ _____
MIB   NB   DB   BNT
☐ Want   Orig. Retail $3.00
NB $6   **MIB** Sec. Mkt. **$12**

QXM 404-6
TEA WITH TEDDY
15/16" tall, Dated 1994.
Artist: Anita Marra Rogers
☐ Purchased 19___ Pd $ _____
MIB   NB   DB   BNT
☐ Want   Orig. Retail $7.25
NB $8   **MIB** Sec. Mkt. **$14**

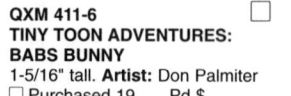

QXM 411-6
**TINY TOON ADVENTURES:
BABS BUNNY**
1-5/16" tall. **Artist:** Don Palmiter
☐ Purchased 19___ Pd $ _____
MIB   NB   DB   BNT
☐ Want   Orig. Retail $5.75
NB $9   **MIB** Sec. Mkt. **$15**

QXM 516-3
**TINY TOON ADVENTURES:
BUSTER BUNNY**
1-5/16" tall. **Artist:** Don Palmiter
☐ Purchased 19___ Pd $ _____
MIB   NB   DB   BNT
☐ Want   Orig. Retail $5.75
NB $7   **MIB** Sec. Mkt. **$13**

QXM 413-3
**TINY TOON ADVENTURES:
DIZZY DEVIL**
15/16" tall. **Artist:** Don Palmiter
☐ Purchased 19___ Pd $ _____
MIB   NB   DB   BNT
☐ Want   Orig. Retail $5.75
NB $8   **MIB** Sec. Mkt. **$15**

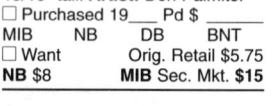

QXM 412-6
**TINY TOON ADVENTURES:
HAMTON**
1-1/16" tall. **Artist:** Don Palmiter
☐ Purchased 19___ Pd $ _____
MIB   NB   DB   BNT
☐ Want   Orig. Retail $5.75
NB $8   **MIB** Sec. Mkt. **$13**

QXM 412-3
**TINY TOON ADVENTURES:
PLUCKY DUCK**
1-1/8" tall. **Artist:** Don Palmiter
☐ Purchased 19___ Pd $ _____
MIB   NB   DB   BNT
☐ Want   Orig. Retail $5.75
NB $7   **MIB** Sec. Mkt. **$13**

1994 Easter Ornament Collection

QEO 815-3
BABY'S FIRST EASTER
2" tall, Dated 1994. Sleeping bunny in basket.
Artist: John Francis (Collin)
☐ Purchased 19___ Pd $ _____
MIB   NB   DB   BNT
☐ Want   Orig. Retail $6.75
NB $9   **MIB** Sec. Mkt. **$20**

QEO 823-3
COLLECTOR'S PLATE
FIRST IN SERIES, Porcelain, 3" dia. Caption: "Gathering Sunny Memories 1994."
Artist: LaDene Votruba.
☐ Purchased 19___ Pd $ _____
MIB   NB   DB   BNT
☐ Want   Orig. Retail $7.75
NB $15   **MIB** Sec. Mkt. **$32**

QEO 816-6
COLORFUL SPRING
3" tall. Caption: "Crayola® Crayon 1994" Was very popular.
Artist: Ken Crow
☐ Purchased 19___ Pd $ _____
MIB   NB   DB   BNT
☐ Want   Orig. Retail $7.75
NB $13   **MIB** Sec. Mkt. **$29**

QEO 815-6
DAUGHTER
2" tall, Dated 1994.
Artist: Patricia Andrews.
Girl bunny in yellow dress.
☐ Purchased 19___ Pd $ _____
MIB   NB   DB   BNT
☐ Want **NB** $25 Orig. Retail $5.75
NB $8   **MIB** Sec. Mkt. **$15**

QEO 818-3
DIVINE DUET
2" tall. Caption: "Easter Hymns."
Artist: LaDene Votruba
☐ Purchased 19___ Pd $ _____
MIB   NB   DB   BNT
☐ Want   Orig. Retail $6.75
NB $7   **MIB** Sec. Mkt. **$17**

QEO 819-3
EASTER ART SHOW
2-1/4" tall, Dated 1994. Stringer Ornament, hangs from two branches. **Artist:** LaDene Votruba
☐ Purchased 19___ Pd $ _____
MIB   NB   DB   BNT
☐ Want   Orig. Retail $7.75
NB $12   **MIB** Sec. Mkt. **$18**

QEO 813-6
EASTER PARADE
Third and Final in Series, 1-1/4" tall, Dated 1994.
Artist: Dill Rhodus
☐ Purchased 19___ Pd $ _____
MIB   NB   DB   BNT
☐ Want   Orig. Retail $6.75
NB $7   **MIB** Sec. Mkt. **$20**

QEO 813-3
EGGS IN SPORTS
Third and Final in Series, 2" tall. Final? Too bad-a great series. Caption: "Golf Club 94."
Artist: Bob Siedler
☐ Purchased 19___ Pd $ _____
MIB   NB   DB   BNT
☐ Want   Orig. Retail $6.75
NB $7   **MIB** Sec. Mkt. **$20**

QXC 484-6
FIRST HELLO
Dated 1994.
☐ Purchased 19___ Pd $ _____
MIB   NB   DB   BNT
☐ Want   Orig. Retail Free gift to a member who enrolled a new club member using a special gift application.   **MIB** Sec. Mkt. **N.E.**

QEO 809-3
HERE COMES EASTER
FIRST IN SERIES, 1-3/4" tall.
Caption: "Hop-N-Go 1994."
Artist: Ken Crow
☐ Purchased 19___ Pd $ _____
MIB   NB   DB   BNT
☐ Want   Orig. Retail $7.75
NB $15   **MIB** Sec. Mkt. **$30**

QEO 820-6
JOYFUL LAMB
1-3/4" tall. **Artist:** Duane Unruh
☐ Purchased 19___ Pd $ _____
MIB   NB   DB   BNT
☐ Want   Orig. Retail $5.75
NB $6   **MIB** Sec. Mkt. **$15**

QEO 817-6
PEANUTS®
2-1/4" tall, Caption: "Easter Beagle 1994." Was the hottest Easter ornament for 1994.
Artist: Duane Unruh
☐ Purchased 19___ Pd $ _____
MIB   NB   DB   BNT
☐ Want   Orig. Retail $7.75
NB $36   **MIB** Sec. Mkt. **$50**

QEO 820-3
PEEPING OUT
1-1/4" tall. **Artist:** Duane Unruh
☐ Purchased 19___ Pd $ _____
MIB   NB   DB   BNT
☐ Want   Orig. Retail $6.75
NB $7   **MIB** Sec. Mkt. **$15**

QEO 821-3
RIDING A BREEZE
2-1/2" tall. Caption: "Happy
Spring '94." **Artist:** Don Palmiter
☐ Purchased 19___ Pd $ _____
MIB   NB   DB   BNT
☐ Want   Orig. Retail $5.75
NB $6   **MIB** Sec. Mkt. **$15**

QEO 816-3
SON
2" tall, Dated 1994.
Artist: Patricia Andrews
☐ Purchased 19___ Pd $ _____
MIB   NB   DB   BNT
☐ Want   Orig. Retail $5.75
NB $6   **MIB** Sec. Mkt. **$15**

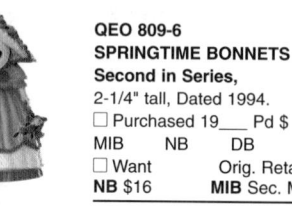

QEO 809-6
SPRINGTIME BONNETS
Second in Series,
2-1/4" tall, Dated 1994.
☐ Purchased 19___ Pd $ _____
MIB   NB   DB   BNT
☐ Want   Orig. Retail $7.75
NB $16   **MIB** Sec. Mkt. **$25**

QEO 813-6
SUNNY BUNNY GARDEN
1-1/4" tall, Set of Three. Caption:
"Teeny Tiny Daisies 1994."
Artist: Ed Seale
☐ Purchased 19___ Pd $ _____
MIB   NB   DB   BNT
☐ Want   Orig. Retail $15.00
NB $15   **MIB** Sec. Mkt. **$30**

QEO 808-6
SWEET AS SUGAR
2-3/4" tall, Dated 1994.
Artist: Anita Marra Rogers
☐ Purchased 19___ Pd $ _____
MIB   NB   DB   BNT
☐ Want   Orig. Retail $8.75
NB $9   **MIB** Sec. Mkt. **$20**

QEO 819-6
SWEET EASTER WISHES
Tender Touches, 2" tall. Caption:
"94 EB." Popular one.
☐ Purchased 19___ Pd $ _____
MIB   NB   DB   BNT
☐ Want   Orig. Retail $8.75
NB $15   **MIB** Sec. Mkt. **$25**

QXC 825-6
**TILLING TIME: CLUB
EXCLUSIVE**
Was also a "Membership" Club
Gift in 1994 that some received
instead of "First Hello."
☐ Purchased 19___ Pd $ _____
MIB   NB   DB   BNT
☐ Want   Orig. Retail $8.75
NB $35   **MIB** Sec. Mkt. **$60**

QEO 818-6
TREETOP COTTAGE
2" tall, Dated 1994.
Artist: Linda Sickman
☐ Purchased 19___ Pd $ _____
MIB   NB   DB   BNT
☐ Want   Orig. Retail $9.75
NB $11   **MIB** Sec. Mkt. **$20**

QEO 814-3
YUMMY RECIPE
2-1/4" tall. Caption: "Anita '94."
Recipe for carrot cake in box.
Artist: Anita Marra Rogers
☐ Purchased 19___ Pd $ _____
MIB   NB   DB   BNT
☐ Want   Orig. Retail $7.75
NB $8   **MIB** Sec. Mkt. **$22**

The Obstacle In Our Path

In ancient times, a king had a boulder placed on a roadway. Then he hid himself and watched to see if anyone would remove the huge rock.

Some of the king's wealthiest merchants and courtiers came by and simply walked around it. Many loudly blamed the king for not keeping the roads clear, but none did anything about getting the big stone out of the way.

Then a peasant came along carrying a load of vegetables. On approaching the boulder, the peasant laid down his burden and tried to move the stone to the side of the road. After much pushing and straining, he finally succeeded. As the peasant picked up his load of vegetables, he noticed a purse lying in the road where the boulder had been.

The purse contained many gold coins and a note from the king indicating that the gold was for the person who removed the boulder from the roadway.

The peasant learned what many others never understand: Every obstacle presents an opportunity to improve one's condition.

1995 Collection

QXC 416-7   1958 FORD EDSEL CITATION KEEPSAKE: ☐
CLUB CONVERTIBLE

Comments: Handcrafted, 2-3/8" tall, Dated 1995.
Complements the Classic American Car Series. Price could go
to $100 easily if not "stockpiled" by Club Members. Will indeed
be a good money maker for the wise investor.
Artist: Don Palmiter
☐ Purchased 19 __Pd $____MIB   NB   DB   BNT
☐ Want   Orig. Ret. $12.95 **NB** $55   **MIB** Sec. Mkt. **$75**

QX 592-9   ACORN 500 ☐
Comments: Handcrafted, 1-7/8" tall, Dated 1995.
A speedy chipmunk pulls into the winner's circle in his bright
red race car, waving the victory flag. Caption: " '95 Good
Cheer." **Artist:** Bob Siedler
☐ Purchased 19 __Pd $____MIB   NB   DB   BNT
☐ Want   Orig. Ret. $10.95 **NB** $12   **MIB** Sec. Mkt. **$20**

QX 584-7   ACROSS THE MILES ☐
Comments: Handcrafted, 2-1/8", Dated 1995.
"How many miles will I travel tonight?" wonders Santa chip-
munk. The compass arrow on this clip-on ornament moves.
Caption: "Across the Miles." **Artist:** John Francis (Collin)
☐ Purchased 19 __Pd $____MIB   NB   DB   BNT
☐ Want   Orig. Ret. $8.95 **NB** $10   **MIB** Sec. Mkt. **$20**

QX 597-7   AIR EXPRESS ☐
Comments: Handcrafted, 1-5/16" tall, Dated 1995.
Flying through the skies, this chipmunk makes sure Santa's
letters get to him on time. Caption: "Air Express."
Artist: Ed Seale
☐ Purchased 19 __Pd $____MIB   NB   DB   BNT
☐ Want   Orig. Ret. $7.95 **NB** $10   **MIB** Sec. Mkt. **$18**

QX 552-7   ALL-AMERICAN TRUCKS: ☐
1956 FORD TRUCK
Comments: **FIRST IN SERIES.** Handcrafted, 1-3/4" tall,
Dated 1995. Celebrate Christmas with a tree and a shiny new
Ford truck. Wheels turn. **Artist:** Don Palmiter
☐ Purchased 19 __Pd $____MIB   NB   DB   BNT
☐ Want   Orig. Ret. $13.95 **NB** $25   **MIB** Sec. Mkt. **$32**

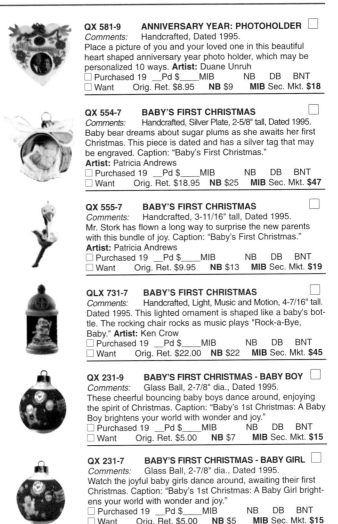

QX 581-9   ANNIVERSARY YEAR: PHOTOHOLDER ☐
Comments: Handcrafted, Dated 1995.
Place a picture of you and your loved one in this beautiful
heart shaped anniversary year photo holder, which may be
personalized 10 ways. **Artist:** Duane Unruh
☐ Purchased 19 __Pd $____MIB   NB   DB   BNT
☐ Want   Orig. Ret. $8.95 **NB** $9   **MIB** Sec. Mkt. **$18**

QX 554-7   BABY'S FIRST CHRISTMAS ☐
Comments: Handcrafted, Silver Plate, 2-5/8" tall, Dated 1995.
Baby bear dreams about sugar plums as she awaits her first
Christmas. This piece is dated and has a silver tag that may
be engraved. Caption: "Baby's First Christmas."
Artist: Patricia Andrews
☐ Purchased 19 __Pd $____MIB   NB   DB   BNT
☐ Want   Orig. Ret. $18.95 **NB** $25   **MIB** Sec. Mkt. **$47**

QX 555-7   BABY'S FIRST CHRISTMAS ☐
Comments: Handcrafted, 3-11/16" tall, Dated 1995.
Mr. Stork has flown a long way to surprise the new parents
with this bundle of joy. Caption: "Baby's First Christmas."
Artist: Patricia Andrews
☐ Purchased 19 __Pd $____MIB   NB   DB   BNT
☐ Want   Orig. Ret. $9.95 **NB** $13   **MIB** Sec. Mkt. **$19**

QLX 731-7   BABY'S FIRST CHRISTMAS ☐
Comments: Handcrafted, Light, Music and Motion, 4-7/16" tall.
Dated 1995. This lighted ornament is shaped like a baby's bot-
tle. The rocking chair rocks as music plays "Rock-a-Bye,
Baby." **Artist:** Ken Crow
☐ Purchased 19 __Pd $____MIB   NB   DB   BNT
☐ Want   Orig. Ret. $22.00 **NB** $22   **MIB** Sec. Mkt. **$45**

QX 231-9   BABY'S FIRST CHRISTMAS - BABY BOY ☐
Comments: Glass Ball, 2-7/8" dia., Dated 1995.
These cheerful bouncing baby boys dance around, enjoying
the spirit of Christmas. Caption: "Baby's 1st Christmas: A Baby
Boy brightens your world with wonder and joy."
☐ Purchased 19 __Pd $____MIB   NB   DB   BNT
☐ Want   Orig. Ret. $5.00 **NB** $7   **MIB** Sec. Mkt. **$15**

QX 231-7   BABY'S FIRST CHRISTMAS - BABY GIRL ☐
Comments: Glass Ball, 2-7/8" dia., Dated 1995.
Watch the joyful baby girls dance around, awaiting their first
Christmas. Caption: "Baby's 1st Christmas: A Baby Girl bright-
ens your world with wonder and joy."
☐ Purchased 19 __Pd $____MIB   NB   DB   BNT
☐ Want   Orig. Ret. $5.00 **NB** $5   **MIB** Sec. Mkt. **$15**

QX 554-9   BABY'S FIRST CHRISTMAS: ☐
　　　　　　PHOTOHOLDER
Comments:　　Handcrafted, 4-7/16" tall, Dated 1995.
Place your baby's first Christmas picture in this baby block
photoholder. Caption: "Baby's First Christmas."
Artist: LaDene Votruba
☐ Purchased 19 __Pd $____MIB　　　NB　　DB　　BNT
☐ Want　　　Orig. Ret. $7.95　**NB** $8　　**MIB** Sec. Mkt. **$18**

QX 555-9   BABY'S FIRST CHRISTMAS: ☐
　　　　　　TEDDY BEAR YEARS COLLECTION
Comments:　　Handcrafted, 2-3/16" tall, Dated 1995.
Baby celebrates its first Christmas with a stocking and star-
shaped Christmas cookie. Design is repeated from 1994.
Caption: "Baby's 1st Christmas." **Artist:** Ken Crow
☐ Purchased 19 __Pd $____MIB　　　NB　　DB　　BNT
☐ Want　　　Orig. Ret. $7.95　**NB** $15　　**MIB** Sec. Mkt. **$21**

QX 556-7   BABY'S SECOND CHRISTMAS: ☐
　　　　　　TEDDY BEAR YEARS COLLECTION
Comments:　　Handcrafted, 2-3/8" tall, Dated 1995.
Teddy wears a red and white bow tie and holds a Christmas
stocking with a tree-shaped cookie. Caption: "Baby's 2nd
Christmas." Design is repeated from '94. **Artist:** Ken Crow
☐ Purchased 19 __Pd $____MIB　　　NB　　DB　　BNT
☐ Want　　　Orig. Ret. $7.95　**NB** $10　　**MIB** Sec. Mkt. **$23**

QXC 539-7   BARBIE™: BRUNETTE DEBUT-1959 ☐
　　　　　　KEEPSAKE CLUB
Comments:　　Handcrafted, Dated 1995.
This brunette beauty dresses for summer in her black and white
bathing suit. Wasn't the most popular Barbie ornament.
Artist: Patricia Andrews
☐ Purchased 19 __Pd $____MIB　　　NB　　DB　　BNT
☐ Want　　　Orig. Ret. $14.95　**NB** $55　　**MIB** Sec. Mkt. **$75**

QXI 504-9   BARBIE™: SOLO IN THE SPOTLIGHT ☐
Comments:　　**Second in Series.** Handcrafted, 4-3/8" tall,
Dated. 1995. Barbie sings the wonderful sounds of Christmas
in her strapless black sequin mermaid dress. Caption: "Solo in
the Spotlight 1995 Edition." **Artist:** Patricia Andrews
☐ Purchased 19 __Pd $____MIB　　　NB　　DB　　BNT
☐ Want　　　Orig. Ret. $14.95　**NB** $23　　**MIB** Sec. Mkt. **$30**

QX 518-9   BARREL-BACK RIDER ☐
Comments:　　Handcrafted, 2-5/16" tall, Dated 1995.
Cowboy bear is ready for the rodeo!
Artist: John Francis　　(Collin)
☐ Purchased 19 __Pd $____MIB　　　NB　　DB　　BNT
☐ Want　　　Orig. Ret. $9.95　**NB** $11　　**MIB** Sec. Mkt. **$25**

QX 502-9   BASEBALL HEROES: LOU GEHRIG ☐
Comments:　　**Second in Series,** Handcrafted, 3-3/8" dia.,
Dated 1995. Caption: "Lou Gehrig '95, 2,130 Consecutive
Games American League MVP 1927, Batting Triple Crown
1934, .340 Lifetime Batting Average, Elected to Hall of Fame
1939." **Artist:** Dill Rhodus
☐ Purchased 19 __Pd $____MIB　　　NB　　DB　　BNT
☐ Want　　Orig. Ret. $12.95　**NB** $18　　**MIB** Sec. Mkt. **$24**

QX 573-9   BATMOBILE ☐
Comments:　　Handcrafted, 1-1/16" tall, Dated 1995.
Batman and Robin rush off in their Batmobile to rescue
Gotham City. **Artist:** Don Palmiter
☐ Purchased 19 __Pd $____MIB　　　NB　　DB　　BNT
☐ Want　　Orig. Ret. $14.95　**NB** $16　　**MIB** Sec. Mkt. **$28**

QX 541-7   BETTY AND WILMA: THE FLINTSTONES® ☐
Comments:　　Handcrafted, Dated 1995. Betty and Wilma are
headed home from their Christmas shopping spree.
Artist: Dill Rhodus
☐ Purchased 19 __Pd $____MIB　　　NB　　DB　　BNT
☐ Want　　Orig. Ret. $14.95 **NB** $12　　**MIB** Sec. Mkt. **$25**

QX 525-9   BEVERLY AND TEDDY: SPECIAL EDITION ☐
Comments:　　Handcrafted, 2-7/8" tall, Dated 1995.
Beverly and Teddy enjoy the true Christmas spirit. Caption:
"Carols." **Artist:** Duane Unruh
☐ Purchased 19 __Pd $____MIB　　　NB　　DB　　BNT
☐ Want　　Orig. Ret. $21.75 **NB** $13　　**MIB** Sec. Mkt. **$30**

QX 591-9   BINGO BEAR ☐
Comments:　　Handcrafted, 2-3/4" tall, Dated 1995.
Bingo! Mr. Bear wins with the diagonal 1995. Caption: "Bingo."
Artist: LaDene Votruba
☐ Purchased 19 __Pd $____MIB　　　NB　　DB　　BNT
☐ Want　　Orig. Ret. $7.95　**NB** $8　　**MIB** Sec. Mkt. **$19**

QX 587-9   BOBBIN' ALONG ☐
Comments:　　Handcrafted, 2-1/4" tall, Dated 1995.
Bucky beaver takes a nap on a mallard decoy, while hoping to
catch his dinner at the same time. **Artist:** Ken Crow
☐ Purchased 19 __Pd $____MIB　　　NB　　DB　　BNT
☐ Want　　Orig. Ret. $8.95　**NB** $14　　**MIB** Sec. Mkt. **$40**

QX 567-9   BROTHER ☐
Comments:　　Handcrafted, 2-9/16" tall, Dated 1995.
Snowboarding brother is the coolest one around in his brightly
colored shades and scarf. Caption: "Brother."
Artist: Joyce Lyle
☐ Purchased 19 __Pd $____MIB　　　NB　　DB　　BNT
☐ Want　　Orig. Ret. $6.95　**NB** $7　　**MIB** Sec. Mkt. **$14**

QX 509-7   CAT NAPS
Comments: **Second in Series,** Handcrafted, 1-9/16" tall.
Dated 1995. A fluffy white cat takes a nap on a warm pot hold-
er. Clips on tree branch. **Artist:** Dill Rhodus
☐ Purchased 19 __Pd $____MIB   NB   DB   BNT
☐ Want   Orig. Ret. $7.95   **NB** $14   **MIB** Sec. Mkt. **$30**

QX 589-9   CATCH THE SPIRIT
Comments: Handcrafted, 2-5/8" tall, Dated 1995.
An enthused baseball fan is ready to enjoy the game with his
popcorn and hot dog. Caption: "Wilson®." **Artist:** Bob Siedler
☐ Purchased 19 __Pd $____MIB   NB   DB   BNT
☐ Want   Orig. Ret. $7.95   **NB** $8   **MIB** Sec. Mkt. **$20**

QX 507-7   CELEBRATION OF ANGELS
Comments: **FIRST IN SERIES,** Handcrafted, 4-3/4" tall,
Dated 1995. Seemed to be more available than most first edi-
tions during late buying season. Not as sought after a first edi-
tion as some. **Artist:** Patricia Andrews
☐ Purchased 19 __Pd $____MIB   NB   DB   BNT
☐ Want   Orig. Ret. $12.95   **NB** $15   **MIB** Sec. Mkt. **$25**

QRP 422-7   CHARLIE BROWN CHRISTMAS:
BASE WITH WOODSTOCK AND TREE
Comments: Handcrafted. This display base features
Woodstock perched on a branch of the Christmas tree with
one red ornament on it. Peanuts®.
☐ Purchased 19 __Pd $____MIB   NB   DB   BNT
☐ Want   Orig. Ret. $3.95   **NB** $9   **MIB** Sec. Mkt. **$18**

QRP 420-9   CHARLIE BROWN CHRISTMAS: LUCY
Comments: Handcrafted. Lucy is wearing a red stocking hat
and holds a candy cane in her hand for the tree. Peanuts®.
☐ Purchased 19 __Pd $____MIB   NB   DB   BNT
☐ Want   Orig. Ret. $3.95   **NB** $11   **MIB** Sec. Mkt. **$18**

QRP 421-7   CHARLIE BROWN CHRISTMAS: LINUS
Comments: Handcrafted. Peanuts®.
☐ Purchased 19 __Pd $____MIB   NB   DB   BNT
☐ Want   Orig. Ret. $3.95   **NB** $15   **MIB** Sec. Mkt. **$20**

QRP 420-7   CHARLIE BROWN CHRISTMAS:
CHARLIE BROWN
Comments: Handcrafted. Charlie Brown is ringing in the
Christmas spirit with his bell. Peanuts®.
☐ Purchased 19 __Pd $____MIB   NB   DB   BNT
☐ Want   Orig. Ret. $3.95   **NB** $11   **MIB** Sec. Mkt. **$23**

QRP 421-9   CHARLIE BROWN CHRISTMAS: SNOOPY
Comments: Handcrafted. Snoopy is joining in the gang with
his black top hat. Peanuts®.
☐ Purchased 19 __Pd $____MIB   NB   DB   BNT
☐ Want   Orig. Ret. $3.95   **NB** $11   **MIB** Sec. Mkt. **$22**

QX 563-7   CHILD'S FIFTH CHRISTMAS:
TEDDY BEAR YEARS COLLECTION
Comments: Handcrafted, 2-3/8" tall, Dated 1995.
Any five year old will love this special ornament. Design is
repeated from '89. **Artist:** Dill Rhodus
☐ Purchased 19 __Pd $____MIB   NB   DB   BNT
☐ Want   Orig. Ret. $6.95   **NB** $9   **MIB** Sec. Mkt. **$17**

QX 562-9   CHILD'S FOURTH CHRISTMAS:
TEDDY BEAR YEARS COLLECTION
Comments: Handcrafted, 3" tall, Dated 1995.
This toddler teddy smiles cheerfully as he holds a red, green
and white numeral 4. Caption: "My 4th Christmas." Design is
repeated from '89. **Artist:** John Francis (Collin)
☐ Purchased 19 __Pd $____MIB   NB   DB   BNT
☐ Want   Orig. Ret. $6.95   **NB** $10   **MIB** Sec. Mkt. **$19**

QX 596-7   CHRISTMAS FEVER
Comments: Handcrafted, 2-1/16" tall, Dated 1995.
If you have Christmas fever, this li'l "Angel of Mercy" can help
you out! **Artist:** Nina Aube
☐ Purchased 19 __Pd $____MIB   NB   DB   BNT
☐ Want   Orig. Ret. $7.95   **NB** $10   **MIB** Sec. Mkt. **$20**

Love is a game two can play and both can win.

QX 562-7 CHILD'S THIRD CHRISTMAS: TEDDY BEAR YEARS COLLECTION

Comments: Handcrafted, 2-9/16" tall, Dated 1995.
Teddy holds onto his stocking filled with a frosted bell shaped cookie with the numeral 3 written on it. Caption: "My 3rd Christmas." **Artist:** Ken Crow

☐ Purchased 19 __Pd $____MIB   NB   DB   BNT
☐ Want   Orig. Ret. $7.95   **NB** $10   **MIB** Sec. Mkt. **$20**

QLX 730-7 CHRIS MOUSE TREE

Comments: **Eleventh in Series,** Lighted, Handcrafted, 3-5/8" tall, Dated 1995. Chris Mouse climbs to the top of his cheese tree to put his gold star on top. The tree glows.
Artist: Anita Marra Rogers

☐ Purchased 19 __Pd $____MIB   NB   DB   BNT
☐ Want   Orig. Ret. $12.50   **NB** $25   **MIB** Sec. Mkt. **$30**

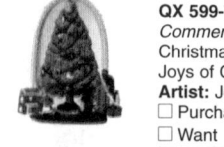

QX 599-7 CHRISTMAS MORNING

Comments: Handcrafted, 3-5/16" tall, Dated 1995. Christmas morning just before the rush! Caption: "How Bright Joys of Christmas, How Warm the Memories."
Artist: John Francis

☐ Purchased 19 __Pd $____MIB   NB   DB   BNT
☐ Want   Orig. Ret. $10.95   **NB** $12   **MIB** Sec. Mkt. **$18**

QX 595-9 CHRISTMAS PATROL

Comments: Handcrafted, 2-1/8" tall, Dated 1995.
Do you have the Christmas blues? This little car won't let you; he'll pull you over and ticket you for being a scrooge.
Artist: Patricia Andrews

☐ Purchased 19 __Pd $____MIB   NB   DB   BNT
☐ Want   Orig. Ret. $7.95   **NB** $9   **MIB** Sec. Mkt. **$18**

QX 508-7 CHRISTMAS VISITORS: ST. NICHOLAS

Comments: **FIRST IN SERIES,** Handcrafted, 4-9/16" tall, Dated 1995. St. Nicholas was well known and loved in the 4th century for his kindness and love for children. His staff is brass with a satin brushed finish. **Artist:** Anita Marra Rogers

☐ Purchased 19 __Pd $____MIB   NB   DB   BNT
☐ Want   Orig. Ret. $14.95   **NB** $25   **MIB** Sec. Mkt. **$30**

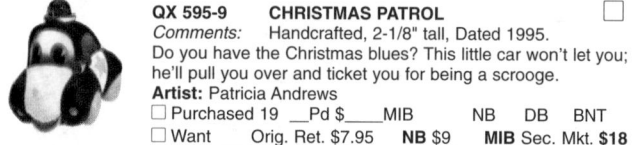

QX 523-9 CLASSIC AMERICAN CARS: 1969 CHEVROLET CAMARO

Comments: **Fifth in Series,** Handcrafted, 1-5/16" tall, Dated 1995. This classic American car races down the street to get home before anyone wakes up on Christmas morning. The wheels really turn! **Artist:** Don Palmiter

☐ Purchased 19 __Pd $____MIB   NB   DB   BNT
☐ Want   Orig. Ret. $12.95   **NB** $19   **MIB** Sec. Mkt. **$24**

QX 551-9 COLORFUL WORLD: CRAYOLA®

Comments: Handcrafted, 3-3/16" tall, Dated 1995.
Multi-Cultural mouse draws his friends with all the colors of the world. Captions: "Crayola® Multi-Cultural 16 Crayons" (front of box), "16 Crayola® Crayons" (side of box), "1995" (back of box). **Artist:** Ken Crow

☐ Purchased 19 __Pd $____MIB   NB   DB   BNT
☐ Want   Orig. Ret. $10.95   **NB** $15   **MIB** Sec. Mkt. **$25**

QXC 411-7 COLLECTING MEMORIES: KEEPSAKE CLUB

Comments: Handcrafted, Dated 1995. Mr. Beaver enjoys displaying his favorite Keepsake Ornaments in a wooden display. **Artist:** Bob Siedler

☐ Purchased 19 __Pd $____MIB   NB   DB   BNT
☐ Want   Membership Fee $20 **NB** $10 **MIB** Sec. Mkt. **$15**

QLX 736-9 COMING TO SEE SANTA

Comments: Handcrafted, Light, Motion and Voice, 3-11/16" tall, Dated 1995. Santa says "Ho! Ho! Ho!" when the children come to see him. **Artist:** Don Palmiter

☐ Purchased 19 __Pd $____MIB   NB   DB   BNT
☐ Want   Orig. Ret. $32.00   **NB** $32   **MIB** Sec. Mkt. **$65**

QX 599-9 COWS OF BALI

Comments: Handcrafted, 3" tall, Dated 1995.
Santa's helper cow is ready for an island Christmas celebration in his grass skirt and Christmas tree bikini top. Designed from Shoebox Greetings. **Artist:** Patricia Andrews

☐ Purchased 19 __Pd $____MIB   NB   DB   BNT
☐ Want   Orig. Ret. $8.95   **NB** $12   **MIB** Sec. Mkt. **$19**

QX 524-7 CRAYOLA® CRAYON: BRIGHT 'N SUNNY TEPEE

Comments: **Seventh in Series,** Handcrafted, 2-11/16" tall, Dated 1995. A little Indian bear peeks out the door of his tepee to give everyone a colorful Christmas hello. Caption: "1995 Crayola® Crayons." **Artist:** Patricia Andrews

☐ Purchased 19 __Pd $____MIB   NB   DB   BNT
☐ Want   Orig. Ret. $10.95   **NB** $15   **MIB** Sec. Mkt. **$19**

QX 564-9 DAD

Comments: Handcrafted, Dated 1995. Dad is ready for Christmas as he pulls the family Christmas tree behind him.
Artist: Bob Siedler

☐ Purchased 19 __Pd $____MIB   NB   DB   BNT
☐ Want   Orig. Ret. $7.95   **NB** $8   **MIB** Sec. Mkt. **$18**

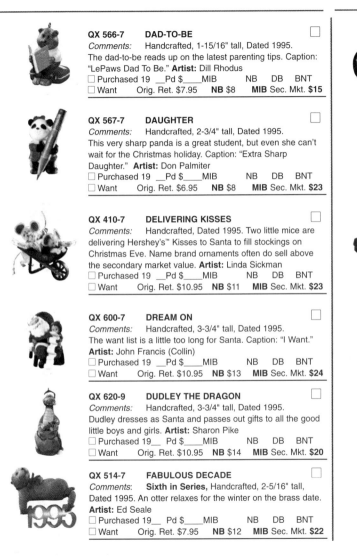

QX 566-7   DAD-TO-BE   ☐
Comments: Handcrafted, 1-15/16" tall, Dated 1995.
The dad-to-be reads up on the latest parenting tips. Caption:
"LePaws Dad To Be." **Artist:** Dill Rhodus
☐ Purchased 19 __Pd $____MIB   NB   DB   BNT
☐ Want   Orig. Ret. $7.95   **NB** $8   **MIB** Sec. Mkt. **$15**

QX 567-7   DAUGHTER   ☐
Comments: Handcrafted, 2-3/4" tall, Dated 1995.
This very sharp panda is a great student, but even she can't
wait for the Christmas holiday. Caption: "Extra Sharp
Daughter." **Artist:** Don Palmiter
☐ Purchased 19 __Pd $____MIB   NB   DB   BNT
☐ Want   Orig. Ret. $6.95   **NB** $8   **MIB** Sec. Mkt. **$23**

QX 410-7   DELIVERING KISSES   ☐
Comments: Handcrafted, Dated 1995. Two little mice are
delivering Hershey's™ Kisses to Santa to fill stockings on
Christmas Eve. Name brand ornaments often do sell above
the secondary market value. **Artist:** Linda Sickman
☐ Purchased 19 __Pd $____MIB   NB   DB   BNT
☐ Want   Orig. Ret. $10.95   **NB** $11   **MIB** Sec. Mkt. **$23**

QX 600-7   DREAM ON   ☐
Comments: Handcrafted, 3-3/4" tall, Dated 1995.
The want list is a little too long for Santa. Caption: "I Want."
Artist: John Francis (Collin)
☐ Purchased 19 __Pd $____MIB   NB   DB   BNT
☐ Want   Orig. Ret. $10.95   **NB** $13   **MIB** Sec. Mkt. **$24**

QX 620-9   DUDLEY THE DRAGON   ☐
Comments: Handcrafted, 3-3/4" tall, Dated 1995.
Dudley dresses as Santa and passes out gifts to all the good
little boys and girls. **Artist:** Sharon Pike
☐ Purchased 19__ Pd $____MIB   NB   DB   BNT
☐ Want   Orig. Ret. $10.95   **NB** $14   **MIB** Sec. Mkt. **$20**

QX 514-7   FABULOUS DECADE   ☐
Comments: **Sixth in Series,** Handcrafted, 2-5/16" tall,
Dated 1995. An otter relaxes for the winter on the brass date.
Artist: Ed Seale
☐ Purchased 19__ Pd $____MIB   NB   DB   BNT
☐ Want   Orig. Ret. $7.95   **NB** $12   **MIB** Sec. Mkt. **$22**

QX 589-7   FAITHFUL FAN   ☐
Comments: Handcrafted, 2-9/16" tall, Dated 1995.
This spirited beaver is cheering for his favorite team, The
Snowflakes. Caption: "Go Team." **Artist:** Bob Siedler
☐ Purchased 19__ Pd $____MIB   NB   DB   BNT
☐ Want   Orig. Ret. $8.95   **NB** $9   **MIB** Sec. Mkt. **$19**

QX 586-9   FELIZ NAVIDAD   ☐
Comments: Handcrafted, 3-1/16" tall, Dated 1995.
A mouse sends warm holiday wishes from inside his bunch of
hot peppers. Caption: "Feliz Navidad." **Artist:** Dill Rhodus
☐ Purchased 19__ Pd $____MIB   NB   DB   BNT
☐ Want   Orig. Ret. $7.95   **NB** $11   **MIB** Sec. Mkt. **$20**

QXC 520-7   FISHING FOR FUN: KEEPSAKE CLUB   ☐
Comments: Handcrafted, Dated 1995. Santa enjoys fishing
with one of his reindeer when he is not busy delivering pres-
ents. The Collectors' Club has "Arctic" misspelled on many of
the ornaments as "Artic."
Artist: Ed Seale
☐ Purchased 19__ Pd $____MIB   NB   DB   BNT
☐ Want   Club Fee $20   **NB** $15   **MIB** Sec. Mkt. **$20**

QXI 620-7   FOOTBALL LEGENDS: JOE MONTANA   ☐
Comments: Handcrafted, 4-7/16" tall, Dated 1995.
The 1995 Joe Montana ornament in the **Kansas City** red,
white and yellow uniform was added to the Keepsake line in
direct response to consumer demand. (He played for two
teams.) The secondary market price reflects sports enthusiasts' demands for this piece. This piece was more limited than
Montana in San Francisco uniform. Caption: **"Montana 19"**
(back of shirt) **"19"** (front of shirt and on sleeve). Box is red
with "Kansas City" written on it. **Artist:** Dill Rhodus
☐ Purchased 19__ Pd $____MIB   NB   DB   BNT
☐ Want   Orig. Ret. $14.95   **NB** $75   **MIB** Sec. Mkt. **$120**

QXI 575-9   FOOTBALL LEGENDS: JOE MONTANA   ☐
Comments: **FIRST IN SERIES,** Handcrafted, 4-7/16" tall,
Dated 1995. Joe Montana in the **San Francisco 49ers** red
and white uniform. There are only 45 seconds in the last quarter and Joe Montana pulls back his arm and fires the winning
touchdown! Box is white with the words "San Francisco" written on it. Caption: **"Montana 16"** (back of shirt) **"16"** (front of
shirt and on sleeve). **Artist:** Dill Rhodus
☐ Purchased 19__ Pd $____MIB   NB   DB   BNT
☐ Want   Orig. Ret. $14.95   **NB** $25   **MIB** Sec. Mkt. **$50**

QX 572-9   FOR MY GRANDMA: PHOTOHOLDER ☐
Comments: Handcrafted, 4-1/6" tall, Dated 1995.
Keep that special picture of you and your grandma in this
frosted gingerbread house picture frame. Caption: "For My
Grandma, I Love You! From _____." **Artist:** Don Palmiter
☐ Purchased 19__ Pd $____MIB   NB   DB   BNT
☐ Want   Orig. Ret. $6.95   **NB** $7   **MIB** Sec. Mkt. **$15**

QLX 729-9   FOREST FROLICS ☐
Comments: **Seventh and Final in Series,** Handcrafted,
Motion. 4-1/8" tall, Dated 1995. The forest animals enjoy
swinging back and forth on their wooden swing. Caption:
"1995 Merry Christmas." **Artist:** Sharon Pike
☐ Purchased 19__ Pd $____MIB   NB   DB   BNT
☐ Want   Orig. Ret. $28.00   **NB** $30   **MIB** Sec. Mkt. **$46**

QX 525-8   FOREVER FRIENDS BEAR ☐
Comments: Handcrafted, 2-3/8" tall, Dated 1995.
Give your special friend a bear they will always remember you
by. This bear has holly berries to share with his friends. **Artist:**
Andrew Brownsword
☐ Purchased 19__ Pd $____MIB   NB   DB   BNT
☐ Want   Orig. Ret. $8.95   **NB** $15   **MIB** Sec. Mkt. **$25**

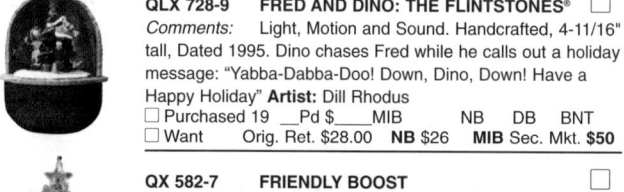

QLX 728-9   FRED AND DINO: THE FLINTSTONES® ☐
Comments: Light, Motion and Sound. Handcrafted, 4-11/16"
tall, Dated 1995. Dino chases Fred while he calls out a holiday
message: "Yabba-Dabba-Doo! Down, Dino, Down! Have a
Happy Holiday" **Artist:** Dill Rhodus
☐ Purchased 19__ Pd $____MIB   NB   DB   BNT
☐ Want   Orig. Ret. $28.00   **NB** $26   **MIB** Sec. Mkt. **$50**

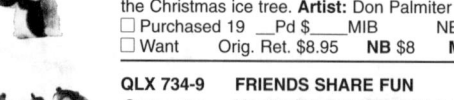

QX 582-7   FRIENDLY BOOST ☐
Comments: Handcrafted and Acrylic, 3-3/16" tall, Dated 1995.
A little penguin gets help from his buddy putting the star atop
the Christmas ice tree. **Artist:** Don Palmiter
☐ Purchased 19__ Pd $____MIB   NB   DB   BNT
☐ Want   Orig. Ret. $8.95   **NB** $8   **MIB** Sec. Mkt. **$24**

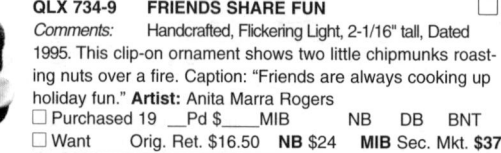

QLX 734-9   FRIENDS SHARE FUN ☐
Comments: Handcrafted, Flickering Light, 2-1/16" tall, Dated
1995. This clip-on ornament shows two little chipmunks roast-
ing nuts over a fire. Caption: "Friends are always cooking up
holiday fun." **Artist:** Anita Marra Rogers
☐ Purchased 19__ Pd $____MIB   NB   DB   BNT
☐ Want   Orig. Ret. $16.50   **NB** $24   **MIB** Sec. Mkt. **$37**

QX 516-9   FROSTY FRIENDS ☐
Comments: **Sixteenth is Series,** Handcrafted, 2-9/16" tall,
Dated 1995. A friendly eskimo takes some presents across the
ice on his snowmobile with a little friend. Caption: "To Santa."
How much longer will this series continue to grow?
Artist: Ed Seale
☐ Purchased 19__ Pd $____MIB   NB   DB   BNT
☐ Want   Orig. Ret. $10.95 **NB** $24   **MIB** Sec. Mkt. **$32**

QX 500-7   GARFIELD® ☐
Comments: Handcrafted, 2-3/16" tall, Dated 1995.
Garfield tries to be a sweet little angel for a minute as he toots
his horn.
☐ Purchased 19__ Pd $____MIB   NB   DB   BNT
☐ Want   Orig. Ret. $10.95   **NB** $12   **MIB** Sec. Mkt. **$25**

QX 570-7   GODCHILD ☐
Comments: Handcrafted, 2-3/16" tall, Dated 1995.
A little bear angel with brass halo plays Christmas music for
his godparents. Caption: "Godchild." **Artist:** Don Palmiter
☐ Purchased 19__ Pd $____MIB   NB   DB   BNT
☐ Want   Orig. Ret. $7.95   **NB** $16   **MIB** Sec. Mkt. **$25**

QX 241-7   GODPARENT ☐
Comments: Glass Ball, 2-7/8" dia., Dated 1995.
Little bear angels watch over their godparent. Caption: "A
Godparent is someone special at Christmas time and always."
Artist: LaDene Votruba
☐ Purchased 19__ Pd $____MIB   NB   DB   BNT
☐ Want   Orig. Ret. $5.00   **NB** $6   **MIB** Sec. Mkt. **$17**

QLX 736-7   GOODY GUMBALLS! ☐
Comments: Handcrafted, Lighted, 2-7/8" tall, Dated 1995.
Two little mice raid the gumball machine. The globe of the
gumball machine glows. **Artist:** Bob Siedler
☐ Purchased 19__ Pd $____MIB   NB   DB   BNT
☐ Want   Orig. Ret. $12.50   **NB** $14   **MIB** Sec. Mkt. **$33**

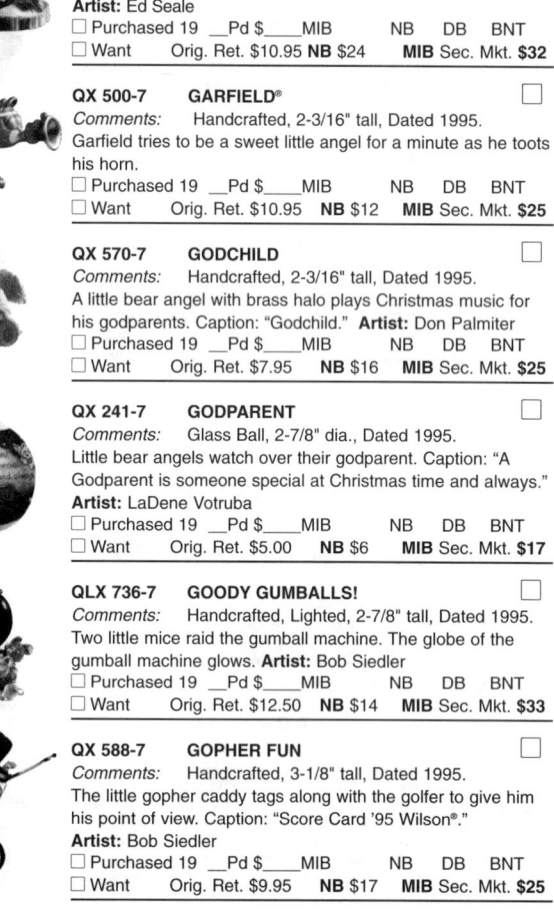

QX 588-7   GOPHER FUN ☐
Comments: Handcrafted, 3-1/8" tall, Dated 1995.
The little gopher caddy tags along with the golfer to give him
his point of view. Caption: "Score Card '95 Wilson®."
Artist: Bob Siedler
☐ Purchased 19__ Pd $____MIB   NB   DB   BNT
☐ Want   Orig. Ret. $9.95   **NB** $17   **MIB** Sec. Mkt. **$25**

QX 577-7   GRANDCHILD'S FIRST CHRISTMAS ☐
Comments: Handcrafted, 1-7/16" tall, Dated 1995.
This grandchild fell fast asleep waiting for Santa to come.
Caption: "Grandchild's 1st Christmas."
Artist: John Francis (Collin)
☐ Purchased 19 __Pd $____MIB   NB   DB   BNT
☐ Want   Orig. Ret. $7.95   **NB** $8   **MIB** Sec. Mkt. **$16**

QX 577-9   GRANDDAUGHTER ☐
Comments: Handcrafted, 2-5/16" tall, Dated 1995.
Little bunny dressed up for the holidays receives a special lol-
lipop from her grandparents. Caption: "Granddaughter-You're
So Sweet." **Artist:** Anita Marra Rogers
☐ Purchased 19 __Pd $____MIB   NB   DB   BNT
☐ Want   Orig. Ret. $6.95   **NB** $12   **MIB** Sec. Mkt. **$20**

QX 576-7   GRANDMOTHER ☐
Comments: Handcrafted, 1-15/16" tall, Dated 1995.
A bluebird on the end of her watering can keeps Grandma
company while watering her flowers. Caption: "For
Grandmother With Love." **Artist:** Patricia Andrews
☐ Purchased 19 __Pd $____MIB   NB   DB   BNT
☐ Want   Orig. Ret. $7.95   **NB** $16   **MIB** Sec. Mkt. **$28**

QX 576-9   GRANDPA ☐
Comments: Handcrafted, 3-1/16" tall, Dated 1995.
Grandpa bear pulls up a tree stump and shares a story with
his grandson over warm cookies and a glass of milk. Caption:
"I ♥ Grandpa." **Artist:** Ken Crow
☐ Purchased 19 __Pd $____MIB   NB   DB   BNT
☐ Want   Orig. Ret. $8.95   **NB** $9   **MIB** Sec. Mkt. **$18**

QX 241-9   GRANDPARENTS ☐
Comments: Glass Ball, 2-7/8" dia., Dated 1995.
The picture perfect scene at Grandma and Grandpa's house
Christmas day is shown on this dated ball. Caption: "Merry
Christmas, Grandparents Fill Our Hearts And Our Lives With
Their Love." **Artist:** Joyce Lyle
☐ Purchased 19 __Pd $____MIB   NB   DB   BNT
☐ Want   Orig. Ret. $5.00   **NB** $8   **MIB** Sec. Mkt. **$12**

QX 578-7   GRANDSON ☐
Comments: Handcrafted, 2-7/16" tall, Dated 1995.
This happy bunny holds a most treasured "treat" given by his
grandparents. Caption: "Grandson – You're a Treat!"
Artist: Anita Marra Rogers
☐ Purchased 19 __Pd $____MIB   NB   DB   BNT
☐ Want   Orig. Ret. $6.95   **NB** $7   **MIB** Sec. Mkt. **$18**

QX 630-7   HAPPY HOLIDAYS: PHOTOHOLDER ☐
Comments: Handcrafted, 3-7/16" tall.
Included with this photo album is a photo of Hallmark's
Keepsake artists, or put your favorite photo inside. A little
mouse swings from a ribbon. Was available at Ornament
Premieres in July. **Artist:** LaDene Votruba
☐ Purchased 19 __Pd $____MIB   NB   DB   BNT
☐ Want Orig. Ret. $2.95 with any purchase
                              NB $4   **MIB** Sec. Mkt. **$10**

QX 603-7   HAPPY WRAPPERS ☐
Comments: Handcrafted, 2-1/8" tall, Dated 1995.
Two little elves each wrap a Christmas gift for Santa.
Artist: Ken Crow
☐ Purchased 19 __Pd $____MIB   NB   DB   BNT
☐ Want   Orig. Ret. $10.95 **NB** $12   **MIB** Sec. Mkt. **$20**

QLX 732-7   HEADIN' HOME ☐
Comments: Blinking Lights, Handcrafted, 1-13/16" tall,
Dated 1995. Santa flies his reindeer home for the holidays in
this red and white airplane. Lights glow on the inside and blink
on the wings. Caption: "Polar Air." **Artist:** Julia Lee
☐ Purchased 19 __Pd $____MIB   NB   DB   BNT
☐ Want   Orig. Ret. $22.00 **NB** $38   **MIB** Sec. Mkt. **$50**

QX 605-7   HEAVEN'S GIFT ☐
Comments: Handcrafted, Joseph 4-9/16" tall, Mary/Baby
2-15/16" tall, Dated 1995. The set of two ornaments rejoice in
Heaven's gift of life to the world. **Artist:** Patricia Andrews
☐ Purchased 19 __Pd $____MIB   NB   DB   BNT
☐ Want   Orig. Ret. $20.00 **NB** $25   **MIB** Sec. Mkt. **$45**

QX 517-9   HERE COMES SANTA: SANTA'S ROADSTER ☐
Comments: **Seventeenth in Series,** Handcrafted, 2-13/16"
tall, Dated 1995. Santa zooms down the highway in his roadster with a Christmas tree for the Elves and Mrs. Claus to decorate. Caption: "KRUZ-N." **Artist:** Linda Sickman
☐ Purchased 19 __Pd $____MIB   NB   DB   BNT
☐ Want   Orig. Ret. $14.95 **NB** $15   **MIB** Sec. Mkt. **$30**

QX 591-7   HOCKEY PUP ☐
Comments: Handcrafted, 3-5/16" tall, Dated 1995.
Tucked into an oversized ice skate, this Christmas dressed
puppy shoots for the winning goal. Caption: "Hockey Pup
1995." **Artist:** Ken Crow
☐ Purchased 19 __Pd $____MIB   NB   DB   BNT
☐ Want   Orig. Ret. $9.95   **NB** $15   **MIB** Sec. Mkt. **$24**

QXI 505-7   HOLIDAY BARBIE™
Comments: **Third in Series,** Handcrafted, Dated 1995.
Barbie is ready for holiday parties in her green and white
Christmas dress. She accents her gown with little silver and
white bulb earrings. Caption: "Holiday Barbie™."
Artist: Patricia Andrews
☐ Purchased 19 __Pd $____MIB   NB   DB   BNT
☐ Want   Orig. Ret. $14.95 **NB** $27   **MIB** Sec. Mkt. **$40**

QLX 731-9   HOLIDAY SWIM
Comments: Lighted, Handcrafted, Acrylic, 3-9/16" tall,
Dated 1995. Delightful aquarium glows while a festive little fish
swims among seaweed decorated with Christmas lights.
Artist: Anita Marra Rogers
☐ Purchased 19 __Pd $____MIB   NB   DB   BNT
☐ Want   Orig. Ret. $18.50 **NB** $18   **MIB** Sec. Mkt. **$40**

QXC 105-9   HOME FROM THE WOODS:
                KEEPSAKE CLUB
Comments: Handcrafted, 2-1/4" tall, Dated 1995.
A little man is on his way home from cutting down his
Christmas tree. Complements the Folk Art Americana
Collection. **Artist:** Linda Sickman
☐ Purchased 19 __Pd $____MIB   NB   DB   BNT
☐ Want   Orig. Ret. $15.95 **NB** $31   **MIB** Sec. Mkt. **$59**

QXI 551-7   HOOP STARS: SHAQUILLE O'NEAL
Comments: **FIRST IN SERIES,** Handcrafted, 5-1/2" tall,
Dated 1995. It's the last possible shot as Shaq slam dunks the
ball for an Orlando Magic win! Caption: "32." With Shaq
changing teams to the Lakers, perhaps this ornament will
become more sought after.
☐ Purchased 19 __Pd $____MIB   NB   DB   BNT
☐ Want   Orig. Ret. $14.95 **NB** $26   **MIB** Sec. Mkt. **$55**

QX 594-7   IMPORTANT MEMO
Comments: Handcrafted, 2-3/16" tall, Dated 1995.
A little mouse is exhausted from the holiday season and takes
a nap under an important memo. Caption: "MEMO, Closed for
the Holidays 1995." **Artist:** Linda Sickman
☐ Purchased 19 __Pd $____MIB   NB   DB   BNT
☐ Want   Orig. Ret. $8.95 **NB** $9   **MIB** Sec. Mkt. **$19**

QX 581-7   IN A HEARTBEAT
Comments: Handcrafted, Dated 1995. With every heart-
beat, these two little mice grow closer together.
Artist: Patricia Andrews
☐ Purchased 19 __Pd $____MIB   NB   DB   BNT
☐ Want   Orig. Ret. $8.95 **NB** $14   **MIB** Sec. Mkt. **$22**

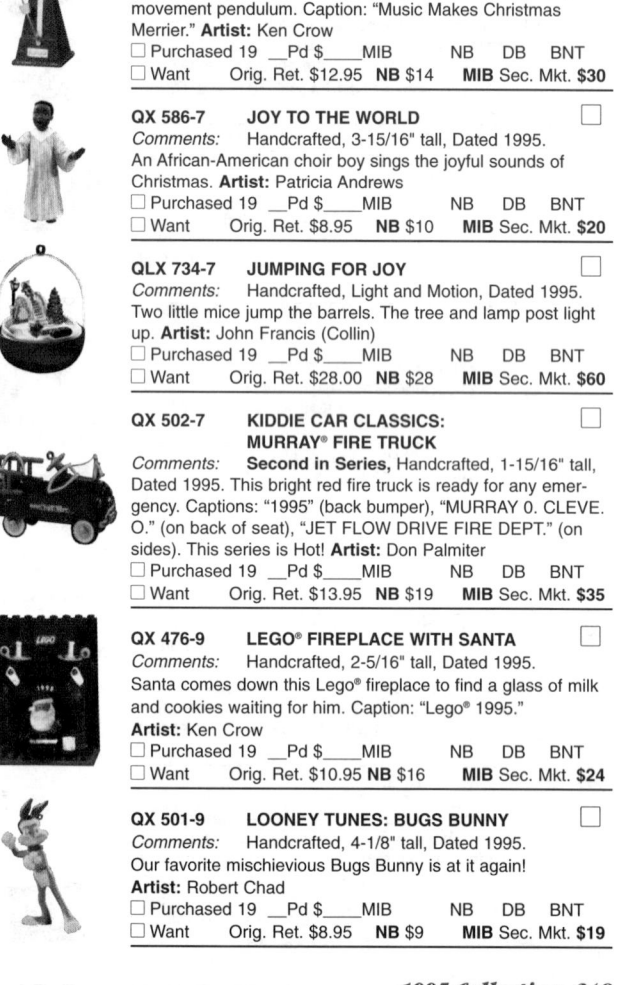

QX 604-9   IN TIME WITH CHRISTMAS
Comments: Handcrafted, 3-3/4" tall, Dated 1995.
It's easy for this little violinist to keep time with the windup
movement pendulum. Caption: "Music Makes Christmas
Merrier." **Artist:** Ken Crow
☐ Purchased 19 __Pd $____MIB   NB   DB   BNT
☐ Want   Orig. Ret. $12.95 **NB** $14   **MIB** Sec. Mkt. **$30**

QX 586-7   JOY TO THE WORLD
Comments: Handcrafted, 3-15/16" tall, Dated 1995.
An African-American choir boy sings the joyful sounds of
Christmas. **Artist:** Patricia Andrews
☐ Purchased 19 __Pd $____MIB   NB   DB   BNT
☐ Want   Orig. Ret. $8.95 **NB** $10   **MIB** Sec. Mkt. **$20**

QLX 734-7   JUMPING FOR JOY
Comments: Handcrafted, Light and Motion, Dated 1995.
Two little mice jump the barrels. The tree and lamp post light
up. **Artist:** John Francis (Collin)
☐ Purchased 19 __Pd $____MIB   NB   DB   BNT
☐ Want   Orig. Ret. $28.00 **NB** $28   **MIB** Sec. Mkt. **$60**

QX 502-7   KIDDIE CAR CLASSICS:
                MURRAY® FIRE TRUCK
Comments: **Second in Series,** Handcrafted, 1-15/16" tall,
Dated 1995. This bright red fire truck is ready for any emer-
gency. Captions: "1995" (back bumper), "MURRAY 0. CLEVE.
O." (on back of seat), "JET FLOW DRIVE FIRE DEPT." (on
sides). This series is Hot! **Artist:** Don Palmiter
☐ Purchased 19 __Pd $____MIB   NB   DB   BNT
☐ Want   Orig. Ret. $13.95 **NB** $19   **MIB** Sec. Mkt. **$35**

QX 476-9   LEGO® FIREPLACE WITH SANTA
Comments: Handcrafted, 2-5/16" tall, Dated 1995.
Santa comes down this Lego® fireplace to find a glass of milk
and cookies waiting for him. Caption: "Lego® 1995."
Artist: Ken Crow
☐ Purchased 19 __Pd $____MIB   NB   DB   BNT
☐ Want   Orig. Ret. $10.95 **NB** $16   **MIB** Sec. Mkt. **$24**

QX 501-9   LOONEY TUNES: BUGS BUNNY
Comments: Handcrafted, 4-1/8" tall, Dated 1995.
Our favorite mischievous Bugs Bunny is at it again!
Artist: Robert Chad
☐ Purchased 19 __Pd $____MIB   NB   DB   BNT
☐ Want   Orig. Ret. $8.95 **NB** $9   **MIB** Sec. Mkt. **$19**

QX 501-7 LOONEY TUNES:
SYLVESTER AND TWEETY
Comments: Handcrafted, Sylvester 4-9/16" tall,
Tweety 1-5/8" tall, Dated 1995. Sylvester still has his eye on a
Tweety for dinner. Set of 2 hang-together ornaments.
Artist: Robert Chad
☐ Purchased 19 __Pd $____MIB   NB   DB   BNT
☐ Want   Orig. Ret. $13.95 **NB** $18   **MIB** Sec. Mkt. **$24**

QX 406-9 LOU RANKIN BEAR
Comments: Handcrafted, 2-5/16" tall, Dated 1995.
This cute and cuddly bear is an ornament that would make
anyone smile. Caption: "Rankin." **Artist:** Bob Siedler
☐ Purchased 19 __Pd $____MIB   NB   DB   BNT
☐ Want   Orig. Ret. $9.95 **NB** $12   **MIB** Sec. Mkt. **$23**

QX 584-9 MAGIC SCHOOL BUS™, THE
Comments: Handcrafted.
Here they go again on another trip – this time to the North
Pole in the holiday decorated Magic School Bus.
Artist: Dill Rhodus
☐ Purchased 19 __Pd $____MIB   NB   DB   BNT
☐ Want   Orig. Ret. $10.95 **NB** $15   **MIB** Sec. Mkt. **$21**

QX 240-9 MARY ENGELBREIT
Comments: Glass Ball, Dated 1995.
This brightly colored ball pictures a jolly Santa ready for the
holiday season. Mary Engelbreit collectibles have been more
evident in different markets recently.
☐ Purchased 19 __Pd $____MIB   NB   DB   BNT
☐ Want   Orig. Ret. $5.00 **NB** $8   **MIB** Sec. Mkt. **$16**

QX 514-9 MARY'S ANGELS: CAMELLIA
Comments: **Eighth in Series,** Handcrafted/Acrylic, 2-5/8" tall.
Oh, to sing like an angel… Camellia sings a duet with a feath-
ered friend perched on her finger. Caption: "Mary."
Artist: Robert Chad
☐ Purchased 19 __Pd $____MIB   NB   DB   BNT
☐ Want   Orig. Ret. $6.95 **NB** $17   **MIB** Sec. Mkt. **$22**

QX 513-9 MERRY OLDE SANTA
Comments: **Sixth in Series,** Handcrafted, 4-5/16" tall,
Dated 1995. Brass bells on a gold cord enhance Santa as he
carries his goodies to children's homes.
Artist: Patricia Andrews
☐ Purchased 19 __Pd $____MIB   NB   DB   BNT
☐ Want   Orig. Ret. $14.95 **NB** $15   **MIB** Sec. Mkt. **$29**

QX 602-7 MERRY RV
Comments: Handcrafted, 2-1/2" tall, Dated 1995.
Santa and Mrs. Claus begin their trip around the country in
their holiday dressed RV on December 27th. (Santa slept all
day on the 26th.) Caption: "The Claus's Merry-We-Go."
Artist: Don Palmiter
☐ Purchased 19 __Pd $____MIB   NB   DB   BNT
☐ Want   Orig. Ret. $12.95 **NB** $15   **MIB** Sec. Mkt. **$30**

QX 564-7 MOM
Comments: Handcrafted, Dated 1995.
Mom is getting ready to decorate her Christmas tree with the
popcorn she is stringing. **Artist:** Bob Siedler
☐ Purchased 19 __Pd $____MIB   NB   DB   BNT
☐ Want   Orig. Ret. $7.95 **NB** $8   **MIB** Sec. Mkt. **$17**

QX 565-7 MOM AND DAD
Comments: Handcrafted, Dated 1995.
Mom and Dad snowmen snuggle together to keep warm.
Artist: Anita Marra Rogers
☐ Purchased 19 __Pd $____MIB   NB   DB   BNT
☐ Want   Orig. Ret. $9.95 **NB** $18   **MIB** Sec. Mkt. **$22**

QX 565-9 MOM-TO-BE
Comments: Handcrafted, Dated 1995.
Mom-to-be reads up on the latest bear facts about child bear-
ing. **Artist:** Dill Rhodus
☐ Purchased 19 __Pd $____MIB   NB   DB   BNT
☐ Want   Orig. Ret. $7.95 **NB** $8   **MIB** Sec. Mkt. **$16**

QX 509-9 MOTHER GOOSE: JACK AND JILL
Comments: **Third in Series,** Handcrafted, 2-1/2" tall, Dated
1995. The Mother Goose book opens to display the verse and
a 3-D depiction. Caption: "Christmas 1995," "Mother Goose,"
"Nursery Rhymes," "Jack and Jill went up the hill …" Many
sales reported. **Artist:** Ed Seale/LaDene Votruba
☐ Purchased 19 __Pd $____MIB   NB   DB   BNT
☐ Want   Orig. Ret. $13.95 **NB** $18   **MIB** Sec. Mkt. **$25**

QX 515-7 MR. AND MRS. CLAUS: CHRISTMAS EVE KISS
Comments: **Tenth and Final in Series,** Handcrafted, 3-
3/16" tall. Dated 1995. Mrs. Claus gives her sweetie a kiss
before he heads off on his annual trip around the world.
Artist: Duane Unruh
☐ Purchased 19 __Pd $____MIB   NB   DB   BNT
☐ Want   Orig. Ret. $14.95 **NB** $28   **MIB** Sec. Mkt. **$32**

QX 600-9   **MULETIDE GREETINGS** ☐
Comments: Handcrafted, 3-1/16" tall, Dated 1995.
Mr. Mule takes a rest from delivering gifts this holiday season.
Designed from Shoebox Greetings. Caption: "Muletide
Greetings." **Artist:** Robert Chad
☐ Purchased 19 __Pd $____MIB   NB   DB   BNT
☐ Want   Orig. Ret. $7.95   **NB** $9   **MIB** Sec. Mkt. **$18**

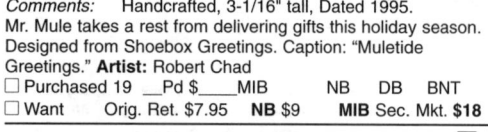

QLX 727-9   **MY FIRST HOT WHEELS™** ☐
Comments: Light and Motion, Handcrafted, 4-1/8" tall,
Dated 1995. Children watch their Hot Wheels™ go 'round and
'round. Tree lights up and the car goes around the track.
Artist: Ken Crow
☐ Purchased 19 __Pd $____MIB   NB   DB   BNT
☐ Want   Orig. Ret. $28.00 **NB** $23   **MIB** Sec. Mkt. **$45**

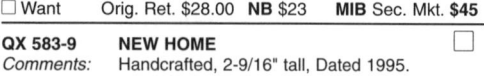

QX 583-9   **NEW HOME** ☐
Comments: Handcrafted, 2-9/16" tall, Dated 1995.
This cute little house dusts off the welcome mat for anyone
who might come visit. Caption: "Welcome New Home 1995."
New home ornaments are not readily asked for, so those who
do buy up extra usually ask double the retail, as only a few
offer these. **Artist:** Patricia Andrews
☐ Purchased 19 __Pd $____MIB   NB   DB   BNT
☐ Want   Orig. Ret. $8.95   **NB** $10   **MIB** Sec. Mkt. **$18**

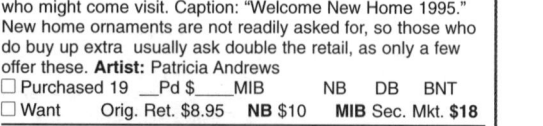

QX 595-7   **NORTH POLE 911** ☐
Comments: Handcrafted, 3-7/8" tall, Dated 1995.
Fireman chipmunk is ready for any emergency. "In Case of
Emergency" he can break the glass to get a candy cane.
Candy cane inside box dangles. Caption: "In Case of
Emergency Break Glass." **Artist:** Ed Seale
☐ Purchased 19 __Pd $____MIB   NB   DB   BNT
☐ Want   Orig. Ret. $10.95 **NB** $12   **MIB** Sec. Mkt. **$24**

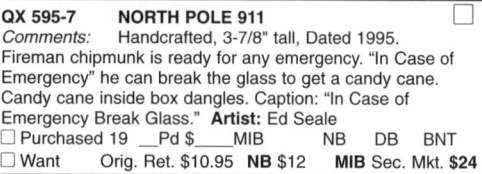

QX 508-9   **NOSTALGIC HOUSES AND SHOPS:** ☐
         COLLECTOR'S SERIES ACCESSORIES
Comments: Handcrafted, Street Lamp, 1-9/16" tall;
Evergreen, 15/16" tall; Roadster, 13/16" tall. Dated 1995.
These cute accessories will add conversation to any collection
of Nostalgic Houses and Shops. **Artist:** Julia Lee
☐ Purchased 19 __Pd $____MIB   NB   DB   BNT
☐ Want   Orig. Ret. $8.95   **NB** $9   **MIB** Sec. Mkt. **$14**

QX 515-9   **NOSTALGIC HOUSES AND SHOPS:** ☐
         TOWN CHURCH
Comments: **Twelfth in Series,** Handcrafted, 4-11/16" tall,
Dated 1995. An excellent choice for this favorite series. Easily
found. **Artist:** Don Palmiter
☐ Purchased 19 __Pd $____MIB   NB   DB   BNT
☐ Want   Orig. Ret. $14.95 **NB** $18   **MIB** Sec. Mkt. **$32**

QX 594-9   **NUMBER ONE TEACHER** ☐
Comments: Handcrafted, 1-11/16" tall, Dated 1995.
This little mouse slides down the bookmark to say, "You're
number one in my book." A more outstanding teacher orna-
ment than others. **Artist:** Ed Seale
☐ Purchased 19 __Pd $____MIB   NB   DB   BNT
☐ Want   Orig. Ret. $7.95   **NB** $8   **MIB** Sec. Mkt. **$17**

QX316-9   **OLYMPIC SPIRIT, THE** ☐
         CENTENNIAL GAMES ATLANTA 1996
Comments: Acrylic, Dated 1995.
The '96 Olympic Games logo graces this oval acrylic orna-
ment. May go higher this year.
☐ Purchased 19 __Pd $____MIB   NB   DB   BNT
☐ Want   Orig. Ret. $7.95   **NB** $10   **MIB** Sec. Mkt. **$20**

QX 604-7   **ON THE ICE** ☐
Comments: Handcrafted, 2-3/16" tall, Dated 1995.
On a cold winter day this Christmas mouse straps blocks of
ice to his feet and enjoys himself. **Artist:** Ken Crow
☐ Purchased 19 __Pd $____MIB   NB   DB   BNT
☐ Want   Orig. Ret. $7.95   **NB** $8   **MIB** Sec. Mkt. **$22**

QX 580-9   **OUR CHRISTMAS TOGETHER** ☐
Comments: Handcrafted, 3-9/16" tall, Dated 1995.
Mr. and Mrs. Bunny decorate their new home for the holidays
and their first Christmas together. Caption: "Our Christmas
Together." **Artist:** Joyce Lyle
☐ Purchased 19 __Pd $____MIB   NB   DB   BNT
☐ Want   Orig. Ret. $9.95   **NB** $9   **MIB** Sec. Mkt. **$18**

QX 570-9   **OUR FAMILY** ☐
Comments: Handcrafted, 3-5/16" tall, Dated 1995.
A treasure trunk full of family mementos and, on the outside of
the treasure chest, you can picture your family. Caption: "Our
Family" and "Christmas Is Meant To Be Shared."
Artist: Robert Chad
☐ Purchased 19 __Pd $____MIB   NB   DB   BNT
☐ Want   Orig. Ret. $7.95   **NB** $8   **MIB** Sec. Mkt. **$15**

QX 317-7   **OUR FIRST CHRISTMAS TOGETHER** ☐
Comments: Acrylic, 3-1/4" tall, Dated 1995.
Heart shaped acrylic ornament is dated to remind you of the
first Christmas you spent together. Caption: "Our First
Christmas Together." **Artist:** Joyce Lyle
☐ Purchased 19 __Pd $____MIB   NB   DB   BNT
☐ Want   Orig. Ret. $6.95   **NB** $13   **MIB** Sec. Mkt. **$18**

QX 579-7   OUR FIRST CHRISTMAS TOGETHER ☐
Comments: Handcrafted, 2-3/8" tall, Dated 1995.
These two lovable bears spend their first Christmas together watching the snow fall outside their window. Caption: "Our First Christmas Together." "Christmas dreams come true when they're dreamed by two." **Artist:** Joyce Lyle
☐ Purchased 19 __Pd $____MIB   NB   DB   BNT
☐ Want   Orig. Ret. $16.95 **NB** $16   **MIB** Sec. Mkt. **$34**

QX 579-9   OUR FIRST CHRISTMAS TOGETHER ☐
Comments: Handcrafted , 2-15/16" tall, Dated 1995.
Two mice have the key to each others' hearts as they spend their first Christmas together. Caption: "Our First Christmas Together." **Artist:** Bob Siedler
☐ Purchased 19 __Pd $____MIB   NB   DB   BNT
☐ Want   Orig. Ret. $8.95 **NB** $9   **MIB** Sec. Mkt. **$20**

QX 580-7   OUR FIRST CHRISTMAS TOGETHER: ☐
                PHOTOHOLDER
Comments: Handcrafted, 3-11/16" tall, Dated 1995.
Put your favorite picture of you and yours in this "Love Bug" photoholder. Caption: "Our First Christmas Together."
Artist: Ed Seale
☐ Purchased 19 __Pd $____MIB   NB   DB   BNT
☐ Want   Orig. Ret. $8.95 **NB** $10   **MIB** Sec. Mkt. **$19**

QX 520-9   OUR LITTLE BLESSINGS ☐
Comments: Handcrafted, 3-9/16" tall, Dated 1995.
Two children sit side by side discussing what they want Santa to bring them for Christmas. **Artist:** Ken Crow
☐ Purchased 19 __Pd $____MIB   NB   DB   BNT
☐ Want   Orig. Ret. $12.95 **NB** $14   **MIB** Sec. Mkt. **$26**

QX 563-9   PACKED WITH MEMORIES ☐
                PHOTOHOLDER
Comments: Handcrafted, 3-5/8" tall, Dated 1995.
New commemorative ornament. Keep your child's first school photo in this cute little pouch with a bear peeking out. **Artist:** Ed Seale
☐ Purchased 19 __Pd $____MIB   NB   DB   BNT
☐ Want   Orig. Ret. $7.95 **NB** $9   **MIB** Sec. Mkt. **$20**

QLX 727-7   PEANUTS® ☐
Comments: **Fifth and Final in Series,** Light and Motion. Handcrafted, 4-1/8" tall, Dated 1995. Snoopy spins gracefully on the ice. His message: "Merry Christmas."
Artist: Dill Rhodus
☐ Purchased 19 __Pd $____MIB   NB   DB   BNT
☐ Want   Orig. Ret. $24.50 **NB** $35   **MIB** Sec. Mkt. **$55**

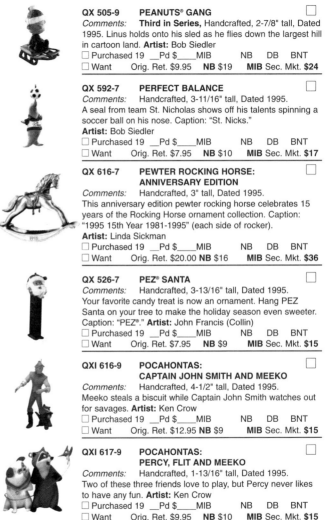

QX 505-9   PEANUTS® GANG ☐
Comments: **Third in Series,** Handcrafted, 2-7/8" tall, Dated 1995. Linus holds onto his sled as he flies down the largest hill in cartoon land. **Artist:** Bob Siedler
☐ Purchased 19 __Pd $____MIB   NB   DB   BNT
☐ Want   Orig. Ret. $9.95 **NB** $19   **MIB** Sec. Mkt. **$24**

QX 592-7   PERFECT BALANCE ☐
Comments: Handcrafted, 3-11/16" tall, Dated 1995.
A seal from team St. Nicholas shows off his talents spinning a soccer ball on his nose. Caption: "St. Nicks."
Artist: Bob Siedler
☐ Purchased 19 __Pd $____MIB   NB   DB   BNT
☐ Want   Orig. Ret. $7.95 **NB** $10   **MIB** Sec. Mkt. **$17**

QX 616-7   PEWTER ROCKING HORSE: ☐
                ANNIVERSARY EDITION
Comments: Handcrafted, 3" tall, Dated 1995.
This anniversary edition pewter rocking horse celebrates 15 years of the Rocking Horse ornament collection. Caption: "1995 15th Year 1981-1995" (each side of rocker).
Artist: Linda Sickman
☐ Purchased 19 __Pd $____MIB   NB   DB   BNT
☐ Want   Orig. Ret. $20.00 **NB** $16   **MIB** Sec. Mkt. **$36**

QX 526-7   PEZ® SANTA ☐
Comments: Handcrafted, 3-13/16" tall, Dated 1995.
Your favorite candy treat is now an ornament. Hang PEZ Santa on your tree to make the holiday season even sweeter. Caption: "PEZ®." **Artist:** John Francis (Collin)
☐ Purchased 19 __Pd $____MIB   NB   DB   BNT
☐ Want   Orig. Ret. $7.95 **NB** $9   **MIB** Sec. Mkt. **$15**

QXI 616-9   POCAHONTAS: ☐
                CAPTAIN JOHN SMITH AND MEEKO
Comments: Handcrafted, 4-1/2" tall, Dated 1995.
Meeko steals a biscuit while Captain John Smith watches out for savages. **Artist:** Ken Crow
☐ Purchased 19 __Pd $____MIB   NB   DB   BNT
☐ Want   Orig. Ret. $12.95 **NB** $9   **MIB** Sec. Mkt. **$15**

QXI 617-9   POCAHONTAS: ☐
                PERCY, FLIT AND MEEKO
Comments: Handcrafted, 1-13/16" tall, Dated 1995.
Two of these three friends love to play, but Percy never likes to have any fun. **Artist:** Ken Crow
☐ Purchased 19 __Pd $____MIB   NB   DB   BNT
☐ Want   Orig. Ret. $9.95 **NB** $10   **MIB** Sec. Mkt. **$15**

QXI 617-7 POCAHONTAS
Comments: Handcrafted, 2-15/16" tall, Dated 1995.
Pocahontas paddles "just around the river bend" with her little
hummingbird friend, Flit. **Artist:** Ken Crow
☐ Purchased 19 __Pd $____MIB   NB   DB   BNT
☐ Want   Orig. Ret. $12.95 **NB** $7   **MIB** Sec. Mkt. **$18**

QXI 619-7 POCAHONTAS:
POCAHONTAS AND CAPTAIN JOHN SMITH
Comments: Handcrafted, 2-9/16" tall, Dated 1995.
You will fall in love at first sight just like these two did, when
you see this ornament! **Artist:** Ken Crow
☐ Purchased 19 __Pd $____MIB   NB   DB   BNT
☐ Want   Orig. Ret. $14.95 **NB** $15   **MIB** Sec. Mkt. **$26**

QX 611-7 POLAR COASTER
Comments: Handcrafted, 2-1/2" tall, Dated 1995.
It's winter fun at its best when this li'l penguin is sliding off his
polar bear friend''s back. **Artist:** Ken Crow
☐ Purchased 19 __Pd $____MIB   NB   DB   BNT
☐ Want   Orig. Ret. $8.95 **NB** $14   **MIB** Sec. Mkt. **$30**

QX 525-7 POPEYE
Comments: Handcrafted, 3-11/16" tall, Dated 1995.
No turkey or ham for him! Even on Christmas Day, spinach is
the only thing Popeye eats. Caption: "SPINACH."
Artist: Robert Chad
☐ Purchased 19 __Pd $____MIB   NB   DB   BNT
☐ Want   Orig. Ret. $10.95 **NB** $15   **MIB** Sec. Mkt. **$25**

QX 513-7 PUPPY LOVE
Comments: **Fifth in Series,** Handcrafted, 2-1/16" tall,
Dated 1995. A brown and black puppy tries his best to help
with wrapping presents, but all he really wants to do is play.
Artist: Anita Marra Rogers
☐ Purchased 19 __Pd $____MIB   NB   DB   BNT
☐ Want   Orig. Ret. $7.95 **NB** $12   **MIB** Sec. Mkt. **$22**

QX 406-7 REFRESHING GIFT
Comments: Handcrafted, Dated 1995.
Santa stocks up on cold Coca-Cola® for all his little helpers.
Artist: Duane Unruh
☐ Purchased 19 __Pd $____MIB   NB   DB   BNT
☐ Want   Orig. Ret. $14.95 **NB** $22   **MIB** Sec. Mkt. **$30**

QX 598-7 REJOICE!
Comments: Handcrafted, 3-15/16" tall, Dated 1995.
Everyone rejoices with the birth of baby Jesus. Caption: "A
Child is Born. The world rejoices!" **Artist:** Joyce Lyle
☐ Purchased 19 __Pd $____MIB   NB   DB   BNT
☐ Want   Orig. Ret. $10.95 **NB** $15   **MIB** Sec. Mkt. **$25**

QX 516-7 ROCKING HORSE
Comments: **Fifteenth in Series,** Handcrafted, 3" tall, Dated
1995. A painted pony with red saddle and green rockers joins
this popular series. **Artist:** Linda Sickman
☐ Purchased 19 __Pd $____MIB   NB   DB   BNT
☐ Want   Orig. Ret. $10.95 **NB** $25   **MIB** Sec. Mkt. **$30**

QX 593-7 ROLLER WHIZ
Comments: Handcrafted, 2-1/2" tall, Dated 1995.
A turtle roller blades his way home to open the gifts he
received. **Artist:** Ed Seale
☐ Purchased 19 __Pd $____MIB   NB   DB   BNT
☐ Want   Orig. Ret. $7.95 **NB** $10   **MIB** Sec. Mkt. **$20**

QX 587-7 SANTA IN PARIS
Comments: Handcrafted, 3-9/16" tall, Dated 1995.
Santa climbs the Eiffel Tower to decorate it with real garland
for Christmas. Caption: "Joyeux Noel 1995."
Artist: Linda Sickman
☐ Purchased 19 __Pd $____MIB   NB   DB   BNT
☐ Want   Orig. Ret. $8.95 **NB** $15   **MIB** Sec. Mkt. **$30**

QLX 733-7 SANTA'S DINER
Comments: Handcrafted, Lighted, 2" tall, Dated 1995.
Santa stands at the door and greets customers into his diner.
Sign glows. Caption: "Santa's Diner." **Artist:** LaDene Votruba
☐ Purchased 19 __Pd $____MIB   NB   DB   BNT
☐ Want   Orig. Ret. $24.50 **NB** $18   **MIB** Sec. Mkt. **$25**

QX 601-7   SANTA'S SERENADE ☐
Comments: Handcrafted, 3" tall, Dated 1995.
Cowboy Santa sings Christmas carols with the help of Mr. Owl
on his hat who is playing the harmonica. **Artist:** Ken Crow
☐ Purchased 19 __Pd $____MIB   NB   DB   BNT
☐ Want   Orig. Ret. $8.95   **NB** $12   **MIB** Sec. Mkt. **$20**

QX 240-7   SANTA'S VISITORS: NORMAN ROCKWELL ☐
Comments: Glass Ball, Dated 1995.
Santa makes sure he checks his list for these two little ones
as they tell him what they want for Christmas.
Artist: Norman Rockwell
☐ Purchased 19 __Pd $____MIB   NB   DB   BNT
☐ Want   Orig. Ret. $5.00   **NB** $12   **MIB** Sec. Mkt. **$20**

QX 615-9   SIMBA, PUMBAA AND TIMON: ☐
**   THE LION KING**
Comments: Handcrafted, 3-1/16" tall, Dated 1995.
Simba, Pumbaa and Timon walk across a log singing their
favorite song. Caption: "Hakuna Matata." **Artist:** Ken Crow
☐ Purchased 19 __Pd $____MIB   NB   DB   BNT
☐ Want   Orig. Ret. $12.95   **NB** $13   **MIB** Sec. Mkt. **$21**

QX 568-7   SISTER ☐
Comments: Handcrafted, 2-5/8" tall, Dated 1995.
Skier sister is heading for the slopes. Caption: "Sister."
Artist: Joyce Lyle
☐ Purchased 19 __Pd $____MIB   NB   DB   BNT
☐ Want   Orig. Ret. $6.95   **NB** $7   **MIB** Sec. Mkt. **$14**

QX 568-9   SISTER TO SISTER ☐
Comments: Handcrafted, 2-3/4" tall, Dated 1995.
These two sisters share everything with each other, from
secrets to spices. Caption: "SPICES" and "Sisters Add Spice
to the Holidays." **Artist:** LaDene Votruba
☐ Purchased 19 __Pd $____MIB   NB   DB   BNT
☐ Want   Orig. Ret. $8.95   **NB** $12   **MIB** Sec. Mkt. **$20**

QX 590-9   SKI HOUND ☐
Comments: Handcrafted, 1-15/16" tall, Dated 1995.
One ski, one dachshund – off he goes. **Artist:** Dill Rhodus
☐ Purchased 19 __Pd $____MIB   NB   DB   BNT
☐ Want   Orig. Ret. $8.95   **NB** $9   **MIB** Sec. Mkt. **$18**

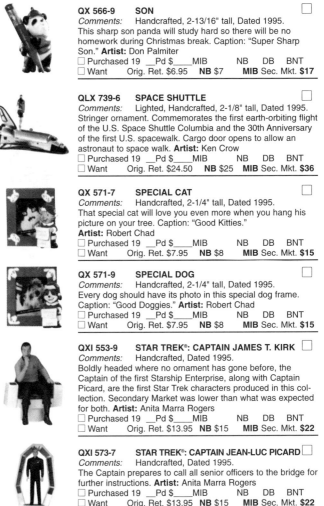

QX 566-9   SON ☐
Comments: Handcrafted, 2-13/16" tall, Dated 1995.
This sharp son panda will study hard so there will be no
homework during Christmas break. Caption: "Super Sharp
Son." **Artist:** Don Palmiter
☐ Purchased 19 __Pd $____MIB   NB   DB   BNT
☐ Want   Orig. Ret. $6.95   **NB** $7   **MIB** Sec. Mkt. **$17**

QLX 739-6   SPACE SHUTTLE ☐
Comments: Lighted, Handcrafted, 2-1/8" tall, Dated 1995.
Stringer ornament. Commemorates the first earth-orbiting flight
of the U.S. Space Shuttle Columbia and the 30th Anniversary
of the first U.S. spacewalk. Cargo door opens to allow an
astronaut to space walk. **Artist:** Ken Crow
☐ Purchased 19 __Pd $____MIB   NB   DB   BNT
☐ Want   Orig. Ret. $24.50   **NB** $25   **MIB** Sec. Mkt. **$36**

QX 571-7   SPECIAL CAT ☐
Comments: Handcrafted, 2-1/4" tall, Dated 1995.
That special cat will love you even more when you hang his
picture on your tree. Caption: "Good Kitties."
Artist: Robert Chad
☐ Purchased 19 __Pd $____MIB   NB   DB   BNT
☐ Want   Orig. Ret. $7.95   **NB** $8   **MIB** Sec. Mkt. **$15**

QX 571-9   SPECIAL DOG ☐
Comments: Handcrafted, 2-1/4" tall, Dated 1995.
Every dog should have its photo in this special dog frame.
Caption: "Good Doggies." **Artist:** Robert Chad
☐ Purchased 19 __Pd $____MIB   NB   DB   BNT
☐ Want   Orig. Ret. $7.95   **NB** $8   **MIB** Sec. Mkt. **$15**

QXI 553-9   STAR TREK®: CAPTAIN JAMES T. KIRK ☐
Comments: Handcrafted, Dated 1995.
Boldly headed where no ornament has gone before, the
Captain of the first Starship Enterprise, along with Captain
Picard, are the first Star Trek characters produced in this col-
lection. Secondary Market was lower than what was expected
for both. **Artist:** Anita Marra Rogers
☐ Purchased 19 __Pd $____MIB   NB   DB   BNT
☐ Want   Orig. Ret. $13.95   **NB** $15   **MIB** Sec. Mkt. **$22**

QXI 573-7   STAR TREK®: CAPTAIN JEAN-LUC PICARD ☐
Comments: Handcrafted, Dated 1995.
The Captain prepares to call all senior officers to the bridge for
further instructions. **Artist:** Anita Marra Rogers
☐ Purchased 19 __Pd $____MIB   NB   DB   BNT
☐ Want   Orig. Ret. $13.95   **NB** $15   **MIB** Sec. Mkt. **$22**

QXI 726-7 STAR TREK THE NEXT GENERATION: ☐
ROMULAN WARBIRD™
Comments: Handcrafted, Lighted, 1-7/8" tall, Dated 1995.
Caption: "Romulans have been the bad guys of the Star Trek universe since the beginning." It looks like this ship forgot its cloaking device. **Artist:** Lynn Norton
☐ Purchased 19 __Pd $____MIB   NB   DB   BNT
☐ Want   Orig. Ret. $24.00   **NB** $25   **MIB** Sec. Mkt. **$35**

QLX 730-9 SUPERMAN™ ☐
Comments: Handcrafted, Light and Motion, 5-1/8" tall, Dated 1995.The sign on top of the telephone booth glows as Clark Kent turns into Superman. Rotates.
Artist: Robert Chad
☐ Purchased 19 __Pd $____MIB   NB   DB   BNT
☐ Want   Orig. Ret. $28.00   **NB** $33   **MIB** Sec. Mkt. **$46**

QX 601-9 SURFIN' SANTA ☐
Comments: Handcrafted, 2-5/8" tall, Dated 1995.
Santa rips a few tides on his break from delivering presents.
Caption: "Yuletide." **Artist:** Ken Crow
☐ Purchased 19 __Pd $____MIB   NB   DB   BNT
☐ Want   Orig. Ret. $9.95   **NB** $12   **MIB** Sec. Mkt. **$25**

QX 602-9 TAKIN' A HIKE ☐
Comments: Handcrafted, 2-1/16" tall, Dated 1995.
This mouse tags along anywhere you may go on your Christmas journeys. **Artist:** John Francis (Collin)
☐ Purchased 19 __Pd $____MIB   NB   DB   BNT
☐ Want   Orig. Ret. $7.95   **NB** $10   **MIB** Sec. Mkt. **$19**

QX 590-7 TENNIS, ANYONE? ☐
Comments: Handcrafted, 3-7/8" tall, Dated 1995.
Play tennis with this little mouse; she is sure to help with your game. **Artist:** Nina Aube
☐ Purchased 19 __Pd $____MIB   NB   DB   BNT
☐ Want   Orig. Ret. $7.95   **NB** $8   **MIB** Sec. Mkt. **$19**

QX 585-7 THOMAS THE TANK ENGINE – NO. 1 ☐
Comments: Handcrafted, 1-11/16" tall, Dated 1995.
Thomas the Tank Engine makes it up another hill to teach the young children all about Christmas. **Artist:** Dill Rhodus
☐ Purchased 19 __Pd $____MIB   NB   DB   BNT
☐ Want   Orig. Ret. $9.95   **NB** $16   **MIB** Sec. Mkt. **$34**

QX 597-9 THREE WISHES ☐
Comments: Handcrafted, 2-5/16" tall, Dated 1995.
The little girl dreams of her three wishes: love, joy and peace.
Caption: "Love Joy Peace." **Artist:** Patricia Andrews
☐ Purchased 19 __Pd $____MIB   NB   DB   BNT
☐ Want   Orig. Ret. $7.95   **NB** $12   **MIB** Sec. Mkt. **$20**

QX 506-9 TOBIN FRALEY CARROUSEL ☐
Comments: **Fourth and Final in Series,** Handpainted Fine Porcelain. 5-7/8" tall, Dated 1995. This handpainted porcelain carrousel is decorated for the Christmas season with its gold star and red and green trimmings.
Artist: Tobin Fraley
☐ Purchased 19 __Pd $____MIB   NB   DB   BNT
☐ Want   Orig. Ret. $28.00 **NB** $28   **MIB** Sec. Mkt. **$50**

QLX 726-9 TOBIN FRALEY HOLIDAY CARROUSEL ☐
Comments: **Second in Series,** Handcrafted, Light and Music. 5-9/16" tall, Dated 1995. A horse prances inside a lighted carrousel. Plays "Over The Waves." **Artist:** Tobin Fraley
☐ Purchased 19 __Pd $____MIB   NB   DB   BNT
☐ Want   Orig. Ret. $32.00   **NB** $32   **MIB** Sec. Mkt. **$55**

QX 300-9 TWELVE DAYS OF CHRISTMAS: ☐
TWELVE DRUMMERS DRUMMING
Comments: **Twelfth and Final in Series,** Handcrafted, 3-7/8" tall, Dated 1995. As soon as you see this piece you will start singing the Twelve Days of Christmas. Caption: "The Twelve Days of Christmas 1995" "...twelve drummers drumming..."
☐ Purchased 19 __Pd $____MIB   NB   DB   BNT
☐ Want   Orig. Ret. $6.95   **NB** $14   **MIB** Sec. Mkt. **$20**

QX 582-9 TWO FOR TEA ☐
Comments: Handcrafted, 1-11/16" tall, Dated 1995.
Two mice join together in a cup of tea. Caption: "Friendship is a Special Gift." **Artist:** Julia Lee
☐ Purchased 19 __Pd $____MIB   NB   DB   BNT
☐ Want   Orig. Ret. $9.95   **NB** $16   **MIB** Sec. Mkt. **$30**

QX 506-7   U.S. CHRISTMAS STAMPS ☐
Comments: **Third and Final in Series,** Handcrafted,
3-3/8" tall Send your love to anyone with this Christmas greet-
ings postage stamp. Caption: "25 USA Greetings," "1995
Christmas" and "Christmas Tree."
☐ Purchased 19 __Pd $____MIB   NB   DB   BNT
☐ Want   Orig. Ret. $10.95   **NB** $13   MIB Sec. Mkt. **$25**

QX 553-7   VERA THE MOUSE ☐
Comments: Fine Porcelain, 3-7/32" dia., Dated 1995.
This fine porcelain Marjolein Bastin collector's plate includes a
stand, or it may be hung on your tree. **Artist:** Marjolein Bastin
☐ Purchased 19 __Pd $____MIB   NB   DB   BNT
☐ Want   Orig. Ret. $8.95   **NB** $9   **MIB** Sec. Mkt. **$18**

QLX 735-7   VICTORIAN TOY BOX: SPECIAL EDITION ☐
Comments: Handcrafted, Light, Motion and Music, 4-5/16"
tall. The Christmas tree glows, jack-in-the-box goes up and
down, top spins and Santa wobbles. Plays "Toyland."
Artist: Joyce Lyle
☐ Purchased 19 __Pd $____MIB   NB   DB   BNT
☐ Want   Orig. Ret. $42.00   **NB** $45   **MIB** Sec. Mkt. **$60**

QX 610-6   WAITING UP FOR SANTA ☐
Comments: Handcrafted, 2-9/16" tall, Dated 1995.
This tired little bear drags his toy bear along while waiting up
for Santa. **Artist:** Don Palmiter
☐ Purchased 19 __Pd $____MIB   NB   DB   BNT
☐ Want   Orig. Ret. $8.95   **NB** $9   **MIB** Sec. Mkt. **$19**

QX 603-9   WATER SPORTS ☐
Comments: Handcrafted, Boat 1-5/8" tall, Mrs. Claus
1-15/16" tall, Dated 1995. A set of two clip-on ornaments.
Santa takes time from his busy schedule to enjoy the summer
sport of water skiing with Mrs. Claus. **Artist:** Bob Siedler
☐ Purchased 19 __Pd $____MIB   NB   DB   BNT
☐ Want   Orig. Ret. $14.95   **NB** $25   **MIB** Sec. Mkt. **$31**

QLX 732-9   WEE LITTLE CHRISTMAS ☐
Comments: Lighted, Handcrafted, 3" tall, Dated 1995.
The Christmas tree glows when Santa comes to deliver his
gifts. There is a surprise Christmas scene behind the wall.
Artist: Ken Crow
☐ Purchased 19 __Pd $____MIB   NB   DB   BNT
☐ Want   Orig. Ret. $22.00   **NB** $22   **MIB** Sec. Mkt. **$40**

QX 618-7   WHEEL OF FORTUNE®: ☐
                ANNIVERSARY EDITION
Comments: Handcrafted, Dated 1995.
Check your luck to see if the letters spell out what you want
for Christmas. Caption: "Wheel of Fortune You're A Winner
1995" and "Wheel of Fortune 20 Years 1975-1995." Popular
ornament. **Artist:** Linda Sickman
☐ Purchased 19 __Pd $____MIB   NB   DB   BNT
☐ Want   Orig. Ret. $12.95   **NB** $16   **MIB** Sec. Mkt. **$25**

QX 588-9   WINNING PLAY, THE ☐
Comments: Handcrafted, 1-7/8" tall, Dated 1995.
The athletic mouse takes the court. He dribbles left then right,
shoots and scores! The Christmas mice win the game.
Artist: Bob Siedler
☐ Purchased 19 __Pd $____MIB   NB   DB   BNT
☐ Want   Orig. Ret. $7.95   **NB** $10   **MIB** Sec. Mkt. **$24**

QX 500-9   WINNIE THE POOH AND TIGGER ☐
Comments: Handcrafted, Dated 1995.
Tigger gives Pooh a boost to put the star atop the tree.
Artist: Bob Siedler
☐ Purchased 19 __Pd $____MIB   NB   DB   BNT
☐ Want   Orig. Ret. $12.95 **NB** $22   **MIB** Sec. Mkt. **$30**

QLX 729-7   WINNIE THE POOH – TOO MUCH HUNNY ☐
Comments: Handcrafted, Motion, 4-1/8" tall, Dated 1995.
Tigger is pulling the hunny loving Pooh through the narrow
hole at "Rabbit's House." **Artist:** Bob Siedler
☐ Purchased 19 __Pd $____MIB   NB   DB   BNT
☐ Want   Orig. Ret. $24.50   **NB** $30   MIB Sec. Mkt. **$55**

QX 585-9   WISH LIST: ORNAMENT PREMIERE ☐
Comments: Handcrafted, 2-3/8" tall, Dated 1995.
A small Tender Touches mouse writes a letter "To Santa."
Artist: Ed Seale
☐ Purchased 19 __Pd $____MIB   NB   DB   BNT
☐ Want   Orig. Ret. $15.00   **NB** $18   **MIB** Sec. Mkt. **$30**

QX 574-9   WIZARD OF OZ™: ☐
                GLINDA, WITCH OF THE NORTH
Comments: Handcrafted, 4-3/8" tall, Dated 1995.
Last year's Wizard of Oz characters were happy to have
Glinda join them in 1995. **Artist:** Joyce Lyle
☐ Purchased 19 __Pd $____MIB   NB   DB   BNT
☐ Want   Orig. Ret. $13.95   **NB** $18   **MIB** Sec. Mkt. **$30**

QX 507-9   YULETIDE CENTRAL

Comments: **Second in Series,** Pressed Tin, 2" tall, Dated 1995. A little train car carries the goodies for children on Christmas Day. **Artist:** Linda Sickman

☐ Purchased 19 __Pd $____MIB   NB   DB   BNT
☐ Want   Orig. Ret. $18.95   **NB** $18   **MIB** Sec. Mkt. **$30**

Hallmark Personalized Keepsake Ornaments

No past sales found on these ornaments. Any ornament with a personal message is not likely to bring a significant secondary market price.

QP 615-7   BABY BEAR

Comments: Handcrafted, 2-5/8" tall, New Design. Personalize this baby bear's bib to commemorate the birth of your little bundle of joy. **Artist:** Patricia Andrews

☐ Purchased 19 __Pd $____MIB   NB   DB   BNT
☐ Want   Orig. Ret. $12.95   **MIB** Sec. Mkt. **N.E.**

QP 612-7   CHAMP, THE

Comments: Handcrafted, 2-9/16" tall. Baby chipmunk holds onto a winners cup. **Artist:** LaDene Votruba

☐ Purchased 19 __Pd $____MIB   NB   DB   BNT
☐ Want   Orig. Ret.$12.95   **MIB** Sec. Mkt. **N.E.**

QP 604-6   COMPUTER CAT 'N MOUSE

Comments: Handcrafted, 2-3/4" tall. A little kitten watches over your mouse from the top of the computer. Caption: "Happy Holidata." **Artist:** Ed Seale

☐ Purchased 19 __Pd $____MIB   NB   DB   BNT
☐ Want   Orig. Ret. $12.95   **MIB** Sec. Mkt. **N.E.**

QP 607-3   COOKIE TIME

Comments: Handcrafted, 2-3/4" tall. An iced Christmas cookie will make your tree even sweeter. **Artist:** LaDene Vortruba

☐ Purchased 19 __Pd $____MIB   NB   DB   BNT
☐ Want   Orig. Ret. $12.95   **MIB** Sec. Mkt. **N.E.**

QP 600-6   ETCH-A-SKETCH®

Comments: Handcrafted, 2-1/4" tall. A little bear sketches a warm Christmas wish to you. Caption: "Etch-A-Sketch®." **Artist:** Ken Crow

☐ Purchased 19 __Pd $____MIB   NB   DB   BNT
☐ Want   Orig. Ret. $12.95   **MIB** Sec. Mkt. **N.E.**

QP 603-6   FROM THE HEART

Comments: Handcrafted, 1-15/16" tall. This little raccoon is willing to brave the cold snow to show his sweetheart how much he loves her. **Artist:** Dill Rhodus

☐ Purchased 19 __Pd $____MIB   NB   DB   BNT
☐ Want   Orig. Ret. $14.95   **MIB** Sec. Mkt. **N.E.**

QP 614-9   KEY NOTE

Comments: Handcrafted, 2-5/8" tall. A li'l mouse holds the golden key to your new home. The tag he sits on can be personalized. **Artist:** Ed Seale

☐ Purchased 19 __Pd $____MIB   NB   DB   BNT
☐ Want   Orig. Ret. $12.95   **MIB** Sec. Mkt. **N.E.**

QP 601-5   MAILBOX DELIVERY

Comments: Handcrafted, 1-7/8" tall. What a surprise when Mr. Raccoon delivers the mail in person. Mail box opens. **Artist:** Ken Crow

☐ Purchased 19 __Pd $____MIB   NB   DB   BNT
☐ Want   Orig. Ret. $14.95   **MIB** Sec. Mkt. **N.E.**

QP 606-6   NOVEL IDEA

Comments: Handcrafted, 2-7/16" tall. Mr. Mouse will help deliver your message on this "novel" ornament. **Artist:** LaDene Votruba

☐ Purchased 19 __Pd $____MIB   NB   DB   BNT
☐ Want   Orig. Ret. $12.95   **MIB** Sec. Mkt. **N.E.**

QP 602-2   ON THE BILLBOARD

Comments: Handcrafted, 2-1/8" tall. Have Santa's helper paint a Christmas message on a billboard for you. Caption: "Santa Sign Co." **Artist:** Ken Crow

☐ Purchased 19 __Pd $____MIB   NB   DB   BNT
☐ Want   Orig. Ret. $12.95   **MIB** Sec. Mkt. **N.E.**

QP 603-2   PLAYING BALL ☐
Comments: Handcrafted, 3-11/16" tall.
This little bear is ready to play ball. He carries a bat that can be personalized for your "little winner."
Artist: John Francis (Collin)
☐ Purchased 19 __Pd $____MIB   NB   DB   BNT
☐ Want   Orig. Ret. $12.95   **MIB** Sec. Mkt. **N.E.**

QP 605-6   REINDEER ROOTERS ☐
Comments: Handcrafted, 2-15/16" tall.
Reissued from 1994. This peppy squad of reindeer will help anyone send that special Christmas message. **Artist:** Ken Crow
☐ Purchased 19 __Pd $____MIB   NB   DB   BNT
☐ Want   Orig. Ret. $12.95   **MIB** Sec. Mkt. **N.E.**

Hallmark Keepsake Showcase Ornaments

Offered by Gold Crown Stores only.

Turn of the Century Parade

QK 102-7   THE FIREMAN ☐
Comments: ***FIRST IN SERIES,*** Die-cast metal, 3-1/8" tal, Dated 1995. No fire truck would be complete without a brass bell and red ribbon; the wheels turn and bell rings.
Artist: Ken Crow
☐ Purchased 19 __Pd $____MIB   NB   DB   BNT
☐ Want   Orig. Ret. $16.95 **NB** $30 **MIB** Sec. Mkt. **$39**

Holiday Enchantment

QK 109-7   AWAY IN A MANGER ☐
Comments: Fine Porcelain, 4-5/16" tall, Dated 1995.
Caption: "...The Little Lord Jesus, Asleep on the Hay" "Away in a Manger." **Artist:** LaDene Votruba
☐ Purchased 19 __Pd $____MIB   NB   DB   BNT
☐ Want   Orig. Ret. $13.95 **NB** $20 **MIB** Sec. Mkt. **$26**

QK 109-9   FOLLOWING THE STAR ☐
Comments: Fine Porcelain, 3-7/16" dia., Dated 1995.
Caption: "...We have seen his star in the east, and are come to worship him. Matthew 2:2." **Artist:** LaDene Votruba
☐ Purchased 19 __Pd $____MIB   NB   DB   BNT
☐ Want   Orig. Ret. $13.95 **NB** $20 **MIB** Sec. Mkt. **$26**

Nature's Sketchbook

QK 106-9   BACKYARD ORCHARD ☐
Comments: Handcrafted, 3-3/16" tall, Dated 1995.
This basket full of fruit feeds everyone from the birds to the butterflies. In '96, Hallmark debuted Marjolein Bastin's "bird" card and accessories.
Artists: Marjolein Bastin and John Francis (Collin)
☐ Purchased 19 __Pd $____MIB   NB   DB   BNT
☐ Want   Orig. Ret. $18.95 **NB** $25   **MIB** Sec. Mkt. **$30**

QK 107-7   CHRISTMAS CARDINAL ☐
Comments: Handcrafted, 3-5/8" tall, Dated 1995.
This red cardinal makes a striking contrast to the scenery.
Artists: Marjolein Bastin and Joyce Lyle
☐ Purchased 19 __Pd $____MIB   NB   DB   BNT
☐ Want   Orig. Ret. $18.95 **NB** $35   **MIB** Sec. Mkt. **$40**

QK 106-7   RAISING A FAMILY ☐
Comments: Handcrafted, 3-5/8" diameter, Dated 1995.
This handcrafted ornament pictures Mama bird feeding her baby bird. Gorgeous! **Artists:** Marjolein Bastin and Joyce Lyle
☐ Purchased 19 __Pd $____MIB   NB   DB   BNT
☐ Want   Orig. Ret. $18.95 **NB** $25   **MIB** Sec. Mkt. **$30**

QK 107-9   VIOLETS AND BUTTERFLIES ☐
Comments: Handcrafted, 4-1/8" tall, Dated 1995.
This two-sided, handcrafted ornament depicts a lovely spring scene of wildflowers and butterflies. Nice!
Artists: Marjolein Bastin and Joyce Lyle
☐ Purchased 19 __Pd $____MIB   NB   DB   BNT
☐ Want   Orig. Ret. $16.95 **NB** $25   **MIB** Sec. Mkt. **$30**

Symbols of Christmas

QK 108-7   JOLLY SANTA ☐
Comments: Handcrafted, Hand Painted, 2-1/4" tall, Dated 1995.Jolly Santa brings home a Christmas tree for the family to enjoy. **Artists:** Patricia Andrews
☐ Purchased 19 __Pd $____MIB   NB   DB   BNT
☐ Want   Orig. Ret. $15.95 **NB** $28   **MIB** Sec. Mkt. **$30**

QK 108-9   SWEET SONG ☐
Comments: Handcrafted, Hand Painted, 2-5/16" tall, Dated 1995.
This hand painted caroler sings her favorite Christmas carols.
Artists: Patricia Andrews
☐ Purchased 19 __Pd $____MIB   NB   DB   BNT
☐ Want   Orig. Ret. $15.95 **NB** $24   **MIB** Sec. Mkt. **$30**

Invitation To Tea

The handle, spout and removable lid of each ornament
are concealed in the design of the teapot.

QK 112-7   COZY COTTAGE TEAPOT ☐
Comments: Handcrafted, 2-7/16" tall, Dated 1995.
A quaint cottage with an ivy covered arch makes a lovely
teapot design. **Artist:** Patricia Andrews
☐ Purchased 19 __Pd $____MIB   NB   DB   BNT
☐ Want   Orig. Ret. $15.95 **NB** $25   **MIB** Sec. Mkt. **$30**

QK 112-9   EUROPEAN CASTLE TEAPOT ☐
Comments: Handcrafted, 3-5/16" tall, Dated 1995.
Turrets and balconies add to the charm of this ivory castle.
Artist: Patricia Andrews
☐ Purchased 19 __Pd $____MIB   NB   DB   BNT
☐ Want   Orig. Ret. $15.95 **NB** $25   **MIB** Sec. Mkt. **$30**

QX 111-9   VICTORIAN HOME TEAPOT ☐
Comments: Handcrafted, 2-7/16" tall, Dated 1995.
All the elegance and style of a Victorian home are captured in
this unique teapot. **Artist:** Patricia Andrews
☐ Purchased 19 __Pd $____MIB   NB   DB   BNT
☐ Want   Orig. Ret. $15.95 **NB** $30   **MIB** Sec. Mkt. **$35**

All Is Bright

QK 115-9   ANGEL OF LIGHT ☐
Comments: Handcrafted, 4-9/16" tall, Dated 1995.
This beautiful angel has a holiday glow; she dreams of the joy
of Christmas. "Gold leaf" look. **Artist:** Patricia Andrews
☐ Purchased 19 __Pd $____MIB   NB   DB   BNT
☐ Want   Orig. Ret. $11.95 **NB** $20   **MIB** Sec. Mkt. **$25**

QK 115-7   GENTLE LULLABY ☐
Comments: Handcrafted, 4-5/16" tall, Dated 1995.
A beautiful golden angel rocks her precious baby to sleep.
"Gold leaf" look. **Artist:** Patricia Andrews
☐ Purchased 19 __Pd $____MIB   NB   DB   BNT
☐ Want   Orig. Ret. $11.95 **NB** $20   **MIB** Sec. Mkt. **$25**

Angel Bells

QK 114-7   CAROLE ☐
Comments: Fine Porcelain, 3-5/8" tall, Dated 1995.
A lovely Asian angel; her feet are the clapper for the bell.
Artist: LaDene Votruba
☐ Purchased 19 __Pd $____MIB   NB   DB   BNT
☐ Want   Orig. Ret. $12.95 **NB** $19   **MIB** Sec. Mkt. **$26**

QK 113-7   JOY ☐
Comments: Fine Porcelain, 3-1/2" tall, Dated 1995.
The Joy bell ornament seemed to be the hardest one to find.
All three were not abundantly produced. Found in box labeled
Carole. **Artist:** LaDene Votruba
☐ Purchased 19 __Pd $____MIB   NB   DB   BNT
☐ Want   Orig. Ret. $12.95 **NB** $25   **MIB** Sec. Mkt. **$30**

QK 113-9   NOELLE ☐
Comments: Fine Porcelain, 3-9/16" tall, Dated 1995.
Noelle is a devout African-American angel. Her feet are the
clapper for the bell. **Artist:** LaDene Votruba
☐ Purchased 19 __Pd $____MIB   NB   DB   BNT
☐ Want   Orig. Ret. $12.95 **NB** $20   **MIB** Sec. Mkt. **$25**

Folk Art Americana

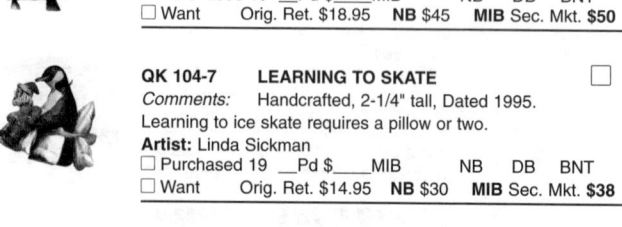

QK105-7   FETCHING THE FIREWOOD ☐
Comments: Handcrafted, Dated 1995.
A li'l man gives his dog a well-deserved hug after a long day
on the trail. **Artist:** Linda Sickman
☐ Purchased 19 __Pd $____MIB   NB   DB   BNT
☐ Want   Orig. Ret. $16.95 **NB** $30   **MIB** Sec. Mkt. **$38**

QK 103-9   FISHING PARTY ☐
Comments: Handcrafted, 1-7/8" tall, Dated 1995.
Everyone should have a pet walrus. **Artist:** Linda Sickman
☐ Purchased 19 __Pd $____MIB   NB   DB   BNT
☐ Want   Orig. Ret. $15.95 **NB** $30   **MIB** Sec. Mkt. **$35**

QK 103-7   GUIDING SANTA ☐
Comments: Handcrafted, 3-3/8" tall, Dated 1995.
A little angel guides Santa as he takes an unusual ride.
Artist: Linda Sickman
☐ Purchased 19 __Pd $____MIB   NB   DB   BNT
☐ Want   Orig. Ret. $18.95 **NB** $45   **MIB** Sec. Mkt. **$50**

QK 104-7   LEARNING TO SKATE ☐
Comments: Handcrafted, 2-1/4" tall, Dated 1995.
Learning to ice skate requires a pillow or two.
Artist: Linda Sickman
☐ Purchased 19 __Pd $____MIB   NB   DB   BNT
☐ Want   Orig. Ret. $14.95 **NB** $30   **MIB** Sec. Mkt. **$38**

Expo 1995

1956 FORD TRUCK ORNAMENT, SPECIAL EDITION ☐
Comments: Handcrafted.
Available only to Expo '95 attendees by special drawing.
☐ Purchased 19 ___ Pd $____ MIB   NB   DB   BNT
☐ Want   Orig. Ret. Free   **NB** $27   **MIB** Sec. Mkt. **$35**

ARTISTS' CARICATURE BALL ORNAMENT ☐
Comments: Signed.
☐ Purchased 19 ___ Pd $____ MIB   NB   DB   BNT
☐ Want   Orig. Ret. $7.95   **NB** $20   **MIB** Sec. Mkt. **$25**

QXC 404-9   CHRISTMAS EVE BAKE-OFF ☐
Comments: Handcrafted, Dated 1995.
Mrs. Claus is baking all kinds of Christmas goodies for Santa
and his elves. Mrs. Santa is a lift-off ornament.
Artist: All 14 Studio Artists.
☐ Purchased 19 ___ Pd $____ MIB   NB   DB   BNT
☐ Want   Orig. Ret. $60   **NB** $100   **MIB** Sec. Mkt. **$120**

COOKIE TIME – SPECIAL EDITION ☐
Comments: Handcrafted, Dated 1995.
Caption: "EXPO '95 Cooking Up Fun!"
☐ Purchased 19 ___ Pd $____ MIB   NB   DB   BNT
☐ Want   Orig. Ret. $12.95   **NB** $14   **MIB** Sec. Mkt. **$19**

KIDDIE CAR CLASSICS – SPECIAL EDITION ☐
Comments: Die Cast Metal.
Available only to Expo '95 attendees by special drawing.
☐ Purchased 19 ___ Pd $____ MIB   NB   DB   BNT
☐ Want   Orig. Ret. Free   **MIB** Sec. Mkt. **N.E.**

MURRAY FIRE TRUCK – SPECIAL EDITION ☐
Comments: Die Cast Metal.
Available only to Expo '95 attendees by special drawing.
☐ Purchased 19 ___ Pd $____ MIB   NB   DB   BNT
☐ Want   Orig. Ret. Free   **MIB** Sec. Mkt. **N.E.**

MURRAY CHAMPION ORNAMENT – SPECIAL EDITION ☐
Comments: Die Cast Metal Miniature Ornament.
Available only to Expo '95 attendees by special drawing.
☐ Purchased 19 ___ Pd $____ MIB   NB   DB   BNT
☐ Want   Orig. Ret. Free   **MIB** Sec. Mkt. **N.E.**

QX616-7   ROCKING HORSE ORNAMENT ☐
SPECIAL EDITION
Comments: Pewter Miniature Ornament.
Hot! Collectors were seeking unwanted redemption forms for
this ornament during the Expos!
☐ Purchased 19 ___ Pd $____ MIB   NB   DB   BNT
☐ Want   Orig. Ret. $9.75   **NB** $27   **MIB** Sec. Mkt. **$50**

Expo '95 Prizes

1995 Keepsake Signature Collection Piece, Signed.
Expo-Exclusive Ball Ornament, Signed.
Kiddie Car Classics Collectible, Expo Special Edition.
Murray® Fire Truck Ornament, Expo Special Edition.
1956 Ford Truck Ornament, Expo Special Edition.
Miniature Murray® Champion Ornament, Expo Special Edition.
Holiday Memories™ Barbie® Doll.
Regional NFL Ornament Collection.
Expo Artists' Caricatures Original Sketch, Signed.
When You Care Enough, Book Signed by.
Don Hall, Sr. and Don Hall, Jr.

NFL Ornaments

☐ ✱ Philadelphia Eagles™	☐ Carolina Panthers™	☐ New England Patriots™
☐ ✱ Washington Redskins™	☐ Kansas City Chiefs™	☐ ✱ Dallas Cowboys™
☐ Chicago Bears™	☐ Minnesota Vikings™	☐ ✱ Los Angeles Raiders™
☐ ✱ San Francisco 49ers™		

Not all Hallmark stores carried these. Some only offered "their" area team's logo.

FOOTBALL HELMET ORNAMENTS
Those listed above with the ✱ are highly sought after and com-
mand a higher secondary market value of $25-$30. All others
would be $20.
Comments: Handcrafted, Dated 1995.
☐ Purchased 19 ___ Pd $____ MIB   NB   DB   BNT
☐ Want   Orig. Ret. $9.95   **NB** $15   **MIB** Sec. Mkt. **$20**

NFL BALL ORNAMENTS
Comments: Glass Ball, Dated 1995. Quite attractive.
☐ Purchased 19 ___ Pd $____ MIB   NB   DB   BNT
☐ Want   Orig. Ret. $5.95   **NB** $7   **MIB** Sec. Mkt. **$15**

1995 Miniature Ornament Collection

QXC 412-9
A GIFT FROM RODNEY:
KEEPSAKE CLUB
Dated 1995.
Artist: Linda Sickman
☐ Purchased 19___ Pd $_____
MIB   NB   DB   BNT
☐ Want   Free with '95 Club
                        Membership
NB $7   **MIB** Sec. Mkt. **$17**

QXM 483-9
A MOUSTERSHIRE
CHRISTMAS: SPECIAL EDITION
13/16" tall, House 2-5/8" tall, Dated
1995. A. Moustershire Cottage
B. Robin C. Violet D. Dunne
Artist: Dill Rhodus
☐ Purchased 19___ Pd $_____
MIB   NB   DB   BNT
☐ Want   Orig. Retail $24.50
NB $28   **MIB** Sec. Mkt. **$45**

QXM 477-7
ALICE IN WONDERLAND
FIRST IN SERIES, 1-7/16" tall,
Dated 1995.
Artist: Patricia Andrews
☐ Purchased 19___ Pd $_____
MIB   NB   DB   BNT
☐ Want   Orig. Retail $6.75
NB $8   **MIB** Sec. Mkt. **$15**

QXM 402-7
BABY'S FIRST CHRISTMAS
1-1/16" tall, Dated 1995.
Artist: Ed Seale
☐ Purchased 19___ Pd $_____
MIB   NB   DB   BNT
☐ Want   Orig. Retail $4.75
NB $7   **MIB** Sec. Mkt. **$14**

QXM 478-9
CENTURIES OF SANTA
Second in Series, 1-1/4" tall,
Dated 1995.
Artist: Linda Sickman
☐ Purchased 19___ Pd $_____
MIB   NB   DB   BNT
☐ Want   Orig. Retail $5.75
NB $12   **MIB** Sec. Mkt. **$22**

QXM 400-7
CHRISTMAS BELLS
FIRST IN SERIES, Metal, 1-1/4"
tall, Dated 1995. A popular series!
Artist: Ed Seale
☐ Purchased 19___ Pd $_____
MIB   NB   DB   BNT
☐ Want   Orig. Retail $4.75
NB $10   **MIB** Sec. Mkt. **$20**

QXM 408-7
CHRISTMAS WISHES
1-1/16" tall, Dated 1995.
Artist: Ed Seale
☐ Purchased 19___ Pd $_____
MIB   NB   DB   BNT
☐ Want   Orig. Retail $3.75
NB $7   **MIB** Sec. Mkt. **$14**

QXM 401-7
CLOISONNÉ PARTRIDGE:
PRECIOUS EDITION
Cloisonné, 1" dia.
Artist: LaDene Votruba
☐ Purchased 19___ Pd $_____
MIB   NB   DB   BNT
☐ Want   Orig. Retail $9.75
NB $10   **MIB** Sec. Mkt. **$20**

QXC 445-7
COOL SANTA: KEEPSAKE CLUB
"Coca-Cola®"
Artist: John Francis (Collin)
☐ Purchased 19___ Pd $_____
MIB   NB   DB   BNT
I Want   Free with '95
                        Club Membership
NB $8   **MIB** Sec. Mkt. **$12**

QXC 411-9
COZY CHRISTMAS: KEEPSAKE
COLLECTOR'S CLUB
1-3/16" dia. Caption: "Santa's
Club Soda."
Artist: John Francis (Collin)
☐ Purchased 19___ Pd $_____
MIB   NB   DB   BNT
☐ Want   Orig. Retail - Included
with Membership Kit
NB $7   **MIB** Sec. Mkt. **$15**

QXM 483-7
DOWNHILL DOUBLE
5/8" tall, Dated 1995.
Artist: Don Palmiter
☐ Purchased 19___ Pd $_____
MIB   NB   DB   BNT
☐ Want   Orig. Retail $4.75
NB $8   **MIB** Sec. Mkt. **$13**

QXM 401-9
FRIENDSHIP DUET
1-1/4" tall, Dated 1995.
Artist: Duane Unruh
☐ Purchased 19___ Pd $_____
MIB   NB   DB   BNT
☐ Want   Orig. Retail $4.75
NB $8   **MIB** Sec. Mkt. **$13**

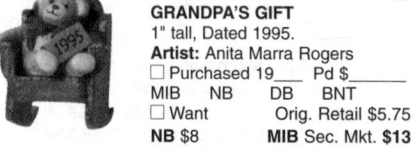

QXM 482-9
GRANDPA'S GIFT
1" tall, Dated 1995.
Artist: Anita Marra Rogers
☐ Purchased 19___ Pd $_____
MIB   NB   DB   BNT
☐ Want   Orig. Retail $5.75
NB $8   **MIB** Sec. Mkt. **$13**

QXM 403-7
HEAVENLY PRAISES
1-5/16" tall, Dated 1995.
Artist: Patricia Andrews
☐ Purchased 19___ Pd $_____
MIB   NB   DB   BNT
☐ Want   Orig. Retail $5.75
NB $8   **MIB** Sec. Mkt. **$13**

QXM 545-2
HOLIDAY EXPRESS
Tree Base, able to hold any standard miniature tree. Train moves on track. 4-1/4" tall.
Artist: Linda Sickman
☐ Purchased 19___ Pd $_____
MIB   NB   DB   BNT
☐ Want   Orig. Retail $50.00
NB $38   **MIB** Sec. Mkt. **$74**

QXM 408-9
JOYFUL SANTA
1-1/8" tall, Dated 1995.
Artist: Duane Unruh
☐ Purchased 19___ Pd $_____
MIB   NB   DB   BNT
☐ Want   Orig. Retail $4.75
NB $6   **MIB** Sec. Mkt. **$12**

QXM 479-9
MARCH OF THE TEDDY BEARS
Third in Series, 1-5/16" tall,
Dated 1995. **Artist:** Duane Unruh
☐ Purchased 19___ Pd $_____
MIB   NB   DB   BNT
☐ Want   Orig. Retail $4.75
NB $8   **MIB** Sec. Mkt. **$14**

QXM 409-7
MINIATURE CLOTHESPIN SOLDIER
FIRST IN SERIES, 1-1/8" tall.
Artist: Linda Sickman
☐ Purchased 19___ Pd $_____
MIB   NB   DB   BNT
☐ Want   Orig. Retail $3.75
NB $9   **MIB** Sec. Mkt. **$17**

QXM 407-9
MINIATURE KIDDIE CAR CLASSICS: MURRAY® BLUE
FIRST IN SERIES, "Champion"
Die Cast Metal, 9/16" tall, Dated 1995. Hot! Disappeared from shelves early in buying season! Secondary market dealers were big buyers.
Artist: Don Palmiter
☐ Purchased 19___ Pd $_____
MIB   NB   DB   BNT
☐ Want   Orig. Retail $5.75
NB $11   **MIB** Sec. Mkt. **$20**

QXM 480-9
NATURE'S ANGELS
Sixth in Series, Brass Halo,
1-1/8" tall. **Artist:** Patricia Andrews
☐ Purchased 19___ Pd $_____
MIB   NB   DB   BNT
☐ Want   Orig. Retail $4.75
NB $11   **MIB** Sec. Mkt. **$20**

QXM 480-7
NIGHT BEFORE CHRISTMAS, THE
Fourth in Series, 1-1/4" tall,
Dated 1995. **Artist:** Duane Unruh
☐ Purchased 19___ Pd $_____
MIB   NB   DB   BNT
☐ Want   Orig. Retail $4.75
NB $11   **MIB** Sec. Mkt. **$20**

QXM 405-7
NOAH'S ARK:
MERRY WALRUSES
9/16" tall. Addition to Noah's Ark Special Edition (1994). A nice series! **Artist:** Linda Sickman
☐ Purchased 19___ Pd $_____
MIB   NB   DB   BNT
☐ Want   Orig. Retail $5.75
NB $11   **MIB** Sec. Mkt. **$20**

QXM 405-9
NOAH'S ARK:
PLAYFUL PENGUINS
11/16" tall. Addition to Noah's Ark Special Edition (1994).
Artist: Linda Sickman
☐ Purchased 19___ Pd $_____
MIB   NB   DB   BNT
☐ Want   Orig. Retail $5.75
NB $11   **MIB** Sec. Mkt. **$20**

QXM 481-7
NOEL R.R.: MILK TANK CAR
Seventh in Series, 13/16" tall,
Dated 1995. **Artist:** Linda Sickman
☐ Purchased 19___ Pd $_____
MIB   NB   DB   BNT
☐ Want   Orig. Retail $6.75
NB $9   **MIB** Sec. Mkt. **$18**

QXM 478-7
NUTCRACKER GUILD
Second in Series, 1-1/8" tall,
Dated 1995. **Artist:** LindaSickman
☐ Purchased 19___ Pd $_____
MIB   NB   DB   BNT
☐ Want   Orig. Retail $5.75
NB $10   **MIB** Sec. Mkt. **$20**

QXM 481-9
OLD ENGLISH VILLAGE:
TUDOR HOUSE
Eighth in Series, 1" tall, Dated 1995. **Artist:** Julia Lee
☐ Purchased 19___ Pd $_____
MIB   NB   DB   BNT
☐ Want   Orig. Retail $6.75
NB $10   **MIB** Sec. Mkt. **$19**

QXM 479-7
ON THE ROAD
Pressed Tin, 7/16" tall, Dated 1995. **Artist:** Linda Sickman
☐ Purchased 19___ Pd $_____
MIB   NB   DB   BNT
☐ Want   Orig. Retail $5.75
NB $8   **MIB** Sec. Mkt. **$16**

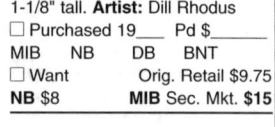

QXM 475-7
PEBBLES AND BAMM-BAMM: THE FLINTSTONES®
1-1/8" tall. **Artist:** Dill Rhodus
☐ Purchased 19___ Pd $_____
MIB   NB   DB   BNT
☐ Want   Orig. Retail $9.75
NB $8   **MIB** Sec. Mkt. **$15**

QXM 407-7
PRECIOUS CREATIONS
1-1/4" tall, Dated 1995.
Artist: Linda Sickman
☐ Purchased 19___ Pd $_____
MIB   NB   DB   BNT
☐ Want   Orig. Retail $9.75
NB $11   **MIB** Sec. Mkt. **$19**

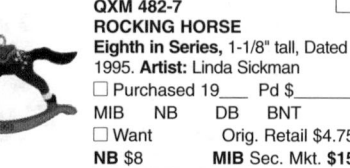

QXM 482-7
ROCKING HORSE
Eighth in Series, 1-1/8" tall, Dated 1995. **Artist:** Linda Sickman
☐ Purchased 19___ Pd $_____
MIB   NB   DB   BNT
☐ Want   Orig. Retail $4.75
NB $8   **MIB** Sec. Mkt. **$15**

QXM 477-9
SANTA'S LITTLE BIG TOP
FIRST IN SERIES, 1-5/8" tall, Dated 1995. **Artist:** Ken Crow
☐ Purchased 19___ Pd $_____
MIB   NB   DB   BNT
☐ Want   Orig. Retail $6.75
NB $11   **MIB** Sec. Mkt. **$19**

QXM 404-7
SANTA'S VISIT
Lighted, Batteries included,
1-7/16" tall, Dated 1995.
Artist: Ken Crow
☐ Purchased 19___ Pd $_____
MIB   NB   DB   BNT
☐ Want   Orig. Retail $7.75
NB $9   **MIB** Sec. Mkt. **$17**

QXM 414-1
SHINING STAR TREE-TOPPER
Dimensional Brass
☐ Purchased 19___ Pd $_____
MIB   NB   DB   BNT
☐ Want   Orig. Retail $9.95
NB $12   **MIB** Sec. Mkt. **$21**

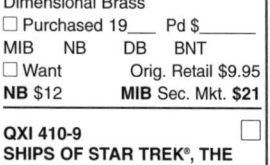

QXI 410-9
SHIPS OF STAR TREK®, THE
Set of three, Dated 1995.
☐ Purchased 19___ Pd $_____
MIB   NB   DB   BNT
☐ Want   Orig. Retail $19.95
NB $13   **MIB** Sec. Mkt. **$22**

QXM 403-9
STARLIT NATIVITY
Lighted, Batteries included,
1-7/16" tall, Dated 1995.
Artist: Duane Unruh
☐ Purchased 19___ Pd $_____
MIB   NB   DB   BNT
☐ Want   Orig. Retail $7.75
NB $10   **MIB** Sec. Mkt. **$20**

QXM 409-9
SUGARPLUM DREAMS,
15/16" tall, Dated 1995.
Artist: Ken Crow
☐ Purchased 19___ Pd $_____
MIB   NB   DB   BNT
☐ Want   Orig. Retail $4.75
NB $8   **MIB** Sec. Mkt. **$15**

QXM 446-7
TINY TOON ADVENTURES: CALAMITY COYOTE
1-7/16" tall.
Artist: Anita Marra Rogers
☐ Purchased 19___ Pd $_____
MIB   NB   DB   BNT
☐ Want   Orig. Retail $6.75
NB $9   **MIB** Sec. Mkt. **$16**

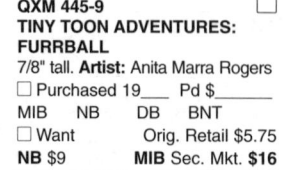

QXM 445-9
TINY TOON ADVENTURES: FURRBALL
7/8" tall. **Artist:** Anita Marra Rogers
☐ Purchased 19___ Pd $_____
MIB   NB   DB   BNT
☐ Want   Orig. Retail $5.75
NB $9   **MIB** Sec. Mkt. **$16**

QXM 446-9
TINY TOON ADVENTURES: LITTLE BEEPER
3/4" tall. **Artist:** Anita Marra Rogers
☐ Purchased 19___ Pd $_____
MIB   NB   DB   BNT
☐ Want   Orig. Retail $5.75
NB $9   **MIB** Sec. Mkt. **$16**

TINY TREASURES
Set of Six Ornaments, 5/8" tall to
1-3/8" tall, Dated 1995.
Precious Gem, Smelling Sweet,
Glamour Girl, All Tied Up, Powder
Puff Pal, Just Reflecting
Artist: Ed Seale
☐ Purchased 19___ Pd $_____
MIB   NB   DB   BNT
☐ Want   Orig. Retail $29.00
NB $23   **MIB** Sec. Mkt. **$45**

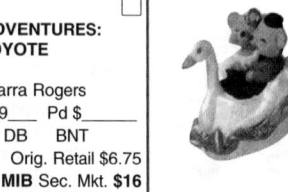

QXM 402-9
TUNNEL OF LOVE
13/16" tall, Dated 1995.
Artist: Ken Crow
☐ Purchased 19___ Pd $_____
MIB   NB   DB   BNT
☐ Want   Orig. Retail $4.75
NB $7   **MIB** Sec. Mkt. **$12**

1995
Easter Ornament Collection

QEO 820-7 ☐
APPLE BLOSSOM LANE
FIRST IN SERIES, Dated 1995.
☐ Purchased 19___ Pd $_____
MIB   NB   DB   BNT
☐ Want   Orig. Retail $8.95
NB $10   **MIB** Sec. Mkt. **$20**

QEO 825-3 ☐
APRIL SHOWERS
Dated 1995.
☐ Purchased 19___ Pd $_____
MIB   NB   DB   BNT
☐ Want   Orig. Retail $6.95
NB $7   **MIB** Sec. Mkt. **$15**

QEO 823-7 ☐
BABY'S FIRST EASTER
Dated 1995.
☐ Purchased 19___ Pd $_____
MIB   NB   DB   BNT
☐ Want   Orig. Retail $7.95
NB $9   **MIB** Sec. Mkt. **$18**

QEO 821-9 ☐
COLLECTOR'S PLATE:
CATCHING THE BREEZE
Second in Series, Porcelain,
Dated 1995.
☐ Purchased 19___ Pd $_____
MIB   NB   DB   BNT
☐ Want   Orig. Retail $7.95
NB $10   **MIB** Sec. Mkt. **$19**

QEO 824-9 ☐
CRAYOLA®:
"PICTURE PERFECT"
Dated 1995.
☐ Purchased 19___ Pd $_____
MIB   NB   DB   BNT
☐ Want   Orig. Retail $7.95
NB $10   **MIB** Sec. Mkt. **$19**

QEO 823-9 ☐
DAUGHTER
Dated 1995.
☐ Purchased 19___ Pd $_____
MIB   NB   DB   BNT
☐ Want   Orig. Retail $5.95
NB $7   **MIB** Sec. Mkt. **$15**

QEO 820-9 ☐
GARDEN CLUB
FIRST IN SERIES, Dated 1995.
☐ Purchased 19___ Pd $_____
MIB   NB   DB   BNT
☐ Want   Orig. Retail $7.95
NB $10   **MIB** Sec. Mkt. **$21**

QEO 827-7 ☐
HAM 'N EGGS
☐ Purchased 19___ Pd $_____
MIB   NB   DB   BNT
☐ Want   Orig. Retail $7.95
NB $7   **MIB** Sec. Mkt. **$14**

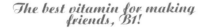

The best vitamin for making friends, B1!

QEO 821-7 ☐
HERE COMES EASTER
Second in Series, Dated 1995.
☐ Purchased 19___ Pd $_____
MIB   NB   DB   BNT
☐ Want   Orig. Retail $7.95
NB $8   **MIB** Sec. Mkt. **$19**

QEO 826-7 ☐
LILY
Brass.
☐ Purchased 19___ Pd $_____
MIB   NB   DB   BNT
☐ Want   Orig. Retail $6.95
NB $6   **MIB** Sec. Mkt. **$12**

QEO 827-9 ☐
LOONEY TUNES: BUGS BUNNY
☐ Purchased 19___ Pd $_____
MIB   NB   DB   BNT
☐ Want   Orig. Retail $8.95
NB $10   **MIB** Sec. Mkt. **$20**

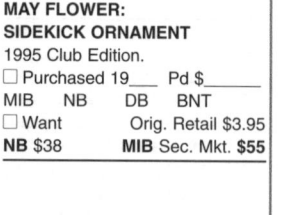

QXC 824-6
MAY FLOWER:
SIDEKICK ORNAMENT
1995 Club Edition.
☐ Purchased 19___ Pd $_____
MIB   NB   DB   BNT
☐ Want   Orig. Retail $3.95
NB $38   **MIB** Sec. Mkt. **$55**

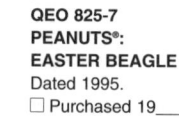

QEO 826-9
MINIATURE TRAIN
"EASTER EGGSPRESS"
Dated 1995.
☐ Purchased 19___ Pd $_____
MIB   NB   DB   BNT
☐ Want   Orig. Retail $4.95
NB $7   **MIB** Sec. Mkt. **$14**

QEO 825-7
PEANUTS®:
EASTER BEAGLE
Dated 1995.
☐ Purchased 19___ Pd $_____
MIB   NB   DB   BNT
☐ Want   Orig. Retail $7.95
NB $16   **MIB** Sec. Mkt. **$24**

QEO 824-7
SON
Dated 1995.
☐ Purchased 19___ Pd $_____
MIB   NB   DB   BNT
☐ Want   Orig. Retail $5.95
NB $7   **MIB** Sec. Mkt. **$15**

QEO 806-9
SPRINGTIME BARBIE
FIRST IN SERIES.
☐ Purchased 19___ Pd $_____
MIB   NB   DB   BNT
☐ Want   Orig. Retail $12.95
NB $17   **MIB** Sec. Mkt. **$35**

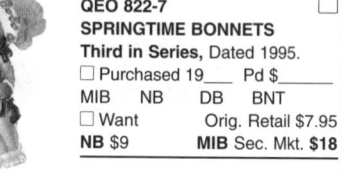

QEO 822-7
SPRINGTIME BONNETS
Third in Series, Dated 1995.
☐ Purchased 19___ Pd $_____
MIB   NB   DB   BNT
☐ Want   Orig. Retail $7.95
NB $9   **MIB** Sec. Mkt. **$18**

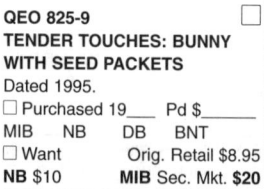

QEO 825-9
TENDER TOUCHES: BUNNY
WITH SEED PACKETS
Dated 1995.
☐ Purchased 19___ Pd $_____
MIB   NB   DB   BNT
☐ Want   Orig. Retail $8.95
NB $10   **MIB** Sec. Mkt. **$20**

QEO 822-9
THREE FLOWERPOT FRIENDS
Dated 1995.
☐ Purchased 19___ Pd $_____
MIB   NB   DB   BNT
☐ Want   Orig. Retail $14.95
NB $17   **MIB** Sec. Mkt. **$25**

-R. STUBLER-

"Next time I put goodies in the
back of the truck for the hired
hand, have some self control!"

1996 Collection

QXC 417-4   1937 STEELCRAFT AUBURN BY MURRAY®: KEEPSAKE CLUB ☐

Comments: Die-cast metal, Dated 1996.
Based on a 1935 Auburn pedal car design. Available to club members only. **Artist:** Don Palmiter

☐ Purchased 19__ Pd $____ MIB   NB   DB   BNT
☐ Want   Orig. Ret. $14.95   **MIB** Sec.Mkt. **$50**

AIRMAIL FOR SANTA ☐

Comments: Handcrafted, Dated 1996.
A flying red bird carries a special envelope addressed to Mr. and Mrs. S. Claus and Elves. Gift membership bonus ornament available only to club members who enrolled a new member in 1996.

☐ Purchased 19__ Pd $____ MIB   NB   DB   BNT
☐ Want   Orig. Ret. Membership Bonus
                      MIB Sec.Mkt. **$20**

QX 621-1   A LITTLE SONG AND DANCE ☐

Comments: Handcrafted, Dated 1996.
These two little mice sing and dance as they play their horn.
Artist: Ken Crow

☐ Purchased 19__ Pd $____ MIB   NB   DB   BNT
☐ Want   Orig. Ret. $9.95   **MIB** Sec. Mkt. **$15**

QX 550-7   A TREE FOR SNOOPY ☐

Comments: Handcrafted, Dated 1996.
Complements "A Tree for WOODSTOCK" Miniature Ornament. Snoopy is bringing home his Christmas tree on his sled.
Artist: Bob Siedler

☐ Purchased 19__ Pd $____ MIB   NB   DB   BNT
☐ Want   Orig. Ret. $8.95   **MIB** Sec. Mkt. **$20**

QX 524-1   ALL-AMERICAN TRUCKS: 1955 CHEVROLET CAMEO ☐

Comments: **Second in Series**, Handcrafted, Dated 1996.
This '55 Chevy is bringing home the Christmas tree for the holidays. **Artist:** Don Palmiter

☐ Purchased 19__ Pd $____ MIB   NB   DB   BNT
☐ Want   Orig. Ret. $13.95   **MIB** Sec. Mkt. **$25**

QX 556-4   ALL GOD'S CHILDREN: CHRISTY ☐

Comments: **FIRST IN SERIES**, Handcrafted, Dated 1996.
A precious African American child holds a star which she has painted with great care. **Artist:** M. Root

☐ Purchased 19 __Pd $____MIB   NB   DB   BNT
☐ Want   Orig. Ret. $12.95   **MIB** Sec. Mkt. **$23**

QX 590-1   ANTLERS AWEIGH! ☐

Comments: Handcrafted, Dated 1996.
Those who love the water, will enjoy this reindeer on his waverunner. **Artist:** Robert Chad

☐ Purchased 19__ Pd $____ MIB   NB   DB   BNT
☐ Want   Orig. Ret. $9.95   **MIB** Sec. Mkt. **$17**

QX 612-1   APPLE FOR TEACHER ☐

Comments: Handcrafted, Dated 1996.
A special gift for that special teacher. **Artist:** Nina Aube

☐ Purchased 19__ Pd $____ MIB   NB   DB   BNT
☐ Want   Orig. Ret. $7.95   **MIB** Sec. Mkt. **$14**

QXI 571-1   AT THE BALL PARK: NOLAN RYAN ☐

Comments: **FIRST IN SERIES**, Handcrafted, Dated 1996.
Ryan is up for the final pitch to decide who will win the game. Has been found with an errored stamp that reads "NLB" instead of "MLB". This was a top seller during the '96-'97 selling season.
Artist: Dill Rhodus

☐ Purchased 19__ Pd $____ MIB   NB   DB   BNT
☐ Want   Orig. Ret. $14.95   **MIB** Sec. Mkt. **$30**

QX 575-1   BABY'S FIRST CHRISTMAS ☐

Comments: Fine Porcelain Collector's Plate, Dated 1996.
Artist: Bessie Pease Gutmann

☐ Purchased 19__ Pd $____ MIB   NB   DB   BNT
☐ Want   Orig. Ret. $10.95   **MIB** Sec. Mkt. **$21**

QX 575-4   BABY'S FIRST CHRISTMAS ☐

Comments: Handcrafted, Dated 1996.
An infant's shoe holds the little one's rattle and bear. "Baby's First Christmas" is written on side of shoe. **Artist:** Patricia Andrews

☐ Purchased 19__ Pd $____ MIB   NB   DB   BNT
☐ Want   Orig. Ret. $9.95   **MIB** Sec. Mkt. **$20**

QX 576-1   BABY'S FIRST CHRISTMAS ☐

Comments: Photo holder, Dated 1996.
A yellow diaper pin opens to display a photo of your baby.
Artist: Ed Seale

☐ Purchased 19__ Pd $____ MIB   NB   DB   BNT
☐ Want   Orig. Ret. $7.95   **MIB** Sec. Mkt. **$18**

QX 574-4 BABY'S FIRST CHRISTMAS: BEATRIX POTTER™ ☐

Comments: Fine Porcelain, Dated 1996.
A mama rabbit rocks her little one to sleep.
Artist: LaDene Votruba

☐ Purchased 19__ Pd $____ MIB   NB   DB   BNT
☐ Want   Orig. Ret. $18.95   **MIB** Sec. Mkt. **$29**

QX 576-4 BABY'S FIRST CHRISTMAS: CHILD'S AGE COLLECTION ☐

Comments: Handcrafted, Dated 1996.
This little bear, with a pacifier in its mouth, is trying to hold onto its stocking and cookie with a number 1 on it.
Artist: Ken Crow

☐ Purchased 19__ Pd $____ MIB   NB   DB   BNT
☐ Want   Orig. Ret. $7.95   **MIB** Sec. Mkt. **$17**

QLX 740-4 BABY'S FIRST CHRISTMAS ☐

Comments: Light and Music, Dated 1996.
This angel is holding a glowing star "night light" while baby sleeps. Plays "Brahm's Lullaby." **Artist:** John Francis (Collin)

☐ Purchased 19__ Pd $____ MIB   NB   DB   BNT
☐ Want   Orig. Ret. $22.00   **MIB** Sec. Mkt.**$29**

QX 577-1 BABY'S SECOND CHRISTMAS: CHILD'S AGE COLLECTION ☐

Comments: Handcrafted, Dated 1996.
A sugar cookie with a number two has been found with this little bear's stocking. **Artist:** Ken Crow

☐ Purchased 19__ Pd $____ MIB   NB   DB   BNT
☐ Want   Orig. Ret. $7.95   **MIB** Sec. Mkt. **$19**

QXI 654-1 BARBIE™: ENCHANTED EVENING BARBIE® DOLL ☐

Comments: **Third in Series**, Handcrafted, Dated 1996.
Barbie, in one of her favorite evening gowns, is ready for a romantic night on the town. This was a top seller during the '96-'97 selling season. **Artist:** Patricia Andrews

☐ Purchased 19__ Pd $____ MIB   NB   DB   BNT
☐ Want   Orig. Ret. $14.95   **MIB** Sec. Mkt. **$25**

QXC 418-1 BARBIE®: BASED ON THE 1988 HAPPY HOLIDAYS KEEPSAKE CLUB ☐

Comments: **FIRST IN SERIES**, Handcrafted.
Complements the Keepsake Ornament Holiday Barbie™.
Available to club members only. **Artist:** Patricia Andrews

☐ Purchased 19__ Pd $____ MIB   NB   DB   BNT
☐ Want   Orig. Ret. $14.95   **MIB** Sec. Mkt. **$33**

QX 530-4 BASEBALL HEROES: SATCHEL PAIGE ☐

Comments: **Third in Series**, Handcrafted, Dated 1996.
This series continues with a tribute to baseball great Satchel Paige. **Artist:** Dill Rhodus

☐ Purchased 19__ Pd $____ MIB   NB   DB   BNT
☐ Want   Orig. Ret. $12.95   **MIB** Sec. Mkt. **$24**

QX 603-1 BOUNCE PASS ☐

Comments: Handcrafted, Dated 1996.
Look at #96 go down that court! Ball bounces on a spring.
Artist: Bob Siedler

☐ Purchased 19__ Pd $____ MIB   NB   DB   BNT
☐ Want   Orig. Ret. $7.95   **MIB** Sec. Mkt. **$13**

QX 601-4 BOWL 'EM OVER ☐

Comments: Handcrafted, Dated 1996.
This mouse is going for a strike with his big purple bowling ball. **Artist:** Bob Siedler

☐ Purchased 19__ Pd $____ MIB   NB   DB   BNT
☐ Want   Orig. Ret. $7.95   **MIB** Sec. Mkt. **$14**

QX 554-1 BOY SCOUTS OF AMERICA GROWTH OF A LEADER ☐

Comments: Ceramic, Dated 1996.
Artwork by Norman Rockwell.

☐ Purchased 19__ Pd $____ MIB   NB   DB   BNT
☐ Want   Orig. Ret. $9.95   **MIB** Sec. Mkt. **$12**

QX 564-1 CAT NAPS ☐

Comments: **Third in Series**, Handcrafted, Dated 1996.
This lazy Siamese cat has found her favorite sleeping place in a fabric lined basket. **Artist:** Dill Rhodus

☐ Purchased 19__ Pd $____ MIB   NB   DB   BNT
☐ Want   Orig. Ret. $7.95 **NB** $10   **MIB** Sec. Mkt. **$20**

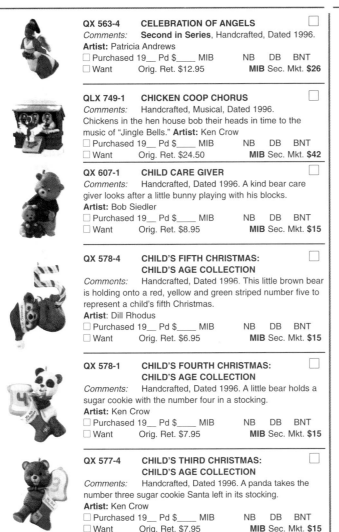
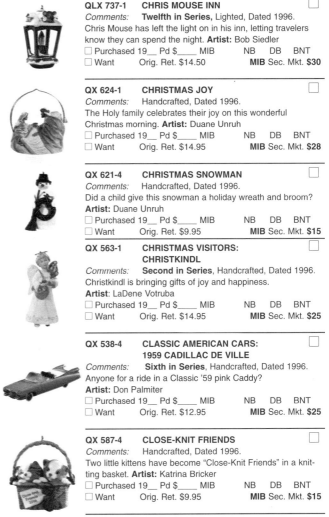

QX 563-4   **CELEBRATION OF ANGELS**
Comments: **Second in Series,** Handcrafted, Dated 1996.
Artist: Patricia Andrews
☐ Purchased 19__   Pd $____   MIB   NB   DB   BNT
☐ Want   Orig. Ret. $12.95   **MIB** Sec. Mkt. **$26**

QLX 749-1   **CHICKEN COOP CHORUS**
Comments: Handcrafted, Musical, Dated 1996.
Chickens in the hen house bob their heads in time to the
music of "Jingle Bells." **Artist:** Ken Crow
☐ Purchased 19__   Pd $____   MIB   NB   DB   BNT
☐ Want   Orig. Ret. $24.50   **MIB** Sec. Mkt. **$42**

QX 607-1   **CHILD CARE GIVER**
Comments: Handcrafted, Dated 1996. A kind bear care
giver looks after a little bunny playing with his blocks.
Artist: Bob Siedler
☐ Purchased 19__   Pd $____   MIB   NB   DB   BNT
☐ Want   Orig. Ret. $8.95   **MIB** Sec. Mkt. **$15**

QX 578-4   **CHILD'S FIFTH CHRISTMAS:**
                CHILD'S AGE COLLECTION
Comments: Handcrafted, Dated 1996. This little brown bear
is holding onto a red, yellow and green striped number five to
represent a child's fifth Christmas.
Artist: Dill Rhodus
☐ Purchased 19__   Pd $____   MIB   NB   DB   BNT
☐ Want   Orig. Ret. $6.95   **MIB** Sec. Mkt. **$15**

QX 578-1   **CHILD'S FOURTH CHRISTMAS:**
                CHILD'S AGE COLLECTION
Comments: Handcrafted, Dated 1996. A little bear holds a
sugar cookie with the number four in a stocking.
Artist: Ken Crow
☐ Purchased 19__   Pd $____   MIB   NB   DB   BNT
☐ Want   Orig. Ret. $7.95   **MIB** Sec. Mkt. **$15**

QX 577-4   **CHILD'S THIRD CHRISTMAS:**
                CHILD'S AGE COLLECTION
Comments: Handcrafted, Dated 1996. A panda takes the
number three sugar cookie Santa left in its stocking.
Artist: Ken Crow
☐ Purchased 19__   Pd $____   MIB   NB   DB   BNT
☐ Want   Orig. Ret. $7.95   **MIB** Sec. Mkt. **$15**

QLX 737-1   **CHRIS MOUSE INN**
Comments: **Twelfth in Series,** Lighted, Dated 1996.
Chris Mouse has left the light on in his inn, letting travelers
know they can spend the night. **Artist:** Bob Siedler
☐ Purchased 19__   Pd $____   MIB   NB   DB   BNT
☐ Want   Orig. Ret. $14.50   **MIB** Sec. Mkt. **$30**

QX 624-1   **CHRISTMAS JOY**
Comments: Handcrafted, Dated 1996.
The Holy family celebrates their joy on this wonderful
Christmas morning. **Artist:** Duane Unruh
☐ Purchased 19__   Pd $____   MIB   NB   DB   BNT
☐ Want   Orig. Ret. $14.95   **MIB** Sec. Mkt. **$28**

QX 621-4   **CHRISTMAS SNOWMAN**
Comments: Handcrafted, Dated 1996.
Did a child give this snowman a holiday wreath and broom?
Artist: Duane Unruh
☐ Purchased 19__   Pd $____   MIB   NB   DB   BNT
☐ Want   Orig. Ret. $9.95   **MIB** Sec. Mkt. **$15**

QX 563-1   **CHRISTMAS VISITORS:**
                CHRISTKINDL
Comments: **Second in Series,** Handcrafted, Dated 1996.
Christkindl is bringing gifts of joy and happiness.
Artist: LaDene Votruba
☐ Purchased 19__   Pd $____   MIB   NB   DB   BNT
☐ Want   Orig. Ret. $14.95   **MIB** Sec. Mkt. **$25**

QX 538-4   **CLASSIC AMERICAN CARS:**
                1959 CADILLAC DE VILLE
Comments: **Sixth in Series,** Handcrafted, Dated 1996.
Anyone for a ride in a Classic '59 pink Caddy?
Artist: Don Palmiter
☐ Purchased 19__   Pd $____   MIB   NB   DB   BNT
☐ Want   Orig. Ret. $12.95   **MIB** Sec. Mkt. **$25**

QX 587-4   **CLOSE-KNIT FRIENDS**
Comments: Handcrafted, Dated 1996.
Two little kittens have become "Close-Knit Friends" in a knit-
ting basket. **Artist:** Katrina Bricker
☐ Purchased 19__   Pd $____   MIB   NB   DB   BNT
☐ Want   Orig. Ret. $9.95   **MIB** Sec. Mkt. **$15**

QX 580-1 COLLECTOR'S PLATE: ☐
OUR FIRST CHRISTMAS TOGETHER
Comments: Fine Porcelain, Dated 1996
A tender moment is depicted on this plate, as two children kiss in a doorway. Display stand included.
☐ Purchased 19__ Pd $____ MIB   NB   DB   BNT
☐ Want   Orig. Ret. $10.95   **MIB** Sec. Mkt. **$20**

QX 624-4 COME ALL YE FAITHFUL: ☐
COLLECTOR'S CHOICE
Comments: Handcrafted, Dated 1996. The church opens to reveal a Nativity scene at the altar. **Artist:** Ken Crow
☐ Purchased 19__ Pd $____ MIB   NB   DB   BNT
☐ Want   Orig. Ret. $12.95   **MIB** Sec. Mkt. **$24**

QX 539-1 CRAYOLA® SERIES: ☐
BRIGHT FLYING COLORS
Comments: **Eighth in Series**, Handcrafted, Dated 1996.
This little mouse is ready for a colorful high flying experience. Propeller spins and wheels turn. **Artist:** Ken Crow
☐ Purchased 19__ Pd $____ MIB   NB   DB   BNT
☐ Want   Orig. Ret. $10.95   **MIB** Sec. Mkt. **$25**

QX 583-1 DAD ☐
Comments: Handcrafted, Dated 1996.
Dad won't miss a thing this Christmas with his new video camera. **Artist:** Bob Siedler
☐ Purchased 19__ Pd $____ MIB   NB   DB   BNT
☐ Want   Orig. Ret. $7.95   **MIB** Sec. Mkt. **$16**

QX 607-7 DAUGHTER ☐
Comments: Handcrafted, Dated 1996.
A little bear is playing with her Jack-in-the-box trying to see what makes it pop. **Artist:** Don Palmiter
☐ Purchased 19__ Pd $____ MIB   NB   DB   BNT
☐ Want   Orig. Ret. $8.95   **MIB** Sec. Mkt. **$19**

QX 556-1 DOLLS OF THE WORLD: ☐
NATIVE AMERICAN BARBIE
Comments: *FIRST IN SERIES*, Handcrafted, Dated 1996.
This traditional Barbie with the jewelry and clothing of Native Americans was a top seller during the '96-'97 selling season. **Artist:** Patricia Andrews
☐ Purchased 19__ Pd $____ MIB   NB   DB   BNT
☐ Want   Orig. Ret. $14.95   **MIB** Sec. Mkt. **$30-35**

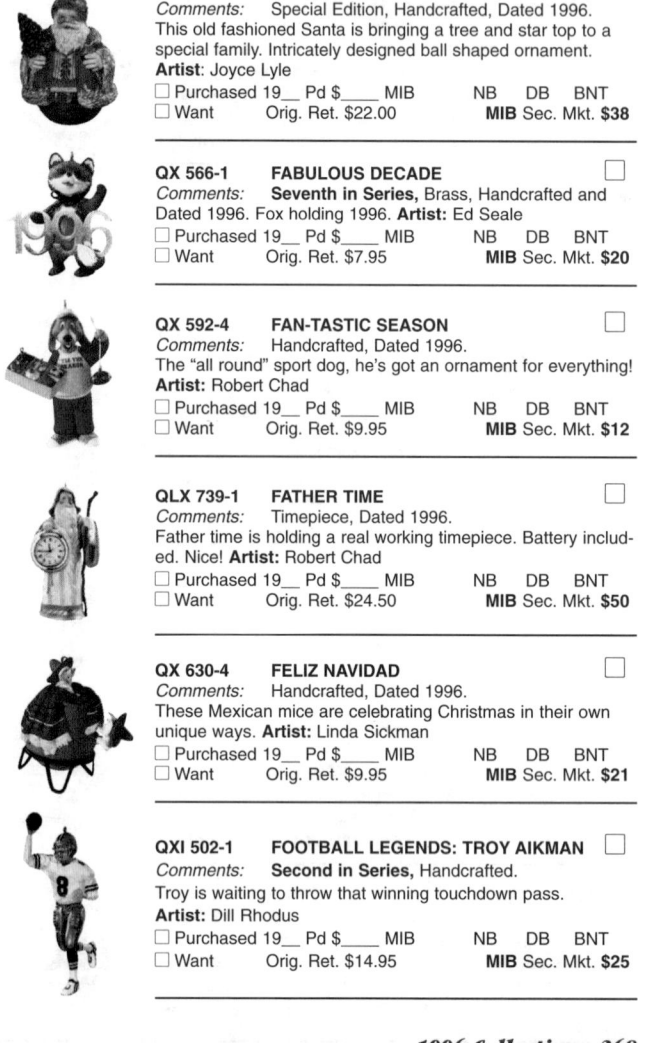

QX 571-4 EVERGREEN SANTA: SPECIAL EDITION ☐
Comments: Special Edition, Handcrafted, Dated 1996.
This old fashioned Santa is bringing a tree and star top to a special family. Intricately designed ball shaped ornament.
Artist: Joyce Lyle
☐ Purchased 19__ Pd $____ MIB   NB   DB   BNT
☐ Want   Orig. Ret. $22.00   **MIB** Sec. Mkt. **$38**

QX 566-1 FABULOUS DECADE ☐
Comments: **Seventh in Series,** Brass, Handcrafted and Dated 1996. Fox holding 1996. **Artist:** Ed Seale
☐ Purchased 19__ Pd $____ MIB   NB   DB   BNT
☐ Want   Orig. Ret. $7.95   **MIB** Sec. Mkt. **$20**

QX 592-4 FAN-TASTIC SEASON ☐
Comments: Handcrafted, Dated 1996.
The "all round" sport dog, he's got an ornament for everything!
Artist: Robert Chad
☐ Purchased 19__ Pd $____ MIB   NB   DB   BNT
☐ Want   Orig. Ret. $9.95   **MIB** Sec. Mkt. **$12**

QLX 739-1 FATHER TIME ☐
Comments: Timepiece, Dated 1996.
Father time is holding a real working timepiece. Battery included. Nice! **Artist:** Robert Chad
☐ Purchased 19__ Pd $____ MIB   NB   DB   BNT
☐ Want   Orig. Ret. $24.50   **MIB** Sec. Mkt. **$50**

QX 630-4 FELIZ NAVIDAD ☐
Comments: Handcrafted, Dated 1996.
These Mexican mice are celebrating Christmas in their own unique ways. **Artist:** Linda Sickman
☐ Purchased 19__ Pd $____ MIB   NB   DB   BNT
☐ Want   Orig. Ret. $9.95   **MIB** Sec. Mkt. **$21**

QXI 502-1 FOOTBALL LEGENDS: TROY AIKMAN ☐
Comments: **Second in Series**, Handcrafted.
Troy is waiting to throw that winning touchdown pass.
Artist: Dill Rhodus
☐ Purchased 19__ Pd $____ MIB   NB   DB   BNT
☐ Want   Orig. Ret. $14.95   **MIB** Sec. Mkt. **$25**

QX 568-1   FROSTY FRIENDS
Comments: **Seventeenth in Series**, Handcrafted, Dated
1996. With icicles for pool cues, these two famous friends play
a game of ice pool. **Artist:** Ed Seale
☐ Purchased 19__ Pd $____ MIB   NB   DB   BNT
☐ Want   Orig. Ret. $10.95   **MIB** Sec. Mkt. **$19**

QX 623-1   GLAD TIDINGS
Comments: Handcrafted, Dated 1996.
This angel is bringing glad tidings from the heavens above.
Artist: Joyce Lyle
☐ Purchased 19__ Pd $____ MIB   NB   DB   BNT
☐ Want   Orig. Ret. $14.95   **MIB** Sec. Mkt. **$28**

QX 600-1   GOAL LINE GLORY
Comments: Handcrafted, Dated 1996. Set of 2. These pen-
guins are out on the ice playing a little hockey.
Artist: Ed Seale
☐ Purchased 19__ Pd $____ MIB   NB   DB   BNT
☐ Want   Orig. Ret. $12.95   **MIB** Sec. Mkt. **$27**

QX 584-1   GODCHILD
Comments: Handcrafted, Dated 1996.
A little mouse says his prayers before going to bed.
Artist: Anita Marra Rogers
☐ Purchased 19__ Pd $____ MIB   NB   DB   BNT
☐ Want   Orig. Ret. $8.95   **MIB** Sec. Mkt. **$17**

QX 569-7   GRANDDAUGHTER
Comments: Handcrafted, Dated 1996.
A black and white kitten, with holly in her bow, rides on her
sled. "Granddaughter" is written on her yellow bow.
Artist: Anita Marra Rogers
☐ Purchased 19__ Pd $____ MIB   NB   DB   BNT
☐ Want   Orig. Ret. $7.95   **MIB** Sec. Mkt. **$17**

QX 584-4   GRANDMA
Comments: Handcrafted, Dated 1996.
A little bear gives a special Christmas card to Grandma bear.
Artist: LaDene Votruba
☐ Purchased 19__ Pd $____ MIB   NB   DB   BNT
☐ Want   Orig. Ret. $8.95   **MIB** Sec. Mkt. **$19**

QX 585-1   GRANDPA
Comments: Handcrafted, Dated 1996.
Hold on tight as Grandpa and Grand "pup" fly down the hill on
their red sled. **Artist:** LaDene Votruba
☐ Purchased 19__ Pd $____ MIB   NB   DB   BNT
☐ Want   Orig. Ret. $8.95   **MIB** Sec. Mkt. **$16**

QX 569-9   GRANDSON
Comments: Handcrafted, Dated 1996. A Dalmatian puppy
rides on his sled. Grandson is written on his purple bow.
Artist: Anita Marra Rogers
☐ Purchased 19__ Pd $____ MIB   NB   DB   BNT
☐ Want   Orig. Ret. $7.95   **MIB** Sec. Mkt. **$15**

QX 590-4   HAPPY HOLI-DOZE
Comments: Handcrafted, Dated 1996.
After a good holiday meal and game, this bear is ready for a
long winter nap. **Artist:** Dill Rhodus
☐ Purchased 19__ Pd $____ MIB   NB   DB   BNT
☐ Want   Orig. Ret. $9.95   **MIB** Sec. Mkt. **$15**

QX 581-4   HEARTS FULL OF LOVE
Comment: Handcrafted, Dated 1996.
These two loveable mice are blowing a big heart full of love.
First production had "1996" printed on the wrong side of the
clear acrylic heart and it was backwards. This was corrected.
(Errored $25 up)**Artist:** Dill Rhodus
☐ Purchased 19__ Pd $____ MIB   NB   DB   BNT
☐ Want   Orig. Ret. $9.95   **MIB** Sec. Mkt. **$18**

QX 568-4   HERE COMES SANTA: SANTA'S 4X4
Comments: **Eighteenth in Series**, Handcrafted, Dated
1996. Here comes Santa in his 4X4; there is no stopping him
now. **Artist:** Ed Seale
☐ Purchased 19__ Pd $____ MIB   NB   DB   BNT
☐ Want   Orig. Ret. $14.95   **MIB** Sec. Mkt. **$32**

QX 606-4   HIGH STYLE
Comments: Handcrafted, Dated 1996.
This woman is really in the holiday spirit with her Christmas
tree hair style. **Artist:** Robert Chad
☐ Purchased 19__ Pd $____ MIB   NB   DB   BNT
☐ Want   Orig. Ret. $8.95   **MIB** Sec. Mkt. **$19**

QX 613-4   HILLSIDE EXPRESS ☐
Comments: Handcrafted, Dated 1996.
A toboggan ride for these forest friends is a lot of fun.
Artist: Nina Aube
☐ Purchased 19__ Pd $____ MIB   NB   DB   BNT
☐ Want   Orig. Ret. $12.95
                                    MIB Sec. Mkt. **$25**

QXI 537-1   HOLIDAY BARBIE™ ☐
Comments: **Fourth in Series**, Handcrafted, Dated 1996.
Barbie is dressed in a gold three tier dress with an overcoat
trimmed with white fur. Her white fur hat and muff complete
her ensemble. **Artist:** Patricia Andrews
☐ Purchased 19__ Pd $____ MIB   NB   DB   BNT
☐ Want   Orig. Ret. $14.95
                                    MIB Sec. Mkt. **$30**

QX 620-1   HOLIDAY HAUL ☐
Comments: Handcrafted, Dated 1996.
One of Santa's reindeer uses his John Deere tractor to haul in
his Christmas tree. **Artist:** Linda Sickman
☐ Purchased 19__ Pd $____ MIB   NB   DB   BNT
☐ Want   Orig. Ret. $14.95
                                    MIB Sec. Mkt. **$32**

HOLIDAY WISHES: 101 DALMATIANS ☐
Comments: Handpainted porcelain, 3-1/4" dia., Dated 1996.
Hallmark and Disney teamed their efforts with this delightful
collector's plate ornament, created to commemorate the live-
action version of 101 Dalmatians.
☐ Purchased 19__ Pd $____ MIB   NB   DB   BNT
☐ Want   Orig. Ret. $14.95   **MIB** Sec. Mkt. **$20**

QXI 501-4   HOOP STARS: LARRY BIRD ☐
Comments: **Second in Series**, Handcrafted.
Bird is up for that three point shot to win the game.
Artist: Dill Rhodus
☐ Purchased 19__ Pd $____ MIB   NB   DB   BNT
☐ Want   Orig. Ret. $14.95
                                    MIB Sec. Mkt. **$25**

QXI 635-1   HUNCHBACK OF NOTRE DAME, THE: ☐
               ESMERALDA AND DJALI
Comments: Handcrafted.
The gypsy girl Esmeralda and her goat Djali dance to entertain
us all.**Artist:** Ken Crow
☐ Purchased 19__ Pd $____ MIB   NB   DB   BNT
☐ Want   Orig. Ret. $14.95   **MIB** Sec. Mkt. **$36**

QXI 635-4   HUNCHBACK OF NOTRE DAME, THE: ☐
               LAVERNE, VICTOR AND HUGO
Comments: Handcrafted.
Three comedic gargoyle friends of Quasimodo. **Artist:** Ken Crow
☐ Purchased 19__ Pd $____ MIB   NB   DB   BNT
☐ Want   Orig. Ret. $12.95   **MIB** Sec. Mkt. **$23**

QXI 634-1   HUNCHBACK OF NOTRE DAME, THE: ☐
               QUASIMODO
Comments: Handcrafted, Dated 1996.
The hunchback, Quasimodo, swings in to wish you a Merry
Christmas. **Artist:** Ken Crow
☐ Purchased 19__ Pd $____ MIB   NB   DB   BNT
☐ Want   Orig. Ret. $9.95
               NB $10   **MIB** Sec. Mkt. **$14**

QX 607-4   HURRYING DOWNSTAIRS ☐
Comments: Handcrafted, Dated 1996.
This little one doesn't want to be last downstairs as he slides
down the fire pole. **Artist:** John Francis (Collin)
☐ Purchased 19__ Pd $____ MIB   NB   DB   BNT
☐ Want   Orig. Ret. $8.95
                                    MIB Sec. Mkt. **$17**

QX 589-1   I DIG GOLF ☐
Comments: Clip-on, Dated 1996.
This gopher is going to make it in one hole or the other.
Artist: Dill Rhodus
☐ Purchased 19__ Pd $____ MIB   NB   DB   BNT
☐ Want   Orig. Ret. $10.95   **MIB** Sec. Mkt. **$20**

QXI 653-1   IT'S A WONDERFUL LIFE™ ☐
Comments: Handcrafted, Dated 1996.
Anniversary Edition, Celebrating 50 years of this beloved film.
The bell rings to show that another angel has received its
wings. This ornament debuted late in '96. This was a top seller
during the '96-'97 selling season. **Artist:** Ken Crow
☐ Purchased 19__ Pd $____ MIB   NB   DB   BNT
☐ Want   Orig. Ret. $14.95
                                    MIB Sec. Mkt. **$30**

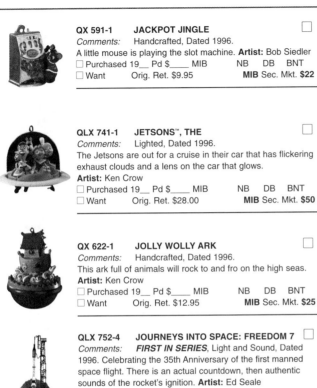

QX 591-1   JACKPOT JINGLE ☐
Comments: Handcrafted, Dated 1996.
A little mouse is playing the slot machine. **Artist:** Bob Siedler
☐ Purchased 19__ Pd $____ MIB   NB DB BNT
☐ Want   Orig. Ret. $9.95   **MIB** Sec. Mkt. **$22**

QLX 741-1   JETSONS™, THE ☐
Comments: Lighted, Dated 1996.
The Jetsons are out for a cruise in their car that has flickering
exhaust clouds and a lens on the car that glows.
Artist: Ken Crow
☐ Purchased 19__ Pd $____ MIB   NB DB BNT
☐ Want   Orig. Ret. $28.00   **MIB** Sec. Mkt. **$50**

QX 622-1   JOLLY WOLLY ARK ☐
Comments: Handcrafted, Dated 1996.
This ark full of animals will rock to and fro on the high seas.
Artist: Ken Crow
☐ Purchased 19__ Pd $____ MIB   NB DB BNT
☐ Want   Orig. Ret. $12.95   **MIB** Sec. Mkt. **$25**

QLX 752-4   JOURNEYS INTO SPACE: FREEDOM 7 ☐
Comments: **FIRST IN SERIES**, Light and Sound, Dated
1996. Celebrating the 35th Anniversary of the first manned
space flight. There is an actual countdown, then authentic
sounds of the rocket's ignition. **Artist:** Ed Seale
☐ Purchased 19__ Pd $____ MIB   NB DB BNT
☐ Want   Orig. Ret. $24.00   **MIB** Sec. Mkt. **$50**

QLX 733-9   JUKEBOX PARTY ☐
Comments: Light and Music, Dated 1996.
This glowing musical jukebox plays "Rockin' Around the
Christmas Tree." by Brenda Lee. **Artist:** Don Palmiter
☐ Purchased 19__ Pd $____ MIB   NB DB BNT
☐ Want   Orig. Ret. $24.50   **MIB** Sec. Mkt. **$55**

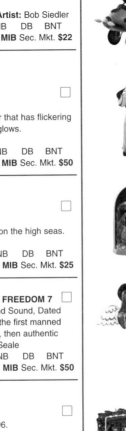

QX 536-4   KIDDIE CAR CLASSICS: ☐
MURRAY® AIRPLANE
Comments: **Third in Series**, Die-cast Metal, Dated 1996. A
great ornament! Popular series. **Artist:** Don Palmiter
☐ Purchased 19__ Pd $____ MIB   NB DB BNT
☐ Want   Orig. Ret. $13.95   **MIB** Sec. Mkt. **$26**

QX 627-4   KINDLY SHEPHERD ☐
Comments: Handcrafted, Dated 1996.
The kind shepherd is bringing one of his lost lambs back to
the herd. **Artist:** Patricia Andrews
☐ Purchased 19__ Pd $____ MIB   NB DB BNT
☐ Want   Orig. Ret. $12.95   **MIB** Sec. Mkt. **$27**

QLX 738-1   LET US ADORE HIM ☐
Comments: Lighted, Dated 1996.
The wise men have brought their gifts for Jesus to show their
adoration. **Artist:** Joyce Lyle
☐ Purchased 19__ Pd $____ MIB   NB DB BNT
☐ Want   Orig. Ret. $16.50   **MIB** Sec. Mkt. **$37**

QX 612-4   LIGHTING THE WAY ☐
Comments: Handcrafted, Dated 1996.
This angel is lighting the way for all late night travelers.
Artist: Robert Chad
☐ Purchased 19__ Pd $____ MIB   NB DB BNT
☐ Want   Orig. Ret. $12.95   **MIB** Sec. Mkt. **$26**

QX 553-1   LIONEL®: 700 E HUDSON ☐
STEAM LOCOMOTIVE
Comments: **FIRST IN SERIES,** Die-cast Metal, Dated 1996.
Replica of the original electric steam power train of the 1900s.
Should prove to be popular with train collectors. Plenty for sale
in first shipment.
☐ Purchased 19__ Pd $____ MIB   NB DB BNT
☐ Want   Orig. Ret. $18.95   **MIB** Sec. Mkt. **$45**

QX 550-4   LITTLE SPOONERS ☐
Comments: Handcrafted, Dated 1996.
Artwork by Norman Rockwell. Two fishing love birds watch the sun go down on a beautiful day. **Artist:** Duane Unruh
☐ Purchased 19___ Pd $_____ MIB   NB   DB   BNT
☐ Want   Orig. Ret. $12.95   **MIB** Sec. Mkt. **$20**

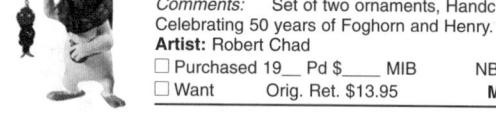

QX 544-4   LOONEY TUNES COLLECTION:
            FOGHORN LEGHORN AND HENRY HAWK ☐
Comments: Set of two ornaments, Handcrafted.
Celebrating 50 years of Foghorn and Henry.
Artist: Robert Chad
☐ Purchased 19___ Pd $_____ MIB   NB   DB   BNT
☐ Want   Orig. Ret. $13.95   **MIB** Sec. Mkt. **$20**

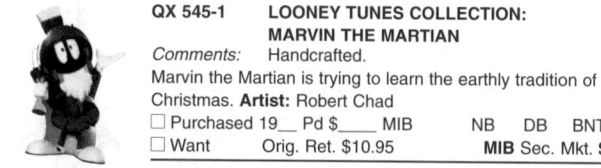

QX 545-1   LOONEY TUNES COLLECTION:
            MARVIN THE MARTIAN ☐
Comments: Handcrafted.
Marvin the Martian is trying to learn the earthly tradition of Christmas. **Artist:** Robert Chad
☐ Purchased 19___ Pd $_____ MIB   NB   DB   BNT
☐ Want   Orig. Ret. $10.95   **MIB** Sec. Mkt. **$22**

QX 631-1   MADAME ALEXANDER: CINDERELLA –1995 ☐
Comments: ***FIRST IN SERIES***, Handcrafted, Dated 1996.
Madame Alexander dolls are very popular because of their beautiful detail. Cinderella is ready for the ball.
Artist: John Francis (Collin)
☐ Purchased 19___ Pd $_____ MIB   NB   DB   BNT
☐ Want   Orig. Ret. $14.95   **MIB** Sec. Mkt. **$35**

QX 632-4   MADONNA AND CHILD ☐
Comments: Stamped tin, Dated 1996.
This picture of Madonna and Child celebrate peace, love, and hope. **Painted** by Jusepe de Ribera.
Frame **Sculpted** by Linda Sickman.
☐ Purchased 19___ Pd $_____ MIB   NB   DB   BNT
☐ Want   Orig. Ret. $12.95   **MIB** Sec. Mkt. **$12**

QX 627-1   MAKING HIS ROUNDS ☐
Comments: Handcrafted, Dated 1996.
Santa has a bag full of presents to give to all of those children who have been good. **Artist:** John Francis (Collin)
☐ Purchased 19___ Pd $_____ MIB   NB   DB   BNT
☐ Want   Orig. Ret. $14.95   **MIB** Sec. Mkt. **$25**

QX 566-4   MARY'S ANGELS: VIOLET ☐
Comments: **Ninth in Series**, Handcrafted, Dated 1996. A little angel is taking extra special care of this lost lamb.
Artist: Robert Chad
☐ Purchased 19___ Pd $_____ MIB   NB   DB   BNT
☐ Want   Orig. Ret. $6.95   **MIB** Sec. Mkt. **$16**

QX 606-1   MATCHLESS MEMORIES ☐
Comments: Handcrafted, Dated 1996.
This little mouse is playing some hot tunes on his "match box" piano! Ornament actually says "Matchless Melodies."
Artist: Ken Crow
☐ Purchased 19___ Pd $_____ MIB   NB   DB   BNT
☐ Want   Orig. Ret. $9.95   **MIB** Sec. Mkt. **$18**

QX 622-4   MAXINE ☐
Comments: Handcrafted, Dated 1996. 10th Anniversary of Shoebox Greetings, Character by John Wagner. Maxine is decked out from head to toe in Christmas clothing.
Artist: Sharon Pike
☐ Purchased 19___ Pd $_____ MIB   NB   DB   BNT
☐ Want   Orig. Ret. $9.95   **MIB** Sec. Mkt. **$25**

QX 588-4   MERRY CARPOOLERS ☐
Comments: Handcrafted, Dated 1996. Santa and his reindeer are going to have a little skiing fun after their ride up the ski lift. A li'l crowded. **Artist:** Ken Crow
☐ Purchased 19___ Pd $_____ MIB   NB   DB   BNT
☐ Want   Orig. Ret. $14.95   **MIB** Sec. Mkt. **$26**

QX 565-4   MERRY OLDE SANTA ☐
Comments: **Seventh in Series**, Handcrafted, Dated 1996.
This Santa is all dressed up in Fourth of July style.
Artist: Ken Crow
☐ Purchased 19___ Pd $_____ MIB   NB   DB   BNT
☐ Want   Orig. Ret. $14.95   **MIB** Sec. Mkt. **$32**

QX 582-4   MOM
Comments: Handcrafted, Dated 1996.
She's trying not to blush with such a large gift that reads "A Mom is a Special Gift 1996." This ornament was found with the signature "LaDene" on the bottom instead of the correct artist signature. Does anyone have one with the correct signature? **Artist:** Joyce Lyle
☐ Purchased 19__ Pd $____ MIB   NB   DB   BNT
☐ Want   Orig. Ret. $7.95   **MIB** Sec. Mkt. **$17**

QX 582-1   MOM AND DAD
Comments: Handcrafted, Dated 1996.
Time for a bear hug to show our love. **Artist:** Dill Rhodus
☐ Purchased 19__ Pd $____ MIB   NB   DB   BNT
☐ Want   Orig. Ret. $9.95   **MIB** Sec. Mkt. **$20**

QX 579-1   MOM-TO-BE
Comments: Handcrafted, Dated 1996.
This mom is all ready for her special delivery, with a bottle and rattle. **Artist:** Duane Unruh
☐ Purchased 19__ Pd $____ MIB   NB   DB   BNT
☐ Want   Orig. Ret. $7.95   **MIB** Sec. Mkt. **$15**

QX 564-4   MOTHER GOOSE:
MARY HAD A LITTLE LAMB
Comments: **Fourth in Series**, Handcrafted, Dated 1996.
Book opens to display a verse. **Artist:** Ed Seale
☐ Purchased 19__ Pd $____ MIB   NB   DB   BNT
☐ Want   Orig. Ret. $13.95   **MIB** Sec. Mkt. **$20**

QX 588-1   NEW HOME
Comments: Handcrafted, Dated 1996.
This little squirrel has found his new home in your mailbox.
Artist: Ed Seale
☐ Purchased 19__ Pd $____ MIB   NB   DB   BNT
☐ Want   Orig. Ret. $8.95   **MIB** Sec. Mkt. **$19**

QLX 747-1   NORTH POLE VOLUNTEERS
Comments: Light, Motion and Sound, Dated 1996.
Fire Chief Santa pulls the cord that makes the bell swing and clang. The sirens wail, mascot barks and the wheels turn on this vintage fire engine. **Artist:** Ed Seale
☐ Purchased 19__ Pd $____ MIB   NB   DB   BNT
☐ Want   Orig. Ret. $42.00   **MIB** Sec. Mkt. **$80**

QX 567-1   NOSTALGIC HOUSES AND SHOPS:
VICTORIAN PAINTED LADY
Comments: **Thirteenth in Series**, Dated 1996.
Artist: Don Palmiter
☐ Purchased 19__ Pd $____ MIB   NB   DB   BNT
☐ Want   Orig. Ret. $14.95   **MIB** Sec. Mkt. **$26**

QX 548-1   OLIVE OYL AND SWEE' PEA
Comments: Handcrafted
The whimsical look of Olive Oyl holding Swee' Pea brings out the child in all of us. Very colorful! **Artist:** Robert Chad
☐ Purchased 19__ Pd $____ MIB   NB   DB   BNT
☐ Want   Orig. Ret. $10.95   **MIB** Sec. Mkt. **$22**

QX 586-1   ON MY WAY – PHOTO HOLDER
Comments: Handcrafted, Dated 1996.
Keep your child's school photo in this nifty bus frame.
Artist: Sue Tague
☐ Purchased 19__ Pd $____ MIB   NB   DB   BNT
☐ Want   Orig. Ret. $7.95   **MIB** Sec. Mkt. **$15**

QX 579-4   OUR CHRISTMAS TOGETHER
Comments: Handcrafted, Dated 1996.
A special couple sit together in this romantic gazebo. Was very popular! **Artist:** Don Palmiter
☐ Purchased 19__ Pd $____ MIB   NB   DB   BNT
☐ Want   Orig. Ret. $18.95   **MIB** Sec. Mkt. **$35**

QX 580-4   OUR CHRISTMAS TOGETHER
PHOTO HOLDER
Comments: Handcrafted, Dated 1996.
Mr. and Mrs. Claus are at the drive-in theatre, where the feature on the big screen happens to be you and that favorite person! **Artist:** Ken Crow
☐ Purchased 19__ Pd $____ MIB   NB   DB   BNT
☐ Want   Orig. Ret. $8.95   **MIB** Sec. Mkt. **$18**

QX 581-1   OUR FIRST CHRISTMAS TOGETHER
Comments: Handcrafted, Dated 1996.
Two loveable mice are sitting on a sliver of cheese shaped like the moon. **Artist:** Don Palmiter
☐ Purchased 19__ Pd $____ MIB   NB   DB   BNT
☐ Want   Orig. Ret. $9.95   **MIB** Sec. Mkt. **$20**

QX 305-1   OUR FIRST CHRISTMAS TOGETHER ☐
Comments: Acrylic, Dated 1996.
Two white doves represent a couple's first Christmas together.
Artist: LaDene Votruba
☐ Purchased 19__ Pd $____ MIB   NB   DB   BNT
☐ Want   Orig. Ret. $6.95   **MIB** Sec. Mkt. **$14**

QLX 737-4   OVER THE ROOFTOPS ☐
Comments: Lighted, Dated 1996.
Within this ornament, reminiscent of a snow globe, Santa flies
over rooftops on Christmas Eve, making his deliveries.
Artist: Ed Seale
☐ Purchased 19__ Pd $____ MIB   NB   DB   BNT
☐ Want   Orig. Ret. $14.50   **MIB** Sec. Mkt. **$26**

QX 538-1   PEANUTS® GANG, THE ☐
Comments: **Fourth and Final in Series,** Handcrafted,
Dated 1996. Sally is making out her Christmas wish list for
Santa. **Artist:** John Francis (Collin)
☐ Purchased 19__ Pd $____ MIB   NB   DB   BNT
☐ Want   Orig. Ret. $9.95   **MIB** Sec. Mkt. **$15**

QLX 739-4   PEANUTS®: SCHROEDER AND LUCY ☐
Comments: Musical, Dated 1996.
Schroeder is playing "Linus and Lucy" on the piano as Lucy
looks on. **Artist:** Robert Chad
☐ Purchased 19__ Pd $____ MIB   NB   DB   BNT
☐ Want   Orig. Ret. $18.50   **MIB** Sec. Mkt. **$38**

QX 623-4   PEPPERMINT SURPRISE ☐
Comments: Handcrafted, Dated 1996.
Can a mouse be so happy to receive this peppermint candy?
From the look on its face, it certainly can. **Artist:** Sharon Pike
☐ Purchased 19__ Pd $____ MIB   NB   DB   BNT
☐ Want   Orig. Ret. $7.95   **MIB** Sec. Mkt. **$17**

QX 653-4   PEZ® SNOWMAN ☐
Comments: Handcrafted, Dated 1996.
Anyone for some frozen Pez Candy?
☐ Purchased 19__ Pd $____ MIB   NB   DB   BNT
☐ Want   Orig. Ret. $7.95   **MIB** Sec. Mkt. **$16**

QLX 745-1   PINBALL WONDER ☐
Comments: Light, Sound and Movement, Dated 1996.
Santa is racking up points as he plays this nostalgic pinball
machine. **Artist:** Ken Crow
☐ Purchased 19__ Pd $____ MIB   NB   DB   BNT
☐ Want   Orig. Ret. $28.00   **MIB** Sec. Mkt. **$56**

QX 603-4   POLAR CYCLE ☐
Comments: Handcrafted, Dated 1996.
A little penguin enjoys his ride on the front of a bicycle ridden
by none other than a polar bear. **Artist:** Duane Unruh
☐ Purchased 19__ Pd $____ MIB   NB   DB   BNT
☐ Want   Orig. Ret. $12.95   **MIB** Sec. Mkt. **$23**

QX 626-1   PRAYER FOR PEACE ☐
Comments: Handcrafted, Dated 1996.
A kneeling little girl, her candle and Bible in hand, says her
prayers. **Artist:** Joyce Lyle
☐ Purchased 19__ Pd $____ MIB   NB   DB   BNT
☐ Want   Orig. Ret. $14.95   **MIB** Sec. Mkt. **$115**

QX 625-1   PRECIOUS CHILD ☐
Comments: Handcrafted, Dated 1996.
The Holy Mother and Child are surrounded by gold on this
special ornament. **Artist:** LaDene Votruba
☐ Purchased 19__ Pd $____ MIB   NB   DB   BNT
☐ Want   Orig. Ret. $8.95   **MIB** Sec. Mkt. **$14**

QX 601-1   PUP-TENTING ☐
Comments: Handcrafted, Dated 1996.
The outdoor person will find the humor in this pup and his dec-
orated tent. **Artist:** Don Palmiter
☐ Purchased 19__ Pd $____ MIB   NB   DB   BNT
☐ Want   Orig. Ret. $7.95   **MIB** Sec. Mkt. **$16**

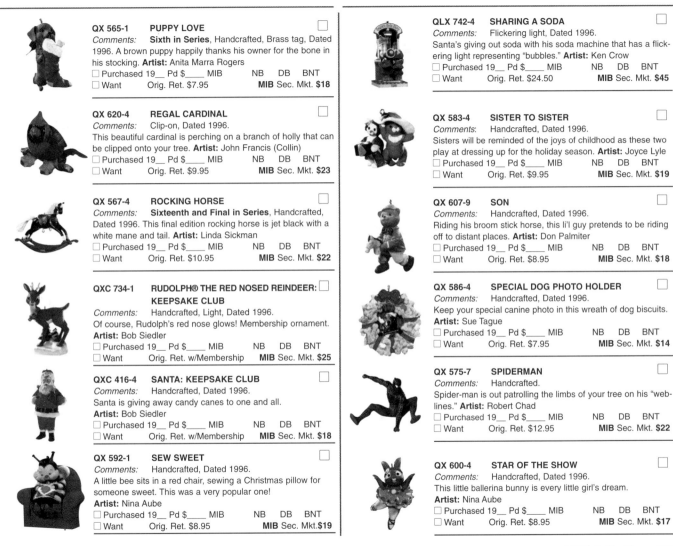

QX 565-1   PUPPY LOVE
Comments: **Sixth in Series**, Handcrafted, Brass tag, Dated 1996. A brown puppy happily thanks his owner for the bone in his stocking. **Artist:** Anita Marra Rogers
☐ Purchased 19__ Pd $____ MIB   NB   DB   BNT
☐ Want   Orig. Ret. $7.95   **MIB** Sec. Mkt. **$18**

QX 620-4   REGAL CARDINAL
Comments: Clip-on, Dated 1996.
This beautiful cardinal is perching on a branch of holly that can be clipped onto your tree. **Artist:** John Francis (Collin)
☐ Purchased 19__ Pd $____ MIB   NB   DB   BNT
☐ Want   Orig. Ret. $9.95   **MIB** Sec. Mkt. **$23**

QX 567-4   ROCKING HORSE
Comments: **Sixteenth and Final in Series**, Handcrafted, Dated 1996. This final edition rocking horse is jet black with a white mane and tail. **Artist:** Linda Sickman
☐ Purchased 19__ Pd $____ MIB   NB   DB   BNT
☐ Want   Orig. Ret. $10.95   **MIB** Sec. Mkt. **$22**

QXC 734-1   RUDOLPH® THE RED NOSED REINDEER: KEEPSAKE CLUB
Comments: Handcrafted, Light, Dated 1996.
Of course, Rudolph's red nose glows! Membership ornament. **Artist:** Bob Siedler
☐ Purchased 19__ Pd $____ MIB   NB   DB   BNT
☐ Want   Orig. Ret. w/Membership   **MIB** Sec. Mkt. **$25**

QXC 416-4   SANTA: KEEPSAKE CLUB
Comments: Handcrafted, Dated 1996.
Santa is giving away candy canes to one and all.
Artist: Bob Siedler
☐ Purchased 19__ Pd $____ MIB   NB   DB   BNT
☐ Want   Orig. Ret. w/Membership   **MIB** Sec. Mkt. **$18**

QX 592-1   SEW SWEET
Comments: Handcrafted, Dated 1996.
A little bee sits in a red chair, sewing a Christmas pillow for someone sweet. This was a very popular one!
Artist: Nina Aube
☐ Purchased 19__ Pd $____ MIB   NB   DB   BNT
☐ Want   Orig. Ret. $8.95   **MIB** Sec. Mkt.**$19**

QLX 742-4   SHARING A SODA
Comments: Flickering light, Dated 1996.
Santa's giving out soda with his soda machine that has a flickering light representing "bubbles." **Artist:** Ken Crow
☐ Purchased 19__ Pd $____ MIB   NB   DB   BNT
☐ Want   Orig. Ret. $24.50   **MIB** Sec. Mkt. **$45**

QX 583-4   SISTER TO SISTER
Comments: Handcrafted, Dated 1996.
Sisters will be reminded of the joys of childhood as these two play at dressing up for the holiday season. **Artist:** Joyce Lyle
☐ Purchased 19__ Pd $____ MIB   NB   DB   BNT
☐ Want   Orig. Ret. $9.95   **MIB** Sec. Mkt. **$19**

QX 607-9   SON
Comments: Handcrafted, Dated 1996.
Riding his broom stick horse, this li'l guy pretends to be riding off to distant places. **Artist:** Don Palmiter
☐ Purchased 19__ Pd $____ MIB   NB   DB   BNT
☐ Want   Orig. Ret. $8.95   **MIB** Sec. Mkt. **$18**

QX 586-4   SPECIAL DOG PHOTO HOLDER
Comments: Handcrafted, Dated 1996.
Keep your special canine photo in this wreath of dog biscuits.
Artist: Sue Tague
☐ Purchased 19__ Pd $____ MIB   NB   DB   BNT
☐ Want   Orig. Ret. $7.95   **MIB** Sec. Mkt. **$14**

QX 575-7   SPIDERMAN
Comments: Handcrafted.
Spider-man is out patrolling the limbs of your tree on his "web-lines." **Artist:** Robert Chad
☐ Purchased 19__ Pd $____ MIB   NB   DB   BNT
☐ Want   Orig. Ret. $12.95   **MIB** Sec. Mkt. **$22**

QX 600-4   STAR OF THE SHOW
Comments: Handcrafted, Dated 1996.
This little ballerina bunny is every little girl's dream.
Artist: Nina Aube
☐ Purchased 19__ Pd $____ MIB   NB   DB   BNT
☐ Want   Orig. Ret. $8.95   **MIB** Sec. Mkt. **$17**

QXI 554-4   **STAR TREK®: MR. SPOCK** ☐
Comments: Handcrafted, Dated 1996.
Mr. Spock is giving the damage report of the latest Klingon attack. **Artist:** Anita M. Rogers
☐ Purchased 19 __Pd $____MIB   NB   DB   BNT
☐ Want   Orig. Ret. $14.95   **MIB** Sec. Mkt. **$19**

QXI 555-1   **STAR TREK® THE NEXT GENERATION™:** ☐
               COMMANDER WILLIAM T. RIKER™
Comments: Handcrafted, Dated 1996.
Commander Riker is poised ready, should danger strike.
Artist: Anita M. Rogers
☐ Purchased 19 __Pd $____MIB   NB   DB   BNT
☐ Want   Orig. Ret. $14.95   **MIB** Sec. Mkt. **$19**

QXI 753-4   **STAR TREK®: U.S.S. ENTERPRISE™ AND** ☐
               GALILEO SHUTTLECRAFT™
Comments: Die-cast Metal, set of two, Dated 1996. Galileo Shuttlecraft is getting ready to dock onto the U.S.S. Enterprise.**Artists:** Lynn Norton and Dill Rhodus
☐ Purchased 19 __Pd $____MIB   NB   DB   BNT
☐ Want   Orig. Ret. $46.00   **MIB** Sec. Mkt.**$75**

QXI 754-4   **STAR TREK®: U.S.S. VOYAGER™** ☐
Comments: Light, Dated 1996.
The Star ship made famous in the fourth television series of Star Trek.® **Artist:** Lynn Norton
☐ Purchased 19 __Pd $____MIB   NB   DB   BNT
☐ Want   Orig. Ret. $24.00   **MIB** Sec. Mkt. **$45**

QLX 747-4   **STAR WARS™: MILLENNIUM FALCON** ☐
Comments: Light, Dated 1996.
The Millennium Falcon is flying through the heavens with lighted thrusters. This was a top seller!
☐ Purchased 19 __Pd $____MIB   NB   DB   BNT
☐ Want   Orig. Ret. $24.00   **MIB** Sec. Mkt. **$47**

QLX 742-1   **STATUE OF LIBERTY, THE** ☐
Comments: Music and Light, Dated 1996.
Lady Liberty's torch and crown light up. Plays "The Star Spangled Banner." Includes special collector's card. Very Nice!
Artist: Ed Seale
☐ Purchased 19 __Pd $____MIB   NB   DB   BNT
☐ Want   Orig. Ret. $24.50   **MIB** Sec. Mkt. **$45**

QX 630-1   **TAMIKA** ☐
Comments: Handcrafted, Dated 1996.
Tamika, one of the Penda Kids™, celebrates peace, hope and love. **Artists:** Cathy Johnson and Katrina Bricker
☐ Purchased 19 __Pd $____MIB   NB   DB   BNT
☐ Want   Orig. Ret. $7.95   **MIB** Sec. Mkt. **$15**

QX 611-4   **TENDER LOVIN' CARE** ☐
Comments: Handcrafted, Dated 1996.
This little nurse has her stethoscope and thermometer ready to check you out. **Artist:** Ed Seale
☐ Purchased 19 __Pd $____MIB   NB   DB   BNT
☐ Want   Orig. Ret. $7.95   **MIB** Sec. Mkt. **$16**

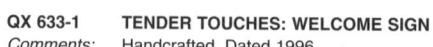

QX 633-1   **TENDER TOUCHES: WELCOME SIGN** ☐
Comments: Handcrafted, Dated 1996.
Available only during the Keepsake Ornament Premier July 20-21. This bear is hanging a wreath in his window to welcome travelers into his home. **Artist:** Ed Seale
☐ Purchased 19 __Pd $____MIB   NB   DB   BNT
☐ Want   Orig. Ret. $15.00   **MIB** Sec. Mkt. **$20**

QX 585-4   **THANK YOU, SANTA PHOTO HOLDER** ☐
Comments: Handcrafted, Dated 1996.
Place your family photo behind Santa's glass of milk and plate of cookies. **Artist:** Katrina Bricker
☐ Purchased 19 __Pd $____MIB   NB   DB   BNT
☐ Want   Orig. Ret. $7.95   **MIB** Sec. Mkt. **$16**

QX 591-4   **THIS BIG!** ☐
Comments: Handcrafted, Dated 1996.
Now Santa, don't s-t-r-e-t-c-h the truth about how big that fish was. Cute! **Artist:** Ed Seale
☐ Purchased 19 __Pd $____MIB   NB   DB   BNT
☐ Want   Orig. Ret. $9.95   **MIB** Sec. Mkt. **$18**

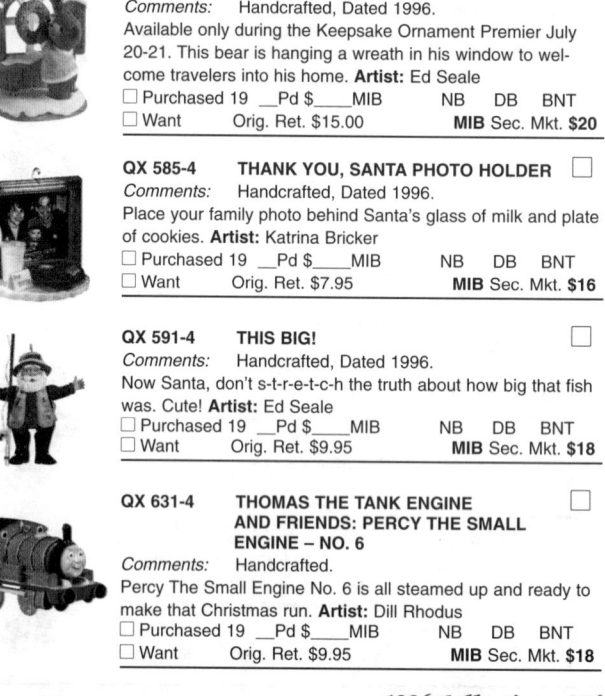

QX 631-4   **THOMAS THE TANK ENGINE** ☐
               AND FRIENDS: PERCY THE SMALL
               ENGINE – NO. 6
Comments: Handcrafted.
Percy The Small Engine No. 6 is all steamed up and ready to make that Christmas run. **Artist:** Dill Rhodus
☐ Purchased 19 __Pd $____MIB   NB   DB   BNT
☐ Want   Orig. Ret. $9.95   **MIB** Sec. Mkt. **$18**

QX 546-4　TIME FOR A TREAT ☐
Comments:　Handcrafted, Dated 1996.
It's time for a Hershey's chocolate run down the hill.
Artist: Linda Sickman
☐ Purchased 19 __Pd $____MIB　　NB　DB　BNT
☐ Want　　Orig. Ret. $11.95　　**MIB** Sec. Mkt. **$30**

QLX 746-1　TOBIN FRALEY HOLIDAY CARROUSEL ☐
Comments:　**Third and Final in Series**, Light and Music,
Dated 1996. This gray carrousel horse plays "On the Beautiful
Blue Danube." **Artist:** John Francis (Collin)
☐ Purchased 19 __Pd $____MIB　　NB　DB　BNT
☐ Want　　Orig. Ret. $32.00　　**MIB** Sec. Mkt. **$50**

QX 632-1　TONKA® MIGHTY DUMP TRUCK ☐
Comments:　Die-cast Metal, Dated 1996.
Replica of the toy many played with as children. Nice!
☐ Purchased 19 __Pd $____MIB　　NB　DB　BNT
☐ Want　　Orig. Ret. $13.95　　**MIB** Sec. Mkt. **$30**

QLX 738-4　TREASURED MEMORIES ☐
Comments:　Lighted, Dated 1996.
This design represents the 22 foot Christmas tree at the home
of collector Jim Reid. **Artist:** Linda Sickman
☐ Purchased 19 __Pd $____MIB　　NB　DB　BNT
☐ Want　　Orig. Ret. $18.50　　**MIB** Sec. Mkt. **$40**

QLX 743-1　VIDEO PARTY ☐
Comments:　Light and Changing Screen, Dated 1996.
Two little mice are having fun playing their video game,
"Making a snowman." Different! **Artist:** Bob Siedler
☐ Purchased 19 __Pd $____MIB　　NB　DB　BNT
☐ Want　　Orig. Ret. $28.00　　**MIB** Sec. Mkt. **$55**

QX 539-4　WELCOME GUEST ☐
Comments:　Handcrafted, Dated 1996.
Santa welcomes his guests with an ice cold Coca-Cola.
Artist: Duane Unruh
☐ Purchased 19 __Pd $____MIB　　NB　DB　BNT
☐ Want　　Orig. Ret. $14.95　　**MIB** Sec. Mkt. **$25**

QX 626-4　WELCOME HIM ☐
Comments:　Handcrafted, Dated 1996.
The animals are in the manger welcoming the new Baby to the
world. **Artist:** Sue Tague
☐ Purchased 19 __Pd $____MIB　　NB　DB　BNT
☐ Want　　Orig. Ret. $8.95　　**MIB** Sec. Mkt. **$17**

QX 545-4　WINNIE THE POOH AND PIGLET ☐
Comments:　Handcrafted, Dated 1996.
Winnie the Pooh and Piglet are out for a winter walk, talking
about Pooh's "hunny" supply for the winter. **Artist:** Bob Siedler
☐ Purchased 19 __Pd $____MIB　　NB　DB　BNT
☐ Want　　Orig. Ret. $12.95　　**MIB** Sec. Mkt. **$30**

QLX 741-4　WINNIE THE POOH: SLIPPERY DAY ☐
Comments:　Motion, Handcrafted.
Winnie the Pooh, Tigger, Piglet and Eeyore are sliding around
on the ice pond, enjoying a wintery day. **Artist:** Bob Siedler
☐ Purchased 19 __Pd $____MIB　　NB　DB　BNT
☐ Want　　Orig. Ret. $24.50　　**MIB** Sec. Mkt. **$58**

QLX 745-4　WIZARD OF OZ™: EMERALD CITY ☐
Comments:　Light, motion, and music.
Dorothy and friends spin around on a rotating road with a
glowing Emerald City while playing "We're Off to See the
Wizard." **Artist:** Ken Crow
☐ Purchased 19 __Pd $____MIB　　NB　DB　BNT
☐ Want　　Orig. Ret. $32.00　　**MIB** Sec. Mkt. **$63**

QX 555-4　WIZARD OF OZ™: WITCH OF THE WEST ☐
Comments:　Handcrafted.
The wicked Witch of theWest is ready to cast her awful spell
on Dorothy and her friends. **Artist:** Joyce Lyle
☐ Purchased 19 __Pd $____MIB　　NB　DB　BNT
☐ Want　　Orig. Ret. $13.95　　**MIB** Sec. Mkt. **$25**

QXC 416-1　WIZARD OF OZ™: WIZARD
**　　　　　　　KEEPSAKE CLUB** ☐
Comments:　Handcrafted.
This ornament depicts a memorable scene from the movie, the
wizard leaving without Dorothy. For Keepsake Club Members
Only. **Artist:** Anita Marra Rogers
☐ Purchased 19 __Pd $____MIB　　NB　DB　BNT
☐ Want　　Orig. Ret. $12.95　　**MIB** Sec. Mkt. **$50**

QX 594-1   WONDER WOMAN   ☐
Comments: Handcrafted.
Wonder Woman is on the lookout for low-down no gooders.
Artist: Anita Marra Rogers
☐ Purchased 19 __Pd $____MIB   NB   DB   BNT
☐ Want   Orig. Ret. $12.95   **MIB** Sec. Mkt. **$26**

QX 613-1   WOODLAND SANTA   ☐
Comments: Pressed tin.
Santa carries on his shoulder the perfect tree for Mrs. Claus.
Artist: Linda Sickman
☐ Purchased 19 __Pd $____MIB   NB   DB   BNT
☐ Want   Orig. Ret. $12.95   **MIB** Sec. Mkt. **$28**

QX 552-1   YOGI BEAR™ AND BOO BOO™   ☐
Comments: Handcrafted.
Yogi and Boo Boo can't wait to see what is in the picnic basket
that is intended for Mr. Ranger.
Artist: Anita Marra Rogers
☐ Purchased 19 __Pd $____MIB   NB   DB   BNT
☐ Want   Orig. Ret. $12.95   **MIB** Sec. Mkt. **$23**

QX 501-1   YULETIDE CENTRAL   ☐
Comments: **Third in Series**, Pressed Tin, Dated 1996.
A mail car is next in line on the track of Yuletide Central.
Artist: Linda Sickman
☐ Purchased 19 __Pd $____MIB   NB   DB   BNT
☐ Want   Orig. Ret. $18.95   **MIB** Sec. Mkt. **$38**

QX 605-4   YULETIDE CHEER   ☐
Comments: Handcrafted, Dated 1996.
This cheerleader is spreading the cheer with her megaphone.
Artist: LaDene Votruba
☐ Purchased 19 __Pd $____MIB   NB   DB   BNT
☐ Want   Orig. Ret. $7.95   **MIB** Sec. Mkt. **$15**

QX 652-4   ZIGGY®   ☐
Comments: 25th Anniversary Handcrafted, Dated 1996.
Ziggy is all dressed up like Santa. **Artist:** Robert Chad
☐ Purchased 19 __Pd $____MIB   NB   DB   BNT
☐ Want   Orig. Ret. $9.95   **MIB** Sec. Mkt. **$28**

Hallmark Keepsake
Showcase Ornaments - 1996
Cookie Jar Friends

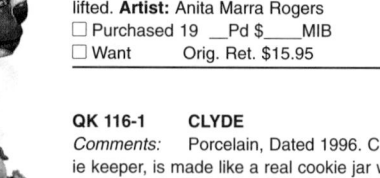

QK 116-4   CARMEN   ☐
Comments: Porcelain, Dated 1996. Carmen the feline cook-
ie keeper is made like a real cookie jar with a lid that can be
lifted. **Artist:** Anita Marra Rogers
☐ Purchased 19 __Pd $____MIB   NB   DB   BNT
☐ Want   Orig. Ret. $15.95   **MIB** Sec. Mkt. **$30**

QK 116-1   CLYDE   ☐
Comments: Porcelain, Dated 1996. Clyde, the canine cook-
ie keeper, is made like a real cookie jar with a lid that can be
lifted. **Artist:** Nina Aube
☐ Purchased 19 __Pd $____MIB   NB   DB   BNT
☐ Want   Orig. Ret. $15.95   **MIB**Sec. Mkt. **$20**

Folk Art Americana

QK 113-4   CAROLING ANGEL   ☐
Comments: Handcrafted, Dated 1996.
This angel with wings of stamped copper is singing praises.
Artist: Linda Sickman
☐ Purchased 19 __Pd $____MIB   NB   DB   BNT
☐ Want   Orig. Ret. $16.95   **MIB** Sec. Mkt. **$30**

QK 120-4   MRS. CLAUS   ☐
Comments: Handcrafted, Dated 1996.
Mrs. Claus is bringing the last of the gifts to Santa with her
copper lantern and bear under her arm. **Artist:** Linda Sickman
☐ Purchased 19 __Pd $____MIB   NB   DB   BNT
☐ Want   Orig. Ret. $18.95   **MIB** Sec. Mkt. **$32**

QK 112-4   SANTA'S GIFTS   ☐
Comments: Handcrafted, Dated 1996.
This Santa is bringing gifts to the "good little boys and girls"
with his brass bells in his hand, train under his arm and an
angel with copper wings on his arm. **Artist:** Linda Sickman
☐ Purchased 19 __Pd $____MIB   NB   DB   BNT
☐ Want   Orig. Ret. $18.95   **MIB** Sec. Mkt. **$40**

Magi Bells

QK 117-4   BALTHASAR (FRANKINCENSE) ☐
Comments: Fine Porcelain Bell. Bathasar is bringing his gift of frankincense to the newborn babe. **Artist:** LaDene Votruba
☐ Purchased 19 __Pd $____MIB   NB   DB   BNT
☐ Want   Orig. Ret. $13.95   **MIB** Sec. Mkt. **$26**

QK 118-4   CASPAR (MYRRH) ☐
Comments: Fine Porcelain Bell. Caspar is bringing his gift of Myrrh to the newborn babe.
Artist: LaDene Votruba
☐ Purchased 19 __Pd $____MIB   NB   DB   BNT
☐ Want   Orig. Ret. $13.95   **MIB** Sec. Mkt. **$26**

QK 118-1   MELCHIOR (GOLD) ☐
Comments: Fine Porcelain Bell. Melchior is bringing his gift of gold to the newborn babe.
.**Artist:** LaDene Votruba
☐ Purchased 19 __Pd $____MIB   NB   DB   BNT
☐ Want   Orig. Ret. $13.95   **MIB** Sec. Mkt. **$26**

Nature's Sketchbook

QK 110-4   CHRISTMAS BUNNY ☐
Comments: Handcrafted, Dated 1996. **Design by Marjolein Bastin.** This curious rabbit has come to inspect the water jug buried deep in winter's snow.
Artist: John Francis (Collin)
☐ Purchased 19 __Pd $____MIB   NB   DB   BNT
☐ Want   Orig. Ret. $18.95   **MIB** Sec. Mkt. **$40**

QK 111-4   THE BIRDS' CHRISTMAS TREE ☐
Comments: Handcrafted, Dated 1996. **Design by Marjolein Bastin.** The birds feed at this lovely Christmas tree decorated especially for them.
Artist: Duane Unruh
☐ Purchased 19 __Pd $____MIB   NB   DB   BNT
☐ Want   Orig. Ret. $18.95   **MIB** Sec. Mkt. **$35**

QK 109-4   THE HOLLY BASKET ☐
Comments: Handcrafted, Dated 1996. **Design by Marjolein Bastin.** A bird sits on a basket full of holly. **Artist:** Joyce Lyle
☐ Purchased 19 __Pd $____MIB   NB   DB   BNT
☐ Want   Orig. Ret. $18.95   **MIB** Sec. Mkt. **$30**

Sacred Masterworks

QK 114-4   MADONNA AND CHILD ☐
Comments: Handcrafted, Dated 1996.
This pays tribute to the19th century lithograph published by Marcus Ward after the painting by Raphael.
Artist: Linda Sickman
☐ Purchased 19 __Pd $____MIB   NB   DB   BNT
☐ Want   Orig. Ret. $15.95   **MIB** Sec. Mkt. **$30**

QK 115-4   PRAYING MADONNA ☐
Comments: Handcrafted, Dated 1996.
This pays tribute to the 19th century lithograph published by Marcus Ward after the painting by Sassoferrato.
Artist: Linda Sickman
☐ Purchased 19 __Pd $____MIB   NB   DB   BNT
☐ Want   Orig. Ret. $15.95   **MIB** Sec. Mkt. **$30**

The Languuage of Flowers

QK 117-1   PANSY ☐
Comments: **FIRST IN SERIES**, Handcrafted, Dated 1996. Pansy is dressed in Victorian tradition, carting a delicate Silver plated container filled with the flowers for which she was named. This was a top seller during the '96-'97 selling season.
Artist: Sue Tague
☐ Purchased 19 __Pd $____MIB   NB   DB   BNT
☐ Want   Orig. Ret. $15.95   **MIB** Sec. Mkt. **$45**

Turn of the Century Parade

QK 108-4   UNCLE SAM ☐
Comments: **Second in Series**, Dated 1996.
A tribute to mechanical tin toys made with die-cast metal with a brass bell that rings. Dated **Artist:** Ken Crow
☐ Purchased 19 __Pd $____MIB   NB   DB   BNT
☐ Want   Orig. Ret. $16.95   **MIB** Sec. Mkt. **$30**

A Little Instruction for Life:
Judge your success by what you had to give up in order to get it.

Olympic Ornaments

QXE 404-1　CLOISONNÉ MEDALLION ☐
Comments:　1" in diameter, Dated 1996.
This miniature ornament features the artwork for the Atlanta Olympic Games for 1996. **Artist:** Diana McGehee
☐ Purchased 19 __Pd $____MIB　　NB　DB　BNT
☐ Want　　Orig. Ret. $9.75　　**MIB** Sec. Mkt. **$20**

QXE 551- 1　INVITATION TO THE GAMES ☐
Comments:　3-1/2" x 2-1/2", Dated 1996.
These two ceramic plaque ornaments feature posters from the 1896 and 1996 Olympics. Each comes with display stand and commemorative copy. **Artist:** Diana McGehee
☐ Purchased 19 __Pd $____MIB　　NB　DB　BNT
☐ Want　　Orig. Ret. $14.95　　**MIB** Sec. Mkt. **$28**

QXE 572-4　IZZY – THE MASCOT ☐
Comments:　3-11/16" x 2-11/16", Dated 1996.
Here's Izzy, the official 1996 Olympic mascot.
☐ Purchased 19 __Pd $____MIB　　NB　DB　BNT
☐ Want　　Orig. Ret. $9.95　　**MIB** Sec. Mkt. **$18**

QXE 744-4　LIGHTING THE FLAME ☐
Comments:　4-15/16" x 2-5/8", battery operated, Dated 1996. Plays Bugler's Dream from the Opening Ceremony. Features commemorative copy and a flickering light.
Artist: Duane Unruh
☐ Purchased 19 __Pd $____MIB　　NB　DB　BNT
☐ Want　　Orig. Ret. $28　　**MIB** Sec. Mkt. **$50**

QXE 573-1　OLYMPIC TRIUMPH KEEPSAKE ORNAMENT ☐
Comments:　4-1/16" x 2-13/16", Dated 1996.
This sculpted discus thrower includes commemorative copy.
Artist: Ed Seale
☐ Purchased 19 __Pd $____MIB　　NB　DB　BNT
☐ Want　　Orig. Ret. $10.95　　**MIB** Sec. Mkt. **$20**

QXE 574-1　PARADE OF NATIONS ☐
Comments:　3-3/16" diameter, Porcelain, Dated 1996.
Includes display stand and features flags from various nations.
☐ Purchased 19 __Pd $____MIB　　NB　DB　BNT
☐ Want　　Orig. Ret. $10.95　　**MIB** Sec. Mkt. **$22**

Artist on Tour 1996

QXC 420-1　SANTA'S TOY SHOP ☐
Comments:　Handcrafted, Dated 1996.
Two Keepsake Ornaments with display. All the elves have their own jobs in preparing Santa for his deliveries.
Artist: All 17 Studio Artists
☐ Purchased 19 __Pd $____MIB　　NB　DB　BNT
☐ Want　　Orig. Ret. $60.00　　**MIB** Sec. Mkt. **$120**

TOY SHOP SANTA ☐
Comments:　Handcrafted, Dated 1996.
To complement Santa's Toy Shop. **Artist:** Duane Unruh
☐ Purchased 19 __Pd $____MIB　　NB　DB　BNT
☐ Want　　Orig. Ret. $14.95　　**MIB** Sec. Mkt. **$35**

24 KT GOLD PLATED ROCKING HORSE ☐
Comments:　Handcrafted, Dated 1996.
Miniature rocking horse. **Artist:** Linda Sickman
☐ Purchased 19 __Pd $____MIB　　NB　DB　BNT
☐ Want　　Orig. Ret. $12.95　　**MIB** Sec. Mkt. **$40**

NFL Ornaments

QSR 643-4 ☐ Houston Oilers™
QSR 648-1 ☐ Phildelphia Eagles™
QSR 649-1 ☐ Pittsburgh Steelers™
QSR 644-4 ☐ St. Louis Rams™
QSR 650-4 ☐ Seatle Seahawks™
QSR 651-1 ☐ Tampa Bay Buccaneers™
QSR 651-4 ☐ Washington Redskins™
QSR 638-4 ☐ Cincinnati Bengals™
QSR 646-1 ☐ New England Patriots™

QSR 648-4 ☐ Arizona Cardinals™
QSR 636-4 ☐ Atlanta Falcon™
QSR 639-1 ☐ Browns™
QSR 637-1 ☐ Buffalo Bills™
QSR 637-4 ☐ Carolina Panthers™
QSR 638-1 ☐ Chicago Bears™
QSR 639-4 ☐ Dallas Cowboys™
QSR 641-1 ☐ Denver Broncos™
QSR 641-4 ☐ Detroit Lions™
QSR 642-1 ☐ Green Bay Packers™
QSR 643-1 ☐ Indianapolis Colts™

QSR 643-4 ☐ Jacksonville Jaguars™
QSR 632-1 ☐ Kansas City Chiefs™
QSR 645-1 ☐ Miami Dolphins™
QSR 645-4 ☐ Minnesota Vikings™
QSR 646-4 ☐ New Orleans Saints™
QSR 647-1 ☐ New York Giants™
QSR 647-4 ☐ New York Jets™
QSR 644-1 ☐ Oakland Raiders™
QSR 649-4 ☐ San Diego Chargers™
QSR 650-1 ☐ San Francisco 49ers™

QSR 632-1　KANSAS CITY CHIEFS™ ☐
Comments:　Handcrafted, Dated 1996. Artist: Duane Unruh
☐ Purchased 19 __Pd $____MIB　　NB　DB　BNT
☐ Want　　Orig. Ret. $9.95　　**MIB.** Sec. Mkt. **$15**

NFL BALL ORNAMENTS ☐
Comments:　Glass Ball, Dated 1996. Four other teams were added to the list of ten from 1995. Those teams were Green Bay Packers™, Pittsburgh Steelers™, St. Louis Rams™ and Buffalo Bills™.
☐ Purchased 19 __Pd $____MIB　　NB　DB　BNT
☐ Want　　Orig. Ret. $5.95　　**MIB** Sec. Mkt.**$15**

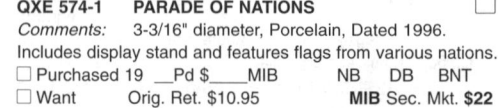

1996
Miniature Ornament Collection

QXM 423-4
A CHILD'S GIFTS
Dated 1996. **Artist:** Patricia Andrews
☐ Purchased 19___ Pd $_____
MIB   NB   DB   BNT
☐ Want   Orig. Retail $6.75
MIB Sec. Mkt. **$12**

QXM 476-7
A TREE FOR WOODSTOCK
Dated 1996. **Artist:** Bob Siedler
☐ Purchased 19___ Pd $_____
MIB   NB   DB   BNT
☐ Want   Orig. Retail $5.75
MIB Sec. Mkt. **$15**

QXM 422-4
AFRICAN ELEPHANTS
Artist: Linda Sickman
☐ Purchased 19___ Pd $_____
MIB   NB   DB   BNT
☐ Want   Orig. Retail $5.75
MIB Sec. Mkt. **$15**

QXM 407-4
ALICE IN WONDERLAND:
MAD HATTER; Second in Series,
Dated 1996. **Artist:** Patricia Andrews
☐ Purchased 19___ Pd $_____
MIB   NB   DB   BNT
☐ Want   Orig. Retail $6.75
MIB Sec. Mkt. **$15**

QXM 409-1
CENTURIES OF SANTA
Third in Series, Dated 1996.
Artist: Linda Sickman
☐ Purchased 19___ Pd $_____
MIB   NB   DB   BNT
☐ Want   Orig. Retail $5.75
MIB Sec. Mkt. **$16**

QXM 424-1
CHRISTMAS BEAR
This is adorable! **Artist:** Ed Seale
☐ Purchased 19___ Pd $_____
MIB   NB   DB   BNT
☐ Want   Orig. Retail $4.75
MIB Sec. Mkt. **$12**

QXM 407-1
CHRISTMAS BELLS
Second in Series Dated 1996.
Very popular! **Artist:** Ed Seale
☐ Purchased 19___ Pd $_____
MIB   NB   DB   BNT
☐ Want   Orig. Retail $4.75
MIB Sec. Mkt. **$15**

QXE 404-1
CLOISONNE MEDALLION:
OLYMPIC SPIRIT COLLECTION
Dated "Atlanta 1996."
Artist: Diana McGehee
☐ Purchased 19___ Pd $_____
MIB   NB   DB   BNT
☐ Want   Orig. Retail $9.75
MIB Sec. Mkt. **$22**

QXM 402-1
COOL DELIVERY COCA-COLA®
Artist: Sharon Pike
☐ Purchased 19___ Pd $_____
MIB   NB   DB   BNT
☐ Want   Orig. Retail $5.75
MIB Sec. Mkt. **$15**

QXM 421-1
GONE WITH THE WIND™
Set of three, 60th Anniversary,
Dated 1996.
Artist: Patricia Andrews
☐ Purchased 19___ Pd $_____
MIB   NB   DB   BNT
☐ Want   Orig. Retail $19.95
MIB Sec. Mkt. **$40**

QXM 425-1
HATTIE CHAPEAU
Dated 1996. Complements "A
Moustershire Christmas" set from
'95, **Artist:** Dill Rhodus
☐ Purchased 19___ Pd $_____
MIB   NB   DB   BNT
☐ Want   Orig. Retail $4.75
MIB Sec. Mkt. **$10**

QXC 419-1
HOLIDAY BUNNY: KEEPSAKE
CLUB
Collector's Club, Dated 1996.
Artist: John Francis (Collin)
☐ Purchased 19___ Pd $_____
MIB   NB   DB   BNT
☐ Want   Free with '96 Club
                    Membership
MIB Sec. Mkt. **$13**

QXM 423-1
JOYOUS ANGEL
Dated 1996. **Artist:** Patricia Andrews
☐ Purchased 19___ Pd $_____
MIB   NB   DB   BNT
☐ Want   Orig. Retail $4.75
MIB Sec. Mkt. **$7**

QXM 424-4
LONG WINTER'S NAP
Dated 1996. **Artist:** Patricia Andrews
☐ Purchased 19___ Pd $_____
MIB   NB   DB   BNT
☐ Want   Orig. Retail $5.75
MIB Sec. Mkt.**$12**

QXM 415-4
LOONY TUNES LOVABLES:
BABY SYLVESTER
Artist: Don Palmiter
☐ Purchased 19___ Pd $_____
MIB   NB   DB   BNT
☐ Want   Orig. Retail $5.75
MIB Sec. Mkt. **$15**

QXM 401-4
LOONY TUNES LOVABLES:
BABY TWEETY
Artist: Don Palmiter
☐ Purchased 19___ Pd $_____
MIB   NB   DB   BNT
☐ Want   Orig. Retail $5.75
                      MIB Sec. Mkt. $25

QXM 409-4
MARCH OF THE TEDDY BEARS
Fourth and Final in Series,
Dated 1996. **Artist:** Duane Unruh
☐ Purchased 19___ Pd $_____
MIB   NB   DB   BNT
☐ Want   Orig. Retail $4.75
                      MIB Sec. Mkt. $13

QXM 425-4
MESSAGE FOR SANTA
Dated 1996. **Artist:** Ed Seale
☐ Purchased 19___ Pd $_____
MIB   NB   DB   BNT
☐ Want   Orig. Retail $6.75
                      MIB Sec. Mkt. $15

QXM 414-4
MINIATURE CLOTHESPIN
SOLDIER; Second in Series,
Artist: Linda Sickman
☐ Purchased 19___ Pd $_____
MIB   NB   DB   BNT
☐ Want   Orig. Retail $4.75
                      MIB Sec. Mkt. $13

QXM 403-1
MINIATURE KIDDIE CAR
CLASSICS: MURRAY®
"FIRE TRUCK"
Second in Series, Die-cast
Metal, Dated 1996.
Artist: Don Palmiter
☐ Purchased 19___ Pd $_____
MIB   NB   DB   BNT
☐ Want   Orig. Retail $6.75
                      MIB Sec. Mkt. $18

QXM 411-1
NATURE'S ANGELS
Seventh and Final in Series,
Artist: Sharon Pike
☐ Purchased 19___ Pd $_____
MIB   NB   DB   BNT
☐ Want   Orig. Retail $4.75
                      MIB Sec. Mkt. $13

QXM 410-4
NIGHT BEFORE CHRISTMAS, THE
Fifth /Final in Series, Dated
1996. **Artist:** Duane Unruh
☐ Purchased 19___ Pd $_____
MIB   NB   DB   BNT
☐ Want   Orig. Retail $5.75
                      MIB Sec. Mkt. $14

QXM 411-4
NOEL R.R.: COOKIE CAR
Eighth in Series, Dated 1996.
Artist: Linda Sickman
☐ Purchased 19___ Pd $_____
MIB   NB   DB   BNT
☐ Want   Orig. Retail $6.75
                      MIB Sec. Mkt. $20

QXM 406-4
NUTCRACKER BALLET, THE
FIRST IN SERIES , Dated 1996.
Comes with display stage.
Artist: LaDene Votruba
☐ Purchased 19___ Pd $_____
MIB   NB   DB   BNT
☐ Want   Orig. Retail $14.75
                      MIB Sec. Mkt. $30

QXM 408-4
NUTCRACKER GUILD
Third in Series, Dated 1996.
Artist: Linda Sickman
☐ Purchased 19___ Pd $_____
MIB   NB   DB   BNT
☐ Want   Orig. Retail $5.75
                      MIB Sec. Mkt. $16

QXM 420-4
O HOLY NIGHT
Set of Four, Dated 1996. Comes
with dated display piece.
Artist: Dill Rhodus
☐ Purchased 19___ Pd $_____
MIB   NB   DB   BNT
☐ Want   Orig. Retail $24.50
                      MIB Sec. Mkt. $40

QXM 412-4
OLD ENGLISH VILLAGE:
VILLAGE MILL;
Ninth in Series, Dated 1996.
Artist: Dill Rhodus
☐ Purchased 19___ Pd $_____
MIB   NB   DB   BNT
☐ Want   Orig. Retail $6.75
                      MIB Sec. Mkt. $16

QXM 410-1
ON THE ROAD
Fourth in Series, Pressed tin.
Artist: Linda Sickman
☐ Purchased 19___ Pd $_____
MIB   NB   DB   BNT
☐ Want   Orig. Retail $5.75
                      MIB Sec. Mkt. $13

QXM 421-4
PEACEFUL CHRISTMAS
Dated 1996. **Artist:** Duane Unruh
☐ Purchased 19___ Pd $_____
MIB   NB   DB   BNT
☐ Want   Orig. Retail $4.75
                      MIB Sec. Mkt. $13

QXM 412-1
ROCKING HORSE
Ninth in Series, Dated 1996.
Artist: Linda Sickman
☐ Purchased 19___ Pd $_____
MIB   NB   DB   BNT
☐ Want   Orig. Retail $4.75
                      MIB Sec. Mkt. $16

QXC 4171
RUDOLPH'S HELPER:
KEEPSAKE CLUB
Dated 1996. **Artist:** Bob Siedler
☐ Purchased 19___ Pd $_____
MIB   NB   DB   BNT
☐ Want   Free with '96 Club
                        Membership
                MIB Sec. Mkt. **$10**

QXM 408-1
SANTA'S LITTLE BIG TOP
Second in Series, Dated 1996.
Artist: Ken Crow
☐ Purchased 19___ Pd $_____
MIB   NB   DB   BNT
☐ Want   Orig. Retail $6.75
                MIB Sec. Mkt. **$15**

QXM 414-1
SHINING STAR TREE-TOPPER
Dimensional Brass.
☐ Purchased 19___ Pd $_____
MIB   NB   DB   BNT
☐ Want   Orig. Retail $9.95
                MIB Sec. Mkt. **$15**

QXM 426-4
SPARKLING CRYSTAL ANGEL:
PRECIOUS EDITION;
Lead crystal and silver plate,
Dated 1996. **Artist:** LaDene
Votruba
☐ Purchased 19___ Pd $_____
MIB   NB   DB   BNT
☐ Want   Orig. Retail $9.75
                MIB Sec. Mkt. **$15**

QXM 426-1
TINY CHRISTMAS HELPERS
Set of Six, Dated 1996.
Artist: Ed Seale
☐ Purchased 19___ Pd $_____
MIB   NB   DB   BNT
☐ Want   Orig. Retail $29.00
                MIB Sec. Mkt. **$50**

QXM 402-4
VEHICLES OF STAR WARS™, THE
Set of Three, Dated 1996.
In this set of three, many sets
were found with the TIE Fighter
(as pictured left center) having the
hook placed on the bottom in the
first production. This was correct-
ed in later productions.
Artist: Dill Rhodus
☐ Purchased 19___ Pd $_____
MIB   NB   DB   BNT
☐ Want   Orig. Retail $19.95
                MIB Sec. Mkt. **$35**

QXM 404-4
WINNIE THE POOH AND
TIGGER
Dated 1996. **Artist:** Bob Siedler
☐ Purchased 19___ Pd $_____
MIB   NB   DB   BNT
☐ Want   Orig. Retail $9.75
                MIB Sec. Mkt. **$20**

From the Staff at Rosie Wells Enterprises, Inc.

1996
Easter Ornament Collection

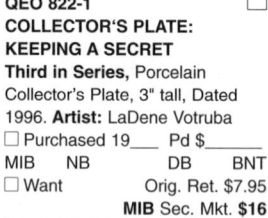

QEO 808-4
APPLE BLOSSOM LANE
Second in Series, 2-1/2" tall,
Dated 1996.
Artist: John Francis (Collin)
☐ Purchased 19___ Pd $_____
MIB   NB   DB   BNT
☐ Want   Orig. Ret. $8.95
            MIB Sec. Mkt. **$18**

QEO 807-1
BEATRIX POTTER:
PETER RABBIT™
FIRST IN SERIES, Beatrix Potter™
series, 2-1/2" tall, Dated 1996.
Artist: LaDene Votruba
☐ Purchased 19___ Pd $_____
MIB   NB   DB   BNT
☐ Want   Orig. Ret. $8.95
            MIB Sec. Mkt. **$75**

QEO 822-1
COLLECTOR'S PLATE:
KEEPING A SECRET
Third in Series, Porcelain
Collector's Plate, 3" tall, Dated
1996. **Artist:** LaDene Votruba
☐ Purchased 19___ Pd $_____
MIB   NB   DB   BNT
☐ Want   Orig. Ret. $7.95
            MIB Sec. Mkt. **$16**

QEO 807-4
COTTON TAIL EXPRESS:
LOCOMOTIVE
FIRST IN SERIES, Cottontail
Express series, 2" tall, Dated
1996. **Artist:** Ken Crow
☐ Purchased 19___ Pd $_____
MIB   NB   DB   BNT
☐ Want   Orig. Ret.$8.95
            MIB Sec. Mkt. **$40**

QEO 814-4
CRAYOLA® CRAYON: HIPPITY
HOP DELIVERY
2" tall, Dated 1996.
Artist: Ken Crow
☐ Purchased 19___ Pd $_____
MIB   NB   DB   BNT
☐ Want   Orig. Ret. $7.95
            MIB Sec. Mkt. **$19**

QEO 816-4
EASTER MORNING
2-1/4" tall, Dated 1996.
Artist: Duane Unruh
☐ Purchased 19___ Pd $_____
MIB   NB   DB   BNT
☐ Want   Orig. Ret. $7.95
            MIB Sec. Mkt. **$12**

QEO 809-1
GARDEN CLUB
Second in Series, 1-1/4" tall,
Dated 1996. **Artist:** Don Palmiter
☐ Purchased 19___ Pd $_____
MIB   NB   DB   BNT
☐ Want   Orig. Ret. $7.95
            MIB Sec. Mkt. **$15**

QEO 809-4
HERE COMES EASTER
Third in Series, 2" tall, Dated
1996. **Artist:** Ken Crow
☐ Purchased 19___ Pd $_____
MIB   NB   DB   BNT
☐ Want   Orig. Ret. $7.95
            MIB Sec. Mkt. **$17**

QEO 818-4
JOYFUL ANGELS
FIRST IN SERIES, 3" tall, Dated
1996. **Artist:** Joyce Lyle
☐ Purchased 19___ Pd $_____
MIB   NB   DB   BNT
☐ Want   Orig. Ret. $9.95
            MIB Sec. Mkt. **$30**

QEO 818-1
LOOK WHAT I FOUND!
1-1/2" tall, Dated 1996.
Artist: John Francis (Collin)
☐ Purchased 19___ Pd $_____
MIB   NB   DB   BNT
☐ Want   Orig. Ret. $7.95
            MIB Sec. Mkt. **$15**

QEO 815-4
LOONEY TUNES™: DAFFY
DUCK
Looney Tunes™, 2-1/2" tall.
Artist: Anita Marra Rogers
☐ Purchased 19___ Pd $_____
MIB   NB   DB   BNT
☐ Want   Orig. Ret. $8.95
            MIB Sec. Mkt. **$17**

QEO 815-1
PEANUTS®: PARADE PALS
Peanuts®, 2-1/4" tall, Dated 1996.
Artist: Dill Rhodus
☐ Purchased 19___ Pd $_____
MIB   NB   DB   BNT
☐ Want   Orig. Ret. $7.95
          MIB Sec. Mkt. **$18**

QEO 817-4
PORK 'N BEANS
2" tall, Dated 1996. **Artist:** Robert Chad
☐ Purchased 19___ Pd $_____
MIB   NB   DB   BNT
☐ Want   Orig. Ret. $7.95
          MIB Sec. Mkt. **$15**

QEO 808-1
SPRINGTIME BARBIE™
Second in Series,
Artist: Patricia Andrews
☐ Purchased 19___ Pd $_____
MIB   NB   DB   BNT
☐ Want   Orig. Ret. $12.95
          MIB Sec. Mkt. **$28**

QEO 813-4
SPRINGTIME BONNETS
Fourth in Series.
Artist: Sharon Pike
☐ Purchased 19___ Pd $_____
MIB   NB   DB   BNT
☐ Want   Orig. Ret. $7.95
          MIB Sec. Mkt. **$25**

QEO 817-1
STRAWBERRY PATCH
3" tall, Dated 1996.
Artist: Ed Seale
☐ Purchased 19___ Pd $_____
MIB   NB   DB   BNT
☐ Want   Orig. Ret. $6.95
          MIB Sec. Mkt. **$15**

QEO 814-1
STRIKE UP THE BAND!
Dated 1996, Set of three: Bugle Bunny, 2-1/4" tall; Tweedle-Dee Duck, 1-1/2" tall; Nutty Squirrel, 1-1/2" tall. **Artist:** Duane Unruh
☐ Purchased 19___ Pd $_____
MIB   NB   DB   BNT
☐ Want   Orig. Ret. $14.95
          MIB Sec. Mkt. **$25**

QEO 816-1
TENDER TOUCHES:
EGGSTRA SPECIAL SURPRISE
Tender Touches, 2-1/4" tall, Dated 1996. **Artist:** Ed Seale
☐ Purchased 19___ Pd $_____
MIB   NB   DB   BNT
☐ Want   Orig. Ret. $8.95
          MIB Sec. Mkt. **$20**

—R. STUBLER—

"Keep your cotton-pick in' hands off that ornament!"

I collect ornaments because it relaxes my nerves.

1997 Collection

QXD 401-5 101 DALMATIANS: TWO-TONE

Comments: Handcrafted. Spotted on one side and all white on the other, this little Dalmatian looks like he is ready to be yours.

☐ Purchased 19____ Pd $_____ MIB NB DB BNT
☐ Want Orig. Ret. $9.95 **MIB** Sec. Mkt. **$14**

1937 STEELCRAFT AIRFLOW BY MURRAY® KEEPSAKE CLUB

Comments: Die-cast Metal, Dated 1997. Based on the 1937 Steelcraft pedal car design by Murray. Available to club members only. **Artist:** Don Palmiter

☐ Purchased 19____ Pd $_____ MIB NB DB BNT
☐ Want Orig. Ret. $15.95 **MIB** Sec. Mkt. **$55**

QXI 645-5 1997 CORVETTE

Comments: Die-cast Metal, Dated 1997. Wheels turn on this 1997 red Corvette. **Artist:** Don Palmiter

☐ Purchased 19____ Pd $_____ MIB NB DB BNT
☐ Want Orig. Ret. $13.95 **MIB** Sec. Mkt. **$22**

QX 617-5 A CELEBRATION OF ANGELS: CELEBRATION OF ANGELS

Comments: **Third in Series,** Handcrafted, Dated 1997. African-American angel dressed in ethnic garb including red turban. **Artist:** Patricia Andrews

☐ Purchased 19____ Pd $_____ MIB NB DB BNT
☐ Want Orig. Ret. $13.95 **MIB** Sec. Mkt. **$16**

QXD 406-2 ALADDIN & THE KING OF THIEVES: JASMINE & ALADDIN

Comments: Handcrafted, Dated 1997. Jasmine and Aladdin sit holding hands on a wonderful magic carpet.

☐ Purchased 19____ Pd $_____ MIB NB DB BNT
☐ Want Orig. Ret. $14.95 **MIB** Sec. Mkt. **$18**

QX 610-5 ALL AMERICAN TRUCKS: 1953 GMC

Comments: **Third in Series,** Die-cast Metal, Dated 1997. Wheels turn on this replica 1953 GMC. **Artist:** Don Palmiter

☐ Purchased 19____ Pd $_____ MIB NB DB BNT
☐ Want Orig. Ret. $13.95 **MIB** Sec. Mkt. **$18**

QX 614-2 ALL GOD'S CHILDREN®: NIKKI

Comments: **Second in Series,** Handcrafted, Dated 1997. Two piece set. This cute child is busy cooking with her teddy bear. **Artist:** Martha Root.

☐ Purchased 19____ Pd $_____ MIB NB DB BNT
☐ Want Orig. Ret. $12.95 **MIB** Sec. Mkt. **$12**

QX 639-2 ALL-ROUND SPORTS FAN

Comments: Handcrafted, Dated 1997. Perfect ornament for the sports fan. Every sport is cleverly used to make a sports man in the likeness of a snowman. **Artist:** Nello Williams

☐ Purchased 19____ Pd $_____ MIB NB DB BNT
☐ Want Orig. Ret. $8.95 **MIB** Sec. Mkt. **$13**

QX 641-5 ALL-WEATHER WALKER

Comments: Handcrafted, Dated 1997. This little bunny is ready to take off at a fast pace to enjoy his sport of walking. **Artist:** Nello Williams

☐ Purchased 19____ Pd $_____ MIB NB DB BNT
☐ Want Orig. Ret. $8.95 **MIB** Sec. Mkt. **$11**

QXI 615-2 AT THE BALLPARK: HANK AARON

Comments: **Second in Series,** Handcrafted, Dated 1997. Hank Aaron is ready to hit a home run. **Artist:** Dill Rhodus

☐ Purchased 19____ Pd $_____ MIB NB DB BNT
☐ Want Orig. Ret. $14.95 **MIB** Sec. Mkt. **$22**

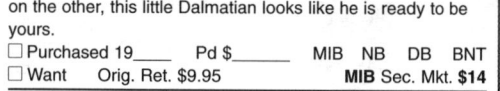

AWAY TO THE WINDOW: KEEPSAKE CLUB

Comments: Handcrafted, Dated 1997. To celebrate the 175th anniversary of Clement C. Moore's "The Night Before Christmas," this and three other ornaments were offered to those who joined the Keepsake Ornament Collector's Club in 1997. **Artist:** Nello Williams

☐ Purchased 19____ Pd $_____ MIB NB DB BNT
☐ Want Price: Came with Club Membership of $22.50
  NB **$10** **MIB** Sec. Mkt. **$20**

QX 653-5   BABY'S FIRST CHRISTMAS

Comments: Fine Porcelain, Dated 1997. A yellow giraffe, a blue elephant and a brown bear ride in a boat with a purple, ruffled sail. Captioned on the sail are the words "Baby's First Christmas." **Artist:** LaDene Votruba

☐ Purchased 19____   Pd $_____   MIB NB DB BNT
☐ Want   Orig. Ret. $14.95   **MIB** Sec. Mkt. **$23**

QX 648-5   BABY'S FIRST CHRISTMAS

Comments: Fine Porcelain, Dated 1997. Colored, ruffled pillows surround baby in a heart shaped ornament. Captioned: "Baby's First Christmas." **Artist:** LaDene Votruba

☐ Purchased 19____   Pd $_____   MIB NB DB BNT
☐ Want   Orig. Ret. $9.95   **MIB** Sec. Mkt. **$24**

QX 649-2   BABY'S FIRST CHRISTMAS

Comments: Handcrafted, Dated 1997. An African-American infant lies in a beautiful basket reproduced pursuant to exclusive license of Harlem Textile Works™. Captioned: "Baby's First Christmas." **Artist:** Patricia Andrews

☐ Purchased 19____   Pd $_____   MIB NB DB BNT
☐ Want   Orig. Ret. $9.95   **MIB** Sec. Mkt. **$18**

QX 648-2   BABY'S FIRST CHRISTMAS

Comments: Handcrafted, Dated 1997. A yellow looking glass with two bears pictured on it becomes a photo holder for Baby. Captioned: "Baby's First Christmas."

☐ Purchased 19____   Pd $_____   MIB NB DB BNT
☐ Want   Orig. Ret. $7.95   **MIB** Sec. Mkt. **$14**

QX 649-5   BABY'S FIRST CHRISTMAS:
CHILD'S AGE COLLECTION

Comments: Handcrafted, Dated 1997. This little bear, with a pacifier in its mout,h is trying to hold onto its stocking and cookie, which has the numeral "1" on it. This seems more sought after than other Baby's First ornaments.
Artist: Ken Crow

☐ Purchased 19____   Pd $_____   MIB NB DB BNT
☐ Want   Orig. Ret. $7.95   **MIB** Sec. Mkt. **$20**

QX 650-2   BABY'S SECOND CHRISTMAS:
CHILD'S AGE COLLECTION

Comments: Handcrafted, Dated 1997. A sugar cookie with a numeral "2" has been found with this little bear's stocking.
Artist: Ken Crow

☐ Purchased 19____   Pd $_____   MIB NB DB BNT
☐ Want   Orig. Ret. $7.95   **MIB** Sec. Mkt. **$18**

QXC 516-2   BARBIE™:
BASED ON THE 1989 HAPPY HOLIDAYS
KEEPSAKE CLUB

Comments: **Second in Series,** Dated 1997. Complements the Keepsake Ornament Holiday **BARBIE™** Collector's series which has depicted Mattel's annual doll since 1993. Available to club members only.

☐ Purchased 19____   Pd $_____   MIB NB DB BNT
☐ Want   Orig. Ret. $15.95   **MIB** Sec. Mkt. **$38**

QXI 681-5   BARBIE™ AND KEN™: WEDDING DAY

Comments: Handcrafted, Dated 1997. Set of two ornaments. A brunette Barbie and Ken are dressed in wedding attire. Complements the BARBIE™ Keepsake Ornament in the Collectors' Series. **Artist for BARBIE™:** Patricia Andrews **Artist for KEN™:** Don Palmiter. Very popular during premiere!!

☐ Purchased 19____   Pd $_____   MIB NB DB BNT
☐ Want   Orig. Ret. $35.00   **MIB** Sec. Mkt. **$50**

QXI 681-2   BARBIE™: WEDDING DAY 1959-1962

Comments: **Fourth in Series,** Handcrafted, Dated 1997. A blonde Barbie is dressed in wedding attire.
Artist: Patricia Andrews

☐ Purchased 19____   Pd $_____   MIB NB DB BNT
☐ Want   Orig. Ret. $15.95   **NB** $13   **MIB** Sec. Mkt. **$16**

QX 620-2   BASEBALL HEROES:
JACKIE ROBINSON

Comments: **Fourth and Final in Series,** Handcrafted, Dated 1997. Celebrating the 50th Anniversary of Baseball, 1947-1997. Jackie Robinson comes sliding into home plate on this the final in the series of Baseball Heroes.
Artist: Dill Rhodus

☐ Purchased 19____   Pd $_____   MIB NB DB BNT
☐ Want   Orig. Ret. $12.95   **NB** $13   **MIB** Sec. Mkt. **$16**

QX 668-2   BIKING BUDDIES

Comments: Handcrafted, Dated 1997. A boy dressed in a green sweater, hat and brown scarf rides his tricycle while carrying his puppy in the front basket. **Artist:** Don Palmiter

☐ Purchased 19____   Pd $_____   MIB NB DB BNT
☐ Want   Orig. Ret. $12.95   **MIB** Sec. Mkt. **$18**

QX 664-5   BOOK OF THE YEAR

Comments: Handcrafted, Dated 1997. An open book, with a small Christmas mouse sitting in front of it, becomes a photo holder. **Artist:** Katrina Bricker

☐ Purchased 19____   Pd $_____   MIB NB DB BNT
☐ Want   Orig. Ret. $7.95   **MIB** Sec. Mkt. **$14**

QX 645-2   BOY SCOUTS OF AMERICA: TOMORROW'S LEADER

Comments: Ceramic, Dated 1997. A beautiful rendition of Norman Rockwell's artwork.

☐ Purchased 19____   Pd $_____   MIB NB DB BNT
☐ Want   Orig. Ret. $9.95   **MIB** Sec. Mkt. **$12**

QX 672-2   BREEZIN' ALONG

Comments: Handcrafted, Dated 1997. A little mouse skates along, holding two leaves to catch the breeze. **Artist:** Ed Seale

☐ Purchased 19____   Pd $_____   MIB NB DB BNT
☐ Want   Orig. Ret. $8.95   **MIB** Sec. Mkt. **$18**

QX 638-2   BUCKET BRIGADE

Comments: Handcrafted, Dated 1997. A fireman Dalmatian dog carries a bucket, ready to put out the fire. **Artist:** John Francis (Collin)

☐ Purchased 19____   Pd $_____   MIB NB DB BNT
☐ Want   Orig. Ret. $8.95   **MIB** Sec. Mkt. **$12**

QX 620-5   CAT NAPS: CAT NAPS

Comments: **Fourth in Series,** Handcrafted, Dated 1997. A yellow cat sleeps in a suitcase, not wanting to miss that Christmas trip! **Artist:** Katrina Bricker

☐ Purchased 19____   Pd $_____   MIB NB DB BNT
☐ Want   Orig. Ret. $8.95   **MIB** Sec. Mkt. **$11**

QX 671-2   CATCH OF THE DAY

Comments: Handcrafted, Dated 1997. A funny bear, dressed in his fishing clothes, gets a fish in the face. **Artist:** Sue Tague

☐ Purchased 19____   Pd $_____   MIB NB DB BNT
☐ Want   Orig. Ret. $9.95   **MIB** Sec. Mkt. **$13**

QX 651-5   CHILD'S FIFTH CHRISTMAS: CHILD'S AGE COLLECTION

Comments: Handcrafted, Dated 1997. This little bear holds the number five cookie in his Christmas stocking. **Artist:** Ken Crow

☐ Purchased 19____   Pd $_____   MIB NB DB BNT
☐ Want   Orig. Ret. $7.95   **MIB** Sec. Mkt. **$12**

QX 651-2   CHILD'S FOURTH CHRISTMAS CHILD'S AGE COLLECTION

Comments: Handcrafted, Dated 1997. A panda bear holds the number four cookie in his Christmas stocking. **Artist:** Ken Crow

☐ Purchased 19____   Pd $_____   MIB NB DB BNT
☐ Want   Orig. Ret. $7.95   **MIB** Sec. Mkt. **$12**

QX 650-5   CHILD'S THIRD CHRISTMAS CHILD'S AGE COLLECTION

Comments: Handcrafted, Dated 1997. A bear holds the number three cookie in his Christmas stocking. **Artist:** Ken Crow

☐ Purchased 19____   Pd $_____   MIB NB DB BNT
☐ Want   Orig. Ret. $7.95   **MIB** Sec. Mkt. **$12**

QLX 752-5   CHRIS MOUSE: CHRIS MOUSE LUMINARIA

Comments: **Thirteenth and Final in Series,** Handcrafted, Dated 1997. A little mouse stands poised atop a pine cone lighting the "candle" inside the luminaria. A "candle" glows softly behind the outlined snowman. I feel this is one of the best in this series! **Artist:** Bob Siedler

☐ Purchased 19____   Pd $_____   MIB NB DB BNT
☐ Want   Orig. Ret. $14.95   **MIB** Sec. Mkt. **$28**

QX 638-5   CHRISTMAS CHECKUP

Comments: Handcrafted, Dated 1997. A little mouse, dressed in a doctor's coat, takes the temperature of a snowman. I assume is temperature is below 98.6°, don't you? **Artist:** Bob Siedler

☐ Purchased 19____   Pd $_____   MIB NB DB BNT
☐ Want   Orig. Ret. $7.95   **MIB** Sec. Mkt. **$14**

QX 617-2   CHRISTMAS VISITORS: KOLYADA ☐

Comments: **Third and Final in Series,** Handcrafted, Dated 1997. Dressed in a white dress and coat, this lady comes bearing gifts of food in her bag. **Artist:** LaDene Votruba

☐ Purchased 19____   Pd $_____   MIB NB DB BNT
☐ Want   Orig. Ret. $14.95   **MIB** Sec. Mkt. **$18**

QXD 405-2   CINDERELLA: GUS & JAQ ☐

Comments: Handcrafted, Dated 1997. Two famous mice from the movie "Cinderella" attempt to decorate her shoe. Sooooo cute!

☐ Purchased 19____   Pd $_____   MIB NB DB BNT
☐ Want   Orig. Ret. $12.95   **MIB** Sec. Mkt. **$18**

QX 610-2   CLASSIC AMERICAN CARS: ☐
1969 HURST OLDSMOBILE 442

Comments: **Seventh in Series,** Handcrafted, Dated 1997. What automobile collector could resist this fine replica of a 1969 Hurst Oldsmobile? **Artist:** Don Palmiter

☐ Purchased 19____   Pd $_____   MIB NB DB BNT
☐ Want   Orig. Ret. $13.95   **MIB** Sec. Mkt. **$17.50**

QX 680-5   CLASSIC CROSS ☐

Comments: Precious Metal, Dated 1997.
Artist: LaDene Votruba

☐ Purchased 19____   Pd $_____   MIB NB DB BNT
☐ Want   Orig. Ret. $13.95   **MIB** Sec. Mkt. **$15**

QX 611-2   CLAUSES ON VACATION, THE: ☐
THE CLAUSES ON VACATION

Comments: **FIRST IN SERIES,** Handcrafted, Dated 1997. The Clauses are off on their fishing vacation. Santa carries a tackle box, pole and reel. Mrs. Clause holds the stringer with one fish (and she probably caught it). **Artist:** Bob Siedler

☐ Purchased 19____   Pd $_____   MIB NB DB BNT
☐ Want   Orig. Ret. $14.95   **MIB** Sec. Mkt. **$18**

QX 644-5   CLEVER CAMPER ☐

Comments: Handcrafted, Dated 1997. This clever beaver sits atop his camp knife all prepared to enjoy his marshmallow. Clever idea for an ornament. **Artist:** Robert Chad

☐ Purchased 19____   Pd $_____   MIB NB DB BNT
☐ Want   Orig. Ret. $7.95   **MIB** Sec. Mkt. **$16**

QX 623-5   CRAYOLA® CRAYON: ☐
BRIGHT ROCKING COLORS

Comments: **Ninth in Series,** Handcrafted, Dated 1997.

A little bear rides his Crayola rocking horse. Always a popular series. **Artist:** Sue Tague

☐ Purchased 19____   Pd $_____   MIB NB DB BNT
☐ Want   Orig. Ret. $12.95   **MIB** Sec. Mkt. **$18.50**

QX 642-5   CYCLING SANTA ☐

Comments: Handcrafted, Dated 1997. The wheels actually turn on this bike on which rides a slimmed down backpacking Santa rides upon. **Artist:** Nello Williams

☐ Purchased 19____   Pd $_____   MIB NB DB BNT
☐ Want   Orig. Ret. $14.95   **MIB** Sec. Mkt. **$25**

QX 653-2   DAD ☐

Comments: Handcrafted, Dated 1997. A gray mouse sits atop a shaving mug which is captioned "DAD."
Artist: Bob Siedler

☐ Purchased 19____   Pd $_____   MIB NB DB BNT
☐ Want   Orig. Ret. $8.95   **MIB** Sec. Mkt. **$16**

QX 661-2   DAUGHTER ☐

Comments: Pressed Tin, Dated 1997. A special daughter should receive this stocking designed with an angel, blowing a trumpet. Pressed tin ornaments always good sellers!

Artist: Katrina Bricker

☐ Purchased 19____   Pd $_____   MIB NB DB BNT
☐ Want   Orig. Ret. $7.95   **MIB** Sec. Mkt. **$16**

QXD 404-5   DISNEY: CINDERELLA ☐

Comments: **FIRST IN SERIES,** Handcrafted, Dated 1997. Later series name was changed to The Enchanted Memories Collection. Second in series is Walt Disney's Snow White.

☐ Purchased 19____   Pd $_____   MIB NB DB BNT
☐ Want   Orig. Ret. $14.95   **MIB** Sec. Mkt. **$22**

QX 616-2   DOLLS OF THE WORLD: ☐
CHINESE BARBIE™

Comments: **Second in Series,** Handcrafted, Dated 1997. Dressed in a traditional Chinese costume, this ornament is popular among BARBIE™ collectors. **Artist:** Anita Marra Rogers

☐ Purchased 19____   Pd $_____   MIB NB DB BNT
☐ Want   Orig. Ret. $14.95   **MIB** Sec. Mkt. **$16**

QX 670-5　DOWNHILL RUN　☐

Comments:　Handcrafted, Dated 1997. Santa and three of his reindeer, with heads bobbin', race down the hill in their bobsled. A great ornamen! **Artist:** Ken Crow

☐ Purchased 19____　　Pd $_____　　MIB　NB　DB　BNT
☐ Want　　Orig. Ret. $9.95　　　　　　**MIB** Sec. Mkt. **$19**

QX 643-2　ELEGANCE ON ICE　☐

Comments:　Handcrafted, Dated 1997. With arms raised, a young skater takes to the ice. Use with a revolving ornament hook. Excellent motion for an ornament! **Artist:** Joyce Lyle

☐ Purchased 19____　　Pd $_____　　MIB　NB　DB　BNT
☐ Want　　Orig. Ret. $9.95　　　　　　**MIB** Sec. Mkt. **$18**

QX 637-5　EXPRESSLY FOR TEACHER　☐

Comments:　Handcrafted, Dated 1997. A small bear holds an apple while sitting on a paper airplane. I'll bet teachers have seen this way of sending messages before! **Artist:** Sue Tague

☐ Purchased 19____　　Pd $_____　　MIB　NB　DB　BNT
☐ Want　　Orig. Ret. $7.95　　　　　　**MIB** Sec. Mkt. **$12**

QX 623-2　FABULOUS DECADE　☐

Comments:　**Eighth in Series,** Brass, Dated 1997. Our forest friend holds the year 1997.

Artist: Ed Seale

☐ Purchased 19____　　Pd $_____　　MIB　NB　DB　BNT
☐ Want　　Orig. Ret. $7.95　　　　　　**MIB** Sec. Mkt. **$14**

QX 666-5　FELIZ NAVIDAD　☐

Comments:　Handcrafted, Dated 1997. A little Mexican mouse decorates his sombrero with colored lights to get ready for the festivities. **Artist:** Ed Seale

☐ Purchased 19____　　Pd $_____　　MIB　NB　DB　BNT
☐ Want　　Orig. Ret. $8.95　　　　　　**MIB** Sec. Mkt. **$18**

QX 678-2　FOLK ART AMERICANA COLLECTION:　☐
　　　　　LEADING THE WAY

Comments:　Handcrafted, Dated 1997. An elf sits atop a moose and prepares to take a holiday ride. Very attractive ornament! **Artist:** Linda Sickman

☐ Purchased 19____　　Pd $_____　　MIB　NB　DB　BNT
☐ Want　　Orig. Ret. $16.95　　　　　**MIB** Sec. Mkt. **$24**

QX 678-5　FOLK ART AMERICANA COLLECTION:　☐
　　　　　SANTA'S MERRY PATH

Comments:　Handcrafted, Dated 1997. Santa stands ready, with his Canadian goose and bag full of goodies, to make his trip. Very creative piece! **Artist:** Linda Sickman

☐ Purchased 19____　　Pd $_____　　MIB　NB　DB　BNT
☐ Want　　Orig. Ret. $16.95　　　　　**MIB** Sec. Mkt. **$25**

QXI 618-2　FOOTBALL LEGENDS: JOE NAMATH　☐

Comments:　**Third in Series,** Handcrafted. Joe Namath in his number 12 football jersey stands ready to throw the pass. **Artist:** Dill Rhodus

☐ Purchased 19____　　Pd $_____　　MIB　NB　DB　BNT
☐ Want　　Orig. Ret. $14.95　　　　　**MIB** Sec. Mkt. **$18**

QX 665-5　FRIENDSHIP BLEND　☐

Comments:　Handcrafted, Dated 1997. Two mice sit atop a tea envelope ready to partake of some Holiday Tea. **Artists:** Ed Seale and Tracy Larsen

☐ Purchased 19____　　Pd $_____　　MIB　NB　DB　BNT
☐ Want　　Orig. Ret. $9.95　　　　　　**MIB** Sec. Mkt. **$18**

QX 625-5　FROSTY FRIENDS: FROSTY FRIENDS　☐

Comments:　**Eighteenth in Series,** Handcrafted, Dated 1997. Two famous friends ride their sailboat across the ice. **Artist:** Ed Seale

☐ Purchased 19____　　Pd $_____　　MIB　NB　DB　BNT
☐ Want　　Orig. Ret. $10.95　　　　　**MIB** Sec. Mkt. **$18**

QLX 743-5　GLOWING ANGEL　☐

Comments:　Lighted, Dated 1997. The angel's wings and halo create a soft heavenly glow. **Artist:** LaDene Votruba

☐ Purchased 19____　　Pd $_____　　MIB　NB　DB　BNT
☐ Want　　Orig. Ret. $18.95　　　　　**MIB** Sec. Mkt. **$22**

QX 679-2　GOD'S GIFT OF LOVE　☐

Comments:　Bisque Porcelain, Dated 1997. Joseph and Mary sit holding God's gift to the world, the baby Jesus. **Artist:** Joyce Lyle

☐ Purchased 19____　　Pd $_____　　MIB　NB　DB　BNT
☐ Want　　Orig. Ret. $17　　　　　　　**MIB** Sec. Mkt. **$20**

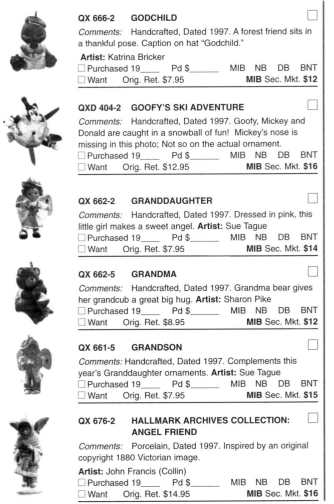

QX 666-2   GODCHILD

Comments: Handcrafted, Dated 1997. A forest friend sits in a thankful pose. Caption on hat "Godchild."

Artist: Katrina Bricker

☐ Purchased 19____   Pd $_____   MIB   NB   DB   BNT
☐ Want   Orig. Ret. $7.95   **MIB** Sec. Mkt. **$12**

QXD 404-2   GOOFY'S SKI ADVENTURE

Comments: Handcrafted, Dated 1997. Goofy, Mickey and Donald are caught in a snowball of fun! Mickey's nose is missing in this photo; Not so on the actual ornament.

☐ Purchased 19____   Pd $_____   MIB   NB   DB   BNT
☐ Want   Orig. Ret. $12.95   **MIB** Sec. Mkt. **$16**

QX 662-2   GRANDDAUGHTER

Comments: Handcrafted, Dated 1997. Dressed in pink, this little girl makes a sweet angel. **Artist:** Sue Tague

☐ Purchased 19____   Pd $_____   MIB   NB   DB   BNT
☐ Want   Orig. Ret. $7.95   **MIB** Sec. Mkt. **$14**

QX 662-5   GRANDMA

Comments: Handcrafted, Dated 1997. Grandma bear gives her grandcub a great big hug. **Artist:** Sharon Pike

☐ Purchased 19____   Pd $_____   MIB   NB   DB   BNT
☐ Want   Orig. Ret. $8.95   **MIB** Sec. Mkt. **$12**

QX 661-5   GRANDSON

Comments: Handcrafted, Dated 1997. Complements this year's Granddaughter ornaments. **Artist:** Sue Tague

☐ Purchased 19____   Pd $_____   MIB   NB   DB   BNT
☐ Want   Orig. Ret. $7.95   **MIB** Sec. Mkt. **$15**

**QX 676-2   HALLMARK ARCHIVES COLLECTION:
ANGEL FRIEND**

Comments: Porcelain, Dated 1997. Inspired by an original copyright 1880 Victorian image.

Artist: John Francis (Collin)

☐ Purchased 19____   Pd $_____   MIB   NB   DB   BNT
☐ Want   Orig. Ret. $14.95   **MIB** Sec. Mkt. **$16**

**QX 679-5   HALLMARK ARCHIVES COLLECTION:
HEAVENLY SONG**

Comments: Acrylic. This ornament has the look of a stained glass window. **Artist:** LaDene Votruba

☐ Purchased 19____   Pd $_____   MIB   NB   DB   BNT
☐ Want   Orig. Ret. $12.95   **MIB** Sec. Mkt. **$14**

**QXD 402-5   HALLMARK ARCHIVES:
DONALD'S SURPRISING GIFT**

Comments: **FIRST IN SERIES,** Handcrafted, Dated 1997. Donald is busy trying to wrap a gift while including himself. Includes Collector's card.

☐ Purchased 19____   Pd $_____   MIB   NB   DB   BNT
☐ Want   Orig. Ret. $12.95   **MIB** Sec. Mkt. **$22**

**QX 675-5   HALLMARK ARCHIVES COLLECTION :
SANTA'S POLAR FRIEND**

Comments: Handcrafted, Dated 1997. This ornament was inspired by an original copyright 1880 Victorian design.

Artist: Robert Chad

☐ Purchased 19____   Pd $_____   MIB   NB   DB   BNT
☐ Want   Orig. Ret. $16.95   **MIB** Sec. Mkt. **$20**

**HAPPY CHRISTMAS TO ALL
KEEPSAKE CLUB**

Comments: Handcrafted, Dated 1997. Celebrating the 175th anniversary of Clement C. Moore's The Night Before Christmas, this ornament captures the essence of that favorite holiday story. Available to club members only.

Artist: Nello Williams.

☐ Purchased 19____   Pd $_____   MIB   NB   DB   BNT
☐ Want Orig. Ret. (club members)   **MIB** Sec. Mkt. **$18**

**QXI 400-5   HERCULES COLLECTION, THE:
HERCULES**

Comments: Handcrafted. This ornament was available beginning in August, 1997. Hercules draws his bow, ready to fight against the evils of the world.

☐ Purchased 19____   Pd $_____   MIB   NB   DB   BNT
☐ Want   Orig. Ret. $14.95   **MIB** Sec. Mkt. **$18**

QXI 401-2   HERCULES COLLECTION, THE: ☐
MEGARA & PEGASUS

Comments: Handcrafted. Megara rides the beautiful
Pegasus to find her true love.

☐ Purchased 19____   Pd $_____   MIB   NB   DB   BNT
☐ Want   Orig. Ret. $16.95   **MIB** Sec. Mkt. **$22**

QX 626-2   HERE COMES SANTA: ☐
THE CLAUS-MOBILE

Comments: **Nineteenth in Series,** Handcrafted, Dated
1997. Santa comes riding in his homemade soap box derby
car. **Artist:** Sue Tague

☐ Purchased 19____   Pd $_____   MIB   NB   DB   BNT
☐ Want   Orig. Ret. $14.95   **MIB** Sec. Mkt. **$22**

QX 632-5   HERSHEY'S™: SWEET DISCOVERY ☐

Comments: Handcrafted, Dated 1997. Two mice share the
sweet discovery of finding Hershey's™ chocolate milk.
Artist: Linda Sickman

☐ Purchased 19____   Pd $_____   MIB   NB   DB   BNT
☐ Want   Orig. Ret. $11.95   **MIB** Sec. Mkt. **$16**

QXI 627-5   HOCKEY GREATS: WAYNE GRETZKY ☐

Comments: **FIRST IN SERIES,** Handcrafted, Dated 1997.
Skating for the Rangers, Wayne Gretzky glides to victory.
Artist: Duane Unruh

☐ Purchased 19____   Pd $_____   MIB   NB   DB   BNT
☐ Want   Orig. Ret. $15.95   **MIB** Sec. Mkt. **$19**

QXI 621-2   HOLIDAY BARBIE™ ☐

Comments: **Fifth in Series,** Handcrafted, Dated 1997.
Brunette Barbie dressed in red and white.
Artist: Patricia Andrews

☐ Purchased 19____   Pd $_____   MIB   NB   DB   BNT
☐ Want   Orig. Ret. $15.95   **MIB** Sec. Mkt. **$20**

QLX 748-5   HOLIDAY SERENADE ☐

Comments: Light/Sound, Dated 1997. Cardinals sing outside the lighted birdhouse. **Artist:** John Francis (Collin)

☐ Purchased 19____   Pd $_____   MIB   NB   DB   BNT
☐ Want   Orig. Ret. $24.00   **MIB** Sec. Mkt. **$30**

HOLIDAY TRADITIONS™ BARBIE™ ☐

Comments: Handcrafted. This ornament matches the new
series of Hallmark exclusive Special Edition Barbie® dolls from
the Holiday Homecoming Collection.

☐ Purchased 19____   Pd $_____   MIB   NB   DB   BNT
☐ Want   Orig. Ret. $14.95   **MIB** Sec. Mkt. **$15**

QXI 683-2   HOOP STARS: MAGIC JOHNSON ☐

Comments: **Third in Series,** Handcrafted. Magic Johnson
jumps to make an easy layup in this third of the Hoop Stars
series.

☐ Purchased 19____   Pd $_____   MIB   NB   DB   BNT
☐ Want   Orig. Ret. $14.95   **MIB** Sec. Mkt. **$18**

QX 627-2   HOWDY DOODY™ ☐

Comments: **Anniversary Edition,** Handcrafted, Dated
1997. Guess what time it is? It's Howdy Doody time! Very
popular! **Artist:** Tracy Larsen

☐ Purchased 19____   Pd $_____   MIB   NB   DB   BNT
☐ Want   Orig. Ret. $12.95   **MIB** Sec. Mkt. **$24**

QXD 634-4   HUNCHBACK OF NOTRE DAME, THE: ☐
PHOEBUS & ESMERALDA

Comments: Handcrafted. Phoebus sweeps Esmeralda off
her feet to show how much he loves her.

☐ Purchased 19____   Pd $_____   MIB   NB   DB   BNT
☐ Want   Orig. Ret. $14.95   **MIB** Sec. Mkt. **$19**

QX 669-5   JINGLE BELL JESTER ☐

Comments: Handcrafted, Dated 1997. A playful squirrel
plays with a bell on a red string. **Artist:** Sharon Pike

☐ Purchased 19____   Pd $_____   MIB   NB   DB   BNT
☐ Want   Orig. Ret. $9.95   **MIB** Sec. Mkt. **$14**

QLX 753-2   JOURNEYS INTO SPACE: FRIENDSHIP 7 ☐

Comments: **Second in Series,** Light/Voice, Dated 1997.
Commemorated the first American manned orbital spaceflight
which took place 35 years ago. **Artist:** Ed Seale

☐ Purchased 19____   Pd $_____   MIB   NB   DB   BNT
☐ Want   Orig. Ret. $24.00   **MIB** Sec. Mkt. **$32**

QLX 751-2   JOY TO THE WORLD

Comments: Lighted, Dated 1997. A little trumpet player announces "Joy" to the world on which he stands upon. Very nice! **Artist**: Sue Tague

☐ Purchased 19____   Pd $_____   MIB NB DB BNT
☐ Want   Orig. Ret. $14.95   **MIB** Sec. Mkt. **$25**

QX 659-5   JUGGLING STARS

Comments: Handcrafted, Dated 1997. Dressed in blue, this angel holds the stars in the palm of her hand.
Artist: Sue Tague

☐ Purchased 19____   Pd $_____   MIB NB DB BNT
☐ Want   Orig. Ret. $9.95   **MIB** Sec. Mkt. **$15**

**QX 619-5   KIDDIE CAR CLASSICS:
MURRAY® DUMP TRUCK**

Comments: **Fourth in Series,** Die-cast Metal, Dated1997. Ready to go, this yellow dump truck is a perfect addition to the Kiddie Car Classics series. **Artist:** Don Palmiter

☐ Purchased 19____   Pd $_____   MIB NB DB BNT
☐ Want   Orig. Ret. $13.95   **MIB** Sec. Mkt. **$18.50**

**QX 109-5   LANGUAGE OF FLOWERS, THE:
SNOWDROP ANGEL**

Comments: **Second in Series,** Silver Plated, Dated 1997. Carrying a basket of little white flowers, the Snowdrop Angel descends to your tree. **Artist:** Sue Tague

☐ Purchased 19____   Pd $_____   MIB NB DB BNT
☐ Want   Orig. Ret. $15.95   **MIB** Sec. Mkt. **$21**

**QX 655-2   LEGEND OF THREE KINGS COLLECTION:
KING NOOR–FIRST KING**

Comments: Handcrafted, Dated 1997. The legend begins this year with King Noor dressed in his blue robe, carrying his gift to the Magi. **Artist:** Patricia Andrews

☐ Purchased 19____   Pd $_____   MIB NB DB BNT
☐ Want   Orig. Ret. $12.95   **MIB** Sec. Mkt. **$18**

**QLX 744-2   LIGHTHOUSE GREETING:
LIGHTHOUSE GREETING**

Comments: **FIRST IN SERIES**, Lighted, Dated 1997. A beacon light flashes while a light glows warmly inside home and on the Christmas tree. Received great reviews.
Artist: John Francis (Collin)

☐ Purchased 19____   Pd $_____   MIB NB DB BNT
☐ Want   Orig. Ret. $24.00   **MIB** Sec. Mkt. **$30**

QLX 752-2   LINCOLN MEMORIAL, THE

Comments: Lighted Musical, Dated 1997.
Plays: "America the Beautiful." Includes a collector card.
Artist: Ed Seale

☐ Purchased 19____   Pd $_____   MIB NB DB BNT
☐ Want   Orig. Ret. $24.00   **MIB** Sec. Mkt. **$28**

QX 660-2   LION AND LAMB

Comments: Handcrafted, Dated 1997.
As is it is written, the peaceable kingdom will happen when the lion lays down with the lamb. **Artist:** Nello Williams

☐ Purchased 19____   Pd $_____   MIB NB DB BNT
☐ Want   Orig. Ret. $7.95   **MIB** Sec. Mkt. **$18**

QXD 406-5   LION KING, THE: TIMON & PUMBAA

Comments: Handcrafted, Dated 1997.
From the classic movie, "The Lion King," Timon and Pumbaa decorate your tree.

☐ Purchased 19____   Pd $_____   MIB NB DB BNT
☐ Want   Orig. Ret. $12.95   **MIB** Sec. Mkt. **$18**

**QX 614-5   LIONEL®: 1950 SANTA FE F3 DIESEL
LOCOMOTIVE**

Comments: **Second in Series**, Die Cast Metal, Dated 1997.Great for train collectors young and old alike. Excellent!

☐ Purchased 19____   Pd $_____   MIB NB DB BNT
☐ Want   Orig. Ret. $18.95   **MIB** Sec. Mkt. **$32**

QXI 407-2   LITTLE MERMAID, THE: ARIEL

Comments: Ariel plays with her little friends of the sea.

☐ Purchased 19____   Pd $_____   MIB NB DB BNT
☐ Want   Orig. Ret. $12.95   **MIB** Sec. Mkt. **$17**

QX 626-5 LONE RANGER™, THE
Comments: Pressed tin, Dated 1997.
The Lone Ranger rides again on this ornament. Spring '98 debuted with the second lunch box ornament.
Artist: Steve Goslin
☐ Purchased 19____ Pd $_____ MIB NB DB BNT
☐ Want Orig. Ret. $12.95 **MIB** Sec. Mkt.**$35**

QLX 750-2 LOONEY TUNES™: DECORATOR TAZ
Comments: Light/Motion, Dated 1997.
In his whirlwind fashion, Taz circles the Christmas tree which encloses a baffled Daffy Duck. **Artist:** Robert Chad
☐ Purchased 19____ Pd $_____ MIB NB DB BNT
☐ Want Orig. Ret. $30 **MIB** Sec. Mkt.**$35**

QX 633-2 LOONEY TUNES™: MICHIGAN J. FROG
Comments: Handcrafted.
Michigan J. Frog looks very dapper as he get ready to sing a song, wearing his top hat and posing with his candy cane.
Artist: Robert Chad
☐ Purchased 19____ Pd $_____ MIB NB DB BNT
☐ Want Orig. Ret. $9.95 **MIB** Sec. Mkt.**$17**

QX 643-5 LOVE TO SEW
Comments: Handcrafted, Dated 1997.
Laying on a pin cushion, this little angel uses the heads of pins to spell "Love." **Artist:** Sue Tague
☐ Purchased 19____ Pd $_____ MIB NB DB BNT
☐ Want Orig. Ret. $7.95 **MIB** Sec. Mkt.**$16**

QX 615-5 MADAME ALEXANDER™:
LITTLE RED RIDING HOOD – 1991
Comments: **Second in Series**, Handcrafted, Dated 1997.
Little Red Riding Hood as portrayed by Madame Alexander's™ doll which was introduced in 1991.
Artist: John Francis (Collin)
☐ Purchased 19____ Pd $_____ MIB NB DB BNT
☐ Want Orig. Ret. $14.95 **MIB** Sec. Mkt.**$26**

QLX 742-5 MADONNA AND CHILD
Comments: Lighted, Dated 1997.
A beautiful ornament, the light softly highlights the cherubs in the clouds which surround the Madonna and Child.
Artist: Joyce Lyle
☐ Purchased 19____ Pd $_____ MIB NB DB BNT
☐ Want Orig. Ret. $20 **MIB** Sec. Mkt.**$25**

QX 654-5 MADONNA DEL ROSARIO
Comments: Handcrafted, Dated 1997.
This ornament is a reproduction of the painting done by Bartolomé Esteban Murillo. **Artist:** Linda Sickman
☐ Purchased 19____ Pd $_____ MIB NB DB BNT
☐ Want Orig. Ret. $12.95 **MIB** Sec. Mkt. **$14**

QX 569-4 MAJESTIC WILDERNESS:
SNOWSHOE RABBITS IN WINTER
– MARK NEWMAN
Comments: **FIRST IN SERIES**, Handcrafted, Dated 1997.
Two rabbits huddle in their home against the chill of winter. This is a really great ornament! The second one in this series will determine how popular the series will be.
☐ Purchased 19____ Pd $_____ MIB NB DB BNT
☐ Want Orig. Ret. $9.95 **MIB** Sec. Mkt. **$22**

QX 570-4 MARILYN MONROE: MARILYN MONROE
Comments: **FIRST IN SERIES**, Handcrafted, Dated 1997.
One of Hollywood's most notable personalities, Marilyn looks beautiful in her pink evening gown. **Artist:** Patricia Andrews
☐ Purchased 19____ Pd $_____ MIB NB DB BNT
☐ Want Orig. Ret. $14.95 **MIB** Sec. Mkt. **$18**

QX 624-2 MARY'S ANGELS: DAISY
Comments: **Tenth in Series**, Handcrafted.
Daisy uses a watering can to water her namesake flower.
Artists: Mary Hamilton and Robert Chad
☐ Purchased 19____ Pd $_____ MIB NB DB BNT
☐ Want Orig. Ret. $7.95 **MIB** Sec. Mkt. **$14**

QX 671-5 MEADOW SNOWMAN
Comments: Pressed Tin, Dated 1997.
A perfect snowman for the perfect tree. **Artist:** Linda Sickman
☐ Purchased 19____ Pd $_____ MIB NB DB BNT
☐ Want Orig. Ret. $12.95 **MIB** Sec. Mkt. **$28**

QX 622-5 MERRY OLDE SANTA: MERRY OLDE SANTA
Comments: **Eighth in Series**, Handcrafted, Dated 1997.
With the look of Christmas past, this Santa seems ready to wish everyone a "Merry Christmas." **Artist:** Joyce Lyle
☐ Purchased 19____ Pd $_____ MIB NB DB BNT
☐ Want Orig. Ret. $14.95 **MIB** Sec. Mkt. **$24**

QXD 402-2 MICKEY'S HOLIDAY PARADE: BANDLEADER MICKEY

Comments: **FIRST IN SERIES**, Handcrafted, Dated 1997. Mickey leads the band with the beat of his big bass drum. So many Disney ornaments! May or may not be hot! Watch and see!
☐ Purchased 19____   Pd $_____   MIB   NB   DB   BNT
☐ Want   Orig. Ret. $13.95   **MIB** Sec. Mkt. **$26**

QXD 641-2 MICKEY'S LONG SHOT

Comments: Handcrafted, Dated 1997.
Mickey prepares to make his long shot in golf.
☐ Purchased 19____   Pd $_____   MIB   NB   DB   BNT
☐ Want   Orig. Ret. $10.95   **MIB** Sec. Mkt. **$16**

QXD 403-5 MICKEY'S SNOW ANGEL

Comments: Handcrafted, Dated 1997.
Mickey makes a perfect mouse shape in the snow.
☐ Purchased 19____   Pd $_____   MIB   NB   DB   BNT
☐ Want   Orig. Ret. $9.95   **MIB** Sec. Mkt. **$18**

QX 652-5 MOM

Comments: Handcrafted, Dated 1997. A little mouse sits on the teapot titled "MOM." **Artist:** Bob Siedler
☐ Purchased 19____   Pd $_____   MIB   NB   DB   BNT
☐ Want   Orig. Ret. $8.95   **MIB** Sec. Mkt. **$16**

QX 652-2 MOM AND DAD

Comments: Handcrafted, Dated 1997.
A little mouse carries the packages marked "Mom" and "Dad" while his partner rides atop. **Artist:** Bob Siedler
☐ Purchased 19____   Pd $_____   MIB   NB   DB   BNT
☐ Want   Orig. Ret. $9.95   **MIB** Sec. Mkt. **$17**

QX 621-5 MOTHER GOOSE: LITTLE BOY BLUE

Comments: **Fifth and Final in Series,** Handcrafted, Dated 1997. Book opens to display this favorite childhood verse. **Artists:** Ed Seale and LaDene Votruba
☐ Purchased 19____   Pd $_____   MIB   NB   DB   BNT
☐ Want   Orig. Ret. $13.95   **MIB** Sec. Mkt. **$18**

QLX 749-5 MOTORCYCLE CHUMS

Comments: Lighted, Dated 1997.
Santa and his favorite reindeer try to find their way on a motorcycle with side car. **Artist:** Ed Seale
☐ Purchased 19____   Pd $_____   MIB   NB   DB   BNT
☐ Want   Orig. Ret. $24.00   **MIB** Sec. Mkt. **$40**

QX 633-5 MR. POTATO HEAD®

Comments: Handcrafted, Dated 1997.
Still a favorite toy of the young and a popular ornament for those remembering the little guy. Larger than most ornaments. **Artist:** Bob Siedler
☐ Purchased 19____   Pd $_____   MIB   NB   DB   BNT
☐ Want   Orig. Ret. $10.95   **MIB** Sec. Mkt. **$18**

QX 657-5 NATIVITY TREE

Comments: Handcrafted, Dated 1997.
A true nativity tree decorated with all who participated that holy night. **Artist:** Duane Unruh
☐ Purchased 19____   Pd $_____   MIB   NB   DB   BNT
☐ Want   Orig. Ret. $14.95   **MIB** Sec. Mkt. **$18**

QX 675-2 NATURE'S SKETCHBOOK: GARDEN BOUQUET

Comments: Handcrafted, Dated 1997.
Beautiful flowers designed by Marjolein Bastin. Beautiful, but her Wildlife is more favored. **Artist:** Joyce Lyle
☐ Purchased 19____   Pd $_____   MIB   NB   DB   BNT
☐ Want   Orig. Ret. $14.95   **MIB** Sec. Mkt. **$21**

QX 674-5 NATURE'S SKETCHBOOK: HONORED GUESTS

Comments: Handcrafted, Dated 1997. Little birds come to feed at this winter feeder. **Artist:** John Francis (Collin)
☐ Purchased 19____   Pd $_____   MIB   NB   DB   BNT
☐ Want   Orig. Ret. $14.95   **MIB** Sec. Mkt. **$21**

QX 665-2 NEW HOME

Comments: Handcrafted, Dated 1997.
Two little mice make their home in a Christmas stocking. **Artist:** Sharon Pike
☐ Purchased 19____   Pd $_____   MIB   NB   DB   BNT
☐ Want   Orig. Ret. $8.95   **MIB** Sec. Mkt. $12

QXD 403-2 NEW PAIR OF SKATES

Comments: Handcrafted, Dated 1997.
Mickey tries on new skates while Minnie patiently helps.
☐ Purchased 19____   Pd $_____   MIB   NB   DB   BNT
☐ Want   Orig. Ret. $13.95   **MIB** Sec. Mkt. **$22**

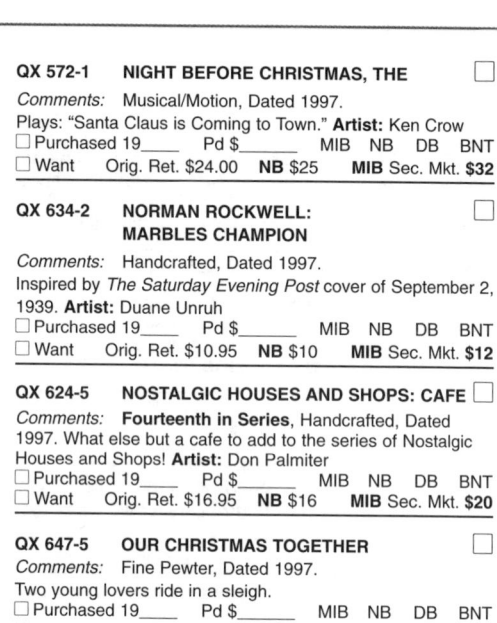

QX 572-1　NIGHT BEFORE CHRISTMAS, THE　☐

Comments: Musical/Motion, Dated 1997.
Plays: "Santa Claus is Coming to Town." **Artist:** Ken Crow
☐ Purchased 19____　Pd $_____　MIB　NB　DB　BNT
☐ Want　Orig. Ret. $24.00　**NB** $25　**MIB** Sec. Mkt. **$32**

QX 634-2　NORMAN ROCKWELL:
　　　　　MARBLES CHAMPION　☐

Comments: Handcrafted, Dated 1997.
Inspired by *The Saturday Evening Post* cover of September 2,
1939. **Artist:** Duane Unruh
☐ Purchased 19____　Pd $_____　MIB　NB　DB　BNT
☐ Want　Orig. Ret. $10.95　**NB** $10　**MIB** Sec. Mkt. **$12**

QX 624-5　NOSTALGIC HOUSES AND SHOPS: CAFE　☐

Comments: **Fourteenth in Series**, Handcrafted, Dated
1997. What else but a cafe to add to the series of Nostalgic
Houses and Shops! **Artist:** Don Palmiter
☐ Purchased 19____　Pd $_____　MIB　NB　DB　BNT
☐ Want　Orig. Ret. $16.95　**NB** $16　**MIB** Sec. Mkt. **$20**

QX 647-5　OUR CHRISTMAS TOGETHER　☐

Comments: Fine Pewter, Dated 1997.
Two young lovers ride in a sleigh.
☐ Purchased 19____　Pd $_____　MIB　NB　DB　BNT
☐ Want　Orig. Ret. $16.95　**NB** $18　**MIB** Sec. Mkt. **$20**

QX 646-5　OUR FIRST CHRISTMAS TOGETHER　☐

Comments: Handcrafted, Dated 1997.
The acorn home of these two little chipmunks sways to and fro
on the Christmas tree. **Artist:** Ed Seale
☐ Purchased 19____　Pd $_____　MIB　NB　DB　BNT
☐ Want　Orig. Ret. $10.95　**NB** $11　**MIB** Sec. Mkt. **$23**

QX 647-2　OUR FIRST CHRISTMAS TOGETHER　☐

Comments: Photo Holder, Dated 1997.
A heart which opens becomes the frame to hold a special pic-
ture. **Artist:** Sharon Pike
☐ Purchased 19____　Pd $_____　MIB　NB　DB　BNT
☐ Want　Orig. Ret. $8.95　**NB** $9　**MIB** Sec. Mkt. **$14**

QX 318-2　OUR FIRST CHRISTMAS TOGETHER　☐

Comments: Acrylic, Dated 1997.
Frosted edged heart encloses the words "Our First Christmas
Together 1997."
☐ Purchased 19____　Pd $_____　MIB　NB　DB　BNT
☐ Want　Orig. Ret. $7.95　**MIB** Sec. Mkt. **$14**

QLX 747-5　PEANUTS®: SNOOPY PLAYS SANTA　☐

Comments: Motion, Dated 1997.
Snoopy rides in a special doghouse sleigh as it circles the
house below. **Artist:** Anita Marra Rogers
☐ Purchased 19____　Pd $_____　MIB　NB　DB　BNT
☐ Want　Orig. Ret. $22.00　**MIB** Sec. Mkt. **$26**

QX 659-2　PLAYFUL SHEPHERD　☐

Comments: Handcrafted, Dated 1997.
A little shepherd rides a special rocking horse-type lamb.
Artist: Sue Tague
☐ Purchased 19____　Pd $_____　MIB　NB　DB　BNT
☐ Want　Orig. Ret. $9.95　**MIB** Sec. Mkt. **$14**

QX 677-2　PORCELAIN HINGED BOX　☐

Comments: Porcelain, Dated 1997.
A snowman opens at the waist to become an unusual hinged
box. Sure to be a collectors' item! **Artist:** LaDene Votruba
☐ Purchased 19____　Pd $_____　MIB　NB　DB　BNT
☐ Want　Orig. Ret. $14.95　**MIB** Sec. Mkt. **$28**

QX 654-2　PRAISE HIM　☐

Comments: Handcrafted, Dated 1997.
A uniquely designed ornament which portrays the birth of
Christ. **Artist:** Linda Sickman
☐ Purchased 19____　Pd $_____　MIB　NB　DB　BNT
☐ Want　Orig. Ret. $8.95　**MIB** Sec. Mkt. **$12**

QX 667-5　PRIZE TOPIARY　☐

Comments: Clip-on, Dated 1997.
Santa trims his hedge in the shape of his favorite animal.
Clever design! **Artist:** Ed Seale
☐ Purchased 19____　Pd $_____　MIB　NB　DB　BNT
☐ Want　Orig. Ret. $14.95　**MIB** Sec. Mkt. **$26**

QX 622-2 PUPPY LOVE: PUPPY LOVE ☐
Comments: **Seventh in Series**, Brass tag, Dated 1997.
A special puppy holds his owner's slipper.
Artist: Anita Marra Rogers
☐ Purchased 19____ Pd $_____ MIB NB DB BNT
☐ Want Orig. Ret. $7.95 **MIB** Sec. Mkt. **$12**

QX 676-5 SAILOR BEAR ☐
Comments: Handcrafted, Dated 1997.
Ready to play with his sailboat, this little bear is dressed in his
sailor outfit complete with cap. **Artist:** Duane Unruh
☐ Purchased 19____ Pd $_____ MIB NB DB BNT
☐ Want Orig. Ret. $14.95 **MIB** Sec. Mkt. **$20**

QX 670-2 SANTA MAIL ☐
Comments: Handcrafted, Dated 1997.
As a little child places mail in the Post Office box, out of the
child's view sits Santa, ready to read the new letter addressed
to him. Such a clever design! **Artist:** Nello Williams
☐ Purchased 19____ Pd $_____ MIB NB DB BNT
☐ Want Orig. Ret. $10.95 **MIB** Sec. Mkt. **$20**

QX 668-5 SANTA'S FRIEND ☐
Comments: Handcrafted, Dated 1997.
A puppy becomes Santa's special friend. Could the puppy be a
gift? **Artist:** Marjolein Bastin and Duane Unruh
☐ Purchased 19____ Pd $_____ MIB NB DB BNT
☐ Want Orig. Ret. $12.95 **MIB** Sec. Mkt. **$22**

QX 667-2 SANTA'S MAGICAL SLEIGH ☐
Comments: Handcrafted, Dated 1997. A very colorful orna-
ment is this Santa and sleigh. **Artist:** Duane Unruh
☐ Purchased 19____ Pd $_____ MIB NB DB BNT
☐ Want Orig. Ret. $24.00 **MIB** Sec. Mkt. **$30**

QLX 745-5 SANTA'S SECRET GIFT ☐
Comments: Musical, Dated 1997.
Plays: " Jolly Old St. Nicholas." Santa holds a gift bag which
can be used to hold a small gift or message.
Artist: Robert Chad
☐ Purchased 19____ Pd $_____ MIB NB DB BNT
☐ Want Orig. Ret. $24.00 **MIB** Sec. Mkt. **$30**

QLX 746-5 SANTA'S SHOWBOAT ☐
Comments: Light and Motion, Musical, Dated 1997.
Plays: "Jingle Bells." The paddle wheel of this riverboat turns,
while the light flickers above the steamboat's chimneys and
portholes glow. Could be used in a table top display.
Artist: Ken Crow
☐ Purchased 19____ Pd $_____ MIB NB DB BNT
☐ Want Orig. Ret. $42.00 **MIB** Sec. Mkt. **$75**

QX 642-2 SANTA'S SKI ADVENTURE ☐
Comments: Handcrafted, Dated 1997.
Santa's skills at skiing are tested when his reindeer friend runs
into him! **Artist:** Robert Chad
☐ Purchased 19____ Pd $_____ MIB NB DB BNT
☐ Want Orig. Ret. $12.95 **MIB** Sec. Mkt. **$20**

QX 612-5 SCARLETT O'HARA™: SCARLETT O'HARA™ ☐
Comments: **FIRST IN SERIES**, Handcrafted, Dated 1997.
The face on this ornament is not an exact protrayal of Vivian
Leigh, who played the part of Scarlett. Future "Gone With the
Wind" characters may enhance this ornament.
Artist: Patricia Andrews
☐ Purchased 19____ Pd $_____ MIB NB DB BNT
☐ Want Orig. Ret. $14.95 **MIB** Sec. Mkt. **$18.50**

QX 663-5 SISTER TO SISTER ☐
Comments: Handcrafted, Dated 1997.
Sisters are truly treasured friends, as these sisters know very
well. Don't forget "sis" when buying your Hallmark Ornaments!
Artist: Sharon Pike
☐ Purchased 19____ Pd $_____ MIB NB DB BNT
☐ Want Orig. Ret. $9.95 **MIB** Sec. Mkt. **$16**

QX 557-4 SKY'S THE LIMIT: THE FLIGHT AT KITTY HAWK ☐
Comments: **FIRST IN SERIES**, Handcrafted, Dated 1997.
The Wright brothers' infamous plane is represented in this high-
ly detailed ornament. A must for airplane buffs!
Artist: Lynn Norton
☐ Purchased 19____ Pd $_____ MIB NB DB BNT
☐ Want Orig. Ret. $14.95 **MIB** Sec. Mkt. **$22**

QX 639-5 SNOW BOWLING ☐
Comments: Handcrafted, Dated 1997.
A bowling pin is used to make this happy snowman.
Artist: Nello Williams
☐ Purchased 19____   Pd $_____   MIB NB DB BNT
☐ Want   Orig. Ret. $6.95   **MIB** Sec. Mkt. **$16**

QXD 405-5 SNOW WHITE ☐
Comments: **Anniversary Edition**, Handcrafted, Dated
1997. Set of two ornaments. Snow White opens a package
which happens to be Dopey.
☐ Purchased 19____   Pd $_____   MIB NB DB BNT
☐ Want   Orig. Ret. $16.95   **MIB** Sec. Mkt. **$30**

QX 656-2 SNOWGIRL ☐
Comments: Handcrafted, Dated 1997.
This African-American beauty holds a golden star ready to
place on the Christmas tree. **Artist:** Sue Tague
☐ Purchased 19____   Pd $_____   MIB NB DB BNT
☐ Want   Orig. Ret. $7.95   **MIB** Sec. Mkt. **$15**

QX 660-5 SON ☐
Comments: Pressed Tin, Dated 1997.
A Christmas stocking, imprinted with "Santa" and made of
pressed tin, becomes the special ornament for a special son.
Artist: Katrina Bricker
☐ Purchased 19____   Pd $_____   MIB NB DB BNT
☐ Want   Orig. Ret. $7.95   **MIB** Sec. Mkt. **$14**

QX 663-2 SPECIAL DOG ☐
Comments: Photo Holder, Dated 1997.
What every dog owner should have, a place to display a photo
of their favorite canine. **Artist:** Katrina Bricker
☐ Purchased 19____   Pd $_____   MIB NB DB BNT
☐ Want   Orig. Ret. $7.95   **MIB** Sec. Mkt. **$12**

QX 658-5 SPIRIT OF CHRISTMAS, THE ☐
Comments: Collectors' Plate.
This collector plate comes with a display stand.
Artist: Tracy Larsen
☐ Purchased 19____   Pd $_____   MIB NB DB BNT
☐ Want   Orig. Ret. $9.95   **MIB** Sec. Mkt. **$11**

QXI 635-2 STAR TREK™: DR. LEONARD H. MCCOY™ ☐
Comments: Handcrafted, Dated 1997. Dr. McCoy is ready to
beam to your home. **Artist:** Anita Marra Rogers
☐ Purchased 19____   Pd $_____   MIB NB DB BNT
☐ Want   Orig. Ret. $14.95   **MIB** Sec. Mkt. **$20**

QXI 634-5 STAR TREK™ THE NEXT GENERATION™: ☐
COMMANDER DATA™
Comments: Handcrafted, Dated 1997. Commander Data sits
at the controls. **Artist:** Anita Marra Rogers
☐ Purchased 19____   Pd $_____   MIB NB DB BNT
☐ Want   Orig. Ret. $14.95   **MIB** Sec. Mkt. **$20**

QXI 748-1 STAR TREK™: U.S.S. DEFIANT™ ☐
Comments: Lighted, Dated 1997.
A reproduction of the U.S.S. Defiant™ from the television pro-
gram Deep Space Nine comes with blinking lights.
Artist: Lynn Norton
☐ Purchased 19____   Pd $_____   MIB NB DB BNT
☐ Want   Orig. Ret. $24.00   **MIB** Sec. Mkt. **$30**

QXI 753-1 STAR WARS™: DARTH VADER™ ☐
Comments: Lighted, Voice, Dated 1997.
Darth Vader™ with lightsaber which glows as he says, " The
Force is with you, young Skywalker. But you are not a Jedi yet!"
Artist: Dill Rhodus
☐ Purchased 19____   Pd $_____   MIB NB DB BNT
☐ Want   Orig. Ret. $24.00   **MIB** Sec. Mkt. **$25**

QXI 548-4 STAR WARS™: LUKE SKYWALKER™ ☐
Comments: **FIRST IN SERIES**, Handcrafted, Dated 1997.
Luke holds a lightsaber, ready to take on the Evil Empire.
Artist: Dill Rhodus
☐ Purchased 19____   Pd $_____   MIB NB DB BNT
☐ Want   Orig. Ret. $13.95   **MIB** Sec. Mkt. **$25**

QXI 635-5 STAR WARS™: YODA™ ☐
Comments: Handcrafted. Completing the Star Wars set is
Luke Skywalker's teacher, Yoda. **Artist:** Katrina Bricker
☐ Purchased 19____   Pd $_____   MIB NB DB BNT
☐ Want   Orig. Ret. $9.95   **MIB** Sec. Mkt. **$32**

QX 655-5   STEALING A KISS ☐
Comments: Handcrafted, Dated 1997.
An African-American Santa kisses the Missus before leaving to deliver toys. His red coat is trimmed in green and gold.
Artist: Sue Tague
☐ Purchased 19_____   Pd $_____   MIB   NB   DB   BNT
☐ Want   Orig. Ret. $14.95   **MIB** Sec. Mkt. **$16**

QXI 616-5   STOCK CAR CHAMPIONS: JEFF GORDON® ☐
Comments: **FIRST IN SERIES**, Handcrafted.
With the checkered flag behind him and #24 in front, Jeff Gordon is ready to win another stock car race! **Artist:** Ed Seale
☐ Purchased 19_____   Pd $_____   MIB   NB   DB   BNT
☐ Want   Orig. Ret. $15.95   **MIB** Sec. Mkt. **$18-24**

QX 673-2   SWEET DREAMER ☐
Comments: Handcrafted, Dated 1997.
A little bunny sleeps warm and cozy inside Santa's stocking cap. **Artist:** Katrina Bricker
☐ Purchased 19_____   Pd $_____   MIB   NB   DB   BNT
☐ Want   Orig. Ret. $6.95   **MIB** Sec. Mkt. **$8**

QX 677-5   SWINGING IN THE SNOW ☐
Comments: Glass, Dated 1997.
This bell is clear except for printed white snowflakes. The clapper is a little girl dressed to play in the new fallen snow.
Artist: Sue Tague
☐ Purchased 19_____   Pd $_____   MIB   NB   DB   BNT
☐ Want   Orig. Ret. $12.95   **MIB** Sec. Mkt. **$15**

QX 630-5   TAKING A BREAK ☐
Comments: Handcrafted, Dated 1997.
Santa Claus sits in a sleigh-like chair, holding up a Coca-Cola bottle. **Artist:** Duane Unruh
☐ Purchased 19_____   Pd $_____   MIB   NB   DB   BNT
☐ Want   Orig. Ret. $14.95   **MIB** Sec. Mkt. **$18**

QLX 748-2   TEAPOT PARTY ☐
Comments: Lighted, Dated 1997.
The light inside the white teapot illuminates a doll and teddy bear's Christmas party. **Artist:** Sue Tague
☐ Purchased 19_____   Pd $_____   MIB   NB   DB   BNT
☐ Want   Orig. Ret. $18.95   **MIB** Sec. Mkt. **$24**

QXC 518-2   TENDER TOUCHES: FARMER'S MARKET ☐
Comments: Club Edition, Handcrafted, Dated 1997.
Farmer Bunny sells carrots, tomatoes, lettuce, corn, and more at his "Fresh Veggies" stand. **Artist:** Ed Seale
☐ Purchased 19_____   Pd $_____   MIB   NB   DB   BNT
☐ Want   Orig. Ret. $15.00   **MIB** Sec. Mkt. **$24**

QX 657-2   TENDER TOUCHES: THE PERFECT TREE ☐
Comments: Handcrafted, Dated 1997.
Mother Mouse and her son decorate the family Christmas tree with red holly berries. **Artist:** Ed Seale
☐ Purchased 19_____   Pd $_____   MIB   NB   DB   BNT
☐ Want   Orig. Ret. $15.00   **MIB** Sec. Mkt. **$20**

QX 547-1   THE INCREDIBLE HULK™ ☐
Comments: Handcrafted.
A cartoon favorite, this green Incredible Hulk™ character went from being weak to very strong, to fight the wrongs of the world.
☐ Purchased 19_____   Pd $_____   MIB   NB   DB   BNT
☐ Want   Orig. Ret. $12.95   **MIB** Sec. Mkt. **$17**

QXI 754-5   THOMAS KINKADE: THE WARMTH OF HOME ☐
Comments: Lighted, Dated 1997.
A lit house stands prominently in this mountain scape. Thomas Kinkade is known as the painter of light. **Artist:** Tracy Larsen
☐ Purchased 19_____   Pd $_____   MIB   NB   DB   BNT
☐ Want   Orig. Ret. $18.95   **MIB** Sec. Mkt. **$24**

QXI 613-5   THOMAS KINKADE: VICTORIAN CHRISTMAS ☐
Comments: **FIRST IN SERIES**, Porcelain, Dated 1997.
A Victorian house shows the glow of a turn-of-the-century Christmas party. Kinkade Collectors will decide the secondary market demand in the future.
☐ Purchased 19_____   Pd $_____   MIB   NB   DB   BNT
☐ Want   Orig. Ret. $10.95   **MIB** Sec. Mkt. **$18**

QX 636-2   TONKA® MIGHTY FRONT LOADER ☐
Comments: Die-cast Metal, Dated 1997.
The front bucket assembly pivots and the wheels turn on this dated, yellow Tonka ornament.
☐ Purchased 19_____   Pd $_____   MIB   NB   DB   BNT
☐ Want   Orig. Ret. $13.95   **MIB** Sec. Mkt. **$18**

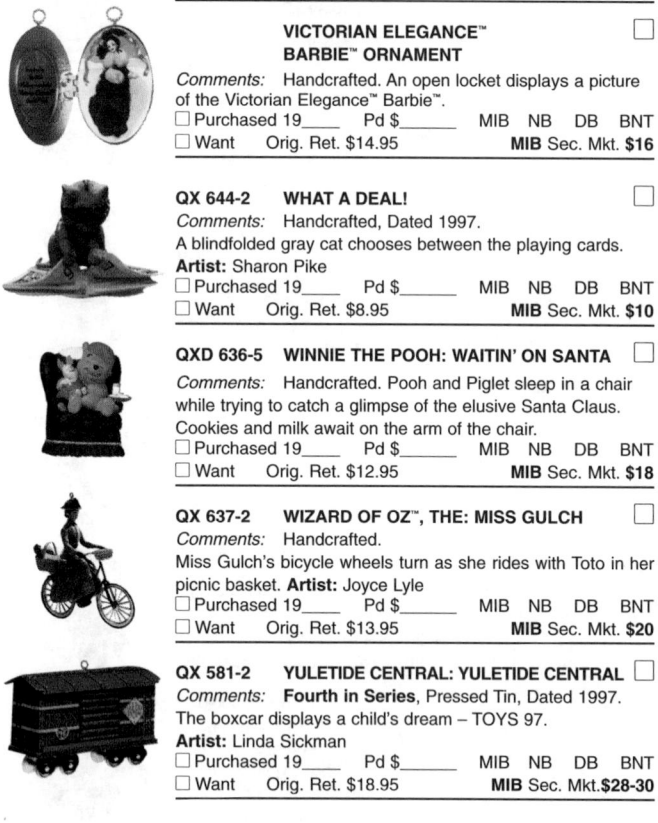

QX 121-5 TURN-OF-THE-CENTURY PARADE: SANTA CLAUS ☐

Comments: **Third and Final in Series,** Die-cast Metal/Brass, Dated 1997. Santa Claus rides a green horse that is sitting on a gold bell with red wheels. **Artist:** Ken Crow
☐ Purchased 19____ Pd $_____ MIB NB DB BNT
☐ Want   Orig. Ret. $16.95   **MIB** Sec. Mkt. **$20**

VICTORIAN ELEGANCE™ BARBIE™ ORNAMENT ☐

Comments: Handcrafted. An open locket displays a picture of the Victorian Elegance™ Barbie™.
☐ Purchased 19____ Pd $_____ MIB NB DB BNT
☐ Want   Orig. Ret. $14.95   **MIB** Sec. Mkt. **$16**

QX 644-2 WHAT A DEAL! ☐

Comments: Handcrafted, Dated 1997.
A blindfolded gray cat chooses between the playing cards.
Artist: Sharon Pike
☐ Purchased 19____ Pd $_____ MIB NB DB BNT
☐ Want   Orig. Ret. $8.95   **MIB** Sec. Mkt. **$10**

QXD 636-5 WINNIE THE POOH: WAITIN' ON SANTA ☐

Comments: Handcrafted. Pooh and Piglet sleep in a chair while trying to catch a glimpse of the elusive Santa Claus. Cookies and milk await on the arm of the chair.
☐ Purchased 19____ Pd $_____ MIB NB DB BNT
☐ Want   Orig. Ret. $12.95   **MIB** Sec. Mkt. **$18**

QX 637-2 WIZARD OF OZ™, THE: MISS GULCH ☐

Comments: Handcrafted.
Miss Gulch's bicycle wheels turn as she rides with Toto in her picnic basket. **Artist:** Joyce Lyle
☐ Purchased 19____ Pd $_____ MIB NB DB BNT
☐ Want   Orig. Ret. $13.95   **MIB** Sec. Mkt. **$20**

QX 581-2 YULETIDE CENTRAL: YULETIDE CENTRAL ☐

Comments: **Fourth in Series,** Pressed Tin, Dated 1997.
The boxcar displays a child's dream – TOYS 97.
Artist: Linda Sickman
☐ Purchased 19____ Pd $_____ MIB NB DB BNT
☐ Want   Orig. Ret. $18.95   **MIB** Sec. Mkt.**$28-30**

NFL Collection

☐ QSR 550-5	Arizona Cardinals™	☐ QSR 530-5	Atlanta Falcons™
☐ QSR 535-2	Baltimore Ravens™	☐ QSR 531-2	Buffalo Bills™
☐ QSR 531-5	Carolina Panthers™	☐ QSR 532-2	Chicago Bears™
☐ QSR 532-5	Cincinnati Bengals™	☐ QSR 535-5	Dallas Cowboys™
☐ QSR 536-2	Denver Broncos™	☐ QSR 536-5	Detroit Lions™
☐ QSR 537-2	Green Bay Packers™	☐ QSR 537-5	Houston Oilers™
☐ QSR 541-1	Indianapolis Colts™	☐ QSR 541-5	Jacksonville Jaguars™
☐ QSR 530-2	Kansas City Chiefs™	☐ QSR 547-2	Miami Dolphins™
☐ QSR 547-5	Minnesota Vikings™	☐ QSR 548-2	New England Patriots™
☐ QSR 548-5	New Orleans Saints™	☐ QSR 549-2	New York Giants™
☐ QSR 549-5	New York Jets™	☐ QSR 542-2	Oakland Raiders™
☐ QSR 550-2	Philadelphia Eagles™	☐ QSR 551-2	Pittsburgh Steelers™
☐ QSR 551-5	San Diego Chargers™	☐ QSR 552-2	San Francisco 49ers™
☐ QSR 552-5	Seattle Seahawks™	☐ QSR 542-5	St. Louis Rams™
☐ QSR 553-2	Tampa Bay Buccaneers™	☐ QSR 553-5	Washington Redskins™

NFL FOOTBALL BLIMP ☐

Comments: Handcrafte, Dated 1997.
Santa Claus rides in a football blimp engraved with a favorite team logo. **Artist:** Bob Siedler.
☐ Purchased 19____ Pd $_____ MIB NB DB BNT
☐ Want   Orig. Ret. $9.95   **MIB** Sec. Mkt. **N.E.**

NBA Collection

☐ QSR 122-2 Charlotte Hornets™	☐ QSR 126-2 Los Angeles Lakers™	
☐ QSR 123-2 Chicago Bulls™	☐ QSR 127-2 New York Knickerbockers™	
☐ QSR 124-2 Detroit Pistons™	☐ QSR 128-2 Orlando Magic™	
☐ QSR 124-5 Houston Rockets™	☐ QSR 129-2 Pheonix Suns™	
☐ QSR 125-2 Indiana Pacers™	☐ QSR 129-5 Seattle Supersonics™	

NBA KEEPSAKE ORNAMENT PLAQUES ☐

Comments: Ceramic, Dated 1997.
The team's official logo appears on the front of each plaque, while the team's statistics and highlights are detailed on the back.
☐ Purchased 19____ Pd $_____ MIB NB DB BNT
☐ Want   Orig. Ret. $9.95   **MIB** Sec. Mkt. **N.E.**

1997
Miniature Ornament Collection

QXM 414-2
ALICE IN WONDERLAND:
WHITE RABBIT
Third in Series, Dated 1997.
Artist: Patricia Andrews
☐ Purchased 19___ Pd $ _____
MIB   NB   DB   BNT
☐ Want   Orig. Retail $6.95
MIB Sec. Mkt. **$12**

QXM 418-5
ANTIQUE TRACTOR
FIRST IN SERIES, Die-cast
metal, Dated 1997.
Artist: Linda Sickman
☐ Purchased 19___ Pd $ _____
MIB   NB   DB   BNT
☐ Want   Orig. Retail $6.95
MIB Sec. Mkt. **$16**

QXM 427-2
CASABLANCA™
Three piece set, Dated 1997.
Artist: Patricia Andrews
☐ Purchased 19___ Pd $ _____
MIB   NB   DB   BNT
☐ Want   Orig. Retail $19.95
MIB Sec. Mkt. **$25**

QXM 429-5
CENTURIES OF SANTA
Fourth in Series, Dated 1997.
Artist: Linda Sickman
☐ Purchased 19___ Pd $ _____
MIB   NB   DB   BNT
☐ Want   Orig. Retail $5.95
MIB Sec. Mkt. **$12**

QXM 416-2
CHRISTMAS BELLS
Third in Series, Metal, Dated
1997. **Artist:** Ed Seale
☐ Purchased 19___ Pd $ _____
MIB   NB   DB   BNT
☐ Want   Orig. Retail $4.95
MIB Sec. Mkt. **$8-10**

QXI 432-2
CORVETTE
Dated 1997. **Artist:** Don Palmiter
☐ Purchased 19___ Pd $ _____
MIB   NB   DB   BNT
☐ Want   Orig. Retail $6.95
MIB Sec. Mkt. **$12**

QXM 423-2
FUTURE STAR
Dated 1997. **Artist:** Sharon Pike
☐ Purchased 19___ Pd $ _____
MIB   NB   DB   BNT
☐ Want   Orig. Retail $5.95
MIB Sec. Mkt. **$10**

QXM 422-1
GENTLE GIRAFFES
Dated 1997. Complements
"Noah's Ark" Special Edition Set
introduced in 1994.
Artist: Linda Sickman
☐ Purchased 19___ Pd $ _____
MIB   NB   DB   BNT
☐ Want   Orig. Retail $5.95
MIB Sec. Mkt. **$15**

QXM 423-5
HE IS BORN
Dated 1997.
Artist: LaDene Votruba
☐ Purchased 19___ Pd $ _____
MIB   NB   DB   BNT
☐ Want   Orig. Retail $7.95
MIB Sec. Mkt. **$13**

QXM 429-2
HEAVENLY MUSIC
Dated 1997. **Artist:** Sue Tague
☐ Purchased 19___ Pd $ _____
MIB   NB   DB   BNT
☐ Want   Orig. Retail $5.95
MIB Sec. Mkt. **$11**

QXM 422-2
HOME SWEET HOME
Dated 1997. **Artist:** Ed Seale
☐ Purchased 19___ Pd $ _____
MIB   NB   DB   BNT
☐ Want   Orig. Retail $5.95
MIB Sec. Mkt. **$12**

QXM 425-2
ICE COLD COCA-COLA®
Dated 1997. **Artist:** Robert Chad
☐ Purchased 19___ Pd $ _____
MIB   NB   DB   BNT
☐ Want   Orig. Retail $6.95
MIB Sec. Mkt. **$12**

JOLLY OLD SANTA
Dated 1997.
☐ Purchased 19___ Pd $ _____
MIB   NB   DB   BNT
☐ Want   Keepsake Membership
MIB Sec. Mkt. **$12**

QXM 415-5
MINIATURE CLOTHESPIN SOLDIER
Third in Series, Arms move, Dated 1997. **Artist:** Linda Sickman
☐ Purchased 19___ Pd $ _____
MIB   NB   DB   BNT
☐ Want   Orig. Retail $4.95
MIB Sec. Mkt. **$8**

QXM 413-2
**MINIATURE KIDDIE CAR CLASSIC: MURRAY INC.®
"PURSUIT" AIRPLANE**
Dated 1997. **Artist:** Robert Chad
☐ Purchased 19___ Pd $ _____
MIB   NB   DB   BNT
☐ Want   Orig. Retail $6.95
MIB Sec. Mkt. **$14**

QXM 417-5
NOEL R.R.: CANDY CAR
Ninth in Series, Dated 1997.
Artist: Linda Sickman
☐ Purchased 19___ Pd $ _____
MIB   NB   DB   BNT
☐ Want   Orig. Retail $6.95
MIB Sec. Mkt. **$10**

QXM 413-5
**NUTCRACKER BALLET:
HERR DROSSELMEYER**
Second in Series, Dated 1997.
Artist: LaDene Votruba
☐ Purchased 19___ Pd $ _____
MIB   NB   DB   BNT
☐ Want   Orig. Retail $5.95
MIB Sec. Mkt. **$9**

QXM 416-5
NUTCRACKER GUILD
Fourth in Series, Dated 1997.
Artist: Linda Sickman
☐ Purchased 19___ Pd $ _____
MIB   NB   DB   BNT
☐ Want   Orig. Retail $6.95
MIB Sec. Mkt. **$10**

QXM 418-2
**OLD ENGLISH VILLAGE:
VILLAGE DEPOT**
Tenth and Final in Series, Dated 1997. **Artist:** Tracy Larsen
☐ Purchased 19___ Pd $ _____
MIB   NB   DB   BNT
☐ Want   Orig. Retail $6.95
MIB Sec. Mkt. **$8**

QXM 417-2
ON THE ROAD: ON THE ROAD
Fifth in Series, Pressed Tin, Dated 1997.
Artist: Linda Sickman
☐ Purchased 19___ Pd $ _____
MIB   NB   DB   BNT
☐ Want   Orig. Retail $5.95
MIB Sec. Mkt. **$12**

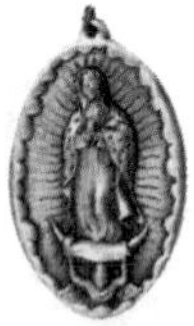

QXM 427-5
OUR LADY OF GUADALUPE
Fine Pewter, Dated 1997.
Artist: Robert Chad
☐ Purchased 19___ Pd $ _____
MIB   NB   DB   BNT
☐ Want   Orig. Retail $8.95
MIB Sec. Mkt. **$10**

QXM 431-2
PEPPERMINT PAINTER
Dated 1997. **Artist:** Sue Tague
☐ Purchased 19___ Pd $ _____
MIB   NB   DB   BNT
☐ Want   Orig. Retail $4.95
MIB Sec. Mkt. **$10**

QXM 433-2
POLAR BUDDIES
Dated 1997.
Artist: John Francis (Collin)
☐ Purchased 19___ Pd $ _____
MIB   NB   DB   BNT
☐ Want   Orig. Retail $4.95
MIB Sec. Mkt. **$8**

QXM 430-2
ROCKING HORSE
Tenth and Final in Series, Dated 1997. **Artist:** Linda Sickman
☐ Purchased 19___ Pd $ _____
MIB   NB   DB   BNT
☐ Want   Orig. Retail $4.95
MIB Sec. Mkt. **$8**

READY FOR SANTA
Dated 1997.
☐ Purchased 19___ Pd $ _____
MIB   NB   DB   BNT
☐ Want   Keepsake Membership
MIB Sec. Mkt. **$9**

QXM 415-2
SANTA'S LITTLE BIG TOP
Third and Final in Series, Dated 1997. **Artist:** Ken Crow
☐ Purchased 19___ Pd $ _____
MIB   NB   DB   BNT
☐ Want   Orig. Ret. $6.95
MIB Sec. Mkt. **$8**

QXM 424-2
SEEDS OF JOY
Dated 1997. **Artist:** Sue Tague
☐ Purchased 19___ Pd $ _____
MIB   NB   DB   BNT
☐ Want   Orig. Ret.$6.95
MIB Sec. Mkt. **$9**

QXM 414-1
SHINING STAR TREE-TOPPER
Brass Tree-Topper, Dated 1997.
☐ Purchased 19___ Pd $ _____
MIB   NB   DB   BNT
☐ Want   Orig. Ret.$9.95
        MIB Sec. Mkt. **$10**

QXM 421-2
SHUTTERBUG
Dated 1997. **Artist:** Sue Tague
☐ Purchased 19___ Pd $ _____
MIB   NB   DB   BNT
☐ Want   Orig. Ret.$5.95
        MIB Sec. Mkt. **$12**

QXM 431-5
SNOWBOARD BUNNY
Dated 1997. **Artist:** Sue Tague
☐ Purchased 19___ Pd $ _____
MIB   NB   DB   BNT
☐ Want   Orig. Ret. $4.95
        MIB Sec. Mkt. **$8**

QXM 419-2
SNOWFLAKE BALLET
FIRST IN SERIES, Dated 1997.
Artist: Patrcia Andrews
☐ Purchased 19___ Pd $ _____
MIB   NB   DB   BNT
☐ Want   Orig. Ret. $5.95
        MIB Sec. Mkt. **$15**

QXI 426-5
STAR WARS™:
C-3PO™ AND R2-D2™
FIRST IN SERIES, Dated 1997.
Artist: Dill Rhodus
☐ Purchased 19___ Pd $ _____
MIB   NB   DB   BNT
☐ Want   Orig. Ret. $12.95
NB $7   **MIB** Sec. Mkt. **$18**

QXM 421-5
TEDDY-BEAR STYLE
FIRST IN SERIES, Dated 1997.
Artist: Duane Unruh
☐ Purchased 19___ Pd $ _____
MIB   NB   DB   BNT
☐ Want   Orig. Ret. $5.95
        MIB Sec. Mkt. **$10**

QXM 428-2
TINY HOME IMPROVERS
Six Piece Set, Dated 1997.
Artist: Ed Seale
☐ Purchased 19___ Pd $ _____
MIB   NB   DB   BNT
☐ Want   Orig. Ret. $29.00
        MIB Sec. Mkt. **$32**

QXM 430-5
VICTORIAN SKATER
Dated 1997. **Artist:** Duane Unruh
☐ Purchased 19___ Pd $ _____
MIB   NB   DB   BNT
☐ Want   Orig. Ret. $5.95
        MIB Sec. Mkt. **$6**

QXM 420-5
WELCOME FRIENDS
FIRST IN SERIES, Dated 1997.
Artist: Sharon Pike
☐ Purchased 19___ Pd $ _____
MIB   NB   DB   BNT
☐ Want   Orig. Ret. $6.95
        MIB Sec. Mkt. **$10**

QXD 425-5
WINNIE THE POOH:
HONEY OF A GIFT
☐ Purchased 19___ Pd $ _____
MIB   NB   DB   BNT
☐ Want   Orig. Ret.$6.95
        MIB Sec. Mkt. **$10**

QXM 426-2
WIZARD OF OZ™, THE:
KING OF THE FOREST
Four Piece Set, Dated 1997.
Artist: Anita Marra Rogers
☐ Purchased 19___ Pd $ _____
MIB   NB   DB   BNT
☐ Want   Orig. Ret. $24.00
        MIB Sec. Mkt. **$30**

1997
Spring Ornament Collection

QEO 871-5
A PURR-FECT PRINCESS
2-3/16" tall, Dated 1997.
Artist: Sharon Pike
☐ Purchased 19___ Pd $ _____
MIB   NB   DB   BNT
☐ Want   Orig. Retail $7.95
MIB Sec. Mkt. **$14**

QEO 866-2
APPLE BLOSSOM LANE
Third and Final in Series,
2-5/16" tall, Dated 1997.
Artist: John Francis (Collin)
☐ Purchased 19___ Pd $ _____
MIB   NB   DB   BNT
☐ Want   Orig. Retail $8.95
MIB Sec. Mkt. **$18**

QEO 864-5
BEATRIX POTTER™:
JEMIMA PUDDLE-DUCK™
Second in Series, 2-1/2" tall,
Dated 1997. Projected pricing…
Depends on quantities produced -
1st in Series took retailers by
surprise
Artist: LaDene Votruba
☐ Purchased 19___ Pd $ _____
MIB   NB   DB   BNT
☐ Want   Orig. Retail $8.95
MIB Sec. Mkt. **$20**

QEO 873-5
BUMPER CROP – TENDER TOUCHES
Set of three. Grade A Packer, 2"
tall; First Taster, 1-1/2" tall;
24-Carrot Dreams, 1-5/8" tall.
Artist: Ed Seale
☐ Purchased 19___ Pd $ _____
MIB   NB   DB   BNT
☐ Want   Orig. Retail $14.95
MIB Sec. Mkt. **$21**

QEO 863-5
CHILDREN'S COLLECTOR
BARBIE™: BARBIE™ AS
RAPUNZEL
FIRST IN SERIES, 3-1/2" tall,
Dated 1997. A very popular
series! **Artist:** Anita Marra Rogers
☐ Purchased 19___ Pd $ _____
MIB   NB   DB   BNT
☐ Want   Orig. Retail $14.95
MIB Sec. Mkt. **$25**

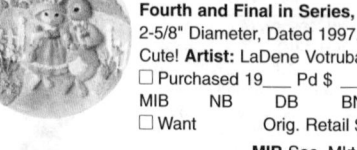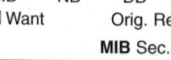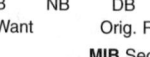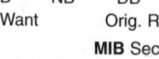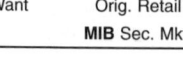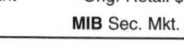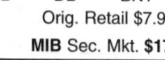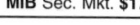

QEO 867-5
COLLECTOR'S PLATE:
SUNNY SUNDAY BEST
Fourth and Final in Series,
2-5/8" Diameter, Dated 1997.
Cute! **Artist:** LaDene Votruba
☐ Purchased 19___ Pd $ _____
MIB   NB   DB   BNT
☐ Want   Orig. Retail $7.95
MIB Sec. Mkt. **$17**

QEO 865-2
COTTONTAIL EXPRESS:
COLORFUL COAL CAR
Second in Series, 1-1/2" tall,
Dated 1997. **Artist:** Ken Crow
☐ Purchased 19___ Pd $ _____
MIB   NB   DB   BNT
☐ Want   Orig. Retail $8.95
MIB Sec. Mkt. **$16**

QEO 869-5
CRAYOLA®:
EGGS-PERT ARTIST
1-1/2" tall, Dated 1997. Still hard
to find. **Artist:** Sue Tague
☐ Purchased 19___ Pd $ _____
MIB   NB   DB   BNT
☐ Want   Orig. Retail $8.95
MIB Sec. Mkt. **$16**

QEO 871-2
DIGGING IN
2-3/16" tall, Dated 1997.
Artist: Ed Seale
☐ Purchased 19___ Pd $ _____
MIB   NB   DB   BNT
☐ Want   Orig. Retail $7.95
MIB Sec. Mkt. **$10**

QEO 866-5
GARDEN CLUB
Third in Series, 1-1/2" tall, Dated
1997. **Artist:** Katrina Bricker
☐ Purchased 19___ Pd $ _____
MIB   NB   DB   BNT
☐ Want   Orig. Retail $7.95
MIB Sec. Mkt. **$14**

QEO 873-2
GENTLE GUARDIAN
3" tall. **Artist:** Tracy Larsen
☐ Purchased 19___ Pd $ _____
MIB   NB   DB   BNT
☐ Want   Orig. Retail $6.95
MIB Sec. Mkt. **$9**

QEO 868-2
HERE COMES EASTER
Fourth and Final in Series,
2-1/8" tall, Dated 1997.
Artist: Ken Crow
☐ Purchased 19___ Pd $ _____
MIB   NB   DB   BNT
☐ Want   Orig. Retail $7.95
MIB Sec. Mkt. **$15**

QEO 865-5
JOYFUL ANGELS
Second in Series, 3-11/16" tall,
Dated 1997. **Artist:** Joyce Lyle
☐ Purchased 19___ Pd $ _____
MIB   NB   DB   BNT
☐ Want   Orig. Retail $10.95
MIB Sec. Mkt. **$18**

QEO 870-2
NATURE'S SKETCHBOOK:
GARDEN BUNNIES
3" tall, Dated 1997.
Artist: Duane Unruh
☐ Purchased 19___ Pd $ _____
MIB   NB   DB   BNT
☐ Want   Orig. Retail $14.95
MIB Sec. Mkt. **$20**

QEO 863-2
SIDEWALK CRUISERS: 1935
STEELCRAFT STREAMLINE
VELOCIPEDE BY MURRAY®
FIRST IN SERIES, 1-6/8" tall,
Dated 1997. Don't miss getting
this one! **Artist:** Dill Rhodus
☐ Purchased 19___ Pd $ _____
MIB   NB   DB   BNT
☐ Want   Orig. Retail $12.95
MIB Sec. Mkt. **$19**

QEO 864-2
SPRINGTIME BARBIE™
Third and Final in Series, 3-1/2"
tall, Dated 1997. This dress was
designed by artist, not Mattel.
Artist: Patricia Andrews
☐ Purchased 19___ Pd $ _____
MIB   NB   DB   BNT
☐ Want   Orig. Retail $12.95
MIB Sec. Mkt. **$17**

QEO 867-2
SPRINGTIME BONNETS
Fifth and Final in Series, 2-5/16"
tall, Dated 1997. Pretty! Pretty!
Artist: Sharon Pike
☐ Purchased 19___ Pd $ _____
MIB   NB   DB   BNT
☐ Want   Orig. Retail $7.95
MIB Sec. Mkt. **$14**

QEO 870-5
SWING-TIME
3-1/4" tall, Dated 1997.
Artist: Sue Tague
☐ Purchased 19___ Pd $ _____
MIB   NB   DB   BNT
☐ Want   Orig. Retail $7.95
MIB Sec. Mkt. **$10**

QEO 872-5
VICTORIAN CROSS
Pewter, 2-1/4" tall.
☐ Purchased 19___ Pd $ _____
MIB   NB   DB   BNT
☐ Want   Orig. Retail $8.95
MIB Sec. Mkt. **$14**

Added Attractions 1997

QXE 683-5   GIFT OF FRIENDSHIP WINNIE THE POOH ☐
Comments: Hallmark Gold Crown Gift Catalog Store
Exclusive.
☐ Purchased 19____   Pd $_____   MIB   NB   DB   BNT
☐ Want   Orig. Ret. $12.95   **MIB** Sec. Mkt. **$24**

Tree by Constance Timper

Artists on Tour 1997

TRIMMING SANTA'S TREE ☐
Comments: Handcrafted, Dated 1997. Celebrating the talents of the Keepsake Ornament Studio Artists. All 19 Artist signatures have been preprinted onto the underside of the piece.
Artists: All 19 Studio Artists
☐ Purchased 19____   Pd $_____   MIB   NB   DB   BNT
☐ Want   Orig. Ret. $60.00   **MIB** Sec. Mkt. **$100**

MRS. CLAUS'S STORY ☐
Comments: Handcrafted, Dated 1997. Mrs. Claus sits in her easy chair reading a favorite story, "The Night Before Christmas" **Artist:** All 19 Studio Artists
☐ Purchased 19____   Pd $_____   MIB   NB   DB   BNT
☐ Want   Orig. Ret. $14.95   **MIB** Sec. Mkt. **$25**

AIRMAIL FOR SANTA ☐
Comments: Handcrafted, Dated 1997. A 1996 Membership gift ornament changed to read on the ornament, "1997 Artists on Tour, Ima Collector." Secondary market value still not established.
☐ Purchased 19____   Pd $_____   MIB   NB   DB   BNT
☐ Want   Orig. Ret. gift to attendees
                                          MIB Sec. Mkt. **$N.E.**

Prizes Awarded

1997 Murray® Dump Truck Ornament - orange and black
1997 GMC Ornament - white
Holiday Traditions™ BARBIE® Doll
1996 Murray® Airplane
1953 GMC Truck - special paint color and signed by the artist.
(QX 610-5)

Club Prizes Awarded

1997 Santa's Magical Sleigh - painted with bright colors and
personally hand signed by Duane Unruh
Secondary market sales have not been reported on the above prizes.

1998 Collection

QXC 449-3   1935 STEELCRAFT BY MURRAY®
Comments: Dated1998.
This classic peldal car was reproduced as a scale-model
Luxury Edition Hallmark collectible in 1996.
Artist: Don Palmiter
☐ Purchased 19____   Pd $_____   MIB   NB   DB   BNT
☐ Want   Orig. Ret. $15.95   **Projected** Sec. Mkt. **$20-25**

QBG 690-9   1955 MURRAY® FIRE TRUCK
Comments: Dated1998.
Hand blown 1955 Murray® red and white fire engine. Picture
shown is a prototype. Holiday gifts have been piled into the
back of the fire truck.
Artist: Tammy Haddix
☐ Purchased 19____   Pd $_____   MIB   NB   DB   BNT
☐ Want   Orig. Ret. $35.00   **Projected** Sec. Mkt. **$40-45**

QLX 760-5   1998 CORVETTE®
Comments: Dated 1998.
This 1998 Corvette® features a glowing spotlight above and
red "chase" lights, which circle the turntable.
Artist: Don Palmiter
☐ Purchased 19____   Pd $_____   MIB   NB   DB   BNT
☐ Want   Orig. Ret. $24.00   **Projected** Sec. Mkt. **$26-28**

QX 641-6   1998 CORVETTE® CONVERTIBLE
Comments: Dated 1998.
This blue 1998 Corvette® convertible features wheels that
turn. **Artist:** Don Palmiter
☐ Purchased 19____   Pd $_____   MIB   NB   DB   BNT
☐ Want   Orig. Ret. $13.95   **Projected** Sec. Mkt. **$19-24**

QX 636-6   A CELEBRATION OF ANGELS
Comments: **Fourth and Final in Series,** Dated 1998.
This unusual angel carries a gift of corn.
Artist: Patricia Andrews
☐ Purchased 19____   Pd $_____   MIB   NB   DB   BNT
☐ Want   Orig. Ret. $13.95   **Projected** Sec. Mkt. **$20-25**

QX 617-6   A CHILD IS BORN
Comments: Dated 1998.
This ornament features the blessed event, the birth of Christ.
Artist: LaDene Votruba
☐ Purchased 19____   Pd $_____   MIB   NB   DB   BNT
☐ Want   Orig. Ret. $12.95   **Projected** Sec. Mkt. **$15-17**

**QX 687-3   A CHRISTMAS EVE STORY:
                    BECKY KELLY**
Comments: Dated 1998.
A little girl reads a story while Santa and his sleigh fly by her
window. Can be featured with a miniature light string to give a
glowing effect.
Artists: Becky Kelly and Sue Tague
☐ Purchased 19____   Pd $_____   MIB   NB   DB   BNT
☐ Want   Orig. Ret. $13.95   **Projected** Sec. Mkt. **$15-18**

QX 663-3   A PERFECT MATCH
Comments: Dated 1998.
A couple of mice snuggle in front of their matchbox fireplace
that has "Our Christmas Together" written on it.
Artist: Dill Rhodus
☐ Purchased 19____   Pd $_____   MIB   NB   DB   BNT
☐ Want   Orig. Ret. $10.95   **Projected** Sec. Mkt. **$14-16**

**QX 631-6   A PONY FOR CHRISTMAS:
                    A PONY FOR CHRISTMAS**
Comments: **FIRST IN SERIES.** Dated 1998.
Nostalgic designs. Teddy bear riding a nostalgic designed toy
pony. **Artist:** Linda Sickman
☐ Purchased 19____   Pd $_____   MIB   NB   DB   BNT
☐ Want   Orig. Ret. $10.95   **Projected** Sec. Mkt. **$15-20**

**QX 693-6   AFRICAN-AMERICAN
                    HOLIDAY BARBIE™**
Comments: **FIRST IN SERIES,** Dated 1998.
She looks exquisite in her black and silver beaded evening
gown with a pink stand up collar.
Artist: Patricia Andrews
☐ Purchased 19____   Pd $_____   MIB   NB   DB   BNT
☐ Want   Orig. Ret. $15.95   **Projected** Sec. Mkt. **$20-25**

QX 626-3   ALL-AMERICAN TRUCKS: 1937 FORD V-8 ☐

Comments: **Fourth in Series.** Dated 1998.
This 1937 Ford features Christmas presents in the back and has wheels that turn. **Artist:** Don Palmiter

☐ Purchased 19____   Pd $_____   MIB   NB   DB   BNT
☐ Want   Orig. Ret. $13.95   **Projected** Sec. Mkt. **$20-25**

QX 636-3   ALL GOD'S CHILDREN®: RICKY ☐

Comments: **Third and Final in Series.** Dated 1998.
It looks as if Ricky is headed for a never ending, popcorn stringing adventure, thanks to his little helper! **Artist:** Martha Root

☐ Purchased 19____   Pd $_____   MIB   NB   DB   BNT
☐ Want   Orig. Ret. $12.95   **Projected** Sec. Mkt. **$15-20**

QXI 414-6   ANGELIC FLIGHT ☐

Comments: **25th Anniversary Edition.**
This Gold Crown Exclusive is a true angel in flight. She is Silver Plated with Lead Crystal and includes a collector's card. Limited Edition of 25,000 and is not dated 1998. **Artists:** Bob Haas & Patricia Andrews

☐ Purchased 19____   Pd $_____   MIB   NB   DB   BNT
☐ Want   Orig. Ret. $85.00   **Projected** Sec. Mkt. **$90-95**

QX 658-3   ARTIST'S STUDIO COLLECTION: SANTA'S DEER FRIEND ☐

Comments: Dated 1998.
Kind-hearted Santa cares for the North Pole animals. **Artist:** Robert Chad

☐ Purchased 19____   Pd $_____   MIB   NB   DB   BNT
☐ Want   Orig. Ret. $24.00   **Projected** Sec. Mkt. **$28-32**

QXI 403-3   AT THE BALLPARK: CAL RIPKEN, JR. ☐

Comments: **Third in Series,** Dated 1998.
For all baseball enthusiasts, a special ornament to represent Cal Ripken. An exclusive trading card is included with this ornament. **Artist:** Dill Rhodus

☐ Purchased 19____   Pd $_____   MIB   NB   DB   BNT
☐ Want   Orig. Ret. $14.95   **Projected** Sec. Mkt. **$20-25**

QX 658-6   BABY'S FIRST CHRISTMAS ☐

Comments: Dated 1998.
A thumb-sucking teddy bear snuggles with a Christmas stocking that has "Baby's 1st Christmas, 1998" written on it. **Artist:** Joanne Eschrich

☐ Purchased 19____   Pd $_____   MIB   NB   DB   BNT
☐ Want   Orig. Ret. $9.95   **Projected** Sec. Mkt. **$12-14**

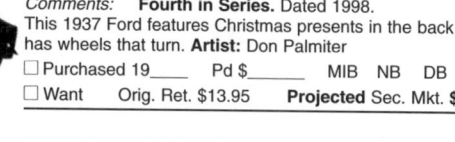

QX 623-3   BABY'S FIRST CHRISTMAS ☐

Comments: Dated 1998.
It features a baby holding a teddy bear while swinging from a star. **Artist:** Sue Tague

☐ Purchased 19____   Pd $_____   MIB   NB   DB   BNT
☐ Want   Orig. Ret. $9.95   **Projected** Sec. Mkt. **$12-14**

QX 659-6   BABY'S FIRST CHRISTMAS ☐

Comments: Dated 1998.
Toys are overflowing out of this photo holder toy chest. **Artist:** Kristina Kline

☐ Purchased 19____   Pd $_____   MIB   NB   DB   BNT
☐ Want   Orig. Ret. $8.95   **Projected** Sec. Mkt. **$11-13**

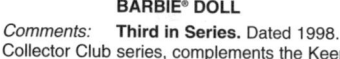

QXC449-3   BARBIE™: BASED ON THE 1990 HAPPY HOLIDAYS® BARBIE® DOLL ☐

Comments: **Third in Series.** Dated 1998.
Collector Club series, complements the Keepsake Ornament Holiday BARBIE™. **Artist:** Patricia Andrews

☐ Purchased 19____   Pd $_____   MIB   NB   DB   BNT
☐ Want   Orig. Ret. $15.95   **Projected** Sec. Mkt. **$40**

QXI 404-3 BARBIE™
SILKEN FLAMES™
Comments: **Fifth in Series,** Dated 1998.
Barbie is dressed in a flaming red and white dress with a matching red coat and hat. Of course, her red shoes match her outfit perfectly.
Artist: Patricia Andrews
☐ Purchased 19_____   Pd $_____   MIB NB DB BNT
☐ Want   Orig. Ret. $15.95   **Projected** Sec. Mkt. **$20-25**

QXD 409-6 BOUNCY BABY-SITTER
Comments: Dated 1998.
Tigger keeps Roo entertained by being his bouncing baby-sitter. A Christmas wreath is featured around Tigger's neck.
☐ Purchased 19_____   Pd $_____   MIB NB DB BNT
☐ Want   Orig. Ret. $12.95   **Projected** Sec. Mkt. **$20-25**

QXD 413-3 BUILDING A SNOWMAN
Comments: Dated 1998.
Piglet and Pooh build a snowman.
☐ Purchased 19_____   Pd $_____   MIB NB DB BNT
☐ Want   Orig. Ret. $14.95   **Projected** Sec. Mkt. **$20-25**

QXD 406-6 BUZZ LIGHTYEAR
Comments: Dated 1998.
Walt Disney's Toy Story. Part human, part airplane it's Buzz the flying machine.
☐ Purchased 19_____   Pd $_____   MIB NB DB BNT
☐ Want   Orig. Ret. $14.95   **Projected** Sec. Mkt. **$18-22**

QLX 763-6 CANDLELIGHT SERVICES:
THE STONE CHURCH
Comments: **FIRST IN SERIES.**, Dated 1998.
Beautiful stone church with light shining through stained glass windows.
Artist: Ed Seale
☐ Purchased 19_____   Pd $_____   MIB NB DB BNT
☐ Want   Orig. Ret. $18.95   **Projected** Sec. Mkt. **$21-26**

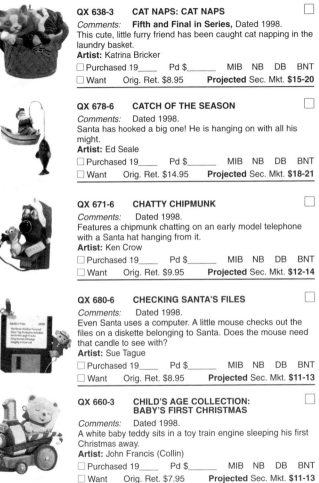

QX 638-3 CAT NAPS: CAT NAPS
Comments: **Fifth and Final in Series,** Dated 1998.
This cute, little furry friend has been caught cat napping in the laundry basket.
Artist: Katrina Bricker
☐ Purchased 19_____   Pd $_____   MIB NB DB BNT
☐ Want   Orig. Ret. $8.95   **Projected** Sec. Mkt. **$15-20**

QX 678-6 CATCH OF THE SEASON
Comments: Dated 1998.
Santa has hooked a big one! He is hanging on with all his might.
Artist: Ed Seale
☐ Purchased 19_____   Pd $_____   MIB NB DB BNT
☐ Want   Orig. Ret. $14.95   **Projected** Sec. Mkt. **$18-21**

QX 671-6 CHATTY CHIPMUNK
Comments: Dated 1998.
Features a chipmunk chatting on an early model telephone with a Santa hat hanging from it.
Artist: Ken Crow
☐ Purchased 19_____   Pd $_____   MIB NB DB BNT
☐ Want   Orig. Ret. $9.95   **Projected** Sec. Mkt. **$12-14**

QX 680-6 CHECKING SANTA'S FILES
Comments: Dated 1998.
Even Santa uses a computer. A little mouse checks out the files on a diskette belonging to Santa. Does the mouse need that candle to see with?
Artist: Sue Tague
☐ Purchased 19_____   Pd $_____   MIB NB DB BNT
☐ Want   Orig. Ret. $8.95   **Projected** Sec. Mkt. **$11-13**

QX 660-3 CHILD'S AGE COLLECTION:
BABY'S FIRST CHRISTMAS
Comments: Dated 1998.
A white baby teddy sits in a toy train engine sleeping his first Christmas away.
Artist: John Francis (Collin)
☐ Purchased 19_____   Pd $_____   MIB NB DB BNT
☐ Want   Orig. Ret. $7.95   **Projected** Sec. Mkt. **$11-13**

**QX 660-6 CHILD'S AGE COLLECTION:
BABY'S SECOND CHRISTMAS** ☐

Comments: Dated 1998.
Teddy holding stocking with an iced Christmas tree cookie
decorated with the number two.
Artist: Ken Crow

☐ Purchased 19____ Pd $_____ MIB NB DB BNT
☐ Want Orig. Ret. $7.95 **Projected** Sec. Mkt. **$11-13**

**QX 661-3 CHILD'S AGE COLLECTION:
CHILD'S THIRD CHRISTMAS** ☐

Comments: Dated 1998.
Teddy holding stocking with an iced bell cookie decorated with
the number three.
Artist: Ken Crow

☐ Purchased 19____ Pd $_____ MIB NB DB BNT
☐ Want Orig. Ret. $7.95 **Projected** Sec. Mkt. **$11-13**

**QX 661-6 CHILD'S AGE COLLECTION:
CHILD'S FOURTH CHRISTMAS** ☐

Comments: Dated 1998.
Panda bear holding stocking with an iced cookie decorated
with the number four.
Artist: Ken Crow

☐ Purchased 19____ Pd $_____ MIB NB DB BNT
☐ Want Orig. Ret. $7.95 **Projected** Sec. Mkt. **$11-13**

**QX 662-3 CHILD'S AGE COLLECTION:
CHILD'S FIFTH CHRISTMAS** ☐

Comments: Dated 1998.
Teddy bear holding stocking with an iced cookie decorated
with the number five.
Artist: Ken Crow

☐ Purchased 19____ Pd $_____ MIB NB DB BNT
☐ Want Orig. Ret. $7.95 **Projected** Sec. Mkt. **$11-13**

QX 619-3 CHRISTMAS REQUEST ☐

Comments: Dated 1998.
African-American Santa listens as the little boy on his lap
whispers his Christmas list.
Artist: John Francis (Collin)

☐ Purchased 19____ Pd $_____ MIB NB DB BNT
☐ Want Orig. Ret. $14.95 **Projected** Sec. Mkt. **$17-19**

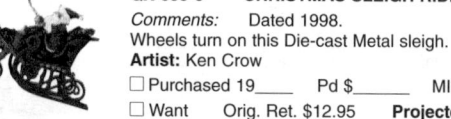

QX 655-6 CHRISTMAS SLEIGH RIDE ☐

Comments: Dated 1998.
Wheels turn on this Die-cast Metal sleigh.
Artist: Ken Crow

☐ Purchased 19____ Pd $_____ MIB NB DB BNT
☐ Want Orig. Ret. $12.95 **Projected** Sec. Mkt. **$16-19**

QXD 757-6 CINDERELLA AT THE BALL ☐

Comments: Walt Disney's "Cinderella", Dated 1998.
Cinderella and the Prince actually waltz around the dance
floor under the lighted chandelier.

☐ Purchased 19____ Pd $_____ MIB NB DB BNT
☐ Want Orig. Ret. $24.00 **Projected** Sec. Mkt. **$30-35**

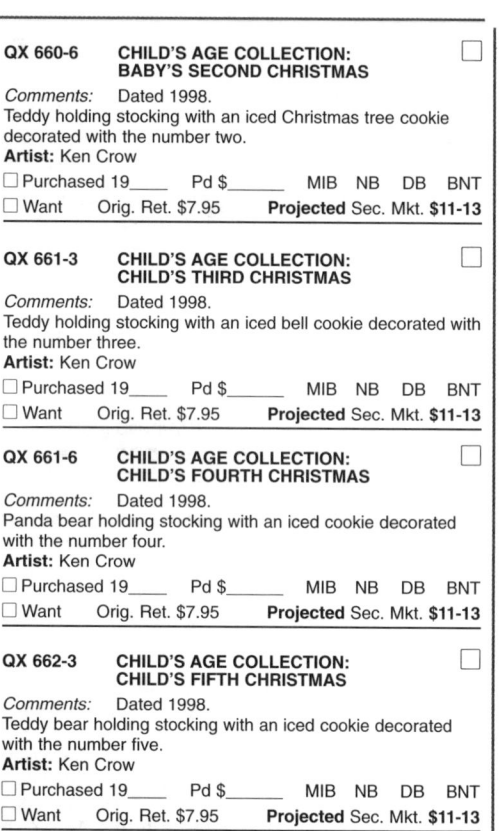

QXD 408-3 CINDERELLA'S COACH ☐

Comments: Walt Disney's "Cinderella", Dated 1998.
Cinderella's elegant coach, white with blue and gold trim, is
guaranteed not to turn into a pumpkin at the stroke of
midnight.

☐ Purchased 19____ Pd $_____ MIB NB DB BNT
☐ Want Orig. Ret. $14.95 **Projected** Sec. Mkt. **$18-21**

**QX 625-6 CLASSIC AMERICAN CARS:
1970 PLYMOUTH HEMI 'CUDA** ☐

Comments: **Eighth in Series,** Dated 1998.
Red replica of a 1970 Plymouth has wheels that turn.
Artist: Don Palmiter

☐ Purchased 19____ Pd $_____ MIB NB DB BNT
☐ Want Orig. Ret. $13.95 **Projected** Sec. Mkt. **$20-25**

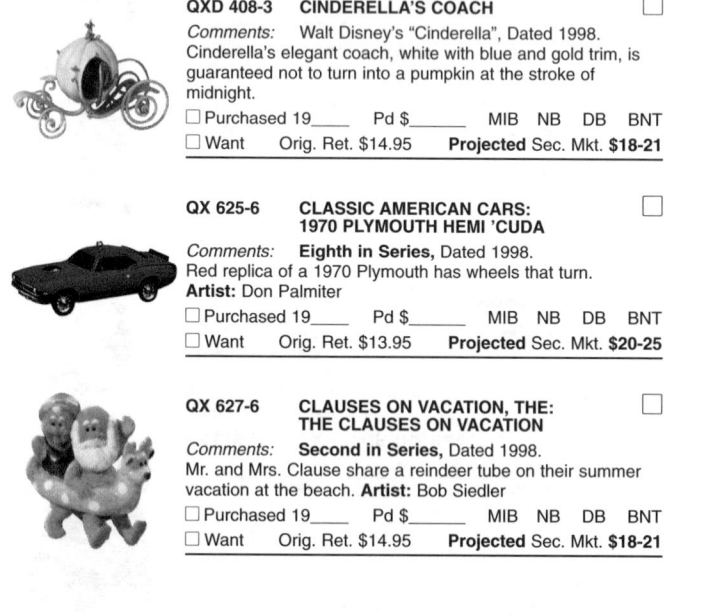

**QX 627-6 CLAUSES ON VACATION, THE:
THE CLAUSES ON VACATION** ☐

Comments: **Second in Series,** Dated 1998.
Mr. and Mrs. Clause share a reindeer tube on their summer
vacation at the beach. **Artist:** Bob Siedler

☐ Purchased 19____ Pd $_____ MIB NB DB BNT
☐ Want Orig. Ret. $14.95 **Projected** Sec. Mkt. **$18-21**

QX 676-6   COMPACT SKATER

Comments: Dated 1998.
A compact is used for this skater's ice rink.
Artist: Sue Tague

☐ Purchased 19____   Pd $_____   MIB NB DB BNT
☐ Want   Orig. Ret. $9.95   **Projected** Sec. Mkt. **$12-14**

QX 616-6   CRAYOLA® CRAYON: BRIGHT SLEDDING COLORS

Comments: **Tenth and Final in Series,** Dated 1998.
Bear wearing a Crayola hat takes a ride on his sled of many colors. **Artist:** Sue Tague

☐ Purchased 19____   Pd $_____   MIB NB DB BNT
☐ Want   Orig. Ret. $12.95   **Projected** Sec. Mkt. **$15-20**

QX 685-6   CROSS OF PEACE

Comments: Dated 1998.
Unique multi colored metal cross. **Artist:** Kristina Kline

☐ Purchased 19____   Pd $_____   MIB NB DB BNT
☐ Want   Orig. Ret. $9.95   **Projected** Sec. Mkt. **$12-14**

QX 619-6   CRUISING INTO CHRISTMAS

Comments: Handcrafted, Tin, Dated 1998.
Santa steams ahead in this tin, handcrafted cruise liner.
Artist: Ken Crow

☐ Purchased 19____   Pd $_____   MIB NB DB BNT
☐ Want   Orig. Ret. $16.95   **Projected** Sec. Mkt. **$20-23**

QX 666-3   DAD

Comments: Dated 1998.
Papa bear paints his gingerbread house. **Artist:** Kristina Kline

☐ Purchased 19____   Pd $_____   MIB NB DB BNT
☐ Want   Orig. Ret. $8.95   **Projected** Sec. Mkt. **$12-15**

QX 667-3   DAUGHTER

Comments: Dated 1998.
Opening and closing, similar to a nutcracker, this ornament is perfect for the perfect daughter. **Artist:** Nina Aubé

☐ Purchased 19____   Pd $_____   MIB NB DB BNT
☐ Want   Orig. Ret. $8.95   **Projected** Sec. Mkt. **$11-13**

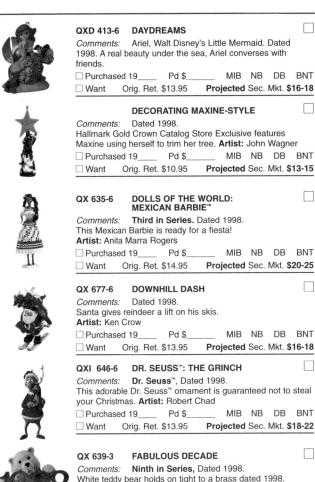

QXD 413-6   DAYDREAMS

Comments: Ariel, Walt Disney's Little Mermaid. Dated 1998. A real beauty under the sea, Ariel converses with friends.

☐ Purchased 19____   Pd $_____   MIB NB DB BNT
☐ Want   Orig. Ret. $13.95   **Projected** Sec. Mkt. **$16-18**

DECORATING MAXINE-STYLE

Comments: Dated 1998.
Hallmark Gold Crown Catalog Store Exclusive features Maxine using herself to trim her tree. **Artist:** John Wagner

☐ Purchased 19____   Pd $_____   MIB NB DB BNT
☐ Want   Orig. Ret. $10.95   **Projected** Sec. Mkt. **$13-15**

QX 635-6   DOLLS OF THE WORLD: MEXICAN BARBIE™

Comments: **Third in Series.** Dated 1998.
This Mexican Barbie is ready for a fiesta!
Artist: Anita Marra Rogers

☐ Purchased 19____   Pd $_____   MIB NB DB BNT
☐ Want   Orig. Ret. $14.95   **Projected** Sec. Mkt. **$20-25**

QX 677-6   DOWNHILL DASH

Comments: Dated 1998.
Santa gives reindeer a lift on his skis.
Artist: Ken Crow

☐ Purchased 19____   Pd $_____   MIB NB DB BNT
☐ Want   Orig. Ret. $13.95   **Projected** Sec. Mkt. **$16-18**

QXI 646-6   DR. SEUSS™: THE GRINCH

Comments: **Dr. Seuss™**, Dated 1998.
This adorable Dr. Seuss™ ornament is guaranteed not to steal your Christmas. **Artist:** Robert Chad

☐ Purchased 19____   Pd $_____   MIB NB DB BNT
☐ Want   Orig. Ret. $13.95   **Projected** Sec. Mkt. **$18-22**

QX 639-3   FABULOUS DECADE

Comments: **Ninth in Series,** Dated 1998.
White teddy bear holds on tight to a brass dated 1998.
Artist: Sharon Pike

☐ Purchased 19____   Pd $_____   MIB NB DB BNT
☐ Want   Orig. Ret. $7.95   **Projected** Sec. Mkt. **$10-12**

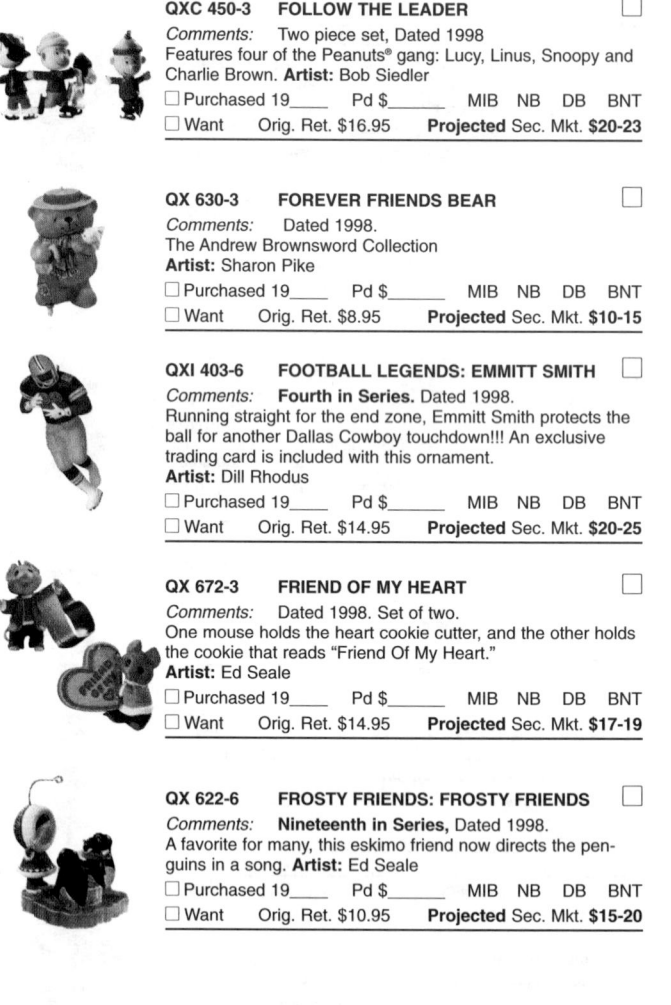

QX 653-6   FANCY FOOTWORK   ☐

Comments: Dated 1998.
A smiling snowman and his little friend waltz together on your tree. **Artist:** LaDene Votruba

☐ Purchased 19____   Pd $_____   MIB   NB   DB   BNT
☐ Want   Orig. Ret. $8.95   **Projected** Sec. Mkt. **$11-13**

QX 617-3   FELIZ NAVIDAD   ☐

Comments: Dated 1998.
Mouse painting white stripes on a red Jalapeño pepper to make it appear as a candy cane. **Artist:** Robert Chad

☐ Purchased 19____   Pd $_____   MIB   NB   DB   BNT
☐ Want   Orig. Ret. $8.95   **Projected** Sec. Mkt. **$11-13**

QBG 690-3   FESTIVE LOCOMOTIVE   ☐

Comments: Dated 1998.
Hand blown Locomotive featured in red, silver, blue and gold colors. **Artist:** Sue Tague

☐ Purchased 19____   Pd $_____   MIB   NB   DB   BNT
☐ Want   Orig. Ret. $35.00   **Projected** Sec. Mkt. **$40-45**

QXD 415-3   FLIK   ☐

Comments: Walt Disney's "A Bug's Life", Dated 1998.
This bug is out of here with his leaf skis and acorn poles.
Artist: Sue Tague

☐ Purchased 19____   Pd $_____   MIB   NB   DB   BNT
☐ Want   Orig. Ret. $12.95   **Projected** Sec. Mkt. **$15-17**

QX 621-3   FOLK ART AMERICANA COLLECTION: ☐
            SOARING WITH ANGELS

Comments: **FIRST IN SERIES,** Dated 1998.
This angel is soaring high with her copper wings, beaded stole and feathered friend. Very unusual.
Artist: Linda Sickman

☐ Purchased 19____   Pd $_____   MIB   NB   DB   BNT
☐ Want   Orig. Ret. $16.95   **Projected** Sec. Mkt. **$20-23**

QXC 450-3   FOLLOW THE LEADER   ☐

Comments: Two piece set, Dated 1998
Features four of the Peanuts® gang: Lucy, Linus, Snoopy and Charlie Brown. **Artist:** Bob Siedler

☐ Purchased 19____   Pd $_____   MIB   NB   DB   BNT
☐ Want   Orig. Ret. $16.95   **Projected** Sec. Mkt. **$20-23**

QX 630-3   FOREVER FRIENDS BEAR   ☐

Comments: Dated 1998.
The Andrew Brownsword Collection
Artist: Sharon Pike

☐ Purchased 19____   Pd $_____   MIB   NB   DB   BNT
☐ Want   Orig. Ret. $8.95   **Projected** Sec. Mkt. **$10-15**

QXI 403-6   FOOTBALL LEGENDS: EMMITT SMITH   ☐

Comments: **Fourth in Series.** Dated 1998.
Running straight for the end zone, Emmitt Smith protects the ball for another Dallas Cowboy touchdown!!! An exclusive trading card is included with this ornament.
Artist: Dill Rhodus

☐ Purchased 19____   Pd $_____   MIB   NB   DB   BNT
☐ Want   Orig. Ret. $14.95   **Projected** Sec. Mkt. **$20-25**

QX 672-3   FRIEND OF MY HEART   ☐

Comments: Dated 1998. Set of two.
One mouse holds the heart cookie cutter, and the other holds the cookie that reads "Friend Of My Heart."
Artist: Ed Seale

☐ Purchased 19____   Pd $_____   MIB   NB   DB   BNT
☐ Want   Orig. Ret. $14.95   **Projected** Sec. Mkt. **$17-19**

QX 622-6   FROSTY FRIENDS: FROSTY FRIENDS   ☐

Comments: **Nineteenth in Series,** Dated 1998.
A favorite for many, this eskimo friend now directs the penguins in a song. **Artist:** Ed Seale

☐ Purchased 19____   Pd $_____   MIB   NB   DB   BNT
☐ Want   Orig. Ret. $10.95   **Projected** Sec. Mkt. **$15-20**

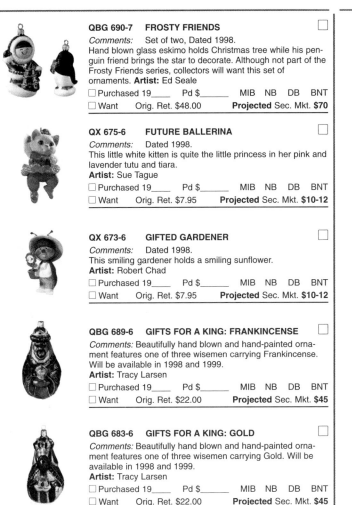

QBG 690-7   FROSTY FRIENDS

Comments: Set of two, Dated 1998.
Hand blown glass eskimo holds Christmas tree while his penguin friend brings the star to decorate. Although not part of the Frosty Friends series, collectors will want this set of ornaments. **Artist:** Ed Seale

☐ Purchased 19____   Pd $_____   MIB   NB   DB   BNT
☐ Want   Orig. Ret. $48.00   **Projected** Sec. Mkt. **$70**

QX 675-6   FUTURE BALLERINA

Comments: Dated 1998.
This little white kitten is quite the little princess in her pink and lavender tutu and tiara.
Artist: Sue Tague

☐ Purchased 19____   Pd $_____   MIB   NB   DB   BNT
☐ Want   Orig. Ret. $7.95   **Projected** Sec. Mkt. **$10-12**

QX 673-6   GIFTED GARDENER

Comments: Dated 1998.
This smiling gardener holds a smiling sunflower.
Artist: Robert Chad

☐ Purchased 19____   Pd $_____   MIB   NB   DB   BNT
☐ Want   Orig. Ret. $7.95   **Projected** Sec. Mkt. **$10-12**

QBG 689-6   GIFTS FOR A KING: FRANKINCENSE

Comments: Beautifully hand blown and hand-painted ornament features one of three wisemen carrying Frankincense. Will be available in 1998 and 1999.
Artist: Tracy Larsen

☐ Purchased 19____   Pd $_____   MIB   NB   DB   BNT
☐ Want   Orig. Ret. $22.00   **Projected** Sec. Mkt. **$45**

QBG 683-6   GIFTS FOR A KING: GOLD

Comments: Beautifully hand blown and hand-painted ornament features one of three wisemen carrying Gold. Will be available in 1998 and 1999.
Artist: Tracy Larsen

☐ Purchased 19____   Pd $_____   MIB   NB   DB   BNT
☐ Want   Orig. Ret. $22.00   **Projected** Sec. Mkt. **$45**

QBG 689-3   GIFTS FOR A KING: MYRRH

Comments: Beautiful hand blown and hand-painted ornament features one of three wisemen carrying Myrrh. Will be available in 1998 and 1999. **Artist:** Tracy Larsen

☐ Purchased 19____   Pd $_____   MIB   NB   DB   BNT
☐ Want   Orig. Ret. $22.00   **Projected** Sec. Mkt. **$45**

QX 670-3   GODCHILD

Comments: Dated 1998.
Wearing his santa hat and hugging his stuffed animals, this cute little teddy is the perfect gift for that favorite godchild.
Artist: Robert Chad

☐ Purchased 19____   Pd $_____   MIB   NB   DB   BNT
☐ Want   Orig. Ret. $7.95   **Projected** Sec. Mkt. **$10-12**

QX 681-3   GOOD LUCK DICE

Comments: Dated 1998.
Jester popping out of a good luck dice isn't joking around when it comes to luck; he has a four leaf clover and lucky horseshoe in hand. **Artist:** Tammy Haddix

☐ Purchased 19____   Pd $_____   MIB   NB   DB   BNT
☐ Want   Orig. Ret. $9.95   **Projected** Sec. Mkt. **$12-14**

QXD 412-3   GOOFY SOCCER STAR

Comments: Dated 1998.
Get a kick out of this ornament. Goofy, a soccer star?

☐ Purchased 19____   Pd $_____   MIB   NB   DB   BNT
☐ Want   Orig. Ret. $10.95   **Projected** Sec. Mkt. **$15-20**

QX 668-3   GRANDDAUGHTER

Comments: Dated 1998.
Granddaughter dressed in a cute little sailor suit.
Artist: John Francis (Collin)

☐ Purchased 19____   Pd $_____   MIB   NB   DB   BNT
☐ Want   Orig. Ret. $7.95   **Projected** Sec. Mkt. **$10-12**

QX 668-6   **GRANDMA'S MEMORIES** ☐

Comments: Dated 1998.
Grandma reminiscing while looking through her photo album.
Artist: Kristina Kline

☐ Purchased 19____   Pd $_____   MIB   NB   DB   BNT
☐ Want   Orig. Ret. $8.95   **Projected** Sec. Mkt. **$10-12**

QX 667-6   **GRANDSON** ☐

Comments: Dated 1998.
Grandson waving, dressed in his little sailor suit.
Artist: John Francis (Collin)

☐ Purchased 19____   Pd $_____   MIB   NB   DB   BNT
☐ Want   Orig. Ret. $7.95   **Projected** Sec. Mkt. **$10-12**

QX 654-3   **GUARDIAN FRIEND** ☐

Comments: Dated 1998.
This little guardian angel keeps a watchful eye while holding
her fuzzy white kitten. **Artist:** Joyce Lyle

☐ Purchased 19____   Pd $_____   MIB   NB   DB   BNT
☐ Want   Orig. Ret. $8.95   **Projected** Sec. Mkt. **$11-13**

QXD 400-6   **HALLMARK ARCHIVES:** ☐
                READY FOR CHRISTMAS

Comments: **Second in Series,** Dated 1998.
Mickey does a balancing act trying to carry his Christmas
gifts. Includes collector's card.

☐ Purchased 19____   Pd $_____   MIB   NB   DB   BNT
☐ Want   Orig. Ret. $12.95   **Projected** Sec. Mkt. **$15-20**

QX 657-6   **HALLMARK ARCHIVES COLLECTION:** ☐
                HEAVENLY MELODY

Comments: Dated 1998.
A Masterworks Collection, Hallmark Archives angel plays her
harp. **Artists:** LaDene Votruba and Bob Haas

☐ Purchased 19____   Pd $_____   MIB   NB   DB   BNT
☐ Want   Orig. Ret. $18.95   **Projected** Sec. Mkt. **$22-25**

QX 664-3   **HALLMARK ARCHIVES COLLECTION:** ☐
                OUR FIRST CHRISTMAS TOGETHER

Comments: Dated 1998.
Beautifully designed brass and porcelain ornament features a
couple in love sharing their first Christmas together.
Artist: LaDene Votruba

☐ Purchased 19____   Pd $_____   MIB   NB   DB   BNT
☐ Want   Orig. Ret. $18.95   **Projected** Sec. Mkt. **$20-22**

QX 683-3   **HALLS STATION** ☐

Comments: **25th Anniversary Edition,** Dated 1998.
This 25th Anniversary Edition complements the Nostalgic
Houses and Shops with a couple waiting patiently for their
luggage and ride. **Artist:** Don Palmiter

☐ Purchased 19____   Pd $_____   MIB   NB   DB   BNT
☐ Want   Orig. Ret. $25.00   **Projected** Sec. Mkt. **$30-35**

QX 628-3   **HERE COMES SANTA:** ☐
                SANTA'S BUMPER CAR

Comments: **Twentieth in Series.** Dated 1998.
Watch out! Make way for Santa in his shiny red bumper car.
Artist: Sue Tague

☐ Purchased 19____   Pd $_____   MIB   NB   DB   BNT
☐ Want   Orig. Ret. $14.95   **Projected** Sec. Mkt. **$18-21**

QX 643-3   **HERSHEY'S®: SWEET TREAT** ☐

Comments: Dated 1998.
Two mice cling to a red Hershey's® Kiss.
Artist: Kristina Kline

☐ Purchased 19____   Pd $_____   MIB   NB   DB   BNT
☐ Want   Orig. Ret. $10.95   **Projected** Sec. Mkt. **$15-19**

QXI 647-6   **HOCKEY GREATS: MARIO LEMIEUX** ☐

Comments: **Second in Series,** Dated 1998.
Mario glides in for a slapshot. An exclusive trading card is
included with this ornament. **Artist:** John Francis (Collin)

☐ Purchased 19____   Pd $_____   MIB   NB   DB   BNT
☐ Want   Orig. Ret. $15.95   **Projected** Sec. Mkt. **$20-25**

QXI 402-3   HOLIDAY BARBIE™

Comments: **Sixth in Series,** Dated 1998.
Wearing a black and silver beaded evening gown with a pink stand up collar adds a touch of elegance to this Holiday BARBIE™
Artist: Patricia Andrews

☐ Purchased 19_____   Pd $_____   MIB NB DB BNT
☐ Want   Orig. Ret. $15.95   **Projected** Sec. Mkt. **$20-25**

QX 678-3   HOLIDAY CAMPER

Comments: Dated 1998.
This raccoon is ready for hiking with his backpack, walking stick and compass that really works. **Artist:** Ed Seale

☐ Purchased 19_____   Pd $_____   MIB NB DB BNT
☐ Want   Orig. Ret. $12.95   **Projected** Sec. Mkt. **$14-16**

QX 656-6   HOLIDAY DECORATOR

Comments: Dated 1998.
This mouse is getting ready for Christmas by stenciling his window. Has a nice lighting effect when used with a miniature light string. **Artist:** Nello Williams

☐ Purchased 19_____   Pd $_____   MIB NB DB BNT
☐ Want   Orig. Ret. $13.95   **Projected** Sec. Mkt. **$18-22**

**QHB 602-0   HOLIDAY MEMORIES™
BARBIE™ ORNAMENT**

Comments: **Limited Time Edition.** Dated 1998.
From the Victorian Christmas Collection, Barbie is pictured inside a locket ornament. She is based on the 1995 doll.

☐ Purchased 19_____   Pd $_____   MIB NB DB BNT
☐ Want   Orig. Ret. $14.95   **Projected** Sec. Mkt. **$20-25**

**QBG 690-6   HOLIDAY TRADITIONS:
RED POINSETTIAS**

Comments: Glass, Hand blown and hand painted.
☐ Purchased 19_____   Pd $_____   MIB NB DB BNT
☐ Want   Orig. Ret. $35.00   **Projected** Sec. Mkt. **$39-43**

**QHB 601-6   HOLIDAY VOYAGE™
BARBIE™ ORNAMENT**

Comments: Inspired by the 1920's, this Barbie holds a Christmas present. Available for a limited time.

☐ Purchased 19_____   Pd $_____   MIB NB DB BNT
☐ Want   Orig. Ret. $14.95   **Projected** Sec. Mkt. **$20-25**

QXI 684-6   HOOP STARS: GRANT HILL

Comments: **Fourth in Series.**
Thanks to his Fila shoes, Grant Hill successfully dribbles down the court, makes the shot and wins for the Detroit Pistons! An exclusive trading card is included with this ornament. **Artist:** Duane Unruh

☐ Purchased 19_____   Pd $_____   MIB NB DB BNT
☐ Want   Orig. Ret. $14.95   **Projected** Sec. Mkt. **$20-25**

QX 643-6   HOT WHEELS™

Comments: **30th Anniversary.** Dated 1998.
This blue Hot Wheels celebrates the 30th Anniversary.
Artist: Ken Crow

☐ Purchased 19_____   Pd $_____   MIB NB DB BNT
☐ Want   Orig. Ret. $13.95   **Projected** Sec. Mkt. **$18-22**

QXD 407-6   IAGO, ABU AND THE GENIE

Comments: Walt Disney's "Aladdin." Dated 1998.
Right out of Disney's movie, Aladdin.

☐ Purchased 19_____   Pd $_____   MIB NB DB BNT
☐ Want   Orig. Ret. $12.95   **Projected** Sec. Mkt. **$14-16**

QXI 684-3   JOE MONTANA: NOTRE DAME

Comments: Dated 1998.
Avoiding a sack, Joe takes a few steps to throw a completed pass, getting another first down for Notre Dame.
Artist: Duane Unruh

☐ Purchased 19_____   Pd $_____   MIB NB DB BNT
☐ Want   Orig. Ret. $14.95   **Projected** Sec. Mkt. **$20-25**

QX 622-3   JOURNEY TO BETHLEHEM

Comments: **Collector's Choice,** Dated 1998.
Named as 1998 Collector's Choice. Truly an exquisite ornament.
Artist: Duane Unruh

☐ Purchased 19____   Pd $_____   MIB   NB   DB   BNT
☐ Want   Orig. Ret. $16.95   **Projected** Sec. Mkt. **$20-23**

**QLX 754-3   JOURNEYS INTO SPACE:
APOLLO LUNAR MODULE**

Comments: **Third in Series,** Dated 1998.
U.S. astronauts used the Lunar Module to carry them from
their Apollo spacecraft to the moon and back. It features a
message from the Apollo 14 mission.

☐ Purchased 19____   Pd $_____   MIB   NB   DB   BNT
☐ Want   Orig. Ret. $24.00   **Projected** Sec. Mkt. **$28-32**

QX 1673-3   JOYFUL MESSENGER

Comments: **25th Anniversary Edition,** Silver plated, Dated
1998. What a beautiful ornament for all you angel collectors.
This angel is a Gold Crown Exclusive 25th Anniversary
Edition holding a Silver Plated Medallion.
Artist: Joyce Lyle

☐ Purchased 19____   Pd $_____   MIB   NB   DB   BNT
☐ Want   Orig. Ret. $18.95   **Projected** Sec. Mkt. **$21-23**

**QX 637-6   KIDDIE CAR CLASSICS:
1955 MURRAY® TRACTOR AND TRAILER**

Comments: **Fifth in Series.** Dated 1998.
Set of two, Die cast Metal red tractor and trailer with wheels
that turn. **Artist:** Don Palmiter

☐ Purchased 19____   Pd $_____   MIB   NB   DB   BNT
☐ Want   Orig. Ret. $16.95   **Projected** Sec. Mkt. **$20-25**

**QX 615-6   LANGUAGE OF FLOWERS, THE:
IRIS ANGEL**

Comments: **Third in Series,** Dated 1998.
Angel carrying silver-plated basket of irises.
Artist: Sue Tague

☐ Purchased 19____   Pd $_____   MIB   NB   DB   BNT
☐ Want   Orig. Ret. $15.95   **Projected** Sec. Mkt. **$18-20**

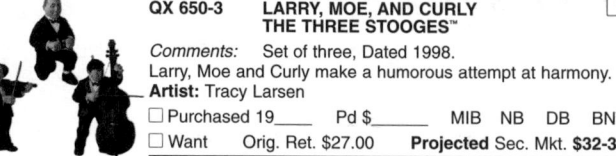

**QX 650-3   LARRY, MOE, AND CURLY
THE THREE STOOGES™**

Comments: Set of three, Dated 1998.
Larry, Moe and Curly make a humorous attempt at harmony.
Artist: Tracy Larsen

☐ Purchased 19____   Pd $_____   MIB   NB   DB   BNT
☐ Want   Orig. Ret. $27.00   **Projected** Sec. Mkt. **$32-37**

**QX 618-6   LEGEND OF THREE KINGS COLLECTION:
KING KHAROOF – SECOND KING**

Comments: Dated 1998.
Comes with Collector's Card. **Artist:** Patricia Andrews

☐ Purchased 19____   Pd $_____   MIB   NB   DB   BNT
☐ Want   Orig. Ret. $12.95   **Projected** Sec. Mkt. **$15-17**

**QLX 753-6   LIGHTHOUSE GREETINGS:
LIGHTHOUSE GREETINGS**

Comments: **Second in Series,** Dated 1998.
Light house featured with flashing light.
Artist: John Francis (Collin)

☐ Purchased 19____   Pd $_____   MIB   NB   DB   BNT
☐ Want   Orig. Ret. $24.00   **Projected** Sec. Mkt. **$26-28**

**QX 634-6   LIONEL®:
PENNSYLVANIA GG-I LOCOMOTIVE**

Comments: **Third in Series,** Dated 1998.
This Pennsylvania GG-1 Locomotive is a must for all Lionel
train collectors. This die-cast metal train features wheels that
turn.

☐ Purchased 19____   Pd $_____   MIB   NB   DB   BNT
☐ Want   Orig. Ret. $18.95   **Projected** Sec. Mkt. **$23-27**

**QX 644-3   LOONEY TUNES:
BUGS BUNNY**

Comments: Bugs is featured wearing a fruit basket hat.
Artist: Robert Chad

☐ Purchased 19____   Pd $_____   MIB   NB   DB   BNT
☐ Want   Orig. Ret. $13.95   **Projected** Sec. Mkt. **$15-20**

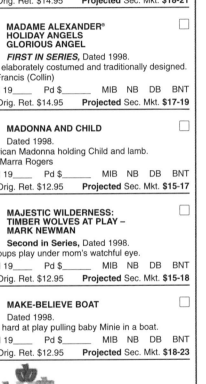

QX 635-3   MADAME ALEXANDER®:
                 MOP TOP WENDY

Comments: **Third in Series,** Dated 1998.
Quite cute, this little Raggedy Ann look alike!
Artist: John Francis (Collin)

☐ Purchased 19____   Pd $_____   MIB   NB   DB   BNT
☐ Want   Orig. Ret. $14.95   **Projected** Sec. Mkt. **$18-21**

QX 649-3   MADAME ALEXANDER®
                 HOLIDAY ANGELS
                 GLORIOUS ANGEL

Comments: ***FIRST IN SERIES,*** Dated 1998.
This angel is elaborately costumed and traditionally designed.
Artist: John Francis (Collin)

☐ Purchased 19____   Pd $_____   MIB   NB   DB   BNT
☐ Want   Orig. Ret. $14.95   **Projected** Sec. Mkt. **$17-19**

QX 651-6   MADONNA AND CHILD

Comments: Dated 1998.
African-American Madonna holding Child and lamb.
Artist: Anita Marra Rogers

☐ Purchased 19____   Pd $_____   MIB   NB   DB   BNT
☐ Want   Orig. Ret. $12.95   **Projected** Sec. Mkt. **$15-17**

QX 627-3   MAJESTIC WILDERNESS:
                 TIMBER WOLVES AT PLAY –
                 MARK NEWMAN

Comments: **Second in Series,** Dated 1998.
Timber wolf pups play under mom's watchful eye.

☐ Purchased 19____   Pd $_____   MIB   NB   DB   BNT
☐ Want   Orig. Ret. $12.95   **Projected** Sec. Mkt. **$15-18**

QXD 411-3   MAKE-BELIEVE BOAT

Comments: Dated 1998.
Baby Mickey hard at play pulling baby Minie in a boat.

☐ Purchased 19____   Pd $_____   MIB   NB   DB   BNT
☐ Want   Orig. Ret. $12.95   **Projected** Sec. Mkt. **$18-23**

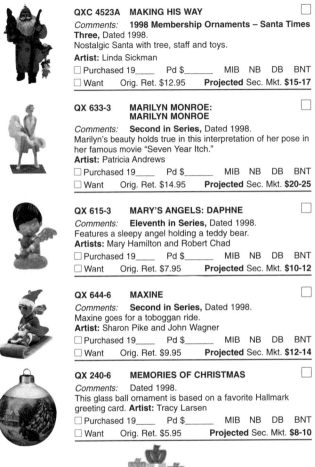

QXC 4523A   MAKING HIS WAY

Comments: **1998 Membership Ornaments – Santa Times**
Three, Dated 1998.
Nostalgic Santa with tree, staff and toys.
Artist: Linda Sickman

☐ Purchased 19____   Pd $_____   MIB   NB   DB   BNT
☐ Want   Orig. Ret. $12.95   **Projected** Sec. Mkt. **$15-17**

QX 633-3   MARILYN MONROE:
                 MARILYN MONROE

Comments: **Second in Series,** Dated 1998.
Marilyn's beauty holds true in this interpretation of her pose in
her famous movie "Seven Year Itch."
Artist: Patricia Andrews

☐ Purchased 19____   Pd $_____   MIB   NB   DB   BNT
☐ Want   Orig. Ret. $14.95   **Projected** Sec. Mkt. **$20-25**

QX 615-3   MARY'S ANGELS: DAPHNE

Comments: **Eleventh in Series,** Dated 1998.
Features a sleepy angel holding a teddy bear.
Artists: Mary Hamilton and Robert Chad

☐ Purchased 19____   Pd $_____   MIB   NB   DB   BNT
☐ Want   Orig. Ret. $7.95   **Projected** Sec. Mkt. **$10-12**

QX 644-6   MAXINE

Comments: **Second in Series,** Dated 1998.
Maxine goes for a toboggan ride.
Artist: Sharon Pike and John Wagner

☐ Purchased 19____   Pd $_____   MIB   NB   DB   BNT
☐ Want   Orig. Ret. $9.95   **Projected** Sec. Mkt. **$12-14**

QX 240-6   MEMORIES OF CHRISTMAS

Comments: Dated 1998.
This glass ball ornament is based on a favorite Hallmark
greeting card. **Artist:** Tracy Larsen

☐ Purchased 19____   Pd $_____   MIB   NB   DB   BNT
☐ Want   Orig. Ret. $5.95   **Projected** Sec. Mkt. **$8-10**

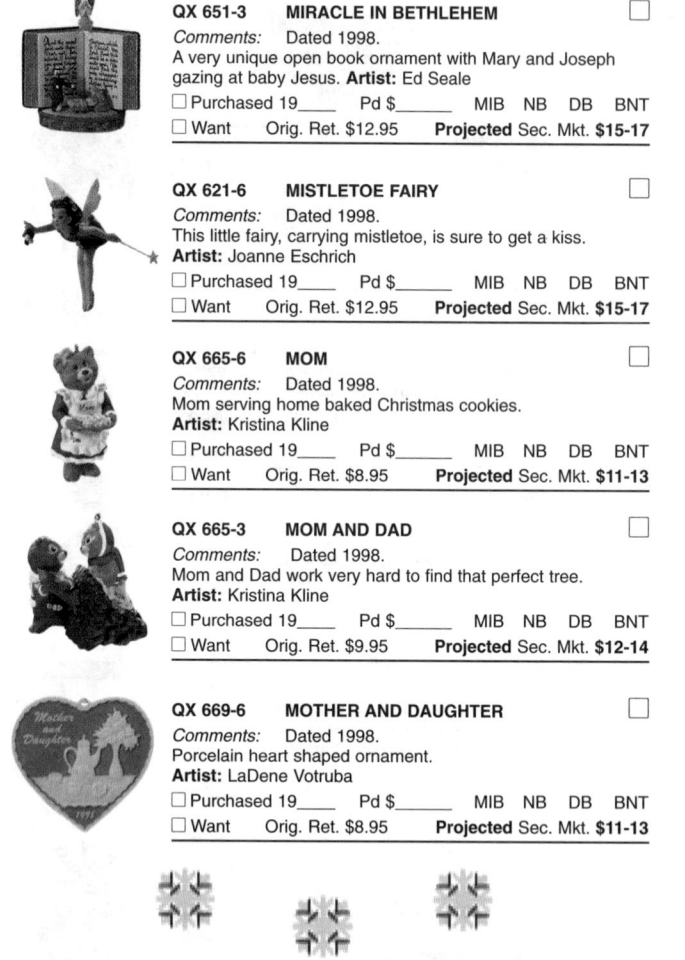

QX 669-2   MERRY CHIME ☐

Comments: Dated 1998.
This peppermint candy wind chime has a mouse dangling from a string. **Artist:** Ken Crow

☐ Purchased 19_____   Pd $_____   MIB   NB   DB   BNT
☐ Want   Orig. Ret. $9.95   **Projected** Sec. Mkt. **$12-14**

QX 638-6   MERRY OLDE SANTA:
MERRY OLDE SANTA ☐

Comments: **Ninth in Series,** Dated 1998.
Santa wishing a Merry Christmas to all with out-reached arms. **Artist:** Duane Unruh

☐ Purchased 19_____   Pd $_____   MIB   NB   DB   BNT
☐ Want   Orig. Ret. $15.95   **Projected** Sec. Mkt. **$18-20**

QXD 758-6   MICKEY'S COMET ☐

Comments: Dated 1998.
This magic ornament features lights that flicker as Mickey hangs on for dear life to Goofy in his M.M. Comet.

☐ Purchased 19_____   Pd $_____   MIB   NB   DB   BNT
☐ Want   Orig. Ret. $24.00   **Projected** Sec. Mkt. **$29-34**

QXD 401-3   MICKEY'S FAVORITE REINDEER ☐

Comments: Dated 1998.
Mickey chuckles as Pluto shows him a little affection.

☐ Purchased 19_____   Pd $_____   MIB   NB   DB   BNT
☐ Want   Orig. Ret. $13.95   **Projected** Sec. Mkt. **$19-24**

QXD 410-6   MICKEY'S HOLIDAY PARADE:
MINNIE PLAYS THE FLUTE ☐

Comments: **Second in Series,** Dated 1998.
Minnie dressed in her band uniform marches proudly in the Disney parade, playing her flute.

☐ Purchased 19_____   Pd $_____   MIB   NB   DB   BNT
☐ Want   Orig. Ret. $13.95   **Projected** Sec. Mkt. **$19-24**

QX 651-3   MIRACLE IN BETHLEHEM ☐

Comments: Dated 1998.
A very unique open book ornament with Mary and Joseph gazing at baby Jesus. **Artist:** Ed Seale

☐ Purchased 19_____   Pd $_____   MIB   NB   DB   BNT
☐ Want   Orig. Ret. $12.95   **Projected** Sec. Mkt. **$15-17**

QX 621-6   MISTLETOE FAIRY ☐

Comments: Dated 1998.
This little fairy, carrying mistletoe, is sure to get a kiss. **Artist:** Joanne Eschrich

☐ Purchased 19_____   Pd $_____   MIB   NB   DB   BNT
☐ Want   Orig. Ret. $12.95   **Projected** Sec. Mkt. **$15-17**

QX 665-6   MOM ☐

Comments: Dated 1998.
Mom serving home baked Christmas cookies. **Artist:** Kristina Kline

☐ Purchased 19_____   Pd $_____   MIB   NB   DB   BNT
☐ Want   Orig. Ret. $8.95   **Projected** Sec. Mkt. **$11-13**

QX 665-3   MOM AND DAD ☐

Comments: Dated 1998.
Mom and Dad work very hard to find that perfect tree. **Artist:** Kristina Kline

☐ Purchased 19_____   Pd $_____   MIB   NB   DB   BNT
☐ Want   Orig. Ret. $9.95   **Projected** Sec. Mkt. **$12-14**

QX 669-6   MOTHER AND DAUGHTER ☐

Comments: Dated 1998.
Porcelain heart shaped ornament. **Artist:** LaDene Votruba

☐ Purchased 19_____   Pd $_____   MIB   NB   DB   BNT
☐ Want   Orig. Ret. $8.95   **Projected** Sec. Mkt. **$11-13**

QX 688-6   MRS. POTATO HEAD®
Comments: Dated 1998.
Mrs. Potato Head is headed for a shopping spree.
☐ Purchased 19_____   Pd $_____   MIB NB DB BNT
☐ Want   Orig. Ret. $10.95   **Projected** Sec. Mkt. **$13-15**

QXD 415-6   MULAN, MUSHU AND CRI-KEE
Comments: Set of two, Dated 1998.
Mulan, Mushu and Cri-kee from the Disney movie "Mulan".
☐ Purchased 19_____   Pd $_____   MIB NB DB BNT
☐ Want   Orig. Ret. $14.95   **Projected** Sec. Mkt. **$20-25**

QX 646-3   MUNCHKINLAND™
               MAYOR AND CORONER
Comments: The coroner, with Certificate in hand, and the
Mayor holding his hat and pocket watch, are grateful to
Dorothy for ridding them of the wicked Witch. "Wizard of Oz."
Artist: Joyce Lyle
☐ Purchased 19_____   Pd $_____   MIB NB DB BNT
☐ Want   Orig. Ret. $13.95   **Projected** Sec. Mkt. **$25-30**

QX 629-3   NATIONAL SALUTE
Comments: Dated 1998.
Give a salute to this 1998 Armed Forces ornament.
Artist: Dill Rhodus
☐ Purchased 19_____   Pd $_____   MIB NB DB BNT
☐ Want   Orig. Ret. $8.95   **Projected** Sec. Mkt. **$12-15**

QX 517-2   NATURE'S SKETCH BOOK:
               COUNTRY HOME – MARJOLEIN BASTIN
Comments: Dated 1998.
Bird perching on his bird house.
Artist: Marjolein Bastin and John Francis (Collin)
☐ Purchased 19_____   Pd $_____   MIB NB DB BNT
☐ Want   Orig. Ret. $10.95   **Projected** Sec. Mkt. **$15-19**

QX 630-6   NEW ARRIVAL
Comments: Porcelain, Dated 1998.
Couple holding their bundle of joy. **Artist:** LaDene Votruba
☐ Purchased 19_____   Pd $_____   MIB NB DB BNT
☐ Want   Orig. Ret. $18.95   **Projected** Sec. Mkt. **$21-23**

NEW CHRISTMAS FRIEND
Comments: 1998 Membership Ornaments-Santa Times
Three, Dated 1998.
Inspired by a 1982 holiday card. **Artist:** Joanne Eschrich
☐ Purchased 19_____   Pd $_____   MIB NB DB BNT
☐ Want   Orig. Ret. $18.95   **Projected** Sec. Mkt. **$22-25**

QX 671-3   NEW HOME
Comments: Dated 1998.
This threshold, with big red bow, is a wonderful house warm-
ing gift. Will be offered in 1998 and 1999.
Artist: Ed Seale
☐ Purchased 19_____   Pd $_____   MIB NB DB BNT
☐ Want   Orig. Ret. $9.95   **Projected** Sec. Mkt. **$12-14**

QX 686-3   NICK'S WISH LIST
Comments: Dated 1998.
Santa is checking his list, not once but twice, to see if you
have been naughty or nice.
Artist: Patricia Andrews
☐ Purchased 19_____   Pd $_____   MIB NB DB BNT
☐ Want   Orig. Ret. $8.95   **Projected** Sec. Mkt. **$11-13**

QX 672-5   NIGHT WATCH
Comments: Dated 1998.
Mouse sleeps atop a winking night watch.
Artist: Bob Siedler
☐ Purchased 19_____   Pd $_____   MIB NB DB BNT
☐ Want   Orig. Ret. $9.95   **Projected** Sec. Mkt. **$12-14**

QX 680-3　NORTH POLE RESERVE ☐

Comments:　Dated 1998.
With hose in hand, this little fire fighter is ready when needed.
Artist: Ed Seale

☐ Purchased 19____　Pd $_____　MIB　NB　DB　BNT
☐ Want　Orig. Ret. $10.95　**Projected** Sec. Mkt. **$14-18**

QX 626-6　NOSTALGIC HOUSES AND SHOPS: GROCERY STORE ☐

Comments:　**Fifteenth in Series,** Dated 1998.
Artist: Don Palmiter

☐ Purchased 19____　Pd $_____　MIB　NB　DB　BNT
☐ Want　Orig. Ret. $16.95　**Projected** Sec. Mkt. **$20-25**

QX 664-6　#1 STUDENT ☐

Comments:　Dated 1998.
Teacher, this photo holder makes an excellent gift for those favorite students!

☐ Purchased 19____　Pd $_____　MIB　NB　DB　BNT
☐ Want　Orig. Ret. $7.95　**Projected** Sec. Mkt. **$10-12**

QX 632-3　OLD WEST: PONY EXPRESS RIDER ☐

Comments:　**FIRST IN SERIES,** Dated 1998.
First in the Old West series of legendary characters.
Artist: Duane Unruh

☐ Purchased 19____　Pd $_____　MIB　NB　DB　BNT
☐ Want　Orig. Ret. $13.95　**Projected** Sec. Mkt. **$16-19**

QX 663-6　OUR FIRST CHRISTMAS TOGETHER ☐

Comments:　Dated 1998.
Two love stricken penguins sit atop this dated photo holder.
Artist: Sue Tague

☐ Purchased 19____　Pd $_____　MIB　NB　DB　BNT
☐ Want　Orig. Ret. $8.95　**Projected** Sec. Mkt. **$11-13**

QX 319-3　OUR FIRST CHRISTMAS TOGETHER ☐

Comments:　Acrylic, Dated 1998.
Beautiful ornament with "Our First Christmas Together, 1998" written in gold. **Artist:** LaDene Votruba

☐ Purchased 19____　Pd $_____　MIB　NB　DB　BNT
☐ Want　Orig. Ret. $7.95　**Projected** Sec. Mkt. **$10-12**

QX 618-3　OUR SONG ☐

Comments:　Ceramic with display stand. Beautiful ornament featuring choir. **Artist:** Brenda Joysmith

☐ Purchased 19____　Pd $_____　MIB　NB　DB　BNT
☐ Want　Orig. Ret. $9.95　**Projected** Sec. Mkt. **$12-14**

QX 656-3　PEEKABOO BEARS ☐

Comments:　Dated 1998.
Three bears sneak a peek from the Christmas tree.
Artist: Ken Crow

☐ Purchased 19____　Pd $_____　MIB　NB　DB　BNT
☐ Want　Orig. Ret. $12.95　**Projected** Sec. Mkt. **$15-17**

QBG 692-6　PINK POINSETTIAS ☐

Comments:　Complements Holiday Traditions Series. Hand blown glass, pink poinsettias ornament.

☐ Purchased 19____　Pd $_____　MIB　NB　DB　BNT
☐ Want　Orig. Ret. $25.00　**Projected** Sec. Mkt. **$30-35**

QX 674-6　POLAR BOWLER ☐

Comments:　Dated 1998.
Looks like this polar bear is headed for a strike.
Artist: Joanne Eschrich

☐ Purchased 19____　Pd $_____　MIB　NB　DB　BNT
☐ Want　Orig. Ret. $7.95　**Projected** Sec. Mkt. **$10-12**

QX 681-6　PREMIERE EXCLUSIVE: SANTA'S MERRY WORKSHOP ☐

Comments:　Musical, Motion, Dated 1998.
Wind up this musical figurine and watch Mr. & Mrs. Claus and one of their favorite elves working hard to the tune of "Here Comes Santa Claus." They revolve in and out of the workshop, getting ready for Christmas Eve.
Artist: Ed Seale

☐ Purchased 19____　Pd $_____　MIB　NB　DB　BNT
☐ Want　Orig. Ret. $32.00　**Projected** Sec. Mkt. **$45-50**

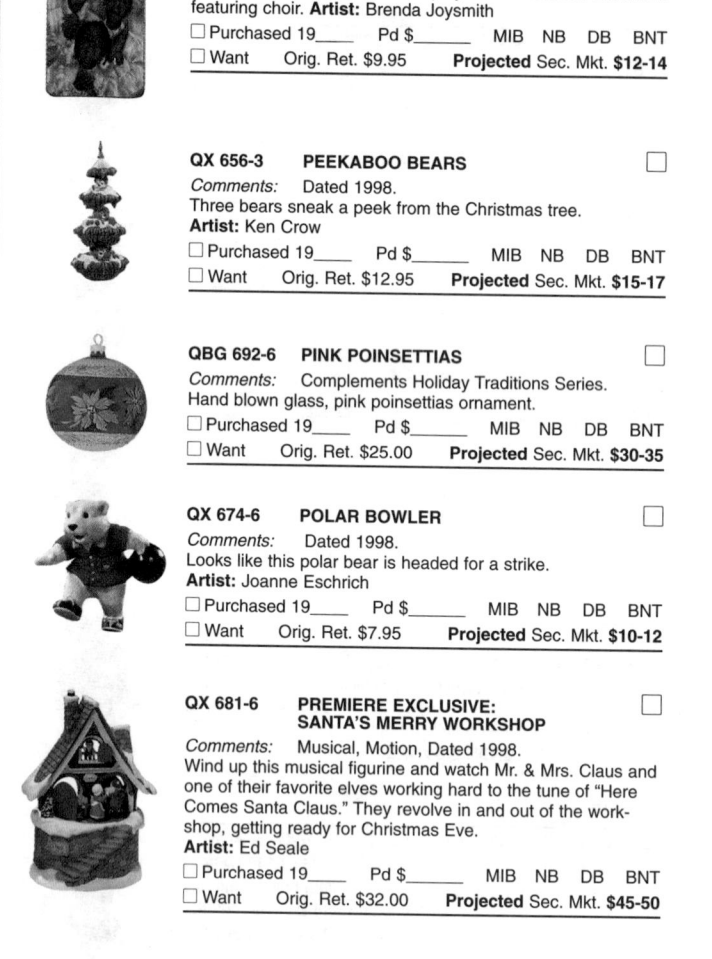

QXD 412-6   PRINCESS AURORA

Comments: **FIRST IN SERIES**, Set of two, Dated 1998.
Walt Disney's *Sleeping Beauty*. Princess Aurora has her fairy
godmothers (not pictured) to thank for watching over her.

☐ Purchased 19____   Pd $_____   MIB   NB   DB   BNT
☐ Want   Orig. Ret. $12.95   **Projected** Sec. Mkt. **$16-19**

QX 616-3   PUPPY LOVE: PUPPY LOVE

Comments: **Eighth in Series**, Dated 1998.
Adorable puppy tangled in string of Christmas lights wears a
brass tag around neck. According to the artist, this is a Black
Labrador puppy.
Artist: Anita Marra Rogers

☐ Purchased 19____   Pd $_____   MIB   NB   DB   BNT
☐ Want   Orig. Ret. $7.95   **Projected** Sec. Mkt. **$10-12**

QX 652-6   PURR-FECT LITTLE DEER

Comments: Dated 1998.
This adorable kitten wearing antlers and bell harness, is a cat
lover's must. **Artist:** Sharon Pike

☐ Purchased 19____   Pd $_____   MIB   NB   DB   BNT
☐ Want   Orig. Ret. $7.95   **Projected** Sec. Mkt. **$10-12**

QX 676-3   PUTTIN' AROUND

Comments: Dated 1998.
Standing on a chunk of Swiss cheese, it looks as if this little
mouse will get a hole in one. **Artist:** Dill Rhodus

☐ Purchased 19____   Pd $_____   MIB   NB   DB   BNT
☐ Want   Orig. Ret. $8.95   **Projected** Sec. Mkt. **$11-13**

QX 679-3   ROCKET TO SUCCESS

Comments: Dated 1998.
This rocket pencil ornament will be at the head of its class.
Teachers love it! **Artist:** Sharon Pike

☐ Purchased 19____   Pd $_____   MIB   NB   DB   BNT
☐ Want   Orig. Ret. $8.95   **Projected** Sec. Mkt. **$11-13**

**QXD 410-3   ROMANTIC VACATIONS:
DONALD AND DAISY IN VENICE**

Comments: **FIRST IN SERIES,** Dated 1998.
Donald gives Daisy a romantic ride in a gondola, in Venice.

☐ Purchased 19____   Pd $_____   MIB   NB   DB   BNT
☐ Want   Orig. Ret. $14.95   **Projected** Sec. Mkt. **$20-25**

QXD 400-3   RUNAWAY TOBOGGAN

Comments: Set of two, Dated 1998.
Mickey and Donald leave Goofy behind, holding the hat.

☐ Purchased 19____   Pd $_____   MIB   NB   DB   BNT
☐ Want   Orig. Ret. $16.95   **Projected** Sec. Mkt. **$20-25**

QX 657-3   SANTA'S FLYING MACHINE

Comments: Handcrafted, Tin, Dated 1998.
Santa lifts off in his flying machine with working rotor blades
and wheels. Will his new flying machine replace his reindeer?
Artist: Ed Seale

☐ Purchased 19____   Pd $_____   MIB   NB   DB   BNT
☐ Want   Orig. Ret. $16.95   **Projected** Sec. Mkt. **$20-23**

QX 691-3   SANTA'S HIDDEN SURPRISE

Comments: Ceramic, Dated 1998.
This Santa opens at the waist and has a hidden surprise.

☐ Purchased 19____   Pd $_____   MIB   NB   DB   BNT
☐ Want   Orig. Ret. $14.95   **Projected** Sec. Mkt. **$18-21**

QLX 756-6   SANTA'S SHOW 'N TELL

Comments: Lighted, Dated 1998.
Features Santa putting on a shadow show for his young
friend. Just turn the wheel in the back of the ornament, and
the shadows will appear. **Artist:** Ken Crow

☐ Purchased 19____   Pd $_____   MIB   NB   DB   BNT
☐ Want   Orig. Ret. $18.95   **Projected** Sec. Mkt. **$22-25**

QLX 757-3   SANTA'S SPIN TOP

Comments: Motion, Dated 1998.
Rudolph pulls Santa and his sleigh around the striped pole. Wonderfully designed, this top will hold the interest of young and old alike.
Artist: Sue Tague

☐ Purchased 19____   Pd $_____   MIB   NB   DB   BNT
☐ Want   Orig. Ret. $22.00   **Projected** Sec. Mkt. **$25-28**

QX 633-6   SCARLETT O'HARA™:
                    SCARLETT O'HARA™

Comments: **Second in Series.** Dated 1998.
Another Scarlett O'Hara dressed in her green and white spring dress; still does not resemble Vivian Leigh.
Artist: Patricia Andrews

☐ Purchased 19____   Pd $_____   MIB   NB   DB   BNT
☐ Want   Orig. Ret. $14.95   **Projected** Sec. Mkt. **$20-25**

QX 674-3   "SEW" GIFTED

Comments: Dated 1998.
Sitting in a thimble, this little guy holds a threaded needle in one hand and a button in the other.
Artist: Sue Tague

☐ Purchased 19____   Pd $_____   MIB   NB   DB   BNT
☐ Want   Orig. Ret. $7.95   **Projected** Sec. Mkt. **$10-12**

QXD 407-3   SIMBA & NALA

Comments: Dated 1998.
Walt Disney's *Simba's Pride.* Simba and Nala from Disney's "Lion King" embracing.

☐ Purchased 19____   Pd $_____   MIB   NB   DB   BNT
☐ Want   Orig. Ret. $13.95   **Projected** Sec. Mkt. **$18-22**

QX 669-3   SISTER TO SISTER

Comments: Dated 1998.
These two sisters have shopped the day away.
Artist: Sharon Pike

☐ Purchased 19____   Pd $_____   MIB   NB   DB   BNT
☐ Want   Orig. Ret. $8.95   **Projected** Sec. Mkt. **$11-13**

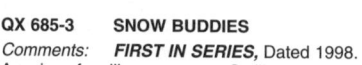

QX 628-6   SKY'S THE LIMIT:
                    1917 CURTISS JN-4D "JENNY"

Comments: **Second in Series,** Dated 1998.
Airplane buffs will enjoy this 1917 Curtis JN-4D "Jenny" to add to their collection. **Artist:** Lynn Norton

☐ Purchased 19____   Pd $_____   MIB   NB   DB   BNT
☐ Want   Orig. Ret. $14.95   **Projected** Sec. Mkt. **$18-21**

QX 685-3   SNOW BUDDIES

Comments: **FIRST IN SERIES,** Dated 1998.
A series of smiling snowmen. Smiling snowman happily greets rabbit with a pat. **Artist:** Tammy Haddix

☐ Purchased 19____   Pd $_____   MIB   NB   DB   BNT
☐ Want   Orig. Ret. $7.95   **Projected** Sec. Mkt. **$10-12**

QX 666-6   SON

Comments: Dated 1998.
This boy opens and closes like a real nutcracker.
Artist: Nina Aubé

☐ Purchased 19____   Pd $_____   MIB   NB   DB   BNT
☐ Want   Orig. Ret. $8.95   **Projected** Sec. Mkt. **$11-13**

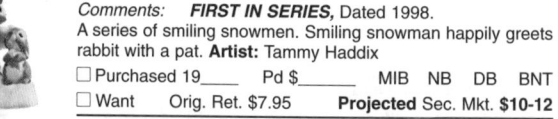

QX 670-6   SPECIAL DOG

Comments: Dated 1998.
An excellent way to display your favorite photo of your family dog.

☐ Purchased 19____   Pd $_____   MIB   NB   DB   BNT
☐ Want   Orig. Ret. $7.95   **Projected** Sec. Mkt. **$10-12**

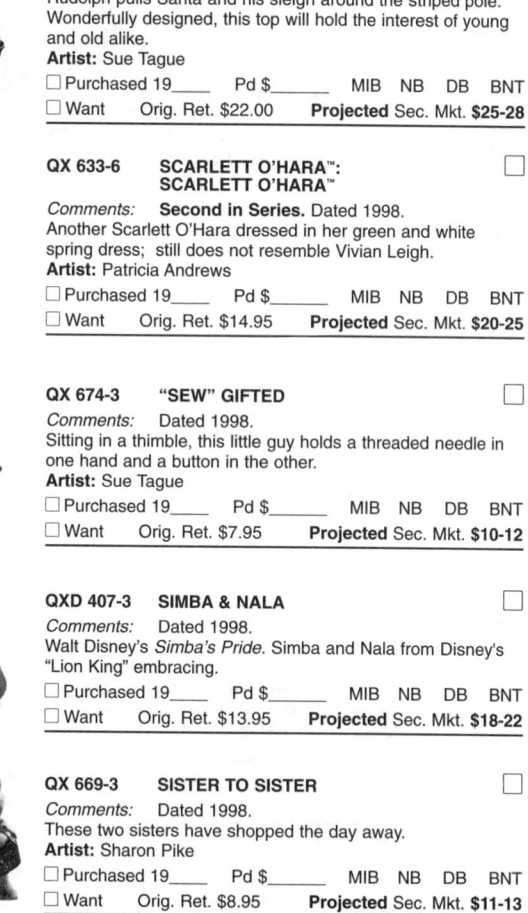

QX 679-6   SPOONFUL OF LOVE

Comments: Dated 1998.
With her spoon full of love, this little nurse helps the medicine go down. **Artist:** Sue Tague

☐ Purchased 19____   Pd $_____   MIB   NB   DB   BNT
☐ Want   Orig. Ret. $8.95   **Projected** Sec. Mkt. **$10-12**

QX 645-3   SPOTLIGHT ON SNOOPY SERIES:
JOE COOL

Comments: **FIRST IN SERIES,** Dated 1998.
Snoopy is just too cool in his santa suit and shades.
Artist: Bob Siedler

☐ Purchased 19____   Pd $_____   MIB   NB   DB   BNT
☐ Want   Orig. Ret. $9.95   **Projected** Sec. Mkt. **$15-20**

QXI 763-3   STAR TREK™: FIRST CONTACT
U.S.S. ENTERPRISE™ NCC-1701-E

Comments: Stardated. Both warp engines, the front deflector shield and the impulse engines are lit.
Artist: Lynn Norton

☐ Purchased 19____   Pd $_____   MIB   NB   DB   BNT
☐ Want   Orig. Ret. $24.00   **Projected** Sec. Mkt. **$30-35**

QXI 404-6   STAR TREK™: VOYAGER™
CAPTAIN KATHRYN JANEWAY™

Comments: Stardated.
Artist: Anita Marra Rogers

☐ Purchased 19____   Pd $_____   MIB   NB   DB   BNT
☐ Want   Orig. Ret. $14.95   **Projected** Sec. Mkt. **$20-25**

QXI 405-3   STAR WARS™:
BOBA FETT™

Comments: The perfect gift for that Star Wars™ lover. This ornament has been found with an error. The symbol on his left shoulder is upside down.
Artist: Dill Rhodus

☐ Purchased 19____   Pd $_____   MIB   NB   DB   BNT
☐ Want   Orig. Ret. $14.95   **Projected** Sec. Mkt. **$20-25**

QXI 402-6   STAR WARS™:
PRINCESS LEIA™

Comments: **Second in Series,** Dated 1998.
Princess Leia, dressed in white, awaits her fate.
Artist: Dill Rhodus

☐ Purchased 19____   Pd $_____   MIB   NB   DB   BNT
☐ Want   Orig. Ret. $13.95   **Projected** Sec. Mkt. **$19-24**

QXI 759-6   STAR WARS™:
X-WING STARFIGHTER™

Comments: Dated 1998.
The four engine pods feature red glowing lights.
Artist: Dill Rhodus

☐ Purchased 19____   Pd $_____   MIB   NB   DB   BNT
☐ Want   Orig. Ret. $24.00   **Projected** Sec. Mkt. **$30-35**

QXI 414-3   STOCK CAR CHAMPIONS:
RICHARD PETTY

Comments: **Second in Series.**
Richard Petty receives a checkered flag in his blue number 43 NASCAR. Included with this ornament is an exclusive trading card. **Artist:** Ed Seale

☐ Purchased 19____   Pd $_____   MIB   NB   DB   BNT
☐ Want   Orig. Ret. $15.95   **Projected** Sec. Mkt. **$20-25**

QBG 691-7   SUGARPLUM COTTAGE

Comments: Beautiful hand blown cottage full of color.
Artist: Tammy Haddix

☐ Purchased 19____   Pd $_____   MIB   NB   DB   BNT
☐ Want   Orig. Ret. $35.00   **Projected** Sec. Mkt. **$40-45**

QX 642-3   SUPERMAN™

Comments: **Commemorative Edition,** Dated 1998.
It's a bird! It's a plane! No ,it's a Superman™ pressed tin lunch box which really opens and closes! Found inside this lunch box, a picture of a BARBIE® lunch box ornament to debut Spring 1999.

☐ Purchased 19____   Pd $_____   MIB   NB   DB   BNT
☐ Want   Orig. Ret. $12.95   **Projected** Sec. Mkt. **$16-19**

QX 675-3   SURPRISE CATCH

Comments: Dated 1998.
The crowd went wild when this little guy, surprisingly, caught the ball and made the winning out.
Artist: John Francis (Collin)

☐ Purchased 19____   Pd $_____   MIB   NB   DB   BNT
☐ Want   Orig. Ret. $7.95   **Projected** Sec. Mkt. **$10-12**

QBG 693-3   SWEET MEMORIES

Comments: Set of eight hand blown Christmas candy ornaments.
Artist: Kristina Kline

☐ Purchased 19____   Pd $_____   MIB   NB   DB   BNT
☐ Want   Orig. Ret. $45.00   **Projected** Sec. Mkt. **$50-55**

QX 687-6   SWEET REMEMBERINGS

Comments: Dated 1998.
Little girl holding her candy cane and gingerbread man.
Artist: Sue Tague

☐ Purchased 19____   Pd $_____   MIB   NB   DB   BNT
☐ Want   Orig. Ret. $8.95   **Projected** Sec. Mkt. **$11-13**

QXD 405-6   THE ENCHANTED MEMORIES COLLECTION: WALT DISNEY'S *SNOW WHITE*

Comments: **Second in Series,** Dated 1998.
Holding a small blue bird on her uplifted finger, Snow White and her animal friends sit visiting in the Enchanted Forest.

☐ Purchased 19____   Pd $_____   MIB   NB   DB   BNT
☐ Want   Orig. Ret. $14.95   **Projected** Sec. Mkt. **$20-25**

QX 652-3   THE HOLY FAMILY

Comments: Blessed Nativity Collection, Dated 1998.
This set of three fine porcelain figures from the Blessed Nativity Collection feature Mary, Joseph and baby Jesus.
Artist: Joyce Lyle

☐ Purchased 19____   Pd $_____   MIB   NB   DB   BNT
☐ Want   Orig. Ret. $25.00   **Projected** Sec. Mkt. **$29-33**

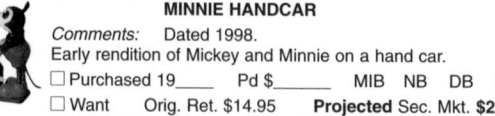

QXD 411-6   THE MICKEY AND MINNIE HANDCAR

Comments: Dated 1998.
Early rendition of Mickey and Minnie on a hand car.

☐ Purchased 19____   Pd $_____   MIB   NB   DB   BNT
☐ Want   Orig. Ret. $14.95   **Projected** Sec. Mkt. **$20-25**

QLX 755-3   THE WASHINGTON MONUMENT

Comments: Light, Sound, Dated 1998.
With sounds of real fireworks and flashes of light, this Washington Monument ornament is a true piece of art.
Artist: Ed Seale

☐ Purchased 19____   Pd $_____   MIB   NB   DB   BNT
☐ Want   Orig. Ret. $24.00   **Projected** Sec. Mkt. **$30-35**

QXI 755-6   THOMAS KINKADE, PAINTER OF LIGHT™ ST. NICHOLAS CIRCLE

Comments: Gold Crown Exclusive, Dated 1998.
This lighted ornament features a glowing background.
Artist: Duane Unruh

☐ Purchased 19____   Pd $_____   MIB   NB   DB   BNT
☐ Want   Orig. Ret. $18.95   **Projected** Sec. Mkt. **$22-24**

QX 634-3   THOMAS KINKADE, PAINTER OF LIGHT™ VICTORIAN CHRISTMAS II

Comments: **Second in Series,** Dated 1998.
Ceramic. Gold Crown Exclusive.

☐ Purchased 19____   Pd $_____   MIB   NB   DB   BNT
☐ Want   Orig. Ret. $10.95   **Projected** Sec. Mkt. **$14-18**

QX 682-6   TIN LOCOMOTIVE

Comments: **25th Anniversary Edition.** Dated 1998.
This tin locomotive ornament would complement any tree.
Artist: Linda Sickman

☐ Purchased 19____   Pd $_____   MIB   NB   DB   BNT
☐ Want   Orig. Ret. $25.00   **Projected** Sec. Mkt. **$30-35**

QX 648-3   TONKA® ROAD GRADER

Comments: Die-cast metal, Dated 1998.
Tonka road grader with pivoting front section and grader.

☐ Purchased 19____   Pd $_____   MIB   NB   DB   BNT
☐ Want   Orig. Ret. $13.95   **Projected** Sec. Mkt. **$18-22**

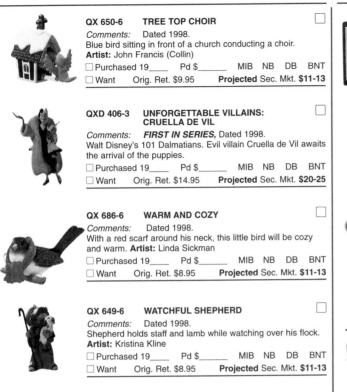

QX 650-6   TREE TOP CHOIR ☐

Comments: Dated 1998.
Blue bird sitting in front of a church conducting a choir.
Artist: John Francis (Collin)

☐ Purchased 19____   Pd $_____   MIB   NB   DB   BNT
☐ Want   Orig. Ret. $9.95   **Projected** Sec. Mkt. **$11-13**

QXD 406-3   UNFORGETTABLE VILLAINS: ☐
CRUELLA DE VIL

Comments: **FIRST IN SERIES,** Dated 1998.
Walt Disney's 101 Dalmatians. Evil villain Cruella de Vil awaits
the arrival of the puppies.

☐ Purchased 19____   Pd $_____   MIB   NB   DB   BNT
☐ Want   Orig. Ret. $14.95   **Projected** Sec. Mkt. **$20-25**

QX 686-6   WARM AND COZY ☐

Comments: Dated 1998.
With a red scarf around his neck, this little bird will be cozy
and warm. **Artist:** Linda Sickman

☐ Purchased 19____   Pd $_____   MIB   NB   DB   BNT
☐ Want   Orig. Ret. $8.95   **Projected** Sec. Mkt. **$11-13**

QX 649-6   WATCHFUL SHEPHERD ☐

Comments: Dated 1998.
Shepherd holds staff and lamb while watching over his flock.
Artist: Kristina Kline

☐ Purchased 19____   Pd $_____   MIB   NB   DB   BNT
☐ Want   Orig. Ret. $8.95   **Projected** Sec. Mkt. **$11-13**

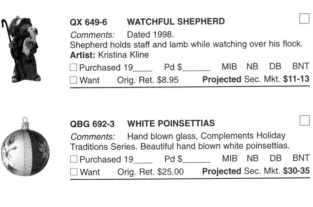

QBG 692-3   WHITE POINSETTIAS ☐

Comments: Hand blown glass, Complements Holiday
Traditions Series. Beautiful hand blown white poinsettias.

☐ Purchased 19____   Pd $_____   MIB   NB   DB   BNT
☐ Want   Orig. Ret. $25.00   **Projected** Sec. Mkt. **$30-35**

QXD 408-6   WINNIE THE POOH: ☐
A VISIT FROM PIGLET

Comments: **FIRST IN SERIES,** Dated 1998.
Piglet visits with Pooh inside this book-style ornament that
opens and closes.

☐ Purchased 19____   Pd $_____   MIB   NB   DB   BNT
☐ Want   Orig. Ret. $13.95   **Projected** Sec. Mkt. **$20-25**

QXD 416-3   WOODY THE SHERIFF ☐

Comments: Walt Disney's *Toy Story*, Dated 1998.
Sheriff Woody uses a string of Christmas lights for a lasso.

☐ Purchased 19____   Pd $_____   MIB   NB   DB   BNT
☐ Want   Orig. Ret. $14.95   **Projected** Sec. Mkt. **$18-22**

QX 653-3   WRITING TO SANTA ☐

Comments: Dated 1998.
Even if his pencil is bigger than he is, it's not going to stop
this determined little guy from writing to Santa.
Artist: Nina Aubé

☐ Purchased 19____   Pd $_____   MIB   NB   DB   BNT
☐ Want   Orig. Ret. $7.95   **Projected** Sec. Mkt. **$11-13**

QX 637-3   YULETIDE CENTRAL: ☐
YULETIDE CENTRAL

Comments: **Fifth and Final in Series,** Dated 1998.
Pressed tin caboose with turning wheels.
Artist: Linda Sickman

☐ Purchased 19____   Pd $_____   MIB   NB   DB   BNT
☐ Want   Orig. Ret. $18.95   **Projected** Sec. Mkt. **$22-25**

NFL Collection

☐	QSR 502-6	Carolina Panthers™		
☐	QSR 503-3	Chicago Bears™		
☐	QSR 504-6	Dallas Cowboys™		
☐	QSR 505-3	Denver Broncos™		
☐	QSR 506-3	Green Bay Packers™		
☐	QSR 501-3	Kansas City Chiefs™		
☐	QSR 509-6	Miami Dolphins™		
☐	QSR 512-6	Minnesota Vikings™		

☐ QSR 514-3	New York Giants™
☐ QSR 508-6	Oakland Raiders™
☐ QSR 515-3	Philadelphia Eagles™
☐ QSR 516-3	Pittsburgh Steelers™
☐ QSR 517-3	San Francisco 49ers™
☐ QSR 509-3	St. Louis Rams™
☐ QSR 518-6	Washington Redskins™

NFL FOOTBALL HELMETS

Comments: Dated 1998. Handcrafted helmets and referees for the most-watched list.
Artist: John Francis (Collin)

☐ Purchased 19____   Pd $_____   MIB   NB   DB   BNT
☐ Want   Orig. Ret. $9.95   **Projected** Sec. Mkt. **$20-25**

NBA Collection

☐ QSR 103-3	Charlotte Hornets™
☐ QSR 103-6	Chicago Bulls™
☐ QSR 104-3	Detroit Pistons™
☐ QSR 104-6	Houston Rockets™
☐ QSR 105-3	Indiana Pacers™

☐ QSR 105-6	Los Angeles Lakers™
☐ QSR 106-3	New York Knickerbockers™
☐ QSR 106-6	Orlando Magic™
☐ QSR 107-6	Seattle Supersonics™
☐ QSR 108-3	Utah Jazz™

NBA SLAM-DUNK

Comments: Handcrafted, Dated 1998.
The favorite team mouse adds drama to the courts during the holidays. **Artist:** Bob Siedler

☐ Purchased 19____   Pd $_____   MIB   NB   DB   BNT
☐ Want   Orig. Ret. $9.95   **Projected** Sec. Mkt. **$20-25**

Collegiate Collection

☐ QSR 231-6	Florida State Seminoles™
☐ QSR 232-3	Michigan Wolverines™
☐ QSR 231-3	Notre Dame® Fighting Irish™
☐ QSR 233-3	North Carolina Tar Heels™
☐ QSR 232-6	Penn State Nittany Lions™

COLLEGIATE KEEPSAKE SNOWMEN

Comments: Handcrafted, Dated 1998.
Cheering for some of the best known schools.
Artist: Tammy Haddix

☐ Purchased 19____   Pd $_____   MIB   NB   DB   BNT
☐ Want   Orig. Ret. $9.95   **Projected** Sec. Mkt. **$15 -20**

School Days Lunch Boxes

Inspired by real lunch boxes, these feature some of the best-loved characters of yesteryear.
Replicas are 75% scale: 6⅛"L x 2¾"W x 5⅛"H

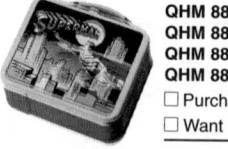

QHM 8801	1950s HOWDY DOODY™
QHM 8802	1950s LONE RANGER™
QHM 8813	1970s HOT WHEELS™
QHM 8803	1950s SUPERMAN™

☐ Purchased 19____   Pd $_____   MIB   NB   DB   BNT
☐ Want   Orig. Ret. $10.95   **Projected** Sec. Mkt. **$15**

1998 Event Exclusive Ornaments

QXC 450-6   CHRISTMAS EVE PREPARATIONS ☐
Comments: Dated 1998, Studio Edition
In celebration of the 25th Anniversay, offered exclusively during the event held in Kansas City. 21 studio artists worked together to create Santa and his elves getting ready for the special event. **Artists** include: Duane Unruh, Ed Seale, Linda Sickman, Sue Tague, Dill Rhodus, Robert Chad, Kristina Kline, Patricia Andrews, Ken Crow, Jon "Collin" Francis, Tracy Larsen, Anita Marra Rogers, Don Palmiter, Nello Williams, LaDene Votruba, Katrina Bricker, Bob Siedler, Nina Aubé, Sharon Pike, Joyce Lyle and Joanne Eschrich.

☐ Purchased 19____   Pd $_____   MIB   NB   DB   BNT
☐ Want   Orig. Ret. $85   Sec. Mkt. **N.E.**

QXC 4536   A LATE-NIGHT SNACK ☐
Comments: Complements the 1998 Keepsake Ornament studio Editon. **Artists:** Robert Chad and Tammy Haddix
☐ Purchased 19____   Pd $_____   MIB   NB   DB   BNT
☐ Want   Orig. Ret. $19.95   Sec. Mkt. **N.E.**

Given At the Hallmark Keepsake Ornament 25th Anniversary Celebration

A purple and silver tote bag with the event logo on it,
a snowflake with "25" in the center
plus a white t-shirt with the same logo.
1998 first in series, *A Pony for Christmas,* except the
pony was painted black instead of white.
Pewter Kansas City Drummer Boy.

Winners of Photo Contest received
Snow Buddies which, was painted gray instead of brown,
and *Joe Cool* painted in a special color.

First place winner received *Joe Cool* in a special color,
signed by Bob Siedler.

Also received by many attendees was a miniature KC Angel,
Precious Edition.

Many other ornaments were given away during this event.
For a more in depth review, read the Dec./Jan.1999 *Collectors Bulletin.*™

Club Member Surprise

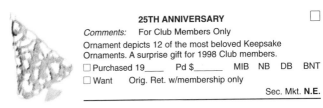

25TH ANNIVERSARY ☐
Comments: For Club Members Only
Ornament depicts 12 of the most beloved Keepsake Ornaments. A surprise gift for 1998 Club members.
☐ Purchased 19____   Pd $_____   MIB   NB   DB   BNT
☐ Want   Orig. Ret. w/membership only
Sec. Mkt. **N.E.**

1998
Miniature Ornament Collection

QXM 418-6
**ALICE IN WONDERLAND
CHESHIRE CAT**
Fourth and Final in Series, Dated 1998. **Artist:** Patricia Andrews
☐ Purchased 19___ Pd $_____
MIB   NB   DB   BNT
☐ Want   Orig. Ret. $6.95
            Projected MIB Sec. Mkt. **$9**

QXM 428-3 ANGEL CHIME
Dated 1998. **Artist:** Sue Tangue
☐ Purchased 19___ Pd $_____
MIB   NB   DB   BNT
☐ Want   Orig. Ret. $8.95
            Projected MIB Sec. Mkt. **$11**

**QXM416-6 ANTIQUE TRACTORS:
ANTIQUE TRACTORS**
Second in Series, Dated 1998.
Artist: Linda Sickman
☐ Purchased 19___ Pd $_____
MIB   NB   DB   BNT
☐ Want   Orig. Ret. $6.95
            Projected MIB Sec. Mkt. **$9**

**QXM 426-3 BETSEY CLARK:
BETSEY'S PRAYER**
Dated 1998. **Artist:** Kristina Kline
☐ Purchased 19___ Pd $_____
MIB   NB   DB   BNT
☐ Want   Orig. Ret. $4.95
            Projected MIB Sec. Mkt. **$7**

QXM 420-6
**CENTURIES OF SANTA:
CENTURIES OF SANTA**
Fifth in Series, Dated 1998.
Artist: Linda Sickman
☐ Purchased 19___ Pd $_____
MIB   NB   DB   BNT
☐ Want   Orig. Ret. $5.95
            Projected MIB Sec. Mkt. **$8**

**QXM 419-6 CHRISTMAS BELLS:
CHRISTMAS BELLS**
Fourth in Series, Dated 1998.
Artist: Ed Seale
☐ Purchased 19___ Pd $_____
MIB   NB   DB   BNT
☐ Want   Orig. Ret. $4.95
            Projected MIB Sec. Mkt. **$7**

QX M 429-6 "COCA-COLA" TIME
Artist: Duane Unruh
☐ Purchased 19___ Pd $_____
MIB   NB   DB   BNT
☐ Want   Orig. Ret. $6.95
            Projected MIB Sec. Mkt. **$10**

QXM 427-6 TASTY SURPRISE
Dated 1998. **Artist:** Joanne Eschrich
☐ Purchased 19___ Pd $_____
MIB   NB   DB   BNT
☐ Want   Orig. Ret. $6.95
            Projected MIB Sec. Mkt. **$9**

QXM 426-6 HOLLY-JOLLY JIG
Dated 1998, **Artist:** Sue Tague.
This jolly old Saint Nick has legs that
dangle.
☐ Purchased 19___ Pd $_____
MIB   NB   DB   BNT
☐ Want   Orig. Ret. $6.95
            Projected MIB Sec. Mkt. **$9**

KRINGLE BELLS
Dated 1998. 1998 Membership
Ornaments – Santa Times Three
Artist: Katrina Bricker.
☐ Purchased 19___ Pd $_____
MIB   NB   DB   BNT
☐ Want   Keepsake Miniature
            Projected MIB Sec. Mkt. **$15**

QXM 419-3
MINIATURE CLOTHESPIN SOLDIER
Fourth in Series. Artist: Linda Sickman
☐ Purchased 19___ Pd $_____
MIB   NB   DB   BNT
☐ Want   Orig. Ret. $4.95
            Projected MIB Sec. Mkt. **$7**

QXM 418-3
**MINIATURE KIDDIE CAR CLASSIC:
MURRAY INC.® DUMP TRUCK**
Fourth in Series, Dated 1998.
Artist: Don Palmiter
☐ Purchased 19___ Pd $_____
MIB   NB   DB   BNT
☐ Want   Orig. Ret. $6.95
            Projected MIB Sec. Mkt. **$10**

QXM 414-3
**MINIATURE KIDDIE CAR LUXURY
EDITION: 1937 STEELCRAFT
AUBURN**
FIRST IN SERIES, Dated 1998.
Artist: Don Palmiter
☐ Purchased 19___ Pd $_____
MIB   NB   DB   BNT
☐ Want   Orig. Ret. $6.95
            Projected MIB Sec. Mkt. **$10**

QXM 421-6 NOEL R.R.: CABOOSE
Tenth and Final in Series, Dated 1998.
Artist: Linda Sickman
☐ Purchased 19___ Pd $_____
MIB   NB   DB   BNT
☐ Want   Orig. Ret. $6.95
            Projected MIB Sec. Mkt. **$10**

QXM 428-6
NOEL R.R. LOCOMOTIVE
1989-1998 Anniversary Edition.
Dated 1998, Fine Pewter.
Artist: Linda Sickman
☐ Purchased 19___ Pd $_____
MIB   NB   DB   BNT
☐ Want   Orig. Ret. $6.95
    Projected MIB Sec. Mkt. **$9**

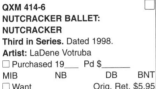

QXM 414-6
NUTCRACKER BALLET:
NUTCRACKER
Third in Series. Dated 1998.
Artist: LaDene Votruba
☐ Purchased 19___ Pd $_____
MIB   NB   DB   BNT
☐ Want   Orig. Ret. $5.95
    Projected MIB Sec. Mkt. **$8**

QXM 420-3 NUTCRACKER GUILD:
NUTCRACKER GUILD
Fifth in Series, Dated 1998.
Artist: Linda Sickman
☐ Purchased 19___ Pd $_____
MIB   NB   DB   BNT
☐ Want   Orig. Ret. $6.95
    Projected MIB Sec. Mkt. **$9**

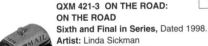

QXM 421-3 ON THE ROAD:
ON THE ROAD
Sixth and Final in Series, Dated 1998.
Artist: Linda Sickman
☐ Purchased 19___ Pd $_____
MIB   NB   DB   BNT
☐ Want   Orig. Ret. $5.95
    Projected MIB Sec. Mkt. **$8**

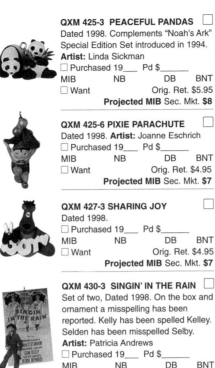

QXM 425-3 PEACEFUL PANDAS
Dated 1998. Complements "Noah's Ark"
Special Edition Set introduced in 1994.
Artist: Linda Sickman
☐ Purchased 19___ Pd $_____
MIB   NB   DB   BNT
☐ Want   Orig. Ret. $5.95
    Projected MIB Sec. Mkt. **$8**

QXM 425-6 PIXIE PARACHUTE
Dated 1998. **Artist:** Joanne Eschrich
☐ Purchased 19___ Pd $_____
MIB   NB   DB   BNT
☐ Want   Orig. Ret. $4.95
    Projected MIB Sec. Mkt. **$7**

QXM 427-3 SHARING JOY
Dated 1998.
☐ Purchased 19___ Pd $_____
MIB   NB   DB   BNT
☐ Want   Orig. Ret. $4.95
    Projected MIB Sec. Mkt. **$7**

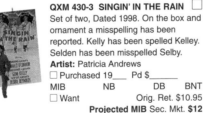

QXM 430-3 SINGIN' IN THE RAIN
Set of two, Dated 1998. On the box and
ornament a misspelling has been
reported. Kelly has been spelled Kelley.
Selden has been misspelled Selby.
Artist: Patricia Andrews
☐ Purchased 19___ Pd $_____
MIB   NB   DB   BNT
☐ Want   Orig. Ret. $10.95
    Projected MIB Sec. Mkt. **$12**

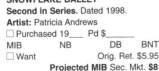

QXM 417-3 SNOWFLAKE BALLET:
SNOWFLAKE BALLET
Second in Series. Dated 1998.
Artist: Patricia Andrews
☐ Purchased 19___ Pd $_____
MIB   NB   DB   BNT
☐ Want   Orig. Ret. $5.95
    Projected MIB Sec. Mkt. **$8**

QXI 422-3
STAR WARS™: EWOKS™
Artist: Katrina Bricker
☐ Purchased 19___ Pd $_____
MIB   NB   DB   BNT
☐ Want   Orig. Ret. $16.95
    Projected MIB Sec. Mkt. **$20**

QXM 431-3
SUPERMAN™ (SET OF 2)
Commemorative Edition Ornament.
Dated 1998. **Artist:** Robert Chad
☐ Purchased 19___ Pd $_____
MIB   NB   DB   BNT
☐ Want   Orig. Ret. $10.95
    Projected MIB Sec. Mkt. **$12**

QXM 417-6
TEDDY-BEAR STYLE: TEDDY-BEAR
STYLE   Second in Series. Dated
1998. **Artist:** Duane Unruh
☐ Purchased 19___ Pd $_____
MIB   NB   DB   BNT
☐ Want   Orig. Ret. $5.95
    Projected MIB Sec. Mkt. **$8**

QXM 415-6
THE NATIVITY
FIRST IN SERIES. Fine Pewter. Dated
1998. **Artist:** Duane Unruh
☐ Purchased 19___ Pd $_____
MIB   NB   DB   BNT
☐ Want   Orig. Ret. $5.95
    Projected MIB Sec. Mkt. **$9**

QXD 423-6 TREE TRIMMIN' TIME ☐
Set of three, Dated 1998. Tigger, Piglet
and Pooh
☐ Purchased 19___ Pd $_____
MIB   NB   DB   BNT
☐ Want   Orig. Ret. $19.95
Projected MIB Sec. Mkt. **$25**

QXM 429-3 ☐
VICTORIAN ANGEL TREE TOPPER
Artist: Joyce Lyle
☐ Purchased 19___ Pd $_____
MIB   NB   DB   BNT
☐ Want   Orig. Ret. $12.95
Projected MIB Sec. Mkt. **$16**

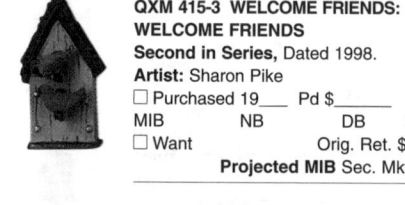

QXM 415-3 WELCOME FRIENDS: ☐
WELCOME FRIENDS
Second in Series, Dated 1998.
Artist: Sharon Pike
☐ Purchased 19___ Pd $_____
MIB   NB   DB   BNT
☐ Want   Orig. Ret. $6.95
Projected MIB Sec. Mkt. **$9**

QXM 424-3 ☐
WINTER FUN WITH SNOOPY®:
WINTER FUN WITH SNOOPY®
FIRST IN SERIES. Dated 1998.
Artist: Tracy Larsen
☐ Purchased 19___ Pd $_____
MIB   NB   DB   BNT
☐ Want   Orig. Ret. $6.95
Projected MIB Sec. Mkt. **$10**

QXM 423-3 WIZARD OF OZ™ THE: ☐
GLINDA, THE GOOD WITCH™ WICKED
WITCH OF THE WEST™
Set of two, **Artist:** Joyce Lyle
☐ Purchased 19___ Pd $_____
MIB   NB   DB   BNT
☐ Want   Orig. Ret. $14.95
Projected MIB Sec. Mkt. **$25**

"Now people will come!"

1998
Spring Ornament Collection

QEO 841-3
35TH ANNIVERSARY MIDGE™
4-3/4" tall, Dated 1998.
Artist: Patricia Andrews
☐ Purchased 19___ Pd $_____
MIB   NB   DB   BNT
☐ Want   Orig. Retail $14.95
          MIB Sec. Mkt. **$25**

QEO 842-3
ANDREW BROWNSWORD COLLECTION: FOREVER FRIENDS; 2-11/16" tall,
Dated 1998. **Artist:** Sharon Pike
☐ Purchased 19___ Pd $_____
MIB   NB   DB   BNT
☐ Want   Orig. Retail $9.95
          MIB Sec. Mkt. **$12**

QEO 844-6
BASHFUL GIFT   2-1/16" tall,
Dated 1998. **Artist:** Nina Aubé
☐ Purchased 19___ Pd $_____
MIB   NB   DB   BNT
☐ Want   Orig. Retail $11.95
          MIB Sec. Mkt. **$14**

QEO 838-3
BEATRIX POTTER™: BENJAMIN BUNNY™ Third in Series,
2-1/2" tall, Dated 1998.
Artist: LaDene Votruba
☐ Purchased 19___ Pd $_____
MIB   NB   DB   BNT
☐ Want   Orig. Retail $8.95
          MIB Sec. Mkt. **$14**

QEO 845-6
BOUQUET OF MEMORIES
2-1/2" tall, Dated 1998.
Artist: Sue Tague
☐ Purchased 19___ Pd $_____
MIB   NB   DB   BNT
☐ Want   Orig. Retail $7.95
          MIB Sec. Mkt. **$14**

QEO 837-3
CHILDREN'S COLLECTOR BARBIE™: BARBIE™ AS LITTLE BO-PEEP Second in Series, 3-1/2" tall, Dated 1998. **Artist:** Anita Marra Rogers
☐ Purchased 19___ Pd $_____
MIB   NB   DB   BNT
☐ Want   Orig. Retail $14.95
          MIB Sec. Mkt. **$18**

QEO 837-6
COTTONTAIL EXPRESS: PASSENGER CAR
Third in Series, 1-15/16" tall,
Dated 1998. **Artist:** Ken Crow
☐ Purchased 19___ Pd $_____
MIB   NB   DB   BNT
☐ Want   Orig. Retail $9.95
          MIB Sec. Mkt. **$12**

QEO 842-6
GARDEN CLUB: GARDEN CLUB   Fourth and Final in Series, 1-9/16" tall, Dated 1998.
Artist: Sharon Pike
☐ Purchased 19___ Pd $_____
MIB   NB   DB   BNT
☐ Want   Orig. Retail $7.95
          MIB Sec. Mkt. **$10**

QEO 847-6
HAPPY DIPLOMA DAY!
2-1/8" tall, Dated 1998. **Artist:**
Tammy Haddix
☐ Purchased 19___ Pd $_____
MIB   NB   DB   BNT
☐ Want   Orig. Retail $7.95
          MIB Sec. Mkt. **$10**

QEO 838-6
JOYFUL ANGELS: JOYFUL ANGELS   Third and Final in Series, 4" tall, Dated 1998.
Artist: Joyce Lyle
☐ Purchased 19___ Pd $_____
MIB   NB   DB   BNT
☐ Want   Orig. Retail $10.95
          MIB Sec. Mkt. **$15**

QEO 839-6
MICKEY & CO.: PRACTICE SWING-DONALD DUCK   3-1/2"
tall, Dated 1998. **Artist:** Disney
☐ Purchased 19___ Pd $_____
MIB   NB   DB   BNT
☐ Want   Orig. Retail $10.95
          MIB Sec. Mkt. **$15**

QEO 843-3
PEANUTS®: GOING UP-CHARLIE BROWN 2" tall, Dated
1998. **Artist:** Sharon Pike
☐ Purchased 19___ Pd $_____
MIB   NB   DB   BNT
☐ Want   Orig. Retail $10.95
          MIB Sec. Mkt. **$15**

QEO 846-3
PRECIOUS BABY 2-5/8" tall,
Dated 1998. **Artist:** Sue Tague
☐ Purchased 19___ Pd $_____
MIB NB DB BNT
☐ Want Orig. Retail $9.95
MIB Sec. Mkt. **$13**

QEO 839-3
SIDEWALK CRUISERS: 1939
MOBO HORSE
Second in Series, 2-5/8" tall,
Dated 1998.
☐ Purchased 19___ Pd $_____
MIB NB DB BNT
☐ Want Orig. Retail $12.95
MIB Sec. Mkt. **$17**

QEO 852-3
SPECIAL FRIENDS
2-7/8" tall, Dated 1998.
Artist: LaDene Wotruba
☐ Purchased 19___ Pd $_____
MIB NB DB BNT
☐ Want Orig. Retail $12.95
MIB Sec. Mkt. **$17**

QEO 840-6 STAR WARS
2-11/16" tall, Dated 1998.
☐ Purchased 19___ Pd $_____
MIB NB DB BNT
☐ Want Orig. Retail $12.95
MIB Sec. Mkt. **$17**

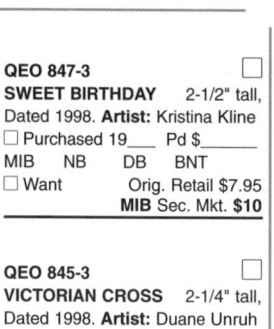

QEO 847-3
SWEET BIRTHDAY 2-1/2" tall,
Dated 1998. **Artist:** Kristina Kline
☐ Purchased 19___ Pd $_____
MIB NB DB BNT
☐ Want Orig. Retail $7.95
MIB Sec. Mkt. **$10**

QEO 845-3
VICTORIAN CROSS 2-1/4" tall,
Dated 1998. **Artist:** Duane Unruh
☐ Purchased 19___ Pd $_____
MIB NB DB BNT
☐ Want Orig. Retail $8.95
MIB Sec. Mkt. **$10**

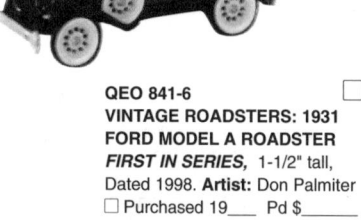

QEO 841-6
VINTAGE ROADSTERS: 1931
FORD MODEL A ROADSTER
FIRST IN SERIES, 1-1/2" tall,
Dated 1998. **Artist:** Don Palmiter
☐ Purchased 19___ Pd $_____
MIB NB DB BNT
☐ Want Orig. Retail $14.95
MIB Sec. Mkt. **$20**

QEO 846-6
WEDDING MEMORIES
4-1/2" tall Dated 1998.
Artist: LaDene Votruba
☐ Purchased 19___ Pd $_____
MIB NB DB BNT
☐ Want Orig. Retail $9.95
MIB Sec. Mkt. **$12**

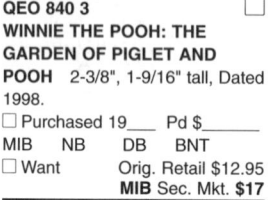

QEO 844-3
WHAT'S YOUR NAME?
1-7/8" tall, Dated 1998.
Artist: Kristina Kline
☐ Purchased 19___ Pd $_____
MIB NB DB BNT
☐ Want Orig. Retail $7.95
MIB Sec. Mkt. **$10**

QEO 840 3
WINNIE THE POOH: THE
GARDEN OF PIGLET AND
POOH 2-3/8", 1-9/16" tall, Dated
1998.
☐ Purchased 19___ Pd $_____
MIB NB DB BNT
☐ Want Orig. Retail $12.95
MIB Sec. Mkt. **$17**

QEO 843-6
WINNIE THE POOH: TIGGER IN
THE GARDEN
Preview Exclusive, 1-5/8" tall,
Dated 1998.
☐ Purchased 19___ Pd $_____
MIB NB DB BNT
☐ Want Orig. Retail $9.95
MIB Sec. Mkt. **$15**

Anniversary Ornaments

Trading on the Secondary Market for the Anniversay and Baby Celebrations Ornaments have not been seen. It is advised that you insure for the values listed.

AGA 786-5   OUR FIRST ANNIVERSARY ☐
Comments: Porcelain, 3-1/4" tall, Dated 1993
Oval white porcelain is trimmed in 14-k gold and says "Our First Anniversary 1993." Caption: "Love Is The Beginning Of Many Happy Memories." Identical to 1992 except date change.
☐ Purchased 19   Pd $ MIB NB   DB   BNT
☐ Want Orig. Ret. $10.00   **NB** $10   **MIB** Sec. Mkt. **$15**

AGA 731-8   OUR FIRST ANNIVERSARY ☐
Comments: Porcelain, 3-1/4" tall, Dated 1992
Oval white porcelain is trimmed in 14-k gold and says "Our First Anniversary 1992." Caption: "Love Is The Beginning Of Many Happy Memories."
☐ Purchased 19   Pd $ MIB NB   DB   BNT
☐ Want Orig. Ret. $10.00   **NB** $10   **MIB** Sec. Mkt. **$15**

AGA 786-6   OUR FIFTH ANNIVERSARY ☐
Comments: Porcelain, 3-1/4" tall, Dated 1993
Oval white porcelain is trimmed in 14-k gold and says "Our Fifth Anniversary 1993." Caption: "Love Is The Beginning Of Many Happy Memories." Identical to 1992 except for the date.
☐ Purchased 19   Pd $ MIB NB   DB   BNT
☐ Want Orig. Ret. $10.00   **NB** $10   **MIB** Sec. Mkt. **$15**

AGA 731-9   OUR FIFTH ANNIVERSARY ☐
Comments: Porcelain, 3-1/4" tall, Dated 1992
Oval white porcelain is trimmed in 14-k gold and says "Our Fifth Anniversary 1992." Caption: "Love Is The Beginning Of Many Happy Memories."
☐ Purchased 19   Pd $ MIB NB   DB   BNT
☐ Want Orig. Ret. $10.00   **NB** $10   **MIB** Sec. Mkt. **$15**

AGA 786-7   OUR TENTH ANNIVERSARY ☐
Comments: Porcelain, 3-1/4" tall, Dated 1993
Oval white porcelain is trimmed in 14-k gold and says "Our Tenth Anniversary 1993." Caption: "Love Is The Beginning Of Many Happy Memories." Identical to 1992 except for the date.
☐ Purchased 19   Pd $ MIB NB   DB   BNT
☐ Want Orig. Ret. $10.00   **NB** $10   **MIB** Sec. Mkt. **$15**

AGA 731-7   OUR TENTH ANNIVERSARY ☐
Comments: Porcelain, 3-1/4" tall, Dated 1992
Oval white porcelain is trimmed in 14-k gold and says "Our Tenth Anniversary 1992." Caption: "Love Is The Beginning Of Many Happy Memories."
☐ Purchased 19   Pd $ MIB NB   DB   BNT
☐ Want Orig. Ret. $10.00   **NB** $10   **MIB** Sec. Mkt. **$15**

AGA 768-6   25 YEARS TOGETHER ☐
Comments: Porcelain, 3-1/4" tall, Dated 1993
Oval white porcelain is trimmed in silver and says "25 Years Together 1993." Caption: "Silver Christmas Memories Are Keepsakes Of The Heart." Identical to 1992 except for the date.
☐ Purchased 19   Pd $ MIB NB   DB   BNT
☐ Want Orig. Ret. $10.00   **NB** $10   **MIB** Sec. Mkt. **$15**

AGA 711-3   25 YEARS TOGETHER ☐
Comments: Porcelain, 3-1/4" tall, Dated 1992
Oval white porcelain is trimmed in silver and says "25 Years Together 1992." Caption: "Silver Christmas Memories Are Keepsakes Of The Heart."
☐ Purchased 19   Pd $ MIB NB   DB   BNT
☐ Want Orig. Ret. $10.00   **NB** $10   **MIB** Sec. Mkt. **$15**

AGA 786-8   40 YEARS TOGETHER ☐
Comments: Porcelain, 3-1/4" tall, Dated 1993
Oval white porcelain is trimmed in 14 k gold and says "40 Years Together 1993." Caption: "Love Is The Beginning Of Many Happy Memories." Identical to 1992 except for the date.
☐ Purchased 19   Pd $ MIB NB   DB   BNT
☐ Want Orig. Ret. $10.00   **NB** $10   **MIB** Sec. Mkt. **$15**

AGA 731-6   40 YEARS TOGETHER ☐
Comments: Porcelain, 3-1/4" tall, Dated 1992
Oval white porcelain is trimmed in 14 k gold and says "40 Years Together 1992." Caption: "Love Is The Beginning Of Many Happy Memories."
☐ Purchased 19   Pd $ MIB NB   DB   BNT
☐ Want Orig. Ret. $10.00   **NB** $10   **MIB** Sec. Mkt. **$15**

AGA 778-7   50 YEARS TOGETHER ☐
Comments: Porcelain, 3-1/4" tall, Dated 1993
Oval white porcelain is trimmed in 14 k gold and says "50 Years Together 1993." Caption: "Golden Christmas Memories Are Keepsakes Of The Heart." Identical to 1992 except for the date.
☐ Purchased 19   Pd $ MIB NB   DB   BNT
☐ Want Orig. Ret. $10.00   **NB** $10   **MIB** Sec. Mkt. **$15**

AGA 721-4   50 YEARS TOGETHER   ☐
Comments: Porcelain, 3-1/4" tall, Dated 1992
Oval white porcelain is trimmed in 14 k gold and says "50 Years Together 1992." Caption: "Golden Christmas Memories Are Keepsakes Of The Heart."
☐ Purchased 19   Pd $ MIB NB   DB   BNT
☐ Want Orig. Ret. $10.00   **NB** $10   **MIB** Sec. Mkt. **$15**

AGA 768-7   25 YEARS TOGETHER ANNIVERSARY BELL ☐
Comments: Porcelain, 3" tall, Dated 1993
White porcelain bell is trimmed in silver and says "25 Years Together 1993." Caption: "Silver Christmas Memories Are Keepsakes Of The Heart." Identical to 1992 except for the date.
☐ Purchased 19   Pd $ MIB NB   DB   BNT
☐ Want Orig. Ret. $10.00   **NB** $10   **MIB** Sec. Mkt. **$15**

AGA 713-4   25 YEARS TOGETHER ANNIVERSARY BELL ☐
Comments: Porcelain, 3" tall, Dated 1992
White porcelain bell is trimmed in silver and says "25 Years Together 1992." Caption: "Silver Christmas Memories Are Keepsakes Of The Heart."
☐ Purchased 19   Pd $ MIB NB   DB   BNT
☐ Want Orig. Ret. $10.00   **NB** $10   **MIB** Sec. Mkt. **$15**

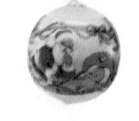

AGA 778-8   50 YEARS TOGETHER ANNIVERSARY BELL ☐
Comments: Porcelain, 3" tall, Dated 1993
White porcelain bell is trimmed in 14 k gold and says "50 Years Together 1993." Caption: "Golden Christmas Memories Are Keepsakes Of The Heart." Identical to 1992 except for the date.
☐ Purchased 19   Pd $ MIB NB   DB   BNT
☐ Want Orig. Ret. $10.00   **NB** $10   **MIB** Sec. Mkt. **$15**

AGA 723-5   50 YEARS TOGETHER ANNIVERSARY BELL ☐
Comments: Porcelain, 3" tall, Dated 1992
White porcelain bell is trimmed in 14 k gold and says "50 Years Together 1992." Caption: "Golden Christmas Memories Are Keepsakes Of The Heart."
☐ Purchased 19   Pd $ MIB NB   DB   BNT
☐ Want Orig. Ret. $10.00   **NB** $10   **MIB** Sec. Mkt. **$15**

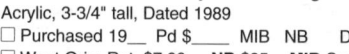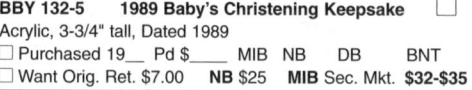

Baby Celebrations
1989

BBY 132-5   1989 Baby's Christening Keepsake   ☐
Acrylic, 3-3/4" tall, Dated 1989
☐ Purchased 19__   Pd $____   MIB NB   DB   BNT
☐ Want Orig. Ret. $7.00   **NB** $25   **MIB** Sec. Mkt. **$32-$35**

BBY 172-9   1989 BABY'S FIRST BIRTHDAY   ☐
Acrylic, 4-1/2" tall, Dated 1989
☐ Purchased 19__   Pd $____   MIB NB   DB   BNT
☐ Want Orig. Ret. $5.50   **NB** $25   **MIB** Sec. Mkt. **$32-$38**

BBY 145-3   1989 BABY'S FIRST CHRISTMAS - BABY BOY ☐
Blue Satin Ball, 2-7/8" dia. Identical to QX 272-5, page 120.
☐ Purchased 19__   Pd $____   MIB NB   DB   BNT
☐ Want Orig. Ret. $4.75   **NB** $10   **MIB** Sec. Mkt. **$12-$16**

BBY 155-3   1989 BABY'S FIRST CHRISTMAS - BABY GIRL ☐
Pink Satin Ball, 2-7/8" dia. Identical to QX 272-2, page 120.
☐ Purchased 19__   Pd $____   MIB NB   DB   BNT
☐ Want Orig. Ret. $4.75   **NB** $8   **MIB** Sec. Mkt. **$10-$14**

1990

BBY 132-6 BABY'S CHRISTENING   ☐
Hand-Painted Porcelain, 2-1/4" tall, Dated 1990
☐ Purchased 19__   Pd $____   MIB NB   DB   BNT
☐ Want Orig. Ret. $10.00 **NB** $15   **MIB** Sec. Mkt. **$25-$30**

BBY 155-4   BABY'S FIRST CHRISTMAS   ☐
Hand-Painted Porcelain, 2-1/8" tall, Dated 1990
☐ Purchased 19__   Pd $____   MIB NB   DB   BNT
☐ Want Orig. Ret. $10.00 **NB** $15   **MIB** Sec. Mkt. **$25-$30**

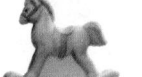

BBY 145-4   BABY'S FIRST CHRISTMAS   ☐
Hand-Painted Porcelain, 2-5/8" tall, Dated 1990
☐ Purchased 19__   Pd $____   MIB NB   DB   BNT
☐ Want Orig. Ret. $10.00 **NB** $15   **MIB** Sec. Mkt. **$25-$30**

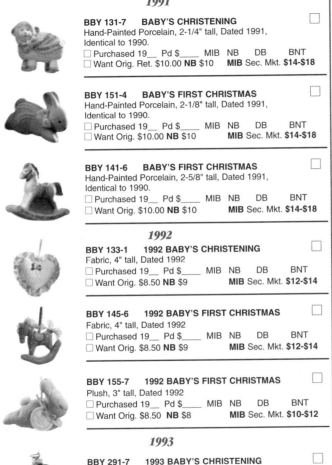

1991

BBY 131-7   BABY'S CHRISTENING
Hand-Painted Porcelain, 2-1/4" tall, Dated 1991,
Identical to 1990.
☐ Purchased 19__ Pd $____ MIB NB   DB   BNT
☐ Want Orig. Ret. $10.00 **NB** $10   **MIB** Sec. Mkt. **$14-$18**

BBY 151-4   BABY'S FIRST CHRISTMAS
Hand-Painted Porcelain, 2-1/8" tall, Dated 1991,
Identical to 1990.
☐ Purchased 19__ Pd $____ MIB NB   DB   BNT
☐ Want Orig. $10.00 **NB** $10   **MIB** Sec. Mkt. **$14-$18**

BBY 141-6   BABY'S FIRST CHRISTMAS
Hand-Painted Porcelain, 2-5/8" tall, Dated 1991,
Identical to 1990.
☐ Purchased 19__ Pd $____ MIB NB   DB   BNT
☐ Want Orig. $10.00 **NB** $10   **MIB** Sec. Mkt. **$14-$18**

1992

BBY 133-1   1992 BABY'S CHRISTENING
Fabric, 4" tall, Dated 1992
☐ Purchased 19__ Pd $____ MIB NB   DB   BNT
☐ Want Orig. $8.50 **NB** $9   **MIB** Sec. Mkt. **$12-$14**

BBY 145-6   1992 BABY'S FIRST CHRISTMAS
Fabric, 4" tall, Dated 1992
☐ Purchased 19__ Pd $____ MIB NB   DB   BNT
☐ Want Orig. $8.50 **NB** $9   **MIB** Sec. Mkt. **$12-$14**

BBY 155-7   1992 BABY'S FIRST CHRISTMAS
Plush, 3" tall, Dated 1992
☐ Purchased 19__ Pd $____ MIB NB   DB   BNT
☐ Want Orig. $8.50 **NB** $8   **MIB** Sec. Mkt. **$10-$12**

1993

BBY 291-7   1993 BABY'S CHRISTENING
3-1/16" tall, Dated 1993
☐ Purchased 19__ Pd $____ MIB NB   DB   BNT
☐ Want Orig. $12.00   **MIB** Sec. Mkt. **$14-$16**

BBY 133-5   1993 BABY'S CHRISTENING
PHOTOHOLDER
Silver-Plated, 2-3/4" dia., Dated 1993
☐ Purchased 19__ Pd $____ MIB NB   DB   BNT
☐ Want Orig. $10.00   **MIB** Sec. Mkt. **$12-$14**

BBY 291-8   1993 BABY'S FIRST CHRISTMAS
1-1/2" tall, Dated 1993
☐ Purchased 19__ Pd $____ MIB NB   DB   BNT
☐ Want Orig. $12.00   **MIB** Sec. Mkt. **$12-$14**

BBY 291-9   1993 BABY'S FIRST CHRISTMAS
2-1/4" tall, Dated 1993
☐ Purchased 19__ Pd $____ MIB NB   DB   BNT
☐ Want Orig. $14.00   **MIB** Sec. Mkt. **$16-$18**

BBY 147-0   1993 BABY'S FIRST CHRISTMAS
PHOTOHOLDER
Silver-Plated, 2-1/4" dia., Dated 1993
☐ Purchased 19__ Pd $____ MIB NB   DB   BNT
☐ Want Orig. $10.00   **MIB** Sec. Mkt. **$12-$15**

BBY 280-2   1993 GRANDDAUGHTER'S
FIRST CHRISTMAS
1-7/8" tall, Dated 1993
☐ Purchased 19__ Pd $____ MIB NB   DB   BNT
☐ Want Orig. $14.00   **MIB** Sec. Mkt. **$16-$18**

BBY 280-1   1993 GRANDSON'S FIRST CHRISTMAS
1-7/8" tall, Dated 1993
☐ Purchased 19__ Pd $____ MIB NB   DB   BNT
☐ Want Orig. $14.00   **MIB** Sec. Mkt. **$16-$19**

Interview with ... *Marjolein Bastin*

by Rose Juergens
Staff of Rosie Wells Ent.

In the last five years, the name Marjolein Bastin has become very well-known in Hallmark circles. Her sketches of nature, so lovingly created, bring a sense of joy to all who view them.

Many people encouraged Marjolein's talent. She received some formal training at a university in Holland. "I also have learned a lot watching birds and animals in nature, and spend much time improving myself every day."

Marjolein's art is featured not only in ornaments, but on greeting cards, books, posters and t-shirts. Such an expansive line draws many collectors to signings. "I love the signings. It's a chance for me to meet collectors and find out what they like and don't like about my work." It is quite apparent that there is much to like about Marjolein's work. It has been noted that people stand in long lines just to have her sign her artwork and perhaps exchange a word or two.

Marjolein's *Nature's Sketchbook* has proven to be a very popular Hallmark line. Marjolein receives hundreds of letters from collectors of the line, some saying they have collected everything she's designed.

Marjolein draws her inspiration from the area surrounding her home. She and her husband, Gaston, have recently built a home near Hallmark. "My prairie home is lovely, built of stone and cedar. We have located it on the edge of the prairie near Kearney, Missouri, nestled in more than 80 acres of forest. We have a beautiful pond for all my feathered friends."

A dedicated artist, Marjolein is said to spend up to 12 hours a day at her work table. She sketches the flowers, birds, plants and insects and transforms these things into beautiful works of art. She was quite excited about the prospect of sketching deer at her Missouri home. "I always hope my artwork will help people gain a greater appreciation for nature, and hope I convey my love for nature through my work."

Marjolein and Gaston have two children. "They have an interest in art, but not as a profession. My daughter is a forest ranger in Holland and my son is a student at (the) University of Kansas, studying international law."

The *Nature's Sketchbook* line, along with Marjolein's ornaments and other artwork, will not fade away anytime soon. When asked about retirement, Marjolein is quick to respond, "Retire? What is that? I don't plan to stop drawing, it's as important to me as breathing."

GARDEN BOUQUET

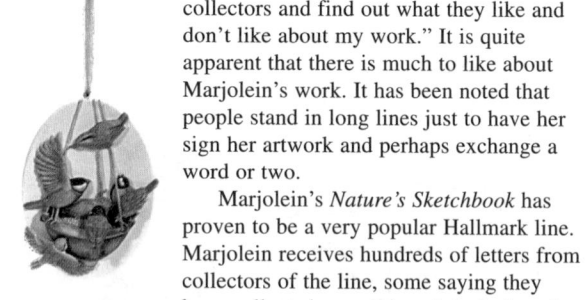

HONORED GUESTS

Marjolein Bastin

HER SKETCHES OF NATURE, SO LOVINGLY CREATED, BRING A SENSE OF JOY TO ALL WHO VIEW THEM.

Hallmark Artists

Anita Marra Rogers ...
joined Hallmark in 1987.
Best known works are
Puppy Love, as well as
Star Trek® characters.

Don Palmiter ...
joined Hallmark in 1967.
Creator of the
Classic American Car series.

Bob Siedler ...
joined Hallmark in 1979.
Some of his creations
are Owliver and
Reindeer Champs.

Diana McGehee ...
was first a book production artist,
then in 1991 became an
ornament designer.
Her favorite ornament is
"Cookies for Santa."

Joyce Lyle ...
joined Hallmark in 1979.
Enjoys sculpting angels,
Victorian figures
and roly-poly Santas.

Ken Crow ...
joined Hallmark in 1979. His
favorite ornament is
"Our Little Blessing" because he
modeled the figures after his own
children.

Robert Chad ...
joined Hallmark in 1987.
Best known design is his
Mary's Angels.

Sharon Pike ...
joined Hallmark in 1963. She
models characters after her own
cat and pet skunk.

Artists

Dill Rhodus ...
joined Hallmark in 1966.
Favorite ornament is
"Nolan Ryan."

Kristina Kline ...
joined Hallmark in 1996.
First project was to sculpt
"Mrs. Claus's Story."

Nina Aubé ...
joined Hallmark in 1981.
She is best known for her
"Bashful Boy" and
"Girl" characters.

Steve Goslin ...
joined Hallmark in 1978.
Most memorable project is
"The Lone Ranger" lunch
box ornament.

Ed Seale ...
joined Hallmark in 1968.
Best known for his
"Frosty Friends" and
"Tender Touches."

Linda Sickman ...
joined Hallmark in 1968.
Best known for her
"Rocking Horse" and
"Tin Locomotive" series.

Sue Tague ...
joined Hallmark in 1964.
Favorite ornament is
"Pansy" in the Language
of Flowers series.

Lynn Norton ...
joined Hallmark in 1966.
Favorite ornament
is the 1997
"The Flight of Kitty Hawk."

1999
Spring Ornament Collection

QEO 839-9 ☐
BARBIE™ ANNIVERSARY EDITION
2-11/16" tall, Pressed Tin, Dated 1999.
☐ Purchased 19___ Pd $_____
MIB   NB   DB   BNT
☐ Want   Orig. Retail $12.95
MIB Sec. Mkt. **N.E.**

QEO 839-7 ☐
BEATRIX POTTER™:
THE TALE OF PETER RABBIT™
Mother, 2-15/32" tall,
3 Rabbits, 1-5/8" tall,
Rabbit with carrot, 1-5/16" tall,
Dated 1999.
Artist: Ladene Votruba
☐ Purchased 19___ Pd $_____
MIB   NB   DB   BNT
☐ Want   Orig. Retail $19.95
MIB Sec. Mkt. **N.E.**

QEO 832-9 ☐
BEATRIX POTTER™:
TOM KITTEN™
Fourth In Series, 2-19/32" tall,
Dated 1999.
Artist: LaDene Votruba
☐ Purchased 19___ Pd $_____
MIB   NB   DB   BNT
☐ Want   Orig. Retail $8.95
MIB Sec. Mkt. **N.E.**

QEO 840-9 ☐
BIRTHDAY CELEBRATION
1-15/16" tall, Dated 1999.
Artist: Nina Aubé
☐ Purchased 19___ Pd $_____
MIB   NB   DB   BNT
☐ Want   Orig. Retail $8.95
MIB Sec. Mkt. **N.E.**

QEO 832-7 ☐
CHILDREN'S COLLECTOR
BARBIE™:
BARBIE® AS CINDERELLA
Third and Final, 3-3/8" tall,
Dated 1999.
Artist: Anita Marra Rogers
☐ Purchased 19___ Pd $_____
MIB   NB   DB   BNT
☐ Want   Orig. Retail $14.95
MIB Sec. Mkt. **N.E.**

QEO 838-7 ☐
COTTONTAIL EXPRESS:
FLATBED CAR
Fourth In Series, 2-3/16" tall,
Dated 1999.
Artist: Ken Crow
☐ Purchased 19___ Pd $_____
MIB   NB   DB   BNT
☐ Want   Orig. Retail $9.95
MIB Sec. Mkt. **N.E.**

QEO 846-7 ☐
CROSS OF FAITH
2-7/16" tall, Precious Metal,
Dated 1999.
Artist: Ladene Votruba
☐ Purchased 19___ Pd $_____
MIB   NB   DB   BNT
☐ Want   Orig. Retail $13.95
MIB Sec. Mkt. **N.E.**

QEO 842-7 ☐
EASTER EGG NEST
1-5/8" tall, Dated 1999.
Artist: Linda Sickman
☐ Purchased 19___ Pd $_____
MIB   NB   DB   BNT
☐ Want   Orig. Retail $7.95
MIB Sec. Mkt. **N.E.**

QEO 837-7 ☐
EASTER EGG SURPRISE
FIRST IN SERIES, 2-27/32 " tall,
Dated 1999.
Artist: Ladene Votruba
☐ Purchased 19___ Pd $_____
MIB   NB   DB   BNT
☐ Want   Orig. Retail $14.95
MIB Sec. Mkt. **N.E.**

QEO 836-9 ☐
FAIRY BERRY BEARS:
STRAWBERRY
FIRST IN SERIES,
2-3/16" tall, Dated 1999.
Artist: Sue Tague
☐ Purchased 19___ Pd $_____
MIB   NB   DB   BNT
☐ Want   Orig. Retail $9.95
MIB Sec. Mkt. **N.E.**

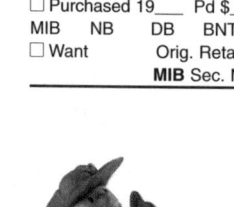

QEO 843-7
HAPPY BUBBLE BLOWER
2-1/2" tall, Dated 1999.
Artist: Sue Tague
☐ Purchased 19___ Pd $_____
MIB   NB   DB   BNT
☐ Want   Orig. Retail $7.95
MIB Sec. Mkt.**N.E**

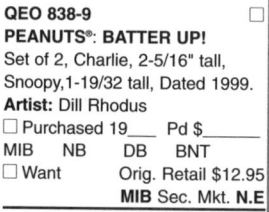

QEO 838-9
PEANUTS®: BATTER UP!
Set of 2, Charlie, 2-5/16" tall,
Snoopy,1-19/32 tall, Dated 1999.
Artist: Dill Rhodus
☐ Purchased 19___ Pd $_____
MIB   NB   DB   BNT
☐ Want   Orig. Retail $12.95
MIB Sec. Mkt. **N.E**

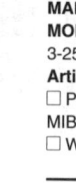

QEO 833-7
MADAME ALEXANDER®:
MOP TOP BILLY
3-25/32" tall, Dated 1999.
Artist: John Francis (Collin)
☐ Purchased 19___ Pd $_____
MIB   NB   DB   BNT
☐ Want   Orig. Retail $14.95
MIB Sec. Mkt. **N.E**

QEO 841-9
MARY'S BEARS:
FRIENDLY DELIVERY
2-9/16" tall, Dated 1999.
Designer: Mary Hamilton
Artist: Kristina Kline
☐ Purchased 19___ Pd $_____
MIB   NB   DB   BNT
☐ Want   Orig. Retail $12.95
MIB Sec. Mkt. **N.E**

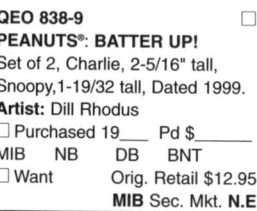

QEO 834-9
MICKEY & CO.: FINAL PUTT –
MINNIE MOUSE
3" tall, Dated 1999.
Artist: Disney
☐ Purchased 19___ Pd $_____
MIB   NB   DB   BNT
☐ Want   Orig. Retail $10.95
MIB Sec. Mkt. **N.E**

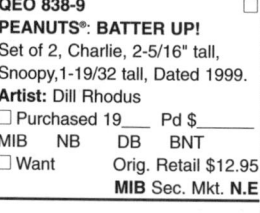

QEO 835-7
MICKEY & CO.
HAPPY DIPLOMA DAY
3" tall, Dated 1999.
Artist: Disney
☐ Purchased 19___ Pd $_____
MIB   NB   DB   BNT
☐ Want   Orig. Retail $10.95
MIB Sec. Mkt. **N.E**

QEO 841-7
PRECIOUS BABY –
COMMEMORATIVE
3-1/16" tall, Dated 1999.
Artist: Joyce Lyle
☐ Purchased 19___ Pd $_____
MIB   NB   DB   BNT
☐ Want   Orig. Retail $9.95
MIB Sec. Mkt. **N.E**

QEO 836-7
SIDEWALK CRUISERS:
1950 GARTON® DELIVERY
CYCLE
Third In Series, 2-1/2" tall,
Dated 1999.
☐ Purchased 19___ Pd $_____
MIB   NB   DB   BNT
☐ Want   Orig. Retail $12.95
MIB Sec. Mkt. **N.E**

QEO 846-9
SPRING CHICK
3-1/2" tall, Blown Glass,
Dated 1999.
☐ Purchased 19___ Pd $_____
MIB   NB   DB   BNT
☐ Want   Orig. Retail $22.00
MIB Sec. Mkt. **N.E**

QEO 842-9
SPRINGTIME HARVEST
2-3/8" tall, Dated 1999.
Artist: Linda Sickman
☐ Purchased 19___ Pd $_____
MIB   NB   DB   BNT
☐ Want   Orig. Retail $7.95
MIB Sec. Mkt. **N.E**

QEO 837-9
VINTAGE ROADSTERS:
1932 CHEVROLET STANDARD
SPORTS ROADSTER
Second In Series, 1-7/16" tall,
Dated 1999.
Artist: Don Palmiter
☐ Purchased 19___ Pd $_____
MIB   NB   DB   BNT
☐ Want   Orig. Retail $14.95
MIB Sec. Mkt. **N.E**

QEO 840-7 ☐
WEDDING MEMORIES
3-1/2" tall, Fine Porcelain,
Dated 1999.
Artist: Duane Unruh
☐ Purchased 19___ Pd $_____
MIB   NB   DB   BNT
☐ Want   Orig. Retail $9.95
MIB Sec. Mkt. **NE**

QEO 847-9 ☐
WINNER'S CIRCLE:
1956 GARTON® HOT ROD
RACER
FIRST IN SERIES, 1-19/32" tall,
Dated 1999.
Artist: Duane Unruh
☐ Purchased 19___ Pd $_____
MIB   NB   DB   BNT
☐ Want   Orig. Retail $13.95
MIB Sec. Mkt. **$14**

QEO 835-9 ☐
WINNIE THE POOH:
TIGGERIFIC EASTER
DELIVERY
2-25/32" tall, Dated 1999.
☐ Purchased 19___ Pd $_____
MIB   NB   DB   BNT
☐ Want   Orig. Retail $10.95
MIB Sec. Mkt. **NE**

Kiddie Car Classics

A special thanks to Michael Belofsky and David Hamrick for photos and helping with our research of prices for this fabulous popular collectible!

1992

The first five Kiddie Car Classics are considered the "hot ones." Notice how scarcity makes a collectible!

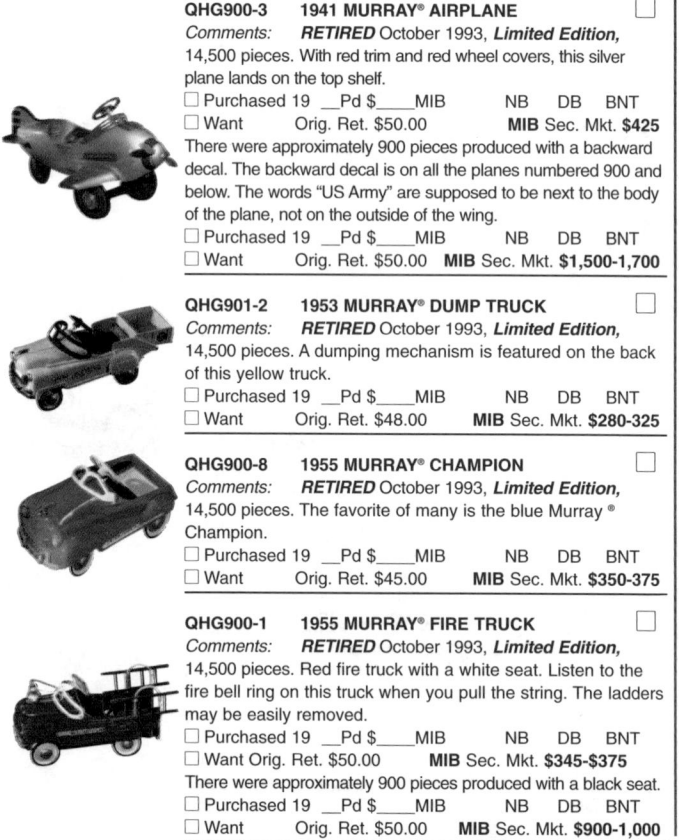

QHG900-3   1941 MURRAY® AIRPLANE ☐
Comments: *RETIRED* October 1993, *Limited Edition,*
14,500 pieces. With red trim and red wheel covers, this silver plane lands on the top shelf.
☐ Purchased 19 __Pd $____MIB   NB   DB   BNT
☐ Want   Orig. Ret. $50.00   **MIB** Sec. Mkt. **$425**
There were approximately 900 pieces produced with a backward decal. The backward decal is on all the planes numbered 900 and below. The words "US Army" are supposed to be next to the body of the plane, not on the outside of the wing.
☐ Purchased 19 __Pd $____MIB   NB   DB   BNT
☐ Want   Orig. Ret. $50.00   **MIB** Sec. Mkt. **$1,500-1,700**

QHG901-2   1953 MURRAY® DUMP TRUCK ☐
Comments: *RETIRED* October 1993, *Limited Edition,*
14,500 pieces. A dumping mechanism is featured on the back of this yellow truck.
☐ Purchased 19 __Pd $____MIB   NB   DB   BNT
☐ Want   Orig. Ret. $48.00   **MIB** Sec. Mkt. **$280-325**

QHG900-8   1955 MURRAY® CHAMPION ☐
Comments: *RETIRED* October 1993, *Limited Edition,*
14,500 pieces. The favorite of many is the blue Murray ® Champion.
☐ Purchased 19 __Pd $____MIB   NB   DB   BNT
☐ Want   Orig. Ret. $45.00   **MIB** Sec. Mkt. **$350-375**

QHG900-1   1955 MURRAY® FIRE TRUCK ☐
Comments: *RETIRED* October 1993, *Limited Edition,*
14,500 pieces. Red fire truck with a white seat. Listen to the fire bell ring on this truck when you pull the string. The ladders may be easily removed.
☐ Purchased 19 __Pd $____MIB   NB   DB   BNT
☐ Want Orig. Ret. $50.00   **MIB** Sec. Mkt. **$345-$375**
There were approximately 900 pieces produced with a black seat.
☐ Purchased 19 __Pd $____MIB   NB   DB   BNT
☐ Want   Orig. Ret. $50.00   **MIB** Sec. Mkt. **$900-1,000**

QHG900-4   1955 MURRAY® TRACTOR AND TRAILER ☐
Comments: *RETIRED* December 1993, *Limited Edition,*
14,500 pieces. Every farm needs this red tractor and trailer, which features a dumping mechanism.
☐ Purchased 19 __Pd $____MIB   NB   DB   BNT
☐ Want   Orig. Ret. $55.00   **MIB** Sec. Mkt. **$355-400**

1993

QHG900-6   1955 MURRAY® FIRE CHIEF ☐
Comments: *RETIRED* January 1996, *Limited Edition,*
19,500 pieces. Listen for the bell as this trim car comes driving down the road of memories. Special Fire Chief decal on both sides of car.
☐ Purchased 19 __Pd $____MIB   NB   DB   BNT
☐ Want   Orig. Ret. $45.00   **MIB** Sec. Mkt. **$125-150**
Approximately the first 15,000 numbered are more expensive and harder to find because they were produced with the left side decal backwards.
☐ Purchased 19 __Pd $____MIB   NB   DB   BNT
☐ Want   Orig. Ret. $45.00   **MIB** Sec. Mkt. **$180-200**

QHG900-5   1968 MURRAY® BOAT JOLLY ROGER ☐
Comments: *RETIRED* February 1996, *Limited Edition,*
19,500 pieces. The white boat has red trim and blue wheels.
☐ Purchased 19 __Pd $____MIB   NB   DB   BNT
☐ Want   Orig. Ret. $50.00   **MIB.** Sec. Mkt. **$90-125**

1994

QHG901-5   1939 STEELCRAFT LINCOLN ZEPHYR ☐
BY MURRAY®
Comments: *RETIRED* July 1996, *Limited Edition*
24,500 pieces. Best seller out of the four released 10/94. This classic black and white Zephyr comes with a French bulb horn.
☐ Purchased 19 __Pd $____MIB   NB   DB   BNT
☐ Want   Orig. Ret. $50.00   **MIB** Sec. Mkt. **$125-150**

QHG900-9   1941 STEELCRAFT SPITFIRE AIRPLANE ☐
BY MURRAY®
Comments: *RETIRED* January 1996, *Limited Edition* 19,500 pieces. Plane of the 40s.
☐ Purchased 19 __Pd $____MIB   NB   DB   BNT
☐ Want   Orig. Ret. $50.00   **MIB** Sec. Mkt. **$175-225**

QHG901-1   1955 MURRAY® DUMP TRUCK ☐
Comments: *RETIRED* March 1996, *Limited Edition,*
19,500 pieces. Black side walls, red hood and dumping mechanism are featured on this dump truck.
☐ Purchased 19 __Pd $____MIB   NB   DB   BNT
☐ Want   Orig. Ret. $48.00   **MIB** Sec. Mkt. **$130-160**

QHG901-0   1955 MURRAY® FIRE TRUCK ☐
Comments: *RETIRED* January 1996, *Limited Edition,*
19,500 pieces. White highlights this fire truck with working bell and movable ladders.
☐ Purchased 19 __Pd $____MIB   NB   DB   BNT
☐ Want   Orig. Ret. $50.00   **MIB** Sec. Mkt. **$275-325**

QHG900-7   1955 MURRAY® RANCH WAGON ☐
Comments: *RETIRED* February 1996, *Limited Edition,*
19,500 pieces. A two-tone green wagon which also features a pull down tailgate.
☐ Purchased 19 __Pd $____MIB   NB   DB   BNT
☐ Want   Orig. Ret. $48.00   **MIB** Sec. Mkt. **$125-150**

QHG900-2   1955 MURRAY® RED CHAMPION ☐
Comments: *RETIRED* March 1996, *Limited Edition*,
19,500 pieces. Another favorite of many is this Murray® Red Champion. Mine is burgundy. What color is yours?
☐ Purchased 19 __Pd $____MIB   NB   DB   BNT
☐ Want   Orig. Ret. $45.00   **MIB** Sec. Mkt. **$125-140**

QHG901-6   1956 GARTON® DRAGNET POLICE CAR ☐
Comments: *RETIRED* May 1997, *Limited Edition,* 24,500 pieces. White and black trimmed police car has a hood scoop and microphone.
☐ Purchased 19 __Pd $____MIB   NB   DB   BNT
☐ Want   Orig. Ret. $50.00   **MIB** Sec. Mkt. **$75-100**

QHX909-4   1956 GARTON® KIDILLAC ☐
Comments: *RETIRED* December 1994. Vintage pink and black Kidillac features side-view mirrors, antenna, spare tire and movable pedals. Antenna found to be easily broken. Not as popular as others.
☐ Purchased 19 __Pd $____MIB   NB   DB   BNT
☐ Want   Orig. Ret. $50.00   **MIB** Sec. Mkt. **$65-95**

QHG902-2   1956 GARTON® MARK V ☐
Comments: *RETIRED* July 1997 *Limited Edition,*
24,500 pieces. The teal painted Mark V features a replica "TOYLAND" license plate; the GARTON® emblem is found above the grille.
☐ Purchased 19 __Pd $____MIB   NB   DB   BNT
☐ Want   Orig. Ret. $45.00   **MIB** Sec. Mkt. **$50-85**

QHG901-8   1958 MURRAY® ATOMIC MISSILE ☐
Comments: *RETIRED* January 1997, *Limited Edition,* 24,500 pieces. Gold and white airplane with red seat has a streamline missile design with control knobs and a steering wheel.
☐ Purchased 19 __Pd $____MIB   NB   DB   BNT
☐ Want   Orig. Ret. $55.00   **MIB** Sec. Mkt. **$75-100**

QHG901-4   1961 MURRAY® CIRCUS CAR ☐
Comments: *RETIRED* November 1997, *Limited Edition*, 24,500 pieces. Tan and red car has gun-sight fender ornaments and a tailgate that can be opened. Notice production going up?
☐ Purchased 19 __Pd $____MIB   NB   DB   BNT
☐ Want   Orig. Ret. $48.00   **MIB** Sec. Mkt. **$55-90**

QHG901-3   1961 MURRAY® SPEEDWAY PACE CAR ☐
Comments: *RETIRED* March 1997, *Limited Edition,*
24,500 pieces. Starting the collectors' race is this white with red trim pace car. Gun-sight fenders and a special checkered flag decal dress up this classic car.
☐ Purchased 19 __Pd $____MIB   NB   DB   BNT
☐ Want   Orig. Ret. $45.00   **MIB** Sec. Mkt. **$75-100**

1995

QHG630-6   1935 STEELCRAFT STREAMLINE
              VELOCIPEDE BY MURRAY® ☐
Comments: *Sidewalk Cruisers Collection*. This green Velocipede has rubber grips, pedals and tires. There is also a spring action seat, simulated headlight and spoked wheels. Also available as miniature 1997 Spring Ornament.
☐ Purchased 19 __Pd $____MIB   NB   DB   BNT
☐ Want   Orig. Ret. $45.00   **MIB** Sec. Mkt. **$50-75**

QHG902-4   1937 STEELCRAFT
              AIRFLOW BY MURRAY® ☐
Comments: *RETIRED* September 1996, **Second in Series,**
Luxury Edition, 24,500 pieces. Working headlights are the main feature on this rich brown car, but also included is a French bulb horn radiator ornament and nickel-plated detailing. Secondary Market will climb when these are sold out.
☐ Purchased 19 __Pd $____MIB   NB   DB   BNT
☐ Want   Orig. Ret. $65.00   **MIB** Sec. Mkt. **$125-150**

QHG902-1 1937 STEELCRAFT AUBURN ☐

Comment: ***FIRST IN SERIES, RETIRED*** April 1996, *Luxury Edition*, 24,500 pieces. The rich black with red trim Steelcraft Auburn has a French bulb horn, nickel-plated exhaust pipes and distinctive windshield. Appears to me to be a favorite!

☐ Purchased 19 __Pd $____MIB   NB   DB   BNT
☐ Want   Orig. Ret. $65.00   **MIB** Sec. Mkt. **$150-200**

**QHG630-1 1937 STEELCRAFT STREAMLINE
            SCOOTER BY MURRAY®** ☐

Comments: ***RETIRED*** October 1997, *Sidewalk Cruisers Collection*. This yellow scooter has a foot mat and handle grips. It also features a parking stand, foot brake and rubber tires.

☐ Purchased 19 __Pd $____MIB   NB   DB   BNT
☐ Want   Orig. Ret. $35.00   **MIB** Sec. Mkt. **$35-75**

QHG630-4 1939 MOBO HORSE ☐

Comments: ***RETIRED*** December 1998, *Sidewalk Cruisers Collection*. Watch this spotted horse go with his realistic spring action legs! Also featured are plastic reins and metal stirrups. Also available as a Spring 1998 ornament.

☐ Purchased 19 __Pd $____MIB   NB   DB   BNT
☐ Want   Orig. Ret. $45.00   **MIB** Sec. Mkt. **$50-75**

QHG630-5 1940 GARTON® AERO FLITE WAGON ☐

Comments: *Sidewalk Cruisers Collection, Limited Edition*, 29,500 pieces. Rubber tires and working headlights show off this wagon. 29,500 pieces is quite a lot of pieces for a Limited Edition, in my opinion.

☐ Purchased 19 __Pd $____MIB   NB   DB   BNT
☐ Want   Orig. Ret. $48.00   **MIB** Sec. Mkt. **$50-75**

QHG902-6 1948 MURRAY® PONTIAC ☐

Comments: ***RETIRED*** June 1998. A radiator ornament and authentic markings adorn this car.

☐ Purchased 19 __Pd $____MIB   NB   DB   BNT
☐ Want   Orig. Ret. $50.00   **MIB** Sec. Mkt. **$60-90**

QHG902-0 1950 MURRAY® TORPEDO ☐

Comments: ***RETIRED*** January 1996. Classic Torpedo ready for the road.

☐ Purchased 19 __Pd $____MIB   NB   DB   BNT
☐ Want   Orig. Ret. $50.00   **MIB** Sec. Mkt. **$135-175**

QHG902-5 1955 MURRAY® ROYAL DELUXE ☐

Comments: *Limited Edition,* 29,500 pieces. (Production higher than last year.) Two-tone paint and continental spare tire make this car very authentic looking. 29,500 seems to be a lot… May take awhile before it is seen on secondary market with the quantity produced.

☐ Purchased 19 __Pd $____MIB   NB   DB   BNT
☐ Want   Orig. Ret. $55.00   **MIB** Sec. Mkt. **$55-90**

QHG901-7 1959 GARTON® DELUXE KIDILLAC ☐

Comments: ***RETIRED*** January 1997. A fully loaded blue and white Kidillac. It has working headlights, side mirrors, decorative trim, non-removable spare tire, hood ornament and antenna.

☐ Purchased 19 __Pd $____MIB   NB   DB   BNT
☐ Want   Orig. Ret. $55.00   **MIB** Sec. Mkt. **$90-125**

**QHG901-9 1961 GARTON® CASEY JONES
            LOCOMOTIVE** ☐

Comments: ***RETIRED*** January 1997. A ringing bell, smokestack, cowcatcher and decals adorn this authentic looking locomotive.

☐ Purchased 19 __Pd $____MIB   NB   DB   BNT
☐ Want   Orig. Ret. $55.00   **MIB** Sec. Mkt. **$90-125**

**QHG909-5 1962 MURRAY® SUPER
            DELUXE FIRETRUCK** ☐

Comments: ***RETIRED*** July 1997. This fire engine comes complete with blinking red light, bell, detachable ladders and realistic looking markings.

☐ Purchased 19 __Pd $____MIB   NB   DB   BNT
☐ Want   Orig. Ret. $55.00   **MIB** Sec. Mkt. **$65-95**

QHG630-3 1963 GARTON® SPEEDSTER ☐

Comments: *Sidewalk Cruisers Collection*. A realistic pump-action handle is featured on this blue speedster. I had one similar to this.

☐ Purchased 19 __Pd $____MIB   NB   DB   BNT
☐ Want   Orig. Ret. $38.00   **MIB** Sec. Mkt. **$40-60**

Peace On Earth!

QHG902-3   1964 GARTON® TIN LIZZIE ☐

Comments: **RETIRED** October 1997. Old-fashioned green and black Tin Lizzie features running boards and fenders. There is also a French bulb horn and a visor-style windshield. Should do well after retirement.

☐ Purchased 19 __ Pd $____ MIB   NB   DB   BNT
☐ Want   Orig. Ret. $50.00   **MIB** Sec. Mkt. **$55-85**

QHG630-2   1966 GARTON® SUPER-SONDA ☐

Comments: **RETIRED** December 1997, *Sidewalk Cruisers Collection.* A special rack on the back of this red scooter can be found, along with a banana-style seat and training wheels.

☐ Purchased 19 __ Pd $____ MIB   NB   DB   BNT
☐ Want   Orig. Ret. $45.00   **MIB** Sec. Mkt. **$50-60**

1996

QHG631-0   1935 AMERICAN AIRFLOW COASTER ☐

Comments: **RETIRED,** October 1997, *Sidewalk Cruisers Collection, Limited Edition,* 29,500 pieces. Working headlights and a handle that turns the front wheels are featured on this royal blue and cream colored wagon.

☐ Purchased 19 __ Pd $____ MIB   NB   DB   BNT
☐ Want   Orig. Ret. $48.00   **MIB** Sec. Mkt. **$50-75**

QHG631-1   1935 SKY KING VELOCIPEDE ☐

Comments: *Sidewalk Cruisers Collection.* This very special tricycle comes complete with a reflective headlight, cruising light, built-in step plates and refined wheel hoods.

☐ Purchased 19 __ Pd $____ MIB   NB   DB   BNT
☐ Want   Orig. Ret. $45.00   **MIB** Sec. Mkt. **$50-75**

QHG902-9   1935 STEELCRAFT BY MURRAY® ☐

Comments: **RETIRED** September 1996, *Third in Series, Luxury Edition,* 24,500 pieces. Classic green and black convertible with working headlights, French bulb horn and luggage rack makes this a special car. Nice! Nice! Should go up quickly when sold out.

☐ Purchased 19 __ Pd $____ MIB   NB   DB   BNT
☐ Want   Orig. Ret. $65.00   **MIB** Sec. Mkt. **$150-175**

QHG903-2   1935 STEELCRAFT AIRPLANE ☐
BY MURRAY®

Comments: **RETIRED** February 1997. *Limited Edition,* 29,500 pieces. Coming in for a three point landing is this green airplane with white tail, wings and sleek wheel hoods. Features a revolving propeller.

☐ Purchased 19 __ Pd $____ MIB   NB   DB   BNT
☐ Want   Orig. Ret. $50.00   **MIB** Sec. Mkt. **$125-140**

QHG630-8   LATE 1940S MOBO SULKY ☐

Comments: *Sidewalk Cruisers Collection, Limited Edition,* 29,500 pieces. A white horse with red plastic reins pulls this red sulky with wooden seat.

☐ Purchased 19 __ Pd $____ MIB   NB   DB   BNT
☐ Want   Orig. Ret. $48.00   **MIB** Sec. Mkt. **$50-75**

QHG631-2   1941 KEYSTONE LOCOMOTIVE ☐

Comments: **RETIRED** December 1998, *Sidewalk Cruisers Collection.* Take a trip back in time with this old fashioned coal locomotive with its coal tender and rubber tires. May be very popular with train collectors, too.

☐ Purchased 19 __ Pd $____ MIB   NB   DB   BNT
☐ Want   Orig. Ret. $45.00   **MIB** Sec. Mkt. **$50-75**

QHG630-9   1950 GARTON® DELIVERY CYCLE ☐

Comments: Ringer bell, rubber handle grips, spoked wheels and attached wagon make this a very unique red cycle.

☐ Purchased 19 __ Pd $____ MIB   NB   DB   BNT
☐ Want   Orig. Ret. $38.00   **MIB** Sec. Mkt. **$40-55**

QHG902-8   1956 GARTON® HOT ROD RACER ☐

Comments: **RETIRED** May 1999, *FIRST IN SERIES, Winner's Circle Series.* First to cross the line is this hot rod racer with nickel-plated hood ornament and hub caps. Always get those first in series!

☐ Purchased 19 __ Pd $____ MIB   NB   DB   BNT
☐ Want   Orig. Ret. $55.00   **MIB** Sec. Mkt. **$60-85**

QHG630-7   1958 MURRAY® POLICE CYCLE ☐

Comments: *Sidewalk Cruisers Collection, Limited Edition,* 29,500 pieces. Working red spotlight, handle grips with streamers, rear door that opens and antenna are featured on this police cycle.

☐ Purchased 19 __ Pd $____ MIB   NB   DB   BNT
☐ Want   Orig. Ret. $55.00   **MIB** Sec. Mkt. **$50-90**

QHG902-7   1961 MURRAY® SUPER DELUXE
TRACTOR WITH TRAILER
Comments: *RETIRED* December 1998. At home on any farm is this yellow single front wheeled tractor with detachable trailer which has a tailgate that opens.
☐ Purchased 19 __Pd $____MIB   NB   DB   BNT
☐ Want   Orig. Ret. $55.00   **MIB** Sec. Mkt. **$55-75**

QHG903-0   1964½ FORD MUSTANG
Comments: Side scoops with racing stripes and wild horse emblems trim this Ford Mustang.
☐ Purchased 19 __Pd $____MIB   NB   DB   BNT
☐ Want   Orig. Ret. $55.00   **MIB** Sec. Mkt. **$60-80**

1997

QHG903-5   1937 GARTON® FORD
Comments: *RETIRED* June 1997, **Fourth in Series, Luxury Edition, Limited Edition,** 24,500 pieces. Extra care is given to detail and workmanship for this luxury car, which is black with ivory to white pin striping and spoke wheels. Great attention getter!
☐ Purchased 19 __Pd $____MIB   NB   DB   BNT
☐ Want   Orig. Ret. $65.00   **MIB** Sec. Mkt. **$125-150**

QHG631-8   1937 SCAMP WAGON
Comments: **Sidewalk Cruiser Collection, Limited Edition,** 29,500 pieces. Aerodynamic fenders accent this wagon. A green handle and working headlights complete the Scamp.
☐ Purchased 19 __Pd $____MIB   NB   DB   BNT
☐ Want   Orig. Ret. $48.00   **MIB** Sec. Mkt. **$50-75**

QHG903-8   1938 GARTON® LINCOLN ZEPHYR
Comments: *RETIRED* December 1997, **Fifth in Series, Luxury Edition, Limited Edition,** 24,500 pieces. The red and white colors and the distinctive grille will make this a popular car.
☐ Purchased 19 __Pd $____MIB   NB   DB   BNT
☐ Want   Orig. Ret. $65.00   **MIB** Sec. Mkt. **$125-150**

QHG631-4   1939 AMERICAN NATIONAL PEDAL BIKE
Comments: **Sidewalk Cruiser Collection.** This pedal bike features a contoured seat with teardrop style fenders and working pedals.
☐ Purchased 19 __Pd $____MIB   NB   DB   BNT
☐ Want   Orig. Ret. $38.00   **MIB** Sec. Mkt. **$40-55**

QHG631-7   1939 GARTON® BAT WING SCOOTER
Comments: Sidewalk Cruiser Collection. This scooter was available in limited supply through 1998 at selected Gold Crown Hallmark stores that were participating in the Hallmark Christmas Catalog program. After this early introduction it will be available to all Gold Crown stores.
☐ Purchased 19 __Pd $____MIB   NB   DB   BNT
☐ Want   Orig. Ret. $38.00   **MIB** Sec. Mkt. **$40-55**

QHG903-4   1939 GARTON® FORD STATION WAGON
Comments: This deep red wagon is a great new design. It has the same wood-look side panels as the Green Ranch Wagon and has a removable surf board. *Groovy!*
☐ Purchased 19 __Pd $____MIB   NB   DB   BNT
☐ Want   Orig. Ret. $55.00   **MIB** Sec. Mkt. **$60-75**

QHG903-7   1940 GENDRON "RED HOT" ROADSTER
Comments: **Second in Series, Winner's Circle Collection.** This shiny red racer has ivory sidewall tires with matching ivory striping, chrome hood ornament and windshield.
☐ Purchased 19 __Pd $____MIB   NB   DB   BNT
☐ Want   Orig. Ret. $55.00   **MIB** Sec. Mkt. **$55-65**

QHG903-1   1941 MURRAY® JUNIOR SERVICE TRUCK
Comments: With the introduction of the Kiddie Car Service Station and accessories, a service truck was needed. This 1941 Murray Junior Service Truck fits the bill nicely. This truck is and comes complete with a tow bar on the back.
☐ Purchased 19 __Pd $____MIB   NB   DB   BNT
☐ Want   Orig. Ret. $55.00   **MIB** Sec. Mkt. **$60-80**

QHG903-6   1941 STEELCRAFT OLDSMOBILE
BY MURRAY®
Comments: A popular design is found in this blue Oldsmobile. White accents the hood, headlights, grille, fenders and spoke wheels.
☐ Purchased 19 __Pd $____MIB   NB   DB   BNT
☐ Want   Orig. Ret. $55.00   **MIB** Sec. Mkt. **$55-75**

QHG903-3   1956 MURRAY® GOLDEN EAGLE
Comments: *RETIRED* July 1997, **Limited Edition ,** 29,500 pieces. Gold and white with a plaid seat, this car comes with a working spotlight.
☐ Purchased 19 __Pd $____MIB   NB   DB   BNT
☐ Want   Orig. Ret. $50.00   **MIB** Sec. Mkt. **$55-85**

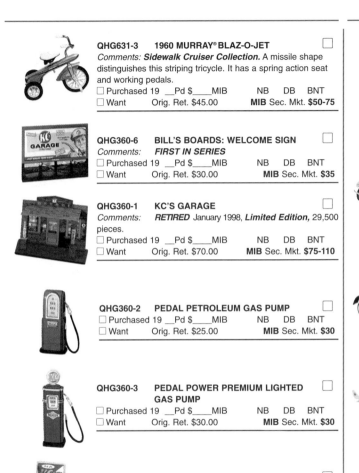

QHG631-3　1960 MURRAY® BLAZ-O-JET ☐
Comments: *Sidewalk Cruiser Collection.* A missile shape distinguishes this striping tricycle. It has a spring action seat and working pedals.
☐ Purchased 19 __Pd $____MIB　　　NB　DB　BNT
☐ Want　　Orig. Ret. $45.00　　　**MIB** Sec. Mkt. **$50-75**

QHG360-6　BILL'S BOARDS: WELCOME SIGN ☐
Comments:　*FIRST IN SERIES*
☐ Purchased 19 __Pd $____MIB　　　NB　DB　BNT
☐ Want　　Orig. Ret. $30.00　　　**MIB** Sec. Mkt. **$35**

QHG360-1　KC'S GARAGE ☐
Comments:　*RETIRED* January 1998, *Limited Edition,* 29,500 pieces.
☐ Purchased 19 __Pd $____MIB　　　NB　DB　BNT
☐ Want　　Orig. Ret. $70.00　　　**MIB** Sec. Mkt. **$75-110**

QHG360-2　PEDAL PETROLEUM GAS PUMP ☐
☐ Purchased 19 __Pd $____MIB　　　NB　DB　BNT
☐ Want　　Orig. Ret. $25.00　　　**MIB** Sec. Mkt. **$30**

QHG360-3　PEDAL POWER PREMIUM LIGHTED GAS PUMP ☐
☐ Purchased 19 __Pd $____MIB　　　NB　DB　BNT
☐ Want　　Orig. Ret. $30.00　　　**MIB** Sec. Mkt. **$30**

QHG360-5　SIDEWALK SALES SIGNS ☐
☐ Purchased 19 __Pd $____MIB　　　NB　DB　BNT
☐ Want　　Orig. Ret. $15.00　　　**MIB.** Sec. Mkt. **$20**

QHG360-4　SIDEWALK SERVICE SIGNS ☐
☐ Purchased 19 __Pd $____MIB　　　NB　DB　BNT
☐ Want　　Orig. Ret. $15.00　　　**MIB** Sec. Mkt. **$20**

1998

1926 STEELCRAFT SPEEDSTER ☐
BY MURRAY®
Comments:　**FIRST IN SERIES, Custom Collection.**
Limited Edition. 29,500 pieces. First in the *Vintage Speedster Series*, this car is packed full of detail that includes leather seats, working suspension and headlights! *Hot Item!*
☐ Purchased 19 __Pd $____MIB　　　NB　DB　BNT
☐ Want　　Orig. Ret. $90.00　　　**MIB** Sec. Mkt. **N.E.**

QHG904-0　1929 STEELCRAFT ROADSTER ☐
BY MURRAY®
Comments:　**Custom Collection, Numbered Edition,**
Limited Edition, 39,500 pieces. *Hot Item!* Featues glass-like windshield, electroplated bright nickel detailing, working pedals and steering wheel.
☐ Purchased 19 __Pd $____MIB　　　NB　DB　BNT
☐ Want　　Orig. Ret. $70.00　　　**MIB** Sec. Mkt. **N.E.**

QHG710-4　1930 CUSTOM BIPLANE ☐
Comments:　**Custom Collection, Numbered Edition,**
10,000 each edition. Yellow 1930 Custom Biplane with striping and star decals, spoked wheels and propeller.
Artist: Don Palmiter
☐ Purchased 19 __Pd $____MIB　　　NB　DB　BNT
☐ Want　　Orig. Ret. $55.00　　　**MIB** Sec. Mkt. **N.E.**

QHG710-5　1930 SPIRIT OF CHRISTMAS ☐
CUSTOM BIPLANE
Comments:　*1998 Hallmark Gold Crown Catalog-Store Exclusive.* The 1930 Spirit of Christmas Custom Biplane is a green plane trimmed in gold, with red wings and propeller. *Hot Item!* **Artist:** Don Palmiter
☐ Purchased 19 __Pd $____MIB　　　NB　DB　BNT
☐ Want　　Orig. Ret. $60.00　　　**MIB** Sec. Mkt. **N.E.**

QHG632-0   1932 KEYSTONE COAST-TO-COAST BUS ☐
Comments: Sidewalk Cruisers Collection, Limited Edition, 29,500 pieces. This 1932 Keystone Coast-to-Coast Bus is blue with a silver top.
☐ Purchased 19 __Pd $____MIB   NB   DB   BNT
☐ Want   Orig. Ret. $45.00   **MIB.** Sec. Mkt. **N.E.**

QHG631-6   1934 MICKEY MOUSE VELOCIPEDE ☐
Comments: Sidewalk Cruisers Collection, Numbered Edition, 10,000 each edition. This 1934 Mickey Mouse Velocipede is green with a brown seat and features Mickey on the fender.
☐ Purchased 19 __Pd $____MIB   NB   DB   BNT
☐ Want   Orig. Ret. $48.00   **MIB** Sec. Mkt. **N.E.**

QHG631-9   1937 DELUXE VELOCIPEDE ☐
Comments: Sidewalk Cruisers Collection, Numbered Edition, 10,000 each edition. The fine lines of this velocipede are enhanced by the pinstriping and chrome-plated body. Also featured are working pedals that turn the front wheel.
☐ Purchased 19 __Pd $____MIB   NB   DB   BNT
☐ Want   Orig. Ret. $45.00   **MIB.** Sec. Mkt. **N.E.**

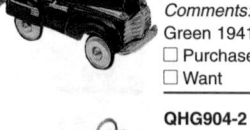

**QHG710-6   1940 CUSTOM ROADSTER
                        WITH TRAILER** ☐
Comments: Custom Collection, Limited Edition, 39,500 pieces. White and red 1940 Custom Roadster with matching trailer.
☐ Purchased 19 __Pd $____MIB   NB   DB   BNT
☐ Want   Orig. Ret. $75.00   **MIB** Sec. Mkt. **N.E.**

**QHG904-4   1941 STEELCRAFT CHRYSLER
                        BY MURRAY®** ☐
Comments: Numbered Edition, 10,000 each edition. Green 1941 Steelcraft Chrysler with silver trim.
☐ Purchased 19 __Pd $____MIB   NB   DB   BNT
☐ Want   Orig. Ret. $55.00   **MIB.** Sec. Mkt. **N.E.**

**QHG904-2   1941 STEELCRAFT FIRE TRUCK
                        BY MURRAY®** ☐
Comments: Custom Collection, Numbered Edition, 10,000 each edition. This traditional red Fire Truck, with green lanterns and working steering wheel and pedals, looks ready for the next alarm.
☐ Purchased 19 __Pd $____MIB   NB   DB   BNT
☐ Want   Orig. Ret. $60.00   **MIB** Sec. Mkt. **N.E.**

QHG710-1   1950 CUSTOM CONVERTIBLE ☐
Comments: Custom Collection, Limited Edition, 10,000 each edition. This numbered edition features a removable convertible, a chrome-like exhaust and a pearlized white finish.
☐ Purchased 19 __Pd $____MIB   NB   DB   BNT
☐ Want   Orig. Ret. $60.00   **MIB** Sec. Mkt. **N.E.**

QHG710-3   1955 CUSTOM CHEVY® ☐
Comments: Custom Collection, Numbered Edition, 10,000 each edition. This 1955 Custom Chevy® is mint green with white.
☐ Purchased 19 __Pd $____MIB   NB   DB   BNT
☐ Want   Orig. Ret. $55.00   **MIB** Sec. Mkt. **N.E.**

QHG904-1   1958 MURRAY® CHAMPION ☐
Comments: Custom Collection, Numbered Edition, 10,000 each edition. The perfect addition to any collection, this Murray Champion features a two-tone color scheme, working pedals and steering wheel which turns the front wheels.
☐ Purchased 19 __Pd $____MIB   NB   DB   BNT
☐ Want   Orig. Ret. $55.00   **MIB** Sec. Mkt. **N.E.**

QHG903-9   1960 EIGHT BALL RACER ☐
Comments: Third in Series, Winner's Circle Collection. A black and white beauty! Black flames roar up the front of the car.
☐ Purchased 19 __Pd $____MIB   NB   DB   BNT
☐ Want   Orig. Ret. $55.00   **MIB** Sec. Mkt. **N.E.**

QHG631-5   1960S SEALTEST MILK TRUCK ☐
Comments: Sidewalk Cruisers Collection.,Numbered Edition, 10,000 each edition. With sliding doors on both sides and a back door which opens, this milk truck is complete with authentic markings.
☐ Purchased 19 __Pd $____MIB   NB   DB   BNT
☐ Want   Orig. Ret. $40.00   **MIB** Sec. Mkt. **N.E.**

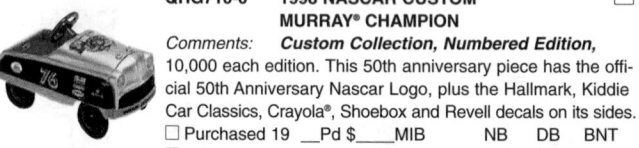

**QHG710-0   1998 NASCAR CUSTOM
                        MURRAY® CHAMPION** ☐
Comments: Custom Collection, Numbered Edition, 10,000 each edition. This 50th anniversary piece has the official 50th Anniversary Nascar Logo, plus the Hallmark, Kiddie Car Classics, Crayola®, Shoebox and Revell decals on its sides.
☐ Purchased 19 __Pd $____MIB   NB   DB   BNT
☐ Want   Orig. Ret. $60.00   **MIB** Sec. Mkt. **N.E.**

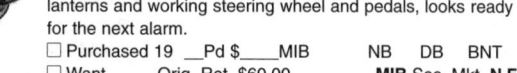

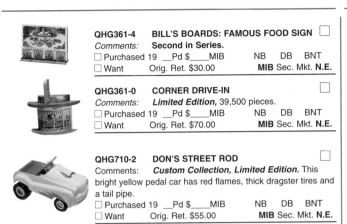

QHG361-4   BILL'S BOARDS: FAMOUS FOOD SIGN ☐
Comments: **Second in Series.**
☐ Purchased 19 __ Pd $____MIB   NB   DB   BNT
☐ Want   Orig. Ret. $30.00   **MIB** Sec. Mkt. **N.E.**

QHG361-0   CORNER DRIVE-IN ☐
Comments: **Limited Edition,** 39,500 pieces.
☐ Purchased 19 __ Pd $____MIB   NB   DB   BNT
☐ Want   Orig. Ret. $70.00   **MIB** Sec. Mkt. **N.E.**

QHG710-2   DON'S STREET ROD ☐
Comments: **Custom Collection, Limited Edition.** This
bright yellow pedal car has red flames, thick dragster tires and
a tail pipe.
☐ Purchased 19 __ Pd $____MIB   NB   DB   BNT
☐ Want   Orig. Ret. $55.00   **MIB** Sec. Mkt. **N.E.**

QHG360-8   MECHANIC'S LIFT ☐
Comments: **Limited Edition.**
☐ Purchased 19 __ Pd $____MIB   NB   DB   BNT
☐ Want   Orig. Ret. $25.00   **MIB** Sec. Mkt. **N.E.**

QHG361-1   MENU STATION WITH FOOD TRAYS ☐
Comments: A nice addition to any collection.
☐ Purchased 19 __ Pd $____MIB   NB   DB   BNT
☐ Want   Orig. Ret. $30.00   **MIB** Sec. Mkt. **N.E.**

QHG361-3   NEWSPAPER BOX & TRASH CAN SET ☐
Comments: A must have for Kiddie Car Collectors.
☐ Purchased 19 __ Pd $____MIB   NB   DB   BNT
☐ Want   Orig. Ret. $20.00   **MIB** Sec. Mkt. **N.E.**

QHG360-9   KC'S OIL CART ☐
Comments: **Limited Edition.**
☐ Purchased 19 __ Pd $____MIB   NB   DB   BNT
☐ Want   Orig. Ret. $15.00   **MIB** Sec. Mkt. **N.E.**

Growing Up With Kiddies!

WOW!
It's a Steelcraft
Auburn, only 24,500
ever made!

CONTACT!

Just look how
Nicholas Hamrick,
son of David and
Janice Hamrick,
has grown!

Merry Miniatures Collection

All values signify mint condition.

1974
Everyday

EPF1433   RAGGEDY ANDY ☐
Issued 1974.
☐ Purch 19__Pd $____   Orig. Ret. $1.25
☐ Want   Sec. Mkt. **$120**

PF1432   RAGGEDY ANN ☐
Issued 1974.
☐ Purch 19__Pd $____   Orig. Ret. $1.25
☐ Want   Sec. Mkt. **$115**

Easter

EPF186   BUNNY ☐
Issued 1974.
☐ Purch 19__Pd $____   Orig. Ret. $.59
☐ Want   Sec. Mkt. **$700**

EPF206   CHICK ☐
Issued 1974.
☐ Purch 19__Pd $____   Orig. Ret. $1.59
☐ Want   Sec. Mkt. **$700**

EPF193   CHILD ☐
Issued 1974.
☐ Purch 19__Pd $____   Orig. Ret. $.50
☐ Want   Sec. Mkt. **$700**

Halloween

HPF   SCARECROW ☐
Issued 1974, *RARE¡*
☐ Purch 19__Pd $____   Orig. Ret. $1.00
☐ Want   Sec. Mkt. **$425**

HPF502   JACK-O-LANTERN ☐
Issued 1974.
☐ Purch 19__Pd $____   Orig. Ret. $.75
☐ Want   Sec. Mkt. **$50**

Thanksgiving

TPF13   PILGRIMS ☐
Issued 1974, *RARE¡*
☐ Purch 19__Pd $____   Orig. Ret. $1.00
☐ Want   Sec. Mkt. **$250**

TPF13   TURKEY ☐
Issued 1974, *RARE¡*
☐ Purch 19__Pd $____   Orig. Ret. $.75
☐ Want   Sec. Mkt. **$380**

Christmas

XPF506   ANGEL ☐
Issued 1974.
☐ Purch 19__Pd $____   Orig. Ret. $1.25
☐ Want   Sec. Mkt. **$380**

XPF493   REINDEER ☐
Issued 1974.
☐ Purch 19__Pd $____   Orig. Ret. $1.25
☐ Want   Sec. Mkt. **$475**

XPF486   SANTA ☐
Issued 1974.
☐ Purch 19__Pd $____   Orig. Ret. $1.25
☐ Want   Sec. Mkt. **$450**

Photo
Not
Available

XPF   SNOWMAN ☐
(waving right hand)
Issued 1974, *RARE¡*
☐ Purch 19__Pd $____   Orig. Ret. $1.25
☐ Want   Sec. Mkt. **N.E.**

XPF473   SNOWMAN ☐
(waving left hand)
Issued 1974.
☐ Purch 19__Pd $____   Orig. Ret. $1.25
☐ Want   Sec. Mkt. **$300**

1975
Everyday

EPF49   BUNNY ☐
Issued 1975.
☐ Purch 19__Pd $____   Orig. Ret. $1.25
☐ Want   Sec. Mkt. **$700**

EPF69   DUCK ☐
Issued 1975.
☐ Purch 19__Pd $____   Orig. Ret. $1.25
☐ Want   Sec. Mkt. **$700**

EPF57   GIRL ☐
Issued 1975, *RARE*
☐ Purch 19__Pd $____   Orig. Ret. $1.25
☐ Want   Sec. Mkt. **$600**

Halloween

HPF29   DEVIL ☐
Issued 1975.
☐ Purch 19__Pd $____   Orig. Ret. $1.25
☐ Want   Sec. Mkt. **$ 380**

Thanksgiving

TPF29   INDIAN ☐
Issued 1975.
☐ Purch 19__Pd $____   Orig. Ret. $1.25
☐ Want   Sec. Mkt. **$65**

Christmas

XPF49   SANTA ☐
Issued 1975.
☐ Purch 19__Pd $____   Orig. Ret. $1.25
☐ Want   Sec. Mkt. **$300**

1976

St. Patrick's Day

SPF266   PIPE
Issued 1976.
☐ Purch 19__ Pd $____   Orig. Ret. $.89
☐ Want   Sec. Mkt. **$150**

Halloween

HPF515   OWL
Issued 1976, *RARE!*
☐ Purch 19__ Pd $____   Orig. Ret. $1.00
☐ Want   Sec. Mkt. **$330**

HPF522   SCARECROW
Issued 1976, *RARE!*
☐ Purch 19__ Pd $____   Orig. Ret. $1.00
☐ Want   Sec. Mkt. **$300**

Thanksgiving

TPF512   TURKEY
Issued 1976. (w/eyelash)
☐ Purch 19__ Pd $____   Orig. Ret. $1.00
☐ Want   Sec. Mkt. **$150**

TPF502   PILGRIMS
"Give Thanks"
Issued 1976.
☐ Purch 19__ Pd $____   Orig. Ret. $1.00
☐ Want   Sec. Mkt. **$225**

Christmas

XPF151   BETSEY CLARK
Issued 1976.
☐ Purch 19__ Pd $____   Orig. Ret. $1.25
☐ Want   Sec. Mkt. **$275**

XPF144   DRUMMER BOY
Issued 1976.
☐ Purch 19__ Pd $____   Orig. Ret. $1.25
☐ Want   Sec. Mkt. **$250**

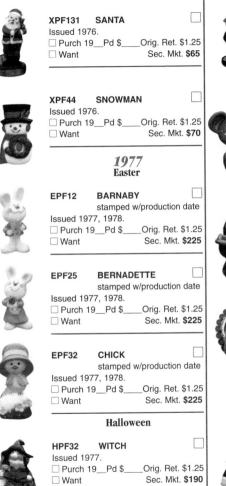

XPF131   SANTA   ☐
Issued 1976.
☐ Purch 19__ Pd $____   Orig. Ret. $1.25
☐ Want   Sec. Mkt. **$65**

XPF44   SNOWMAN   ☐
Issued 1976.
☐ Purch 19__ Pd $____   Orig. Ret. $1.25
☐ Want   Sec. Mkt. **$70**

1977

Easter

EPF12   BARNABY   ☐
stamped w/production date
Issued 1977, 1978.
☐ Purch 19__ Pd $____   Orig. Ret. $1.25
☐ Want   Sec. Mkt. **$225**

EPF25   BERNADETTE   ☐
stamped w/production date
Issued 1977, 1978.
☐ Purch 19__ Pd $____   Orig. Ret. $1.25
☐ Want   Sec. Mkt. **$225**

EPF32   CHICK   ☐
stamped w/production date
Issued 1977, 1978.
☐ Purch 19__ Pd $____   Orig. Ret. $1.25
☐ Want   Sec. Mkt. **$225**

Halloween

HPF32   WITCH   ☐
Issued 1977.
☐ Purch 19__ Pd $____   Orig. Ret. $1.25
☐ Want   Sec. Mkt. **$190**

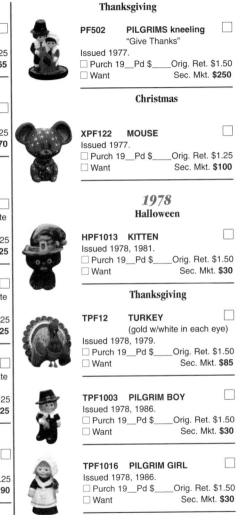

Thanksgiving

PF502   PILGRIMS kneeling   ☐
"Give Thanks"
Issued 1977.
☐ Purch 19__ Pd $____   Orig. Ret. $1.50
☐ Want   Sec. Mkt. **$250**

Christmas

XPF122   MOUSE   ☐
Issued 1977.
☐ Purch 19__ Pd $____   Orig. Ret. $1.25
☐ Want   Sec. Mkt. **$100**

1978

Halloween

HPF1013   KITTEN   ☐
Issued 1978, 1981.
☐ Purch 19__ Pd $____   Orig. Ret. $1.50
☐ Want   Sec. Mkt. **$30**

Thanksgiving

TPF12   TURKEY   ☐
(gold w/white in each eye)
Issued 1978, 1979.
☐ Purch 19__ Pd $____   Orig. Ret. $1.50
☐ Want   Sec. Mkt. **$85**

TPF1003   PILGRIM BOY   ☐
Issued 1978, 1986.
☐ Purch 19__ Pd $____   Orig. Ret. $1.50
☐ Want   Sec. Mkt. **$30**

TPF1016   PILGRIM GIRL   ☐
Issued 1978, 1986.
☐ Purch 19__ Pd $____   Orig. Ret. $1.50
☐ Want   Sec. Mkt. **$30**

Christmas

XPF1003　JOY ELF
Issued 1978.
☐ Purch 19__Pd $____ Orig. Ret. $1.50
☐ Want　　　　　Sec. Mkt. **$120**

Photo
Not
Available

XPF33　SNOWMAN
w/cane & top hat
Issued 1978.
☐ Purch 19__Pd $____ Orig. Ret. $1.50
☐ Want　　　　　Sec. Mkt. **$260**

XPF23　MRS. SNOWMAN
w/purse
Issued 1978, 1979.
☐ Purch 19__Pd $____ Orig. Ret. $1.50
☐ Want　　　　　Sec. Mkt. **$100**

1979
Valentine's Day

VPF1007　LOVE
(resembles carved wood)
Issued 1979 & 1981.
☐ Purch 19__Pd $____ Orig. Ret. $1.50
☐ Want　　　　　Sec. Mkt. **$130**

Easter

EPF397　DUCK
Issued 1979, 1981, Flocked.
☐ Purch 19__Pd $____ Orig. Ret. $2.00
☐ Want　　　　　Sec. Mkt. **$60**

EPF377　BUNNY
Issued 1979, 1980, Flocked.
☐ Purch 19__Pd $____ Orig. Ret. $2.00
☐ Want　　　　　Sec. Mkt. **$95**

Christmas

XPF1017　MOUSE
Issued 1979, 1980.
☐ Purch 19__Pd $____ Orig. Ret. $1.50
☐ Want　　　　　Sec. Mkt. **$125**

1980
Valentine's Day

VPF3451　TURTLE
Issued 1980, 1981
☐ Purch 19__Pd $____ Orig. Ret. $2.00
☐ Want　　　　　Sec. Mkt. **$50**

St. Patrick's Day

SPF1017　PIPE
Issued 1980, *RARE!*
☐ Purch 19__Pd $____ Orig. Ret. $.75
☐ Want　　　　　Sec. Mkt. **$65**

Thanksgiving

TPF3441　TURKEY
Issued 1980.
☐ Purch 19__Pd $____ Orig. Ret. $2.00
☐ Want　　　　　Sec. Mkt. **$85**

Christmas

XPF3471　ANGEL
Issued 1980.
☐ Purch 19__Pd $____ Orig. Ret. $3.00
☐ Want　　　　　Sec. Mkt. **$40**

XPF3421　KITTEN
Issued 1980, 1981.
☐ Purch 19__Pd $____ Orig. Ret. $3.00
☐ Want　　　　　Sec. Mkt. **$40**

XPF39　SANTA
Issued 1980, 1981.
☐ Purch 19__Pd $____ Orig. Ret. $3.00
☐ Want　　　　　Sec. Mkt. **$30**

XPF3451　SLEIGH
Stamped w/production date
Issued 1980, 1981.
☐ Purch 19__Pd $____ Orig. Ret. $3.00
☐ Want　　　　　Sec. Mkt. **$50**

XPF3464　REINDEER
Stamped w/production date
Issued 1980, 1982.
☐ Purch 19__Pd $____ Orig. Ret. $3.00
☐ Want　　　　　Sec. Mkt. **$100**

1981
Valentine's Day

VPF3465　CUPID
Issued 1981, 1982.
☐ Purch 19__Pd $____ Orig. Ret. $3.00
☐ Want　　　　　Sec. Mkt. **$60**

St. Patrick's Day

SHA3415　TUMBLING LEPRECHAUN
Issued 1981.
☐ Purch 19__Pd $____ Orig. Ret. $3.00
☐ Want　　　　　Sec.Mkt. **$60**

Easter

EPF402　LAMB
Issued 1981, 1982, Flocked.
☐ Purch 19__Pd $____ Orig. Ret. $3.00
☐ Want　　　　　Sec. Mkt. **$30**

Halloween

HHA3402 GHOST
Issued 1981, 1982.
☐ Purch 19__ Pd $____ Orig. Ret. $3.00
☐ Want   Sec. Mkt. **$300**

Thanksgiving

THA3402 RACCOON PILGRIM
Issued 1981, 1982.
☐ Purch 19__ Pd $____ Orig. Ret. $3.00
☐ Want   Sec. Mkt. **$50**

THA3415 SQUIRREL INDIAN
        (headband w/real feather)
Issued 1981, 1982.
☐ Purch 19__ Pd $____ Orig. Ret. $3.00
☐ Want   Sec. Mkt. **$50**

THA22   TURKEY
Issued 1981, 1982.
☐ Purch 19__ Pd $____ Orig. Ret. $3.00
☐ Want   Sec. Mkt. **$53**

Christmas

XHA3412 PENGUIN
Issued 1981, 1982.
☐ Purch 19__ Pd $____ Orig. Ret. $3.00
☐ Want   Sec. Mkt. **$100**

XHA3405 REDBIRD
Issued 1981, 1982.
☐ Purch 19__ Pd $____ Orig. Ret. $3.00
☐ Want   Sec. Mkt. **$40**

Table Trimmers

HA4906   KITTEN
Issued 1981.
☐ Purch 19__ Pd $____ Orig. Ret. $6.95
☐ Want   Sec. Mkt. **$150**

HA4905   MOUSE
Issued 1981.
☐ Purch 19__ Pd $____ Orig. Ret. $6.95
☐ Want   Sec. Mkt. **$150**

HA4902   PUPPY
Issued 1981.
☐ Purch 19__ Pd $____ Orig. Ret. $6.95
☐ Want   Sec. Mkt. **$160**

HA4901   SQUIRREL
Issued 1981.
☐ Purch 19__ Pd $____ Orig. Ret. $6.95
☐ Want   Sec. Mkt. **$150**

1982
Valentine's Day

VHA3403 KERMIT
        "Prince of Hearts"
Issued 1982, 1983.
☐ Purch 19__ Pd $____ Orig. Ret. $3.95
☐ Want   Sec. Mkt. **$30**

VHA3416 MISS PIGGY
Issued 1982, 1983.
☐ Purch 19__ Pd $____ Orig. Ret. $3.95
☐ Want   Sec. Mkt. **$30**

Easter

EHA3403 DUCK
Issued 1982, 1983.
☐ Purch 19__ Pd $____ Orig. Ret. $3.95
☐ Want   Sec. Mkt. **$30**

EPF3702 CERAMIC BUNNY
        (Promo Piece)
Issued 1982.
☐ Purch 19__ Pd $____ Orig. Ret. $3.00
☐ Want   Sec. Mkt. **$50**

Halloween

HHA3466 KITTEN
Issued 1982, Flocked.
☐ Purch 19__ Pd $____ Orig. Ret. $3.95
☐ Want   Sec. Mkt. **$55**

HHA3456 WITCH
Issued 1982, *RARE!*
☐ Purch 19__ Pd $____ Orig. Ret. $3.95
☐ Want   Sec. Mkt. **$400**

HHA3446 JACK-O-LANTERN
Issued 1982.
☐ Purch 19__ Pd $____ Orig. Ret. $3.95
☐ Want   Sec. Mkt. **$95**

Thanksgiving

THA3433 PILGRIM MOUSE
Issued 1982, 1983.
☐ Purch 19__ Pd $____ Orig. Ret. $2.95
☐ Want   Sec. Mkt. **$225**

Christmas

XHA5023 MOUSE
Issued 1982, 1983.
☐ Purch 19__ Pd $____ Orig. Ret. $4.50
☐ Want   Sec. Mkt. **$65**

XHA5003 ROCKING HORSE ☐
Issued 1982, 1983.
☐ Purch 19__ Pd $____ Orig. Ret. $4.50
☐ Want   Sec. Mkt. **$100**

XHA5016 SANTA ☐
Issued 1982.
☐ Purch 19__ Pd $____ Orig. Ret. $4.50
☐ Want   Sec. Mkt. **$190**

XHA5013 TEDDY BEAR ☐
Issued 1982, 1985, Container.
☐ Purch 19__ Pd $____ Orig. Ret. $4.50
☐ Want   Sec. Mkt. **$25**

XHA5006 TREE ☐
Issued 1982, 1985.
☐ Purch 19__ Pd $____ Orig. Ret. $4.50
☐ Want   Sec. Mkt. **$150**

Cake Decorations

CDB8820 DRAGON ☐
Issued 1982.
☐ Purch 19__ Pd $____ Orig. Ret. $7.50
☐ Want   Sec. Mkt. **$100**

CDB8818 LITTLE BO PEEP ☐
Issued 1982.
☐ Purch 19__ Pd $____ Orig. Ret. $7.50
☐ Want   Sec. Mkt. **$45**

CDB8821 MICKEY MOUSE,
        The Sorcerer's Apprentice ☐
Issued 1982.
☐ Purch 19__ Pd $____ Orig. Ret. $7.50
☐ Want   Sec. Mkt. **$90**

CDB8819 SOLDIER BOY ☐
Issued 1982.
☐ Purch 19__ Pd $____ Orig. Ret. $7.50
☐ Want   Sec. Mkt. **$40**

Table Trimmers

EHA1053 BUNNY ☐
Issued 1982.
☐ Purch 19__ Pd $____ Orig. Ret. $6.95
☐ Want   Sec. Mkt. **$200**

1983
Valentine's Day

VHA4099 CUPID ☐
Issued 1983, Dated 1983.
☐ Purch 19__ Pd $____ Orig. Ret. $5.50
☐ Want   **MIB**Sec. Mkt. **$350**

VHA3497 CHERUB ☐
Issued 1983, 1984.
☐ Purch 19__ Pd $____ Orig. Ret. $3.50
☐ Want   Sec. Mkt. **$30**

VHA3489 KITTEN ☐
Issued 1983, 1984.
☐ Purch 19__ Pd $____ Orig. Ret. $3.50
☐ Want   Sec. Mkt. **$100**

VHA4107 HEDGEHOG ☐
Issued 1983, 1984, Container.
☐ Purch 19__ Pd $____ Orig. Ret. $3.50
☐ Want   Sec. Mkt. **$100**

St. Patrick's Day

SHA3407 WHITE MOUSE ☐
Issued 1983, 1984, Flocked.
☐ Purch 19__ Pd $____ Orig. Ret. $3.50
☐ Want   Sec. Mkt. **$20**

Easter

EHA2429 BETSEY CLARK ☐
Issued 1983, 1984.
☐ Purch 19__ Pd $____ Orig. Ret. $3.50
☐ Want   Sec. Mkt. **$33**

EHA4117 BUNNY ☐
Issued 1983, Container.
☐ Purch 19__ Pd $____ Orig. Ret. $3.50
☐ Want   Sec. Mkt. **$35**

EHA4089 BUNNY & FLOWER ☐
Issued 1983, 1984, Frosted Lucite.
☐ Purch 19__ Pd $____ Orig. Ret. $6.50
☐ Want   **MIB**Sec. Mkt. **$300**

EHA3469 CHICK ☐
Issued 1983, 1985, Flocked.
☐ Purch 19__ Pd $____ Orig. Ret. $2.50
☐ Want   Sec. Mkt. **$240**

EHA3477 DUCK ☐
Issued 1983, 1985, Flocked.
☐ Purch 19__ Pd $____ Orig. Ret. $2.50
☐ Want   Sec. Mkt. **$240**

EHA3457 BUNNY ☐
Issued 1983, 1987.
☐ Purch 19__ Pd $____ Orig. Ret. $2.50
☐ Want   Sec. Mkt. **$15**

EHA3417 FLOCKED BUNNY ☐
Issued 1983, 1987.
☐ Purch 19__ Pd $____ Orig. Ret. $3.50
☐ Want   Sec. Mkt. **$15**

Halloween

HHA3437 SHIRT TALES
Issued 1983.
☐ Purch 19__ Pd $____ Orig. Ret. $2.95
☐ Want   Sec. Mkt. **$40**

Thanksgiving

THA207 TURKEY
Issued 1983, 1984. (w/wavy blue lines on back)
☐ Purch 19__ Pd $____ Orig. Ret. $2.95
☐ Want   Sec. Mkt. **$43**

Christmas

XHA3467 ANGEL
Issued 1983.
☐ Purch 19__ Pd $____ Orig. Ret. $2.00
☐ Want   Sec. Mkt. **$50**

XHA3487 ANIMALS
Issued 1983, 1985, (Raccoon, Rabbit, Hedgehog).
☐ Purch 19__ Pd $____ Orig. Ret. $7.50
☐ Want   Sec. Mkt. **$40**

XHA3419 DEER
Issued 1983, Flocked.
☐ Purch 19__ Pd $____ Orig. Ret. $3.50
☐ Want   Sec. Mkt. **$53**

XHA3447 KITTEN
Issued 1983, 1985.
☐ Purch 19__ Pd $____ Orig. Ret. $2.00
☐ Want   Sec. Mkt. **$45**

XHA3459 MOUSE
Issued 1983, 1985.
☐ Purch 19__ Pd $____ Orig. Ret. $2.00
☐ Want   Sec. Mkt. **$42**

XHA3439 PENGUIN
Issued 1983, 1985.
☐ Purch 19__ Pd $____ Orig. Ret. $2.95
☐ Want   Sec. Mkt. **$75**

XHA3407 POLAR BEAR
Issued 1983, Dated 1983.
☐ Purch 19__ Pd $____ Orig. Ret. $3.50
☐ Want   Sec. Mkt. **$225**

XHA3427 SANTA
Issued 1983, 1984, Bag reads, "Rooftop Deliveries."
☐ Purch 19__ Pd $____ Orig. Ret. $2.95
☐ Want   Sec. Mkt. **$43**

XHA3479 SNOWMAN
Issued 1983, 1984, (waving left hand).
☐ Purch 19__ Pd $____ Orig. Ret. $2.95
☐ Want   Sec. Mkt. **$40**

1984
Valentine's Day

VHA3451 DOG
Issued 1984,1986, Heart reads, "Be mine."
☐ Purch 19__ Pd $____
Orig. Ret. $2.00
☐ Want   Sec. Mkt. **$55**

VHA3471 PANDA
Issued 1984, 1987, Heart reads, "Luv".
☐ Purch 19__ Pd $____ Orig. Ret. $2.00
☐ Want   Sec. Mkt. **$25**

VHA3464 PENGUIN
Issued 1984, 1985.
☐ Purch 19__ Pd $____ Orig. Ret. $2.00
☐ Want   Sec. Mkt. **$30**

Easter

EHA3461 CHICK
Issued 1984, 1985, Flocked.
☐ Purch 19__ Pd $____ Orig. Ret. $2.00
☐ Want   Sec. Mkt. **$30**

EHA3434 DUCK
Issued 1984, Flocked.
☐ Purch 19__ Pd $____ Orig. Ret. $3.50
☐ Want   Sec. Mkt. **$20**

EHA3401 BROWN BUNNY
Issued 1984, Flocked.
☐ Purch 19__ Pd $____ Orig. Ret. $3.50
☐ Want   Sec. Mkt. **$20**

EHA3474 DUCK
Issued 1984, Flocked.
☐ Purch 19__ Pd $____ Orig. Ret. $2.00
☐ Want   Sec. Mkt. **$33**

EHA4121 EGG
Issued 1984, 1985, Container.
☐ Purch 19__ Pd $____ Orig. Ret. $3.50
☐ Want   Sec. Mkt. **$35**

Halloween

HHA3454 JACK-O-LANTERN
Issued 1984, 1987.
☐ Purch 19__ Pd $____ Orig. Ret. $2.00
☐ Want   Sec. Mkt. **$25**

HHA3441 KITTEN
Issued 1984, 1985, Flocked.
☐ Purch 19__ Pd $____ Orig. Ret. $2.00
☐ Want   Sec. Mkt. **$23**

Thanksgiving

THA3444 HEDGEHOG
Issued 1984, 1985.
☐ Purch 19__ Pd $____ Orig. Ret. $2.00
☐ Want   Sec. Mkt. **$20**

THA3451 MOUSE
Issued 1984, 1985, (w/real feather).
☐ Purch 19__ Pd $____ Orig. Ret. $2.00
☐ Want   Sec. Mkt. **$40**

Christmas

XHA3401 KOALA
Issued 1984, 1985, Flocked.
☐ Purch 19__ Pd $____ Orig. Ret. $2.95
☐ Want   Sec. Mkt. **$30**

XHA3494 PUPPY
Issued 1984, 1985.
☐ Purch 19__ Pd $____ Orig. Ret. $2.00
☐ Want   Sec. Mkt. **$50**

XHA3501 REDBIRD
Issued 1984, 1985.
☐ Purch 19__ Pd $____ Orig. Ret. $2.00
☐ Want   Sec. Mkt. **$45**

XHA3391 RODNEY REINDEER
Issued 1984, 1985.
☐ Purch 19__ Pd $____ Orig. Ret. $2.95
☐ Want   Sec. Mkt. **$38**

XHA3451 SANTA
Issued 1984, 1985, Container.
☐ Purch 19__ Pd $____ Orig. Ret. $4.50
☐ Want   Sec. Mkt. **$30**

XHA3481 SOLDIER
Issued 1984, 1985.
☐ Purch 19__ Pd $____ Orig. Ret. $2.00
☐ Want   Sec. Mkt. **$40**

XHA3464 MOUSE
Issued 1984, 1986.
☐ Purch 19__ Pd $____ Orig. Ret. $4.50
☐ Want   Sec. Mkt. **$40**

Merry Miniatures Greetings

The Merry Miniatures Greetings each came packaged in a box with a cut out, so when the front flap was closed you could see only the faces. Upon opening the flap, the complete Merry Miniatures could be seen.

HA4204 BEAR
Issued 1984, Pot reads, " I Wuv You."
☐ Purch 19__ Pd $____ Orig. Ret. $3.95
☐ Want   **MIB** Sec. Mkt. **$110**

HA4303 BLUEBIRD
Issued 1984, Star reads, " You Brighten My Day."
☐ Purch 19__ Pd $____ Orig. Ret. $3.95
☐ Want   **MIB** Sec. Mkt. **$25**

HA4202 DOG w/scroll
Issued 1984, Scroll reads, "You Are My Sunshine."
☐ Purch 19__ Pd $____ Orig. Ret. $3.95
☐ Want   **MIB** Sec. Mkt. **$125**

HA4301 DUCK
Issued 1984. Kerchief reads, " Howdy."
☐ Purch 19__ Pd $____ Orig. Ret. $3.95
☐ Want   **MIB** Sec. Mkt. **$25**

HA4201 KITTEN
Issued 1984, Banner reads, " Be Happy."
☐ Purch 19__ Pd $____ Orig. Ret. $3.95
☐ Want   **MIB** Sec. Mkt. **$100**

HA4304 LAMB
Issued 1984, Ribbon reads, " Bless You."
☐ Purch 19__ Pd $____ Orig. Ret. $3.95
☐ Want   **MIB** Sec. Mkt. **$60**

HA4203 MOUSE
Issued 1984, Heart reads, "You're Special."
☐ Purch 19__ Pd $____ Orig. Ret. $3.95
☐ Want   **MIB** Sec. Mkt. **$165**

HA4302 RABBIT
Issued 1984, Heart reads, "So Glad We're Friends."
☐ Purch 19__ Pd $____ Orig. Ret. $3.95
☐ Want   **MIB** Sec. Mkt. **$95**

Hugga Bunch

HA3731 BUBBLES
Issued 1984.
☐ Purch 19__ Pd $____ Orig. Ret. $3.25
☐ Want   Sec. Mkt. **$26**

HA3733 HUGGINS
Issued 1984.
☐ Purch 19__ Pd $____ Orig. Ret. $3.25
☐ Want   Sec. Mkt. **$30**

HA3728 HUGSY
Issued 1984.
☐ Purch 19__ Pd $____ Orig. Ret. $3.25
☐ Want   Sec. Mkt. **$19**

HA3734   IMPKINS
Issued 1984.
☐ Purch 19__ Pd $____ Orig. Ret. $3.25
☐ Want   Sec. Mkt. **$20**

HA3721   PATOOTIE
Issued 1984.
☐ Purch 19__ Pd $____ Orig. Ret. $3.25
☐ Want   Sec. Mkt. **$15**

HA3729   PRECIOUS
Issued 1984.
☐ Purch 19__ Pd $____ Orig. Ret. $3.25
☐ Want   Sec. Mkt. **$15**

HA3735   TICKLES
Issued 1984.
☐ Purch 19__ Pd $____ Orig. Ret. $3.25
☐ Want   Sec. Mkt. **$40**

HA3727   TWEAKER
Issued 1984.
☐ Purch 19__ Pd $____ Orig. Ret. $3.25
☐ Want   Sec. Mkt. **$50**

1985
Valentine's Day

VHA3495   KITTEN
Issued 1985, 1986.
☐ Purch 19__ Pd $____ Orig. Ret. $2.00
☐ Want   Sec. Mkt. **$28**

VHA3482   SKUNK
Issued 1985, 1987.
☐ Purch 19__ Pd $____ Orig. Ret. $2.00
☐ Want   Sec. Mkt. **$23**

VHA4112   TEDDY BEAR
Issued 1985, 1987, Container.
☐ Purch 19__ Pd $____ Orig. Ret. $2.00
☐ Want   Sec. Mkt. **$23**

St. Patrick's Day

SHA3452   SHAMROCK
Issued 1985, 1986.
☐ Purch 19__ Pd $____ Orig. Ret. $2.00
☐ Want   Sec. Mkt. **$18**

Easter

EHA3495   BASKET
Issued 1985, 1987.
☐ Purch 19__ Pd $____ Orig. Ret. $2.00
☐ Want   Sec. Mkt. **$43**

EHA3482   BUNNY
Issued 1985, 1987.
☐ Purch 19__ Pd $____ Orig. Ret. $2.00
☐ Want   Sec. Mkt. **$38**

EPR3701   CERAMIC BUNNY
(Promotional piece)
☐ Purch 19__ Pd $____ Orig. Ret. $2.00
☐ Want   Sec. Mkt. **$12**

EHA4132   DUCK
Issued 1985, 1986 Container.
☐ Purch 19__ Pd $____ Orig. Ret. $3.50
☐ Want   Sec. Mkt. **$25**

EHA3442   LAMB
Issued 1985, 1986.
☐ Purch 19__ Pd $____ Orig. Ret. $3.50
☐ Want   Sec. Mkt. **$20**

EHA3455   MOUSE
Issued 1985, 1986, Flocked.
☐ Purch 19__ Pd $____ Orig. Ret. $3.50
☐ Want   Sec. Mkt. **$25**

Halloween
HHA3462   HAUNTED HOUSE
Issued 1985, 1987, Container.
☐ Purch 19__ Pd $____ Orig. Ret. $4.50
☐ Want   Sec. Mkt. **$33**

Thanksgiving
THA3395   TURKEY
Issued 1985, 1986. (Maroon w/orange head).
☐ Purch 19__ Pd $____ Orig. Ret. $2.95
☐ Want   Sec. Mkt. **$20**

Christmas
XHA3392   BEARS
Issued 1985, 1987.
☐ Purch 19__ Pd $____ Orig. Ret. $4.50
☐ Want   Sec. Mkt. **$30**

XHA3482   CAT
Issued 1985, 1987.
☐ Purch 19__ Pd $____ Orig. Ret. $2.00
☐ Want   Sec. Mkt. **$30**

XHA3452   ELF
Issued 1985, 1987, Container.
☐ Purch 19__ Pd $____ Orig. Ret. $4.50
☐ Want   Sec. Mkt. **$25**

XHA3522   GOOSE
Issued 1985, 1987.
☐ Purch 19__ Pd $____ Orig. Ret. $2.50
☐ Want   Sec. Mkt. **$18**

XHA3412 HORSE
Issued 1985, 1987.
☐ Purch 19__ Pd $____ Orig. Ret. $3.50
☐ Want   Sec. Mkt. **$15**

XHA3405 MOUSE
Issued 1985, 1987, "Hallmark" written on candle.
☐ Purch 19__ Pd $____ Orig. Ret. $3.50
☐ Want   Sec. Mkt. **$30**

XHA3495 MR. SANTA
Issued 1985, 1986.
☐ Purch 19__ Pd $____ Orig. Ret. $2.00
☐ Want   Sec. Mkt. **$25**

XHA3502 MRS. SANTA
Issued 1985, 1986.
☐ Purch 19__ Pd $____ Orig. Ret. $2.00
☐ Want   Sec. Mkt. **$35**

XHA3515 ROCKING HORSE
Issued 1985, 1986, Dated 1985, but not in 1986.
☐ Purch 19__ Pd $____ Orig. Ret. $2.00
☐ Want   Sec. Mkt. **$30**

XHA3465 SOLDIER & DRUM
Issued 1985, 1986, Container.
☐ Purch 19__ Pd $____ Orig. Ret. $4.50
☐ Want   Sec. Mkt. **$10**

1986
Valentine's Day

VHA3523 PANDAS
Issued 1986, 1987.
☐ Purch 19__ Pd $____ Orig. Ret. $3.50
☐ Want   Sec. Mkt. **$25**

VHA3516 SEBASTIAN
Issued 1986, 1987.
☐ Purch 19__ Pd $____ Orig. Ret. $2.00
☐ Want   Sec. Mkt. **$80**

VHA3503 UNICORN
Issued 1986, 1987.
☐ Purch 19__ Pd $____ Orig. Ret. $2.00
☐ Want   Sec. Mkt. **$30**

Easter

EHA4143 BASKET
Issued 1986, 1987.
☐ Purch 19__ Pd $____ Orig. Ret. $3.50
☐ Want   Sec. Mkt. **$15**

EPF4133 BUNNY BOY
Issued 1986, 1987.
☐ Purch 19__ Pd $____ Orig. Ret. $2.95
☐ Want   Sec. Mkt. **$19**

EPF4106 BUNNY GIRL
Issued 1986, 1987.
☐ Purch 19__ Pd $____ Orig. Ret. $2.95
☐ Want   Sec. Mkt. **$18**

EHA3476 BUNNY
Issued 1986, 1987.
☐ Purch 19__ Pd $____ Orig. Ret. $3.50
☐ Want   Sec. Mkt. **$18**

EHA3463 DUCK
Issued 1986, 1987.
☐ Purch 19__ Pd $____ Orig. Ret. $2.95
☐ Want   Sec. Mkt. **$15**

EPF4113 DUCK SAILOR
Issued 1986, 1987.
☐ Purch 19__ Pd $____ Orig. Ret. $2.95
☐ Want   Sec. Mkt. **$15**

EHA3503 GIRL BUNNY
Issued 1986, 1987.
☐ Purch 19__ Pd $____ Orig. Ret. $2.00
☐ Want   Sec. Mkt. **$30**

EHA3516 GOOSE
Issued 1986, 1987.
☐ Purch 19__ Pd $____ Orig. Ret. $2.00
☐ Want   Sec. Mkt. **$17**

EPF4126 SHEEP & BELL
Issued 1986, 1987.
☐ Purch 19__ Pd $____ Orig. Ret. $2.95
☐ Want   Sec. Mkt. **$15**

Egg Containers

EHA4156 EGG
Issued 1986, 1989, Geese and Tulips.
☐ Purch 19__ Pd $____ Orig. Ret. $3.50
☐ Want   Sec. Mkt. **$25**

EPF4203 BUTTERFLY
Issued 1986, 1987.
☐ Purch 19__ Pd $____ Orig. Ret. $2.25
☐ Want   Sec. Mkt. **$50**

EPF4163 CHICK
Issued 1986, 1987.
☐ Purch 19__ Pd $____ Orig. Ret. $2.25
☐ Want   Sec. Mkt. **$25**

EPF4246 DUCKS
Issued 1986, 1987.
☐ Purch 19__Pd $____ Orig. Ret. $2.25
☐ Want   Sec. Mkt. **$170**

EPF4183 EGG & RABBITS
Issued 1986, 1987.
☐ Purch 19__Pd $____ Orig. Ret. $2.25
☐ Want   Sec. Mkt. **$25**

EPF4216 FLOWER
Issued 1986, 1987.
☐ Purch 19__Pd $____ Orig. Ret. $2.25
☐ Want   Sec. Mkt. **$40**

EPF4143 HAPPY EASTER
Issued 1986, 1987.
☐ Purch 19__Pd $____ Orig. Ret. $2.25
☐ Want   Sec. Mkt. **$20**

EPF4196 HEARTS
Issued 1986, 1987.
☐ Purch 19__Pd $____ Orig. Ret. $2.25
☐ Want   Sec. Mkt. **$50**

EPF4176 LAMBS
Issued 1986, 1987.
☐ Purch 19__Pd $____ Orig. Ret. $2.25
☐ Want   Sec. Mkt. **$50**

EPF4253 POLKA DOT
Issued 1986, 1987.
☐ Purch 19__Pd $____ Orig. Ret. $2.25
☐ Want   Sec. Mkt. **$25**

EPF4223 RAINBOW
Issued 1986.
☐ Purch 19__Pd $____ Orig. Ret. $2.25
☐ Want   Sec. Mkt. **$25**

EPF4156 STRIPED
Issued 1986, 1987.
☐ Purch 19__Pd $____ Orig. Ret. $2.25
☐ Want   Sec. Mkt. **$20**

EPF4233 TEDDY BEAR
Issued 1986, 1987.
☐ Purch 19__Pd $____ Orig. Ret. $2.25
☐ Want   Sec. Mkt. **$150**

Graduation

GHA3456 OWL
Issued 1986, 1987.
☐ Purch 19__Pd $____ Orig. Ret. $2.00
☐ Want   Sec. Mkt. **$15**

Halloween

HHA3486 CAT
Issued 1986, 1987.
☐ Purch 19__Pd $____ Orig. Ret. $2.00
☐ Want   Sec. Mkt. **$20**

HHS3473 WITCH
Issued 1986.
☐ Purch 19__Pd $____ Orig. Ret. $3.00
☐ Want   Sec. Mkt. **$100**

Thanksgiving

THA3403 MR. SQUIRREL
Issued 1986.
☐ Purch 19__Pd $____ Orig. Ret. $2.00
☐ Want   Sec. Mkt. **$20**

THA3416 MRS. SQUIRREL
Issued 1986.
☐ Purch 19__Pd $____ Orig. Ret. $2.00
☐ Want   Sec. Mkt. **$20**

Christmas

EPF4486 BLUE STAR
Issued 1986, Lucite Container.
☐ Purch 19__Pd $____ Orig. Ret. $2.95
☐ Want   Sec. Mkt. **$35**

XHA3666 KATYBETH
Issued 1986, 1987.
☐ Purch 19__Pd $____ Orig. Ret. $2.00
☐ Want   Sec. Mkt. **$43**

XHA3573 MR. MOUSE
Issued 1986, 1987.
☐ Purch 19__Pd $____ Orig. Ret. $2.00
☐ Want   Sec. Mkt. **$30**

XHA3653 MRS. MOUSE
Issued 1986, 1987.
☐ Purch 19__Pd $____ Orig. Ret. $2.00
☐ Want   Sec. Mkt. **$30**

XHA3533 MOUSE
Issued 1986, 1987.
☐ Purch 19__Pd $____ Orig. Ret. $2.00
☐ Want   Sec. Mkt. **$65**

XHA3473 MOUSE
Issued 1986, 1987, Container.
☐ Purch 19__Pd $____ Orig. Ret. $4.50
☐ Want   Sec. Mkt. **$30**

XHA3486 PENGUIN
Issued 1986, 1987, Container.
☐ Purch 19__ Pd $____ Orig. Ret. $4.50
☐ Want   Sec. Mkt. **$ 25**

XHA4413 PENGUIN
Issued 1986, 1987.
☐ Purch 19__ Pd $____ Orig. Ret. $2.95
☐ Want   Sec. Mkt. **$ 25**

EPF4473 PINK HEART
Issued 1986, Lucite Container.
☐ Purch 19__ Pd $____ Orig. Ret. $2.95
☐ Want   Sec. Mkt. **$70**

XHA3553 RHONDA
Issued 1986, 1987.
☐ Purch 19__ Pd $____ Orig. Ret. $3.50
☐ Want   Sec. Mkt. **$43**

XHA3546 RODNEY
Issued 1986, 1987.
☐ Purch 19__ Pd $____ Orig. Ret. $3.50
☐ Want   Sec. Mkt. **$27**

EPF4466 RODNEY
Issued 1986, Container.
☐ Purch 19__ Pd $____ Orig. Ret. $2.95
☐ Want   Sec. Mkt. **$45**

XHA3673 SANTA
Issued 1986, Container.
☐ Purch 19__ Pd $____ Orig. Ret. $3.50
☐ Want   Sec. Mkt. **$43**

XHA3566 SEBASTIAN
Issued 1986, 1987.
☐ Purch 19__ Pd $____ Orig. Ret. $2.00
☐ Want   Sec. Mkt. **$90**

1987
Valentine's Day

VHA3507 CLOWN TEDDY
Issued 1987.
☐ Purch 19__ Pd $____ Orig. Ret. $2.00
☐ Want   Sec. Mkt. **$15**

VHA3519 GIRAFFE
Issued 1987.
☐ Purch 19__ Pd $____ Orig. Ret. $3.50
☐ Want   Sec. Mkt. **$95**

VHA3527 MOUSE
Issued 1987, Heart reads "Love Ya."
☐ Purch 19__ Pd $____ Orig. Ret. $2.95
☐ Want   Sec. Mkt. **$30**

St. Patrick's Day

SHA3467 MOUSE
Issued 1987.
☐ Purch 19__ Pd $____ Orig. Ret. $2.00
☐ Want   Sec. Mkt. **$15**

Easter

EHA4197 BOY
Issued 1987.
☐ Purch 19__ Pd $____ Orig. Ret. $2.95
☐ Want   Sec. Mkt. **$20**

EHA4179 BUNNY
Issued 1987.
☐ Purch 19__ Pd $____ Orig. Ret. $2.00
☐ Want   Sec. Mkt. **$ 150**

EHA4199 CHICK/EGG
Issued 1987.
☐ Purch 19__ Pd $____ Orig. Ret. $3.50
☐ Want   Sec. Mkt. **$ 15**

EHA4187 GIRL LAMB
Issued 1987.
☐ Purch 19__ Pd $____ Orig. Ret. $2.95
☐ Want   Sec. Mkt. **$ 28**

EHA4167 SEBASTIAN
Issued 1987.
☐ Purch 19__ Pd $____ Orig. Ret. $2.00
☐ Want   Sec. Mkt. **$ 65**

Halloween

HHA3487 RACCOON WITCH
Issued 1987.
☐ Purch 19__ Pd $____ Orig. Ret. $2.00
☐ Want   Sec. Mkt. **$20**

Thanksgiving

THA49 TURKEY
Issued 1987, 1988.
☐ Purch 19__ Pd $____ Orig. Ret. $3.75
☐ Want   Sec. Mkt. **$15**

Christmas

XHA3687   APPLE
Issued 1987, Container.
☐ Purch 19__ Pd $____ Orig. Ret. $4.50
☐ Want   Sec. Mkt. **$23**

XHA3709   BEAR
Issued 1987.
☐ Purch 19__ Pd $____ Orig. Ret. $4.50
☐ Want   Sec. Mkt. **$30**

XHA3729   BUNNY
Issued 1987.
☐ Purch 19__ Pd $____ Orig. Ret. $2.50
☐ Want   Sec. Mkt. **$30**

XHA3737   BUNNY BOY
Issued 1987.
☐ Purch 19__ Pd $____ Orig. Ret. $2.50
☐ Want   Sec. Mkt. **$20**

XHA3749   BUNNY GIRL
Issued 1987.
☐ Purch 19__ Pd $____ Orig. Ret. $2.50
☐ Want   Sec. Mkt. **$20**

XHA3757   FAWN
Issued 1987.
☐ Purch 19__ Pd $____ Orig. Ret. $2.00
☐ Want   Sec. Mkt. **$30**

XHA207   GINGER BEAR
Issued 1987.
☐ Purch 19__ Pd $____ Orig. Ret. $2.00
☐ Want   Sec. Mkt. **$30**

XHA3699   HOUSE
Issued 1987.
☐ Purch 19__ Pd $____ Orig. Ret. $4.50
☐ Want   Sec. Mkt. **$28**

XHA3769   PUPPY
Issued 1987.
☐ Purch 19__ Pd $____ Orig. Ret. $2.00
☐ Want   Sec. Mkt. **$20**

XHA3717   SANTA
Issued 1987, Dated 1987.
☐ Purch 19__ Pd $____ Orig. Ret. $3.50
☐ Want   Sec. Mkt. **$40**

Purrrsonality Cats

PF3847   CALVIN
Issued 1987.
☐ Purch 19__ Pd $____ Orig. Ret. $2.95
☐ Want   Sec. Mkt. **$30**

PF3859   CHUCK
Issued 1987.
☐ Purch 19__ Pd $____ Orig. Ret. $2.95
☐ Want   Sec. Mkt. **$30**

PF3827   ELECTRA
Issued 1987.
☐ Purch 19__ Pd $____ Orig. Ret. $2.95
☐ Want   Sec. Mkt. **$40**

PF3839   FELINA
Issued 1987.
☐ Purch 19__ Pd $____ Orig. Ret. $2.95
☐ Want   Sec. Mkt. **$65**

PF3807   FRANKLIN
Issued 1987.
☐ Purch 19__ Pd $____ Orig. Ret. $2.95
☐ Want   Sec. Mkt. **$150**

PF3879   JOSH
Issued 1987.
☐ Purch 19__ Pd $____ Orig. Ret. $2.95
☐ Want   Sec. Mkt. **$25**

PF3887   LESTER
Issued 1987.
☐ Purch 19__ Pd $____ Orig. Ret. $2.95
☐ Want   Sec. Mkt. **$150**

PF3819   MAUDE
Issued 1987.
☐ Purch 19__ Pd $____ Orig. Ret. $2.95
☐ Want   Sec. Mkt. **$200**

PF3867   TAFFI
Issued 1987.
☐ Purch 19__ Pd $____ Orig. Ret. $2.95
☐ Want   Sec. Mkt. **$30**

1988

Valentine's Day

VHA3624   KOALA
Issued 1988.
☐ Purch 19__ Pd $____ Orig. Ret. $2.00
☐ Want   Sec. Mkt. **$15**

VHA3531 KOALA
Issued 1988.
☐ Purch 19__ Pd $____ Orig. Ret. $2.00
☐ Want   Sec. Mkt. **$10**

VHA3631 KOALA
Issued 1988.
☐ Purch 19__ Pd $____ Orig. Ret. $2.00
☐ Want   Sec. Mkt. **$65**

VHA3651 KOALA
Issued 1988.
☐ Purch 19__ Pd $____ Orig. Ret. $2.00
☐ Want   Sec. Mkt. **$20**

Easter

EBO2591 CHICK
Issued 1988, Mechanical.
☐ Purch 19__ Pd $____ Orig. Ret. $3.50
☐ Want   Sec. Mkt. **$20**

EBO2594 EGG YW
Issued 1988, Mechanical.
☐ Purch 19__ Pd $____ Orig. Ret. $3.50
☐ Want   Sec. Mkt. **$16**

EBO2604 RABBIT
Issued 1988, Wind-up.
☐ Purch 19__ Pd $____ Orig. Ret. $3.50
☐ Want   Sec. Mkt. **$15**

Egg Containers

EBO2384 BUNNIES
Issued 1988.
☐ Purch 19__ Pd $____ Orig. Ret. $1.95
☐ Want   Sec. Mkt. **$18**

EBO2371 CHICK
Issued 1988.
☐ Purch 19__ Pd $____ Orig. Ret. $1.95
☐ Want   Sec. Mkt. **$18**

EBO2381 GOOSE
Issued 1988.
☐ Purch 19__ Pd $____ Orig. Ret. $1.95
☐ Want   Sec. Mkt. **$18**

EBO2374 LAMB
Issued 1988.
☐ Purch 19__ Pd $____ Orig. Ret. $1.95
☐ Want   Sec. Mkt. **$18**

Tin Egg Containers

EBO2314 BOY BUNNY
Issued 1988.
☐ Purch 19__ Pd $____ Orig. Ret. $2.95
☐ Want   Sec. Mkt. **$23**

EBO2311 BUNNY
Issued 1988.
☐ Purch 19__ Pd $____ Orig. Ret. $2.95
☐ Want   Sec. Mkt. **$30**

EBO2321 BUNNY & CARROT
Issued 1988.
☐ Purch 19__ Pd $____ Orig. Ret. $2.95
☐ Want   Sec. Mkt. **$23**

EBO2311 GIRL BUNNY
Issued 1988.
☐ Purch 19__ Pd $____ Orig. Ret. $2.95
☐ Want   Sec. Mkt. **$23**

Graduation

GHA3524 DOG
Issued 1988.
☐ Purch 19__ Pd $____ Orig. Ret. $2.00
☐ Want   Sec. Mkt. **$15**

Halloween

QFM1501 MOUSE/PUMPKIN
Issued 1988.
☐ Purch 19__ Pd $____ Orig. Ret. $2.25
☐ Want   Sec. Mkt. **$65**

QFM1504 OWL
Issued 1988.
☐ Purch 19__ Pd $____ Orig. Ret. $2.25
☐ Want   Sec. Mkt. **$10**

Thanksgiving

QFM1511 INDIAN BEAR
Issued 1988.
☐ Purch 19__ Pd $____ Orig. Ret. $3.25
☐ Want   Sec. Mkt. **$15**

QFM1514 MOUSE
Issued 1988.
☐ Purch 19__ Pd $____ Orig. Ret. $2.25
☐ Want   Sec. Mkt. **$15**

Christmas

QFM1544 KITTEN
Issued 1988.
☐ Purch 19__ Pd $____ Orig. Ret. $2.50
☐ Want   Sec. Mkt. **$20**

QFM1551 MOUSE ANGEL
Issued 1988.
☐ Purch 19__ Pd $____ Orig. Ret. $2.50
☐ Want   Sec. Mkt. **$35**

QFM1521 SANTA
Issued 1988, DATED 1988.
☐ Purch 19__ Pd $____ Orig. Ret. $3.75
☐ Want   Sec. Mkt. **$40**

QFM1541 PENGUIN
Issued 1988.
☐ Purch 19__ Pd $____ Orig. Ret. $3.75
☐ Want   Sec. Mkt. **$22**

QFM1534 SNOWMAN
Issued 1988.
☐ Purch 19__ Pd $____ Orig. Ret. $3.50
☐ Want   Sec. Mkt. **$15**

QFM1524 UNICORN
Issued 1988, Dated 1988.
☐ Purch 19__ Pd $____ Orig. Ret. $3.50
☐ Want   Sec. Mkt. **$40**

QFM1591 TANK CAR
Second in Series, Issued 1988, Dated 1988.
☐ Purch 19__ Pd $____ Orig. Ret. $3.00
☐ Want   Sec. Mkt. **$32**

QFM1531 TRAIN ENGINE
FIRST IN SERIES, Issued 1988.
☐ Purch 19__ Pd $____ Orig. Ret. $3.00
☐ Want   Sec. Mkt. **$20**

Nativity

QFM1581 DONKEY
Issued 1988, 1989.
☐ Purch 19__ Pd $____ Orig. Ret. $2.25
☐ Want   Sec. Mkt. **$10**

QFM1564 JESUS
Issued 1988, 1989.
☐ Purch 19__ Pd $____ Orig. Ret. $2.50
☐ Want   Sec. Mkt. **$25**

QFM1561 JOSEPH
Issued 1988, 1989.
☐ Purch 19__ Pd $____ Orig. Ret. $2.50
☐ Want   Sec. Mkt. **$15**

QFM1574 LAMB
Issued 1988, 1989.
☐ Purch 19__ Pd $____ Orig. Ret. $2.50
☐ Want   Sec. Mkt. **$30**

QFM1554 MARY
Issued 1988, 1989.
☐ Purch 19__ Pd $____ Orig. Ret. $2.50
☐ Want   Sec. Mkt. **$15**

QFM1571 SHEPHERD
Issued 1988, 1989.
☐ Purch 19__ Pd $____ Orig. Ret. $2.50
☐ Want   Sec. Mkt. **$15**

QFM1584 STABLE
Issued 1988, 1989.
☐ Purch 19__ Pd $____ Orig. Ret. $2.50
☐ Want   Sec. Mkt. **$25**

Cosmopolitan Cats
The Cosmopolitan Cats are hand-painted porcelain.
The original came with a small greeting card.

GCT1098 BOY KITTEN
Issued 1988.
☐ Purch 19__ Pd $____ Orig. Ret. $6.50
☐ Want   Sec. Mkt. **$22**

GCT1099 EXERCISE KITTEN
Issued 1988.
☐ Purch 19__ Pd $____ Orig. Ret. $6.50
☐ Want   Sec. Mkt. **$20**

GCT1097 GIRL KITTENS
Issued 1988.
☐ Purch 19__ Pd $____ Orig. Ret. $7.50
☐ Want   Sec. Mkt. **$30**

GCT1096 GIRL KITTENS
Issued 1988.
☐ Purch 19__ Pd $____ Orig. Ret. $7.50
☐ Want   Sec. Mkt. **$30**

GCT1095 GIRL KITTEN
Issued 1988.
☐ Purch 19__ Pd $____ Orig. Ret. $6.50
☐ Want   Sec. Mkt. **$22**

GCT1100 KITTEN/GIFT
Issued 1988.
☐ Purch 19__ Pd $____ Orig. Ret. $6.00
☐ Want   Sec. Mkt. **$20**

GCT1102 KITTEN/HAT
Issued 1988.
☐ Purch 19__ Pd $____ Orig. Ret. $6.00
☐ Want   Sec. Mkt. **$20**

GCT1101 KITTEN/PLANT
Issued 1988.
☐ Purch 19__ Pd $____ Orig. Ret. $6.00
☐ Want   Sec. Mkt. **$20**

QXC5104 SEAL OF FRIENDSHIP
Issued 1988, Dated 1988.
☐ Purch 19__ Pd $____
☐ Want   Sec. Mkt. **$40**

1989
Valentine's Day

QSM1522 BEAR BAKER
Issued 1989.
☐ Purch 19__ Pd $____ Orig. Ret. $3.50
☐ Want   Sec. Mkt. **$18**

QSM1512 BUNNY BALLERINA
Issued 1989.
☐ Purch 19__ Pd $____ Orig. Ret. $2.50
☐ Want   Sec. Mkt. **$19**

QSM1515 DOG & KITTEN
Issued 1989.
☐ Purch 19__ Pd $____ Orig. Ret. $3.50
☐ Want   Sec. Mkt. **$30**

QSM1502 GREY MOUSE
Issued 1989, Heart reads, "Be Mine."
☐ Purch 19__ Pd $____ Orig. Ret. $2.50
☐ Want   Sec. Mkt. **$20**

QSM1505 KITTEN
Issued 1989
☐ Purch 19__ Pd $____ Orig. Ret. $2.50
☐ Want   Sec. Mkt. **$18**

St. Patrick's Day

QSM1525 BEAR WITH MUG
Issued 1989.
☐ Purch 19__ Pd $____ Orig. Ret. $2.50
☐ Want   Sec. Mkt. **$22**

Easter

EBO3092 BUNNY & SKATEBOARD
Issued 1989.
☐ Purch 19__ Pd $____ Orig. Ret. $3.50
☐ Want   Sec. Mkt. **$35**

QSM1552 BUNNY
Issued 1989.
☐ Purch 19__ Pd $____ Orig. Ret. $3.50
☐ Want   Sec. Mkt. **$15**

EBO3215 E. BUNNY
Issued 1989.
☐ Purch 19__ Pd $____ Orig. Ret. $2.95
☐ Want   Sec. Mkt. **$20**

QSM1545 LAMB
Issued 1989.
☐ Purch 19__ Pd $____ Orig. Ret. $3.50
☐ Want   Sec. Mkt. **$20**

Egg Containers

EBO3025 BUNNIES
Issued 1989.
☐ Purch 19__ Pd $____ Orig. Ret. $1.95
☐ Want   Sec. Mkt. **$17**

EBO3032 FLOWERS
Issued 1989.
☐ Purch 19__ Pd $____ Orig. Ret. $1.95
☐ Want   Sec. Mkt. **$17**

EBO3035 HAPPY EASTER
Issued 1989.
☐ Purch 19__ Pd $____ Orig. Ret. $1.95
☐ Want   Sec. Mkt. **$17**

Graduation

QSM1555 OWL
Issued 1989, Dated 1989.
☐ Purch 19__ Pd $____ Orig. Ret. $2.50
☐ Want   Sec. Mkt. **$17**

Halloween

QFM1565 BUNNY GHOST "BOO"
Issued 1989.
☐ Purch 19__ Pd $____ Orig. Ret. $3.00
☐ Want   Sec. Mkt. **$15**

QFM1572 MOUSE WITCH
Issued 1989, Dated 1989.
☐ Purch 19__ Pd $____ Orig. Ret. $2.50
☐ Want   Sec. Mkt. **$20**

QFM1575 RACCOON
Issued 1989, "Happy Halloween"
☐ Purch 19__ Pd $____ Orig. Ret. $3.50
☐ Want   Sec. Mkt. **$10**

Thanksgiving

QFM1585 BABY BOY
Issued 1989, Dated 1989.
☐ Purch 19__ Pd $____ Orig. Ret. $3.00
☐ Want   Sec. Mkt. **$20**

QFM1592 BABY GIRL
Issued 1989, Dated 1989.
☐ Purch 19__ Pd $____ Orig. Ret. $3.00
☐ Want   Sec. Mkt. **$20**

QFM1582 MOMMA BEAR
Issued 1989.
☐ Purch 19__ Pd $____ Orig. Ret. $3.50
☐ Want   Sec. Mkt. **$18**

Christmas

QFM1615   BABY'S 1ST CHRISTMAS
Issued 1989, Dated 1989.
☐ Purch 19__Pd $____Orig. Ret. $3.00
☐ Want   Sec. Mkt. **$15**

QFM1662   BUNNY CAROLER
Issued 1989.
☐ Purch 19__Pd $____Orig. Ret. $3.00
☐ Want   Sec. Mkt. **$15**

QFM1622   ELF
Issued 1989.
☐ Purch 19__Pd $____Orig. Ret. $3.00
☐ Want   Sec. Mkt. **$10**

QFM1605   JOY ELF
Issued 1989.
☐ Purch 19__Pd $____Orig. Ret. $3.00
☐ Want   Sec. Mkt. **$10**

QFM1595   MR. CLAUS
Issued 1989.
☐ Purch 19__Pd $____Orig. Ret. $3.50
☐ Want   Sec. Mkt. **$15**

QFM1602   MRS. CLAUS
Issued 1989.
☐ Purch 19__Pd $____Orig. Ret. $3.50
☐ Want   Sec. Mkt. **$15**

QFM1612   TEACHER ELF
Issued 1989, Dated 1989.
☐ Purch 19__Pd $____Orig. Ret. $3.00
☐ Want   Sec. Mkt. **$9**

QFM1562   TRAIN CAR
Third in Series, Issued 1989.
☐ Purch 19__Pd $____Orig. Ret. $3.50
☐ Want   Sec. Mkt. **$17**

QFM1655   MOUSE CAROLER
Issued 1989.
☐ Purch 19__Pd $____Orig. Ret. $2.50
☐ Want   Sec. Mkt. **$15**

QFM1652   RACCOON CAROLER
Issued 1989.
☐ Purch 19__Pd $____Orig. Ret. $3.50
☐ Want   Sec. Mkt. **$10**

Nativity

QFM1632   BLUE KING
Issued 1989.
☐ Purch 19__Pd $____Orig. Ret. $3.00
☐ Want   Sec. Mkt. **$20**

QFM1642   PINK KING
Issued 1989.
☐ Purch 19__Pd $____Orig. Ret. $3.00
☐ Want   Sec. Mkt. **$10**

QFM1635   YELLOW KING
Issued 1989.
☐ Purch 19__Pd $____Orig. Ret. $3.00
☐ Want   Sec. Mkt. **$12**

QFM1685   STABLE & 9 FIGURINES
Issued 1989, Set included Joseph,
Mary, Jesus, Donkey, Lamb, Shepherd
Stable which debuted in 1988, and the
three Kings.
☐ Purch 19__Pd $___Orig. Ret. $35.50
☐ Want   Sec. Mkt. **$100**

1990
Everyday

QSM1573   ALLIGATOR
Issued 1990.
☐ Purch 19__Pd $____Orig. Ret. $3.00
☐ Want   Sec. Mkt. **$15**

QSM1576   BASEBALL BUNNY
Issued 1990.
☐ Purch 19__Pd $____Orig. Ret. $2.50
☐ Want   Sec. Mkt. **$10**

QFM1716   BEAR & BALLOON
Issued 1990, Balloon reads, "Grin and
Bear It"
☐ Purch 19__Pd $____Orig. Ret. $3.00
☐ Want   Sec. Mkt. **$12**

QFM1706   BIRTHDAY CLOWN
FIRST IN SERIES ,Issued 1990, Dated
1990.
☐ Purch 19__Pd $____Orig. Ret. $3.50
☐ Want   Sec. Mkt. **$20**

QSM1593   BUNNY
Issued 1990
☐ Purch 19__Pd $____Orig. Ret. $3.00
☐ Want   Sec. Mkt. **$11**

QFM1713   BUNNY IN TUX
Issued 1990, Hat reads, "You're Tops."
☐ Purch 19__Pd $____Orig. Ret. $3.00
☐ Want   Sec. Mkt. **$13**

QSM1566   ELEPHANT
Issued 1990, Dated1990, "Happy
Birthday"
☐ Purch 19__Pd $____Orig. Ret. $3.50
☐ Want   Sec. Mkt. **$10**

QFM1703 GET WELL PUPPY
Issued 1990.
☐ Purch 19__ Pd $____ Orig. Ret. $3.00
☐ Want   Sec. Mkt. **$12**

QSM1603 MOUSE
Issued 1990.
☐ Purch 19__ Pd $____ Orig. Ret. $2.50
☐ Want   Sec. Mkt. **$18**

QSM1583 PUPPY
Issued 1990, "100% Huggable."
☐ Purch 19__ Pd $____ Orig. Ret. $2.50
☐ Want   Sec. Mkt. **$15**

QSM1586 RACCOON
Issued 1990.
☐ Purch 19__ Pd $____ Orig. Ret. $3.50
☐ Want   Sec. Mkt. **$14**

Valentine's Day

QSM1533 GRAY MOUSE
Issued 1990.
☐ Purch 19__ Pd $____ Orig. Ret. $2.50
☐ Want   Sec. Mkt. **$15**

QSM1513 HIPPO CUPID
Issued 1990, Dated 1990.
☐ Purch 19__ Pd $____ Orig. Ret. $2.50
☐ Want   Sec. Mkt. **$19**

QSM1516 KITTEN
Issued 1990.
☐ Purch 19__ Pd $____ Orig. Ret. $3.00
☐ Want   Sec. Mkt. **$13**

QSM1526 PIG
Issued 1990.
☐ Purch 19__ Pd $____ Orig. Ret. $3.00
☐ Want   Sec. Mkt. **$17**

QSM1506 STITCHED TEDDY
Issued 1990.
☐ Purch 19__ Pd $____ Orig. Ret. $3.50
☐ Want   Sec. Mkt. **$25**

Easter

QSM1543 ARTIST RACCOON
Issued 1990.
☐ Purch 19__ Pd $____ Orig. Ret. $3.50
☐ Want   Sec. Mkt. **$15**

QSM1536 BABY'S 1ST EASTER
Issued 1990.
☐ Purch 19__ Pd $____ Orig. Ret. $3.00
☐ Want   Sec. Mkt. **$15**

QSM1682 BOY BUNNY
Issued 1990.
☐ Purch 19__ Pd $____ Orig. Ret. $3.00
☐ Want   Sec. Mkt. **$8**

QSM1726 EASTER BUNNY
Issued 1990.
☐ Purch 19__ Pd $____ Orig. Ret. $3.00
☐ Want   Sec. Mkt. **$20**

QSM1675 GIRL BUNNY
Issued 1990.
☐ Purch 19__ Pd $____ Orig. Ret. $3.50
☐ Want   Sec. Mkt. **$15**

QSM1546 MOUSE & BUNNY
Issued 1990, "Happy Easter."
☐ Purch 19__ Pd $____ Orig. Ret. $3.50
☐ Want   Sec. Mkt. **$15**

QSM1553 SQUIRREL
Issued 1990, Dated 1990.
☐ Purch 19__ Pd $____ Orig. Ret. $2.50
☐ Want   Sec. Mkt. **$15**

Graduation

QSM1563 OWL
Issued 1990, "CLASS OF 1990."
☐ Purch 19__ Pd $____ Orig. Ret. $3.00
☐ Want   Sec. Mkt. **$19**

Halloween

QFM1613 GREEN MONSTER
Issued 1990, 1991.
☐ Purch 19__ Pd $____ Orig. Ret. $3.50
☐ Want   Sec. Mkt. **$13**

QFM1616 SCARECROW
Issued 1990, 1991.
☐ Purch 19__ Pd $____ Orig. Ret. $3.50
☐ Want   Sec. Mkt. **$15**

QFM1606 SQUIRREL HOBO
Issued 1990, "Trick or Treat."
☐ Purch 19__ Pd $____ Orig. Ret. $3.00
☐ Want   Sec. Mkt. **$12**

Thanksgiving

QFM1626 INDIAN CHIPMUNK
Issued 1990.
☐ Purch 19__ Pd $____ Orig. Ret. $3.00
☐ Want   Sec. Mkt. **$15**

QFM1636 PILGRIM MOUSE
Issued 1990, 1991.
☐ Purch 19__Pd $____Orig. Ret. $2.50
☐ Want   Sec. Mkt. **$14**

QFM1633 PILGRIM SQUIRREL
Issued 1990, 1991, "Happy
Thanksgiving"
☐ Purch 19__Pd $____Orig. Ret. $3.00
☐ Want   Sec. Mkt. **$14**

QFM1623 THANKFUL TURKEY
FIRST IN SERIES , Issued 1990,
Dated 1990.
☐ Purch 19__Pd $____Orig. Ret. $3.50
☐ Want   Sec. Mkt. **$20**

Christmas
QFM1683 BABY'S 1ST
              POLAR BEAR
Issued 1990, Dated 1990.
☐ Purch 19__Pd $____Orig. Ret. $2.50
☐ Want   Sec. Mkt. **$10**

QFM1693 CANDY CABOOSE
Issued 1990, Dated 1990, 4th in set
☐ Purch 19__Pd $____Orig. Ret. $3.50
☐ Want   Sec. Mkt. **$15**

QFM1686 FIRST CHRISTMAS
              TOGETHER
Issued 1990, Dated 1990.
☐ Purch 19__Pd $____Orig. Ret. $3.50
☐ Want   Sec. Mkt. **$10**

QFM1656 GENTLE PAL — LAMB
FIRST IN SERIES , Issued 1990
☐ Purch 19__Pd $____Orig. Ret. $3.50
☐ Want   Sec. Mkt. **$15**

QFM1663 JINGLE BELL SANTA
FIRST IN SERIES, Issued/Dated 1990.
☐ Purch 19__Pd $____Orig. Ret. $3.50
☐ Want   Sec. Mkt. **$25**

QFM1666 MAMA POLAR BEAR
Issued 1990.
☐ Purch 19__Pd $____Orig. Ret. $3.00
☐ Want   Sec. Mkt. **$15**

QFM1696 SQUIRREL CAROLER
Issued/Dated 1990.
☐ Purch 19__Pd $____Orig. Ret. $3.00
☐ Want   Sec. Mkt. **$20**

QFM1676 TEACHER MOUSE
Issued/Dated 1990.
☐ Purch 19__Pd $____Orig. Ret. $3.00
☐ Want   Sec. Mkt. **$7**

QFM1653 KANGAROO
Issued 1990, 1991, "Hoppy Holidays!"
☐ Purch 19__Pd $____Orig. Ret. $3.50
☐ Want   Sec. Mkt. **$10**

QFM1673 POLAR BEAR & CHILD
Issued 1990, 1991
☐ Purch 19__Pd $____Orig. Ret. $3.50
☐ Want   Sec. Mkt. **$15**

QFM1646 SNOWMAN
Issued 1990, 1991, "Let it Snow."
☐ Purch 19__Pd $____Orig. Ret. $2.50
☐ Want   Sec. Mkt. **$12**

QFM1643 WALRUS
Issued 1990, 1991.
☐ Purch 19__Pd $____Orig. Ret. $2.50
☐ Want   Sec. Mkt. **$14**

QFM1817 AEROBIC BUNNY
Issued 1991
☐ Purch 19__Pd $____Orig. Ret. $2.50
☐ Want   Sec. Mkt. **$20**

QSM1619 BABY BUNNY
Issued 1991, "Baby 1991."
☐ Purch 19__Pd $____Orig. Ret. $3.50
☐ Want   Sec. Mkt. **$12**

QFM1809 BACKPACK
              CHIPMUNK
Issued 1991.
☐ Purch 19__Pd $____Orig. Ret. $2.50
☐ Want   Sec. Mkt. **$18**

QFM1827 BASEBALL BEAR
Issued 1991.
☐ Purch 19__Pd $____Orig. Ret. $3.00
☐ Want   Sec. Mkt. **$21**

QSM1609 BEARS HUGGING
FIRST IN SERIES , Issued/Dated 1991.
☐ Purch 19__Pd $____Orig. Ret. $3.50
☐ Want   Sec. Mkt. **$25**

QSM1617 BIRTHDAY CLOWN
Second in Series, Issued/Dated 1991.
☐ Purch 19__Pd $____Orig. Ret. $3.50
☐ Want   Sec. Mkt. **$20**

QFM1829 FOOTBALL BEAVER
Issued 1991.
☐ Purch 19__Pd $____Orig. Ret. $3.50
☐ Want   Sec. Mkt. **$23**

QSM1657 I LOVE DAD
Issued 1991.
☐ Purch 19__Pd $____ Orig. Ret. $2.50
☐ Want   Sec. Mkt. **$15**

QSM1659 I LOVE MOM
Issued 1991.
☐ Purch 19__Pd $____ Orig. Ret. $2.50
☐ Want   Sec. Mkt. **$15**

QFM1837 SKATING RACCOON
Issued 1991.
☐ Purch 19__Pd $____ Orig. Ret. $3.50
☐ Want   Sec. Mkt. **$23**

QFM1819 SOCCER SKUNK
Issued 1991.
☐ Purch 19__Pd $____ Orig. Ret. $3.00
☐ Want   Sec. Mkt. **$22**

Carrousel Set

QSM1637 BEAR
Issued 1991.
☐ Purch 19__Pd $____ Orig. Ret. $3.00
☐ Want   Sec. Mkt. **$13**

QSM1629 CAMEL
Issued 1991.
☐ Purch 19__Pd $____ Orig. Ret. $3.00
☐ Want   Sec. Mkt. **$13**

QSM1647 ELEPHANT
Issued 1991.
☐ Purch 19__Pd $____ Orig. Ret. $3.00
☐ Want   Sec. Mkt. **$14**

QSM1649 HORSE
Issued 1991.
☐ Purch 19__Pd $____ Orig. Ret. $3.00
☐ Want   Sec. Mkt. **$40**

QSM1639 LION
Issued 1991.
☐ Purch 19__Pd $____ Orig. Ret. $3.00
☐ Want   Sec. Mkt. **$20**

QSM1627 CARROUSEL DISPLAY
Issued 1991.
☐ Purch 19__Pd $____ Orig. Ret. $5.00
☐ Want   Sec. Mkt. **$25**

QSM1667 CARROUSEL GIFT SET
Issued 1991.
☐ Purch 19__Pd $____ Orig. Ret. 20.00
☐ Want   Sec. Mkt. **$125**

Valentine's Day

QSM1519 ARTIST MOUSE
Issued 1991, Dated 1991.
☐ Purch 19__Pd $____ Orig. Ret. $2.50
☐ Want   Sec. Mkt. **$15**

QSM1509 BEAR
FIRST IN SERIES, Issued 1991.
☐ Purch 19__Pd $____ Orig. Ret. $3.50
☐ Want   Sec. Mkt. **$23**

QSM1537 BUNNY
Issued 1991.
☐ Purch 19__Pd $____ Orig. Ret. $3.00
☐ Want   Sec. Mkt. **$15**

QSM1529 PUPPY
Issued 1991.
☐ Purch 19__Pd $____ Orig. Ret. $3.00
☐ Want   Sec. Mkt. **$25**

QSM1517 RACCOON THIEF
Issued 1991, "You Stole My Heart."
☐ Purch 19__Pd $____ Orig. Ret. $3.50
☐ Want   Sec. Mkt. **$13**

St. Patrick's Day

QSM1539 IRISH FROG
Issued 1991.
☐ Purch 19__Pd $____ Orig. Ret. $3.50
☐ Want   Sec. Mkt. **$15**

Easter

QSM1557 BABY'S 1ST — BUNNY
Issued 1991, Dated 1991.
☐ Purch 19__Pd $____ Orig. Ret. $3.50
☐ Want   Sec. Mkt. **$15**

QSM1597 BUNNY PRAYING
Issued 1991
☐ Purch 19__Pd $____ Orig. Ret. $2.50
☐ Want   Sec. Mkt. **$18**

QSM1587 DAUGHTER BUNNY
Issued 1991.
☐ Purch 19__Pd $____ Orig. Ret. $2.50
☐ Want   Sec. Mkt. **$15**

QSM1549 DUCK IN PUDDLE
Issued 1991.
☐ Purch 19__Pd $____ Orig. Ret. $3.00
☐ Want   Sec. Mkt. **$20**

QSM1569 LAMB & DUCK
Issued 1991, "Happy Easter 1991."
☐ Purch 19__ Pd $____ Orig. Ret. $3.50
☐ Want   Sec. Mkt. **$15**

QSM1577 MOTHER BUNNY ☐
Issued 1991.
☐ Purch 19__ Pd $____ Orig. Ret. $3.00
☐ Want   Sec. Mkt. **$15**

Graduation

QSM1607 DOG IN CAP & GOWN ☐
Issued 1991.
☐ Purch 19__ Pd $____ Orig. Ret. $2.50
☐ Want   Sec. Mkt. **$15**

Halloween

QFM1669 BEAR ☐
Issued 1991.
☐ Purch 19__ Pd $____ Orig. Ret. $2.50
☐ Want   Sec. Mkt. **$25**

QFM1677 CAT WITCH ☐
Issued 1991, 1992.
☐ Purch 19__ Pd $____ Orig. Ret. $3.00
☐ Want   Sec. Mkt. **$15**

QFM1679 MUMMY ☐
Issued 1991, 1992.
☐ Purch 19__ Pd $____ Orig. Ret. $2.50
☐ Want   Sec. Mkt. **$15**

Thanksgiving

QFM1689 FOX ☐
Issued 1991, 1992.
☐ Purch 19__ Pd $____ Orig. Ret. $3.50
☐ Want   Sec. Mkt. **$12**

QFM1687 INDIAN MAIDEN MOUSE ☐
Issued 1991, 1992.
☐ Purch 19__ Pd $____ Orig. Ret. $2.50
☐ Want   Sec. Mkt. **$12**

QFM1697 TURKEY ☐
Second in Series, Issued 1991,
Dated 1991.
☐ Purch 19__ Pd $____ Orig. Ret. $3.50
☐ Want   Sec. Mkt. **$20**

Christmas

QFM1797 BABY'S 1ST – ☐
RABBIT
Issued/Dated 1991.
☐ Purch 19__ Pd $____ Orig. Ret. $3.00
☐ Want   Sec. Mkt. **$11**

QFM1769 COOKIE ELF ☐
Issued/Dated 1991.
☐ Purch 19__ Pd $____ Orig. Ret. $3.00
☐ Want   Sec. Mkt. **$10**

QFM1777 COOKIE REINDEER ☐
Issued/Dated 1991.
☐ Purch 19__ Pd $____ Orig. Ret. $3.00
☐ Want   Sec. Mkt. **$10**

QFM1767 COOKIE SANTA ☐
Issued/Dated 1991.
☐ Purch 19__ Pd $____ Orig. Ret. $3.00
☐ Want   Sec. Mkt. **$10**

QFM1799 1ST CHRISTMAS – ☐
KOALAS
Issued/Dated 1991.
☐ Purch 19__ Pd $____ Orig. Ret. $3.50
☐ Want   Sec. Mkt. **$10**

QFM1709 GENTLE PALS KITTEN ☐
Second in Series , Issued/Dated 1991.
☐ Purch 19__ Pd $____ Orig. Ret. $3.50
☐ Want   Sec. Mkt. **$18**

QFM1719 GIFT BRINGER BUNNY ☐
Issued/Dated 1991.
☐ Purch 19__ Pd $____ Orig. Ret. $3.00
☐ Want   Sec. Mkt. **$12**

QFM1729 GIFT BRINGER FROG ☐
Issued/Dated 1991.
☐ Purch 19__ Pd $____ Orig. Ret. $3.00
☐ Want   Sec. Mkt. **$12**

QFM1737 GIFT BRINGER ☐
KITTEN
Issued/Dated 1991.
☐ Purch 19__ Pd $____ Orig. Ret. $3.00
☐ Want   Sec. Mkt. **$12**

QFM1739 GIFT BRINGER PIG ☐
Issued/Dated 1991.
☐ Purch 19__ Pd $____ Orig. Ret. $3.00
☐ Want   Sec. Mkt. **$15**

QFM1727 GIFT BRINGER PUPPY ☐
Issued/Dated 1991.
☐ Purch 19__ Pd $____ Orig. Ret. $3.00
☐ Want   Sec. Mkt. **$14**

QFM1747 GIFT BRINGER TURTLE ☐
Issued/Dated 1991.
☐ Purch 19__ Pd $____ Orig. Ret. $3.00
☐ Want   Sec. Mkt. **$13**

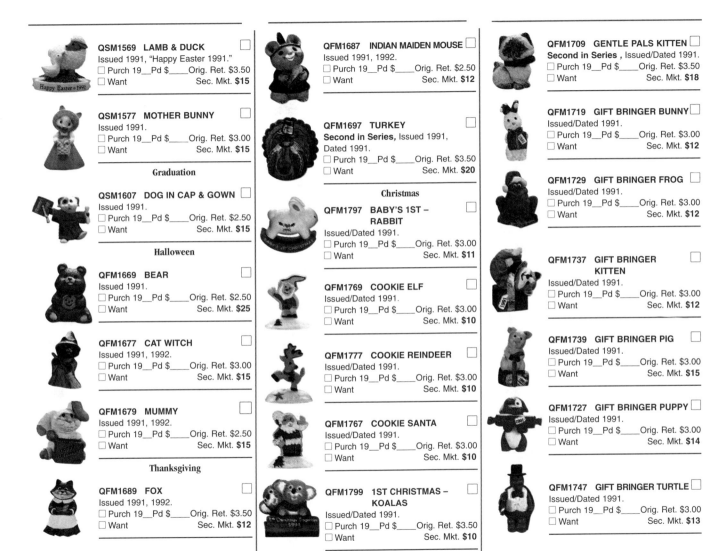

QFM1717 JINGLE BELL SANTA
Second in Series, Issued 1991.
☐ Purch 19__ Pd $____ Orig. Ret. $3.50
☐ Want   Sec. Mkt. **$23**

QFM1789 MOUSE
Issued 1991, 1992.
☐ Purch 19__ Pd $____ Orig. Ret. $2.50
☐ Want   Sec. Mkt. **$10**

QFM1779 MUSIC MAKERS BEAR
FIRST IN SERIES , Issued 1991.
☐ Purch 19__ Pd $____ Orig. Ret. $3.00
☐ Want   Sec. Mkt. **$23**

QFM1787 PUPPY IN BOX
Issued 1991, "Open Me First 1991."
☐ Purch 19__ Pd $____ Orig. Ret. $3.00
☐ Want   Sec. Mkt. **$15**

QFM1749 SNOW BUNNY
Issued 1991,, "Joy."
☐ Purch 19__ Pd $____ Orig. Ret. $2.50
☐ Want   Sec. Mkt. **$12**

QFM1759 SNOW LAMB
Issued 1991, "Peace."
☐ Purch 19__ Pd $____ Orig. Ret. $2.50
☐ Want   Sec. Mkt. **$12**

QFM1757 SNOW MICE
Issued 1991, "Love"
☐ Purch 19__ Pd $____ Orig. Ret. $2.50
☐ Want   Sec. Mkt. **$12**

QFM1807 TEACHER RACCOON
Issued 1991, "For Teacher 91."
☐ Purch 19__ Pd $____ Orig. Ret. $3.50
☐ Want   Sec. Mkt. **$9**

1992
Everyday

QSM9829 KITTEN IN BIB
Issued/Dated 1992.
☐ Purch 19__ Pd $____ Orig. Ret. $3.50
☐ Want   Sec. Mkt. **$12**

QSM9819 BIRTHDAY CLOWN
Third in Series, Issued 1992.
☐ Purch 19__ Pd $____ Orig. Ret. $3.50
☐ Want   Sec. Mkt. **$16**

QSM9847 DOG
Issued 1992.
☐ Purch 19__ Pd $____ Orig. Ret. $3.00
☐ Want   Sec. Mkt. **$18**

QSM9859 HEDGEHOG
Issued 1992.
☐ Purch 19__ Pd $____ Orig. Ret. $2.50
☐ Want   Sec. Mkt. **$12**

QSM9839 KITTEN FOR DAD
Issued 1992, "Best Dad."
☐ Purch 19__ Pd $____ Orig. Ret. $3.50
☐ Want   Sec. Mkt. **$15**

QSM9837 KITTEN FOR MOM
Issued 1992, "Best Mom."
☐ Purch 19__ Pd $____ Orig. Ret. $3.50
☐ Want   Sec. Mkt. **$15**

QFM9191 PARTY DOG
Issued 1992.
☐ Purch 19__ Pd $____ Orig. Ret. $3.00
☐ Want   Sec. Mkt. **$15**

QSM9827 RABBIT & SQUIRREL
Second in Series ,Issued/Dated 1992.
☐ Purch 19__ Pd $____ Orig. Ret. $3.00
☐ Want   Sec. Mkt. **$20**

QFM9201 RABBIT
Issued 1992.
☐ Purch 19__ Pd $____ Orig. Ret. $3.50
☐ Want   Sec. Mkt. **$15**

QSM9849 SEAL
Issued/Dated 1992.
☐ Purch 19__ Pd $____ Orig. Ret. $3.00
☐ Want   Sec. Mkt. **$12**

QFM9184 SKUNK
Issued 1992.
☐ Purch 19__ Pd $____ Orig. Ret. $3.50
☐ Want   Sec. Mkt. **$13**

QFM9194 TEDDY BEAR
Issued 1992.
☐ Purch 19__ Pd $____ Orig. Ret. $2.50
☐ Want   Sec. Mkt. **$15**

QSM9857 TURTLE & MOUSE
Issued 1992.
☐ Purch 19__ Pd $____ Orig. Ret. $3.00
☐ Want   Sec. Mkt. **$25**

Barn Yard Collection

QFM9034 BARNYARD COW ☐
Issued 1992.
☐ Purch 19__Pd $____Orig. Ret. **$2.50**
☐ Want   Sec. Mkt. **$15**

QFM9051 BARNYARD HORSE ☐
Issued 1992.
☐ Purch 19__Pd $____Orig. Ret. **$2.50**
☐ Want   Sec. Mkt. **$19**

QFM9044 BARNYARD LAMB ☐
Issued 1992.
☐ Purch 19__Pd $____Orig. Ret. **$2.50**
☐ Want   Sec. Mkt. **$17**

QFM9041 BARNYARD PIG ☐
Issued 1992.
☐ Purch 19__Pd $____Orig. Ret. **$2.50**
☐ Want   Sec. Mkt. **$20**

Valentine's Day

QSM9759 BALLET PIG ☐
Issued 1992.
☐ Purch 19__Pd $____Orig. Ret. **$2.50**
☐ Want   Sec. Mkt. **$15**

QSM9717 BEAR ☐
Second in Series, Issued 1992.
☐ Purch 19__Pd $____Orig. Ret. **$2.50**
☐ Want   Sec. Mkt. **$20**

QSM9767 PUPPY ☐
Issued 1992.
☐ Purch 19__Pd $____Orig. Ret. **$2.50**
☐ Want   Sec. Mkt. **$27**

QSM9719 LION ☐
Issued 1992.
☐ Purch 19__Pd $____Orig. Ret. **$3.50**
☐ Want   Sec. Mkt. **$13**

QSM9757 PENGUIN IN TUX ☐
Issued/Dated 1992.
☐ Purch 19__Pd $____Orig. Ret. **$3.00**
☐ Want   Sec. Mkt. **$15**

St. Patrick's Day

QSM9769 MOUSE ☐
Issued /Dated 1992.
☐ Purch 19__Pd $____Orig. Ret. **$3.00**
☐ Want   Sec. Mkt. **$11**

Easter

**QSM9777 BABY'S FIRST
        EASTER** ☐
Issued/Dated 1992.
☐ Purch 19__Pd $____Orig. Ret. **$3.50**
☐ Want   Sec. Mkt. **$14**

QSM9779 SWEAT SHIRT BUNNY ☐
Issued 1992.
☐ Purch 19__Pd $____Orig. Ret. **$3.50**
☐ Want   Sec. Mkt. **$17**

QSM9797 PRAYING CHIPMUNK ☐
Issued 1992.
☐ Purch 19__Pd $____Orig. Ret. **$3.00**
☐ Want   Sec. Mkt. **$15**

QSM9789 GOOSE IN BONNET ☐
Issued 1992.
☐ Purch 19__Pd $____Orig. Ret. **$3.00**
☐ Want   Sec. Mkt. **$13**

QSM9787 LAMB ☐
Issued 1992,"Happy Easter 1992."
☐ Purch 19__Pd $____Orig. Ret. **$3.50**
☐ Want   Sec. Mkt. **$15**

QSM9799 BUNNY & CARROT ☐
Issued/Dated 1992.
☐ Purch 19__Pd $____Orig. Ret. **$2.50**
☐ Want   Sec. Mkt. **$15**

Graduation

QSM9817 GRAD DOG ☐
Issued/Dated 1992.
☐ Purch 19__Pd $____Orig. Ret. **$2.50**
☐ Want   Sec. Mkt. **$5**

Halloween

QFM9014 GHOST ☐
Issued 1992, "1992 Boo!"
☐ Purch 19__Pd $____Orig. Ret. **$3.00**
☐ Want   Sec. Mkt. **$15**

QFM9024 HAUNTED HOUSE ☐
Issued 1992.
☐ Purch 19__Pd $____Orig. Ret. **$3.50**
☐ Want   Sec. Mkt. **$13**

QFM9031 MOUSE AS CLOWN ☐
Issued/Dated 1992.
☐ Purch 19__Pd $____Orig. Ret. **$2.50**
☐ Want   Sec. Mkt. **$13**

QFM9021 PUMPKIN ☐
Issued 1992, "Trick or Treat."
☐ Purch 19__Pd $____Orig. Ret. **$3.00**
☐ Want   Sec. Mkt. **$12**

Thanksgiving

QFM9001   TURKEY
Third and Final in Series,
Issued/Dated 1992.
☐ Purch 19__Pd $____Orig. Ret. $3.50
☐ Want   Sec. Mkt. **$20**

QFM9004   INDIAN BUNNIES
Issued 1992.
☐ Purch 19__Pd $____Orig. Ret. $3.50
☐ Want   Sec. Mkt. **$15**

QFM9011   PILGRIM BEAVER
Issued 1992, "Happy Thanksgiving."
☐ Purch 19__Pd $____Orig. Ret. $3.00
☐ Want   Sec. Mkt. **$12**

Christmas

QFM9071   BUNNY in Snow Dome
Issued 1992, Baby's 1st Christmas
1992.
☐ Purch 19__Pd $____Orig. Ret. $4.00
☐ Want   Sec. Mkt. **$10**

QFM9061   BEE
Issued 1992.
☐ Purch 19__Pd $____Orig. Ret. $3.00
☐ Want   Sec. Mkt. **$12**

QFM9144   CHIPMUNK
Issued 1992.
☐ Purch 19__Pd $____Orig. Ret. $2.50
☐ Want   Sec. Mkt. **$10**

QFM9174   CRAB
Issued 1992.
☐ Purch 19__Pd $____Orig. Ret. $3.00
☐ Want   Sec. Mkt. **$10**

QFM9084   DAUGHTER
Issued 1992, "Daughter 1992."
☐ Purch 19__Pd $____Orig. Ret. $3.50
☐ Want   Sec. Mkt. **$14**

QFM9094   GENTLE PAL
Third and Final In Series,
Issued 1992.
☐ Purch 19__Pd $____Orig. Ret. $3.50
☐ Want   Sec. Mkt. **$20**

QFM9141   GIRAFFE AS
**   CHRISTMAS TREE**
Issued 1992.
☐ Purch 19__Pd $____Orig. Ret. $3.00
☐ Want   Sec. Mkt. **$15**

QFM9181   GOLDFISH
Issued 1992.
☐ Purch 19__Pd $____Orig. Ret. $3.00
☐ Want   Sec. Mkt. **$12**

QFM9131   JINGLE BELL SANTA
Third and Final In Series,
Issued/Dated 1992.
☐ Purch 19__Pd $____Orig. Ret. $3.50
☐ Want   Sec. Mkt. **$20**

QFM9114   MOUSE
Issued 1992.
☐ Purch 19__Pd $____Orig. Ret. $3.00
☐ Want   Sec. Mkt. **$13**

QFM9134   MUSIC MAKER BEAR
Second in Series, Issued 1992.
☐ Purch 19__Pd $____Orig. Ret. $3.50
☐ Want   Sec. Mkt. **$15**

QFM9171   OCTOPUS
Issued 1992.
☐ Purch 19__Pd $____Orig. Ret. $3.00
☐ Want   Sec. Mkt. **$10**

QFM9091   PENGUIN ICE SKATING
Issued 1992, "Dinky Rink 92."
☐ Purch 19__Pd $____Orig. Ret. $3.00
☐ Want   Sec. Mkt. **$14**

QFM9151   RABBIT ON SLED
Issued 1992.
☐ Purch 19__Pd $____Orig. Ret. $3.00
☐ Want   Sec. Mkt. **$12**

QFM9121   REINDEER WAVING
Issued/Dated 1992.
☐ Purch 19__Pd $____Orig. Ret. $3.00
☐ Want   Sec. Mkt. **$15**

QFM9081   DOG
Issued 1992, "Son 1992."
☐ Purch 19__Pd $____Orig. Ret. $3.50
☐ Want   Sec. Mkt. **$12**

QFM9064   SQUIRRELS
Issued 1992, "1st Christmas Together
'92."
☐ Purch 19__Pd $____Orig. Ret. $3.50
☐ Want   Sec. Mkt. **$15**

QFM9124   SWEET ANGEL
Issued 1992.
☐ Purch 19__Pd $____Orig. Ret. $3.00
☐ Want   Sec. Mkt. **$23**

QFM9074   TEACHER-CAT
Issued/Dated 1992.
☐ Purch 19__ Pd $____ Orig. Ret. $3.50
☐ Want   Sec. Mkt. **$10**

QFM9054   WALRUS & BIRD
Issued 1992.
☐ Purch 19__ Pd $____ Orig. Ret. $3.50
☐ Want   Sec. Mkt. **$15**

QFM9111   BEAR
Issued 1992.
☐ Purch 19__ Pd $____ Orig. Ret.
☐ Want   **NeverProduced**

Columbus' Ships

QFM9154   NINA SHIP
Issued 1992.
☐ Purch 19__ Pd $____ Orig. Ret. $3.50
☐ Want   Sec. Mkt. **$10**

QFM9161   PINTA SHIP
Issued 1992.
☐ Purch 19__ Pd $____ Orig. Ret. $3.50
☐ Want   Sec. Mkt. **$10**

QFM9164   SANTA MARIA SHIP
Issued 1992.
☐ Purch 19__ Pd $____ Orig. Ret. $3.50
☐ Want   Sec. Mkt. **$10**

1993
Everyday

QFM8055   DISPLAY STAND
Issued 1993.
☐ Purch 19__ Pd $____ Orig. Ret. $6.75
☐ Want   Sec. Mkt. **$7**

At The Beach

QSM8015   BEAR w/SURFBOARD
Issued 1993.
☐ Purch 19__ Pd $____ Orig. Ret. $3.50
☐ Want   Sec. Mkt. **$17**

QSM8005   BUNNY
Issued 1993.
☐ Purch 19__ Pd $____ Orig. Ret. $3.50
☐ Want   Sec. Mkt. **$20**

QSM8002   CHIPMUNK ON INFLATABLE HORSE
Issued 1993.
☐ Purch 19__ Pd $____ Orig. Ret. $3.50
☐ Want   Sec. Mkt. **$15**

QSM8026   HEDGEHOG EATING HOT DOG
Issued 1993.
☐ Purch 19__ Pd $____ Orig. Ret. $3.00
☐ Want   Sec. Mkt. **$10**

QSM8032   HIPPO
Issued 1993.
☐ Purch 19__ Pd $____ Orig. Ret. $3.00
☐ Want   Sec. Mkt. **$14**

QSM8035   MOUSE
Issued 1993.
☐ Purch 19__ Pd $____ Orig. Ret. $2.50
☐ Want   Sec. Mkt. **$15**

QSM8022   PIG IN A BLANKET
Issued 1993.
☐ Purch 19__ Pd $____ Orig. Ret. $3.00
☐ Want   Sec. Mkt. **$20**

QSM8012   PRAIRIE DOG
Issued 1993.
☐ Purch 19__ Pd $____ Orig. Ret. $3.50
☐ Want   Sec. Mkt. **$20**

QSM8045   SANDCASTLE
Issued 1993.
☐ Purch 19__ Pd $____ Orig. Ret. $3.00
☐ Want   Sec. Mkt. **$17**

QSM8042   BEACH SCENE
Issued 1993, Cardboard backdrop.
☐ Purch 19__ Pd $____ Orig. Ret. $1.75
☐ Want   Sec. Mkt. **$6**

Valentine's Day

QSM8095   BOX OF CANDY
Issued 1993.
☐ Purch 19__ Pd $____ Orig. Ret. $2.50
☐ Want   Sec. Mkt. **$20**

QSM8102   CAT HUGGING MOUSE
Third in Series, Issued 1993.
☐ Purch 19__ Pd $____ Orig. Ret. $3.50
☐ Want   Sec. Mkt. **$15**

QSM8092   DOG
Issued 1993, 1994.
☐ Purch 19__ Pd $____ Orig. Ret. $2.50
☐ Want   Sec. Mkt. **$10**

QSM8065   FOX
Issued 1993.
☐ Purch 19__ Pd $____ Orig. Ret. $3.50
☐ Want   Sec. Mkt. **$10**

QSM8082 HEARTLAND FOREST ☐
Issued 1993, Cardboard backdrop.
☐ Purch 19__Pd $____ Orig. Ret. $1.75
☐ Want   Sec. Mkt. **$6**

QSM8105 PANDA ☐
Third in Series, Issued 1993.
☐ Purch 19__Pd $____ Orig. Ret. $3.50
☐ Want   Sec. Mkt. **$15**

**QSM8062 RACCOON WITH
              CUTOUT HEART** ☐
Issued 1993, 1994.
☐ Purch 19__Pd $____ Orig. Ret. $3.50
☐ Want   Sec. Mkt. **$10**

QSM8072 SKUNK ☐
Issued 1993.
☐ Purch 19__Pd $____ Orig. Ret. $3.00
☐ Want   Sec. Mkt. **$10**

**QSM8075 TREE STUMP AND
              PAINT CAN** ☐
Issued 1993, 1994.
☐ Purch 19__Pd $____ Orig. Ret. $3.00
☐ Want   Sec. Mkt. **$13**

Easter

QSM8115 BUNNY PAINTING EGG ☐
Issued 1993.
☐ Purch 19__Pd $____ Orig. Ret. $3.50
☐ Want   Sec. Mkt. **$9**

QSM8142 BUNNY w/BASKET ☐
Issued 1993.
☐ Purch 19__Pd $____ Orig. Ret. $2.50
☐ Want   Sec. Mkt. **$13**

**QSM8125 BUNNY WITH
              CRACKED EGG** ☐
Issued 1993, 1994.
☐ Purch 19__Pd $____ Orig. Ret. $3.00
☐ Want   Sec. Mkt. **$12**

QSM8135 DUCK ☐
Issued 1993.
☐ Purch 19__Pd $____ Orig. Ret. $3.00
☐ Want   Sec. Mkt. **$10**

QSM8145 EASTER BASKET ☐
Issued 1993, 1994.
☐ Purch 19__Pd $____ Orig. Ret. $2.50
☐ Want   Sec. Mkt. **$15**

QSM8152 EASTER GARDEN ☐
Issued 1993, Cardboard backdrop.
☐ Purch 19__Pd $____ Orig. Ret. $1.75
☐ Want   Sec. Mkt. **$6**

**QSM8112 LAMB
              SHEARING SHRUB** ☐
Issued 1993.
☐ Purch 19__Pd $____ Orig. Ret. $3.50
☐ Want   Sec. Mkt. **$10**

**QSM8122 SHERLOCK HOLMES
              DUCK** ☐
Issued 1993.
☐ Purch 19__Pd $____ Orig. Ret. $3.00
☐ Want   Sec. Mkt. **$8**

Patriotic

QSM8472 GOAT UNCLE SAM ☐
Issued 1993.
☐ Purch 19__Pd $____ Orig. Ret. $3.00
☐ Want   Sec. Mkt. **$15**

**QSM8492 HEDGEHOG PATRIOT
              WITH FIFE** ☐
Issued 1993.
☐ Purch 19__Pd $____ Orig. Ret. $3.50
☐ Want   Sec. Mkt. **$10**

**QSM8482 LAMB BETSY ROSS
              w/FLAG** ☐
Issued 1993.
☐ Purch 19__Pd $____ Orig. Ret. $3.50
☐ Want   Sec. Mkt. **$18**

QSM8465 LIBERTY BELL w/Bird ☐
Issued 1993.
☐ Purch 19__Pd $____ Orig. Ret. $2.50
☐ Want   Sec. Mkt. **$17**

**QSM8475 MOUSE STATUE OF
              LIBERTY** ☐
Issued 1993.
☐ Purch 19__Pd $____ Orig. Ret. $3.00
☐ Want   Sec. Mkt. **$18**

QSM8495 PATRIOTIC ☐
Issued 1993, Cardboard backdrop.
☐ Purch 19__Pd $____ Orig. Ret. $1.75
☐ Want   Sec. Mkt. **$10**

Halloween

QFM8285 ANIMATED CAULDRON ☐
Issued 1993.
☐ Purch 19__Pd $____ Orig. Ret. $2.50
☐ Want   Sec. Mkt. **$15**

QFM8285 BEAR Dressed as Bat ☐
Issued 1993.
☐ Purch 19__Pd $____ Orig. Ret. $3.00
☐ Want   Sec. Mkt. **$10**

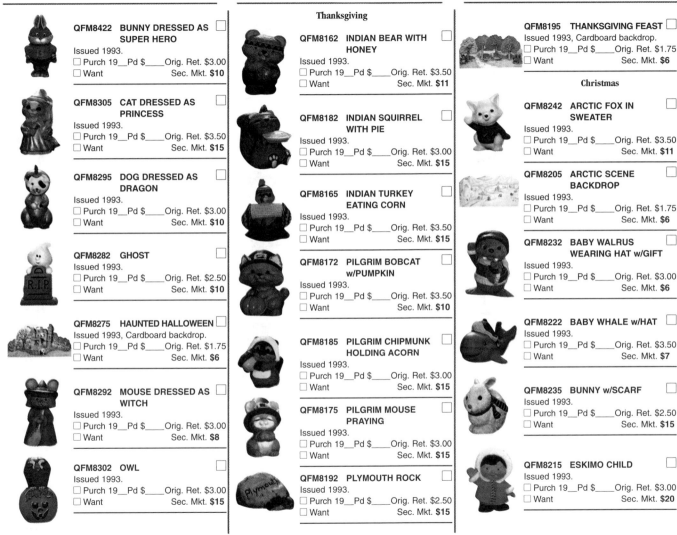

QFM8422 BUNNY DRESSED AS SUPER HERO
Issued 1993.
☐ Purch 19__Pd $____Orig. Ret. $3.00
☐ Want   Sec. Mkt. **$10**

QFM8305 CAT DRESSED AS PRINCESS
Issued 1993.
☐ Purch 19__Pd $____Orig. Ret. $3.50
☐ Want   Sec. Mkt. **$15**

QFM8295 DOG DRESSED AS DRAGON
Issued 1993.
☐ Purch 19__Pd $____Orig. Ret. $3.00
☐ Want   Sec. Mkt. **$10**

QFM8282 GHOST
Issued 1993.
☐ Purch 19__Pd $____Orig. Ret. $2.50
☐ Want   Sec. Mkt. **$10**

QFM8275 HAUNTED HALLOWEEN
Issued 1993, Cardboard backdrop.
☐ Purch 19__Pd $____Orig. Ret. $1.75
☐ Want   Sec. Mkt. **$6**

QFM8292 MOUSE DRESSED AS WITCH
Issued 1993.
☐ Purch 19__Pd $____Orig. Ret. $3.00
☐ Want   Sec. Mkt. **$8**

QFM8302 OWL
Issued 1993.
☐ Purch 19__Pd $____Orig. Ret. $3.00
☐ Want   Sec. Mkt. **$15**

Thanksgiving

QFM8162 INDIAN BEAR WITH HONEY
Issued 1993.
☐ Purch 19__Pd $____Orig. Ret. $3.50
☐ Want   Sec. Mkt. **$11**

QFM8182 INDIAN SQUIRREL WITH PIE
Issued 1993.
☐ Purch 19__Pd $____Orig. Ret. $3.00
☐ Want   Sec. Mkt. **$15**

QFM8165 INDIAN TURKEY EATING CORN
Issued 1993.
☐ Purch 19__Pd $____Orig. Ret. $3.50
☐ Want   Sec. Mkt. **$15**

QFM8172 PILGRIM BOBCAT w/PUMPKIN
Issued 1993.
☐ Purch 19__Pd $____Orig. Ret. $3.50
☐ Want   Sec. Mkt. **$10**

QFM8185 PILGRIM CHIPMUNK HOLDING ACORN
Issued 1993.
☐ Purch 19__Pd $____Orig. Ret. $3.00
☐ Want   Sec. Mkt. **$15**

QFM8175 PILGRIM MOUSE PRAYING
Issued 1993.
☐ Purch 19__Pd $____Orig. Ret. $3.00
☐ Want   Sec. Mkt. **$15**

QFM8192 PLYMOUTH ROCK
Issued 1993.
☐ Purch 19__Pd $____Orig. Ret. $2.50
☐ Want   Sec. Mkt. **$15**

QFM8195 THANKSGIVING FEAST
Issued 1993, Cardboard backdrop.
☐ Purch 19__Pd $____Orig. Ret. $1.75
☐ Want   Sec. Mkt. **$6**

Christmas

QFM8242 ARCTIC FOX IN SWEATER
Issued 1993.
☐ Purch 19__Pd $____Orig. Ret. $3.50
☐ Want   Sec. Mkt. **$11**

QFM8205 ARCTIC SCENE BACKDROP
Issued 1993.
☐ Purch 19__Pd $____Orig. Ret. $1.75
☐ Want   Sec. Mkt. **$6**

QFM8232 BABY WALRUS WEARING HAT w/GIFT
Issued 1993.
☐ Purch 19__Pd $____Orig. Ret. $3.00
☐ Want   Sec. Mkt. **$6**

QFM8222 BABY WHALE w/HAT
Issued 1993.
☐ Purch 19__Pd $____Orig. Ret. $3.50
☐ Want   Sec. Mkt. **$7**

QFM8235 BUNNY w/SCARF
Issued 1993.
☐ Purch 19__Pd $____Orig. Ret. $2.50
☐ Want   Sec. Mkt. **$15**

QFM8215 ESKIMO CHILD
Issued 1993.
☐ Purch 19__Pd $____Orig. Ret. $3.00
☐ Want   Sec. Mkt. **$20**

QFM8245 HUSKY PUPPY
Issued 1993.
☐ Purch 19__ Pd $____ Orig. Ret. $3.50
☐ Want   Sec. Mkt. **$11**

QFM8252 IGLOO
Issued 1993.
☐ Purch 19__ Pd $____ Orig. Ret. $3.00
☐ Want   Sec. Mkt. **$15**

QFM8212 PENGUIN
Issued 1993.
☐ Purch 19__ Pd $____ Orig. Ret. $3.00
☐ Want   Sec. Mkt. **$11**

QFM8265 POLAR BEAR
Third and Final in Series, Issued 1993.
☐ Purch 19__ Pd $____ Orig. Ret. $3.50
☐ Want   Sec. Mkt. **$15**

QFM8262 SANTA ESKIMO
Issued 1993.
☐ Purch 19__ Pd $____ Orig. Ret. $3.50
☐ Want   Sec. Mkt. **$30**

QFM8272 SEAL
Issued 1993.
☐ Purch 19__ Pd $____ Orig. Ret. $2.50
☐ Want   Sec. Mkt. **$8**

1994
Everyday

QSM8076 DOCK
Issued 1994.
☐ Purch 19__ Pd $____ Orig. Ret. $6.75
☐ Want   Sec. Mkt. **$25**

QSM8052 PAIL OF SEASHELLS
Issued 1994.
☐ Purch 19__ Pd $____ Orig. Ret. $2.75
☐ Want   Sec. Mkt. **$25**

QSM8066 RABBIT
Issued 1994.
☐ Purch 19__ Pd $____ Orig. Ret. $2.75
☐ Want   Sec. Mkt. **$15**

QSM8063 RACCOON
Issued 1994.
☐ Purch 19__ Pd $____ Orig. Ret. $3.75
☐ Want   Sec. Mkt. **$20**

Valentine's Day

QSM8006 BEAR MAILMAN
Issued 1994.
☐ Purch 19__ Pd $____ Orig. Ret. $3.75
☐ Want   Sec. Mkt. **$11**

QSM8013 BEAVER
Issued 1994.
☐ Purch 19__ Pd $____ Orig. Ret. $3.75
☐ Want   Sec. Mkt. **$10**

QSM8003 CHIPMUNK
Issued 1994.
☐ Purch 19__ Pd $____ Orig. Ret. $3.75
☐ Want   Sec. Mkt. **$11**

QSM8023 MAILBOX
Issued 1994.
☐ Purch 19__ Pd $____ Orig. Ret. $6.75
☐ Want   Sec. Mkt. **$15**

QSM8085 OWL IN STUMP
Issued 1994.
☐ Purch 19__ Pd $____ Orig. Ret. $2.75
☐ Want   Sec. Mkt. **$10**

QSM8016 RABBIT w/HEART CUTOUTS
Issued 1994.
☐ Purch 19__ Pd $____ Orig. Ret. $3.25
☐ Want   Sec. Mkt. **$10**

Easter

QSM8116 BIRDS IN NEST
Issued 1994.
☐ Purch 19__ Pd $____ Orig. Ret. $3.75
☐ Want   Sec. Mkt. **$15**

QSM8123 CHICK IN WAGON
Issued 1994.
☐ Purch 19__ Pd $____ Orig. Ret. $3.75
☐ Want   Sec. Mkt. **$17**

QSM8033 EGG WISHING WELL
Issued 1994.
☐ Purch 19__ Pd $____ Orig. Ret. $6.75
☐ Want   Sec. Mkt. **$24**

QSM8132 LAMB
Issued 1994.
☐ Purch 19__ Pd $____ Orig. Ret. $3.25
☐ Want   Sec. Mkt. **$10**

QSM8243 MOUSE w/FLOWER
Issued 1994.
☐ Purch 19__ Pd $____ Orig. Ret. $2.75
☐ Want   Sec. Mkt. **$13**

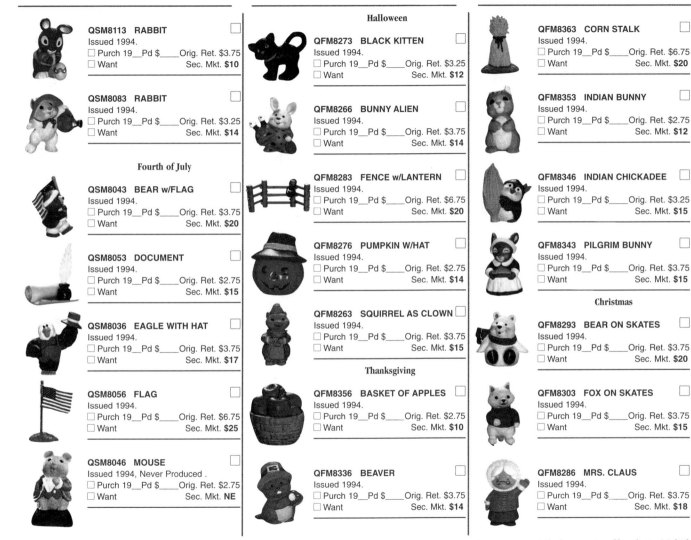

QSM8113 RABBIT
Issued 1994.
☐ Purch 19__Pd $____Orig. Ret. $3.75
☐ Want   Sec. Mkt. **$10**

QSM8083 RABBIT
Issued 1994.
☐ Purch 19__Pd $____Orig. Ret. $3.25
☐ Want   Sec. Mkt. **$14**

Fourth of July

QSM8043 BEAR w/FLAG
Issued 1994.
☐ Purch 19__Pd $____Orig. Ret. $3.75
☐ Want   Sec. Mkt. **$20**

QSM8053 DOCUMENT
Issued 1994.
☐ Purch 19__Pd $____Orig. Ret. $2.75
☐ Want   Sec. Mkt. **$15**

QSM8036 EAGLE WITH HAT
Issued 1994.
☐ Purch 19__Pd $____Orig. Ret. $3.75
☐ Want   Sec. Mkt. **$17**

QSM8056 FLAG
Issued 1994.
☐ Purch 19__Pd $____Orig. Ret. $6.75
☐ Want   Sec. Mkt. **$25**

QSM8046 MOUSE
Issued 1994, Never Produced .
☐ Purch 19__Pd $____Orig. Ret. $2.75
☐ Want   Sec. Mkt. **NE**

Halloween

QFM8273 BLACK KITTEN
Issued 1994.
☐ Purch 19__Pd $____Orig. Ret. $3.25
☐ Want   Sec. Mkt. **$12**

QFM8266 BUNNY ALIEN
Issued 1994.
☐ Purch 19__Pd $____Orig. Ret. $3.75
☐ Want   Sec. Mkt. **$14**

QFM8283 FENCE w/LANTERN
Issued 1994.
☐ Purch 19__Pd $____Orig. Ret. $6.75
☐ Want   Sec. Mkt. **$20**

QFM8276 PUMPKIN W/HAT
Issued 1994.
☐ Purch 19__Pd $____Orig. Ret. $2.75
☐ Want   Sec. Mkt. **$14**

QFM8263 SQUIRREL AS CLOWN
Issued 1994.
☐ Purch 19__Pd $____Orig. Ret. $3.75
☐ Want   Sec. Mkt. **$15**

Thanksgiving

QFM8356 BASKET OF APPLES
Issued 1994.
☐ Purch 19__Pd $____Orig. Ret. $2.75
☐ Want   Sec. Mkt. **$10**

QFM8336 BEAVER
Issued 1994.
☐ Purch 19__Pd $____Orig. Ret. $3.75
☐ Want   Sec. Mkt. **$14**

QFM8363 CORN STALK
Issued 1994.
☐ Purch 19__Pd $____Orig. Ret. $6.75
☐ Want   Sec. Mkt. **$20**

QFM8353 INDIAN BUNNY
Issued 1994.
☐ Purch 19__Pd $____Orig. Ret. $2.75
☐ Want   Sec. Mkt. **$12**

QFM8346 INDIAN CHICKADEE
Issued 1994.
☐ Purch 19__Pd $____Orig. Ret. $3.25
☐ Want   Sec. Mkt. **$15**

QFM8343 PILGRIM BUNNY
Issued 1994.
☐ Purch 19__Pd $____Orig. Ret. $3.75
☐ Want   Sec. Mkt. **$15**

Christmas

QFM8293 BEAR ON SKATES
Issued 1994.
☐ Purch 19__Pd $____Orig. Ret. $3.75
☐ Want   Sec. Mkt. **$20**

QFM8303 FOX ON SKATES
Issued 1994.
☐ Purch 19__Pd $____Orig. Ret. $3.75
☐ Want   Sec. Mkt. **$15**

QFM8286 MRS. CLAUS
Issued 1994.
☐ Purch 19__Pd $____Orig. Ret. $3.75
☐ Want   Sec. Mkt. **$18**

QFM8333 NORTH POLE SIGN ☐
Issued 1994.
☐ Purch 19__ Pd $____ Orig. Ret. $6.75
☐ Want   Sec. Mkt. **$20**

QFM8313 PENGUIN ☐
Issued 1994.
☐ Purch 19__Pd $____ Orig. Ret. $2.75
☐ Want   Sec. Mkt. **$18**

QFM8323 POLAR BEARS ☐
Issued 1994.
☐ Purch 19__Pd $____ Orig. Ret. $3.25
☐ Want   Sec. Mkt. **$15**

QXC4803 PUPPY IN TOTE BAG ☐
Collector's Club Gift Issued 1994.
☐ Purch 19__Pd $____ Orig. Ret. $3.00
☐ Want   Sec. Mkt. **$30**

QFM8306 SLED DOG ☐
Issued 1994.
☐ Purch 19__Pd $____ Orig. Ret. $3.25
☐ Want   Sec. Mkt. **$15**

QFM8316 SNOWMAN ☐
Issued 1994.
☐ Purch 19__Pd $____ Orig. Ret. $2.75
☐ Want   Sec. Mkt. **$10**

QFM8326 TREE ☐
Issued 1994.
☐ Purch 19__Pd $____ Orig. Ret. $2.75
☐ Want   Sec. Mkt. **$20**

1995
Everyday

QSM8057 BIRTHDAY BEAR ☐
Issued 1995.
☐ Purch 19__ Pd $____ Orig. Ret. $3.75
☐ Want   Sec. Mkt. **$10**

QSM8067 BRIDE & GROOM ☐
Issued 1995.
☐ Purch 19__Pd $____ Orig. Ret. $3.75
☐ Want   Sec. Mkt. **$12**

QSM8077 CAMERON w/CAMERA ☐
Issued 1995.
☐ Purch 19__Pd $____ Orig. Ret. $3.75
☐ Want   Sec. Mkt. **$12**

QSM8089 FAIRY GODMOTHER ☐
Issued 1995.
☐ Purch 19__Pd $____ Orig. Ret. $4.00
☐ Want   Sec. Mkt. **$15**

QSM8079 GROUND HOG ☐
Issued 1995.
☐ Purch 19__Pd $____ Orig. Ret. $3.00
☐ Want   Sec. Mkt. **$12**

QSM8087 RACCOON & FLOWER ☐
Issued 1995.
☐ Purch 19__Pd $____ Orig. Ret. $3.00
☐ Want   Sec. Mkt. **$10**

QXC4159 STEPSISTERS ☐
Issued 1995, Members Gift.
☐ Purch 19__Pd $____ Orig. Ret. $3.75
☐ Want   Sec. Mkt. **$40**

Valentine's Day

QSM8107 BASHFUL BOY ☐
Issued 1995.
☐ Purch 19__ Pd $____ Orig. Ret. $3.00
☐ Want   Sec. Mkt. **$17**

QSM8109 BASHFUL GIRL ☐
Issued 1995.
☐ Purch 19__ Pd $____ Orig. Ret. $3.00
☐ Want   Sec. Mkt. **$20**

QSM8009 CAMERON ☐
Issued 1995.
☐ Purch 19__Pd $____ Orig. Ret. $3.75
☐ Want   Sec. Mkt. **$20**

QSM8117 CINDERELLA ☐
Issued 1995.
☐ Purch 19__Pd $____ Orig. Ret. $4.00
☐ Want   Sec. Mkt. **$30**

QSM8019 KOALA BEAR ☐
Issued 1995.
☐ Purch 19__Pd $____ Orig. Ret. $3.75
☐ Want   Sec. Mkt. **$15**

QSM8017 ST. BERNARD ☐
Issued 1995.
☐ Purch 19__Pd $____ Orig. Ret. $3.75
☐ Want   Sec. Mkt. **$15**

QSM8007 TREE ☐
Issued 1995.
☐ Purch 19__Pd $____ Orig. Ret. $6.75
☐ Want   Sec. Mkt. **$20**

St. Patrick's Day

QSM8119 LEPRECHAUN
Issued 1995.
☐ Purch 19__ Pd $____ Orig. Ret. $3.50
☐ Want   Sec. Mkt. **$15**

Easter

QSM8047 BEAUREGARD BUNNY
Issued 1995, Never Produced.
☐ Purch 19__ Pd $____   Orig. Ret. $
☐ Want   **Never Produced**

QSM8029 CAMERON BUNNY
Issued 1995.
☐ Purch 19__ Pd $____ Orig. Ret. $3.75
☐ Want   Sec. Mkt. **$20**

QSM8027 COTTAGE
Issued 1995.
☐ Purch 19__ Pd $____ Orig. Ret. $6.75
☐ Want   Sec. Mkt. **$20**

QSM8049 PRINCE CHARMING
Issued 1995.
☐ Purch 19__ Pd $____ Orig. Ret. $4.00
☐ Want   Sec. Mkt. **$35**

QSM8039 SELBY
Issued 1995.
☐ Purch 19__ Pd $____ Orig. Ret. $3.00
☐ Want   Sec. Mkt. **$15**

QSM8037 STYLISH RABBIT
Issued 1995.
☐ Purch 19__ Pd $____ Orig. Ret. $3.75
☐ Want   Sec. Mkt. **$15**

Halloween

**QFM8147 CAMERON PUMPKIN
IN COSTUME**
Issued 1995.
☐ Purch 19__ Pd $____ Orig. Ret. $3.75
☐ Want   Sec. Mkt. **$18**

QFM8157 CUTE WITCH
Issued 1995.
☐ Purch 19__ Pd $____ Orig. Ret. $3.00
☐ Want   Sec. Mkt. **$13**

QFM8159 FRIENDLY MONSTER
Issued 1995.
☐ Purch 19__ Pd $____ Orig. Ret. $3.00
☐ Want   Sec. Mkt. **$13**

QFM8139 HAUNTED HOUSE
Issued 1995.
☐ Purch 19__ Pd $____ Orig. Ret. $6.75
☐ Want   Sec. Mkt. **$20**

QFM8149 RHINO MUMMY
Issued 1995.
☐ Purch 19__ Pd $____ Orig. Ret. $3.75
☐ Want   Sec. Mkt. **$15**

QSM8099 STEPMOTHER
Issued 1995.
☐ Purch 19__ Pd $____ Orig. Ret. $4.00
☐ Want   Sec. Mkt. **$15**

Thanksgiving

QFM8169 CAMERON PILGRIM
Issued 1995.
☐ Purch 19__ Pd $____ Orig. Ret. $3.75
☐ Want   Sec. Mkt. **$18**

QFM8179 CHIPMUNK w/CORN
Issued 1995.
☐ Purch 19__ Pd $____ Orig. Ret. $3.75
☐ Want   Sec. Mkt. **$7**

**QFM8189 MOUSE
w/CRANBERRIES**
Issued 1995.
☐ Purch 19__ Pd $____ Orig. Ret. $3.00
☐ Want   Sec. Mkt. **$13**

QFM8187 MOUSE w/PUMPKIN
Issued 1995.
☐ Purch 19__ Pd $____ Orig. Ret. $3.00
☐ Want   Sec. Mkt. **$15**

QSM8127 PUMPKIN CARRIAGE
Issued 1995.
☐ Purch 19__ Pd $____ Orig. Ret. $5.00
☐ Want   Sec. Mkt. **$20**

QFM8167 THANKSGIVING
Issued 1995.
☐ Purch 19__ Pd $____ Orig. Ret. $4.75
☐ Want   Sec. Mkt. **$15**

QFM8177 TURKEY
Issued 1995.
☐ Purch 19__ Pd $____ Orig. Ret. $3.75
☐ Want   Sec. Mkt. **$15**

Christmas

QFM8199 CAMERON ON SLED
Issued 1995.
☐ Purch 19__ Pd $____ Orig. Ret. $3.75
☐ Want   Sec. Mkt. **$15**

QFM8307 CAROLING BEAR ☐
Issued 1995.
☐ Purch 19__ Pd $____ Orig. Ret. $3.25
☐ Want   Sec. Mkt. **$15**

QFM8309 CAROLING BUNNY ☐
Issued 1995.
☐ Purch 19__ Pd $____ Orig. Ret. $3.25
☐ Want   Sec. Mkt. **$15**

QFM8317 CAROLING MOUSE ☐
Issued 1995.
☐ Purch 19__ Pd $____ Orig. Ret. $3.00
☐ Want   Sec. Mkt. **$15**

QFM8197 CHRISTMAS TREE ☐
Issued 1995.
☐ Purch 19__ Pd $____ Orig. Ret. $6.75
☐ Want   Sec. Mkt. **$20**

QFM8319 HAMSTER ☐
Issued 1995.
☐ Purch 19__ Pd $____ Orig. Ret. $3.25
☐ Want   Sec. Mkt. **$17**

QFM8287 LION & LAMB ☐
Issued 1995.
☐ Purch 19__ Pd $____ Orig. Ret. $4.00
☐ Want   Sec. Mkt. **$17**

QFM8297 NUTCRACKER ☐
Issued 1995.
☐ Purch 19__ Pd $____ Orig. Ret. $3.75
☐ Want   Sec. Mkt. **$15**

QFM8299 SANTA ☐
Issued 1995.
☐ Purch 19__ Pd $____ Orig. Ret. $3.75
☐ Want   Sec. Mkt. **$15**

QFM8289 TOY MAKER BEAVER ☐
Issued 1995.
☐ Purch 19__ Pd $____ Orig. Ret. $3.75
☐ Want   Sec. Mkt. **$15**

1996
Valentine's Day

QSM8014 ALICE IN WONDERLAND ☐
Issued 1996, 5 pcs., Story Time.
☐ Purch 19__ Pd $____ Orig. Ret. $19.95
MIB   NB   DB   BNT
☐ Want   **MIB** Sec. Mkt. **$40**

QSM8011 PENDA KIDS ☐
Issued 1996, 2 pcs.
☐ Purch 19__ Pd $____ Orig. Ret. $7.95
MIB   NB   DB   BNT
☐ Want   **MIB** Sec. Mkt. **$16**

QSM8004 SWEETHEART CRUISE ☐
Issued 1996, 3 pcs.
☐ Purch 19__ Pd $____ Orig. Ret. $12.95
MIB   NB   DB   BNT
☐ Want   **MIB** Sec. Mkt. **$22**

St. Patrick's Day

QSM8021 LUCKY CAMERON ☐
Issued 1996, 2 pcs.
☐ Purch 19__ Pd $____ Orig. Ret. $7.95
MIB   NB   DB   BNT
☐ Want   **MIB** Sec. Mkt. **$17**

Easter

QSM8064 BLUE RIBBON BUNNY ☐
Issued 1996.
☐ Purch 19__ Pd $____ Orig. Ret. $4.95
MIB   NB   DB   BNT
☐ Want   **MIB** Sec. Mkt. **$20**

QSM8024 EASTER EGG HUNT ☐
Issued 1996.
☐ Purch 19__ Pd $____ Orig. Ret. $4.95
MIB   NB   DB   BNT
☐ Want   **MIB** Sec. Mkt. **$20**

QSM8114 HAPPY BIRTHDAY CLOWNS ☐ Issued 1996, 2 pcs.
☐ Purch 19__ Pd $____ Orig. Ret. $7.95
MIB   NB   DB   BNT
☐ Want   **MIB** Sec. Mkt. **$18**

QSM8111 NOAH AND FRIENDS ☐
Issued 1996, 5 pcs., Story Time.
☐ Purch 19__ Pd $____ Orig. Ret. $19.95
MIB   NB   DB   BNT
☐ Want   **MIB** Sec. Mkt. **$60**

Halloween

QFM8124   HAPPY HAUNTING

Issued 1996, 2 pcs.
- [ ] Purch 19__Pd $____ Orig. Ret. $12.95
- MIB   NB   DB   BNT
- [ ] Want   **MIB** Sec. Mkt. **$30**

QFM8131   PEANUTS™ PUMPKIN PATCH

Issued 1996, 5 pcs.
- [ ] Purch 19__Pd $____ Orig. Ret. $19.95
- MIB   NB   DB   BNT
- [ ] Want   **MIB** Sec. Mkt. **$50**

Thanksgiving

QFM8041   COWBOY CAMERON

Issued 1996, 3 pcs.
- [ ] Purch 19__Pd $____ Orig. Ret. $12.95
- MIB   NB   DB   BNT
- [ ] Want   **MIB** Sec. Mkt. **$30**

QFM8134   GIVING THANKS

Issued 1996, 3 pcs.
- [ ] Purch 19__Pd $____ Orig. Ret. $12.95
- MIB   NB   DB   BNT
- [ ] Want   **MIB** Sec. Mkt. **$27**

Christmas

QFM8054   BASHFUL MISTLETOE

Issued 1996, 3 pcs.
- [ ] Purch 19__Pd $____ Orig. Ret. $12.95
- MIB   NB   DB   BNT
- [ ] Want   **MIB** Sec. Mkt. **$20**

QFM8121   BUSY BAKERS

Issued 1996, 2 pcs.
- [ ] Purch 19__Pd $____ Orig. Ret. $7.95
- MIB   NB   DB   BNT
- [ ] Want   **MIB** Sec. Mkt. **$15**

QFM8044   MR. AND MRS. BEAR CLAUS

Issued 1996, 2 pcs.
- [ ] Purch 19__Pd $____ Orig. Ret. $7.95
- MIB   NB   DB   BNT
- [ ] Want   **MIB** Sec. Mkt. **$18**

QFM8051   SANTA'S HELPERS

Issued 1996, 3 pcs.
- [ ] Purch 19__Pd $____ Orig. Ret. $12.95
- MIB   NB   DB   BNT
- [ ] Want   **MIB** Sec. Mkt. **$26**

QFM8061   THE SEWING CLUB

Issued 1996, 3 pcs.
- [ ] Purch 19__Pd $____ Orig. Ret. $12.95
- MIB   NB   DB   BNT
- [ ] Want   **MIB** Sec. Mkt. **$27**

1997
Every Day

QFM8582 BASHFUL VISITORS ☐
Issued 1997, 3 pcs.
☐ Purch 19__Pd $____ Orig. Ret. $12.95
MIB   NB   DB   BNT
☐ Want   **MIB** Sec. Mkt. **$20**

QSM8565 HAPPY BIRTHDAY ☐
Third and Final in Series
Issued 1997.
☐ Purch 19__Pd $____ Orig. Ret. $4.95
MIB   NB   DB   BNT
☐ Want   **MIB** Sec. Mkt. **$8**

QFM8625 HERSHEY'S™ ☐
FIRST IN SERIES, Issued 1997, 2 pcs.
☐ Purch 19__Pd $____ Orig. Ret. $12.95
MIB   NB   DB   BNT
☐ Want   **MIB** Sec. Mkt.**$20**

**QSM8545 SULU & SARA
PENDA KIDS™** ☐
Issued 1997.
☐ Purch 19__Pd $____ Orig. Ret. $7.95
MIB   NB   DB   BNT
☐ Want   **MIB** Sec. Mkt. **$10**

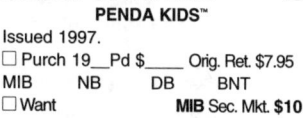

**QFM8642 TEA TIME MARY'S
BEARS** ☐
Issued 1997, 3 pcs.
☐ Purch 19__Pd $____ Orig. Ret. $12.95
MIB   NB   DB   BNT
☐ Want   **MIB** Sec. Mkt. **$15**

Valentine's Day

QSM8552 CUPID CAMERON ☐
Issued 1997.
☐ Purch 19__Pd $____ Orig. Ret. $4.95
MIB   NB   DB   BNT
☐ Want   **MIB** Sec. Mkt. **$10**

Easter

QSM8562 EASTER PARADE ☐
Issued 1997, 2 pcs.
☐ Purch 19__Pd $____ Orig. Ret. $7.95
MIB   NB   DB   BNT
☐ Want   **MIB** Sec. Mkt. **$10**

QSM8575 GETTING READY FOR ☐
SPRING
Issued 1997.
☐ Purch 19__Pd $____ Orig. Ret. $12.95
MIB   NB   DB   BNT
☐ Want   **MIB** Sec. Mkt. **$15**

QSM8572 NOAH'S FRIENDS ☐
Issued 1997, 2 pcs., Story Time.
☐ Purch 19__Pd $____ Orig. Ret. $7.95
MIB   NB   DB   BNT
☐ Want   **MIB** Sec. Mkt. **$20**

QSM8605 PETER PAN ☐
Issued 1997, 5 pcs., Story Time.
☐ Purch 19__Pd $____ Orig. Ret. $19.95
MIB   NB   DB   BNT
☐ Want   **MIB** Sec. Mkt.**$40**

QFM8685 SIX DWARFS
Issued 1997, 3 pcs., Story Time.
☐ Purch 19__ Pd $____ Orig. Ret. $12.95
MIB   NB   DB   BNT
☐ Want   **MIB** Sec. Mkt.**$24**

**QFM8535 SNOW WHITE AND
DANCING DWARFS**
Issued 1997, Story Time
☐ Purch 19__ Pd $____ Orig. Ret. $7.9
MIB   NB   DB   BNT
☐ Want 5   **MIB** Sec. Mkt. **$14**

Thanksgiving

**QFM8585 APPLE HARVEST
MARY'S BEARS**
Issued 1997, 3 pcs.
☐ Purch 19__ Pd $____ Orig. Ret. $12.95
MIB   NB   DB   BNT
☐ Want   **MIB** Sec. Mkt.**$15**

QFM8592 MAKING A WISH
Issued 1997, 2 pcs.
☐ Purch 19__ Pd $____ Orig. Ret. $7.95
MIB   NB   DB   BNT
☐ Want   **MIB** Sec. Mkt. **$10**

Christmas

QFM8612 HOLIDAY HARMONY
Issued 1997, 3 pcs.
☐ Purch 19__ Pd $____ Orig. Ret. $12.95
MIB   NB   DB   BNT
☐ Want   **MIB** Sec. Mkt.**$15**

QFM8615 THE NATIVITY
Issued 1997, 2 pcs.
Christmas Pageant Collection
☐ Purch 19__ Pd $____ Orig. Ret. $7.95
MIB   NB   DB   BNT
☐ Want   MIB Sec. Mkt. $10

QFM8692 THREE WEE KINGS
Issued 1997, 3 pcs.
Christmas Pageant Collection
☐ Purch 19__ Pd $____ Orig. Ret. $12.95
MIB   NB   DB   BNT
☐ Want   **MIB** Sec. Mkt. **$15**

QFM8622 SANTA CAMERON
Issued 1997.
☐ Purch19__ Pd $____ Orig. Ret. $4.95
MIB   NB   DB   BNT
☐ Want   **MIB** Sec. Mkt. **$17**

QFM8602 SNOWBEAR SEASON
Preview Exclusive, Issued 1997, 3 pcs.
☐ Purch 19__ Pd $____ Orig. Ret. $12.95
MIB   NB   DB   BNT
☐ Want   **MIB** Sec. Mkt. **$15**

1998

QSM8483 RAPUNZEL AND PRINCE
Preview Exclusive, Issued 1998, 2pcs.
☐ Purch 19__ Pd $____ Orig. Ret. $12.95
MIB   NB   DB   BNT
☐ Want   **MIB** Sec. Mkt. **$20**

Everyday

QFM 848-6 BRIDE AND GROOM
1996 MADAME
ALEXANDER®
Issued 1998.
☐ Purch 19__ Pd $___Orig. Ret. $12.95
☐ Want   Sec. Mkt. **N.E.**

Christmas

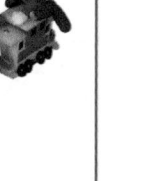

QFM 849-3   HERSHEY'S ™
Second in Series, Issued 1998.
☐ Purch 19__ Pd $___Orig. Ret. $10.95
☐ Want   Sec. Mkt. **N.E.**

QRP 851-3   DONALD'S
             PASSENGER CAR
Issued 1998.
☐ Purch 19__ Pd $____Orig. Ret. $5.95
☐ Want   Sec. Mkt. **N.E.**

QRP 851-6   GOOFY'S
             CABOOSE
Issued 1998.
☐ Purch 19__ Pd $____Orig. Ret. $5.95
☐ Want   Sec. Mkt. **N.E.**

QRP 849-6   MICKEY'S
             LOCOMOTIVE
Issued 1998.
☐ Purch 19__ Pd $____Orig. Ret. $5.95
☐ Want   Sec. Mkt. **N.E.**

QRP 850-6   MINNIE'S LUGGAGE
             CAR
Issued 1998.
☐ Purch 19__ Pd $____Orig. Ret. $5.95
☐ Want   Sec. Mkt. **N.E.**

QRP 850-3   PLUTO'S COAL CAR
Issued 1998.
☐ Purch 19__ Pd $____Orig. Ret. $5.95
☐ Want   Sec. Mkt. **N.E.**

1999

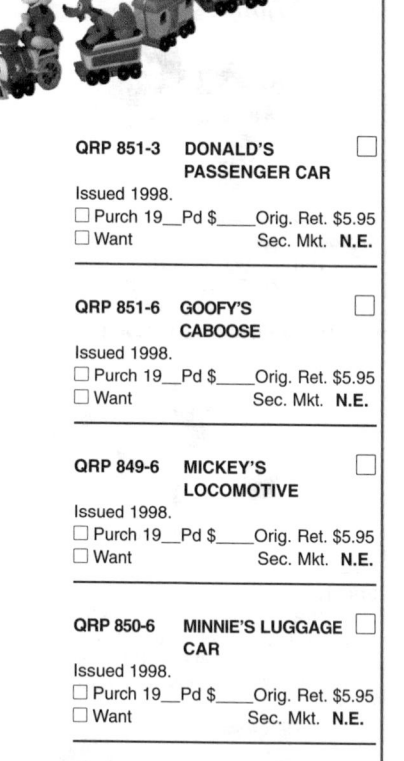

QSP 845-9   BASHFUL BOY
             AND GIRL
             AT GARDN GATE
Issued 1999.
☐ Purch 19__ Pd $___Orig. Ret. $12.95
☐ Want   Sec. Mkt. **N.E.**

Alphabetical Listing of Hallmark Keepsake Easter Ornaments®

Alphabetical Listing of Hallmark Kiddie Car Classics™

Alphabetical Listing of Hallmark Miniature Ornaments®

Subject Listing of
Hallmark™ Miniature Ornaments

THREE MORE SHOPPERS HAVE ARRIVED DOCTOR

DEC 26

HALLMARK SHOPPERS WARD

TOM HIGGINS

Alphabetical Listing of Hallmark Keepsake Ornaments®

F (cont.)

L (cont.)

95 QX 476-9	Lego®
	Fireplace with Santa 248
87 QX 458-9	Let it Snow 99
81 QX 811-5	Let Us Adore Him 37
96 QLX 738-1	Let Us Adore Him 271
89 QX 488-2	Let's Play 127
90 QLX 722-6	Letter to Santa 143
86 QX 419-3	Li'l Jingler 86
87 QX 419-3	Li'l Jingler 100
97 QLX 744-2	Lighthouse Greeting 293
98 QLX 753-6	Lighthouse Greeting 316
79 QX 256-7	Light of Christmas, The.....22
96 QXE 744 4	Lighting the Flame 280
92 QLX 723-1	Lighting the Way 178
96 QX 612-4	Lighting the Way 271
97 QLX 752-2	Lincoln Memorial, The ... 293
97 QX 660-2	Lion and Lamb 293

Lion King, The

94 QX 540-6	Mufasa and Simba 223
95 QX 615-9	Simba,
	Pumbaa and Timon.......253
94 QX 530-3	Simba and Nala 223
97 QXD 406-5	Timon and Pumbaa 293
94 QLX 751-3	Simba, Sarabi
	and Mufasa 224
94 QLX 751-6	Simba, Sarabi
	and Mufasa 224
94 QX 536-6	Timon and Pumbaa........224

97 QX 614-5	Lionel®: 1950 Santa Fe F3
	Diesel Locomotive 293
96 QX 553-1	Lionel®: 700E Steam
	Locomotive.....................271
98 QX 634-6	Lionel®: Pennsylvania
	GG-I Locomotive.............316
90 QX 523-3	Little Drummer Boy 143
93 QX 537-2	Little Drummer Boy 198
86 QX 511-6	Little Drummers 86
88 QX 408-1	Little Jack Horner 111
74 QX 115-1	Little Miracles 2

75 QX 140-1	Little Miracles 5
97 QXI 407-2	Little Mermaid, The: Ariel ...293
85 QLX 711-2	Little Red Schoolhouse.....75
96 QX 550-4	Little Spooners 272

Little Trimmer

79 QX 130-7	Angel Delight 22
78 QX 132-3	Little Trimmer Collection ...17
79 QX 132-7	Matchless Christmas 22
79 QX 159-9	Little Trimmer Set.............22
82 QX 454-3	Christmas Kitten 45
80 QX 131-4	Christmas Owl 29
82 QX 131-4	Christmas Owl 45
80 QX 135-4	Christmas Teddy 29
81 QX 408-2	Clothespin Drummer 37
80 QX 134-1	Clothespin Soldier............30
82 QX 454-6	Cookie Mouse...................46
82 QX 462-3	Dove Love........................46
78 QX 136-3	Drummer Boy....................17
82 QX 477-6	Jingling Teddy 46
81 QX 407-5	Jolly Snowman.................38
82 QX 415-5	Merry Moose.....................46
80 QX 160-1	Merry Redbird...................30
82 QX 459-6	Musical Angel...................46
81 QX 409-5	Perky Penguin...................38
82 QX 409-5	Perky Penguin...................46
78 QX 134-3	Praying Angel....................17
81 QX 406-2	Puppy Love.......................38
78 QX 135-6	Santa................................17
79 QX 135-6	Santa................................22
81 QX 412-2	Stocking Mouse 38
80 QX 130-1	Swingin' on a Star............30
78 QX 133-6	Thimble Series..................17
79 QX 133-6	Thimble Series..................22

87 QX 469-5	Little Whittler 100
97 QX 626-5	Lone Ranger™, The 294
90 QX 470-3	Long Winter's Nap 144
93 QX 568-5	Look for the Wonder 198
92 QLX 709-4	Look! It's Santa 179

Looney Tunes

93 QX 541-2	Bugs Bunny 198

95 QX 501-9	Bugs Bunny 248
98 QX 644-3	Bugs Bunny 316
94 QX 541-5	Daffy Duck 224
97 QLX 750-2	Decorator Taz 294
93 QX 549-5	Elmer Fudd 198
96 QX 544-4	Foghorn and
	Henry Hawk 272
97 QX 633-2	Michigan J. Frog 294
93 QX 565-2	Porky Pig 199
94 QX 560-5	Road Runner
	and Wile E. Coyote 224
94 QX 534-3	Speedy Gonzales 224
93 QX 540-5	Sylvester and Tweety......199
95 QX 501-7	Sylvester and Tweety......249
94 QX 560-5	Tasmanian Devil 224
94 QX 534-6	Yosemite Sam 224

95 QX 502-9	Lou Gehrig 242
95 QX 406-9	Lou Rankin Bear 249
93 QX 574-5	Lou Rankin Polar Bear ...199
94 QX 545-6	Lou Rankin Seal 224
90 QX 547-6	Lovable Dears.................144
77 QX 262-2	Love 12
78 QX 268-3	Love 17
79 QX 258-7	Love 23
80 QX 302-1	Love 30
81 QX 502-2	Love 38
82 QX 209-6	Love 46
82 QX 304-3	Love 46
82 QMB 900-9	Love 46
83 QX 207-9	Love 55
83 QX 310-9	Love 55
83 QX 305-7	Love 55
83 QX 422-7	Love 55
84 QX 255-4	Love 65
81 QX 425-2	Love and Joy
	(Porcelain Chimes) 38
85 QX 371-5	Love at Christmas 75
88 QX 374-4	Love Fills the Heart 111
88 QX 275-4	Love Grows 111
83 QX 223-9	Love Is A Song...............55

87 QX 278-7	Love Is Everywhere 100
88 QX 486-4	Love Santa 112
84 QX 247-4	Love...
	the Spirit of Christmas.........65
97 QX 643-5	Love to Sew 294
92 QX 484-1	Love To Skate 179
85 QLX 702-5	Love Wreath.....................75
88 QX 493-4	Loving Bear 112
87 QLX 701-6	Loving Holiday 100
86 QX 409-3	Loving Memories 86
92 QX 515-1	Loving Shepherd............179
89 QLX 726-2	Loving Spoonful 127
94 QX 481-5	Lucinda and Teddy.........224

M

Madame Alexander®

96 QX 631-1	Cinderella......................272
97 QX 615-5	Little Red Riding Hood,
	1991 294
98 QX 635-3	Mop Top Wendy 317
98 QX 649-3	Holiday Angels:
	Glorious Angel 317

83 QX 428-7	Madonna and Child..........55
84 QX 344-1	Madonna and Child..........65
96 QX 632-4	Madonna and Child........272
96 QK 114-4	Madonna and Child........279
97 QLX 742-5	Madonna and Child 294
98 QX 651-6	Madonna and Child 317
97 QX 654-5	Madonna del Rosario 294
86 QX 272-6	Magi, The 86
93 QK 102-5	Magi, The 208
94 QX 588-3	Magic Carpet Ride 224
97 QXI 683-2	Magic Johnson 292
95 QX584-9	Magic School Bus™, The .249
86 QX 429-3	Magical Unicorn 86
89 QX 452-2	Mail Call 127
93 QP 601-5	Mailbox Delivery 207
94 QP 601-5	Mailbox Delivery 232
95 Qp 601-5	Mailbox Delivery 256
83 QX 415-7	Mailbox Kitten 56

Subject Listing of Hallmark Keepsake Ornaments®

Subject Listing of Hallmark Ornaments (Chipmunk – Disney) **39 (I)**

Alphabetical Listing of Merry Miniatures®

The Merry Miniature section of this guide will have pages numbered 1 - 35(M), the (M) standing for Merry Miniatues.

Year	Code	Item	Pg
93	QSM8265	Polar Bear playing piccolo	27
94	QFM8323	Polar Bears	29
86	EPF4253	Polka Dot	10
93	QSM8012	Prairie Dog w/pail and shovel	24
92	QSM9797	Praying Chipmunk	22
84	HA3729	Precious	8
95	QSM8049	Prince Charming	30
95	QSM8127	Pumpkin Carriage	30
92	QFM9021	Pumpkin, "Trick or Treat"	22
94	QFM8276	Pumpkin w/hat	28
92	QSM9767	Puppy	22
81	HA4902	Puppy in basket w/flowers	4
91	QFM1787	Puppy in box, "Open Me First 1991"	21
84	XHA3494	Puppy in gift box	7
91	QSM1529	Puppy in shoe	19
94	QXC4803	Puppy in tote bag	29
90	QSM1583	Puppy w/shirt "100% Huggable"	17
87	XHA3769	Puppy w/stocking	12

R

Year	Code	Item	Pg
92	QFM9151	Rabbit on sled	23
88	EBO2604	Rabbit on wheels	13
92	QSM9827	Rabbit & Squirrel	21
92	QFM9201	Rabbit w/heart carrot	21
84	HA4302	Rabbit w/pink heart, "So Glad We're Friends"	7
94	QSM8113	Rabbit with croquet	28
94	QSM8083	Rabbit with egg shaped watering can	28
94	QSM8016	Rabbit with heart cutouts	27
94	QSM8066	Rabbit with ice cream	27
89	QFM1652	Raccoon Caroler	16
95	QSM8087	Raccoon & Flower	29
89	QFM1575	Raccoon, "Happy Halloween"	15
94	QSM8063	Raccoon in flippers	27
81	THA3402	Raccoon Pilgrim w/corn	4
91	QSM1517	Raccoon Thief, "You Stole My Heart"	19
90	QSM1586	Raccoon w/pineapple	17
87	HHA3487	Raccoon Witch w/pumpkin	11
93	QSM8062	Raccoon w/cutout heart	25
74	PF1433	Raggedy Andy™	1
74	PF1432	Raggedy Ann™	1
86	EPF4223	Rainbow	10
98	QSM8483	Rapunzel and the Prince (2 pcs.)	34
81	XHA3405	Redbird throwing a snowball	4
84	XHA3501	Redbird w/black boots on snow	7
80	XPF3464	Reindeer on snow base, Stamped with production date	3
92	QFM9121	Reindeer Waving, Dated "92"	23
74	XPF493	Reindeer w/antlers sitting	1
95	QFM8149	Rhino Mummy	30
86	XHA3553	Rhonda	11
82	XHA5003	Rocking Horse	5
85	XHA3515	Rocking Horse	9
86	XHA3546	Rodney	11
86	EPF4466	Rodney container	11
84	XHA3391	Rodney Reindeer w/skates	7

S

Year	Code	Item	Pg
93	QSM8045	Sandcastle	24
76	XPF131	Santa	2
82	XHA5016	Santa	5
95	QFM8299	Santa	31
97	QFM8622	Santa Cameron	34
83	XHA3427	Santa carrying bag w/ "Rooftop Deliveries"	6
86	XHA3673	Santa	11
88	QFM1521	Santa	14
93	QSM8262	Santa Eskimo	27
75	XPF49	Santa holding canes	1
92	QFM9164	Santa Maria ship	24
84	XHA3451	Santa sitting on chimney	7
74	XPF486	Santa standing on peppermint candy	1
87	XHA3717	Santa w/bag, Dated 1987	12
80	XPF39	Santa w/Christmas packages	3
96	QFM8051	Santa's Helpers (3 pcs)	32
90	QFM1616	Scarecrow	17
74	HPF	Scarecrow w/Jack-O-Lantern	1
76	HPF522	Scarecrow w/Jack-O-Lantern	2
92	QSM9849	Seal, Dated 1992	21
88	QXC5104	Seal of Friendship	14
93	QSM8272	Seal w/earmuffs	27
87	EHA4167	Sebastian w/bunny ears	11
86	VHA3516	Sebastian w/heart collar	9
86	XHA3566	Sebastian w/wreath around his neck	11
95	QSM8039	Selby	30
85	SHA3452	Shamrock figure w/face and top hat	8
86	EPF4126	Sheep & Bell	9
88	QFM1571	Shepherd	14
93	QSM8122	Sherlock Holmes Duck	25
83	HHA3437	Shirt Tales™, Raccoon, similar to pin	6
97	QFM8685	Six Dwarfs (3 pcs)	34
91	QFM1837	Skating Raccoon	19
85	VHA3482	Skunk holding heart,	8
92	QFM9184	Skunk w/Butterfly	21
93	QSM8072	Skunk w/lacy heart	25
94	QFM8306	Sled Dog	29
80	XPF3451	Sleigh, red and green	3
91	QFM1749	Snow Bunny, "Joy"	21
91	QFM1759	Snow Lamb, "Peace"	21
91	QFM1757	Snow Mice, "Love"	21
97	QFM8535	Snow White and Dancing Dwarf	34
97	QFM8602	Snowbear Season (3 pcs.)	34
76	XPF44	Snowman	2
88	QFM1534	Snowman	14
94	QFM8316	Snowman	29
83	XHA3479	Snowman in black hat waving left hand	6
90	QFM1646	Snowman, "Let it Snow"	18
74	XPF473	Snowman w/redbird waving right hand	1
78	XPF33	Snowman w/cane & top hat	3
74	XPF	Snowman w/redbird waving left hand	1
91	QFM1819	Soccer Skunk	19
82	CDB8819	Soldier Boy saluting w/dog	5
85	XHA3465	Soldier & Drum, container	9
84	XHA3481	Soldier w/gold drum	7
92	QFM9081	Son dog in p.j.'s "Son 1992"	23
94	QFM8263	Squirrel as clown	28
90	QFM1696	Squirrel Caroler, Dated 1990	18
90	QSM1553	Squirrel, Dated 1990	17
90	QFM1606	Squirrel Hobo, "Trick or Treat"	17
81	HA4901	Squirrel in bucket w/fall leaves	4
81	THA3415	Squirrel Indian, headband w/real feather	4
92	QFM9064	Squirrels in nutshell, 1st Christmas Together '92	23
95	QSM8017	St. Bernard	29
88	QFM1584	Stable	14
89	QFM1685	Stable & 9 Figurines	16
95	QSM8099	Stepmother	30
95	QXC4159	Stepsisters	29
90	QSM1506	Stitched Teddy w/red heart	17
86	EPF4156	Striped	10
95	QSM8037	Stylish Rabbit	30
97	QSM8545	Sulu & Sara, Penda Kids™	33
92	QSM9779	SweatShirt Bunny	22
92	QFM9124	Sweet Angel	23
96	QSM8004	Sweetheart Cruise (3 pcs)	31

T

Year	Code	Item	Pg
87	PF3867	Taffi	12
88	QFM1591	Tank Car	14
89	QFM1612	Teacher Elf	16
90	QFM1676	Teacher Mouse	18
91	QFM1807	Teacher Raccoon, "For Teacher, 91"	21
92	QFM9074	Teacher Cat w/paper	24
97	QFM8642	Tea Time Mary's Bears	33
86	EPF4233	Teddy Bear	10
82	XHA5013	Teddy Bear on a drum, container	5
85	VHA4112	Teddy Bear on red heart, container	8
92	QFM9194	Teddy Bear w/bandage on arm	21
90	QFM1623	Thankful Turkey	18
93	QFM8195	Thanksgiving Feast Backdrop	26
95	QFM8167	Thanksgiving Feast Table	30
97	QFM8615	The Nativity (2 pcs)	34
96	QFM8061	The Sewing Club (3 pcs)	32
97	QFM8692	Three Wee Kings	34
84	HA3735	Tickles	8
95	QSM8289	Toy Maker Beaver	31
89	QFM1562	Train Car	16
88	QFM1531	Train Engine	14
94	QFM8326	Tree	29
95	QSM8007	Tree	29
82	XHA5006	Tree	5
93	QSM8075	Tree Stump and paint can	25
81	SHA3415	Tumbling Leprechaun	3
87	THA49	Turkey	11
95	QFM8177	Turkey	30
91	QFM1697	Turkey	20
92	QFM9001	Turkey	23
78	TPF12	Turkey,	2
85	THA3395	Turkey,	8
74	TPF13	Turkey on grass	1
81	THA22	Turkey	4
76	TPF512	Turkey	2

Subject Listing of Merry Miniatures

Bear (cont.)

94 QFM8323 Polar Bears 29
97 QFM8602 Snowbear Season (3 pcs.)34
90 QSM1506 Stitched Teddy
w/red heart 17
97 QFM8642 Tea Time Mary's Bears . .33

Beaver

94 QFM8336 Beaver eating apple ...28
94 QSM8013 Beaver w/card 27
91 QFM1829 Football Beaver 18
92 QFM9011 Pilgrim Beaver,
"Happy Thanksgiving" . .23
95 QFM8289 Toy Maker Beaver 31

Betsey Clark

76 XPF151 Betsey Clark 2
83 EHA2429 Betsey Clark holding bunny5

Bird

94 QSM8116 Birds in nest 27
84 HA4303 Bluebird w/star,
"You Brighten My Day" ...7
94 QSM8036 Eagle w/hat 28
81 XHA3405 Redbird throwing
snowball 4
84 XHA3501 Redbird w/black boots
on snow 7

Birthday

95 QSM8057 Birthday Bear 29
92 QSM9819 Birthday Clown 21
90 QFM1706 Birthday Clown 16
91 QSM1617 Birthday Clown 18
90 QSM1566 Elephant,
"Happy Birthday" 16
97 QSM8565 Happy Birthday Clowns .33
96 QSM8114 Happy Birthday
Clowns (2 pcs) 31

Bunny

91 QFM1817 Aerobic Bunny 18
90 QSM1576 Baseball Bunny 16
96 QSM8064 Blue Ribbon Bunny 31
88 EBO2314 Boy Bunny 13
90 QSM1682 Boy Bunny 17
94 QFM8266 Bunny Alien 28
87 EHA4179 Bunny asleep 11
89 QSM1512 Bunny Ballerina 15
87 XHA3737 Bunny Boy 12
86 EPF4133 Bunny Boy, ...9

89 QFM1662 Bunny Caroler 16
88 EBO2321 Bunny & Carrot 13
92 QSM9799 Bunny & Carrot 22
93 QFM8422 Bunny Dressed
as super hero 26
79 EPF377 Bunny, flocked 3
83 EHA4089 Bunny & Flower 5
89 QFM1565 Bunny Ghost "Boo" ...15
87 XHA3749 Bunny Girl 12
86 EPF4106 Bunny Girl 9
74 EPF186 Bunny holding little chick .1
82 EHA1053 Bunny in a wicker basket
w/flowers 5
87 XHA3729 Bunny in red w/bear 12
92 QFM9071 Bunny in Snow Dome,
Baby's 1st Christmas
1992 23
90 QFM1713 Bunny in tux, "You're Tops" 16
89 QSM1552 Bunny in wagon 15
83 EHA4117 Bunny lying on egg 5
93 QSM8115 Bunny painting egg 25
91 QSM1597 Bunny Praying 19
89 EBO3092 Bunny & Skateboard 15
83 EHA3457 Bunny, small 5
88 EBO2311 Bunny w/basket 13
86 EHA3476 Bunny w/butterfly 9
90 QSM1593 Bunny w/camera 16
75 EPF49 Bunny w/carrot 1
85 EHA3482 Bunny w/carrot 8
91 QSM1537 Bunny w/heart 19
93 QSM8142 Bunny w/basket 25
93 QSM8125 Bunny w/cracked egg . .25
93 QSM8235 Bunny w/scarf 26
93 QSM8005 Bunny w/seashell 24
95 QFM8309 Caroling Bunny 31
82 EPF3702 Ceramic Bunny
w/basket of eggs 4
85 EPR3701 Ceramic Bunny, purple egg8
91 QSM1587 Daughter Bunny
w/wheelbarrow 19
89 EBO3215 E. Bunny 15
90 QSM1726 E. Bunny w/paint can ..17
96 QSM8024 Easter Egg Hunt 31
83 EHA3417 Flocked Bunny on
hind feet 5
91 QFM1719 Gift Bringer Bunny 20
86 EHA3503 Girl Bunny 9
90 QSM1675 Girl Bunny 17
88 EBO2311 Girl Bunny w/basket 13
91 QSM1577 Mother Bunny
holding basket 20

94 QFM8343 Pilgrim Bunny 28
91 QFM1749 Snow Bunny, "Joy" 21
92 QSM9779 Sweat Shirt Bunny 22

Candy

93 QSM8095 Box of Candy 24
90 QFM1693 Candy Caboose,
4th in set 18
97 QFM8625 HERSHEY'S™ (2 pcs) . . .33

Carousel

91 QSM1637 Bear 19
91 QSM1629 Camel 19
91 QSM1627 Carrousel Display 19
91 QSM1667 Carrousel Gift Set 19
91 QSM1647 Elephant 19
91 QSM1649 Horse 19
91 QSM1639 Lion 19

Cats

87 PF3847 Calvin 12
86 HHA3486 Cat 10
93 QFM8305 Cat dressed as princess .26
93 QSM8102 Cat hugging mouse 24
91 QFM1677 Cat Witch w/broom 20
85 XHA3482 Cat wrapped in
Christmas lights 8
87 PF3859 Chuck 12
87 PF3827 Electra 12
87 PF3839 Felina 12
87 PF3879 Josh 12
87 PF3887 Lester 12
87 PF3819 Maude 12
87 PF3867 Taffi 12

Chick

86 EPF4163 Chick 9
88 EBO2371 Chick 13
88 EBO2591 Chick in egg, mechanical 13
94 QSM8123 Chick in wagon 27
84 EHA3461 Chick on grass, flocked ..6
83 EHA3469 Chick on two legs, flocked 5
77 EPF32 Chick, stamped with
production date 2
74 EPF206 Chick w/egg-shell hat 1
87 EHA4199 Chick/egg 11

Chipmunk

93 QSM8002 Chipmunk on
inflatable horse 24
95 QFM8179 Chipmunk w/corn 30

92 QFM9144 Chipmunk w/ribbon 23
94 QSM8003 Chipmunk w/kite 27
85 XHA3502 Mrs. Santa Chipmunk 9
93 QFM8185 Pilgrim Chipmunk
holding acorn 26
92 QSM9797 Praying Chipmunk 22

Christmas

91 QFM1799 1st Christmas - Koalas,
Dated 1991 20
74 XPF506 Angel holding star 1
83 XHA3467 Angel playing a mandolin .6
80 XPF3471 Angle in blue gown
holding a snowflake 3
83 XHA3487 Animals Raccoon, Rabbit &
Hedgehog Carolers 6
87 XHA3687 Apple, owl w/green scarf,
container 12
93 QFM8242 Arctic Fox in sweater . .26
93 QSM8205 Arctic Scene Backdrop ..26
93 QSM8232 Baby Walrus
wearing hat w/gift 26
93 QSM8222 Baby Whale w/hat 26
89 QFM1615 Baby's 1st Christmas,
Elf, Dated 1989 16
90 QFM1683 Baby's 1st Polar Bear,
Dated 1990 18
91 QFM1797 Baby's 1st - Rabbit,
Dated 1991 20
96 QFM8054 Bashful Mistletoe (3 pcs) 32
94 QFM8293 Bear on skates 28
87 XHA3709 Bear w/ice bear 12
92 QFM9111 Bear w/wheelbarrow ...24
85 XHA3392 Bears on sled 8
92 QFM9061 Bee w/Santa hat 23
76 XPF151 Betsey Clark 2
86 EPF4486 Blue Star 10
87 XHA3737 Bunny Boy 12
89 QFM1662 Bunny Caroler 16
87 XHA3749 Bunny Girl 12
87 XHA3729 Bunny in red w/bear 12
92 QFM9071 Bunny in Snow Dome,
Baby's 1st Christmas '92 23
93 QSM8235 Bunny w/scarf 26
96 QFM8121 Busy Bakers (2 pcs) ...32
95 QFM8199 Cameron on sled 30
90 QFM1693 Candy Caboose,
4th in set 18
95 QFM8307 Caroling Bear 31
95 QFM8309 Caroling Bunny 31
95 QFM8317 Caroling Mouse 31

Christmas (cont.)

85	XHA3482	Cat wrapped in Christmas lights	8
92	QFM9144	Chipmunk w/ribbon	23
95	QFM8197	Christmas Tree	31
91	QFM1769	Cookie Elf	20
91	QFM1777	Cookie Reindeer	20
91	QFM1767	Cookie Santa	20
92	QFM9174	Crab	23
92	QFM9084	Daughter - cat in p.j.'s "Daughter 1992"	23
83	XHA3419	Deer lying down, flocked	6
76	XPF144	Drummer Boy	2
89	QFM1622	Elf	16
85	XHA3452	Elf on gift box, container	8
83	QSM8215	Eskimo Child	26
87	XHA3757	Fawn	12
90	QFM1686	First Christmas Together	18
94	QFM8303	Fox on skates	28
90	QFM1656	Gentle Pal - Lamb	18
92	QFM9094	Gentle Pal - Squirrel	23
91	QFM1709	Gentle Pals Kitten	20
91	QFM1719	Gift Bringer Bunny	20
91	QFM1729	Gift Bringer Frog	20
91	QFM1737	Gift Bringer Kitten	20
91	QFM1739	Gift Bringer Pig	20
91	QFM1727	Gift Bringer Puppy	20
91	QFM1747	Gift Bringer Turtle	20
87	XHA207	Ginger Bear w/red bow	12
92	QFM9141	Giraffe as Christmas Tree	23
92	QFM9181	Goldfish	23
85	XHA3522	Goose w/real plaid ribbon bow	8
95	QFM8319	Hamster w/cookie	31
97	QFM8612	Holiday Harmony (3 pcs)	34
85	XHA3412	Horse on wheels	9
87	XHA3699	House	12
93	QSM8245	Husky puppy w/scarf	27
93	QSM8252	Igloo	27
91	QFM1717	Jingle Bell Santa	21
90	QFM1663	Jingle Bell Santa	18
92	QFM9131	Jingle Bell Santa	23
78	XPF1003	Joy Elf	3
89	QFM1605	Joy Elf	16
90	QFM1653	Kangaroo, "Hoppy Holidays!"	18
86	XHA3666	Katybeth	10
88	QFM1544	Kitten in slipper	13
83	XHA3447	Kitten in stocking cap	6
80	XPF3421	Kitten w/Santa's cap	3
84	XHA3401	Koala w/candy cane	7

95	QFM8287	Lion & Lamb	31
90	QFM1666	Mama Polar Bear	18
77	XPF122	Mouse	2
88	QFM1551	Mouse Angel	13
84	XHA3464	Mouse asleep in matchbox	7
89	QFM1655	Mouse Caroler	16
85	XHA3405	Mouse, Hallmark written on candle	9
91	QFM1789	Mouse in nightshirt	21
92	QFM9114	Mouse in peanut car	23
86	XHA3533	Mouse in shell	10
86	XHA3473	Mouse on ornament	10
79	XPF1017	Mouse w/stocking	3
82	XHA5023	Mouse writing w/real feather pen	4
83	XHA3459	Mouse yawning in green night cap	6
83	XHA3459	Mouse yawning in green night cap	6
96	QFM8044	Mr. and Mrs. Bear Claus (2 pcs)	32
89	QFM1595	Mr. Claus	16
86	XHA3573	Mr. Mouse	10
85	XHA3495	Mr. Santa Chipmunk	9
89	QFM1602	Mrs. Claus	16
94	QFM8286	Mrs. Claus	28
86	XHA3653	Mrs. Mouse	10
85	XHA3502	Mrs. Santa Chipmunk	9
78	XPF23	Mrs. Snowman w/purse	3
92	QFM9134	Music Maker Bear	23
91	QFM1779	Music Makers Bear	21
94	QFM8333	North Pole Sign	29
95	QFM8297	Nutcracker	31
92	QFM9171	Octopus	23
90	QFM1673	Papa Polar Bear & Child	18
94	QFM8313	Penguin	29
92	QFM9091	Penguin Ice Skating, "Dinky Rink 92"	23
86	XHA3486	Penguin on igloo, container	11
81	XHA3412	Penguin riding on a disc sled	4
83	XHA3439	Penguin w/metal skates	6
86	XHA4413	Penguin w/red & green scarf	11
93	QSM8212	Penguin w/ peppermint stick	27
88	QFM1541	Penguin	14
86	EPF4473	Pink Heart	11
83	XHA3407	Polar Bear on block of ice	6
93	QSM8265	Polar Bear playing piccolo	27

94	QFM8323	Polar Bears	29
91	QFM1787	Puppy in box, "Open Me First 1991"	21
84	XHA3494	Puppy in gift box	7
94	QXC4803	Puppy in tote bag	29
87	XHA3769	Puppy w/stocking	12
92	QFM9151	Rabbit on sled	23
89	QFM1652	Raccoon Caroler	16
81	XHA3405	Redbird throwing a snowball	4
84	XHA3501	Redbird w/black boots on snow	7
80	XPF3464	Reindeer on snow base	3
92	QFM9121	Reindeer Waving, Dated "'92"	23
74	XPF493	Reindeer w/antlers sitting	1
86	XHA3553	Rhonda	11
82	XHA5003	Rocking Horse	5
83	XHA3515	Rocking Horse	9
86	XHA3546	Rodney	11
86	EPF4466	Rodney container	11
84	XHA3391	Rodney Reindeer w/skates	7
76	XPF131	Santa	2
82	XHA5016	Santa	5
95	QFM8299	Santa	31
97	QFM8622	Santa Cameron	34
83	XHA3427	Santa carrying bag, w/"Rooftop Deliveries"	6
86	XHA3673	Santa	11
91	QFM1521	Santa	21
93	QSM8262	Santa Eskimo	27
75	XPF49	Santa holding canes	1
84	XHA3451	Santa sitting on chimney	7
74	XPF486	Santa standing on peppermint candy	1
87	XHA3717	Santa w/bag	12
89	XPF39	Santa w/Christmas packages	3
96	QFM8051	Santa's Helpers (3 pcs)	32
93	QSM8272	Seal w/earmuffs	27
86	XHA3566	Sebastian w/wreath around his neck	11
94	QFM8306	Sled Dog	29
80	XPF3451	Sleigh, red and green	3
91	QFM1749	Snow Bunny, "Joy"	21
91	QFM1759	Snow Lamb, "Peace"	21
91	QFM1757	Snow Mice, "Love"	21
97	QFM8602	Snowbear Season (3 pcs.)	34
76	XPF44	Snowman	2
88	QFM1534	Snowman	14
94	QFM8316	Snowman	29
83	XHA3479	Snowman in black	

		hat waving left hand	6
90	QFM1646	Snowman, "Let it Snow"	18
74	XPF473	Snowman w/redbird waving right hand	1
78	XPF33	Snowman w/cane & top hat	3
74	XPF	Snowman waving left hand	1
85	XHA3465	Soldier & Drum, container	9
84	XHA3481	Soldier w/gold drum	7
92	QFM9081	Son - dog in p.j.'s "Son 1992"	23
90	QFM1696	Squirrel Caroler	18
92	QFM9064	Squirrels in nutshell, 1st Christmas Together '92	23
92	QFM9124	Sweet Angel	23
88	QFM1591	Tank Car	14
89	QFM1612	Teacher Elf	16
90	QFM1676	Teacher Mouse	18
91	QFM1807	Teacher Raccoon, "For Teacher '91"	21
92	QFM9074	Teacher-Cat w/paper	24
82	XHA5013	Teddy Bear on drum, container	5
97	QFM8615	The Nativity (2 pcs)	34
96	QFM8061	The Sewing Club (3 pcs)	32
95	QFM8289	Toy Maker Beaver	31
89	QFM1562	Train Car	16
88	QFM1531	Train Engine	14
94	QFM8326	Tree	29
82	XHA5006	Tree, similar to Jolly Christmas tree orn	5
88	QFM1524	Unicorn	14
95	QFM9054	Walrus & Bird w/gift	24
90	QFM1643	Walrus wearing Santa hat	18

Container

86	EPF4486	Blue Star	10
84	EHA4121	Egg wearing overalls	6
85	HHA3462	Haunted House	8
86	EPF4176	Lambs	10
86	EPF4473	Pink Heart	11

Cosmopolitan Cats

88	GCT1098	Boy Kitten, wheelbarrow	14
88	GCT1099	Exercise Kitten	14
88	GCT1095	Girl Kitten, watering can	14
88	GCT1097	Girl Kittens, bouquet and basket	14
88	GCT1096	Girl Kittens, two kittens talking	14
88	GCT1100	Kitten/Gift	14

Cosmopolitan Cats (cont.)

88 GCT1102 Kitten/Hat 14
88 GCT1101 Kitten/Plant 14

Cupid

81 VPF3465 Cupid behind heart,
container, "I Love You" . . .3
97 QSM8552 Cupid Cameron 33
83 VHA4099 Cupid on cloud base 5
90 QSM1513 Hippo Cupid 17

Display

91 QSM1627 Carrousel Display 19
93 QFM8055 Display Stand 24

Dog

93 QFM8295 Dog dressed as dragon . .26
84 VHA3451 Dog holding heart
"Be Mine" 6
91 QSM1607 Dog in cap & gown 20
89 QSM1515 Dog & Kitten 15
88 GHA3524 Dog w/cap 13
84 HA4202 Dog w/scroll,
"You Are My Sunshine" . . .7
93 QSM8092 Dog w/Balloon Heart 24
92 QSM9847 Dog w/Trophy 21
92 QSM9817 Grad Dog 22
92 QFM9191 Party Dog 21
94 QFM8306 Sled Dog 29

Duck

75 EPF69 Duck holding Easter egg . .1
84 EHA3434 Duck in hat, flocked 6
91 QSM1549 Duck in puddle 19
86 EHA3463 Duck in umbrella 9
83 EHA3474 Duck on one leg, flocked . .5
85 EHA4132 Duck pulling flowered cart .8
86 EPF4113 Duck Sailor 9
84 EHA3474 Duck standing in pool
of water 6
79 EPF397 Duck standing on left leg . .3
84 HA4301 Duck w/blue kerchief,
"Howdy" 7
82 EHA3403 Duck w/daisy 4
93 QSM8135 Duck w/egg on spoon . . .25
86 EPF4246 Ducks 10
93 QSM8122 Sherlock Holmes Duck . .25

Easter

90 QSM1543 Artist Raccoon 17
91 QSM1557 Baby's 1st - Bunny 19

90 QSM1536 Baby's 1st Easter, Lamb .17
92 QSM9777 Baby's First Easter 22
77 EPF12 Barnaby 2
86 EHA4143 Basket 9
85 EHA3495 Basket w/bunny 8
95 QSM8047 Beauregard Bunny 30
77 EPF25 Bernadette 2
83 EHA2429 Betsey Clark holding bunny5
94 QSM8116 Birds in nest 27
96 QSM8064 Blue Ribbon Bunny 31
88 EBO2314 Boy Bunny 13
90 QSM1682 Boy Bunny 17
87 EHA4197 Boy lamb w/hat 11
84 EHA3401 Brown Bunny 6
88 EBO2384 Bunnies 13
89 EBO3025 Bunnies 15
87 EHA4179 Bunny asleep 11
86 EPF4133 Bunny Boy 9
88 EBO2321 Bunny & carrot 13
92 QSM9799 Bunny & carrot 22
79 EPF377 Bunny, flocked 3
83 EHA4089 Bunny & Flower 5
86 EPF4106 Bunny Girl, made of rubber .9
74 EPF186 Bunny holding little chick .1
89 QSM1552 Bunny in wagon 15
83 EHA4117 Bunny lying on egg 5
93 QSM8115 Bunny painting egg 25
91 QSM1597 Bunny praying 19
89 EBO3092 Bunny & Skateboard 15
83 EHA3457 Bunny, small 5
88 EBO2311 Bunny w/basket 13
86 EHA3476 Bunny w/butterfly 9
75 EPF49 Bunny w/carrot 1
85 EHA3482 Bunny w/carrot 8
93 QSM8142 Bunny w/Basket 25
93 QSM8125 Bunny w/cracked egg . . .25
95 QSM8029 Cameron Bunny 30
82 EPF3702 Ceramic Bunny w/eggs . . .4
85 EPR3701 Ceramic Bunny w/purple egg .8
88 EBO2371 Chick 13
88 EBO2591 Chick in egg, mechanical 13
94 QSM8123 Chick in wagon 27
84 EHA3461 Chick on grass 6
83 EHA3469 Chick on two legs 5
77 EPF32 Chick 2
74 EPF206 Chick w/egg-shell hat 1
87 EHA4199 Chick/Egg 11
74 EPF193 Child in bunny suit 1
95 QSM8027 Cottage 30
91 QSM1587 Daughter Bunny
w/wheelbarrow 19

75 EPF69 Duck holding Easter Egg .1
84 EHA3434 Duck in hat 6
91 QSM1549 Duck in puddle 19
86 EHA3463 Duck in umbrella 9
83 EHA3474 Duck on one leg 5
85 EHA4132 Duck puling flowered cart .8
86 EPF4113 Duck Sailor 9
84 EHA3474 Duck standing in water . . .6
79 EPF397 Duck standing on left leg . .3
82 EHA3403 Duck w/daisy 4
93 QSM8135 Duck w/egg on spoon . . .25
89 EBO3215 E. Bunny 15
90 QSM1726 E-Bunny w/paint can 17
98 QSM8145 Easter Basket 25
96 QSM8024 Easter Egg Hunt 31
93 QSM8152 Easter Garden Backdrop 25
97 QSM8562 Easter Parade (2 pcs) . . .33
84 EHA4121 Egg wearing overalls 6
94 QSM8033 Egg Wishing Well 27
88 EBO2594 Egg, mechanical 13
89 EHA3417 Flocked Bunny on hind feet5
83 EBO3032 Flowers 15
97 QSM8575 Getting Ready for Spring 33
86 EHA3503 Girl Bunny 9
90 QSM1675 Girl Bunny 17
88 EBO2311 Girl Bunny w/basket 13
87 EHA4187 Girl Lamb w/hat 11
75 EPF57 Girl w/baby ducks 1
88 EBO2381 Goose 13
92 QSM9789 Goose in bonnet 22
86 EHA3516 Goose w/bonnet & bow . .9
96 QSM8114 Happy Birthday
Clowns (2) 31
89 EBO3035 Happy Easter 15
85 EHA3442 Lamb 8
88 EBO2374 Lamb 13
91 QSM1569 Lamb & Duck
"Happy Easter 1991" . . .20
81 EPF402 Lamb 3
92 QSM9787 Lamb, "Happy Easter 1992"22
94 QSM8132 Lamb in Flower Patch . . .27
93 QSM8112 Lamb Shearing Shrub . . .25
89 QSM1545 Lamb w/Easter basket . .15
91 QSM1577 Mother Bunny
holding basket 20
90 QSM1546 Mouse & Bunny,
"Happy Easter" 17
85 EHA3455 Mouse holding violets . . .8
94 QSM8243 Mouse w/flower 27
96 QSM8111 Noah and Friends
(5 pcs) 31

97 QSM8572 Noah's Friends (2 pcs) .33
97 QSM8605 Peter Pan (5 pcs) 33
92 QSM9797 Praying Chipmunk 22
95 QSM8049 Prince Charming 30
88 EBO2604 Rabbit on wheels 13
94 QSM8113 Rabbit w/croquet 28
94 QSM8083 Rabbit w/egg shaped
watering can 28
87 EHA4167 Sebastian w/bunny ears .11
95 QSM8039 Selby 30
86 EPF4126 Sheep & Bell 9
93 QSM8122 Sherlock Holmes Duck . .25
97 QFM8685 Six Dwarfs (3 pcs) 34
97 QFM8535 Snow White and
Dancing Dwarf 34
90 QSM1553 Squirrel 17
95 QSM8037 Stylish Rabbit 30
92 QSM9779 SweatShirt Bunny 22

Egg

88 EBO2384 Bunnies 13
89 EBO3025 Bunnies 15
86 EPF4203 Butterfly 9
86 EHA4156 Egg, Geese and Tulips . .9
86 EPF4183 Egg & Rabbits 10
94 QSM8033 Egg Wishing Well 27
88 EBO2594 Egg, mechanical 13
86 EPF4143 Happy Easter 10
89 EBO3035 Happy Easter 15
86 EPF4196 Hearts 10
86 EPF4253 Polka Dot 10
86 EPF4156 Striped 10

Elf

91 QFM1769 Cookie Elf 20
89 QFM1622 Elf 16
83 XHA3452 Elf on gift box, container . .8
78 XPF1003 Joy Elf 3
89 XPF1605 Joy Elf 16

Fourth of July

94 QSM8043 Bear w/flag 28
94 QSM8053 Document 28
94 QSM8036 Eagle w/hat 28
94 QSM8056 Flag 28
94 QSM8046 Mouse saying pledge . . .28

Fox

93 QFM8242 Arctic Fox in Sweater . . .26
94 QFM8303 Fox on skates 28
91 QFM1689 Fox w/piece of pie 20
93 QSM8065 Fox w/heart wreath 24
87 PF3807 Franklin 1

Ghost

- 81 HHA3402 Ghost jumping from pumpkin 4
- 93 QFM8282 Ghost on Tombstone . .26
- 92 QFM9014 Ghost w/candy corn "1992 Boo!" 22

Goose

- 88 EBO2381 Goose 13
- 92 QSM9789 Goose in bonnet 22
- 86 EHA3516 Goose w/bonnet & bow . .9
- 85 XHA3522 Goose w/real plaid ribbon bow 8

Graduation

- 91 QSM1607 Dog in cap & gown 20
- 88 GHA3524 Dog w/cap 13
- 92 QSM9817 Grad Dog 22
- 90 QSM1563 Owl, "Class of 1990" 17
- 89 QSM1555 Owl 15
- 86 GHA3456 Owl in cap/gown 10

Halloween

- 74 HPF Scarecrow w/Jack-O-Lantern 1
- 74 HPF502 Jack-O-Lantern w/green leaf 1
- 75 HPF29 Devil 1
- 76 HPF515 Owl on Jack-O-Lantern . .2
- 76 HPF522 Scarecrow w/Jack-O-Lantern.........2
- 77 HPF32 Witch w/broom & black cat 2
- 78 HPF1013 Kitten w/green hat 2
- 81 HHA3402 Ghost jumping from pumpkin 4
- 82 HHA3466 Kitten w/real bow, flocked .4
- 82 HHA3456 Witch w/broom, frog on her hat 4
- 82 HHA3446 Jack-O-Lantern 4
- 83 HHA3437 Shirt Tales, Raccoon 6
- 84 HHA3454 Jack-O-Lantern 6
- 84 HHA3441 Kitten crouching, flocked ..6
- 85 HHA3462 Haunted House, container 8
- 86 HHA3486 Cat 10
- 86 HHS3473 Witch w/pumpkin 10
- 87 HHA3487 Raccoon Witch w/pumpkin 11
- 88 QFM1501 Mouse/Pumpkin 13
- 88 QFM1504 Owl w/bag 13
- 89 QFM1565 Bunny Ghost, "Boo" 15
- 89 QFM1572 Mouse Witch 15
- 89 QFM1575 Raccoon "Happy Halloween" 15
- 90 QFM1613 Green Monster 17
- 90 QFM1616 Scarecrow 17
- 91 QFM1669 Bear w/pumpkin cookie . .20
- 91 QFM1677 Cat Witch w/broom 20
- 91 QFM1679 Mummy w/treat sack 20
- 92 QFM9014 Ghost w/candy corn, "1992 Boo!" 22
- 92 QFM9024 Haunted House 22
- 92 QFM9031 Mouse as clown 22
- 92 QFM9021 Pumpkin, "Trick or Treat" 22
- 93 QFM8285 Animated Cauldron 25
- 93 QFM8285 Bear dressed as bat 25
- 93 QFM8422 Bunny dressed as super hero 26
- 93 QFM8305 Cat dressed as princess .26
- 93 QFM8295 Dog dressed As dragon ..26
- 93 QFM8282 Ghost on tombstone 26
- 93 QFM8275 Haunted Halloween Backdrop, Cardboard . .26
- 93 QFM8292 Mouse dressed as witch .26
- 93 QFM8302 Owl popping out of pumpkin 26
- 94 QFM8283 Fence w/lantern 28
- 94 QFM8263 Squirrel as clown 28
- 94 QFM8266 Bunny Alien 28
- 94 QFM8276 Pumpkin w/hat 28
- 94 QFM8273 Black Kitten 28
- 95 QFM8157 Cute Witch 30
- 95 QFM8147 Cameron in pumpkin costume 30
- 95 QFM8159 Friendly Monster 30
- 95 QFM8149 Rhino Mummy 30
- 95 QFM8139 Haunted House 30
- 95 QSM8099 Stepmother 30
- 96 QFM8131 Peanuts™ Pumpkin Patch (5 pcs) 32
- 96 QFM8124 Happy Haunting (2 pcs) .32

Hedgehog

- 92 QSM9859 Hedgehog 21
- 93 QSM8026 Hedgehog eating hot dog 24
- 84 THA3444 Hedgehog holding pilgrim hat behind him 7
- 83 VHA4107 Hedgehog on heart 5

House

- 95 QSM8027 Cottage 30
- 92 QFM9024 Haunted House 22
- 95 QFM8139 Haunted House 30
- 87 XHA3699 House 12
- 93 QSM8252 Igloo 27

Hugga Bunch

- 84 HA3731 Bubbles 7
- 84 HA3733 Huggins 7
- 84 HA3728 Hugsy 7
- 84 HA3734 Impkins 8
- 84 HA3721 Patootie 8
- 84 HA3729 Precious 8
- 84 HA3735 Tickles 8
- 84 HA3727 Tweaker 8

Indian

- 88 QFM1511 Indian Bear 13
- 93 QFM8162 Indian Bear w/honey ...26
- 92 QFM9004 Indian Bunnies w/pumpkin, squaw w/papoose 23
- 94 QFM8353 Indian Bunny 28
- 94 QFM8346 Indian Chickadee 28
- 91 QFM1626 Indian Chipmunk 17
- 91 QFM1687 Indian Maiden Mouse ...20
- 93 QFM8182 Indian Squirrel w/pie 26
- 88 QFM8165 Indian Turkey eating corn 26
- 75 TPF29 Indian w/dog 1

Jingle Bell

- 91 QFM1717 Jingle Bell Santa 21
- 90 QFM1663 Jingle Bell Santa 18
- 92 QFM9131 Jingle Bell Santa 23

Katybeth

- 86 XHA3666 Katybeth 10

Kitten

- 94 QFM8273 Black Kitten 28
- 88 GCT1098 Boy Kitten, wheelbarrow .14
- 88 GCT1099 Exercise Kitten 14
- 91 QFM1709 Gentle Pals Kitten 20
- 91 QFM1737 Gift Bringer Kitten 20
- 88 GCT1095 Girl Kitten, watering can .14
- 88 GCT1097 Girl Kittens, bouquet and basket 14
- 88 GCT1096 Girl Kittens, two kittens talking 14
- 90 QSM1516 Kitten 17
- 84 HHA3441 Kitten crouching, flocked ..6
- 92 QSM9839 Kitten for Dad,"Best Dad" 21
- 92 QSM9837 Kitten for Mom, "Best Mom" 21
- 81 HA4906 Kitten in basket w/flowers .4
- 92 QSM9829 Kitten in bib, Dated 1992 21
- 88 QFM1544 Kitten in slipper 13
- 83 XHA3447 Kitten in stocking cap 6
- 83 VHA3489 Kitten lying on lace pillow .6
- 89 QSM1505 Kitten on pillow 15
- 84 HA4201 Kitten w/banner, bird, "Be Happy" 7
- 78 HPF1013 Kitten w/green hat 2
- 82 HHA3466 Kitten w/real bow, flocked .4
- 80 XPF3421 Kitten w/Santa's cap 3
- 85 VHA3495 Kitten w/heart 8
- 88 GCT1100 Kitten/Gift 14
- 88 GCT1102 Kitten/Hat 14
- 88 GCT1101 Kitten/Plant 14

Koala Bear

- 95 QSM8019 Koala Bear 29
- 88 VHA3531 Koala & Hearts 13
- 88 VHA3651 Koala & Lollipop 13
- 88 VHA3631 Koala & Ruffled Heart ..13
- 84 XHA3401 Koala w/candy cane 7
- 88 VHA3624 Koala w/bow & arrow ..12

Lamb

- 92 QFM9044 Barnyard Lamb 22
- 87 EHA4197 Boy lamb w/hat 11
- 90 QFM1656 Gentle Pal - Lamb 18
- 87 EHA4187 Girl Lamb w/hat 11
- 85 EHA3442 Lamb 8
- 88 EBO2374 Lamb 13
- 88 QFM1574 Lamb 14
- 93 QSM8482 Lamb Betsy Ross w/flag .25
- 91 QSM1569 Lamb & Duck "Happy Easter 1991" ...20
- 81 EPF402 Lamb, flocked 3
- 92 QSM9787 Lamb, "Happy Easter 1992"22
- 94 QSM8132 Lamb in flower patch ...27
- 93 QSM8112 Lamb shearing shrub ...25
- 89 QSM1545 Lamb w/Easter basket ...15
- 84 HA4304 Lamb w/pink ribbon, "Bless You" 7
- 91 QFM1759 Snow Lamb, "Peace" ...21

Lion

- 91 QSM1639 Lion 19
- 95 QFM8287 Lion & Lamb 31
- 92 QSM9719 Lion w/ruffled heart 22

Mouse

- 91 QSM1519 Artist Mouse 19
- 95 QFM8317 Caroling Mouse 31
- 89 QSM1502 Gray Mouse w/heart "Be Mine" 15
- 90 QSM1533 Grey Mouse w/ heart glasses 17
- 77 XPF122 Mouse 2

Mouse (cont.)

92	QFM9031	Mouse as clown	.22
84	XHA3464	Mouse asleep in matchbox	7
90	QSM1546	Mouse & Bunny, "Happy Easter"	.17
89	QFM1655	Mouse Caroler	.16
93	QFM8292	Mouse dressed as witch	.26
85	XHA3405	Mouse, Hallmark written on candle	.9
85	EHA3455	Mouse holding violets	.8
88	QFM1514	Mouse in cornucopia	.13
81	HA4905	Mouse in metal bucket w/poinsettia	.4
91	QFM1789	Mouse in nightshirt	.21
92	QFM9114	Mouse in peanut car	.23
86	XHA3533	Mouse in shell	.10
86	XHA3473	Mouse on ornament	.10
94	QSM8046	Mouse saying Pledge of Allegiance	.28
93	QSM8475	Mouse Statue of Liberty	.25
90	QSM1603	Mouse w/blue life preserver	17
95	QFM8189	Mouse w/cranberries	.30
87	SHA3467	Mouse w/hat & shamrock	11
87	VHA3527	Mouse w/heart says, "Love Ya"	.11
84	HA4203	Mouse w/heart, "You're Special"	.7
95	QFM8187	Mouse w/pumpkin	.30
84	THA3451	Mouse w/real feather in headband/drum	.7
92	QSM9769	Mouse w/shamrock	.22
79	XPF1017	Mouse w/stocking	.3
93	QSM8035	Mouse wearing sunglasses	.24
89	QFM1572	Mouse	.15
94	QSM8243	Mouse w/flower	.27
82	XHA5023	Mouse writing w/real feather pen	.4
83	XHA3459	Mouse yawning in green night cap	.6
88	QFM1501	Mouse/Pumpkin	.13
86	XHA3573	Mr. Mouse	.10
86	XHA3653	Mrs. Mouse	.10
90	QFM1636	Pilgrim Mouse	.18
82	THA3433	Pilgrim Mouse on orange leaf	.4
93	QFM8175	Pilgrim Mouse praying	.26
91	QFM1757	Snow Mice, "Love"	.21
83	SHA3407	White Mouse holding shamrock	.5

Nativity

89	QFM1632	Blue King	.16
88	QFM1581	Donkey	.14
88	QFM1564	Jesus	.14
88	QFM1561	Joseph	.14
88	QFM1574	Lamb	.14
88	QFM1554	Mary	.14
89	QFM1642	Pink King	.16
88	QFM1571	Shepherd	.14
88	QFM1584	Stable	.14
89	QFM1685	Stable & 9 Figurines	.16
89	QFM1635	Yellow King	.16

Owl

87	XHA3687	Apple, owl w/green scarf	.12
90	QSM1563	Owl, "Class of 1990"	.17
89	QSM1555	Owl	.15
86	GHA3456	Owl in cap/gown	.10
94	QSM8085	Owl in stump	.27
76	HPF515	Owl on Jack-O-Lantern	.2
93	QFM8302	Owl popping out of pumpkin	.26
88	QFM1504	Owl w/bag	.13

Patriotic

93	QSM8472	Goat Uncle Sam	.25
93	QSM8492	Hedgehog Patriot w/fife	.25
93	QSM8482	Lamb Betsy Ross w/flag	.25
93	QSM8465	Liberty Bell w/bird	.25
93	QSM8475	Mouse Statue of Liberty	.25
93	QSM8495	Patriotic Backdrop	.25

People

95	QSM8107	Bashful Boy	.29
95	QSM8109	Bashful Girl	.29
97	QFM8582	Bashful Visitors (3 pcs)	.33
89	QFM1632	Blue King	.16
74	EPF193	Child in bunny suit	.1
95	QFM8157	Cute Witch	.30
75	HPF29	Devil	.1
76	XPF144	Drummer Boy	.2
93	QSM8215	Eskimo Child	.26
95	QFM8159	Friendly Monster	.30
75	EPF57	Girl w/baby ducks	.1
88	QFM1564	Jesus	.14
88	QFM1561	Joseph	.14
82	CDB8818	Little Bo Peep w/sheep	.5
96	QSM8011	Penda Kids (2 pcs)	.31
78	TPF1003	Pilgrim Boy w/turkey	.2
78	TPF1016	Pilgrim Girl w/flowers	.2
74	TPF13	Pilgrims	.1

76	TPF502	Pilgrims kneeling, "Give Thanks"	.2
77	TPF502	Pilgrims kneeling, "Give Thanks"	.2
89	QFM1642	Pink King	.16
97	QSM8545	Sulu & Sara, Penda Kids™	.33
89	QFM1635	Yellow King	.16

Pig

92	QSM9759	Ballet Pig w/rose	.22
92	QFM9041	Barnyard Pig	.22
91	QFM1739	Gift Bringer Pig	.20
90	QSM1526	Pig	.17
93	QSM8022	Pig in a blanket	.24

Pipe

76	SPF266	Pipe w/green shamrock	.2
80	SPF1017	Pipe w/green shamrock	.3

Polar Bear

90	QFM1666	Mama Polar Bear	.18
90	QFM1673	Papa Polar Bear & Child	.18
83	XHA3407	Polar Bear on block of ice	.6
93	QSM8265	Polar Bear playing piccolo	.27
94	QFM8323	Polar Bears	.29

Pumpkin

95	QSM8127	Pumpkin Carriage	.30
92	QFM9021	Pumpkin, "Trick or Treat"	22
94	QFM8276	Pumpkin w/hat	.28

Puppy

90	QFM1703	Get Well Puppy	.17
91	QFM1727	Gift Bringer Puppy	.20
93	QSM8245	Husky Puppy w/scarf	.27
92	QSM9767	Puppy	.22
81	HA4902	Puppy in basket w/flowers	4
91	QFM1787	Puppy in box, "Open Me First 1991"	.21
84	XHA3494	Puppy in gift box	.7
91	QSM1529	Puppy in shoe	.19
94	QXC4803	Puppy in tote bag	.29
90	QSM1583	Puppy w/shirt "100% Huggable"	.17
87	XHA3769	Puppy w/stocking	.12

Rabbit

92	QFM9151	Rabbit on Sled	.23
88	EBO2604	Rabbit on wheels	.13
92	QSM9827	Rabbit & Squirrel	.21

92	QFM9201	Rabbit w/heart carrot	.21
84	HA4302	Rabbit w/pink heart, "So Glad We're Friends"	.7
94	QSM8113	Rabbit w/croquet	.28
94	QSM8083	Rabbit w/leg shaped watering can	.28
94	QSM8016	Rabbit w/heart cutouts	.27
94	QSM8066	Rabbit w/ice cream	.27
95	QSM8037	Stylish Rabbit	.30

Raccoon

89	QFM1652	Raccoon Caroler	.16
95	QSM8087	Raccoon & Flower	.29
89	QFM1575	Raccoon "Happy Halloween"	.15
94	QSM8063	Raccoon in flippers	.27
81	THA3402	Raccoon Pilgrim w/corn	.4
91	QSM1517	Raccoon Thief, "You Stole My Heart"	.19
90	QSM1586	Raccoon w/pineapple	.17
87	HHA3487	Raccoon Witch w/pumpkin	11
93	QSM8062	Raccoon w/cutout heart	.25
83	HHA3437	Shirt Tales, Raccoon	.6
91	QFM1837	Skating Raccoon	.19

Reindeer

91	QFM1777	Cookie Reindeer	.20
80	XPF3464	Reindeer on snow base	.3
92	QFM9121	Reindeer Waving	.23
74	XPF493	Reindeer w/antlers/sitting	.1

Rocking Horse

82	XHA5003	Rocking Horse	.5
85	XHA3515	Rocking Horse	.9

Rodney

86	XHA3553	Rhonda	.11
86	XHA3546	Rodney	.11
86	EPF4466	Rodney container	.11
84	XHA3391	Rodney Reindeer w/skates	7

Santa

91	QFM1767	Cookie Santa	.20
91	QFM1717	Jingle Bell Santa	.21
90	QFM1663	Jingle Bell Santa	.18
92	QFM9131	Jingle Bell Santa	.23
89	QFM1595	Mr. Claus	.16
85	XHA3495	Mr. Santa Chipmunk	.9
89	QFM1602	Mrs. Claus	.16
94	QFM8286	Mrs. Claus	.28
76	XPF131	Santa	.2

Unicorn

86	VHA3503	Unicorn 9
88	QFM1524	Unicorn, Dated 1988 14

Valentine's Day

96	QSM8014	Alice in Wonderland (5) .31
91	QSM1519	Artist Mouse 19
92	QSM9759	Ballet Pig w/rose 22
95	QSM8107	Bashful Boy 29
95	QSM8109	Bashful Girl 29
91	QSM1509	Bear 19
92	QSM9717	Bear 22
89	QSM1522	Bear Baker 15
94	QSM8006	Bear Mailman 27
94	QSM8013	Beaver w/Card 27
93	QSM8095	Box of candy 24
89	QSM1512	Bunny Ballerina 15
91	QSM1537	Bunny w/heart 19
95	QSM8009	Cameron 29
93	QSM8102	Cat Hugging Mouse 24
83	VHA3497	Cherub sitting on top of letters "Love" . . .5
94	QSM8003	Chipmunk w/kite 27
95	QSM8117	Cinderella 29
87	VHA3507	Clown Teddy holding heart11
81	VPF3465	Cupid behind heart container, "I Love You" . . .3
97	QSM8552	Cupid Cameron 33
83	VHA4099	Cupid on cloud base, Dated 1983 5
84	VHA3451	Dog holding heart "Be Mine" 6
89	QSM1515	Dog & Kitten 15
93	QSM8092	Dog w/balloon heart 24
93	QSM8065	Fox w/heart wreath 24
87	VHA3519	Giraffe 11
89	QSM1502	Gray Mouse w/heart "Be Mine" 15
90	QSM1533	Gray Mouse w/heart glasses 17
93	QSM8082	Heartland Forest Backdrop, cardboard . . .25
83	VHA4107	Hedgehog on heart, container 5
90	QSM1513	Hippo Cupid 17
82	VHA3403	Kermit on top of red heart, "Prince of Hearts" 4
90	QSM1516	Kitten 17
83	VHA3489	Kitten lying on lace pillow .5
89	QSM1505	Kitten on pillow 15
85	VHA3495	Kitten with heart 8

95	QSM8019	Koala Bear 29
88	VHA3531	Koala & Hearts 13
88	VHA3651	Koala & Lollipop 13
88	VHA3631	Koala & Ruffled Heart . . .13
88	VHA3624	Koala w/bow & arrow . . .12
92	QSM9719	Lion w/ruffled heart 22
79	VPF1007	Love, resembles carved wood 3
94	QSM8023	Mailbox 27
82	VHA3416	Miss Piggy in long gown w/crown 4
87	VHA3527	Mouse w/heart says "Love Ya" 11
94	QSM8085	Owl in stump 27
84	VHA3471	Panda holding heart with "Luv" 6
93	QSM8105	Panda w/foil heart 25
86	VHA3523	Pandas 9
96	QSM8011	Penda Kids (2 pcs) 31
92	QSM9757	Penguin in tux 22
84	VHA3464	Penguin w/top hat & heart 6
90	QSM1526	Pig 17
92	QSM9767	Puppy 22
91	QSM1529	Puppy in shoe 19
94	QSM8016	Rabbit w/heart cutouts . .27
91	QSM1517	Raccoon Thief, ... "You Stole My Heart" . .19
93	QSM8062	Raccoon w/cutout heart .25
86	VHA3516	Sebastian w/heart collar . .9
85	VHA3482	Skunk holding heart, . . .8
93	QSM8072	Skunk w/lacy heart 25
95	QSM8017	St. Bernard 29
90	QSM1506	Stitched Teddy w/red heart 17
96	QSM8004	Sweetheart Cruise (3 pcs)31
85	VHA4112	Teddy Bear on red heart . .8
95	QSM8007	Tree 29
93	QSM8075	Tree Stump and paint can 25
80	VPF3451	Turtle w/red hearts on its shell 3
86	VHA3503	Unicorn 9

Walrus

92	QFM9054	Walrus & Bird w/gift 24
90	QFM1643	Walrus wearing Santa Hat 18

Witch

77	HPF32	Witch w/broom & black cat 2
82	HHA3456	Witch w/broom frog on her hat 4
86	HHS3473	Witch w/pumpkin 10

Hallmark ™ For The Holidays

Willie & Jo Willis
Oregon

Joy Hamel
Washington

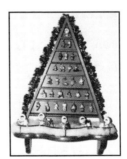

Joan Phillipson
Washington

Deborah Hubschman
Florida

Order your subscription to the Collectors' Bulletin™ Today!
Save $5.00 off the subscription rate
when you use this coupon!

Specializing in Limited Edition Collectibles Since 1983!

~ 6 Issues a year!

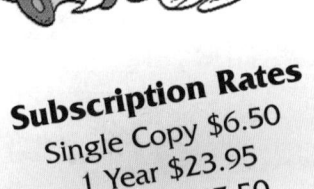

Subscription Rates
Single Copy $6.50
1 Year $23.95
2 Years $47.50

Find the latest
information on many
collectible lines,
including
Hallmark™ Keepsake Ornaments,®
Merry Miniatures® and
Kiddie Car Classic™ news!

Notes

Notes

Notes

1-900-COLLECTORS' LINE©

Buy - Sell - Trade Collectibles Across the U.S.A...
Or be the first to know the week's latest hot news as Rosie reports it!
Place your "VOICE AD™" on Rosie's collector advertising line!
Here's how it works! Call 1-900-740-7575

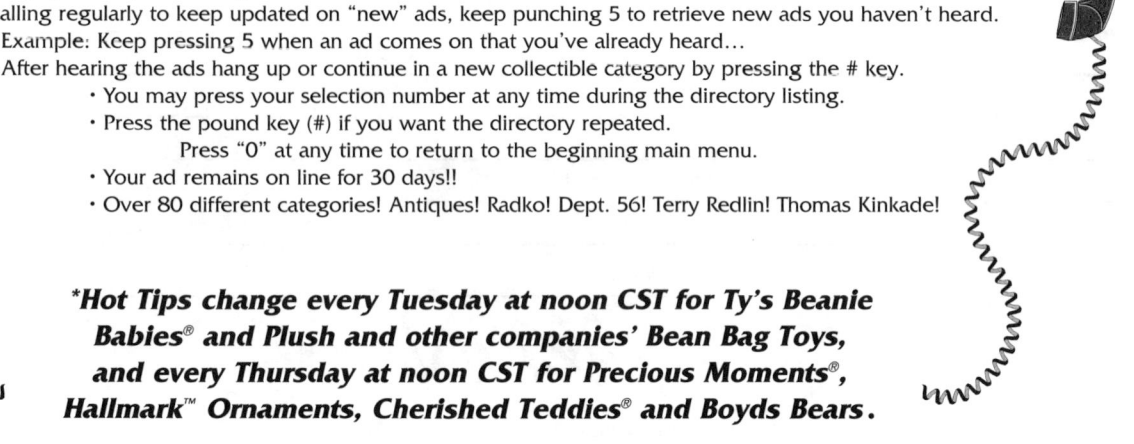

- Listen to Rosie as she directs you to record your own ad or find out what's available for sale!
- You MUST wait until Rosie starts listing the directory before pressing your selection number.
      (She will say, "The following is a directory... ") Then you can press the desired number!
- Once you have pressed your collectible's selection number, you will be given a choice to select
      "1" if you wish to advertise your collectibles for sale or
      "2" if you are trying to locate collectibles for sale, etc.
- Have that paper and pencil ready!
- When calling regularly to keep updated on "new" ads, keep punching 5 to retrieve new ads you haven't heard.
      Example: Keep pressing 5 when an ad comes on that you've already heard...
      After hearing the ads hang up or continue in a new collectible category by pressing the # key.
            - You may press your selection number at any time during the directory listing.
            - Press the pound key (#) if you want the directory repeated.
                  Press "0" at any time to return to the beginning main menu.
            - Your ad remains on line for 30 days!!
            - Over 80 different categories! Antiques! Radko! Dept. 56! Terry Redlin! Thomas Kinkade!

Hot Tips change every Tuesday at noon CST for Ty's Beanie
Babies® and Plush and other companies' Bean Bag Toys,
and every Thursday at noon CST for Precious Moments®,
Hallmark™ Ornaments, Cherished Teddies® and Boyds Bears.

Hot Tips on the following:

*Press 1 - Precious Moments® Collectibles
*Press 2 - Hallmark™ Ornaments
*Press 0 - Cherished Teddies®
*Press *, and then pause for instructions to
      press 1 for Ty's Beanie Babies® and
      Plush and other companies' Bean
      Bag Toys.
*Press *, and then pause for instructions to
      press 2 for Boyds Bears.
(Note: The * is located below the 7 on your keypad.)

To Advertise or Locate:

Press 31 - African-American Memorabilia
Press 12 - All God's Children
Press 69 - Andrea Birds
Press 34 - Antique and Classic Cars
Press 46 - Antique Cookie Jars
Press 33 - Antique Furniture
Press 44 - Antique Toys
Press 42 - Antiques
Press 64 - Ashton Drake Dolls
Press 86 - Barbie® Dolls
Press 27 - Baseball Cards
Press 78 - Beanie Babies®, Ty's
Press 48 - Boyds Bears
Press 60 - Brenders Art Prints
Press 67 - Calico Kittens
Press 74 - Campbell's Soup Collectibles
Press 77 - Carnival Glass
Press 18 - Cherished Teddies®
Press 20 - Coca-Cola Collectibles
Press 36 - Coins

Press 5 - Collectibles Shows and Auctions
Press 19 - Collectible Dolls
Press 11 - Collector Plates
Press 13 - David Winter
Press 7 - Department 56
Press 32 - Depression Glass
Press 22 - Disney Collectibles
Press 76 - Dreamsicles
Press 39 - Duck Decoys
Press 25 - Elvis Collectibles
Press 6 - Enesco, Carlton and other Ornaments
Press 40 - Farm Toys and Tractors
Press 30 - Fenton Glass
Press 71 - Fiesta Ware
Press 84 - Forma Vitrum™
Press 26 - Gone With The Wind Collectibles
Press 58 - Hallmark's™ Barbie® Collectibles
Press 4 - Hallmark™ Ornaments and other
      Hallmark™ Collectibles
Press 83 - Harbour Lights
Press 82 - Harmony Kingdom
Press 15 - Hummels
Press 75 - Indian Relics
Press 43 - Jewelry and Watches
Press 47 - Legends
Press 66 - Lena Liu Collectibles/Prints
Press 14 - Lilliput Lane
Press 70 - Lladro
Press 79 - Longaberger® Baskets
Press 10 - Lowell Davis
Press 73 - Lunch Boxes
Press 68 - Mary's Moo Moos

Press 37 - Matchbox Cars
Press 9 - Memories of Yesterday
Press 52 - McDonald's Collectibles and
      other Food Chain Collectibles
Press 81 - Old Farmall Tractors
Press 80 - Old John Deere Tractors
Press 63 - Old World Ornaments
Press 45 - Paper Dolls, Paper Collectibles
Press 24 - Penni Bears
Press 53 - Phone Cards
Press 50 - Precious Moments™ Applause® Dolls
Press 3 - Precious Moments® Collectibles
Press 49 - Precious Moments® PMC Dolls
Press 85 - PM Rose Art Dolls
Press 57 - Radko Ornaments
Press 72 - Royal Doulton
Press 21 - Sarah's Attic
Press 55 - Shelia's Collectibles
Press 51 - Silver Ornaments
Press 8 - Snowbabies®
Press 29 - Sports Memorabilia
Press 28 - Star Trek Collectibles
Press 35 - Stamps
Press 17 - Swarovski Crystal
Press 62 - Terry Redlin Art Prints
Press 38 - Thomas Kinkade
Press 59 - Thorndike Art Prints
Press 41 - Today's Modern-Day Advertising Tins
Press 16 - Tom Clark Gnomes
Press 54 - Trading Cards
Press 65 - Walt Disney Classics
Press 23 - Wee Forest Folk
Press 61 - Zoland Art Prints

**Our 900 number is approved through
AT&T! $2.00 per minute. Touch-tone
phone required. Must be 18 years of age.
Any questions? Call us at 309/668-2211.
Voice Ads™ (Since 1991)**

**by Rosie Wells Enterprises, Inc.
22341 E. Wells Rd., Canton, IL 61520
E-mail: Rosie@RosieWells.com
Web address: http://www.RosieWells.com**
Collectors' Outreach in Advertising! Buy! Sell! Trade!

Rosie's Secondary Market Price Guides for...

Precious Moments® Company's Dolls

❋ Easy to read format!
❋ Numerical Index
❋ Over 120 pages ❋ Use for insuring ❋ Full color
Co-edited by the nation's leading authority on PMC Dolls, Jan Kropenick.

©1998 Precious Moments, Inc. Licensee, Rosie Wells Enterprises, Inc. "Precious Moments®" is a registered trademark of Precious Moments, Inc. All Rights Reserved.

Precious Moments® Collectibles

❋ Easy to read! ❋ Detailed description and Line Drawing of each piece ❋ Alphabetical Index and Subject Index ❋ Today's Current Value of each piece ❋ 8¹/²" x 6³/⁴" ❋ Over 250 pages ❋ Spiral Bound ❋ Use for insuring! ❋ The avid collectors' and retailers' favorite guide ❋ Call us, or look for this guide at your Precious Moments® Collectibles dealer.

©1998 Precious Moments, Inc. Licensee, Rosie Wells Enterprises, Inc. All Rights Reserved. "Precious Moments" is a registered trademark of Precious Moments, Inc.

Precious Moments™ Applause® Dolls

❋ Premiere Edition ❋ 5¹/²" x 8¹/²"
❋ Over 80 pages ❋ Perfect Bound
❋ Detailed Description with black and white photo of each doll with Today's Current Value ❋ Only guide published for these collectible dolls ❋ Alphabetically Indexed ❋ Use for insuring! ❋ Includes informative articles on Applause® Doll collecting
❋ Call us or look for this guide at your Precious Moments® dealer.

©1998 Precious Moments, Inc. Licensee, Rosie Wells Enterprises, Inc. "Precious Moments" is a registered trademark of Precious Moments, Inc. All Rights Reserved.

TY's Beanie Babies®

❋ Detailed Descriptions and color photos of all Ty's Beanie Babies® to date! ❋ Size: 5¹/²" x 8¹/²"
❋ Over 180 pages ❋ Fun and Informative! ❋ Indexed for your convenience ❋ Birthday, Retirement and Out-of-Production lists
This price guide is produced by Rosie Wells Enterprises, Inc. and is not sponsored or endorsed by Ty, Inc. "Beanie Babies" is a registered trademark of Ty, Inc.

"No Other Guide Can Compare!"

Charming Tails™

❋ Easy to read! ❋ Use for insuring
❋ Retirement lists ❋ Alphabetically indexed ❋ Current value of each piece
❋ Detailed descriptions ❋ Full color
The name "Charming Tails" is a trademark of Fitz & Floyd. ©1998 Fitz & Floyd. ©1998 Roman.

Hallmark™ Ornaments

❋ Easy to read! ❋ Photos for each ornament
❋ Interviews with well-known Hallmark artists
❋ Alphabetical Index and Subject Index
❋ Up-to-date current prices on past years' Hallmark™ Ornaments, Kiddie Car Classics™ and Merry Miniatures® ❋ 8¹/²" x 6³/⁴" ❋ Over 350 pages ❋ Spiral Bound at the top of guide!
❋ Use for insuring! ❋ Call us, or look for this guide at your Hallmark™ dealer.

Ornaments pictured on guide ©1998 Hallmark Cards, Inc. All Rights Reserved.

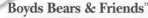

ASK your favorite retailer first for these guides!

Rosie Wells Enterprises, Inc.

22341 E. Wells Rd., Dept. G, Canton, IL 61520

1-800-445-8745

Web Site: http://www.RosieWells.com

**The prices above include bookrate shipping.
For speedier service, add $2 for UPS delivery. Illinois Residents add 6.25% Sales Tax on Price Guides.**

Cherished Teddies® Collection

❋ Detailed Description and Color Photo of each figurine ❋ Today's Current Value for each piece ❋ Alphabetically Indexed ❋ 5¹/²" x 8¹/²" ❋ Over 125 pages ❋ Use for insuring! ❋ This guide will provide the collector with an accurate record of **CHERISHED TEDDIES®** resin collectibles that have been produced to date. Ask your favorite **CHERISHED TEDDIES®** dealer for this guide or call us.

Cherished Teddies ©1991-1998 Priscilla Hillman. Cherished Teddies® is a registered trademark of Enesco Corporation All Rights Reserved.

Boyds Bears & Friends™

❋ 2nd Edition ❋ Detailed Description and Color Photo of each piece with established value ❋ Includes Bearstones™, Folkstones™, Dollstones™ and Shoe Box Bears™ ❋ Alphabetically Indexed ❋ 5¹/²" x 8¹/²" ❋ Over 90 pages ❋ Use for insuring! ❋ Call us, or look for this guide at your Boyds Bears & Friends™ collectibles dealer.

©The Boyds Collection, Ltd.® Boyds Bear & Friends™ All Rights Reserved.

This guide belongs to:

Name _____

Address _____

Phone _____

If found, please Return to Desperate Collector above!